C R S I
DESIGN HANDBOOK

WORKING STRESS DESIGN

REVISED

1963 ACI CODE

Prepared under the Direction
of the
Engineering Practice Committee
Concrete Reinforcing Steel Institute

by

R. C. Reese

Price $8.50

CONCRETE REINFORCING STEEL INSTITUTE
228 NORTH LASALLE STREET, CHICAGO, ILL. 60601

PRINTED IN THE UNITED STATES OF AMERICA

FIRST PRINTING, FIRST EDITION, 1965
SECOND PRINTING, 1966
FIRST PRINTING, SECOND EDITION, 1968
SECOND PRINTING, SECOND EDITION, 1970

CONTENTS

For "black spot" index, see front endpaper.

CONTENTS CONTINUED

SAFE LOAD TABLES CONTINUED

BEAM FIXED BOTH ENDS—NO LOAD—ONE END OFFSET

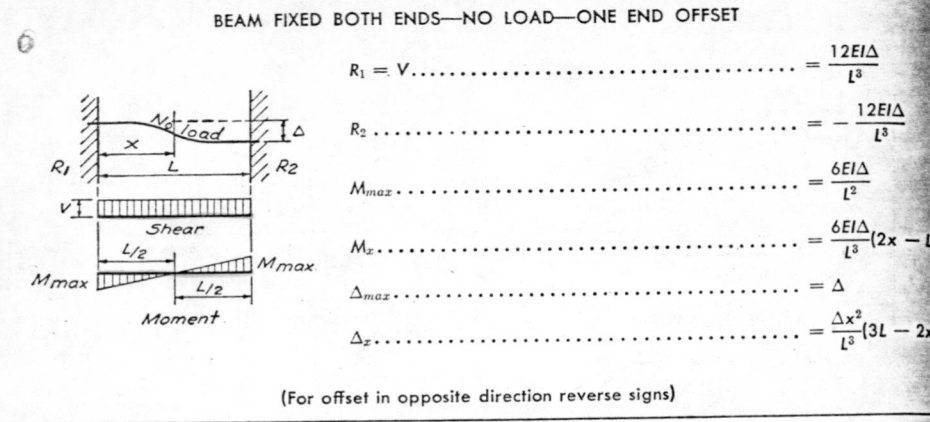

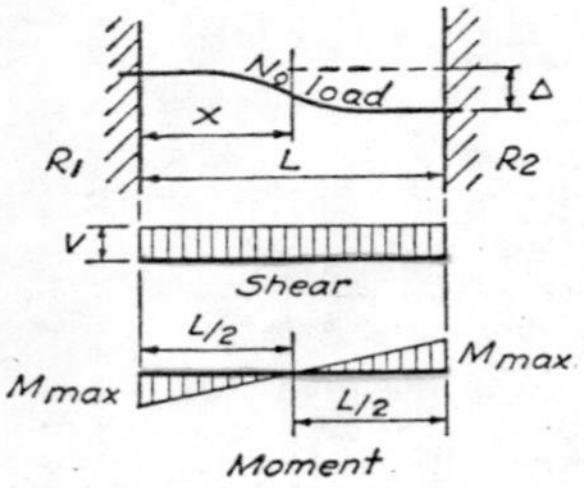

$R_1 = V \ldots\ldots = \frac{12EI\Delta}{L^3}$

$R_2 \ldots\ldots = -\frac{12EI\Delta}{L^3}$

$M_{max} \ldots\ldots = \frac{6EI\Delta}{L^2}$

$M_x \ldots\ldots = \frac{6EI\Delta}{L^3}(2x - L)$

$\Delta_{max} \ldots\ldots = \Delta$

$\Delta_x \ldots\ldots = \frac{\Delta x^2}{L^3}(3L - 2x)$

(For offset in opposite direction reverse signs)

BEAM FIXED ONE END—NO LOAD—ONE END OFFSET

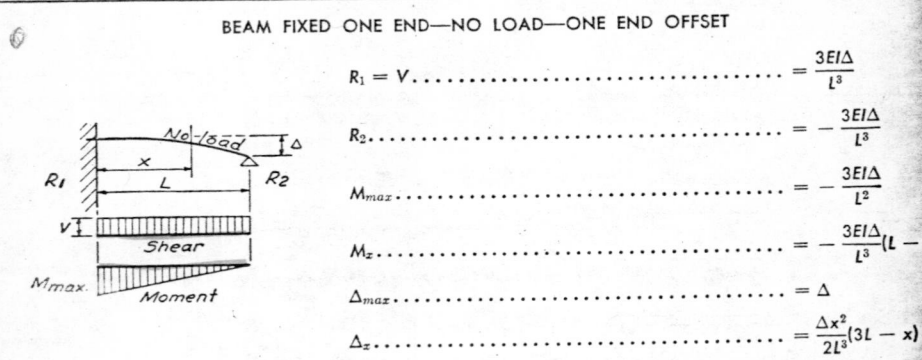

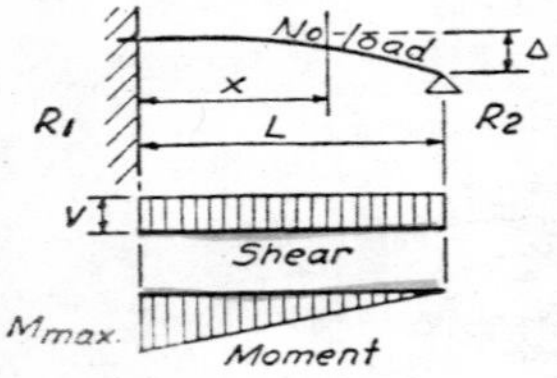

$R_1 = V \ldots\ldots = \frac{3EI\Delta}{L^3}$

$R_2 \ldots\ldots = -\frac{3EI\Delta}{L^3}$

$M_{max} \ldots\ldots = -\frac{3EI\Delta}{L^2}$

$M_x \ldots\ldots = -\frac{3EI\Delta}{L^3}(L - x)$

$\Delta_{max} \ldots\ldots = \Delta$

$\Delta_x \ldots\ldots = \frac{\Delta x^2}{2L^3}(3L - x)$

(For offset in opposite direction reverse signs)

BEAM FIXED BOTH ENDS—NO LOAD—APPLIED MOMENT

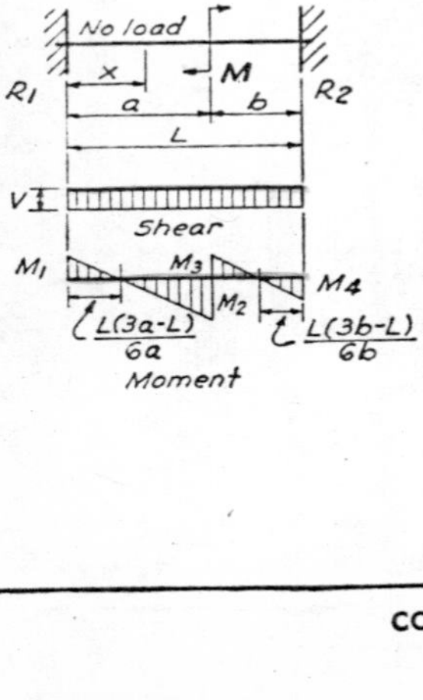

$R_1 = V = -\frac{6Mab}{L^3}$ $\qquad R_2 = \frac{6Mab}{L^3}$

$M_1 \ldots\ldots = +\frac{Mb}{L}\left(1 - 3\frac{a}{L}\right)$ $\qquad M_2 = -\frac{Mb}{L}\left(1 - 3\frac{a}{L} + 6\frac{a^2}{L^2}\right)$

$M_3 \ldots\ldots = \frac{Ma}{L}\left(1 - 3\frac{b}{L} + 6\frac{b^2}{L^2}\right)$ $\qquad M_4 = -\frac{Ma}{L}\left(1 - 3\frac{b}{L}\right)$

M_x (when $x < a$) $\ldots\ldots = -\frac{Mb}{L^3}(L^2 - 3aL + 6ax)$

M_x (when $x > a$) $\ldots\ldots = \frac{Ma}{L^3}(L^2 + 3bL - 6bx)$

Δ_x (when $x < a$) $\ldots\ldots = \frac{Mb}{EIL^3}\left(\frac{L^2x^2}{2} - \frac{3aLx^2}{2} + ax^3\right)$

Δ_x (when $x > a$) $\ldots\ldots = -\frac{Ma}{EIL^3}\left(\frac{L^2x^2}{2} + \frac{3bLx^2}{2} - bx^3 - L^3x + \frac{aL^3}{2}\right)$

$\Delta_a \ldots\ldots = \frac{Ma^2b}{EIL^3}\left(\frac{L^2}{2} - \frac{3aL}{2} + a^2\right) = \frac{Ma^2b^2}{2EIL^3}(L - 2a)$

BEAM FIXED ONE END—NO LOAD—APPLIED MOMENT

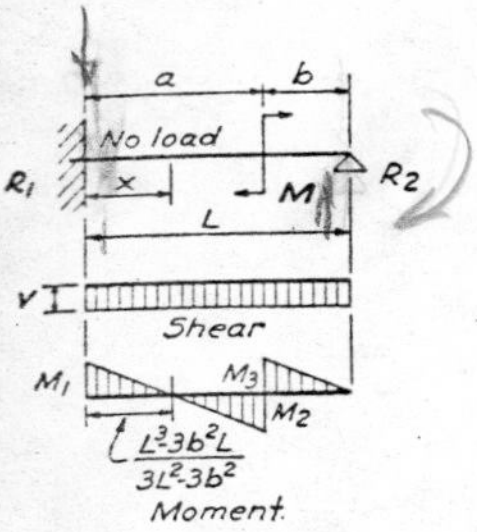

$R_1 = V \ldots\ldots = -\frac{3M}{2L}\left(1 - \frac{b^2}{L^2}\right)$ $\qquad R_2 \ldots\ldots = \frac{3M}{2L}\left(1 - \frac{b^2}{L^2}\right)$

$M_1 \ldots\ldots = \frac{M}{2}\left(1 - 3\frac{b^2}{L^2}\right)$ $\qquad M_2 \ldots\ldots = \frac{3Mb}{2L}\left(1 - \frac{b^2}{L^2}\right) - M$

$M_3 \ldots\ldots = \frac{3Mb}{2L}\left(1 - \frac{b^2}{L^2}\right)$

$M_x \text{ (when } x < a) \ldots = \frac{3M}{2L}\left(1 - \frac{b^2}{L^2}\right)(L - x) - M$

$M_x \text{ (when } x > a) \ldots = \frac{3M}{2L}\left(1 - \frac{b^2}{L^2}\right)(L - x)$

$\Delta_x \text{ (when } x < a) \ldots = \frac{Mx^2}{2EI}\left[\frac{3}{L}\left(1 - \frac{b^2}{L^2}\right)\left(\frac{x}{6} - \frac{L}{2}\right) + 1\right]$

$\Delta_x \text{ (when } x > a) \ldots = \frac{3M}{2EIL}\left(1 - \frac{b^2}{L^2}\right)\left(\frac{L^3}{3} - \frac{Lx^2}{2} + \frac{x^3}{6}\right) - \frac{Ma}{EI}(L - x)$

$\Delta_a \ldots\ldots = \frac{Ma^2}{2EI}\left[\frac{a(2L - a)(a - 3L)}{2L^3} + 1\right]$

SIMPLE BEAM—NO LOAD—APPLIED MOMENT

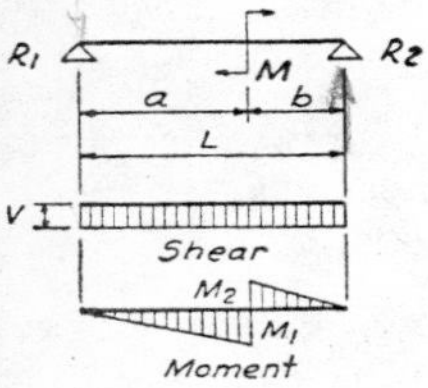

$R_1 = V \ldots\ldots = -\frac{M}{L}$ $\qquad R_2 \ldots\ldots = \frac{M}{L}$

$M_1 \ldots\ldots = -\frac{Ma}{L}$ $\qquad M_2 \ldots\ldots = \frac{Mb}{L}$

$M_{max} \ldots\ldots = M_1 \text{ if } a > b$

$= M_2 \text{ if } a < b$

$M_x \text{ (when } x < a) \ldots = -\frac{Mx}{L}$

$M_x \text{ (when } x > a) \ldots = \frac{M}{L}(L - x)$

$\Delta_x \text{ (when } x < a) \ldots = \frac{Mx}{6EIL^2}(-a^3 - 3a^2b + 2b^3 + Lx^2)$

$\Delta_x \text{ (when } x > a) \ldots = \frac{M(L - x)}{6EIL^2}[-2a^3 + 3ab^2 + b^3 - L(L - x)^2]$

$\Delta_{max}\left(\text{if } a > b, \text{ at } x = \sqrt{-\frac{2}{3}L^2 + 2aL - a^2}\right) =$

$\frac{M\sqrt{-\frac{2}{3}L^2 + 2aL - a^2}}{6EIL^2}\left(-a^3 - 3a^2b + 2b^3 - \frac{2}{3}L^3 + 2aL^2 - a^2L\right)$

$\Delta_{max}\left(\text{if } a < b, \text{ at } (L - x) = \sqrt{-\frac{2}{3}L^2 + 2bL - b^2}\right) =$

$\frac{M\sqrt{-\frac{2L^2}{3} + 2bL - b^2}}{6EIL^2}\left(-2a^3 + 3ab^2 + b^3 + \frac{2}{3}L^3 - 2bL^2 + b^2L\right)$

CANTILEVERED BEAM—NO LOAD—APPLIED MOMENT

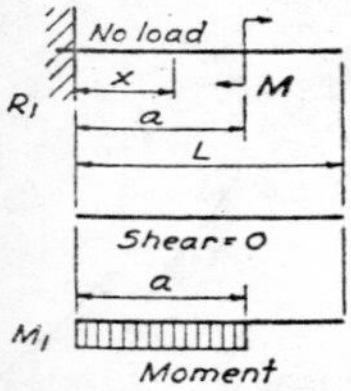

$R = V \ldots\ldots = 0$

$M_1 \ldots\ldots = -M$

$\Delta_x \text{ (when } x \overline{<} a) \ldots = \frac{Mx^2}{2EI}$

$\Delta_x \text{ (when } x \overline{>} a) \ldots = \frac{Ma}{EI}\left(x - \frac{a}{2}\right)$

$\Delta_{max} \text{ (when } x = L) \ldots = \frac{Ma}{EI}\left(L - \frac{a}{2}\right)$

Basis and Use of Tables

Section 1

The Institute does not prepare engineering plans. While every precaution is taken to insure that all data and information furnished are as accurate as possible, the Institute cannot assume responsibility for errors or oversights in the use of such information or in the preparation of engineering plans. The design information given in these tables should prove useful in preliminary estimating, for establishing sizes and clearances and for comparing different types of construction. Obviously, the tables apply only to the particular condition of span, loading and eccentricity specified. The information in this handbook should not replace the judgment of an experienced structural engineer when selecting types of structure, proper loads, stresses, moment factors, eliminating eccentricities, providing proper stiffness and in obtaining the most economical design.

PRECISION OF COMPUTATIONS FOR REINFORCED CONCRETE

If the somewhat involved mathematical methods used in rigid frame analysis lead one to believe that the design of reinforced concrete structures requires a high degree of precision, such is not the case. Moment coefficients in the ACI Building Code are prescribed to two significant figures. The Code permits a 10 percent adjustment of (+) (−) design moments from "exact" analyses. Concrete is a job-made material. Tests or control cylinders that do not vary more than 15 per cent are good. Reinforcing bars may vary in strength above the specified minimum. Formwork also has its variations; generally, ½ to 1 inch. Bars that are held in place to an accuracy of ¼ in. in specified effective depth are extremely well placed. Two-figure accuracy is sufficient for almost all problems in reinforced concrete design.

Concrete is weak in tension; reinforcing steel is supplied to make up that deficiency. The time and effort of the designer is best spent in recognizing and providing for stress concentrations where they exist, not in striving for a high degree of mathematical precision by carrying figures to an excessive number of places.

On the other hand, the bulk of present computing is done on a 10 in. slide rule, reading easily to three significant figures. When numbers are subtracted, significant figures are often lost. It is, therefore, recommended, more for control of the computations, rather than for any effect on the completed structure, that figures be carried to three significant places or to the extent of a 10 in. slide rule. There is no point in computing loads to a fine determination only to lose the results in a moment computation; nor is it logical to carry moments to the suggested three significant figures when the loads were estimated to one-figure precision. For that reason, the following table is suggested as a rough guide, not as any hard and fast rule, but only to give some indication of a satisfactory procedure.

RECORD VALUES TO THE FOLLOWING PRECISION:—

Loads to nearest 1 psf; 10 plf; 100 lb concentration.
Span lengths to about 0.1 ft
Total loads and reactions to 0.1 kip or 3 significant figures
Moments to nearest 1.0 kip-in., or to 3 significant figures.
Individual bar areas to 0.01 sq in.
Concrete sizes to ½ in., except footings.
Effective beam depth to 0.1 in.

BASIS AND USE OF TABLES

Introduction. The purpose of this handbook is to provide completed designs of members in reinforced concrete, by giving outlines of concrete, and sizes and quantities of reinforcement in accordance with the Working Stress Method of "Building Code Requirements for Reinforced Concrete (ACI 318-63)." Selecting completed designs of members from these safe load tables eliminates the need for charts and diagrams. The designer enters the appropriate table with load and span and immediately obtains the concrete outlines and the reinforcing steel.

This handbook is based upon f'_c = 3,000, 3,750, and 5,000 psi controlled concrete, f_s = 24,000 psi (60,000 psi yield point) steel, and the methods of ACI 318-63. The designer will, of course, realize that as higher stresses and more refined methods are used, more accurate appraisal of loading conditions and closer control of construction methods and the quality of materials become necessary.

After many years of use, Volume I of the CRSI Handbook series (first published in 1952) was printed as Volume I in 1964. Volume I was based upon the 1956 ACI Building Code, and is now out-of-print.

Two handbooks by CRSI are available for Ultimate Strength Design:

(1) COLUMNS BY ULTIMATE STRENGTH DESIGN (1967) and (2) FLOOR SYSTEMS BY ULTIMATE STRENGTH DESIGN (1968).

Safe Load Tables instead of Coefficients and Charts. In these days of electronic computers, it is extravagant for designers to multiply loads by spans and divide by stresses repeatedly, when a single careful computer analysis for shear, bond, flexure, and all other criteria can be made once and for all more accurately and completely and tabulated for ready reference and for the designer's convenience. No handbook can replace the judgment of an experienced structural engineer in selecting types of structure, proper loads, stresses, and moment factors, in eliminating eccentricities, in providing adequate stiffness, in compensating for temperature effects and shrinkage, and in obtaining satisfactory and economical structures. Use of these tables, however, eliminates routine calculations and enables the designer to devote that much more time to his real functions. Therefore, Volume II eliminates many of the charts and coefficients given in Volume I, to allow the broadest possible coverage to the safe load tables.

Use of Tables. The general arrangement of the book is quickly noted by reference to the "Section Index" on the front end paper. The black-spot index, repeated on the individual pages, makes it easy to riffle through the edges of the pages to reach the desired section and the individual table. Sections 1 to 5, inclusive, contain information on bar sizes, bar combinations, spacings, bends, and splices, as well as moment tables, continuities, loads, stresses, and all the preliminary requirements of a design. Sections 6 to 14, inclusive, are actual safe load tables, for the types of members or systems listed. Section 14 contains such miscellaneous tables as pits, bins, lintels, pipe columns, and slabs on the ground. Section 15 provides several useful mathematical tables.

More detailed information on the items covered and where they can be located is found in the Table of Contents on page iii.

A rather complete alphabetical Index is included at the end of the book. It is suggested that the front flyleaf and the Contents be studied to get an idea of the arrangement. Then use the Index freely to find the exact material desired.

Tabulated values for flexural members (except beams) give the maximum safe superimposed load obtained by computing the total capacity of a member as limited by flexure, shear, bond, or any other consideration and deducting from the least of these the dead weight of the concrete in the member itself. In the case of beams, where the dead weight of tributary slab is such a large factor, no useful purpose is served by deducting merely the weight of the beam. Therefore, in the beam tables only, the loads given are the **total safe loads** in pounds per lineal foot. In all other safe load tables, the "safe superimposed load" includes live load, partitions, floor finishes, ceilings, and, in fact, everything except the dead weight of the concrete member.

To meet average conditions, tables are given for concrete testing to f'_c in standard 6 x 12 in. cylinders at 28 days and for deformed bars stressed 24,000 psi (f_y = 60,000 psi). Columns are worked also for the richer mix of 5000 psi and for steel with f_y = 75,000 psi.

Caution. Tabulated safe loads are the maximum obtainable within the stresses and factors of "Building Code Requirements for Reinforced Concrete (ACI 318-63)" and should be used only by one familiar with reinforced concrete design. No increase above the tabulated values should be made.

Materials and Specifications. Since all the tables in this book are based upon steel with a yield point of 60,000 psi; that is, Grade 60 bars, it is important that the designer be thoroughly familiar with the ASTM Specifications for these materials and particularly with the required rolled-on grade markings for deformed reinforcing bars with f_y = 60,000 and 75,000 psi.

These specifications are obtainable from the American Society for Testing and Materials or are reproduced in the CRSI Manual of Standard Practice for Reinforced Concrete Construction.*

ASTM Specifications for minimum requirements for the deformations

---

* Available from Concrete Reinforcing Steel Institute, 228 North Lasalle Street, Chicago, Illinois 60601.

of bars establish the projection and spacing of deformations. Under "Building Code Requirements for Reinforced Concrete (ACI 318-63)," increased bond and diagonal tension values are permitted, provided bars meet these specifications. These higher values for shear and bond are used throughout the book. Consequently, **only bars meeting the ASTM requirements for strength and deformations should be used with the tabulated values.**

With the use of higher strength and better quality concrete, the designer must specify precisely what he requires and verify that this is what he obtains. Complete specifications for concrete work can be found in "Suggested Specifications for Structural Concrete for Buildings (ACI 301)" of the American Concrete Institute.*

References. For useful material on reinforced concrete design not reproduced in this Design Handbook, the reader is advised to procure (at a nominal charge) both a copy of the American Concrete Institute * "Building Code Requirements for Reinforced Concrete (ACI 318-63)," which is the recognized authority in this field, also a copy of the "Manual of Standard Practice for Detailing Reinforced Concrete Structures (ACI 315)," which presents approved standards for preparing drawings for the fabrication and placing of reinforcing steel.

The designer should also have a copy of the Concrete Reinforcing Steel Institute † "Manual of Standard Practice for Reinforced Concrete Construction," which covers materials available, standard methods of fabricating, and standard practices of estimating and contracting for such items, as well as the ASTM Specifications for deformed reinforcing bars. Another helpful book available at a nominal charge and covering the actual placement of bars, supports, and welded wire fabric is "CRSI Recommended Practice for Placing Reinforcing Bars." †

The Portland Cement Association ‡ issues material on the techniques of construction and design procedures for reinforced concrete structures, most of which is available upon request.

The American Concrete Institute,* in addition to the codes and manuals described above, issues many reference books and a regular monthly publication, "Journal of the American Concrete Institute," devoted to all phases of the design of reinforced concrete structures and to better procedures for concrete proportioning, mixing, placing, and curing.

Proposed Volume III of this series is mentioned on page 1-3.

Tables are based upon 3000 or 3750 psi concrete of normal weight using ASTM coarse aggregate C33. If lightweight aggregate is used (ASTM 330) with splitting tensile strength as in ACI 318-63, adjust all values accordingly, especially those determined by shear and deflection.

---

* American Concrete Institute, P. O. Box 4754, Redford Station, Detroit 19, Michigan.
† Concrete Reinforcing Steel Institute, 228 N. Lasalle St., Chicago, Ill. 60601.
‡ Portland Cement Association, 33 West Grand Avenue, Chicago 10, Illinois.

HINTS FOR GETTING THE MOST OUT OF THIS BOOK

1. Note black-spot index on front endpaper and on edge of page in text.
2. Scan Table of Contents to see general make-up.
3. Freely use the Index at the back of the book.
4. Sections 1 to 5, inclusive, are general; Sections 6 to 14, inclusive, are safe load tables.
5. Basis for flexural members tabulated: $f'_c = 3{,}000$ psi or 3750 psi, $f_s = 24{,}000$ psi, and the methods of ACI 318-63, working stress design.
6. Columns are tabulated for square tied, square spiralled, and round spiralled in 3750/60,000, 5000/60,000, and 5000/75,000 stress combinations.
7. Observe carefully the significance of headings, zigzag lines, dotted lines, footnotes, boldface and italic type, and all other designations in these tables.

   Serious problems could result from overlooking a mark for tapered ends on joists or stirrups in a beam.
8. Each safe load table is preceded by a few pages of explanation that should be read very carefully to understand limitations and methods of use.
9. Each table is preceded by carefully worked out examples to illustrate the procedures that the electronic computer followed.

Bars, Bar Combinations, Fabric
Section 2

Standard sizes, weights, areas, perimeters of individual bars
Combinations of bars—areas and perimeters
Minimum beam widths to accommodate bars
Laps, splicing and spacing of bars
Maximum number of verticals in spiral and square columns
Hooks, bends, length of trussed bars
Welded wire fabric

WEIGHT, AREA AND PERIMETER OF INDIVIDUAL REINFORCING BARS *

STANDARD REINFORCING BARS

DEFORMED BAR DES-IGNATION	WEIGHT (Pounds per Foot)	NOMINAL DIM.—ROUND SECT.			MAXIMUM OUTSIDE DIAMETER ‡ (In.)
		DIAMETER (Inches)	CROSS SEC. AREA (Sq. In.)	PERIMETER (Inches)	
#3	.376	.375	.11	1.178	7/16
#4	.668	.500	.20	1.571	9/16
#5	1.043	.625	.31	1.963	11/16
#6	1.502	.750	.44	2.356	7/8
#7	2.044	.875	.60	2.749	1
#8	2.670	1.000	.79	3.142	1-1/8
#9	3.400	1.128	1.00	3.544	1-1/4
#10	4.303	1.270	1.27	3.990	1-7/16
#11	5.313	1.410	1.56	4.430	1-5/8

‡ The maximum outside diameter including deformations may be important as when punching holes in structural steel members to accommodate bars, or in fitting couplings, or in nesting or bundling bars. Exact dimensions vary among manufacturers. Tabulated values allow for deformations, longitudinal ribs and out-of-round.

The above weights were adoped as standards by the Institute in 1934.

These weights have been approved through the U. S. Department of Commerce Simplified Practice Recommendation 26.

LARGE DEFORMED REINFORCING BARS

#14	7.65	1.693	2.25	5.32	1-15/16
#18	13.60	2.257	4.00	7.09	2-1/2

Sizes #14 and #18 are large bars generally not carried in regular stock. These sizes available by arrangement with the supplier.

* Copies of the bar card (heavy cardboard and suitable for hanging on the wall or celluloid pocketsize) may be obtained from the Concrete Reinforcing Steel Institute, 228 North LaSalle St., Chicago 1, Illinois.

DIMENSIONAL REQUIREMENTS FOR DEFORMED STEEL BARS FOR CONCRETE REINFORCEMENT, ASTM

Deformed Bar Designation Number	Deformation Requirements		
	Max Avg Spacing (in.)	Min Height (in.)	Max Gap (in.) Chord of 12½ Per Cent of Nominal Perimeter
3	0.262	0.015	0.143
4	0.350	0.020	0.191
5	0.437	0.028	0.239
6	0.525	0.038	0.286
7	0.612	0.044	0.334
8	0.700	0.050	0.383
9	0.790	0.056	0.431
10	0.889	0.064	0.487
11	0.987	0.071	0.540
14	1.185	0.085	0.648
18	1.580	0.102	0.864

AREAS OF VARIOUS COMBINATIONS OF BARS AND MINIMUM WEB WIDTHS FOR BEAMS

For table of areas of various combinations of bars, see pages 2-5 to 2-7 incl.

The table on pages 2-5 to 2-7 gives all practicable combinations of bars, #3 to #11 inclusive, of equal diameters or differing by one or two sizes to produce any desired steel area, A_s, up to 13 sq in.

The same table also gives the minimum width of beam web that will properly cover the bars placed in a single layer, on the basis of $1\frac{1}{2}$ in. protection over $\frac{3}{8}$ stirrup legs, with spaces between the bars equal to one bar diameter or one inch. (See figure below.) Beam widths are given in multiples of one-tenth inch. When bars are of different sizes, smaller bars are placed on outside.

Since #14 and #18 bars are used in very heavy construction which the designer would be laying out in detail, they are not included in these tables of combinations.

Example:—A_s = 2.38 sq in. can be obtained with 4-#6 and 2-#5 bars, requiring a beam width of 13 in. or better, or with 4-#7 bars in a beam width of 10½ in.

Aggregate should be chosen with maximum size three-quarters of the clear space between bars.

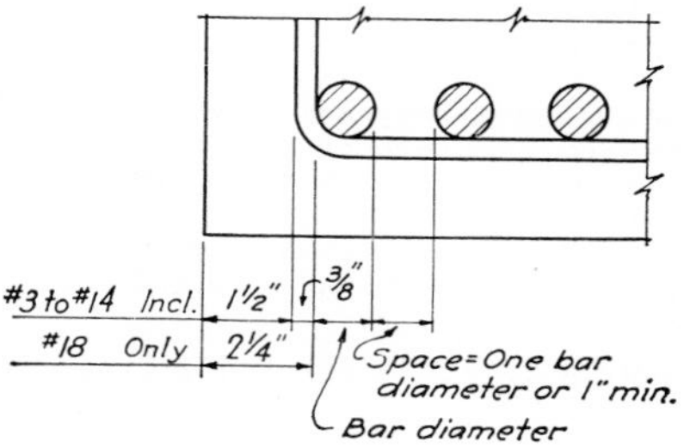

The following table gives minimum beam widths in multiples of one-quarter inch for various numbers of *equal* sized bars spaced as on the figure above:-

MINIMUM BEAM WIDTHS—ACI CODE

Size of Bars	Number of Bars in Single Layer of Reinforcement							add for Each Added Bar
	2	3	4	5	6	7	8	
#4	5¾	7¼	8¾	10¼	11¾	13¼	14¾	1½
#5	6	7¾	9¼	11	12½	14¼	15¾	1⅝
#6	6¼	8	9¾	11½	13¼	15	16¾	1¾
#7	6½	8½	10¼	12¼	14	16	17¾	1⅞
#8	6¾	8¾	10¾	12¾	14¾	16¾	18¾	2
#9	7¼	9½	11¾	14	16¼	18½	20¾	2¼
#10	7¾	10¼	12¾	15¼	17¾	20¼	23	2⅝
#11	8	11	13¾	16½	19½	22¼	25	2⅞
#14	9	12¼	15¾	19	22½	25¾	29¼	3⅜
#18	11¼	15¾	20¼	24¾	29¼	33¾	38½	4½

Table shows minimum beam widths when stirrups are used.
If no stirrups are required, deduct three-quarters of an inch from figures shown.
For additional bars, add dimension in last column for each added bar.
For bars of different sizes, determine from table the beam width for smaller size bars, and then add last column figure for each larger bar used, or see pages 2-5 to 2-7.

AREAS OF VARIOUS COMBINATIONS OF SEPARATE BARS AND MINIMUM WEB WIDTHS FOR BEAMS

A_s (sq in.)	Bar Combination				Min Web Width (in.)	A_s (sq in.)	Bar Combination				Min Web Width (in.)	A_s (sq in.)	Bar Combination				Min Web Width (in.)
	Quant	Size	Quant	Size			Quant	Size	Quant	Size			Quant	Size	Quant	Size	
0.11	1	#3	.....	....	4.2	1.13	3	#5	1	#4	9.2	1.73	3	#5	4	#4	13.7
0.20	1	#4	.....	....	4.3	1.13	4	#4	3	#3	12.9	1.75	5	#5	1	#4	12.4
0.31	1	#5	.....	....	4.4	1.15	3	#4	5	#3	14.2	1.76	4	#6	.....	....	9.8
0.31	1	#4	1	#3	5.7	1.19	2	#6	1	#5	7.9	1.79	1	#9	1	#8	7.0
0.40	2	#4	.....	....	5.8	1.20	2	#7	.....	....	6.5	1.80	3	#7	.....	....	8.4
0.42	1	#4	2	#3	7.0	1.22	2	#5	3	#4	10.5	1.81	2	#6	3	#5	11.2
0.44	1	#6	.....	....	4.5	1.22	1	#7	2	#5	7.9	1.82	2	#7	2	#5	9.8
0.51	1	#5	1	#4	5.9	1.22	5	#4	2	#3	13.0	1.84	1	#7	4	#5	11.2
0.51	2	#4	1	#3	7.2	1.23	1	#8	1	#6	6.5	1.84	4	#5	3	#4	13.8
0.53	1	#4	3	#3	8.4	1.24	4	#5	.....	....	9.3	1.88	2	#6	5	#4	13.8
0.60	1	#7	.....	....	4.7	1.24	1	#6	4	#4	10.5	1.92	1	#7	3	#6	9.9
0.60	3	#4	.....	....	7.3	1.24	4	#4	4	#3	14.3	1.92	3	#6	3	#4	12.5
0.62	2	#5	.....	....	6.0	1.27	1	#10	.....	....	5.1	1.93	3	#5	5	#4	15.2
0.62	2	#4	2	#3	8.5	1.28	2	#6	2	#4	9.3	1.94	3	#6	2	#5	11.3
0.64	1	#4	4	#3	9.8	1.31	1	#5	5	#4	11.9	1.95	5	#5	2	#4	13.9
0.64	1	#6	1	#4	6.0	1.32	3	#6	.....	....	8.0	1.96	4	#6	1	#4	11.3
0.71	1	#5	2	#4	7.4	1.33	3	#5	2	#4	10.7	1.99	1	#8	2	#7	8.5
0.71	3	#4	1	#3	8.7	1.33	5	#4	3	#3	14.4	1.99	1	#6	5	#5	12.7
0.73	2	#4	3	#3	9.9	1.35	4	#4	5	#3	15.7	2.00	2	#9	.....	....	7.2
0.75	1	#6	1	#5	6.2	1.37	1	#6	3	#5	9.4	2.02	2	#8	1	#6	8.5
0.75	1	#4	5	#3	11.2	1.39	1	#8	1	#7	6.7	2.04	4	#5	4	#4	15.3
0.79	1	#8	.....	....	4.8	1.42	2	#5	4	#4	12.0	2.06	1	#10	1	#8	7.2
0.80	4	#4	.....	....	8.8	1.44	4	#5	1	#4	10.8	2.07	4	#6	1	#5	11.4
0.82	2	#5	1	#4	7.5	1.44	1	#6	5	#4	12.0	2.08	2	#7	2	#6	10.0
0.82	3	#4	2	#3	10.0	1.44	5	#4	4	#3	15.8	2.11	1	#8	3	#6	10.0
0.84	2	#4	4	#3	11.3	1.48	1	#7	2	#6	8.2	2.11	3	#7	1	#5	10.0
0.84	1	#6	2	#4	7.5	1.48	2	#6	3	#4	10.8	2.12	2	#6	4	#5	12.8
0.88	2	#6	.....	....	6.3	1.50	2	#6	2	#5	9.5	2.12	3	#6	4	#4	14.0
0.91	1	#5	3	#4	8.9	1.51	2	#7	1	#5	8.2	2.13	2	#7	3	#5	11.4
0.91	1	#7	1	#5	6.3	1.52	3	#6	1	#4	9.5	2.15	1	#7	5	#5	12.8
0.91	4	#4	1	#3	10.2	1.53	1	#7	3	#5	9.5	2.15	5	#5	3	#4	15.4
0.93	3	#5	.....	....	7.7	1.53	3	#5	3	#4	12.2	2.16	4	#6	2	#4	12.8
0.93	3	#4	3	#3	11.4	1.55	5	#5	.....	....	10.9	2.18	2	#8	1	#7	8.7
0.95	2	#4	5	#3	12.7	1.55	5	#4	5	#3	17.2	2.20	1	#9	2	#7	8.7
1.00	1	#9	.....	....	4.9	1.56	1	#11	.....	....	5.2	2.20	5	#6	.....	....	11.5
1.00	5	#4	.....	....	10.3	1.58	2	#8	.....	....	6.8	2.24	4	#5	5	#4	16.8
1.02	2	#5	2	#4	9.0	1.60	1	#9	1	#7	6.9	2.24	3	#7	1	#6	10.2
1.02	4	#4	2	#3	11.5	1.62	2	#5	5	#4	13.5	2.25	3	#6	3	#5	12.9
1.04	1	#7	1	#6	6.4	1.63	3	#6	1	#5	9.7	2.27	1	#10	1	#9	7.4
1.04	3	#4	4	#3	12.8	1.64	4	#5	2	#4	12.3	2.32	3	#6	5	#4	15.5
1.04	1	#6	3	#4	9.0	1.64	2	#7	1	#6	8.3	2.35	5	#5	4	#4	16.9
1.06	1	#6	2	#5	7.8	1.67	1	#8	2	#6	8.3	2.36	1	#7	4	#6	11.7
1.08	2	#6	1	#4	7.8	1.68	1	#6	4	#5	11.0	2.36	4	#6	3	#4	14.3
1.11	1	#5	4	#4	10.4	1.68	2	#6	4	#4	12.3	2.37	3	#8	.....	....	8.8
1.11	5	#4	1	#3	11.7	1.72	3	#6	2	#4	11.0	2.38	4	#6	2	#5	13.0

AREAS OF VARIOUS COMBINATIONS OF SEPARATE BARS AND MINIMUM WEB WIDTHS FOR BEAMS

A_s (sq in.)	Bar Combination				Min Web Width (in.)	A_s (sq in.)	Bar Combination				Min Web Width (in.)	A_s (sq in.)	Bar Combination				Min Web Width (in.)
	Quant	Size	Quant	Size			Quant	Size	Quant	Size			Quant	Size	Quant	Size	
2.40	4	#7	.....	....	10.3	3.12	2	#11	.....	....	8.0	3.98	2	#8	4	#7	14.3
2.40	5	#6	1	#4	13.0	3.12	3	#7	3	#6	13.7	4.00	4	#9	.....	....	11.7
2.42	3	#7	2	#5	11.7	3.13	5	#6	3	#5	16.4	4.00	1	#9	5	#7	14.4
2.43	2	#6	5	#5	14.4	3.16	4	#8	.....	....	10.8	4.00	3	#7	5	#6	17.2
2.44	2	#7	4	#5	13.0	3.19	1	#8	4	#7	12.3	4.04	4	#8	2	#6	14.3
2.46	2	#8	2	#6	10.3	3.20	2	#9	2	#7	11.1	4.10	1	#11	2	#10	10.4
2.51	5	#6	1	#5	13.2	3.20	5	#6	5	#4	19.0	4.12	2	#10	2	#8	11.9
2.52	2	#7	3	#6	11.8	3.25	3	#8	2	#6	12.3	4.12	2	#11	1	#9	10.4
2.54	2	#10	.....	....	7.6	3.27	1	#10	2	#9	9.7	4.13	3	#8	4	#6	15.8
2.55	5	#5	5	#4	18.4	3.28	4	#7	2	#6	13.8	4.16	1	#9	4	#8	13.1
2.55	1	#8	4	#6	11.8	3.31	4	#6	5	#5	17.9	4.16	4	#7	4	#6	17.3
2.56	3	#6	4	#5	14.5	3.31	5	#7	1	#5	13.8	4.17	3	#8	3	#7	14.4
2.56	1	#11	1	#9	7.6	3.33	2	#10	1	#8	9.7	4.20	3	#9	2	#7	13.3
2.56	4	#6	4	#4	15.8	3.33	4	#7	3	#5	15.2	4.24	5	#7	4	#5	18.7
2.58	1	#9	2	#8	9.1	3.34	2	#8	4	#6	13.8	4.27	1	#10	3	#9	12.0
2.59	1	#8	3	#7	10.4	3.35	3	#7	5	#5	16.5	4.32	5	#7	3	#6	17.4
2.60	2	#9	1	#7	9.1	3.37	1	#9	3	#8	11.1	4.36	4	#8	2	#7	14.5
2.60	5	#6	2	#4	14.5	3.38	2	#8	3	#7	12.4	4.37	2	#9	3	#8	13.3
2.68	3	#7	2	#6	11.9	3.40	1	#9	4	#7	12.4	4.39	5	#8	1	#6	14.5
2.69	4	#6	3	#5	14.7	3.40	2	#7	5	#6	15.3	4.39	2	#11	1	#10	10.6
2.71	4	#7	1	#5	11.9	3.44	5	#7	1	#6	13.9	4.40	2	#9	4	#7	14.8
2.73	3	#7	3	#5	13.3	3.44	5	#6	4	#5	18.0	4.43	1	#10	4	#8	13.3
2.75	2	#7	5	#5	14.7	3.54	2	#10	1	#9	9.9	4.48	4	#8	3	#6	16.0
2.76	4	#6	5	#4	17.3	3.56	1	#11	2	#9	10.0	4.54	2	#10	2	#9	12.3
2.78	2	#8	2	#7	10.5	3.56	3	#7	4	#6	15.4	4.55	5	#8	1	#7	14.7
2.79	2	#9	1	#8	9.2	3.57	3	#8	2	#7	12.5	4.55	5	#7	5	#5	20.3
2.80	1	#9	3	#7	10.6	3.58	2	#9	2	#8	11.3	4.56	1	#11	3	#9	12.2
2.80	1	#7	5	#6	13.4	3.60	3	#9	1	#7	11.4	4.57	3	#8	5	#6	17.5
2.80	5	#6	3	#4	16.0	3.60	4	#8	1	#6	12.5	4.58	3	#9	2	#8	13.6
2.81	3	#8	1	#6	10.5	3.62	5	#7	2	#5	15.4	4.58	2	#8	5	#7	16.2
2.82	5	#6	2	#5	14.8	3.64	1	#10	3	#8	11.3	4.60	3	#10	1	#8	12.3
2.83	1	#11	1	#10	7.8	3.64	4	#7	4	#5	16.8	4.60	4	#9	1	#7	13.6
2.84	4	#7	1	#6	12.0	3.69	3	#8	3	#6	14.0	4.60	4	#7	5	#6	19.0
2.85	1	#10	2	#8	9.3	3.72	4	#7	3	#6	15.5	4.68	3	#11	.....	....	10.9
2.87	3	#6	5	#5	16.2	3.75	5	#6	5	#5	19.7	4.76	5	#7	4	#6	19.2
2.88	2	#9	2	#6	10.8	3.76	4	#8	1	#7	12.7	4.77	3	#8	4	#7	16.3
2.96	2	#7	4	#6	13.5	3.78	2	#8	5	#6	15.5	4.79	4	#9	1	#8	13.8
2.97	3	#8	1	#7	10.7	3.79	3	#9	1	#8	11.5	4.80	3	#9	3	#7	15.2
2.99	1	#8	5	#6	13.5	3.79	1	#8	5	#7	14.2	4.81	3	#10	1	#9	12.5
3.00	4	#6	4	#5	16.3	3.80	2	#9	3	#7	12.9	4.83	5	#8	2	#6	16.3
3.00	3	#9	.....	....	9.4	3.81	3	#10	.....	....	10.2	4.91	2	#10	3	#8	13.8
3.00	5	#7	.....	....	12.2	3.88	5	#7	2	#6	15.7	4.92	4	#8	4	#6	17.8
3.00	5	#6	4	#4	17.5	3.93	5	#7	3	#5	17.0	4.95	1	#9	5	#8	15.1
3.02	4	#7	2	#5	13.5	3.95	5	#8	.....	....	12.8	4.96	4	#8	3	#7	16.4
3.04	3	#7	4	#5	14.9	3.95	4	#7	5	#5	18.4	5.00	5	#9	.....	....	14.0

AREAS OF VARIOUS COMBINATIONS OF SEPARATE BARS AND MINIMUM WEB WIDTHS FOR BEAMS

A_s (sq in.)	Bar Combination				Min Web Width (in.)	A_s (sq in.)	Bar Combination				Min Web Width (in.)	A_s (sq in.)	Bar Combination				Min Web Width (in.)
	Quant	Size	Quant	Size			Quant	Size	Quant	Size			Quant	Size	Quant	Size	
5.00	2	#9	5	#7	16.6	6.24	4	#11	.....	....	13.7	8.08	4	#10	3	#9	19.6
5.08	4	#10	.....	....	12.7	6.27	1	#10	5	#9	16.5	8.12	2	#11	5	#9	19.6
5.12	2	#11	2	#9	12.7	6.35	5	#10	.....	....	15.2	8.16	5	#9	4	#8	22.1
5.15	5	#8	2	#7	16.5	6.35	5	#8	4	#7	20.3	8.20	2	#11	4	#10	18.3
5.16	2	#9	4	#8	15.3	6.37	4	#9	3	#8	17.8	8.24	4	#10	4	#8	21.0
5.20	4	#9	2	#7	15.4	6.40	4	#9	4	#7	19.3	8.24	4	#11	2	#9	18.5
5.20	5	#7	5	#6	20.9	6.49	2	#10	5	#8	17.9	8.35	5	#10	2	#9	19.9
5.22	1	#10	5	#8	15.3	6.54	2	#10	4	#9	16.8	8.49	3	#11	3	#10	18.6
5.27	5	#8	3	#6	18.0	6.56	1	#11	5	#9	16.8	8.68	3	#11	4	#9	20.2
5.27	1	#10	4	#9	14.2	6.58	5	#9	2	#8	18.1	8.72	5	#10	3	#8	21.5
5.36	4	#8	5	#6	19.5	6.64	1	#11	4	#10	15.5	8.78	4	#11	2	#10	18.9
5.37	1	#11	3	#10	13.0	6.66	4	#10	2	#8	17.0	8.80	5	#11	1	#9	18.9
5.37	3	#9	3	#8	15.5	6.68	3	#11	2	#9	15.6	8.81	3	#10	5	#9	21.6
5.37	3	#8	5	#7	18.2	6.80	5	#9	3	#7	19.7	8.95	5	#9	5	#8	24.1
5.39	3	#10	2	#8	14.4	6.81	3	#10	3	#9	17.1	9.03	4	#10	5	#8	23.0
5.40	3	#9	4	#7	17.1	6.93	2	#11	3	#10	15.8	9.07	5	#11	1	#10	19.1
5.54	2	#10	3	#9	14.5	6.95	3	#9	5	#8	19.6	9.08	4	#10	4	#9	21.9
5.56	4	#8	4	#7	18.3	6.95	5	#8	5	#7	22.2	9.24	4	#11	3	#9	20.7
5.56	1	#11	4	#9	14.5	6.97	3	#10	4	#8	18.4	9.35	5	#10	3	#9	22.1
5.58	4	#9	2	#8	15.8	7.00	4	#9	5	#7	21.2	9.47	2	#11	5	#10	20.9
5.60	5	#9	1	#7	15.9	7.08	4	#10	2	#9	17.3	9.51	5	#10	4	#8	23.5
5.66	2	#11	2	#10	13.2	7.12	2	#11	4	#9	17.3	9.68	3	#11	5	#9	22.4
5.68	3	#11	1	#9	13.2	7.14	5	#10	1	#8	17.4	9.76	3	#11	4	#10	21.1
5.70	2	#10	4	#8	15.9	7.16	4	#9	4	#8	19.8	9.80	5	#11	2	#9	21.3
5.71	5	#8	4	#6	19.8	7.22	3	#11	2	#10	16.1	10.05	4	#11	3	#10	21.4
5.75	5	#8	3	#7	18.4	7.24	4	#11	1	#9	16.1	10.08	4	#10	5	#9	24.1
5.79	5	#9	1	#8	16.0	7.35	5	#10	1	#9	17.6	10.24	4	#11	4	#9	23.0
5.80	4	#9	3	#7	17.4	7.37	5	#9	3	#8	20.1	10.30	5	#10	5	#8	25.5
5.81	3	#10	2	#9	14.8	7.40	5	#9	4	#7	21.6	10.34	5	#11	2	#10	21.7
5.87	4	#10	1	#8	14.8	7.45	4	#10	3	#8	19.0	10.35	5	#10	4	#9	24.4
5.95	2	#9	5	#8	17.3	7.51	4	#11	1	#10	16.3	10.80	5	#11	3	#9	23.5
5.95	3	#11	1	#10	13.5	7.54	2	#10	5	#9	19.0	11.03	3	#11	5	#10	23.7
6.00	3	#9	5	#7	18.9	7.68	3	#11	3	#9	17.9	11.24	4	#11	5	#9	25.2
6.08	4	#10	1	#9	15.0	7.76	3	#10	5	#8	20.4	11.32	4	#11	4	#10	24.0
6.12	2	#11	3	#9	15.1	7.80	5	#11	.....	....	16.5	11.35	5	#10	5	#9	26.7
6.15	5	#8	5	#6	21.5	7.81	3	#10	4	#9	19.3	11.61	5	#11	3	#10	24.2
6.16	3	#9	4	#8	17.6	7.91	1	#11	5	#10	18.0	11.80	5	#11	4	#9	25.8
6.16	4	#8	5	#7	20.2	7.93	5	#10	2	#8	19.5	12.59	4	#11	5	#10	26.5
6.18	3	#10	3	#8	16.4	7.95	4	#9	5	#8	21.8	12.80	5	#11	5	#9	28.1
6.20	5	#9	2	#7	17.8	8.00	5	#9	5	#7	23.5	12.88	5	#11	4	#10	26.8

PERIMETERS FOR VARIOUS COMBINATIONS OF SEPARATE BARS

		0		1	2	3	4	5		1	2	3	4	5
1		1.6		2.5	3.4	4.2	5.1	6.0						
2		3.1		4.1	5.0	5.8	6.7	7.6						
3	#4	4.7	#3	5.7	6.6	7.4	8.3	9.2						
4		6.3		7.3	8.2	9.0	9.9	10.8						
5		7.9		8.9	9.8	10.6	11.5	12.4						
1		2.0		3.3	4.5	5.8	7.1	8.4						
2		3.9		5.2	6.5	7.8	9.1	10.4						
3	#5	5.9	#4	7.2	8.5	9.8	11.1	12.4						
4		7.9		9.2	10.5	11.8	13.1	14.3						
5		9.8		11.2	12.5	13.8	15.0	16.3						
1		2.4		4.0	5.7	7.3	9.0	10.6		3.4	4.5	5.5	6.6	7.7
2		4.7		6.3	8.0	9.7	11.3	13.0		5.8	6.8	7.9	9.0	10.0
3	#6	7.1	#5	8.7	10.3	12.0	13.7	15.3	#4	8.1	9.2	10.2	11.3	12.4
4		9.4		11.0	12.7	14.3	16.0	17.7		10.5	11.5	12.6	13.7	14.7
5		11.8		13.4	15.0	16.7	18.3	20.0		12.8	13.9	14.9	16.0	17.1
1		2.7		4.8	6.8	8.8	10.8	12.8		4.2	5.6	7.0	8.4	9.8
2		5.5		7.5	9.5	11.5	13.5	15.5		6.9	8.3	9.7	11.2	12.5
3	#7	8.2	#6	10.2	12.3	14.3	16.3	18.3	#5	9.6	11.1	12.5	13.9	15.3
4		11.0		13.0	15.0	17.0	19.0	21.0		12.4	13.8	15.2	16.6	18.1
5		13.7		15.7	17.7	19.7	21.8	23.8		15.1	16.5	18.0	19.4	20.8
1		3.1		5.6	8.0	10.4	12.8	15.2		4.9	6.7	8.4	10.2	12.0
2		6.3		8.7	11.1	13.5	15.9	18.3		8.1	9.8	11.6	13.4	15.1
3	#8	9.4	#7	11.9	14.3	16.7	19.1	21.5	#6	11.2	13.0	14.8	16.5	18.3
4		12.6		15.0	17.4	19.8	22.2	24.6		14.4	16.2	17.9	19.7	21.4
5		15.7		18.2	20.6	23.0	25.4	27.8		17.6	19.3	21.1	22.8	24.6
1		3.5		6.3	9.1	12.0	14.8	17.6		5.7	7.8	9.9	12.1	14.2
2		7.1		9.9	12.7	15.5	18.3	21.1		9.2	11.3	13.5	15.6	17.7
3	#9	10.6	#8	13.4	16.2	19.0	21.8	24.6	#7	12.8	14.9	17.0	19.1	21.3
4		14.2		17.0	19.8	22.6	25.4	28.2		16.3	18.4	20.6	22.7	24.8
5		17.7		20.5	23.3	26.1	28.9	31.7		19.9	22.0	24.1	26.2	28.4
1		4.0		7.1	10.3	13.4	16.6	19.7		6.5	9.0	11.5	14.0	16.4
2		8.0		11.2	14.3	17.4	20.6	23.7		10.5	13.0	15.5	18.0	20.4
3	#10	12.0	#9	15.2	18.3	21.4	24.6	27.7	#8	14.5	17.0	19.5	22.0	24.4
4		16.0		19.2	22.3	25.4	28.6	31.7		18.5	21.0	23.5	26.0	28.4
5		20.0		23.2	26.3	29.4	32.6	35.7		22.5	25.0	27.5	30.0	32.4
1		4.4		8.0	11.6	15.2	18.8	22.4		7.3	10.1	12.9	15.8	18.6
2		8.9		12.5	16.1	19.7	23.3	26.9		11.7	14.5	17.4	20.2	23.0
3	#11	13.3	#10	16.9	20.5	24.1	27.7	31.3	#9	16.1	19.0	21.8	24.6	27.5
4		17.7		21.3	24.9	28.5	32.1	35.7		20.5	23.4	26.2	29.1	31.9
5		22.2		25.7	29.3	32.9	36.5	40.1		25.0	27.8	30.6	33.5	36.3

The column headed 0 contains the total perimeter for bars of the size given in the second column, the number of bars, from 1 to 5, being specified in the first column.

Columns headed 1 2 3 4 5 give the average total perimeter (i.e., $4A_s/D$, where D is the diameter of the largest bar) of combinations of the number of bars called for across the top of the table of the sizes given in the column just to the left of the number of bars when combined with the number and size of bars given in the first two columns.

Examples:—Perimeter of three #4 bars is found on Line 3 in Column 0 as 4.7 in.

Perimeter of three #4 plus four #3 bars is found on Line 3 in Column headed 4 as 8.3 in.

Perimeter of five #11 plus five #9 bars is found in the last line, last column as 36.3 in.

AREAS AND PERIMETERS OF BARS FOR SECTION OF SLAB ONE-FOOT WIDE

The table on pages 2-10 and 2-11 gives the cross-sectional area per foot width of slab for various combinations of equal and unequal size bars. The spacing given is center to center of adjacent bars in inches, whether bars are of the same or different size. When different bar sizes are combined, large and small bars alternate.

The table on page 2-12 gives the total perimeter of bars per foot width of slab for various bar spacings. The spacing selected for entering the table should be that of the bars actually available for bond, disregarding any bars that have been bent out of the plane of stress.

Example in the use of Area Table on page 2-11. An area of 1.18 sq in. per foot width of slab is required. The column headed "#6 + #7" shows that 1.19 sq in. can be obtained with consecutive bars 5¼ * in. c/c. The required area can also be obtained with #5 + #6 @ 3¾ * = 1.20 sq in. However, #6 + #7 @ 5 * = 1.25 sq in. has the advantage of spacing in even inches and will be used.

Example in the use of Perimeter Table on page 2-12. To obtain the perimeter for bond, assume first that this is a single span, so that alternate #6 bars would be bent up and bond figured on #7 @ 10 in. Enter the table and in column headed "#7" at a spacing of 10 in. find a perimeter of 3.3 in.

If this were a continuous span, the #7 bars would be bent up and bond for negative moment would be figured on two sets of #7 @ 10 in., which is equivalent to #7 @ 5 in. In column headed "#7" at a spacing of 5 in. find 6.6 in. Bond for the positive moment bars is figured on #6 @ 10 in. = 2.8 in.

---

* According to "Building Code Requirements for Reinforced Concrete (ACI 318-63)," the spacing between two adjacent bars must not exceed three times the slab thickness, ***t***.

AREAS OF BARS FOR SECTION OF SLAB ONE-FOOT WIDE

	Spacing * (in.)	Combinations of Bar Nos						
		#3 + #3	#3 + #4	#4 + #4	#4 + #5	#5 + #5	#5 + #6	#6 + #6
1	2	0.66	0.93	1.20	1.53	1.86	2.25	2.64
2	2¼	0.59	0.82	1.07	1.36	1.65	2.00	2.35
3	2½	0.53	0.74	0.96	1.22	1.49	1.80	2.11
4	2¾	0.48	0.68	0.87	1.12	1.35	1.64	1.92
5	3	0.44	0.62	0.80	1.02	1.24	1.50	1.76
6	3¼	0.41	0.57	0.74	0.94	1.14	1.38	1.62
7	3½	0.38	0.53	0.69	0.87	1.06	1.28	1.51
8	3¾	0.35	0.50	0.64	0.82	0.99	1.20	1.41
9	4	0.33	0.47	0.60	0.77	0.93	1.13	1.32
10	4¼	0.31	0.44	0.56	0.72	0.88	1.06	1.24
11	4½	0.29	0.42	0.53	0.68	0.83	1.00	1.17
12	4¾	0.28	0.39	0.51	0.64	0.78	0.95	1.11
13	5	0.26	0.37	0.48	0.61	0.74	0.90	1.06
14	5¼	0.25	0.36	0.46	0.58	0.71	0.85	1.01
15	5½	0.24	0.34	0.44	0.56	0.68	0.82	0.96
16	5¾	0.23	0.32	0.42	0.53	0.65	0.78	0.92
17	6	0.22	0.31	0.40	0.51	0.62	0.75	0.88
18	6½	0.20	0.29	0.37	0.47	0.57	0.70	0.81
19	7	0.19	0.27	0.34	0.44	0.53	0.65	0.75
20	7½	0.18	0.25	0.32	0.41	0.50	0.60	0.70
21	8	0.17	0.24	0.30	0.38	0.47	0.56	0.66
22	8½	0.16	0.22	0.28	0.36	0.44	0.53	0.62
23	9	0.15	0.21	0.27	0.34	0.41	0.50	0.59
24	9½	0.14	0.20	0.25	0.32	0.39	0.48	0.56
25	10	0.13	0.19	0.24	0.31	0.37	0.45	0.53
26	10½	0.13	0.18	0.23	0.29	0.35	0.43	0.50
27	11	0.12	0.17	0.22	0.28	0.34	0.41	0.48
28	11½	0.11	0.16	0.21	0.27	0.32	0.39	0.46
29	12	0.11	0.16	0.20	0.26	0.31	0.38	0.44
30	13	0.10	0.14	0.18	0.24	0.29	0.35	0.41
31	14	0.09	0.13	0.17	0.22	0.27	0.33	0.38
32	15	0.09	0.13	0.16	0.21	0.25	0.30	0.35

* According to "Building Code Requirements for Reinforced Concrete (ACI 318-63)," the spacing between two adjacent bars must not exceed three times the slab thickness, *t*.

AREAS OF BARS FOR SECTION OF SLAB ONE-FOOT WIDE

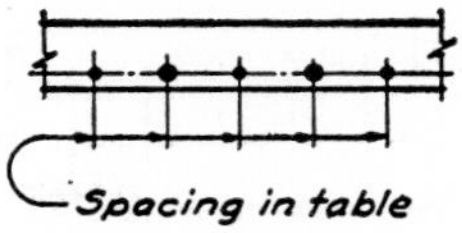

Combinations of Bar Nos

#6+#7	#7+#7	#7+#8	#8+#8	#8+#9	#9+#9	#9+#10	#10+#10	#10+#11	#11+#11	
										1
2.77	3.20									2
2.50	2.88	3.34	3.79							3
2.27	2.62	3.03	3.45							4
2.08	2.40	2.78	3.16	3.58	4.00					5
1.92	2.22	2.57	2.92	3.31	3.69					6
1.78	2.06	2.38	2.71	3.06	3.43	3.89	4.36			7
1.66	1.92	2.22	2.53	2.86	3.20	3.63	4.06	4.53	4.99	8
1.56	1.80	2.09	2.37	2.69	3.00	3.41	3.81	4.25	4.68	9
1.47	1.69	1.97	2.23	2.53	2.82	3.20	3.59	3.99	4.40	10
1.39	1.60	1.85	2.11	2.38	2.67	3.02	3.39	3.77	4.16	11
1.32	1.52	1.76	2.00	2.26	2.53	2.86	3.21	3.57	3.94	12
1.25	1.44	1.67	1.90	2.15	2.40	2.72	3.05	3.39	3.74	13
1.19	1.37	1.59	1.81	2.04	2.29	2.59	2.90	3.23	3.57	14
1.13	1.31	1.51	1.72	1.95	2.18	2.48	2.77	3.09	3.40	15
1.09	1.25	1.45	1.65	1.86	2.09	2.37	2.65	2.96	3.26	16
1.04	1.20	1.39	1.58	1.79	2.00	2.27	2.54	2.83	3.12	17
0.96	1.11	1.28	1.46	1.65	1.85	2.09	2.35	2.61	2.88	18
0.89	1.03	1.19	1.35	1.54	1.71	1.95	2.18	2.43	2.67	19
0.83	0.96	1.11	1.26	1.43	1.60	1.82	2.03	2.27	2.50	20
0.78	0.90	1.04	1.19	1.34	1.50	1.70	1.91	2.12	2.34	21
0.73	0.85	0.98	1.12	1.27	1.41	1.61	1.79	2.00	2.20	22
0.69	0.80	0.93	1.05	1.20	1.33	1.52	1.69	1.89	2.08	23
0.66	0.76	0.88	1.00	1.13	1.26	1.43	1.60	1.79	1.97	24
0.63	0.72	0.84	0.95	1.08	1.20	1.36	1.52	1.70	1.87	25
0.60	0.69	0.80	0.90	1.02	1.14	1.30	1.45	1.62	1.78	26
0.57	0.65	0.76	0.86	0.98	1.09	1.24	1.39	1.55	1.70	27
0.55	0.63	0.73	0.82	0.93	1.04	1.19	1.33	1.48	1.63	28
0.52	0.60	0.70	0.79	0.90	1.00	1.14	1.27	1.42	1.56	29
0.48	0.55	0.64	0.73	0.83	0.92	1.05	1.17	1.31	1.44	30
0.45	0.51	0.60	0.68	0.77	0.86	0.98	1.09	1.22	1.34	31
0.42	0.48	0.56	0.63	0.72	0.80	0.91	1.02	1.14	1.25	32

PERIMETERS OF BARS FOR SECTION OF SLAB ONE-FOOT WIDE

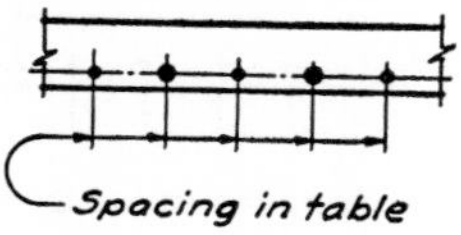

Spacing* (in.)	Bar No. #3	#4	#5	#6	#7	#8	#9	#10	#11
2	7.1	9.4	11.8	14.2					
2¼	6.3	8.4	10.5	12.6	14.7				
2½	5.7	7.5	9.4	11.3	13.2	15.1			
2¾	5.1	6.9	8.6	10.3	12.0	13.7			
3	4.7	6.3	7.8	9.4	11.0	12.6	14.2		
3¼	4.4	5.8	7.2	8.7	10.2	11.6	13.0		
3½	4.0	5.4	6.7	8.1	9.4	10.8	12.1	13.7	
3¾	3.8	5.0	6.3	7.5	8.8	10.0	11.3	12.7	14.2
4	3.5	4.7	5.9	7.1	8.3	9.4	10.6	12.0	13.3
4¼	3.3	4.4	5.5	6.7	7.8	8.9	10.0	11.2	12.5
4½	3.1	4.2	5.2	6.3	7.3	8.4	9.5	10.6	11.8
4¾	3.0	4.0	5.0	6.0	6.9	7.9	8.9	10.0	11.2
5	2.8	3.8	4.7	5.7	6.6	7.5	8.5	9.6	10.6
5¼	2.7	3.6	4.5	5.4	6.3	7.2	8.1	9.1	10.1
5½	2.6	3.4	4.3	5.1	6.0	6.9	7.7	8.7	9.6
5¾	2.5	3.3	4.1	4.9	5.7	6.6	7.4	8.3	9.2
6	2.4	3.1	3.9	4.7	5.5	6.3	7.1	8.0	8.8
6½	2.2	2.9	3.6	4.4	5.1	5.8	6.5	7.4	8.2
7	2.0	2.7	3.4	4.0	4.7	5.4	6.1	6.8	7.6
7½	1.9	2.5	3.1	3.8	4.4	5.0	5.7	6.4	7.1
8	1.8	2.4	2.9	3.5	4.1	4.7	5.3	6.0	6.6
8½	1.7	2.2	2.8	3.3	3.9	4.4	5.0	5.6	6.2
9	1.6	2.1	2.6	3.1	3.7	4.2	4.7	5.3	5.9
9½	1.5	2.0	2.5	3.0	3.5	4.0	4.5	5.0	5.6
10	1.4	1.9	2.4	2.8	3.3	3.8	4.3	4.8	5.3
10½	1.3	1.8	2.2	2.7	3.1	3.6	4.0	4.6	5.0
11	1.3	1.7	2.2	2.6	3.0	3.4	3.9	4.3	4.8
11½	1.2	1.6	2.0	2.5	2.9	3.3	3.7	4.2	4.6
12	1.2	1.6	2.0	2.4	2.8	3.1	3.5	4.0	4.4
13	1.1	1.4	1.8	2.2	2.5	2.9	3.3	3.7	4.1
14	1.0	1.3	1.7	2.0	2.4	2.7	3.0	3.4	3.8
15	0.9	1.3	1.6	1.8	2.1	2.5	2.8	3.2	3.5

* According to "Building Code Requirements for Reinforced Concrete (ACI 318-63)," the spacing between two adjacent bars must not exceed three times the slab thickness, *t*.

BUNDLED BARS

For arrangement of bundled bars in columns see page 2-14.

EFFECTIVE AREA AND PERIMETER OF A BUNDLE

TYPE I   TYPE II   TYPE III   TYPE IV

Type	Effective Number of Bars	Bar Size	Total Area (in.^{2})	Equiv. dia. (in.)	Effective Perimeter of bundle (in.) — At a Splice Bar: Splice bar	Effective Perimeter — At a Splice Bar: Remainder of bundle	Effective Perimeter — Without splice bar	Minimum Clear Distance (in.) — Between Bundles	Minimum Clear Distance (in.) — Bundle to Edge
I	2	#8	1.58	1.42	2.61	5.24	6.28	2⅛	1¾
		#9	2.00	1.60	2.94	5.91	7.09	2½	1¾
		#10	2.54	1.80	3.33	6.65	7.98	2¾	1¾
		#11	3.12	2.00	3.67	7.39	8.86	3	2
II III	3	#8	2.37	1.75	2.35	7.07	7.85	2⅝	1¾
		#9	3.00	1.95	2.65	7.97	8.85	3	2
		#10	3.81	2.20	3.00	8.97	9.97	3⅜	2¼
		#11	4.68	2.44	3.33	9.96	11.06	3¾	2½
IV	4	#8	3.16	2.01	—	—	9.42	3	2
		#9	4.00	2.26	—	—	10.63	3½	2¼
		#10	5.08	2.55	—	—	11.97	3¾	2½
		#11	6.24	2.82	—	—	13.29	4¼	2¾

Bars in a bundle shall terminate with at least 40 bar diameters stagger except where the bundle terminates.

* Splice bars, welding, or positive connection must be provided for splices required to carry full tension or tension in excess of the capacity of the unspliced portion of the bundle. Compression may be transmitted by end-bearing of square-cut ends.

BUNDLED BAR SUBSTITUTIONS—VARIOUS GRADES—FOR #14 AND #18 BARS†

	1-#14		1-#18	
Grade	60	40	60	40
75	3-#8 + 1-#6 1-#10 + 1-#11 1-#10 + 2-#8 2-#9 + 2-#6	1-#10 + 3-#9 2-#11 + 1-#10	4-#10 + — 2-#11 + 2-#9	
60	1-#10 + 1-#9 3-#8 + — 4-#7 + —	1-#9 + 3-#8 2-#10 + 1-#9 1-#11 + 2-#9	4-#9 + — 2-#8 + 2-#10 2-#10 + 1-#11 2-#11 + 1-#9	4-#11 + —
50	1-#11 + — 2-#8 + — 3-#6 + 1-#5 3-#7 + —	1-#10 + 1-#9 3-#8 + — 4-#7 + —	1-#11 + 1-#10 1-#10 + 2-#8 2-#9 + 1-#8 2-#8 + 2-#7	4-#9 + — 2-#8 + 2-#10 2-#10 + 1-#11 2-#11 + 1-#9

† Opposite a single #14 or #18 bar of the grade given in the first column are given the various combinations of equivalent bundles of bars and grades scheduled that will produce the same total tensile capacity.

ARRANGEMENT OF VERTICALS AND TIES IN TIED COLUMNS

Diagrams show arrangement of vertical bars and ties in tied columns. Dotted ties are not required unless distance x exceeds 6 in. (ACI 806(c)).

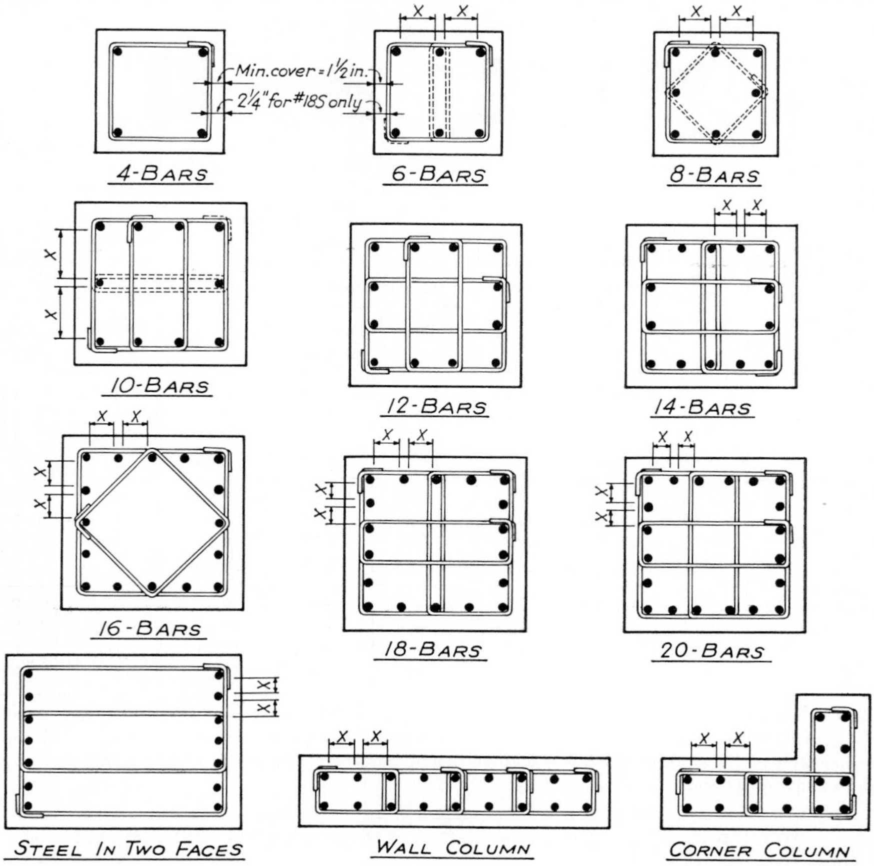

A different pattern of ties may be substituted provided it meets the requirements of the code and the contract drawings.

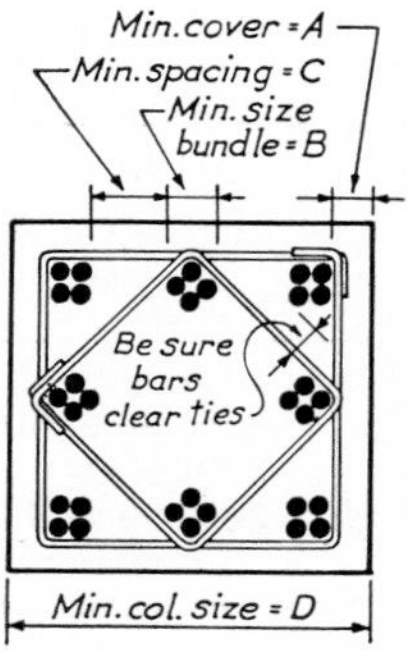

MINIMUM COLUMN DIMENSIONS WITH EIGHT BUNDLES OF BARS *

Bar Size	2-Bar Bundle Minima (in.)					3-Bar Bundle Minima (in.)					4-Bar Bundle Minima (in.)				
	Cover A	Size B	Spacing C	Column Side D	Percent of Steel	Cover A	Size B	Spacing C	Column Side D	Percent of Steel	Cover A	Size B	Spacing C	Column Side D	Percent of Steel
#8	1¾	2	2⅛	14	6½	1¾	2	2⅝	16	*	2	2	3	20	*
#9	1¾	2¼	2½	16	6¼	2	2¼	3	18	*	2¼	2¼	3½	23	*
#10	1¾	2½	2¾	17	7	2¼	2½	3⅜	20	*	2½	2½	3¾	26	*
#11	2	2¾	3	19	7	2½	2¾	3¾	22	*	2¾	2¾	4¼	28	*

* The column sizes are the minimum that will provide proper spacing or cover for the bundles or the minimum size (marked with an asterisk) for which the bundles are 8% or less of the cross section.

SPLICING BARS IN REINFORCED CONCRETE STRUCTURES
Suggestions to the Designer

Bars of the required length cannot always be in one piece. Lengths of around 30 to 40 feet (for #5 bars and larger) are usually easily handled. Small bars (#2 and #3) are frequently limited to 15 or 20 feet. Bars that stand vertically unsupported must be short. Bars up to 60 feet or more are customarily stocked by fabricators. The lengths that can be readily fabricated, delivered and installed depend upon transportation facilities and job equipment and are worked out between fabricator and contractor. Bars as long as 90 feet and over have been supplied under very special conditions.

Splicing. Splices are made by overlapping two bars a certain number of bar diameters in surrounding concrete capable of transmitting the stress from one bar to another; or by welding with a butt, lapped, or reinforced weld; or by fastening in any manner that will reliably transmit stress.

Column verticals are often spliced just above each floor line. Enough bars from below, *to develop in bond the bars above*, project a certain number of bar diameters, as required by grade of concrete and steel, above the floor line. Bars of the story above rest on top of the floor, alongside of the projecting bars (Fig. A). With upturned beams, splices will be at top of upturn. A clear space of 1½ in. or 1½ bar diameters is left between pairs of bars.

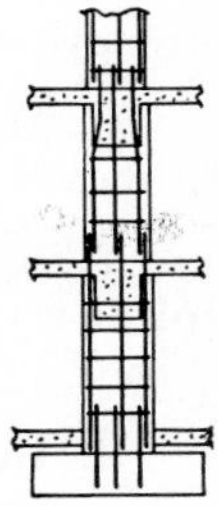

FIG. A

When the size and number of bars cause congestion, the bars, if sufficiently stiff, extend two stories in height, with half the bars spliced at each floor, eliminating half the overlaps at each level (Fig. B).

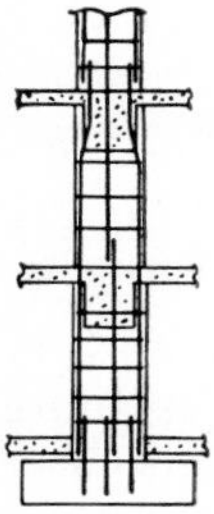

FIG. B

ACI 318-63 recommends butt-welding for #14S and #18S bars, and permits butt-welding of smaller bars also. The joint is to be prepared as shown in Fig. C and is required to develop 125% of the yield strength required by ASTM for the grade of bars specified. All welding shall be done in accordance with American Welding Society Recommendation D12.1.

FIG. C

In columns carrying large bending moments, it may be advantageous to splice bars at mid-story height, where the number of bars to be developed is reduced. Splice at alternate stories (Fig. D).

See pp. 2-19 to 2-21 for maximum number of bars in a column.

Slab, beam, and girder bars may be straight or trussed. Straight bottom bars may be one span length from support to support, or possibly continuous through consecutive spans to maximum length readily placed. Where splices are necessary:—

1. **Do not splice beam bars at points of maximum stress.** For top bars maximum stress will be at support of cantilever or continuous beams; for bottom bars, near midspan of continuous or freely supported beams.

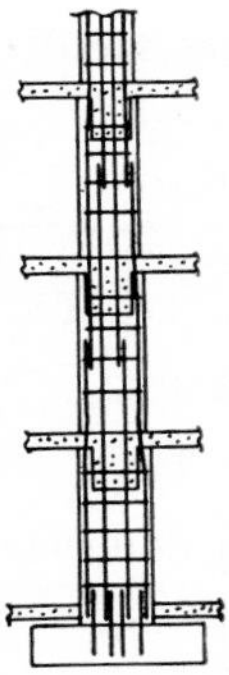

FIG. D

Splices are shown lapped for ease of illustration. They may equally well be butt-welded or mechanically coupled.

SPLICING BARS IN REINFORCED CONCRETE STRUCTURES
Suggestions to the Designer

2. Splice near point of inflection, i.e., fifth point of span for continuous beams of approximately equal spans, loads, and stiffnesses.

3. Stagger splices. Splice only one bar at a time; stagger next splice by 40 or 50 bar diameters. Even in beams with large quantities of reinforcement, splice only a small fraction of all the steel at any one point. Splices arranged symmetrically use the same pair of bars, reversed (Fig. E).

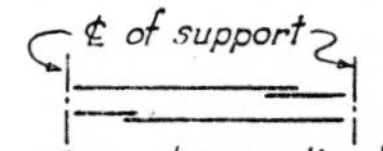

Beam bars spliced at alternate ends of beam. (Plan view)
FIG. E

4. Arrange splices where ample concrete transmits the stress. Avoid splices near holes, re-entrant corners, or sharp changes in section. Avoid points where concrete is highly stressed from other causes (shrinkage, temperature, torsion, etc.). Splices need special attention in beams with narrow stems or high intensities of shear.

5. Lapped splices are most commonly used. Welded splices may be used. Then preparation and performance should follow AWS D12.1. Coupled splices of adequate strength are also acceptable.

6. Wiring overlapped lengths of bar together affords no advantage.

7. A light spiral or closely-spaced ties around the splice reinforce it if there is doubt about surrounding concrete (Fig. F). Suitable for a hanger or tie.

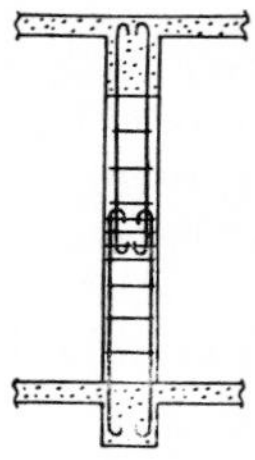
FIG. F
spliced hanger

8. Laps in truss bars follow a similar pattern. Keep splices away from support of a cantilever; supports and midspan (or maximum moment) for continuous beams.

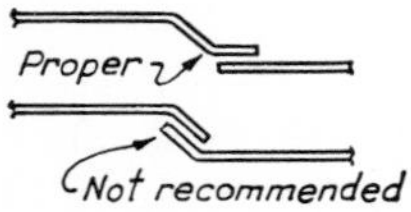

FIG. G

9. Put all bending in one bar when splicing truss bars near point of inflection which is also near where bars are bent up, reducing bending charge (Fig. G), and providing anchorage of bar carrying shear.

10. Detail sets of bars so that simple reversal will automatically provide trussed bar effect (Fig. H).

11. Specify extra stock in overlap in lines of steel. If ring rods around a circular tank are placed farther from the center than the designer planned, a few inches extra length in each bar will prevent insufficient lap or a shortage of steel.

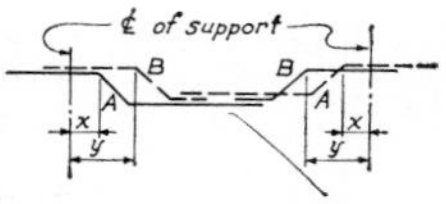

FIG. H

12. Stagger splices in adjacent tiers for grain elevators and tanks where bars are in full tension, as surrounding concrete must transfer the tension.

13. Specify additional horizontal cross bars at splices of retaining wall and footing bars to prevent splitting of concrete where large bars with minimum cover are used at points where all tension bars are spliced simultaneously.

LAPS AND SPACING OF BARS

ACI 318-63 recognizes two positions of bars:

(1) So-called "top bars" where, below an approximately horizontal bar, there are over 12 in. of concrete whose settlement and shrinkage tend to reduce the bond.

(2) "Other than top bars" where full bond resistance can be developed, as, for example, column verticals, bottom bars in slabs, joists, and beams, and vertical wall steel.

TENSION LAPPED SPLICES

ACI 805(b) requires that a tension splice:

(1) Transmit the full computed stress at ¾ of the otherwise allowed bond stress.*

(2) Have a minimum lap of 36 bar diameters for Grade 60 bars, or 12 in.

(3) Have computed lap increased 20 per cent unless bars are spaced 12 bar diameters or more and are over 6 in. or 6 bar diameters from an outside edge or are enclosed in closely-spaced stirrups or spirals.

(4) Not be used for bars larger than #11.

(5) Be away from a point of maximum stress with not over half the bars spliced within a length of 40 bar diameters.

Example I. How much lap is required at a splice of #10 tension bars in the top of a 30 in. deep beam?

Solution. Since these are "top bars," $u = \frac{3}{4}\,\frac{3.4\sqrt{f'_c}}{D} = \frac{2.55\sqrt{3750}}{1.27} = 123$ psi.

Computed lap $= \frac{f_s D}{4u} = \frac{24{,}000 \times 1.27}{4 \times 123} = 62$ in. Unless bars are farther apart than $12 \times 1.27 = 15.24$ in., which is unlikely in a beam, splice length should increase computed lap by 20 per cent to $1.2 \times 62 = 74.4$, say 75 in. (see table below). This exceeds 120 per cent of 36 bar diameters, i.e., $1.2 \times 36 \times 1.27 = 54.9$ in.

If the bars could be spaced 15.24 in. and covered as required (and this would be very unlikely), the lap could be reduced to 62 in.

Example II. If the bars of Example I were in the bottom of the beam, compute the lap.

Solution. With "other than top bars," $u = \frac{3}{4}\,\frac{4.8\sqrt{f'_c}}{D} = \frac{3.6\sqrt{3750}}{1.27} = 173.6$ psi. Computed lap $= \frac{f_s D}{4u} = \frac{24{,}000 \times 1.27}{4 \times 173.6} = 43.9$ in. Splice length, because of lack of surrounding concrete $= 1.2 \times 43.9 = 52.7$, say 53 in., but this is less than 120 per cent of 36 bar diameters, i.e., $1.2 \times 36 \times 1.27 = 54.9$ in., so use 55 in. (see table below).

If the bars could be spaced 15.24 in. and covered as required (again, very unlikely), the lap could be reduced to 44 in.

---

* For plain round bars, these laps shall be doubled in length.

LAPS AND SPACING OF BARS

MINIMUM TENSION LAPPED SPLICE LENGTHS
Grade 60 bars $f'_c = 3750$ psi Concrete

Bar Size	Top Bars		Other Than Top Bars	
	Ordinary Spacing	Widely Spaced and Covered *	Ordinary Spacing	Widely Spaced and Covered *
#3	17″	14″	17″	14″
#4	22″	18″	22″	18″
#5	27″	23″	27″	23″
#6	33″	27″	33″	27″
#7	38″	32″	38″	32″
#8	47″	39″	44″	36″
#9	59″	49″	49″	41″
#10	75″	62″	55″	46″
#11	92″	77″	65″	54″
#14 & #18	Lapped splices not permitted.			

Values above horizontal line are determined by arbitrary bar diameters; values below the horizontal lines, by computed bond.

* Also applies to ordinary spacing with closely-spaced stirrups or spirals enclosing the splice for its full length.

COMPRESSION LAPPED SPLICES

ACI 805(c) requires that a compression lapped splice:

(1) Have a minimum lap of 24 bar diameters for Grade 60 bars or 30 bar diameters for Grade 75 in 3000 psi or more concrete, increased one-third for weaker concrete, or 12 in.

(2) For bars larger than #11, be preferably welded or otherwise positively connected, except that, for compression only, ends may be butted and held in alignment by a collar instead of lapped.

Example III. Design the length of splice for #11 column verticals of Grade 75 in 5000 psi concrete where bars will not be in tension under any likely loading condition.
Solution. Grade 75 bars require 30 bar diameter lap in 3000 psi concrete or more. $30 \times 1.41 = 42.3$, say 43 in.

Example IV. If bars were of Grade 60 in 3750 psi concrete, what is the lap?
Solution. $24 \times 1.41 = 33.84$, say 34 in.

MINIMUM COMPRESSION LAPPED SPLICE LENGTHS
$f'_c = 3750$ or 5000 psi concrete

Bar Size	Grade 60 Bars ($f_s = 24{,}000$ psi basis)	Grade 75 Bars ($f_s = 30{,}000$ psi basis)
#5	15″	19″
#6	18″	23″
#7	21″	27″
#8	24″	30″
#9	28″	34″
#10	31″	39″
#11	34″	43″
#14 & #18	Lapped splices not recommended.	

LAPS AND SPACING OF BARS

MAXIMUM NUMBER OF SPLICED COLUMN VERTICALS IN VARIOUS PATTERNS THAT CAN BE ACCOMMODATED IN SINGLE RING WITHIN COLUMN SPIRALS

BUTT-WELDED **RADIALLY LAPPED** **CIRCUMFERENTIALLY LAPPED**

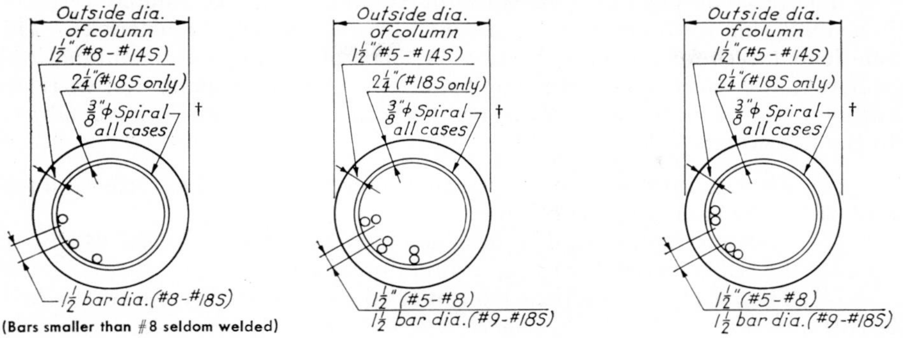

(Bars smaller than #8 seldom welded)

Diameter of Column	Butt-welded #8	#9	#10	#11	#14S	#18S	Radially lapped #5	#6	#7	#8	#9	#10	#11	‡ #14S	‡ #18S	Circumferentially lapped #5	#6	#7	#8	#9	#10	#11	‡ #14S	‡ #18S
10†	6	—	—	—	—	—	6	—	—	—	—	—	—	—	—	6	6	—	—	—	—	—	—	—
11†	7	6	—	—	—	—	8	7	6	—	—	—	—	—	—	7	7	6	—	—	—	—	—	—
12†	9	7	6	—	—	—	9	8	7	6	—	—	—	—	—	8	7	7	6	—	—	—	—	—
13†	10	9	7	6	—	—	10	9	8	7	6	—	—	—	—	9	8	8	7	6	—	—	—	—
14	11	10	8	7	—	—	12	11	10	9	8	6	—	—	—	11	9	9	8	7	6	—	—	—
15	12	11	9	8	6	—	13	12	11	10	8	7	6	—	—	12	11	10	9	8	7	6	—	—
16	14	12	10	9	7	—	15	13	12	11	9	8	6	—	—	13	12	11	10	8	7	6	—	—
17	15	13	11	10	8	—	16	15	14	12	11	9	7	6	—	14	13	11	11	9	8	7	6	—
18	16	14	12	11	9	—	18	16	15	14	12	10	8	6	—	15	14	12	11	10	9	8	6	—
19	17	15	13	12	10	—	19	18	16	15	13	11	9	7	—	16	15	13	12	11	9	8	7	—
20	19	16	14	13	10	6*	21	19	18	16	14	12	10	8	—	17	16	14	13	12	10	9	7	—
21	20	18	15	14	11	7*	22	20	19	17	15	13	11	8	—	18	17	15	14	12	11	10	8	—
22	21	19	16	15	12	7*	23	22	20	18	16	14	11	9	—	20	18	16	15	13	12	10	8	6
23	22	20	17	15	13	8*	25	23	21	20	17	15	12	10	6	21	19	17	16	14	12	11	9	6
24	24	21	18	16	13	9*	26	24	22	21	18	16	13	11	7	22	20	18	17	15	13	11	9	6
25	25	22	19	17	14	9*	28	26	24	22	19	17	14	11	7	23	21	19	18	16	14	12	10	7
26	26	23	20	18	15	10	29	27	25	23	20	18	15	12	8	24	22	20	19	16	14	13	10	7
27	28	24	21	19	16	11	31	28	26	25	21	19	16	13	8	25	23	21	20	17	15	13	11	8
28	29	25	22	20	16	11	32	30	28	26	22	20	17	13	9	26	24	22	20	18	16	14	11	8
29	30	26	23	21	17	12	33	31	29	27	23	21	17	14	9		25	23	21	19	16	15	12	8
30	31	28	24	22	18	12	35	32	30	28	25	22	18	15	10		26	24	22	20	17	15	12	9
31	33	29	25	23	18	13		34	31	29	26	23	19	16	10		27	25	23	20	18	16	13	9
32	34	30	26	23	19	14			33	31	27	24	20	16	11			26	24	21	19	16	14	10
33	35	31	27	24	20	14			34	32	28	25	21	17	12			27	25	22	19	17	14	10
34	36	32	28	25	21	15				33	29	26	22	18	12				26	23	20	18	15	10
35	38	33	29	26	21	15				34	30	26	23	19	13				27	23	21	18	15	11
36		34	30	27	22	16					31	27	24	19	13					24	22	19	16	11
37		35	31	28	23	16					33	29	25	20	14					25	23	20	16	12
38		37	32	29	24	17					33	29	26	21	14					26	24	21	17	12
39		38	33	30	24	17					35	31	27	22	15					27	24	22	17	12
40			34	31	25	18						31	28	22	15						25	22	18	13
41			35	31	26	19						33	29	23	16						26	23	18	13
42			36	32	27	19						33	30	24	17						26	23	19	14
43			37	33	27	20						35	31	25	17						27	24	19	14
44			38	34	28	20							31	25	18							25	20	14
45				35	29	21							33	26	18							25	20	15
46				36	30	21							33	27	19							26	21	15
47				37	30	22							34	28	19							27	22	16
48				38	31	22							35	28	20							27	22	16

* Limited to number of bars that provide a maximum of 8% vertical reinforcement.

† 3/8" spiral too large to meet all code requirements in 10" to 13" columns, but 1/4" spiral not standard.

‡ Lapped splices not recommended for #14S and #18S bars.

LAPS AND SPACING OF BARS

MAXIMUM NUMBER OF SPLICED COLUMN VERTICALS IN VARIOUS PATTERNS THAT CAN BE ACCOMMODATED IN TWO RINGS WITHIN COLUMN SPIRAL

The table on page 2-19 gives the maximum number of column verticals in a single ring (or limited by 8 per cent where noted with an asterisk). The safe load tables for columns, Section 11, generally cover only combinations of bars that conform to the table on page 2-19. A greater number of verticals can be accommodated if they are arranged in two concentric rings, subject to the following:

(1) The total percentage of vertical reinforcement shall not exceed 8 per cent of the gross area of the column.
(2) The outer spiral shall be designed in accordance with ACI 913(b) to provide the entire percentage of spiral reinforcement.*
(3) The spacing of vertical bars in all directions shall conform to ACI 804(d) and (e).
(4) The inner ring of bars can be held in place with circular or polygonal hoops or ties spaced according to the table on page 2-21 for tied columns.

The maximum number that can be accommodated can be determined by combining the maximum number in a single ring within the given column with the tabulated number for a column of smaller diameter, which diameter can be obtained by deducting from the given column diameter the number of inches given in the following table.

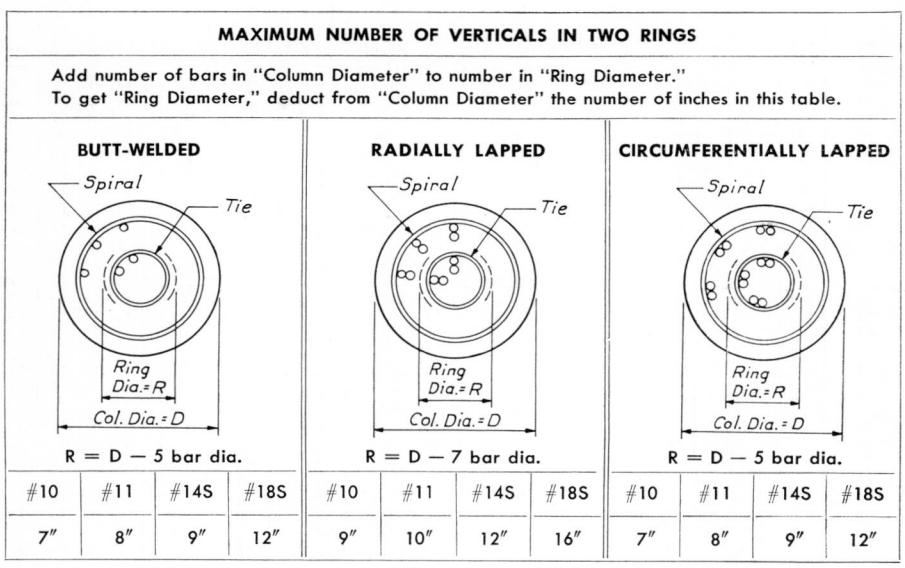

MAXIMUM NUMBER OF VERTICALS IN TWO RINGS

Add number of bars in "Column Diameter" to number in "Ring Diameter."
To get "Ring Diameter," deduct from "Column Diameter" the number of inches in this table.

BUTT-WELDED

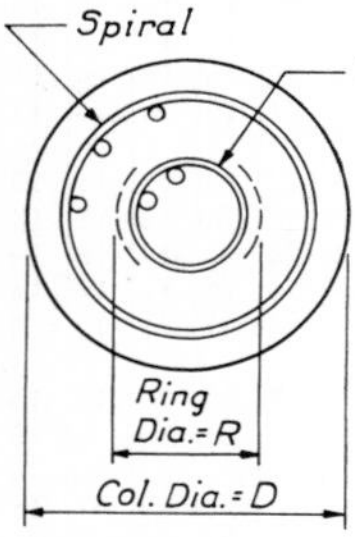

R = D − 5 bar dia.

RADIALLY LAPPED

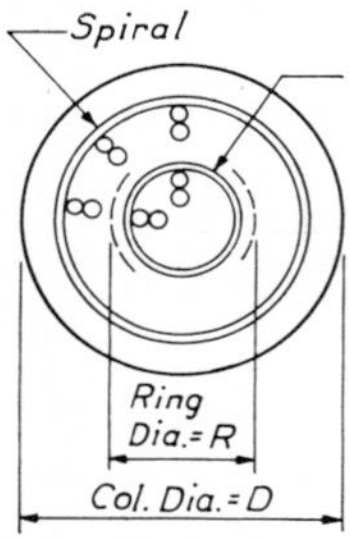

R = D − 7 bar dia.

CIRCUMFERENTIALLY LAPPED

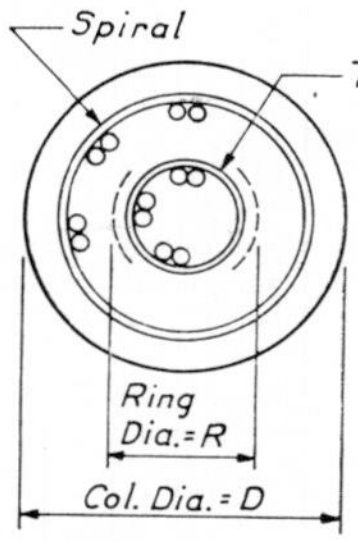

R = D − 5 bar dia.

BUTT-WELDED				RADIALLY LAPPED				CIRCUMFERENTIALLY LAPPED			
#10	#11	#14S	#18S	#10	#11	#14S	#18S	#10	#11	#14S	#18S
7″	8″	9″	12″	9″	10″	12″	16″	7″	8″	9″	12″

* For percentage of spirals in relation to core area, see pages 11-212 and 11-213.

LAPS AND SPACING OF BARS

MAXIMUM SPACING OF COLUMN TIES

Vertical Bar Size	Size and Spacing of Ties in Inches; Maximum Spacing Not to Exceed Least Column Dimension	
	#3	#4
#5	10	10
#6	12	12
#7	14	14
#8	16	16
#9	18	18
#10	18	20
#11	18	22
#14	18	24
#18	18	24

MAXIMUM NUMBER OF BARS IN ONE FACE OF SQUARE TIED COLUMNS

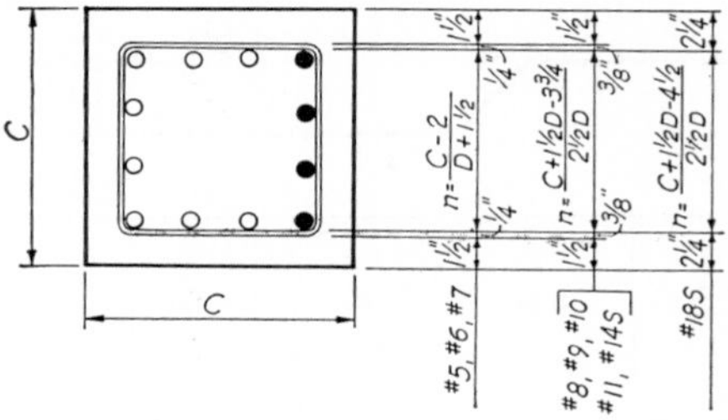

Column Size "C"	Number of Bars of a Size (n)								
	#5	#6	#7	#8	#9	#10	#11	#14S	#18S
10	3	3	3	3	2	2	2	—	—
11	4	4	3	3	3	2	2	2	—
12	4	4	4	3	3	3	2	2	—
13	5	4	4	4	3	3	3	2	—
14	5	5	5	4	4	3	3	3*	—
15	6	5	5	5	4	4	3	3	2
16	6	6	5	5	4	4	4	3	2
17	7	6	6	5	5	4	4	3	2
18	7	7	6	6	5	5	4	3	2
19	8	7	7	6	6	5	4	4	3*
20	8	8	7	7	6	5	5	4	3
21	8	8	8	7	6	6	5	4	3
22	9	8	8	7	7	6	5	4	3
23	9	9	8	8	7	6	6	5	3
24	10	9	9	8	7	6	6	5	4*
25	10	10	9	9	8	7	6	5	4
26	11	10	10	9	8	7	6	5	4
27	11	11	10	9	8	7	7	6	4
28	12	11	10	10	9	8	7	6	4
29	12	12	11	10	9	8	7	6	4
30	13	12	11	11	9	8	8	6	5
31	13	12	12	11	10	9	8	7	5
32	14	13	12	11	10	9	8	7	5
33	14	13	13	12	10	9	8	7	5
34	15	14	13	12	11	10	9	7	5
35	15	14	13	13	11	10	9	7	6
36	16	15	14	13	12	10	9	8	6
37	16	15	14	13	12	11	10	8	6
38	16	16	15	14	12	11	10	8	6
39	17	16	15	14	13	11	10	8	6
40	17	16	16	15	13	12	10	9	6

* If this number of bars is used in each of four faces, p will exceed 8%.

INCHES OF LAP CORRESPONDING TO NUMBER OF BAR DIAMETERS *

Number of Diameters	Size of Bar										
	#3	#4	#5	#6	#7	#8	#9	#10	#11	#14S	#18S
20	—	—	13	15	18	20	23	26	29	34	46
21	—	—	14	16	19	21	24	27	30	36	48
22	—	—	14	17	20	22	25	28	31	38	50
23	—	12	15	18	21	23	26	30	33	39	52
24	—	12	15	18	21	24	28	31	34	41	55
25	—	13	16	19	22	25	29	32	36	43	57
26	—	13	17	20	23	26	30	33	37	45	59
27	—	14	17	21	24	27	31	35	39	46	61
28	—	14	18	21	25	28	32	36	40	48	64
29	—	15	19	22	26	29	33	37	41	50	66
30	12	15	19	23	27	30	34	39	43	51	68
32	12	16	20	24	28	32	36	41	45	55	73
34	13	17	22	26	30	34	39	44	48	58	77
36	14	18	23	27	32	36	41	46	51	61	82
38	15	19	24	29	34	38	43	49	54	65	86
40	15	20	25	30	35	40	46	51	57	68	91
42	16	21	27	32	37	42	48	54	60	71	95
44	17	22	28	33	39	44	50	56	62	75	100
46	18	23	29	35	41	46	52	59	65	78	104
48	18	24	30	36	42	48	55	61	68	82	109
50	1[illegible]	25	32	38	44	50	57	64	71	85	113
52	20	26	33	39	46	52	59	67	74	88	118
54	21	27	34	41	48	54	61	69	77	92	122
56	21	28	35	42	49	56	64	72	79	95	127
58	22	29	37	44	51	58	66	74	82	99	131
60	23	30	38	45	53	60	68	77	85	102	136

Minimum lap equals 12 in.
* Figured to next larger whole inch.

SLANTS AND INCREMENTS FOR 45° BAR BENDS *

See also page 2-23.

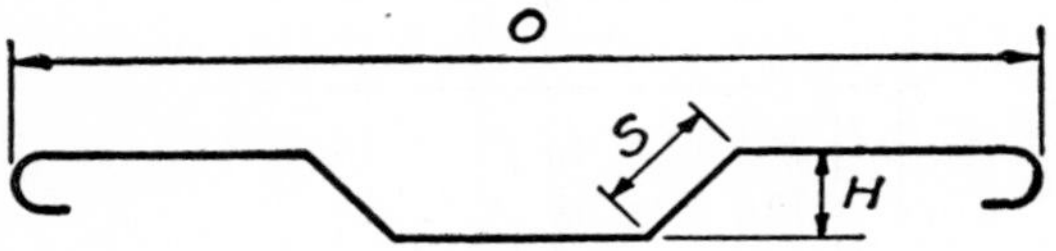

O = Overall Bar Dimension
H = Height of Bend, out to out
S = Slant = 1.414 H to Nearest ½ Inch
I = Increment = S–H

Height H †	Slant S	Increment 2 Slants 2I	Height H †	Slant S	Increment 2 Slants 2I	Height H †	Slant S	Increment 2 Slants 2I
			1-1	1-6½	11	3-1	4-4½	2-7
			1-2	1-8	1-0	3-2	4-5½	2-7
			1-3	1-9	1-0	3-3	4-7	2-8
2	3	2	1-4	1-10½	1-1	3-4	4-8½	2-9
2½	3½	2	1-5	2-0	1-2	3-5	4-10	2-10
3	4	2	1-6	2-1½	1-3	3-6	4-11½	2-11
3½	5	3	1-7	2-3	1-4	3-7	5-1	3-0
4	5½	3	1-8	2-4	1-4	3-8	5-2	3-0
4½	6½	4	1-9	2-5½	1-5	3-9	5-3½	3-1
5	7	4	1-10	2-7	1-6	3-10	5-5	3-2
5½	7½	4	1-11	2-8½	1-7	3-11	5-6½	3-3
6	8½	5	2-0	2-10	1-8	4-0	5-8	3-4
6½	9	5	2-1	2-11½	1-9	4-1	5-9½	3-5
7	10	6	2-2	3-1	1-10	4-2	5-10½	3-5
7½	10½	6	2-3	3-2	1-10	4-3	6-0	3-6
8	11½	7	2-4	3-3½	1-11	4-4	6-1½	3-7
8½	1-0	7	2-5	3-5	2-0	4-5	6-3	3-8
9	1-0½	7	2-6	3-6½	2-1	4-6	6-4½	3-9
9½	1-1½	8	2-7	3-8	2-2	4-7	6-6	3-10
10	1-2	8	2-8	3-9	2-2	4-8	6-7	3-10
10½	1-3	9	2-9	3-10½	2-3	4-9	6-8½	3-11
11	1-3½	9	2-10	4-0	2-4	4-10	6-10	4-0
11½	1-4	9	2-11	4-1½	2-5	4-11	6-11½	4-1
1-0	1-5	10	3-0	4-3	2-6	5-0	7-1	4-2

Increment For 2 Slants = 2 × (S–H)
Length of Truss Bars = 0 + 2I + Hooks.
All Dimensions Are Out To Out of Bar.
Scheduled length of bar is sum of the detail dimensions.

* From "Manual of Standard Practice for Detailing Reinforced Concrete Structures (ACI 315)."

† H = out-to-out vertical drop of truss bar = out-to-out of concrete, less following where applicable:—(1) fireproofing at top, (2) fireproofing at bottom, (3) tie diameter top, (4) stirrup diameter bottom, (5) diameter of cross-over bars, (6) allowance for bottom layer of bars and clearance between bars.

Fireproofing is usually ¾″ at top and ¾″ at bottom for slabs and joists, 1½″ top and 1½″ bottom for beams, to outer side of stirrups.

SLANT DIAGRAM *

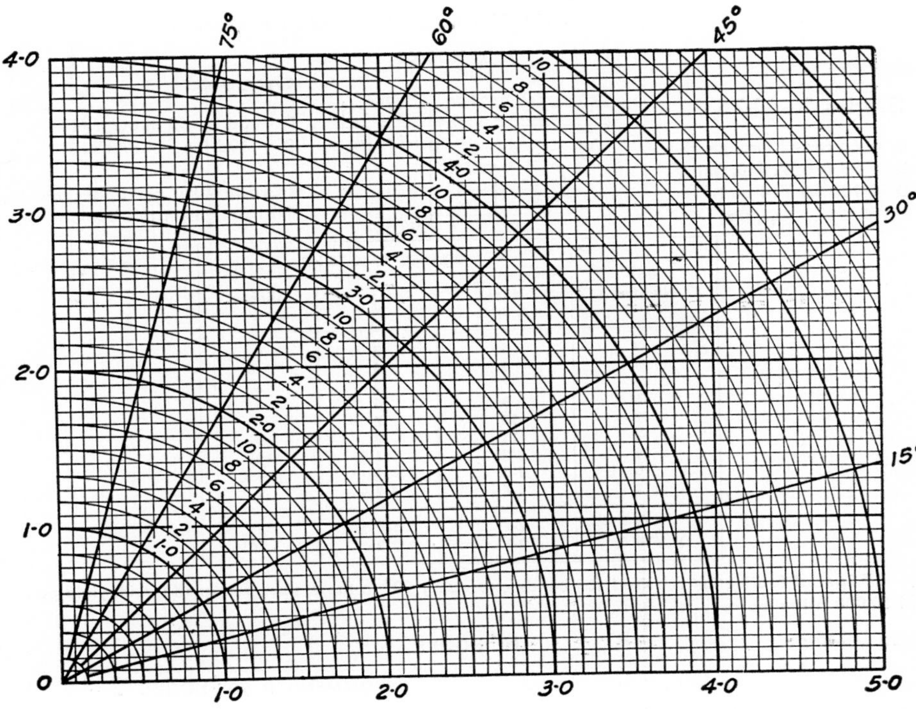

To determine the slant length enter the diagram with the length and height of bend and at the intersection read the slant length on the curved line.

STANDARD HOOKS

HOOKS WHICH MEET ACI 318-63 AND CAN BE FABRICATED WITH STANDARD EQUIPMENT

180° HOOKS

Grades 50-60-75

D = 6d for #3 through #8
D = 8d for #9, #10, and #11
D = 10d for #14 and #18

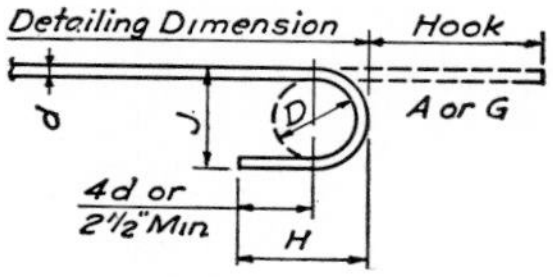

Grade 40 ‡

D = 5d for #3 through #11
D = 10d for #14 and #18

‡ Grade 40 is not applicable to most designs in this book.

Bar Number	GRADES 50-60-75 ksi		
	Hook A or G	J	Approx. H
#3	5	3	4
#4	6	4	4½
#5	7	5	5
#6	8	6	6
#7	10	7	7
#8	11	8	9
#9	1-3	11¼	10¼
#10	1-5	1-0¾	1-0¾
#11	1-7	1-2¼	1-2
#14 *	2-2	1-8½	1-5
#18 *	2-11	2-3	1-10½

* Special fabrication required for bends exceeding 90° in these sizes and grades with yield point of 50,000 psi or more.

90° HOOKS

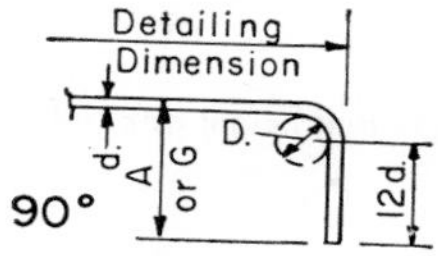

Recommended Bending

D = 6d for #3 through #8
D = 8d for #9, #10, and #11
D = 10d for #14 and #18

RECOMMENDED 90° HOOKS	
Bar Number	ALL GRADES
	Hook A or G
#3	6
#4	8
#5	10
#6	1-0
#7	1-2
#8	1-4
#9	1-7
#10	1-10
#11	2-0
#14	2-7
#18	3-5

STIRRUP AND TIE HOOKS

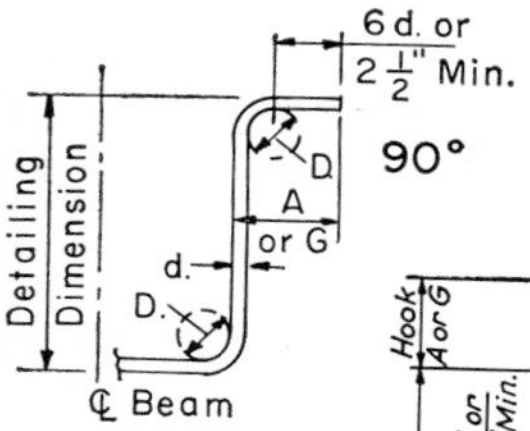

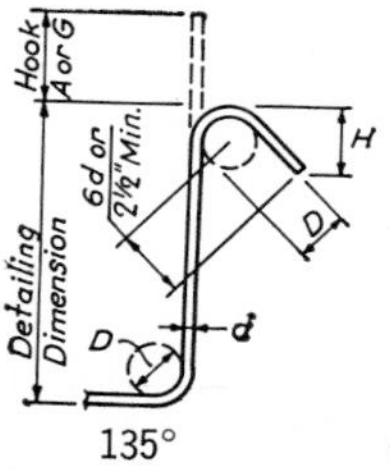

RECOMMENDED STIRRUP AND TIE HOOKS *				
Bar Number	D (in.)	90° Hook	135° Hook	
		Hook A or G	Hook A or G	Approx. H
#3	1½	4	4	2½
#4	2	4½	4½	3
#5	2½	6	5½	3¾
#6	2½	6½	6½	4½

* ASTM Specifications for all bars include bend tests within above limits except rail steel bars.

DATA ON AS&W WIRE GAUGES USED IN WELDED WIRE FABRIC

AS&W Wire Gauge Numbers	Diameter (in.)	Area (sq in.)	Weight (lb/ft)
0000000	0.4900	0.18857	0.6404
000000	0.4615	0.16728	0.5681
00000	0.4305	0.14556	0.4943
0000	0.3938	0.12180	0.4136
000	0.3625	0.10321	0.3505
00	0.3310	0.086049	0.2922
0	0.3065	0.073782	0.2506
1	0.2830	0.062902	0.2136
2	0.2625	0.054119	0.1838
¼″	0.2500	0.049087	0.1667
3	0.2437	0.046645	0.1584
4	0.2253	0.039867	0.1354
5	0.2070	0.033654	0.1143
6	0.1920	0.028953	0.09832
7	0.1770	0.024606	0.08356
8	0.1620	0.020612	0.07000
9	0.1483	0.017273	0.05866
10	0.1350	0.014314	0.04861
11*	0.1205	0.011404	0.03873
12*	0.1055	0.0087417	0.02969
13*	0.0915	0.0065755	0.02233
14*	0.0800	0.0050266	0.01707
15*	0.0720	0.0040715	0.01383
16*	0.0625	0.0030680	0.01042

* Fabric in which both longitudinal and transverse wires are No. 12 gauge or lighter is furnished galvanized only.

Note: Deformed wire sizes are designated D- followed by a number indicating cross-sectional area in hundredths of sq. in. A.S.T.M. Specification A496 lists sizes from D-1 to D-31. Requirements for deformed welded wire fabric are given in A.S.T.M. A497.

COMMON STYLES OF WELDED WIRE FABRIC

Style Designation	Weight (lb per 100 sq ft)	Spacing of Wires (in.)		Size of Wires AS&W Gauge		Sectional Area (sq in. per ft)	
		Longit.	Trans.	Longit.	Trans.	Longit.	Trans.
22-1414 *	21	2	2	14	14	.030	.030
22-1212 *	37	2	2	12	12	.052	.052
22-1010	60	2	2	10	10	.086	.086
212-812	46	2	12	8	12	.124	.009
212-610	66	2	12	6	10	.174	.014
212-48	91	2	12	4	8	.239	.021
212-26	124	2	12	2	6	.325	.029
212-04	169	2	12	0	4	.443	.040
33-1414 *	14	3	3	14	14	.020	.020
33-1212 *	25	3	3	12	12	.035	.035
33-1010	41	3	3	10	10	.057	.057
33-88	58	3	3	8	8	.082	.082
312-812	32	3	12	8	12	.082	.009
312-610	46	3	12	6	10	.116	.014
312-48	64	3	12	4	8	.159	.021
312-26	87	3	12	2	6	.216	.029
312-04	119	3	12	0	4	.295	.040
44-1414 *	11	4	4	14	14	.015	.015
44-1212 *	19	4	4	12	12	.026	.026
44-1010	31	4	4	10	10	.043	.043
44-88	44	4	4	8	8	.062	.062
44-66	62	4	4	6	6	.087	.087
44-44	85	4	4	4	4	.120	.120
48-1214 *	12	4	8	12	14	.026	.008
48-1212 *	14	4	8	12	12	.026	.013
48-1012	20	4	8	10	12	.043	.013
48-812	27	4	8	8	12	.062	.013
412-1012	19	4	12	10	12	.043	.009
412-812	25	4	12	8	12	.062	.009
412-610	36	4	12	6	10	.087	.014
412-48	51	4	12	4	8	.120	.021
412-26	69	4	12	2	6	.162	.029
412-04	94	4	12	0	4	.221	.040
66-1212 *	13	6	6	12	12	.017	.017
66-1010	21	6	6	10	10	.029	.029
66-88	30	6	6	8	8	.041	.041
66-66	42	6	6	6	6	.058	.058
66-46	50	6	6	4	6	.080	.058
66-44	58	6	6	4	4	.080	.080
66-22	78	6	6	2	2	.108	.108
66-00	107	6	6	0	0	.148	.148
612-66	32	6	12	6	6	.058	.029
612-44	44	6	12	4	4	.080	.040
612-22	59	6	12	2	2	.108	.054
612-04	69	6	12	0	4	.148	.040
612-00	81	6	12	0	0	.148	.074
612-2/0 4	78	6	12	2/0	4	.172	.040
612-3/0 4	91	6	12	3/0	4	.206	.040

* Furnished galvanized wire only.

Note: The above listing of styles is a representative listing only, as fabric with virtually any combination of wire gauges and spacings is possible to fit design requirements.

DESIGN FORMULAS AND DATA
Working Stress Method
Section 3

DESIGN FORMULAS AND DATA FOR REINFORCED CONCRETE WORKING STRESS METHOD

NOMENCLATURE

A — Distance in direction of span from center of support to intersection of centerline of slab thickness with extreme 45° diagonal line lying wholly within concrete section of slab and column or other support, including drop panel, capital and bracket.

A_c — Area of concrete within pipe column; area of core of spirally reinforced column measured to outside dia. of spiral; area of concrete within core of composite column.

A_g — Gross area of spirally reinforced or tied column; total area of concrete encasement of combination column; area of concrete of a composite column; gross area of section.

A_r — Area of steel or cast-iron core of composite, combination or pipe column.

A_s — Effective area of available tension reinforcement.

A'_s — Area of compressive reinforcement in flexural members.

A_{st} — Total area of longitudinal reinforcement.

A_v — Total area of web reinforcement in tension within a distance, s, measured in a direction parallel to the longitudinal reinforcement.

A'_v, A''_v, A'''_v — Portions of the total area of web reinforcement for distance d from support, the remaining excess shear prism and an extension of distance d.

a — Base length of shear diagram (inches).

α — Angle between inclined web bars and longitudinal axis of beam.

b — Width of compression face of flexural member.

b' — Width of web in I- and T-sections.

b_o — Periphery of critical section for shear in slabs and footings.

C — Side of a square tied column (inches); compressive force in beam section.

C_c — Resultant of compressive force in concrete only.

C_s — Resultant of compressive force in compressive reinforcement only.

c — Effective support size.

D — Nominal diameter of bar (inches); outside diameter of round column; inside diameter of hook or bend; service dead load in load tests.

D_s — Diameter of circle through centers of the longitudinal reinforcement in spiral columns.

d — Distance from extreme compression fiber to centroid of tension reinforcement.

d' — Distance from extreme compression fiber to centroid of compression reinforcement.

E_c, E_s — Modulus of elasticity of concrete $= w^{1.5}\,33\sqrt{f'_c}$; of steel $=$ 29,000,000 psi.

e — Eccentricity of the resultant load on a column measured from the gravity axis; eccentricity of axial load at end of member measured from plastic centroid of the section, calculated by conventional methods of frame analysis.

e_b — Maximum permissible eccentricity of N_b; eccentricity of load P_b measured from plastic centroid of section.

F_a — $0.34(1 + p_g m)f'_c$.

F_b — Allowable bending stress that would be permitted for bending alone.

F_{sp} — Ratio of splitting tensile strength to the square root of compressive strength.

f_a — Axial load divided by area of member, A_g.

f_{bx}, f_{by} — Bending moment components about the x and y principal axes divided by the section modulus of the respective transformed uncracked section, $2n$ being assumed as the modular ratio for all vertical reinforcement.

f_c — Allowable or computed stress in extreme fiber on compressive side of a reinforced concrete flexural member; allowable or computed stress in concrete of an eccentrically loaded column.

f'_c — Specified compressive strength of concrete in std. 6″ x 12″ cylinders at 28 days.

f_r — Allowable stress in the metal core of a composite column.

f'_r — Allowable stress on unencased metal columns and pipe columns.

f_s — Allowable or computed stress in tensile reinforcement; nominal allowable stress in vertical column reinforcement.

f_v — Tensile stress in web reinforcement.

f_y — Specified minimum yield strength in tension of reinforcement or of spirals.

H — Horizontal force or thrust; story height (feet) of column or support of a flat slab center-to-center of slabs.

h — Actual unsupported length of column; distance from top of slab to bottom of capital; any vertical height or distance.

h' — Effective length of long column.

I — Moment of inertia of beam or column about the neutral axis for bending.

I_c, I_s — Moment of inertia of concrete; of steel.

j — Ratio of distance between centroids of compression and tension to depth d.

K — Stiffness factor in frame design, i.e., the moment of inertia divided by the length.

K_c, K_s — Radii of gyration of concrete in pipe columns; of metal pipe.

k — Ratio of distance from extreme compressive fiber to neutral axis to depth d.

klf — Uniform load in kips per lineal foot.

L — Span length in general; length of embedment to develop bond stress; span length of a

NOMENCLATURE

flat slab panel center-to-center of supports.

l — Span length of slab or beam.

l' — Clear span for positive moment and shear and the average of the two adjacent clear spans for negative moment.

l'', l''' — Corresponding spans adjacent to l'.

M — External bending moment in lb–in.

M_b — Moment capacity at simultaneous crushing of concrete and yielding of tension steel (balanced conditions) $= P_b e_b$.

M_c — Resisting moment determined by concrete.

M_o — Numerical sum of assumed positive and average negative moments at the critical design sections of a flat slab panel.

M_s — Resisting Moment determined by reinforcing steel.

M_u — Moment capacity under combined axial load and bending.

M_{uo} — Ultimate capacity of member in pure bending.

m — $f_y/0.85f'_c$

N — Eccentric load normal to the cross section of a column; number of stirrups in a given length of beam.

$N.A.$ — Neutral axis.

N_b — Value of N below which the allowable eccentricity is controlled by tension and above which, by compression.

n — Ratio of modulus of elasticity of steel to that of concrete $= E_s/E_c = \dfrac{29{,}000{,}000}{w^{1.5}\,33\sqrt{f'_c}}$; number of bars in one face of square tied column.

Σ_o — Sum of perimeters of all effective bars crossing the section on the tension side if of uniform size; for mixed sizes, substitute $4A_s/D$; for bundled bars, the sum of the exposed portions of the perimeters.

P — Allowable axial load on a reinforced concrete column without reduction for length or eccentricity; concentrated load on flexural member; external concentric load on footings or piles; allowable axial load on combination, composite or pipe column without reduction for eccentricity.

P_b — Axial load capacity at simultaneous crushing of concrete and yielding of tension steel (balanced conditions).

P_o — Axial load capacity of actual member when concentrically loaded.

P_u — Axial load capacity under combined axial load and bending.

p — Ratio of area of tension reinforcement to effective area of concrete in rectangular beam or in web of flanged member.

p' — Ratio of compressive reinforcement in flexural member (A'_s/bd).

pcf, *plf* — Pounds per cubic foot; pounds per lineal foot.

p_g — Ratio of area of vertical reinforcement to the gross area A_g.

p_s — Ratio of volume of spiral reinforcement to total volume of core (out-to-out of spirals) of a spirally reinforced concrete or composite column.

psf, *psi* — Pounds per square foot; pounds per square inch.

p_w — $A_s/b'd$.

R — M/bd^2, the constant for flexural computations; outside diameter of hypothetical column that encloses inner ring of steel when two concentric rings of vertical bars are used; a reduction factor for long columns.

R_c — M/bd^2 determined by concrete.

R_s — M/bd^2 determined by steel.

R_n, R_p — Factor for increasing negative moment in flat slab; for increasing positive moment.

r — Radius of gyration of gross concrete area of a column.

r' — $\dfrac{\Sigma K(\text{column})}{\Sigma K(\text{floor members})}$ in a plane at one end of a column.

s — Spacing of stirrups or bent bars in direction parallel to longitudinal reinforcement.

T — Tensile force in beam section.

t — Thickness of flexural member; thickness of flange of a tee beam; over-all depth of rectangular column or the diameter of a round column.

t_1 — Thickness (inches) of slab without drop panels or through drop panel if any.

t_2 — Thickness (inches) of slab with drop panels at points beyond the drop panel.

u — Bond stress.

V — Total shear; total vertical force.

V' — Excess of the total shear over that permitted on the concrete.

v — Mean intensity of shear stress ($V/b'd$).

v_c — Allowable intensity of diagonal tension (shear) resisted by concrete.

W — Total load (wL); total dead and live load on panel.

W_D, W_L — Total dead load on panel; total live load on panel, uniformly distributed.

w — Weight of concrete (lb/cu ft); total uniformly distributed load per unit of length of beam or per unit of area of slab.

z — Distance from compression face to resultant of the compressive stresses.

FORMULAS, TABLES AND DIAGRAMS FOR REINFORCED CONCRETE DESIGN (WORKING STRESS METHOD)

Although the purpose of this book is to provide finished designs giving concrete outlines and reinforcing steel for different loading conditions, it may be helpful to have the formulas for working stress computations of reinforced concrete grouped together in one place for easy reference.

References in this section marked "ACI" are to "Building Code Requirements for Reinforced Concrete (ACI 318-63)."

Transformed Areas

In general, it will be found with practice that it is simpler to use the method of "transformed areas" than to depend upon formulas. This method simply replaces the reinforcement with $n\left(=\frac{E_s}{E_c}\right)$ times as much concrete on the tension side of a member or $(2n - 1)$ times as much on the compression side, ACI 1102(c). It omits any tension concrete and provides the equivalent of a homogeneous member whose neutral axis (under flexure without direct stress) is at the centroid of the transformed area. If stresses are assumed to vary as the distance from the neutral axis, all values can be determined by simple geometrical relationships.

FORMULAS—WORKING STRESS METHOD

1. Rectangular Beams with Tension Reinforcement.*

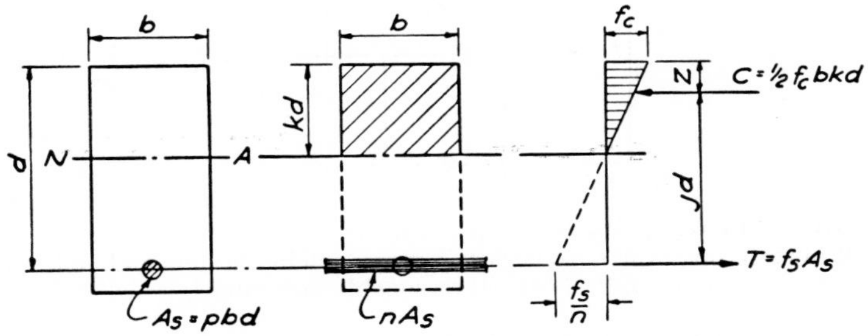

f_s = tensile unit stress in steel.
f_c = compressive unit stress in extreme fiber of concrete.
E_s = modulus of elasticity of steel.
E_c = modulus of elasticity of concrete.

$$n = \frac{E_s}{E_c} = \frac{29{,}000{,}000}{w^{1.5}\, 33\sqrt{f_c'}}$$

M = moment of resistance or bending moment in general.
b = breadth of beam.
d = depth of beam to center of steel.

ACI 1102 (b) permits n to be taken to the nearest integer, e.g. 8 for 3750/24000; it has also been taken to the nearest tenth, as 8.2, or as 8.22 or 8.25 depending upon the method of calculation. These minor variations are of no significance.

* For applications to specific numerical examples, see pages 6-4, 6-20, 10-4, 10-19, 10-30.

FORMULAS, TABLES AND DIAGRAMS

A_s = cross-sectional area of tension steel reinforcement.
k = ratio of depth of neutral axis to depth d.
j = ratio of lever arm of resisting couple to depth d.
z = depth from compression face to resultant of the compressive stresses.
$jd = d - z$ = arm of resisting couple.
p = steel ratio $\frac{A_s}{bd}$

$$M = Tjd = A_s f_s jd = (f_s pj)bd^2 = Cjd = (\tfrac{1}{2} f_c kj)bd^2 = Rbd^2$$

$$R_s = f_s pj \qquad R_c = \tfrac{1}{2} f_c kj$$

$$k = \sqrt{2pn + (pn)^2} - pn \qquad z = \frac{kd}{3} \qquad j = 1 - \frac{k}{3}$$

$$k = \frac{1}{1 + \frac{f_s}{nf_c}} \qquad p = \frac{f_c}{2f_s} k$$

$$f_s = \frac{M}{A_s jd} \qquad f_c = \frac{2M}{kjbd^2}$$

Balanced Reinforcement:—$p = \dfrac{1}{\frac{2f_s}{f_c}\left(\frac{f_s}{nf_c} + 1\right)}$

For tables and diagrams giving values of these constants for different stresses and grades of concrete, see pages 3-14, 3-15, 3-17.

2. Tee Beams with Tension Reinforcement.*

ACI 906 limits b in symmetrical beams to $\frac{L}{4}$ and the projection either side of the stem to $8t$, or one-half the distance to the next beam. In one-sided beams, it limits the projection beyond the stem to $\frac{L}{12}$, $6t$, or one-half the distance to the next beam.

A. Flange thickness down to or below the neutral axis:—

This becomes a rectangular beam (see Item 1) of width b.

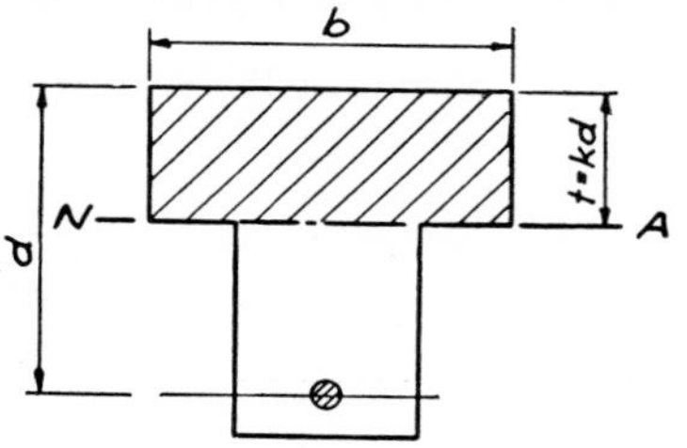

B. Shallow flange, neglecting stem:—

It is always conservative to neglect compression in the stem and, unless the flange is extremely thin (say $t < 0.15d$), reasonably accurate.

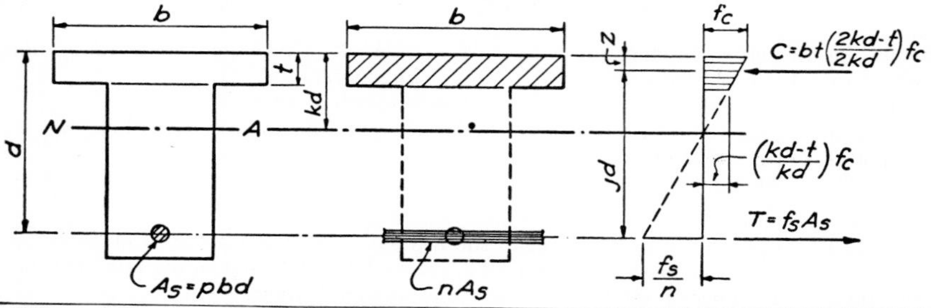

* For application to specific numerical examples, see pages 7-7, 7-34, 7-60, 10-4.

FORMULAS, TABLES AND DIAGRAMS

Symbols have same meaning as for rectangular beams, Item 1 above; also

t = flange thickness.

$$z = \frac{t}{3}\,\frac{(3kd - 2t)}{(2kd - t)}$$

$$jd = d - z = d - \frac{t}{3}\,\frac{(3kd - 2t)}{(2kd - t)}$$

$$M_s = Tjd = A_s f_s jd = f_s jpbd^2 = \left(\frac{f_s}{n}\right)pnjbd^2 = C_s\left(\frac{f_s}{n}\right)bd^2 = R_s bd^2$$

where $C_s = pnj$; $R_s = f_s pj$

$$M_c = Cjd = btj\left(\frac{2kd - t}{2k}\right)f_c = \frac{f_c j \frac{t}{d}}{2k}\left(2k - \frac{t}{d}\right)bd^2 = R_c bd^2 =$$

$$f_c\left(1 - \frac{t}{2kd}\right)\frac{t}{d}jbd^2 = C_c f_c bd^2$$

where $C_c = \left(1 - \frac{t}{2kd}\right)\frac{t}{d}j;]$ $\qquad R_c = f_c j\,\frac{t}{d}\left(\frac{2k - \frac{t}{d}}{2k}\right)$

$$k = \frac{1}{\left(\frac{f_s}{nf_c} + 1\right)}$$

$$kd = \frac{2ndA_s + bt^2}{2nA_s + 2bt}; \qquad k = \frac{2pn + \left(\frac{t}{d}\right)^2}{2pn + 2\left(\frac{t}{d}\right)}$$

$$f_c = \frac{Mkd}{bt\left(kd - \frac{t}{2}\right)jd} = \frac{f_s k}{n(1 - k)} \qquad f_s = \frac{M}{A_s jd} = \frac{f_c n(1 - k)}{k}$$

$$j = \frac{6 - 6\left(\frac{t}{d}\right) + 2\left(\frac{t}{d}\right)^2 + \frac{\left(\frac{t}{d}\right)^3}{2pn}}{6 - 3\left(\frac{t}{d}\right)}$$

C. Shallow flange, including stem:—

No formulas are presented here because this refinement is seldom necessary, no diagrams or tables are readily available, and the method of transformed areas is the simplest attack on the problem.

D. Doubly Reinforced Tee Beams:—

It is possible to reinforce a tee beam for compression, but, additional flange width being far more economical, compressive reinforcement would only be used when both the width and depth of beam are severely limited by space considerations. This relatively unusual case is best solved by the method of transformed areas.

For tables and diagrams giving values of these constants for different stresses and grades of concrete, see page 3-16.

3. Rectangular Beams Reinforced for Both Tension and Compression.*

The doubly reinforced beam (a) (figure on page 3-8), can be thought of as a rectangular beam (b) with balanced tension reinforcement plus a supplementary internal couple (c) of the compression in the top steel and the stress in the additional tension steel, the excess area over that required for balanced reinforcement.

* For applications to examples, see "Negative Moment" on pages 7-36, 7-62 and "Negative Flexure" on pages 10-20 and 10-31.

FORMULAS, TABLES AND DIAGRAMS

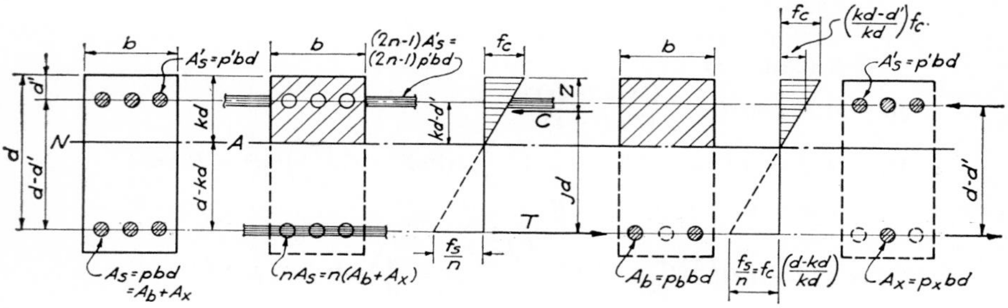

For balanced reinforcement as in (b), R_b is easily computed or available from tables on page 3-14. For the couple in (c), the resisting moment, M_x, is the product of the compressive area $(2n - 1)p'bd$, the stress intensity $\left(\frac{kd - d'}{kd}\right)f_c$ and the arm $(d - d')$. From this, $R_x = \frac{M_x}{bd^2} = (2n - 1)p'\left(1 - \frac{1}{k}\frac{d'}{d}\right)f_c\left(1 - \frac{d'}{d}\right)$ and $R = R_b + R_x$. The extra tension steel, A_x, being further from the neutral axis and not displacing any flexurally stressed concrete, will usually be less than A'_s, so $p_x = \left(\frac{kd - d'}{d - kd}\right)\left(\frac{2n - 1}{n}\right)p'$. If p_b is the ratio for balanced reinforcement, $p = p_b + p_x$. For any given set of stresses and $\frac{d'}{d}$ ratio, the relation of R to p and p' will plot a straight line, so charts are easily constructed for any set of values.

The following formulas can be used, but the procedure just described should be simpler:—

$$k = \sqrt{2pn + \frac{2p'd'}{d}(2n - 1) + [pn - 2p'n + p']^2} - (pn + 2p'n - p')$$

$$z = \frac{\frac{k^3d}{3} + 2(2n - 1)p'd'\left(k - \frac{d}{d'}\right)}{k^2 + 2(2n - 1)p'\left(k - \frac{d'}{d}\right)} \qquad jd = (d - z)$$

$$f_s = \frac{M}{pjbd^2} = \frac{nf_c(1 - k)}{k}$$

$$f'_s = \frac{(2n - 1)f_c\left(k - \frac{d'}{d}\right)}{k}$$

$$f_c = \frac{6M}{bd^2\left[3k - k^2 + \frac{6p'(2n - 1)}{k}\left(k - \frac{d'}{d}\right)\left(1 - \frac{d'}{d}\right)\right]}$$

Note:—The effectiveness of compressive reinforcement is taken as double that indicated by the elastic theory, providing that the unit stress does not then exceed that permitted in tension, $f_s = 24{,}000$ psi (ACI 1102(c)).

FORMULAS, TABLES AND DIAGRAMS

4. Web Reinforcement *:—

Intensity of web shear: $v = \frac{V}{b'd}$ (ACI 1201(a))

Web reinforcement required when:

$v > 1.1\sqrt{f'_c}$ ($1.2\sqrt{f'_c}$ in concrete joists) (ACI 1201(c))

or $> \sqrt{f'_c} + \frac{1300 p_w Vd}{M}$ (but $< 1.75\sqrt{f'_c}$) (ACI 1201(d))

Stirrup spacing: $d/2$ when $v \lesseqgtr 3\sqrt{f'_c}$

(ACI 1206(a))

$d/4$ when $v \lesseqgtr 5\sqrt{f'_c}$

For total web reinforcement: Divide beam into three portions along span length:

(a) *From face of support to distance* d *from face of support:*

$$A'_v = v - v_c \left(\frac{b'd}{f_v}\right)$$

(b) *From distance* d *to point where no web reinforcement is required, called* a:

$a = \left(\frac{v - v_c}{v}\right)$ times distance from a point distant d from face of support to point of zero shear

$$A''_v = (v - v_c)\frac{b'a}{kf_v}$$

$k = 2$ for uniform load

$k = 1$ for center concentrated load

(c) *From* (d + a) *from face of support, a distance* d, *reinforced with a minimum steel ratio of 0.0015*

$$A'''_v = 0.0015\frac{b'd}{f_v}$$

(d) *Total* A_v: $A_v = A'_v + A''_v + A'''_v$

Stress in a series of parallel bent bars (ACI 1204(c)):

$$A_v = \frac{V'_s}{f_v d\,(\text{Sin}\,\alpha + \text{Cos}\,\alpha)}$$

Stress in vertical stirrups: $f_v = \frac{V's}{A_v d}$

Area of stirrups in distance s: $A_v = \frac{V's}{f_v d} = \frac{v'bs}{f_v}$

Spacing of stirrups, where N equals the number of stirrups required:

$$s = \frac{f_v d A_v}{V'};\quad s = a\left(\frac{\sqrt{N} - \sqrt{N - \frac{1}{2}}}{\sqrt{N}}\right);$$

$$a\left(\frac{\sqrt{N} - \sqrt{N - 1\frac{1}{2}}}{\sqrt{N}}\right);\quad a\left(\frac{\sqrt{N} - \sqrt{N - 2\frac{1}{2}}}{\sqrt{N}}\right);\text{ etc.}$$

5. Bond *:—

Bond stress:—$u = \frac{V}{\Sigma o j d} = \frac{vb}{\Sigma o j}$

Length to develop bar:—$L = \frac{f_s D}{4u}$

---

* See further explanation on page 4-23 ff and examples on pp. 10-5, 10-20 and 10-31.

FORMULAS, TABLES AND DIAGRAMS

Allowable bond:—(See Table on page 3-13 (ACI 1301(c)).

Top Bars (horizontal bars with more than 12 in. of concrete underneath) $\not> \frac{3.4\sqrt{f'_c}}{D}$ or 350 psi.

Bars other than top bars $\not> \frac{4.8\sqrt{f'_c}}{D}$ or 500 psi.

6. Columns (Concentric Load)

A. Tied Columns* (ACI 1408(a)):—

$P = A_g\,(0.213f'_c + 0.85f_s p_g)$.
A_g = gross area of concrete.
f'_c = compressive strength of concrete.
f_s = nominal allowable stress in vertical reinforcement (40 per cent of minimum specified yield point, but not to exceed 30,000 psi).
p_g = ratio of area of vertical reinforcement to gross area, A_g.

B. Spirally Reinforced Columns† (ACI 1402(a)):—

$P = A_g\,(0.25f'_c + f_s p_g)$.
where symbols have same meaning as in 6*A* above.

Spiral Reinforcement‡ (ACI 913(b)):—

$$p_s = 0.45\left(\frac{A_g}{A_c} - 1\right)\frac{f'_c}{f_y}.$$

p_s = ratio of volume of spiral reinforcement to volume of core, out-to-out of spirals.
f_y = specified yield strength of spiral reinforcement; 40,000 psi for intermediate grade hot rolled rods; 50,000 psi for hard grade; and 60,000 psi for A432 rod or cold drawn wire (60,000 used in these tables).

C. Long Columns:—

See explanation on pages 11-3 to 11-13 inclusive.

7. Eccentrically Loaded Columns §

Eccentricity which separates control by compression from tension in either principal plane:—(ACI 1407(a))
Symmetrical spiral columns:—$e_b = 0.43\,p_g m D_s + 0.14t$.
Symmetrical tied columns:—$e_b = (0.67p_g m + 0.17)d$.
Unsymmetrical tied columns:—$e_b = \frac{p'm(d - d') + 0.1d}{(p' - p)m + 0.6}$.

A. Axial Load and Bending in One Principal Plane:—

$$\frac{f_a}{F_a} + \frac{f_b}{F_b} \not> 1. \qquad \text{(ACI 1407(b))}$$

$F_a = 0.34\,(1 + p_g m)f'_c$.

B. Axial Load and Bending in Both Principal Planes:—

$$f_a/F_a + f_{bx}/F_b + f_{by}/F_b \not> 1.$$

---

* For application to specific numerical example, see page 11-7 to -9.
† For application to specific numerical example, see page 11-96 and -97, -170 and -171.
‡ For application to specific numerical example, see page 11-211.
§ For applications to specific numerical examples, see pages 11-7 to -9, -96 and -97, -170 and -171.

DESIGN COMMENT

The preceding pages have collected the formulas for working stress design of reinforced concrete members.

The following pages give stresses for use in working stress design. Sections 4 and 5 review design methods, continuity, loads and weights of materials.

Not one of these items, in itself, establishes the size and reinforcement of a member. All must be properly related to each other to produce a well-balanced, economical structure.

A formula appropriate for certain loads and stresses might be quite unreliable for some other combination.

The design of a flexural member includes, among other things, multiplying load by span and dividing by continuity factor and stress constant. A ten per cent variation in any one of these items produces a similar variation in the result. If a designer is cautious and constantly selects conservative values, his design will be more expensive than necessary. If he constantly underestimates values, he will be a like amount on the unsafe side.

The designer who uses the highest of the range of possible loads with high stresses (occasional overloads) or the one who uses the lowest of the range of possible loads with conservative stresses will come out about the same.

The designer aims, above all else, for balance. If he feels he should be conservative in certain values, he will endeavor to offset with tighter appraisals where they tend to balance.

ALLOWABLE UNIT WORKING STRESSES

"Building Code Requirements for Reinforced Concrete (ACI 318-63)."

The table gives the allowable working stresses for various grades of concrete with bars whose deformations meet ASTM A305 and for those which do not. The stresses used throughout this book for bond and diagonal tension in computing safe load tables apply only to bars with deformations conforming to ASTM A305 or A408.

CONCRETE STRESSES

Description		Allowable stresses: For any strength of concrete	Allowable stresses: For strength of concrete shown below: $f_c' =$ 2500 psi	$f_c' =$ 3000 psi	$f_c' =$ 3750 psi	$f_c' =$ 4000 psi	$f_c' =$ 5000 psi
Modulus of elasticity ratio: n							
For concrete weighing 145 lb per cu ft	n	$\frac{29{,}000{,}000}{w^{1.5}33\sqrt{f_c'}}$	10	9	8.25	8	7
Flexure: f_c							
Extreme fiber stress in compression	f_c	$0.45f_c'$	1125	1350	1688	1800	2250
Extreme fiber stress in tension in plain concrete footings and walls	f_c	$1.6\sqrt{f_c'}$	80	88	98	102	113
Shear: v (as a measure of diagonal tension at a distance d from the face of the support)							
Beams with no web reinforcement *	v_c	$1.1\sqrt{f_c'}$	55 *	60 *	67 *	70 *	78 *
Joists with no web reinforcement	v_c	$1.2\sqrt{f_c'}$	61	66	73	77	86
Members with vertical or inclined web reinforcement or properly combined bent bars and vertical stirrups	v	$5\sqrt{f_c'}$	250	274	306	316	354
Slabs and footings (peripheral shear, Section 1207, ACI 318-63) *	v_c	$2\sqrt{f_c'}$	100 *	110 *	122 *	126 *	141 *
Bearing: f_c							
On full area		$0.25f_c'$	625	750	937	1000	1250
On one-third area or less †		$0.375f_c'$	938	1125	1406	1500	1875

* For shear values of lightweight aggregate concrete see Section 1208, ACI 318-63.
† This increase shall be permitted only when the least distance between the edges of the loaded and unloaded areas is a minimum of one-fourth of the parallel side dimension of the loaded area. The allowable bearing stress on a reasonably concentric area greater than one-third but less than the full area shall be interpolated between the values given.

STEEL STRESSES

Unless otherwise provided, steel for concrete reinforcement shall not be stressed in excess of the following limits:

(*a*) *In tension*

For billet-steel or axle-steel concrete reinforcing bars of structural grade . . . . 18,000 psi

For main reinforcement, ⅜ in. or less in diameter, in one-way slabs of not more than 12-ft span, 50 percent of the minimum yield strength specified by the American Society for Testing and Materials for the reinforcement used, but not to exceed . . . . 30,000 psi

ALLOWABLE UNIT WORKING STRESSES

For deformed bars with a yield strength of 60,000 psi or more and in sizes #11 and smaller..24,000 psi
For all other reinforcement..20,000 psi

(*b*) *In compression, vertical column reinforcement*
Spiral columns, 40 percent of the minimum yield strength, but not to exceed . 30,000 psi
Tied columns, 85 percent of the value for spiral columns, but not to exceed . 25,500 psi
Composite and combination columns:
Structural steel sections
For ASTM A 36 Steel..18,000 psi
For ASTM A 7 Steel..16,000 psi
Cast iron sections..10,000 psi
Steel pipe.......................... see limitations of Section 1406, ACI 318-63

(*c*) *In compression, flexural members*
For compression reinforcement in flexural members see Section 1102, ACI 318-63

(*d*) *Spirals* [*yield strength for use in Eq.* (*9–1*), ACI 318-63]
Hot rolled rods, Grade 40..40,000 psi
Hot rolled rods, Grade 50..50,000 psi
Hot rolled rods, Grade 60, and cold-drawn wire........................60,000 psi

STRESSES—WIND AND EARTHQUAKE FORCES

(a) Members subject to stresses produced by wind or earthquake forces combined with other loads may be proportioned for stresses 33⅓ percent greater than those specified provided that the section thus required is not less than that required for the combination of dead and live load.

ALLOWABLE BOND STRESS (TENSION)

Bar No.	TOP BARS #3-#11: $\frac{3.4\sqrt{f_c'}}{D} \not> 350$ psi #14, #18: $2.1\sqrt{f_c'}$					OTHER THAN TOP BARS #3-#11: $\frac{4.8\sqrt{f_c'}}{D} \not> 500$ psi #14, #18: $3\sqrt{f_c'}$				
	f_c' = 2500 psi	f_c' = 3000 psi	f_c' = 3750 psi	f_c' = 4000 psi	f_c' = 5000 psi	f_c' = 2500 psi	f_c' = 3000 psi	f_c' = 3750 psi	f_c' = 4000 psi	f_c' = 5000 psi
3	350	350	350	350	350	500	500	500	500	500
4	340	350	350	350	350	480	500	500	500	500
5	272	298	333	344	350	384	421	470	486	500
6	227	248	278	287	321	320	351	392	405	452
7	194	213	238	246	275	274	300	336	347	388
8	170	186	208	215	240	240	263	294	304	339
9	151	165	185	190	213	213	233	261	269	301
10	134	147	164	169	189	189	207	231	239	267
11	121	132	148	153	171	170	186	208	215	241
14	015	115	129	133	148	150	164	184	190	212
18	105	115	129	133	148	150	164	184	190	212

VALUE OF n, p, k, j, R FOR VARIOUS COMBINATIONS OF STEEL AND CONCRETE STRESSES FOR RECTANGULAR BEAMS AND SLABS

(WORKING STRESS METHOD)

Balanced Design

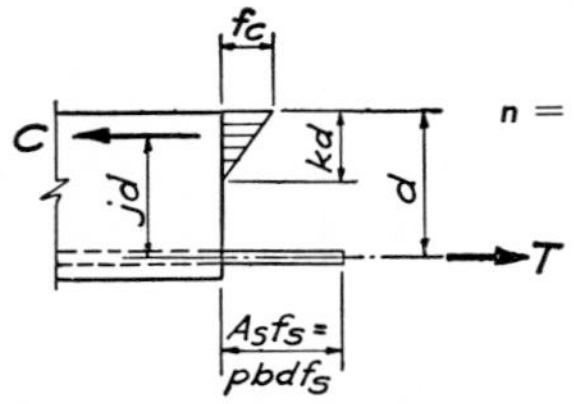

$$n = \frac{29{,}000{,}000}{w^{1.5}33\sqrt{f'_c}} \qquad k = \frac{1}{1 + \frac{f_s}{nf_c}} \qquad p = \frac{f_c k}{2f_s} \qquad j = 1 - \frac{k}{3}$$

$$R = \tfrac{1}{2} f_c k j = p f_s j \qquad f_c = 0.45\, f'_c$$

f'_c	2500.	3000.	3750.	4000.	5000.
f_c	1125.	1350.	1687.	1800.	2250.
n	10.1	9.2	8.2	8.0	7.1
			$f_s = 16000$		
p	0.01460	0.01844	0.02446	0.02664	0.03513
k	0.4153	0.4370	0.4638	0.4737	0.4996
j'	0.8616	0.8543	0.8454	0.8421	0.8335
R	201.3	252.0	330.8	359.0	468.5
			$f_s = 18000$		
p	0.01209	0.01531	0.02037	0.02222	0.02939
k	0.3870	0.4083	0.4346	0.4444	0.4702
j	0.8710	0.8639	0.8551	0.8519	0.8433
R	189.6	238.1	313.6	340.7	446.1
			$f_s = 20000$		
p	0.01019	0.01293	0.01725	0.01884	0.02498
k	0.3623	0.3831	0.4089	0.4186	0.4441
j	0.8792	0.8723	0.8637	0.8605	0.8520
R	179.2	225.6	298.0	324.2	425.6
			$f_s = 24000$		
p	0.00753	0.00959	0.01286	0.01406	0.01873
k	0.3213	0.3410	0.3657	0.3750	0.3996
j	0.8929	0.8863	0.8781	0.8750	0.8668
R	161.4	204.0	271.0	295.3	389.7
			$f_s = 27000$		
p	0.00617	0.00788	0.01059	0.01159	0.01549
k	0.2962	0.3151	0.3388	0.3478	0.3717
j	0.9013	0.8950	0.8871	0.8841	0.8761
R	150.2	190.3	253.6	276.7	366.4
			$f_s = 30000$		
p	0.00515	0.00659	0.00888	0.00973	0.01303
k	0.2747	0.2928	0.3157	0.3243	0.3475
j	0.9084	0.9024	0.8948	0.8919	0.8842
R	140.4	178.3	238.3	260.3	345.6
			$f_s = 33000$		
p	0.00437	0.00559	0.00755	0.00829	0.01112
k	0.2561	0.2734	0.2954	0.3038	0.3262
j	0.9146	0.9089	0.9015	0.8987	0.8913
R	131.8	167.8	224.7	245.7	327.1

DESIGN CONSTANTS—ALL PERCENTAGES REINFORCEMENT
24,000 psi STEEL AND 3750 psi CONCRETE ONLY

(WORKING STRESS METHOD)

$p = \frac{A_s}{bd}$ $\quad k = \sqrt{2pn + (pn)^2} - pn$ $\quad j = 1 - \frac{k}{3}$ $\quad R_s = pf_sj$ $\quad R_c = \frac{1}{2}f_ckj$

p	k	j	R_s	R_c	p	k	j	R_s	R_c
0.0030	0.1986	0.9338	67.2	156.5	0.0120	0.3560	0.8813	253.8	264.7
0.0032	0.2043	0.9319	71.6	160.7	0.0122	0.3583	0.8806	257.8	266.2
0.0034	0.2099	0.9300	75.9	164.7	0.0124	0.3606	0.8798	261.8	267.7
0.0036	0.2152	0.9283	80.2	168.6	0.0126	0.3629	0.8790	265.8	269.1
0.0038	0.2204	0.9265	84.5	172.3	0.0128	0.3651	0.8783	269.8	270.5
					0.01286	**0.3658**	**0.8781**	**271.0**	**271.0**
0.0040	0.2254	0.9249	88.8	175.9	0.0130	0.3673	0.8776	273.8	272.0
0.0042	0.2303	0.9232	93.1	179.4	0.0132	0.3695	0.8768	277.8	273.3
0.0044	0.2350	0.9217	97.3	182.7	0.0134	0.3716	0.8761	281.8	274.7
0.0046	0.2395	0.9202	101.6	186.0	0.0136	0.3737	0.8754	285.7	276.1
0.0048	0.2440	0.9187	105.8	189.1	0.0138	0.3758	0.8747	289.7	277.4
0.0050	0.2483	0.9172	110.1	192.1	0.0140	0.3779	0.8740	293.7	278.7
0.0052	0.2525	0.9158	114.3	195.1	0.0142	0.3800	0.8733	297.6	280.0
0.0054	0.2566	0.9145	118.5	198.0	0.0144	0.3820	0.8727	301.6	281.3
0.0056	0.2606	0.9131	122.7	200.8	0.0146	0.3840	0.8720	305.5	282.6
0.0058	0.2645	0.9118	126.9	203.5	0.0148	0.3860	0.8713	309.5	283.8
0.0060	0.2683	0.9106	131.1	206.1	0.0150	0.3880	0.8707	313.4	285.0
0.0062	0.2721	0.9093	135.3	208.7	0.0152	0.3900	0.8700	317.4	286.3
0.0064	0.2757	0.9081	139.5	211.3	0.0154	0.3919	0.8694	321.3	287.5
0.0066	0.2793	0.9069	143.7	213.7	0.0156	0.3938	0.8687	325.3	288.7
0.0068	0.2828	0.9057	147.8	216.1	0.0158	0.3957	0.8681	329.2	289.8
0.0070	0.2862	0.9046	152.0	218.5	0.0160	0.3976	0.8675	333.1	291.0
0.0072	0.2896	0.9035	156.1	220.8	0.0162	0.3994	0.8669	337.0	292.2
0.0074	0.2929	0.9024	160.3	223.0	0.0164	0.4013	0.8662	341.0	293.3
0.0076	0.2962	0.9013	164.4	225.2	0.0166	0.4031	0.8656	344.9	294.4
0.0078	0.2994	0.9002	168.5	227.4	0.0168	0.4049	0.8650	348.8	295.5
0.0080	0.3025	0.8992	172.6	229.5	0.0170	0.4067	0.8644	352.7	296.6
0.0082	0.3056	0.8981	176.8	231.6	0.0172	0.4085	0.8638	356.6	297.7
0.0084	0.3086	0.8971	180.9	233.6	0.0174	0.4102	0.8633	360.5	298.8
0.0086	0.3116	0.8961	185.0	235.6	0.0176	0.4120	0.8627	364.4	299.9
0.0088	0.3145	0.8952	189.1	237.6	0.0178	0.4137	0.8621	368.3	300.9
0.0090	0.3174	0.8942	193.1	239.5	0.0180	0.4154	0.8615	372.2	302.0
0.0092	0.3203	0.8932	197.2	241.4	0.0182	0.4171	0.8610	376.1	303.0
0.0094	0.3230	0.8923	201.3	243.2	0.0184	0.4188	0.8604	380.0	304.0
0.0096	0.3258	0.8914	205.4	245.0	0.0186	0.4205	0.8598	383.8	305.0
0.0098	0.3285	0.8905	209.4	246.8	0.0188	0.4221	0.8593	387.7	306.0
0.0100	0.3312	0.8896	213.5	248.6	0.0190	0.4237	0.8588	391.6	307.0
0.0102	0.3338	0.8887	217.6	250.3	0.0192	0.4254	0.8582	395.5	308.0
0.0104	0.3364	0.8879	221.6	252.0	0.0194	0.4270	0.8577	399.3	309.0
0.0106	0.3390	0.8870	225.7	253.7	0.0196	0.4286	0.8571	403.2	310.0
0.0108	0.3415	0.8862	229.7	255.3	0.0198	0.4302	0.8566	407.1	310.9
0.0110	0.3440	0.8853	233.7	257.0	0.0200	0.4317	0.8561	410.9	311.9
0.0112	0.3465	0.8845	237.8	258.6	0.0202	0.4333	0.8556	414.8	312.8
0.0114	0.3489	0.8837	241.8	260.1	0.0204	0.4347	0.8551	418.7	313.6
0.0116	0.3513	0.8829	245.8	261.7	0.0206	0.4364	0.8545	422.5	314.7
0.0118	0.3537	0.8821	249.8	263.2	0.0208	0.4380	0.8540	426.3	315.6

VALUES OF $R = \frac{M}{bd^2}$ FOR TEE BEAMS, BALANCED REINFORCEMENT

(WORKING STRESS METHOD)

f_s = 24,000 psi

f'_c and n†	f_c	$\frac{t}{d}$ .06	.08	.10	.12	.14	.16	.18	.20	.24	.28	.32	.36	.40	.44
	725	37	46	54	61	67	71	75	77	*78	*78	*78	*78	*78	*78
	825	42	54	63	72	79	85	89	93	97	*97	*97	*97	*97	*97
2500	925	48	61	72	82	91	98	104	109	115	117	*117	*117	*117	*117
	1025	54	68	82	93	103	112	119	126	134	138	*139	*139	*139	*139
10.1	1125	59	76	91	104	115	126	134	142	153	159	161	*161	*161	*161
	1225	65	83	100	114	127	139	149	158	172	180	184	*185	*185	*185
	1325	71	91	109	125	140	153	164	174	190	201	207	*209	*209	*209
	1425	76	98	118	136	152	166	179	191	209	222	230	233	*234	*234
	1525	82	105	127	146	164	180	194	207	228	243	253	258	*259	*259
	1625	88	113	136	157	176	193	209	223	246	264	276	283	285	*285
	950	49	62	74	84	92	99	105	109	115	*116	*116	*116	*116	*116
	1050	55	70	83	94	104	113	120	126	133	136	*136	*136	*136	*136
3000	1150	60	77	92	105	116	126	135	142	152	157	*158	*158	*158	*158
	1250	66	84	101	115	128	140	150	158	171	178	181	*181	*181	*181
9.2	1350	72	92	110	126	141	153	165	174	189	199	203	*204	*204	*204
	1450	77	99	119	137	153	167	180	191	208	220	226	*228	*228	*228
	1550	83	106	128	147	165	181	195	207	227	241	249	253	*253	*253
	1650	89	114	137	158	177	194	210	223	245	262	272	277	*278	*278
	1750	94	121	146	169	189	208	225	239	264	282	295	302	304	*304
	1850	100	129	155	179	201	221	239	256	283	303	318	327	330	*331
	1287	68	86	103	117	130	141	151	159	170	176	*177	*177	*177	*177
	1387	73	93	112	128	142	155	166	175	189	197	199	*199	*199	*199
3750	1487	79	101	121	139	154	168	181	191	207	217	222	*222	*222	*222
	1587	85	108	130	149	167	182	196	208	226	238	245	*246	*246	*246
8.2	1687	90	116	139	160	179	196	211	224	245	259	268	271	*271	*271
	1787	96	123	148	170	191	209	226	240	263	280	291	295	*296	*296
	1887	102	130	157	181	203	223	241	256	282	301	313	320	*322	*322
	1987	107	138	166	192	215	236	255	273	301	322	336	345	348	*348
	2087	113	145	175	202	227	250	270	289	320	343	359	369	374	*374
	2187	118	153	184	213	239	264	285	305	338	364	382	394	400	*401
	1400	74	94	112	129	143	156	167	176	189	197	*199	*199	*199	*199
	1500	80	102	122	139	155	169	182	192	208	218	222	*222	*222	*222
4000	1600	85	109	131	150	167	183	197	208	227	239	245	*246	*246	*246
	1700	91	116	140	161	180	196	211	225	245	260	268	270	*270	*270
8.0	1800	96	124	149	171	192	210	226	241	264	280	291	295	*295	*295
	1900	102	131	158	182	204	224	241	257	283	301	313	320	*321	*321
	2000	108	138	167	192	216	237	256	273	301	322	336	344	*347	*347
	2100	113	146	176	203	228	251	271	290	320	343	359	369	373	*373
	2200	119	153	185	214	240	264	286	306	339	364	382	393	399	*400
	2300	125	161	194	224	252	278	301	322	358	385	405	418	425	*427
	1850	99	126	151	174	194	213	228	242	264	279	287	*289	*289	*289
	1950	104	134	160	185	207	226	243	259	283	300	309	313	*313	*313
5000	2050	110	141	169	195	219	240	258	275	302	321	332	338	*338	*338
	2150	116	148	178	206	231	253	273	291	320	341	355	362	*364	*364
7.1	2250	121	156	187	217	243	267	288	307	339	362	378	387	*390	*390
	2350	127	163	197	227	255	280	303	324	358	383	401	412	416	*416
	2450	133	170	206	238	267	294	318	340	376	404	424	436	442	*443
	2550	138	178	215	248	279	308	333	356	395	425	447	461	468	*470
	2650	144	185	224	259	291	321	348	372	414	446	469	485	494	*497
	2750	149	193	233	270	304	335	363	389	432	467	492	510	520	524

* The values in boldface type indicate that the neutral axis is within the flange.

† See explanation of value of n on page 3-5.

VALUES OF k AND j FOR RECTANGULAR BEAMS

(WORKING STRESS METHOD)

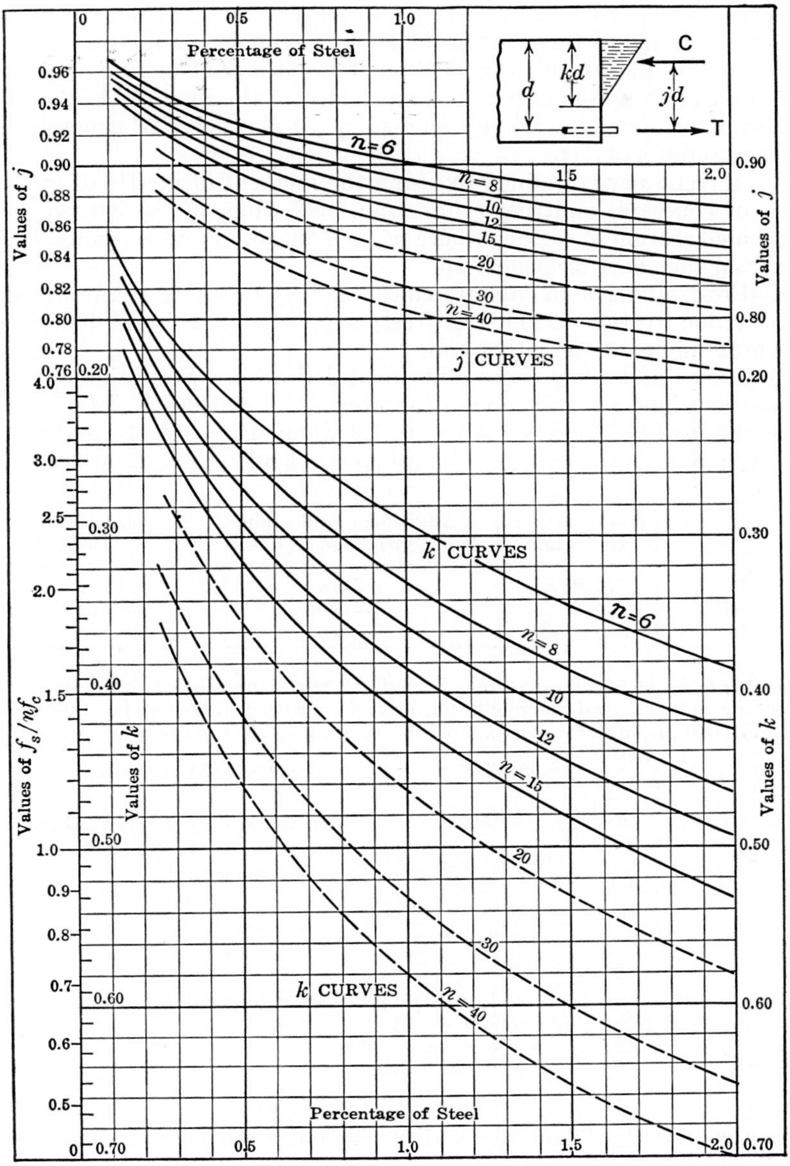

DEFLECTIONS OF REINFORCED CONCRETE BEAMS

The intent of ACI 909 is to prevent excessive deflections. As higher strengths are used, deflections become increasingly important. One way to control deflections is by using deep enough sections; so long as $R = M/bd^2 \leq 250$, beams will be reasonably stiff. Another way is to use compressive reinforcement to minimize creep. The l/t ratios in ACI Table 909(b) do not guarantee that below those ratios deflections cannot be a factor.

The determination of the deflection of a reinforced concrete beam is complicated by (1) a non-homogeneous material, (2) the monolithic character of structure developing restraining moments, (3) shrinkage of concrete during hardening, and (4) creep.

Good results are obtained by using the moment of inertia of gross cross section of concrete, omitting reinforcing steel when $pf_y \leq 500$ psi and the transformed section in regions where $pf_y > 500$ psi. For tee beams, I_c can be taken from the chart on page 4-18.

End restraining moments are considered by breaking the problem into: deflection due to transverse loads (freely supported ends), and deflection due to separate moments on either end.

Shrinkage and creep cause additional deflection. Workable approximations are obtained by multiplying the immediate deflection of the sustained part of the load by 2.0 when $A'_s = 0$, 1.2 when $A'_s = 0.5\ A_s$, and 0.8 when $A'_s = A_s$ (see table where Δ_D = permanent load, Δ_L = temporary load).

A'_s	Instantaneous Deflection	Additional Deflection from Shrinkage & Creep	Total Long-Time Deflection
0	$\Delta_D + \Delta_L$	$2\Delta_D$	$3\Delta_D + \Delta_L$
$0.5A_s$	$\Delta_D + \Delta_L$	$1.2\Delta_D$	$2.2\Delta_D + \Delta_L$
A_s	$\Delta_D + \Delta_L$	$0.8\Delta_D$	$1.8\Delta_D + \Delta_L$

Example I—Determine maximum immediate deflection of single span, freely supported, rectangular reinforced concrete beam, 14 x 18 in., with 3-#7 bottom bars, uniform dead load of 600 plf, uniform live load of 400 plf, span of 20 ft, $f'_c = 3750$ psi, $n = 8\frac{1}{4}$.

$$p = \frac{1.80}{14 \times 16} = 0.00803 < p = \frac{500}{60{,}000} = 0.00833 \text{ (ACI 909(d))}.$$

$$I_c = \frac{bd^3}{12} = \frac{14 \times 18^3}{12} = 6800 \text{ in.}^4 \qquad E_c = w^{1.5}33\sqrt{f'_c} = 3{,}540{,}000 \text{ psi}$$

$$\Delta_D = \frac{w_D L^4}{76.8EI} = \frac{600 \times 20^4 \times 1728}{76.8 \times 3{,}540{,}000 \times 6800} = 0.090 \text{ in.}$$

$$\Delta_L = \frac{w_L L^4}{76.8EI} = \frac{400 \times 20^4 \times 1728}{76.8 \times 3{,}540{,}000 \times 6800} = \underline{0.060 \text{ in.}}$$

$$0.150 \text{ in.} = \frac{L}{1600}$$

Example II—What is probable maximum deflection of beam in Ex. I after five years if maintained under continuous live load?

$$A'_s = 0 \qquad 3\Delta_D = 3 \times 0.090 = 0.270 \text{ in.}$$

$$3\Delta_L = 3 \times 0.060 = \underline{0.180}$$

$$0.450 \text{ in.} = \frac{L}{533}$$

Example III—What is probable maximum deflection of beam in Ex. I after five years if only dead load is continuously in place and live load seldom?

$$3\Delta_D = 3 \times 0.090 = 0.270 \text{ in.}$$

$$1\Delta_L = 1 \times 0.060 = \underline{0.060}$$

$$0.330 \text{ in.} = \frac{L}{726}$$

DEFLECTIONS OF REINFORCED CONCRETE BEAMS

Example IV—Estimate the five-year deflection if 3-#7 top bars are added to Ex. I and live load is seldom realized.

$$A'_s = A_s \qquad 1.8\Delta_D = 1.8 \times 0.090 = 0.162 \text{ in.}$$
$$1\Delta_L = 1 \times 0.060 = 0.060$$
$$0.222 \text{ in.} = \frac{L}{1080}$$

Example V—What is probable short-time deflection of beam similar to Ex. I but 12 in. wide with moment of 200 ki at left end and 300 ki at right? *

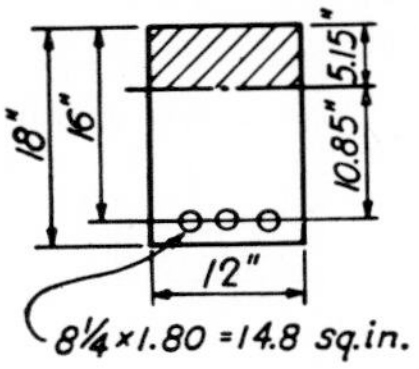

$$p = \frac{1.80}{12 \times 16} = 0.00938 > p = \frac{500}{60{,}000}; \text{ use cracked section}$$
$$pn = 0.00938 \times 8\tfrac{1}{4} = 0.077$$
$$k = \sqrt{0.154 + (0.077)^2} - 0.077 = 0.322$$
$$kd = 5.15 \text{ in.}$$
$$I_c = 12 \times \frac{5.15^3}{3} = 547 \text{ in.}^4$$
$$14.8 \times (10.85)^2 = 1740$$
$$2287 \text{ in.}^4$$

The uniform load produces downward deflection (*a* in fig.), maximum at mid-span. Left end moment produces upward deflection (*b*), maximum left of center; right end moment produces upward deflection (*c*), maximum right of center. A summation for absolute maximum is complicated, but it is sufficiently accurate to add deflections at center (and quarter-points) to obtain the curve (*d*).

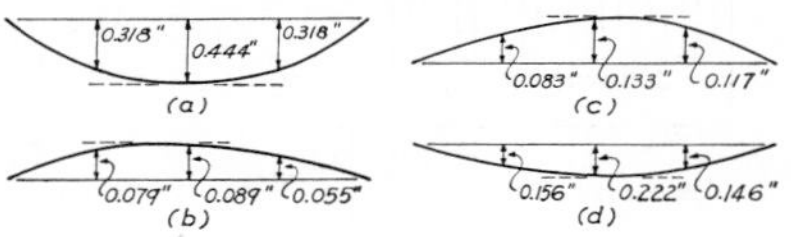

$$\Delta_T \text{ for uniform load} = \frac{+wL^4}{76.8EI} = \frac{1000 \times 20^4 \times 1728}{76.8 \times 3{,}540{,}000 \times 2287} = +0.444 \text{ in.}$$

$$\Delta \text{ for } 200^{ki} \text{ left end moment} = \frac{-3M_AL^2}{48EI} = \frac{-3 \times 200{,}000 \times 20^2 \times 144}{48 \times 3{,}540{,}000 \times 2287} = -0.089 \text{ in.}$$

$$\Delta \text{ for } 300^{ki} \text{ right end moment} = \frac{-3M_BL^2}{48EI} = \frac{-3 \times 300{,}000 \times 20^2 \times 144}{48 \times 3{,}540{,}000 \times 2287} = -0.133 \text{ in.}$$

$$+0.222 \text{ in.}$$

A greater deflection would actually develop as discussed in Ex. VI.

Example VI—What is probable maximum deflection of beam of Ex. V after five years if live load and end moments are all fairly continuously in place?

This example does not lend itself readily to simple mathematical analysis. The end slopes from moments computed by elastic frame methods, while reasonably accurate for short-time loading, might relieve themselves somewhat by creep in the concrete; certainly the deflection of the portion undergoing positive moment will be materially increased by such creep. Recent tests of continuous beams suggest that the long-time actual deflection can best be obtained by multiplying the short-time deflection by a factor, and 2½ at present seems a fair value for this multiplier. Hence, 2½ × 0.144 = 0.36 in.

One of the most effective ways of reducing deflection caused by long-time loading is by the use of compressive reinforcement.

---

* ACI 909(c), for continuous beams, permits using the average moment of inertia of end and center, but the given data are such that only the moment of inertia at mid-span is available.

BEAM DIAGRAMS AND FORMULAS

CANTILEVERED BEAM—UNIFORMLY DISTRIBUTED LOAD

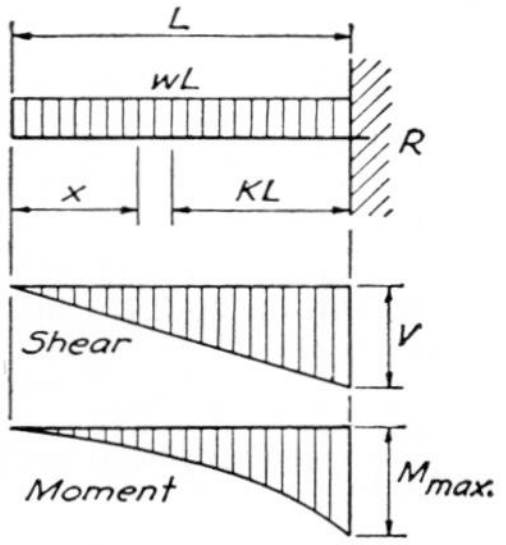

Equivalent Tabular Load.*. . . $= 4wL$

$R = V$ . . . . $= wL$

V_x . . . . $= wx$

M_{max} (at fixed end). . . . . $= \frac{wL^2}{2}$

M_x . . . . $= \frac{wx^2}{2}$

Δ_{max} (at free end). . . . . $= \frac{wL^4}{8EI}$

Δ_x . . . . $= \frac{w}{24EI}(x^4 - 4L^3x + 3L^4)$

* Note: *See explanation on page 3-27.*

CANTILEVERED BEAM—CONCENTRATED LOAD AT FREE END

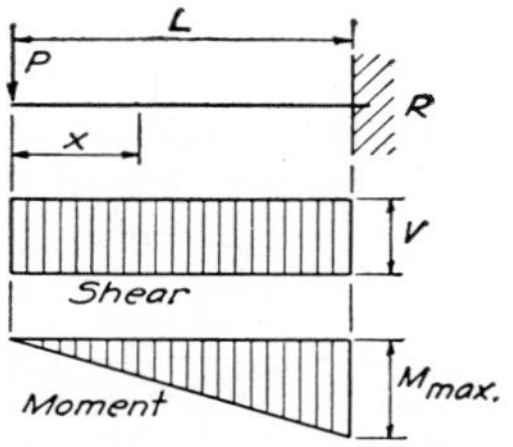

Equivalent Tabular Load.*. . . . $= 8P$

$R = V$ . . . . $= P$

M_{max} (at fixed end). . . . . $= PL$

M_x . . . . $= Px$

Δ_{max} (at free end). . . . . $= \frac{PL^3}{3EI}$

Δ_x . . . . $= \frac{P}{6EI}(2L^3 - 3L^2x + x^3)$

CANTILEVERED BEAM—CONCENTRATED LOAD AT ANY POINT

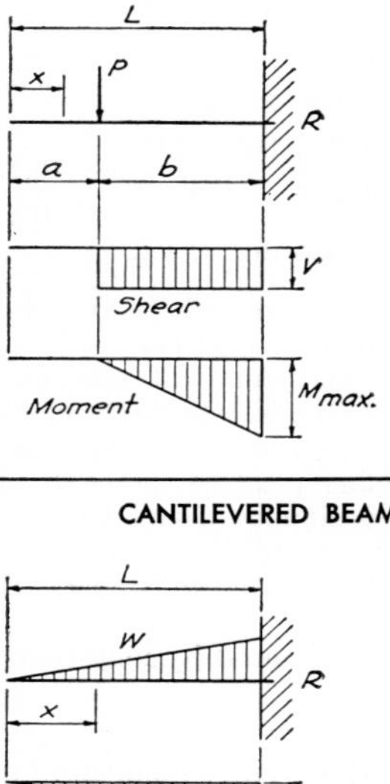

Equivalent Tabular Load.*. . . $= \frac{8Pb}{L}$

$R = V$ (when $x > a$) . . . . $= P$

M_{max} (at fixed end). . . . . . . $= Pb$

M_x (when $x > a$). . . . . $= P(x - a)$

Δ_{max} (at free end). . . . . $= \frac{Pb^2}{6EI}(3L - b)$

Δa (at point of load). . . . . $= \frac{Pb^3}{3EI}$

Δ_x (when $x < a$). . . . . $= \frac{Pb^2}{6EI}(3L - 3x - b)$

Δ_x (when $x > a$). . . . . $= \frac{P(L - x)^2}{6EI}(3b - L + x)$

CANTILEVERED BEAM—LOAD INCREASING UNIFORMLY TO FIXED END

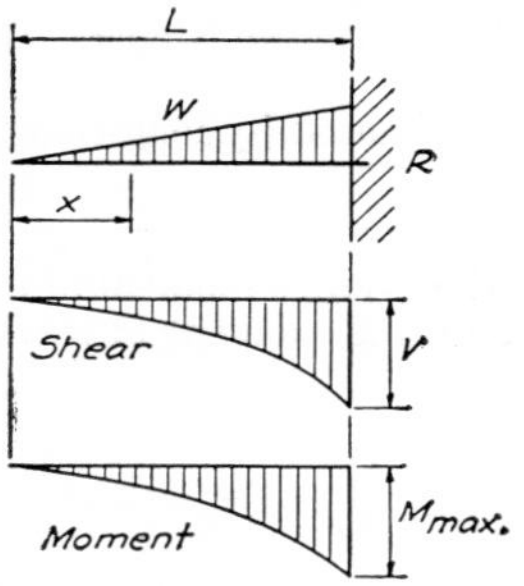

Equivalent Tabular Load.*. . . . . . . $= \frac{8}{3}W$

$R = V$ . . . . $= W$

V_x . . . . $= W\frac{x^2}{L^2}$

M_{max} (at fixed end) . . . . $= \frac{WL}{3}$

M_x . . . . $= \frac{Wx^3}{3L^2}$

Δ_{max} (at free end). . . . . $= \frac{WL^3}{15EI}$

Δ_x . . . . $= \frac{W}{60EIL^2}(x^5 - 5L^4x + 4L^5)$

BEAM DIAGRAMS AND FORMULAS

SIMPLE BEAM—UNIFORMLY DISTRIBUTED LOAD

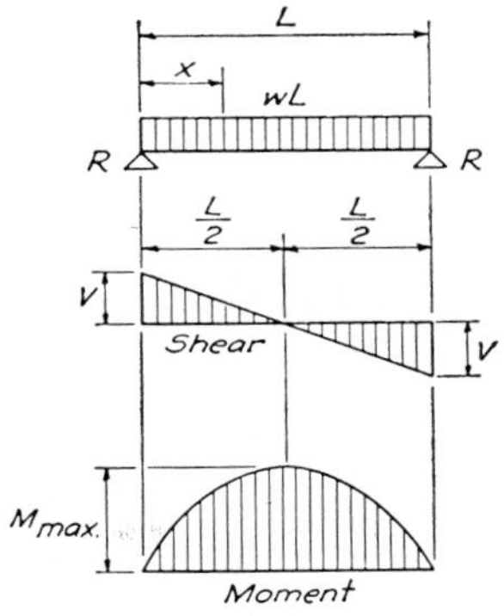

Equivalent Tabular Load * .... $= wL$

$R = V$ .... $= \dfrac{wL}{2}$

V_x .... $= w\left(\dfrac{L}{2} - x\right)$

M_{max} (at center) .... $= \dfrac{wL^2}{8}$

M_x .... $= \dfrac{wx}{2}(L - x)$

Δ_{max} (at center) .... $= \dfrac{5wL^4}{384EI}$

Δ_x .... $= \dfrac{wx}{24EI}(L^3 - 2Lx^2 + x^3)$

* **Note:** *See explanation on page 3-27.*

SIMPLE BEAM—UNIFORM LOAD PARTIALLY DISTRIBUTED

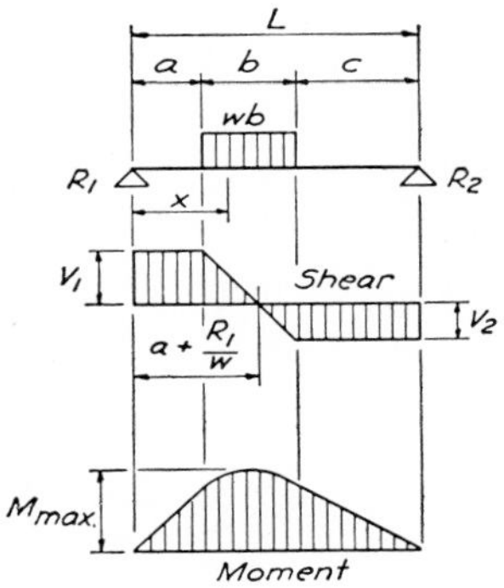

$R_1 = V_1$ (max when $a < c$) ...... $= \dfrac{wb}{2L}(2c + b)$

$R_2 = V_2$ (max when $a > c$) ...... $= \dfrac{wb}{2L}(2a + b)$

V_x [when $x > a$ and $< (a + b)$] $= R_1 - w(x - a)$

$M_{max}\left(\text{at } x = a + \dfrac{R_1}{w}\right)$ .... $= R_1\left(a + \dfrac{R_1}{2w}\right)$

M_x (when $x < a$) .... $= R_1x$

M_x [when $x > a$ and $< (a + b)$] $= R_1x - \dfrac{w}{2}(x - a)^2$

M_x [when $x > (a + b)$] .... $= R_2(L - x)$

SIMPLE BEAM—UNIFORM LOAD PARTIALLY DISTRIBUTED AT ONE END

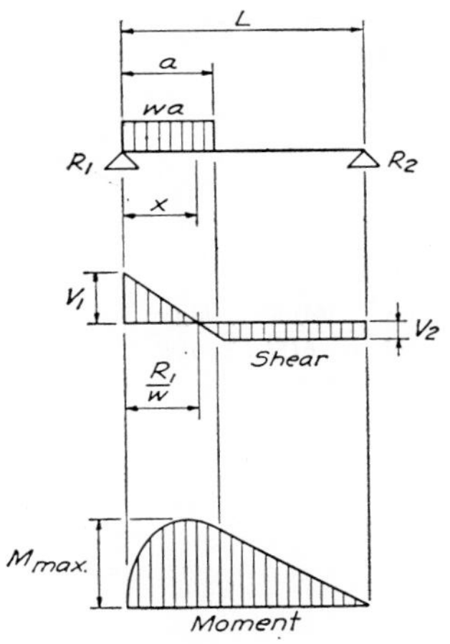

$R_1 = V_{1max}$ .... $= \dfrac{wa}{2L}(2L - a)$

$R_2 = V_2$ .... $= \dfrac{wa^2}{2L}$

V (when $x < a$) .. $= R_1 - wx$

$M_{max}\left(\text{at } x = \dfrac{R_1}{w}\right)$ .. $= \dfrac{R_1^2}{2w}$

M_x (when $x < a$) .. $= R_1x - \dfrac{wx^2}{2}$

M_x (when $x > a$) .. $= R_2(L - x)$

Δ_x (when $x < a$) .. $= \dfrac{wx}{24EIL}[a^2(2L - a)^2 - 2ax^2(2L - a) + Lx^3]$

Δ_x (when $x > a$) .. $= \dfrac{wa^2(L - x)}{24EIL}(4xL - 2x^2 - a^2)$

BEAM DIAGRAMS AND FORMULAS

SIMPLE BEAM—MOMENT ONE END

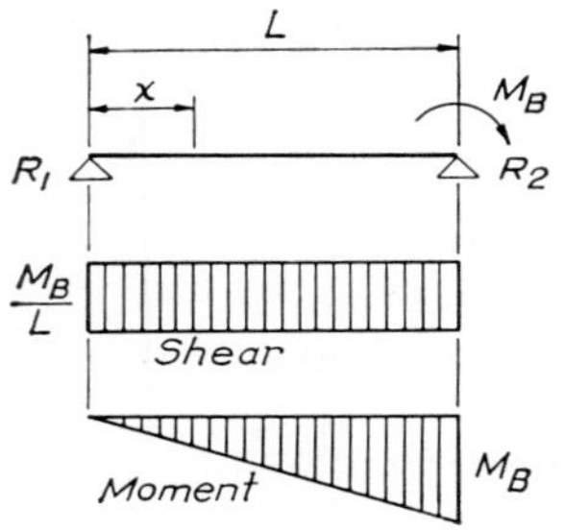

$$R_1 = -R_2 = \frac{M_B}{L}$$

$$V_x = \frac{M_B}{L}$$

$$M_{max} \text{ (at } R_2) = M_B$$

$$M_x \ldots\ldots = \frac{M_B x}{L}$$

$$\Delta_{max} \text{ (at } x = 0.578L) = 0.0642 \frac{M_B L^2}{EI}$$

$$\Delta_x = \frac{M_B L x}{6EI}\left(1 - \frac{x^2}{L^2}\right)$$

$$\Delta \text{ center} = \frac{M_B L^2}{16EI}$$

SIMPLE BEAM—EQUAL MOMENTS EACH END

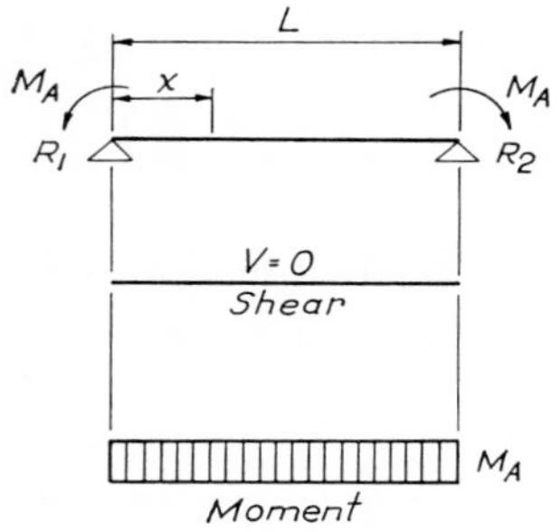

M_A is equal and opposite to M_A

$$R_1 = R_2 = 0$$

$$V_x = 0$$

$$M_x = M_A$$

$$M_{max} = M_A$$

$$\Delta_{max} \text{ (at center)} = \frac{M_A L^2}{8EI}$$

SIMPLE BEAM—UNEQUAL MOMENTS OPPOSITE ENDS

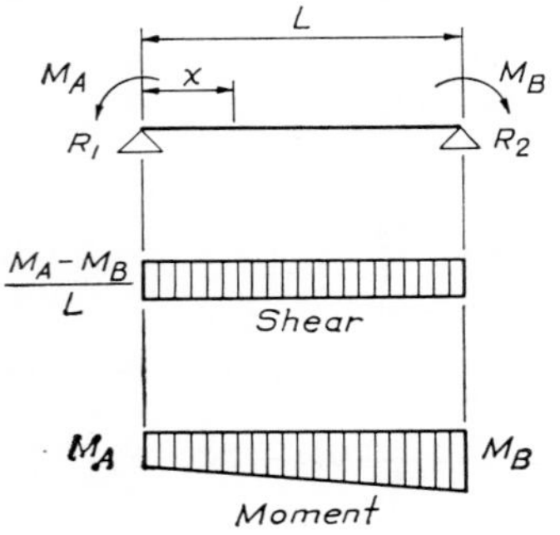

$$R_1 = -R_2 = \frac{M_A - M_B}{L}$$

$$V_x = \frac{M_A - M_B}{L}$$

$$M_x = M_A\left(\frac{1 - x}{L}\right) - M_B \frac{x}{L}$$

$$\Delta_x = \frac{M_A L x}{3EI} + \frac{M_B L x}{6EI} - \frac{M_A x^2}{2EI} - \frac{M_B x^3}{6LEI} + \frac{M_A x^3}{6LEI}$$

$$\Delta_{L/2} = \frac{(M_A + M_B)L^2}{16EI}$$

BEAM DIAGRAMS AND FORMULAS

SIMPLE BEAM—UNIFORM LOAD PARTIALLY DISTRIBUTED AT EACH END

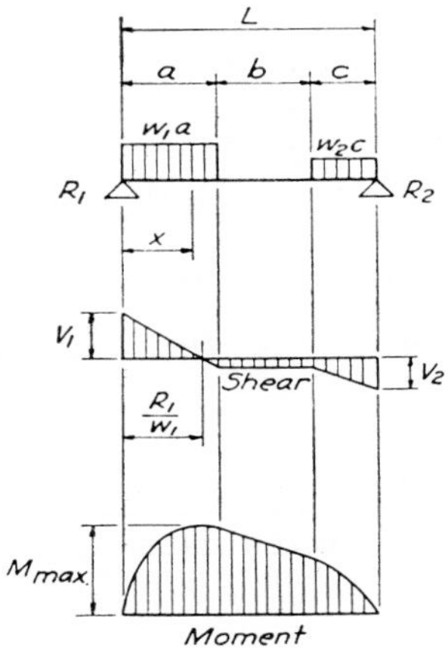

$R_1 = V_1 \ldots\ldots = \dfrac{w_1a(2L - a) + w_2c^2}{2L}$

$R_2 = V_2 \ldots\ldots = \dfrac{w_2c(2L - c) + w_1a^2}{2L}$

V_x (when $x < a$) $\ldots\ldots = R_1 - w_1x$

V_x [when $x > a$ and $<(a + b)$] $\ldots\ldots = R_1 - w_1a$

V_x [when $x > (a + b)$] $\ldots\ldots = R_2 - w_2(L - x)$

$M_{max}\left(\text{at } x = \dfrac{R_1}{w_1} \text{ when } R_1 < w_1a\right) \ldots\ldots = \dfrac{R_1^2}{2w_1}$

$M_{max}\left(\text{at } x = L - \dfrac{R_2}{w_2} \text{ when } R_2 < w_2c\right) \ldots = \dfrac{R_2^2}{2w_2}$

M_x (when $x < a$) $\ldots\ldots = R_1x - \dfrac{w_1x^2}{2}$

M_x [when $x > a$ and $<(a + b)$] $\ldots\ldots = R_1x - \dfrac{w_1a}{2}(2x - a)$

M_x [when $x > (a + b)$] $\ldots\ldots = R_2(L - x) - \dfrac{w_2(L - x)^2}{2}$

SIMPLE BEAM—CONCENTRATED LOAD AT CENTER

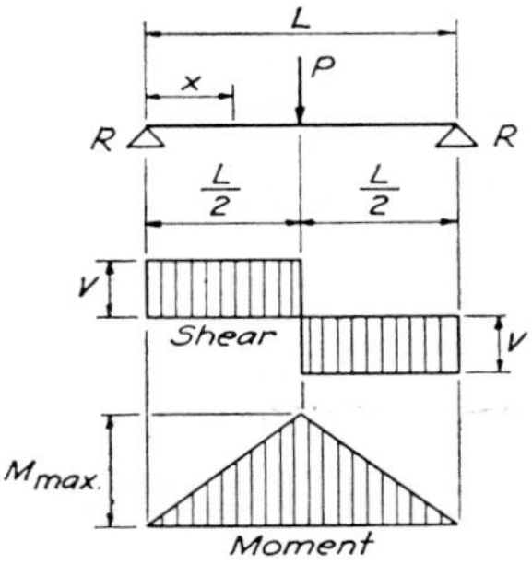

Equivalent Tabular Load.* $\ldots\ldots = 2P$

$R = V \ldots\ldots = \dfrac{P}{2}$

M_{max} (at point of load) $\ldots\ldots = \dfrac{PL}{4}$

$M_x\left(\text{when } x < \dfrac{L}{2}\right) \ldots\ldots = \dfrac{Px}{2}$

Δ_{max} (at point of load) $\ldots\ldots = \dfrac{PL^3}{48EI}$

$\Delta_x\left(\text{when } x < \dfrac{L}{2}\right) \ldots\ldots = \dfrac{Px}{48EI}(3L^2 - 4x^2)$

** Note: See explanation on page 3-27.*

SIMPLE BEAM—CONCENTRATED LOAD AT ANY POINT

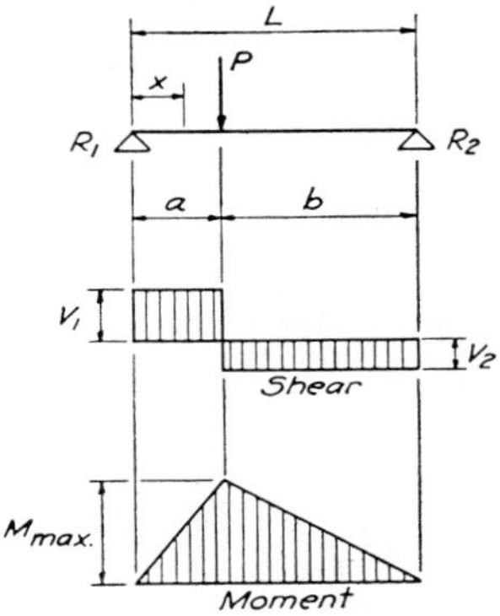

Equivalent Tabular Load.* $\ldots\ldots = \dfrac{8Pab}{L^2}$

$R_1 = V_1$ (max when $a < b$) $\ldots\ldots = \dfrac{Pb}{L}$

$R_2 = V_2$ (max when $a > b$) $\ldots\ldots = \dfrac{Pa}{L}$

M_{max} (at point of load) $\ldots\ldots = \dfrac{Pab}{L}$

M_x (when $x < a$) $\ldots\ldots = \dfrac{Pbx}{L}$

$\Delta_{max}\left[\text{at } x = \sqrt{\dfrac{a(a + 2b)}{3}} \text{ when } a > b\right] = \dfrac{Pab(a + 2b)\sqrt{3a(a + 2b)}}{27EIL}$

Δ_a (at point of load) $\ldots\ldots = \dfrac{Pa^2b^2}{3EIL}$

Δ_x (when $x < a$) $\ldots\ldots = \dfrac{Pbx}{6EIL}(L^2 - b^2 - x^2)$

BEAM DIAGRAMS AND FORMULAS

SIMPLE BEAM—TWO EQUAL CONCENTRATED LOADS SYMMETRICALLY PLACED

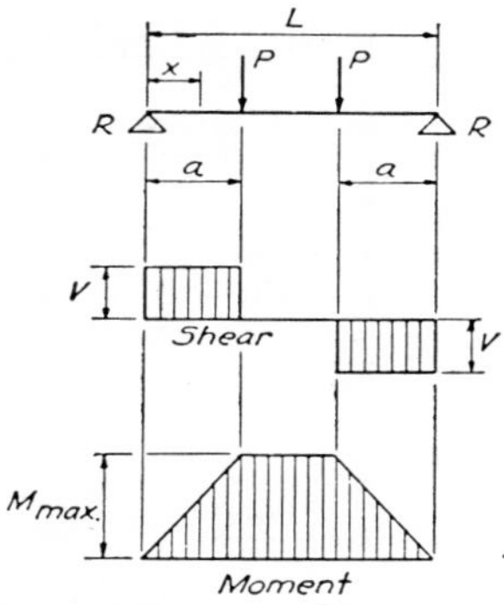

Equivalent Tabular Load * . . . . $= \frac{8Pa}{L}$

$R = V$ [when $x < a$, or $>(L - a)$] . . . . . . $= P$

M_{max} (between loads) . . . . $= Pa$

M_x (when $x < a$) . . . . $= Px$

Δ_{max} (at center) . . . . $= \frac{Pa}{24EI}(3L^2 - 4a^2)$

Δ_x (when $x < a$) . . . . $= \frac{Px}{6EI}(3La - 3a^2 - x^2)$

Δ_x [when $x > a$ and $<(L - a)$] . . . . $= \frac{Pa}{6EI}(3Lx - 3x^2 - a^2)$

---

* *Note:* *See explanation on page 3-27.*

SIMPLE BEAM—TWO EQUAL CONCENTRATED LOADS UNSYMMETRICALLY PLACED

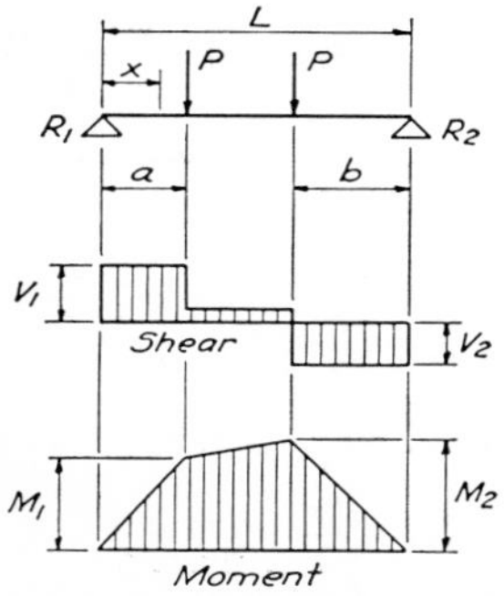

$R_1 = V_1$ (max when $a < b$) . . . . $= \frac{P}{L}(L - a + b)$

$R_2 = V_2$ (max when $a > b$) . . . . $= \frac{P}{L}(L - b + a)$

V_x [when $x > a$ and $<(L - b)$] . . . . $= \frac{P}{L}(b - a)$

M_1 (max when $a > b$) . . . . $= R_1a$

M_2 (max when $a < b$) . . . . $= R_2b$

M_x (when $x < a$) . . . . $= R_1x$

M_x [when $x > a$ and $<(L - b)$] . . . . $= R_1x - P(x - a)$

SIMPLE BEAM—TWO UNEQUAL CONCENTRATED LOADS UNSYMMETRICALLY PLACED

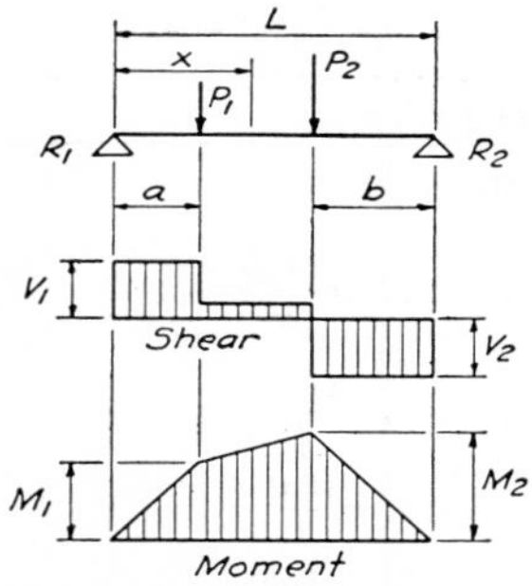

$R_1 = V_1$ . . . . $= \frac{P_1(L - a) + P_2b}{L}$

$R_2 = V_2$ . . . . $= \frac{P_1a + P_2(L - b)}{L}$

V_x [when $x > a$ and $<(L - b)$] . . . . . $= R_1 - P_1$

M_1 (max when $R_1 < P_1$) . . . . $= R_1a$

M_2 (max when $R_2 < P_2$) . . . . $= R_2b$

M_x (when $x < a$) . . . . $= R_1x$

M_x [when $x > a$ and $<(L - b)$] . . . . . $= R_1x - P_1(x - a)$

SIMPLE BEAM—TWO EQUAL CONCENTRATED MOVING LOADS

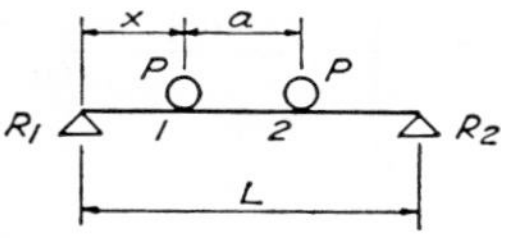

$R_{1max} = V_{1max}$ (at $x = 0$) . . . . $= P\left(2 - \frac{a}{L}\right)$

M_{max}:

- [when $a < (2 - \sqrt{2})L = .586L$ under load 1 at $x = \frac{1}{2}\left(L - \frac{a}{2}\right)$] . . $= \frac{P}{2L}\left(L - \frac{a}{2}\right)^2$
- [when $a > (2 - \sqrt{2})L = .586L$ with one load at center of span] . . $= \frac{PL}{4}$

BEAM DIAGRAMS AND FORMULAS

SIMPLE BEAM—TWO UNEQUAL CONCENTRATED MOVING LOAD

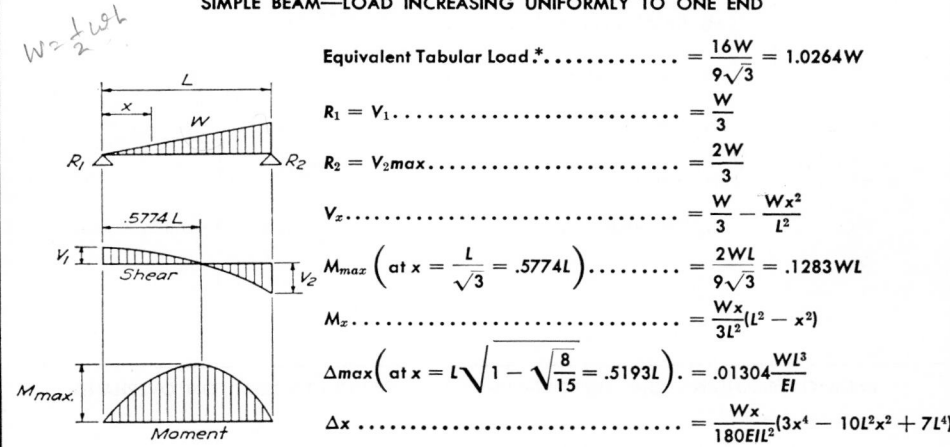

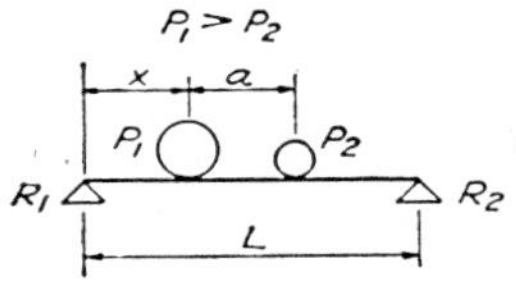

$R_{1max} = V_{1max}$ (at $x = 0$) . . . . $= P_1 + P_2\left(\frac{L-a}{L}\right)$

M_{max}

[under P_1 at $x = \frac{1}{2}\left(L - \frac{P_2 a}{P_1 + P_2}\right)$] . . $= (P_1 + P_2)\frac{x^2}{L}$

[M_{max} may occur with larger load at center of span and other load off span] . . $= \frac{P_1 L}{4}$

SIMPLE BEAM—LOAD INCREASING UNIFORMLY TO ONE END

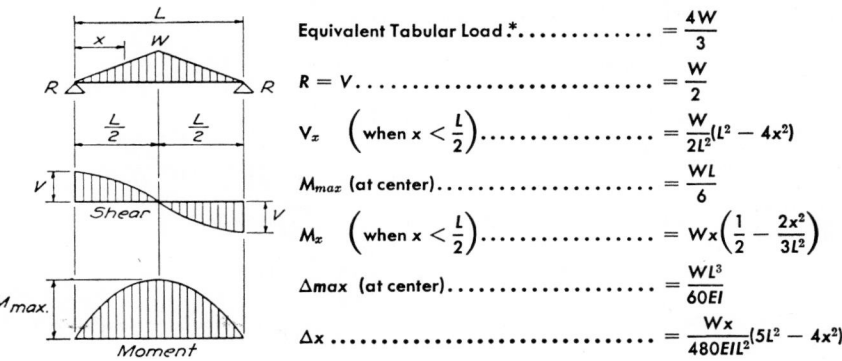

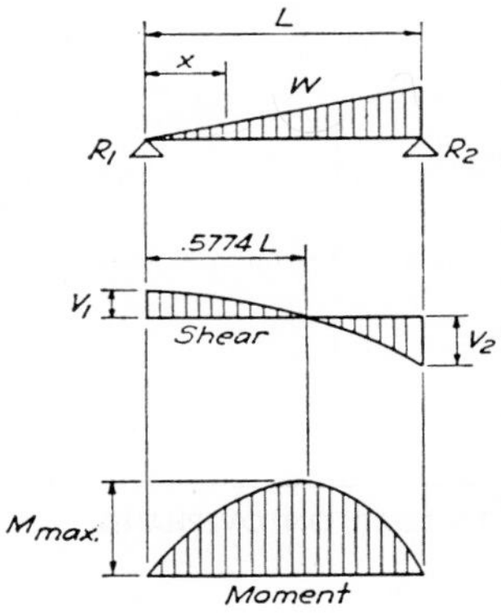

Equivalent Tabular Load * . . . . $= \frac{16W}{9\sqrt{3}} = 1.0264W$

$R_1 = V_1$ . . . . $= \frac{W}{3}$

$R_2 = V_2 max$ . . . . $= \frac{2W}{3}$

V_x . . . . $= \frac{W}{3} - \frac{Wx^2}{L^2}$

M_{max} $\left(\text{at } x = \frac{L}{\sqrt{3}} = .5774L\right)$ . . . . $= \frac{2WL}{9\sqrt{3}} = .1283WL$

M_x . . . . $= \frac{Wx}{3L^2}(L^2 - x^2)$

$\Delta max\left(\text{at } x = L\sqrt{1 - \sqrt{\frac{8}{15}}} = .5193L\right)$. $= .01304\frac{WL^3}{EI}$

Δx . . . . $= \frac{Wx}{180EIL^2}(3x^4 - 10L^2x^2 + 7L^4)$

SIMPLE BEAM—LOAD INCREASING UNIFORMLY TO CENTER

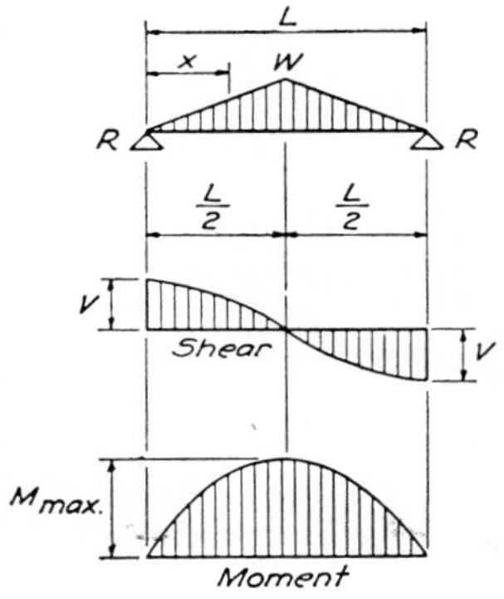

Equivalent Tabular Load * . . . . $= \frac{4W}{3}$

$R = V$ . . . . $= \frac{W}{2}$

V_x $\left(\text{when } x < \frac{L}{2}\right)$ . . . . $= \frac{W}{2L^2}(L^2 - 4x^2)$

M_{max} (at center) . . . . $= \frac{WL}{6}$

M_x $\left(\text{when } x < \frac{L}{2}\right)$ . . . . $= Wx\left(\frac{1}{2} - \frac{2x^2}{3L^2}\right)$

Δmax (at center) . . . . $= \frac{WL^3}{60EI}$

Δx . . . . $= \frac{Wx}{480EIL^2}(5L^2 - 4x^2)^2$

* Note: See explanation on page 3-27.

BEAM DIAGRAMS AND FORMULAS

BEAM OVERHANGING ONE SUPPORT—UNIFORMLY DISTRIBUTED LOAD

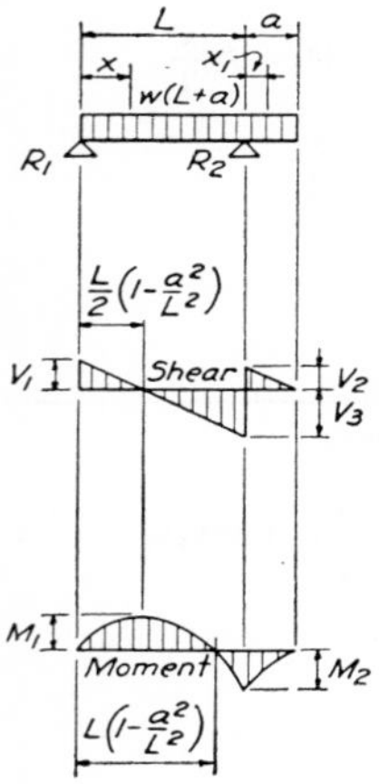

$R_1 = V_1$ .... $= \frac{w}{2L}(L^2 - a^2)$

$R_2 = V_2 + V_3$ .... $= \frac{w}{2L}(L + a)^2$

V_2 .... $= wa$

V_3 .... $= \frac{w}{2L}(L^2 + a^2)$

V_x (between supports) .... $= R_1 - wx$

V_{x_1} (for overhang) .... $= w(a - x_1)$

$M_1 \left(\text{at } x = \frac{L}{2}\left[1 - \frac{a^2}{L^2}\right]\right)$ .... $= \frac{w}{8L^2}(L + a)^2(L - a)^2$

M_2 (at R_2) .... $= \frac{wa^2}{2}$

M_x (between supports) .... $= \frac{wx}{2L}(L^2 - a^2 - xL)$

M_{x_1} (for overhang) .... $= \frac{w}{2}(a - x_1)^2$

Δ_x (between supports) .... $= \frac{wx}{24EIL}(L^4 - 2L^2x^2 + Lx^3 - 2a^2L^2 + 2a^2x^2)$

Δ_{x_1} (for overhang) .... $= \frac{wx_1}{24EI}(4a^2L - L^3 + 6a^2x_1 - 4ax_1^2 + x_1^3)$

BEAM OVERHANGING ONE SUPPORT—UNIFORMLY DISTRIBUTED LOAD ON OVERHANG

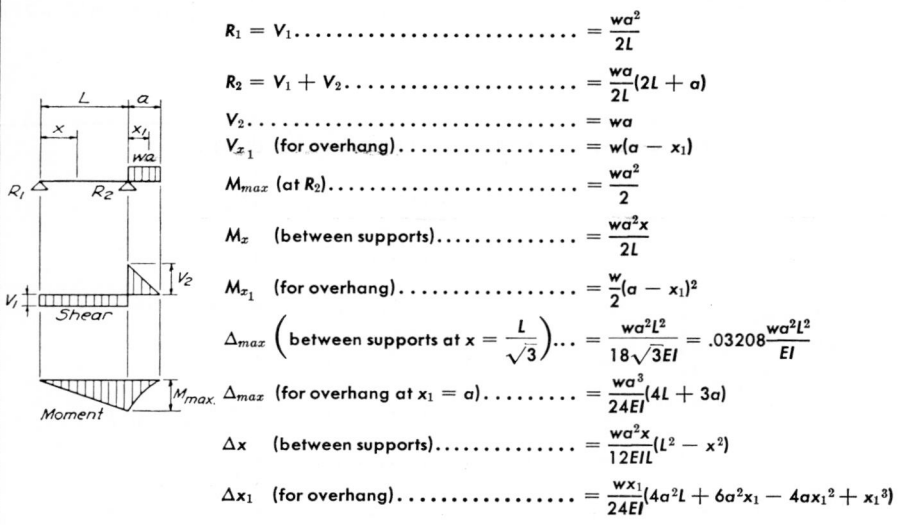

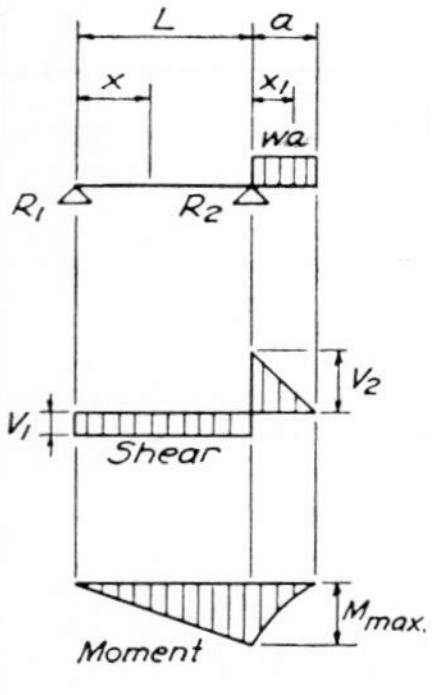

$R_1 = V_1$ .... $= \frac{wa^2}{2L}$

$R_2 = V_1 + V_2$ .... $= \frac{wa}{2L}(2L + a)$

V_2 .... $= wa$

V_{x_1} (for overhang) .... $= w(a - x_1)$

M_{max} (at R_2) .... $= \frac{wa^2}{2}$

M_x (between supports) .... $= \frac{wa^2x}{2L}$

M_{x_1} (for overhang) .... $= \frac{w}{2}(a - x_1)^2$

$\Delta_{max} \left(\text{between supports at } x = \frac{L}{\sqrt{3}}\right)$ ... $= \frac{wa^2L^2}{18\sqrt{3}EI} = .03208\frac{wa^2L^2}{EI}$

Δ_{max} (for overhang at $x_1 = a$) .... $= \frac{wa^3}{24EI}(4L + 3a)$

Δx (between supports) .... $= \frac{wa^2x}{12EIL}(L^2 - x^2)$

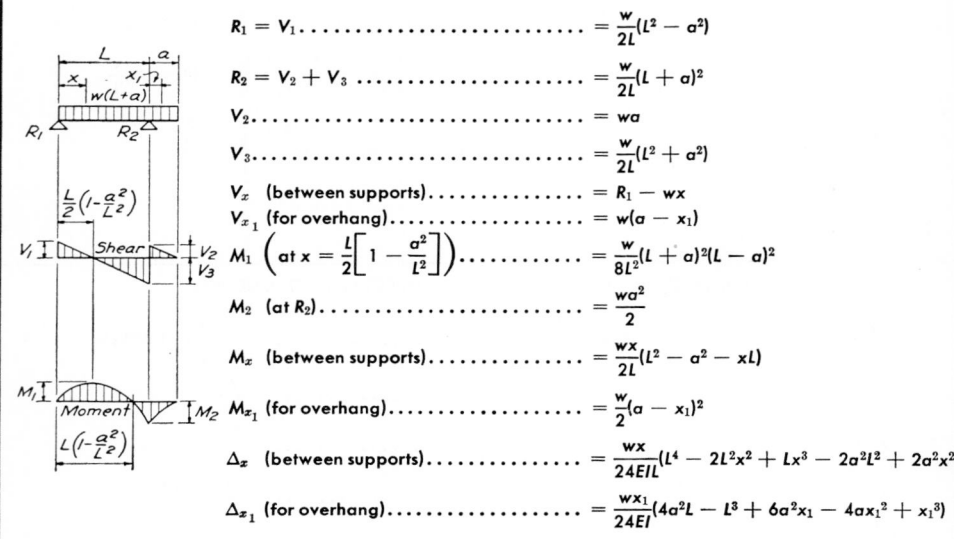

Δx_1 (for overhang) .... $= \frac{wx_1}{24EI}(4a^2L + 6a^2x_1 - 4ax_1^2 + x_1^3)$

BEAM DIAGRAMS AND FORMULAS

BEAM OVERHANGING ONE SUPPORT—UNIFORMLY DISTRIBUTED LOAD BETWEEN SUPPORTS

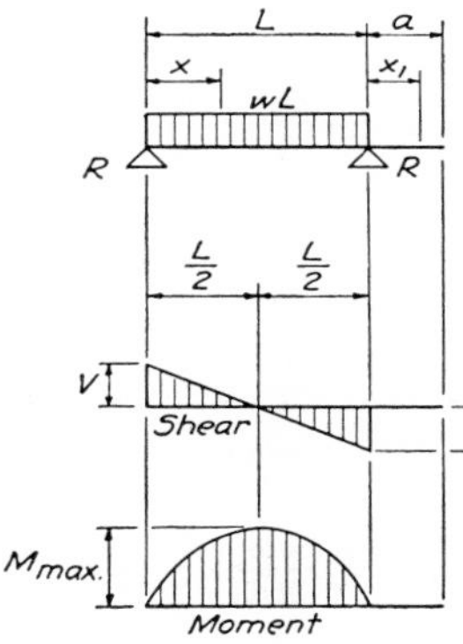

Equivalent Tabular Load.* . . . . $= wL$

$R = V$ . . . . $= \frac{wL}{2}$

V_x . . . . $= w\left(\frac{L}{2} - x\right)$

M_{max} (at center) . . . . $= \frac{wL^2}{8}$

M_x . . . . $= \frac{wx}{2}(L - x)$

Δ_{max} (at center) . . . . $= \frac{5wL^4}{384EI}$

Δx . . . . $= \frac{wx}{24EI}(L^3 - 2Lx^2 + x^3)$

Δx_1 . . . . $= \frac{wL^3x_1}{24EI}$

BEAM OVERHANGING ONE SUPPORT—CONCENTRATED LOAD AT END OF OVERHANG

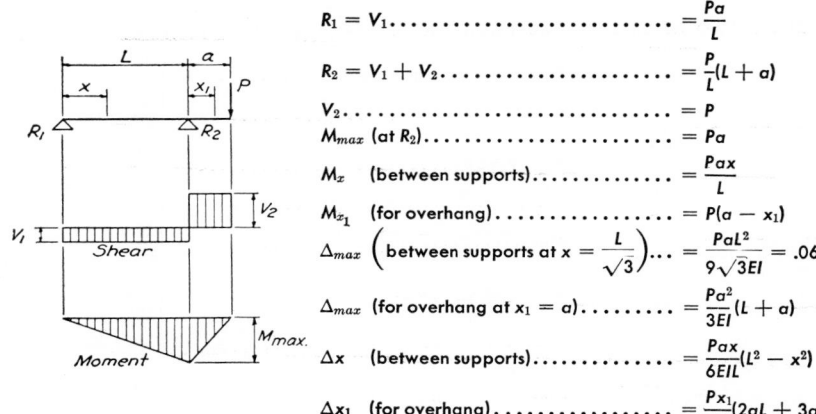

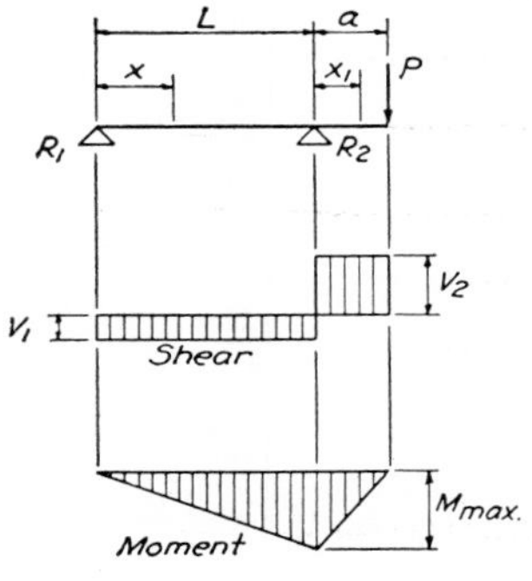

$R_1 = V_1$ . . . . $= \frac{Pa}{L}$

$R_2 = V_1 + V_2$ . . . . $= \frac{P}{L}(L + a)$

V_2 . . . . $= P$

M_{max} (at R_2) . . . . $= Pa$

M_x (between supports) . . . . $= \frac{Pax}{L}$

M_{x_1} (for overhang) . . . . $= P(a - x_1)$

Δ_{max} $\left(\text{between supports at } x = \frac{L}{\sqrt{3}}\right)$ . . . $= \frac{PaL^2}{9\sqrt{3}EI} = .06415\frac{PaL^2}{EI}$

Δ_{max} (for overhang at $x_1 = a$) . . . . $= \frac{Pa^2}{3EI}(L + a)$

Δx (between supports) . . . . $= \frac{Pax}{6EIL}(L^2 - x^2)$

Δx_1 (for overhang) . . . . $= \frac{Px_1}{6EI}(2aL + 3ax_1 - x_1^2)$

** Note that "Equivalent Tabular Load" is the total uniform load that will produce the same bending moment (but probably not the same shear) and must be divided by the span, L, for entering safe load tables in this book.*

BEAM DIAGRAMS AND FORMULAS

BEAM OVERHANGING ONE SUPPORT—CONCENTRATED LOAD AT ANY POINT BETWEEN SUPPORTS

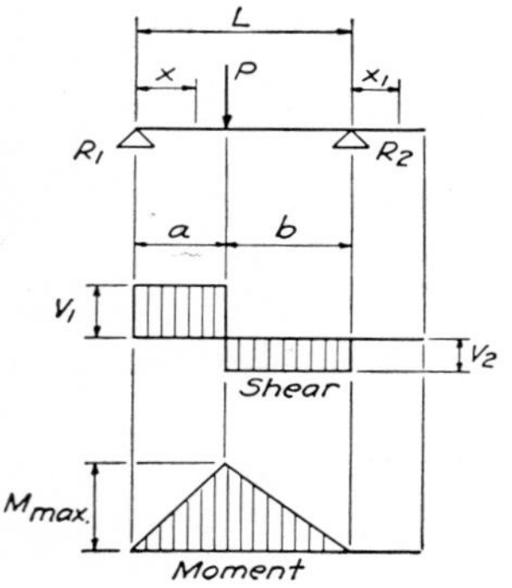

Equivalent Tabular Load.* . . . . $= \frac{8Pab}{L^2}$

$R_1 = V_1$ (max when $a < b$) . . . . $= \frac{Pb}{L}$

$R_2 = V_2$ (max when $a > b$) . . . . $= \frac{Pa}{L}$

M_{max} (at point of load) . . . . $= \frac{Pab}{L}$

M_x (when $x < a$) . . . . $= \frac{Pbx}{L}$

$\Delta_{max}\left[\text{at } x = \sqrt{\frac{a(a+2b)}{3}} \text{ when } a > b\right]$. $= \frac{Pab(a+2b)\sqrt{3a(a+2b)}}{27EIL}$

Δa (at point of load) . . . . $= \frac{Pa^2b^2}{3EIL}$

Δx (when $x < a$) . . . . $= \frac{Pbx}{6EIL}(L^2 - b^2 - x^2)$

Δx (when $x > a$) . . . . $= \frac{Pa(L-x)}{6EIL}(2Lx - x^2 - a^2)$

Δx_1 . . . . $= \frac{Pabx_1}{6EIL}(L + a)$

BEAM FIXED AT ONE END, SUPPORTED AT OTHER—UNIFORMLY DISTRIBUTED LOAD

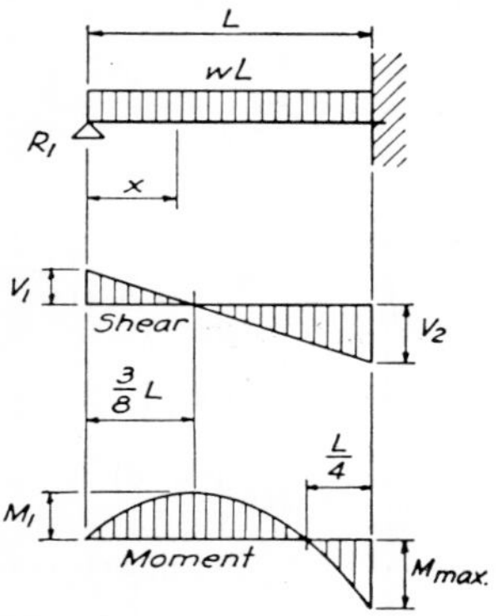

Equivalent Tabular Load.* . . . . $= wL$

$R_1 = V_1$ . . . . $= \frac{3wL}{8}$

$R_2 = V_2 max$ . . . . $= \frac{5wL}{8}$

V_x . . . . $= R_1 - wx$

M_{max} . . . . $= \frac{wL^2}{8}$

$M_1 \left(\text{at } x = \frac{3}{8}L\right)$ . . . . $= \frac{9}{128}wL^2$

M_x . . . . $= R_1x - \frac{wx^2}{2}$

$\Delta max\left[\text{at } x = \frac{L}{16}(1 + \sqrt{33}) = .4215L\right]$. . $= \frac{wL^4}{184.63EI}$

Δx . . . . $= \frac{wx}{48EI}(L^3 - 3Lx^2 + 2x^3)$

* *Note: See explanation on page 3-27.*

BEAM DIAGRAMS AND FORMULAS

BEAM FIXED AT ONE END, SUPPORTED AT OTHER—CONCENTRATED LOAD AT CENTER

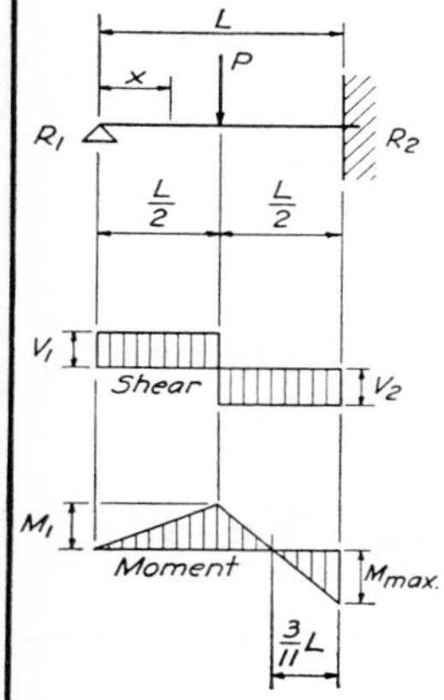

Equivalent Tabular Load.* .... $= \frac{3P}{2}$

$R_1 = V_1$ .... $= \frac{5P}{16}$

$R_2 = V_2 max$ .... $= \frac{11P}{16}$

M_{max} (at fixed end) .... $= \frac{3PL}{16}$

M_1 (at point of load) .... $= \frac{5PL}{32}$

M_x $\left(\text{when } x < \frac{L}{2}\right)$ .... $= \frac{5Px}{16}$

M_x $\left(\text{when } x > \frac{L}{2}\right)$ .... $= P\left(\frac{L}{2} - \frac{11x}{16}\right)$

Δ_{max} $\left(\text{at } x = L\sqrt{\frac{1}{5}} = .4472L\right)$ .... $= \frac{PL^3}{48EI\sqrt{5}} = .009317\frac{PL^3}{EI}$

Δx (at point of load) .... $= \frac{7PL^3}{768EI}$

Δx $\left(\text{when } x < \frac{L}{2}\right)$ .... $= \frac{Px}{96EI}(3L^2 - 5x^2)$

Δx $\left(\text{when } x > \frac{L}{2}\right)$ .... $= \frac{P}{96EI}(x - L)^2(11x - 2L)$

---

* *Note:* *See explanation on page 3-27.*

BEAM FIXED AT ONE END, SUPPORTED AT OTHER—CONCENTRATED LOAD AT ANY POINT

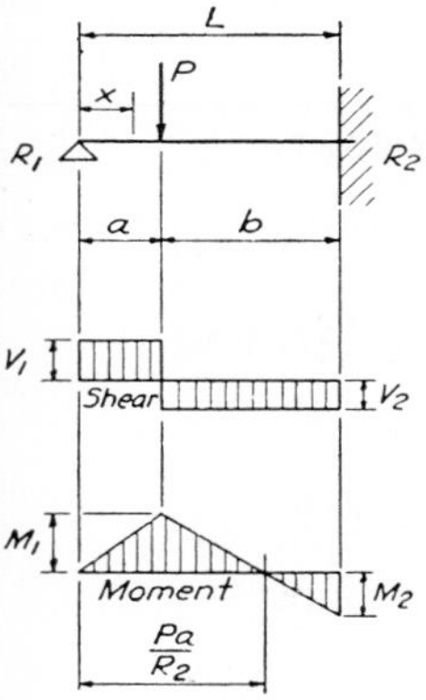

$R_1 = V_1$ .... $= \frac{Pb^2}{2L^3}(a + 2L)$

$R_2 = V_2$ .... $= \frac{Pa}{2L^3}(3L^2 - a^2)$

M_1 (at point of load) .... $= R_1 a$

M_2 (at fixed end) .... $= \frac{Pab}{2L^2}(a + L)$

M_x (when $x < a$) .... $= R_1 x$

M_x (when $x > a$) .... $= R_1 x - P(x - a)$

Δ_{max} $\left(\text{when } a < .414L \text{ at } x = L\frac{L^2 + a^2}{3L^2 - a^2}\right)$ .. $= \frac{Pa(L^2 - a^2)^3}{3EI(3L^2 - a^2)^2}$

Δ_{max} $\left(\text{when } a > .414L \text{ at } x = L\sqrt{\frac{a}{2L + a}}\right)$. $= \frac{Pab^2}{6EI}\sqrt{\frac{a}{2L + a}}$

Δa (at point of load) .... $= \frac{Pa^2b^3}{12EIL^3}(3L + a)$

Δx (when $x < a$) .... $= \frac{Pb^2x}{12EIL^3}(3aL^2 - 2Lx^2 - ax^2)$

Δx (when $x > a$) .... $= \frac{Pa}{12EIL^3}(L - x)^2(3L^2x - a^2x - 2a^2L)$

BEAM DIAGRAMS AND FORMULAS

BEAM FIXED AT BOTH ENDS—UNIFORMLY DISTRIBUTED LOADS

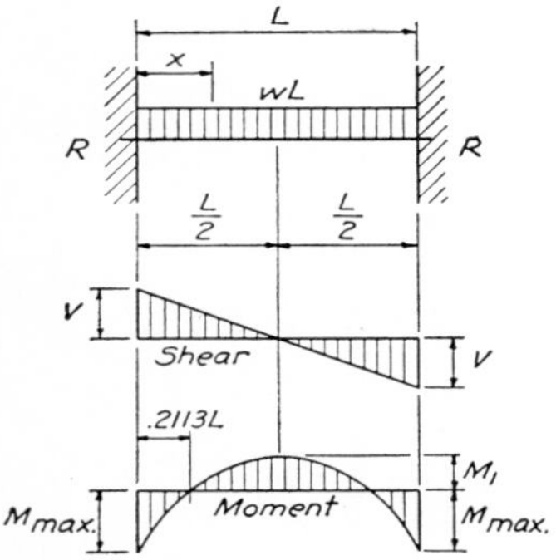

Equivalent Tabular Load *. . . . . $= \frac{2wL}{3}$

$R = V$ . . . . $= \frac{wL}{2}$

V_x . . . . $= w\left(\frac{L}{2} - x\right)$

M_{max} (at ends). . . . . $= \frac{wL^2}{12}$

M_1 (at center). . . . . $= \frac{wL^2}{24}$

M_x . . . . $= \frac{w}{12}(6Lx - L^2 - 6x^2)$

Δ_{max} (at center). . . . . $= \frac{wL^4}{384EI}$

Δx . . . . $= \frac{wx^2}{24EI}(L - x)^2$

BEAM FIXED AT BOTH ENDS—CONCENTRATED LOAD AT CENTER

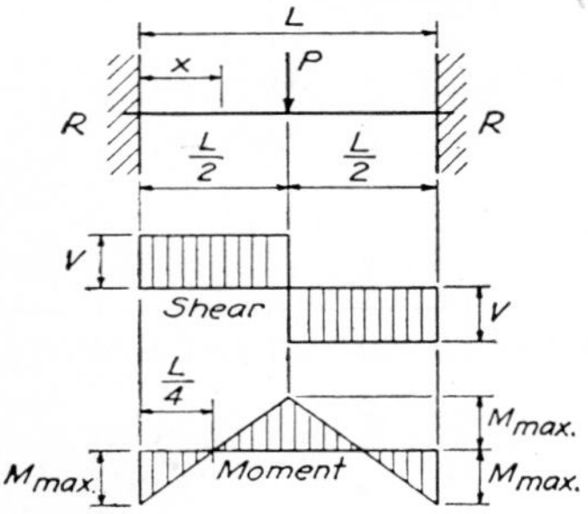

Equivalent Tabular Load *. . . . . $= P$

$R = V$ . . . . $= \frac{P}{2}$

M_{max} (at center and ends). . . . . $= \frac{PL}{8}$

M_x $\left(\text{when } x < \frac{L}{2}\right)$ . . . . $= \frac{P}{8}(4x - L)$

Δ_{max} (at center). . . . . $= \frac{PL^3}{192EI}$

Δx $\left(x < \frac{L}{2}\right)$ . . . . $= \frac{Px^2}{48EI}(3L - 4x)$

BEAM FIXED AT BOTH ENDS—CONCENTRATED LOAD AT ANY POINT

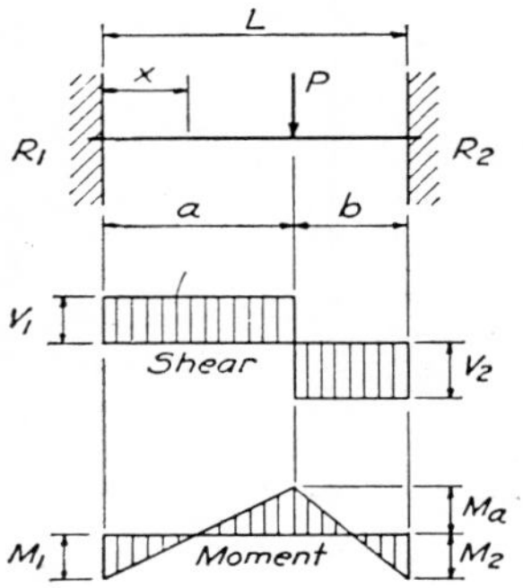

$R_1 = V_1$ (max when $a < b$). . . . . $= \frac{Pb^2}{L^3}(3a + b)$

$R_2 = V_2$ (max when $a > b$). . . . . $= \frac{Pa^2}{L^3}(a + 3b)$

M_1 (max when $a < b$). . . . . $= \frac{Pab^2}{L^2}$

M_2 (max when $a > b$). . . . . $= \frac{Pa^2b}{L^2}$

M_a (at point of load). . . . . $= \frac{2Pa^2b^2}{L^3}$

M_x (when $x < a$). . . . . $= R_1x - \frac{Pab^2}{L^2}$

Δ_{max} $\left(\text{when } a > b \text{ at } x = \frac{2aL}{3a + b}\right)$. . . $= \frac{2Pa^3b^2}{3EI(3a + b)^2}$

Δa (at point of load). . . . . $= \frac{Pa^3b^3}{3EIL^3}$

Δx (when $x < a$). . . . . $= \frac{Pb^2x^2}{6EIL^3}(3aL - 3ax - bx)$

* *Note: See explanation on page 3-27.*

BEAM DIAGRAMS AND FORMULAS

CONTINUOUS BEAM—TWO EQUAL SPANS—UNIFORM LOAD ON ONE SPAN

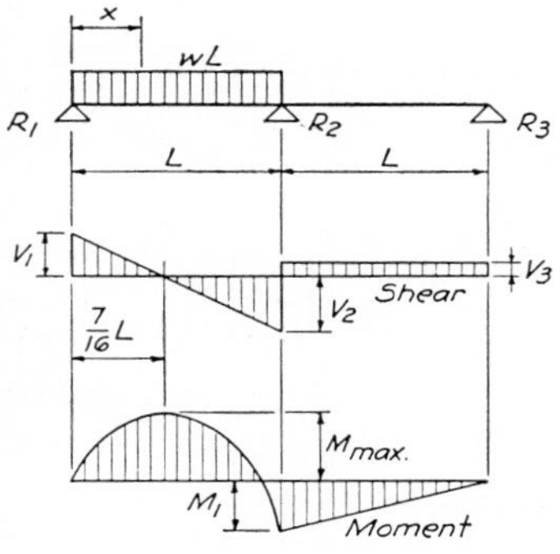

Equivalent Tabular Load * .... $= \frac{49}{64}wL$

$R_1 = V_1$ .... $= \frac{7}{16}wL$

$R_2 = V_2 + V_3$ .... $= \frac{5}{8}wL$

$R_3 = V_3$ .... $= -\frac{1}{16}wL$

V_2 .... $= \frac{9}{16}wL$

$M_{max} \left(\text{at } x = \frac{7}{16}L\right)$ .... $= \frac{49}{512}wL^2$

M_1 (at support R_2) .... $= \frac{1}{16}wL^2$

M_x (when $x < L$) .... $= \frac{wx}{16}(7L - 8x)$

CONTINUOUS BEAM—TWO EQUAL SPANS—CONCENTRATED LOAD AT CENTER OF ONE SPAN

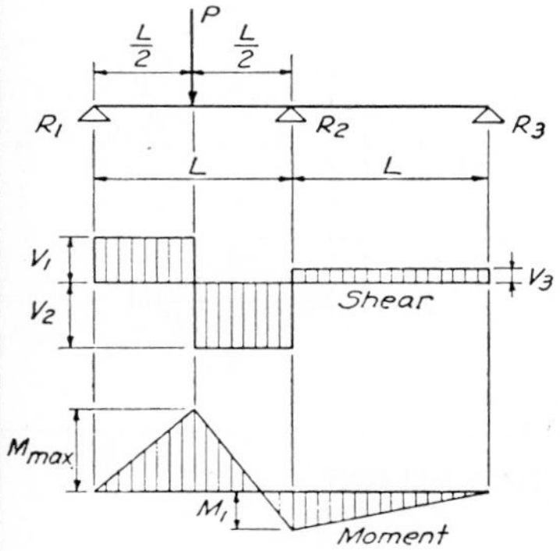

Equivalent Tabular Load * .... $= \frac{13}{8}P$

$R_1 = V_1$ .... $= \frac{13}{32}P$

$R_2 = V_2 + V_3$ .... $= \frac{11}{16}P$

$R_3 = V_3$ .... $= -\frac{3}{32}P$

V_2 .... $= \frac{19}{32}P$

M_{max} (at point of load) .... $= \frac{13}{64}PL$

M_1 (at support R_2) .... $= \frac{3}{32}PL$

CONTINUOUS BEAM—TWO EQUAL SPANS—CONCENTRATED LOAD AT ANY POINT

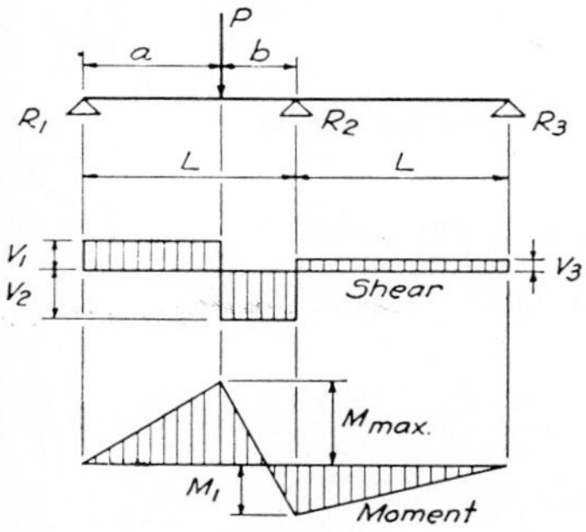

$R_1 = V_1$ .... $= \frac{Pb}{4L^3}[4L^2 - a(L + a)]$

$R_2 = V_2 + V_3$ .... $= \frac{Pa}{2L^3}[2L^2 + b(L + a)]$

$R_3 = V_3$ .... $= -\frac{Pab}{4L^3}(L + a)$

V_2 .... $= \frac{Pa}{4L^3}[4L^2 + b(L + a)]$

M_{max} (at point of load) .... $= \frac{Pab}{4L^3}[4L^2 - a(L + a)]$

M_1 (at support R_2) .... $= \frac{Pab}{4L^2}(L + a)$

* *Note:* *See explanation on page 3-27.*

BEAM DIAGRAMS AND FORMULAS

BEAM FIXED BOTH ENDS—NO LOAD—ONE END OFFSET

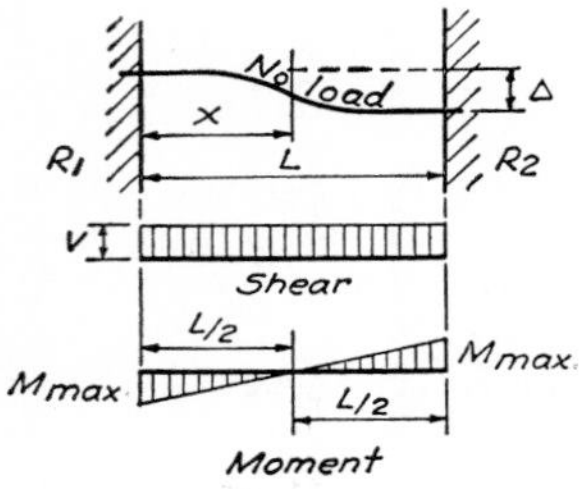

$R_1 = V \dots = \frac{12EI\Delta}{L^3}$

$R_2 \dots = -\frac{12EI\Delta}{L^3}$

$M_{max} \dots = \frac{6EI\Delta}{L^2}$

$M_x \dots = \frac{6EI\Delta}{L^3}(2x - L)$

$\Delta_{max} \dots = \Delta$

$\Delta_x \dots = \frac{\Delta x^2}{L^3}(3L - 2x)$

(For offset in opposite direction reverse signs)

BEAM FIXED ONE END—NO LOAD—ONE END OFFSET

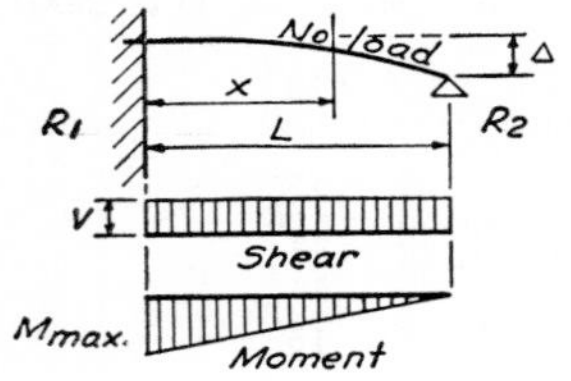

$R_1 = V \dots = \frac{3EI\Delta}{L^3}$

$R_2 \dots = -\frac{3EI\Delta}{L^3}$

$M_{max} \dots = -\frac{3EI\Delta}{L^2}$

$M_x \dots = -\frac{3EI\Delta}{L^3}(L - x)$

$\Delta_{max} \dots = \Delta$

$\Delta_x \dots = \frac{\Delta x^2}{2L^3}(3L - x)$

(For offset in opposite direction reverse signs)

BEAM FIXED BOTH ENDS—NO LOAD—APPLIED MOMENT

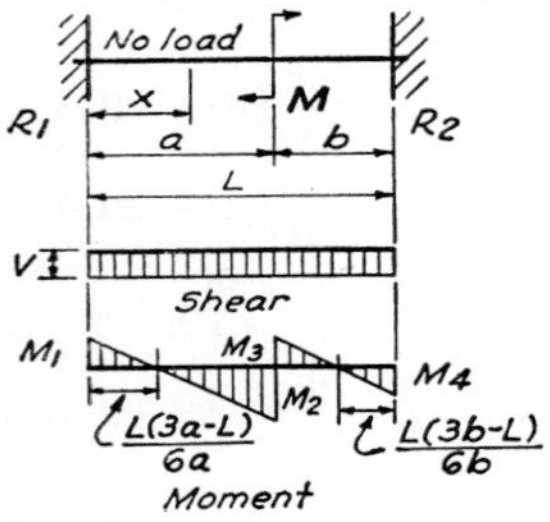

$R_1 = V = -\frac{6Mab}{L^3}$ $\qquad R_2 = \frac{6Mab}{L^3}$

$M_1 \dots = +\frac{Mb}{L}\left(1 - 3\frac{a}{L}\right)$ $\qquad M_2 = -\frac{Mb}{L}\left(1 - 3\frac{a}{L} + 6\frac{a^2}{L^2}\right)$

$M_3 \dots = \frac{Ma}{L}\left(1 - 3\frac{b}{L} + 6\frac{b^2}{L^2}\right)$ $\qquad M_4 = -\frac{Ma}{L}\left(1 - 3\frac{b}{L}\right)$

M_x (when $x < a$) $\dots = -\frac{Mb}{L^3}(L^2 - 3aL + 6ax)$

M_x (when $x > a$) $\dots = \frac{Ma}{L^3}(L^2 + 3bL - 6bx)$

Δ_x (when $x < a$) $\dots = \frac{Mb}{EIL^3}\left(\frac{L^2x^2}{2} - \frac{3aLx^2}{2} + ax^3\right)$

Δ_x (when $x > a$) $\dots = -\frac{Ma}{EIL^3}\left(\frac{L^2x^2}{2} + \frac{3bLx^2}{2} - bx^3 - L^3x + \frac{aL^3}{2}\right)$

$\Delta_a \dots = \frac{Ma^2b}{EIL^3}\left(\frac{L^2}{2} - \frac{3aL}{2} + a^2\right) = \frac{Ma^2b^2}{2EIL^3}(L - 2a)$

BEAM DIAGRAMS AND FORMULAS

BEAM FIXED ONE END—NO LOAD—APPLIED MOMENT

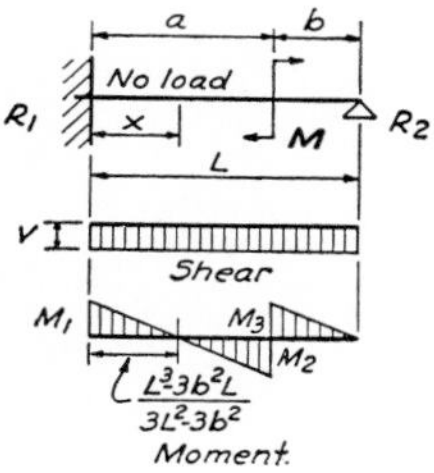

$$R_1 = V \ldots\ldots = -\frac{3M}{2L}\left(1-\frac{b^2}{L^2}\right) \qquad R_2 \ldots\ldots = \frac{3M}{2L}\left(1-\frac{b^2}{L^2}\right)$$

$$M_1 \ldots\ldots = \frac{M}{2}\left(1-3\frac{b^2}{L^2}\right) \qquad M_2 \ldots\ldots = \frac{3Mb}{2L}\left(1-\frac{b^2}{L^2}\right) - M$$

$$M_3 \ldots\ldots = \frac{3Mb}{2L}\left(1-\frac{b^2}{L^2}\right)$$

$$M_x \text{ (when } x < a) \ldots = \frac{3M}{2L}\left(1-\frac{b^2}{L^2}\right)(L-x) - M$$

$$M_x \text{ (when } x > a) \ldots = \frac{3M}{2L}\left(1-\frac{b^2}{L^2}\right)(L-x)$$

$$\Delta_x \text{ (when } x < a) \ldots = \frac{Mx^2}{2EI}\left[\frac{3}{L}\left(1-\frac{b^2}{L^2}\right)\left(\frac{x}{6}-\frac{L}{2}\right)+1\right]$$

$$\Delta_x \text{ (when } x > a) \ldots = \frac{3M}{2EIL}\left(1-\frac{b^2}{L^2}\right)\left(\frac{L^3}{3}-\frac{Lx^2}{2}+\frac{x^3}{6}\right) - \frac{Ma}{EI}(L-x)$$

$$\Delta_a \ldots\ldots = \frac{Ma^2}{2EI}\left[\frac{a(2L-a)(a-3L)}{2L^3}+1\right]$$

SIMPLE BEAM—NO LOAD—APPLIED MOMENT

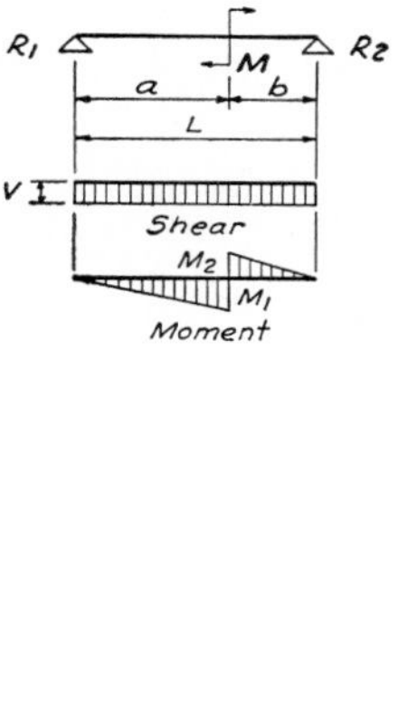

$$R_1 = V \ldots\ldots = -\frac{M}{L} \qquad R_2 \ldots\ldots = \frac{M}{L}$$

$$M_1 \ldots\ldots = -\frac{Ma}{L} \qquad M_2 \ldots\ldots = \frac{Mb}{L}$$

$$M_{max} \ldots\ldots = M_1 \text{ if } a > b$$
$$= M_2 \text{ if } a < b$$

$$M_x \text{ (when } x < a) \ldots = -\frac{Mx}{L}$$

$$M_x \text{ (when } x > a) \ldots = \frac{M}{L}(L-x)$$

$$\Delta_x \text{ (when } x < a) \ldots = \frac{Mx}{6EIL^2}(-a^3-3a^2b+2b^3+Lx^2)$$

$$\Delta_x \text{ (when } x > a) \ldots = \frac{M(L-x)}{6EIL^2}[-2a^3+3ab^2+b^3-L(L-x)^2]$$

$$\Delta_{max}\left(\text{if } a > b, \text{ at } x = \sqrt{-\frac{2}{3}L^2+2aL-a^2}\right) =$$

$$\frac{M\sqrt{-\frac{2}{3}L^2+2aL-a^2}}{6EIL^2}\left(-a^3-3a^2b+2b^3-\frac{2}{3}L^3+2aL^2-a^2L\right)$$

$$\Delta_{max}\left(\text{if } a < b, \text{ at } (L-x) = \sqrt{-\frac{2}{3}L^2+2bL-b^2}\right) =$$

$$\frac{M\sqrt{-\frac{2L^2}{3}+2bL-b^2}}{6EIL^2}\left(-2a^3+3ab^2+b^3+\frac{2}{3}L^3-2bL^2+b^2L\right)$$

CANTILEVERED BEAM—NO LOAD—APPLIED MOMENT

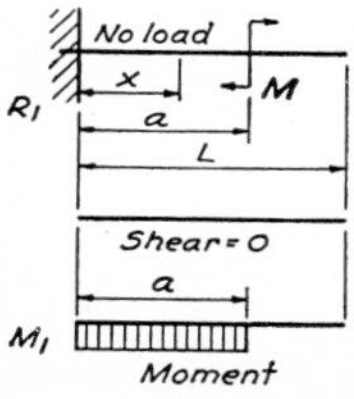

$$R = V \ldots\ldots = 0$$

$$M_1 \ldots\ldots = -M$$

$$\Delta_x \text{ (when } x \leqq a) \ldots = \frac{Mx^2}{2EI}$$

$$\Delta_x \text{ (when } x \geqq a) \ldots = \frac{Ma}{EI}\left(x-\frac{a}{2}\right)$$

$$\Delta_{max} \text{ (when } x = L) \ldots = \frac{Ma}{EI}\left(L-\frac{a}{2}\right)$$

Design Methods, Continuity, Beam Formulas
Section 4

CONTINUITY IN STRUCTURES

All of the tables of safe carrying capacities for flexural members given in this book are based upon loads uniformly distributed along the span length of the member. The ratios of live to dead load (i.e., 3:1, except in some cases so noted), and of span length under consideration to the lengths of adjoining spans (i.e., longer $\leqslant$ 1.20 shorter) are within the limits imposed by ACI "Building Code Requirements for Reinforced Concrete (ACI 318–63)" (904(c)), permitting the use of arbitrary moment coefficients that will produce reasonably safe results.

When span lengths or the ratio of live to dead load vary beyond Code limits, it is best to compute the moments by the Three Moment Equation or by Moment Distribution as illustrated briefly in this section and explained at length in any standard text on continuity.

Equivalent Loads

When concentrated loads are encountered, it is possible to enter the safe uniform load tables with approximately equivalent uniform loads. There is an "equivalent uniform load" that will produce the same *maximum* positive moment as the series of concentrated loads. There is, similarly, an "equivalent uniform load" for the negative moment. These equivalent total loads, $W = wL$, are given for a number of cases in the table on page 4-4, where $+W$ produces the same maximum positive moment and $-W$, the same maximum negative moment as do the concentrated loads. It is obvious that the shears, and the moments at other points than that where moment is maximum, may be quite different from the shears and moments produced by the concentrated loads. Hence the use of such equivalent uniform loading is not a safe way to make the final design of an important flexural member. Equivalent uniform loads may help in making a tentative selection for preliminary estimating purposes or in determining preliminary clearances. The table is given with this explanation as being of some guidance. Those not familiar with the general theory of bending would do well to obtain assistance in design for any cases that depart from the limitations imposed on each set of tables.

Note further that the coefficients in each column on page 4-4 relate to the uniformly loaded case at the head of the column.

EQUIVALENT UNIFORM LOAD FOR MAXIMUM MOMENT

Single Span	End Span	Interior Span
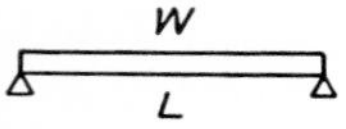 Max $M = \frac{WL}{8}$	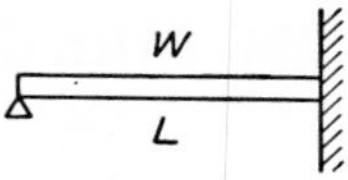 Max. $-M = -\frac{WL}{8}$ Max. $+M = +\frac{9WL}{128}$	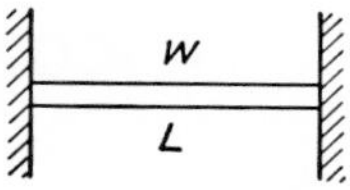 Max. $-M = -\frac{WL}{12}$ Max. $+M = +\frac{WL}{24}$
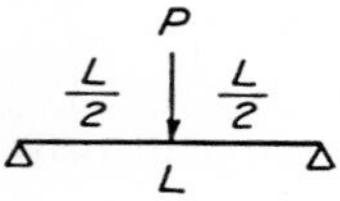 $+W = 2P$ Max. $M = \frac{PL}{4}$	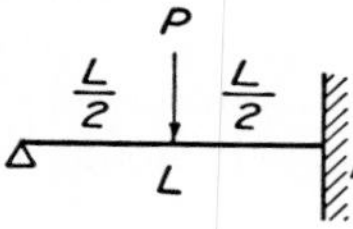 $+W = \frac{20P}{9}$ $-W = \frac{3P}{2}$ Max. $-M = -\frac{3PL}{16}$ Max. $+M = +\frac{5PL}{32}$	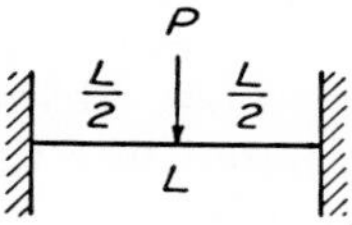 $+W = 3P$ $-W = \frac{3P}{2}$ Max. $-M = -\frac{PL}{8}$ Max. $+M = +\frac{PL}{8}$
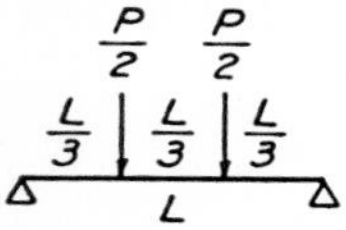 $+W = \frac{4P}{3}$ Max. $M = \frac{PL}{6}$	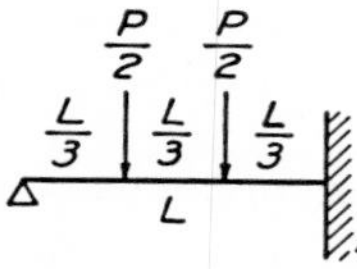 $+W = \frac{128P}{81}$ $-W = \frac{4P}{3}$ Max. $-M = -\frac{PL}{6}$ Max. $+M = +\frac{PL}{9}$	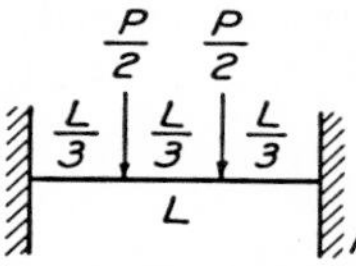 $+W = \frac{4P}{3}$ $-W = \frac{4P}{3}$ Max. $-M = -\frac{PL}{9}$ Max. $+M = +\frac{PL}{18}$
 $+W = \frac{4P}{3}$ Max. $M = \frac{PL}{6}$	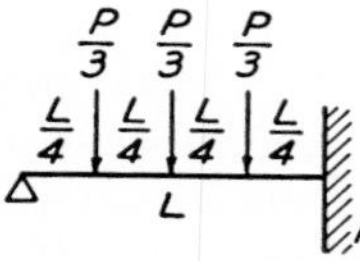 $+W = \frac{34P}{27}$ $-W = \frac{5P}{4}$ Max. $-M = -\frac{5PL}{32}$ Max. $+M = +\frac{17PL}{192}$	 $+W = \frac{3P}{2}$ $-W = \frac{5P}{4}$ Max. $-M = -\frac{5PL}{48}$ Max. $+M = +\frac{3PL}{48}$
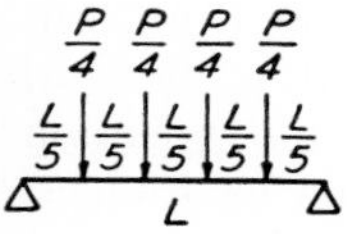 $+W = \frac{6P}{5}$ Max. $M = \frac{3PL}{20}$	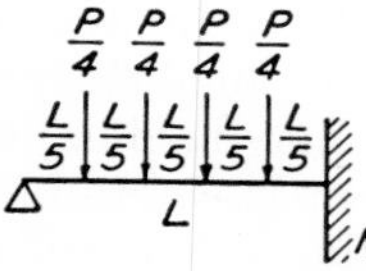 $+W = \frac{128P}{100}$ $-W = \frac{6P}{5}$ Max. $-M = -\frac{3PL}{20}$ Max. $+M = +\frac{9PL}{100}$	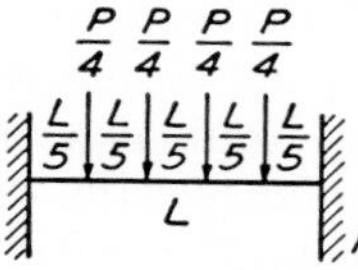 $+W = \frac{6P}{5}$ $-W = \frac{6P}{5}$ Max. $-M = -\frac{PL}{10}$ Max. $+M = +\frac{PL}{20}$

The values of W given in the four lower boxes of each column give in terms of the concentrated loads, P, the equivalent uniformly distributed load, W, for the condition shown in the box at the top of each column.

+W is the uniform load that produces the same positive moment; —W, the same negative moment.

The equivalent uniform load divided by the span gives an approximate value for entering the safe load tables.

These equivalent uniform loads, while reasonably accurate for moments, if properly used, should not be used for estimating shears in the original beam.

CONTINUITY IN STRUCTURES
Three Moment Equation

Frequently the ratios of live to dead load, or especially of span length to adjoining spans exceed the limitations of the ACI Code 318-63 (904c). To take care of such conditions, some understanding of the Theorem of Three Moments * is convenient. It is not practicable to develop the Theorem in a handbook, but the following general form is well known to structural engineers and can be accepted as a starting point:—

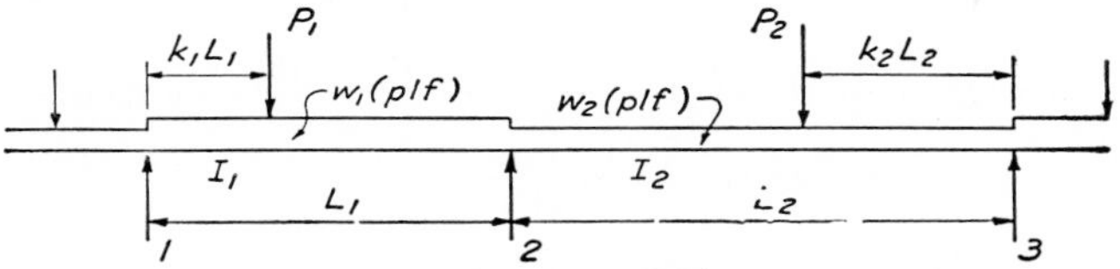

$$M_1\frac{L_1}{I_1} + 2M_2\left(\frac{L_1}{I_1} + \frac{L_2}{I_2}\right) + M_3\left(\frac{L_2}{I_2}\right) = -\frac{w_1L_1^3}{4I_1} - \frac{w_2L_2^3}{4I_2}$$

$$-\frac{1}{I_1}\Sigma\left[P_1L_1^2(k_1 - k_1^3)\right] - \frac{1}{I_2}\Sigma\left[P_2L_2^2(k_2 - k_2^3)\right] + 6E\left(\frac{m}{L_1} + \frac{n}{L_2}\right)$$

where M_1 = the bending moment at support 1 in lb-ft.
M_2 = " " " " " 2 " "
M_3 = " " " " " 3 " "
L_1 = length of first span of any two-span consecutive group (ft).
L_2 = " " second " " " " " " "
I_1 = moment of inertia of the beam in span 1-2.
I_2 = " " " " " " " " 2-3.
m = differential settlement of supports 1 and 2, positive when support 2 is below 1.
n = differential settlement of supports 3 and 2, positive when support 2 is below 3.
w_1 = uniform load on span 1-2 in pounds per lineal foot.
w_2 = " " " " 2-3 " " " " "
P_1 = any concentrated load on span 1-2 at distance k_1L_1 from 1.
P_2 = " " " " " 2-3 " " k_2L_2 " 3.

If the moments of inertia of the spans are equal, their values drop out and the coefficient of the final term becomes $6EI$ instead of $6E$. The signs here used are those for bending moment; positive moment causes compression in the top of the beam.

A few applications of this theorem will be made to illustrate its use:—

Example I—Determine the negative moment over the center support and the positive moment in the longer span of two consecutive spans of lengths L and $0.833L$, loads of $4w$ and w, equal moments of inertia, equal settlements of the support, and no restraint at the outer ends.

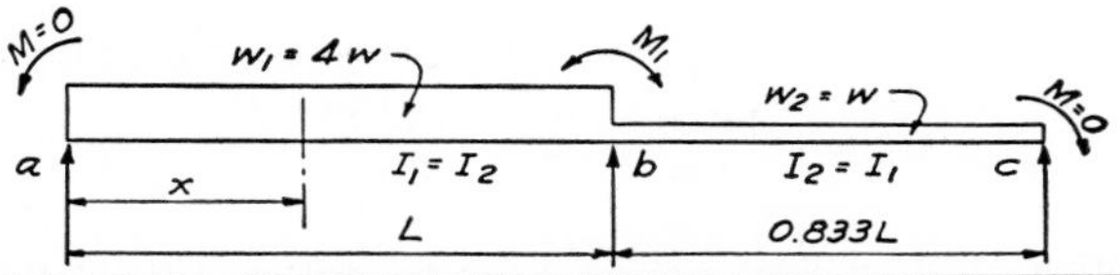

* See any textbook on the Strength of Materials for the derivation of this theorem and any book on Reinforced Concrete Design for its applications to practical problems.

CONTINUITY IN STRUCTURES

Solution:—Write the Three Moment Equation, omitting unnecessary terms:—

$$0 + 2M_1(L + 0.833L) + 0 = -\frac{4wL^3}{4} - \frac{w(0.833L)^3}{4}$$

Solving:—$M_1 = -\frac{(4 + 0.579)wL^2}{4 \times 3.666} = -0.3128wL^2$, which can also be written as $M_1 = -0.0782w_1L^2$.

Determine the left end reaction as $R_L = 2wL - 0.3128wL = 1.6872wL$.

Section for zero shear and max. positive moment:—$x = \frac{1.6872wL}{4w} = 0.4218L$.

Positive moment:—$+M = \frac{R_Lx}{2} = \frac{1.6872wL \times 0.4218L}{2} = 0.356wL^2$, which can also be written as $0.089w_1L^2$, or approx. $\frac{w_1L^2}{11.25}$

Observation—For only two spans, the Three Moment Equation can be written directly.* As the number of spans increases, it is necessary to work progressively across the structure, two spans at a time, resulting in a number of simultaneous equations which may become involved.

The Three Moment Equation can be used with equal facility for numerical or algebraic values; in fact algebraic values are often preferable, as they combine and cancel readily.

Example II—Given four equal spans with equal moments of inertia, no end restraint and no concentrated loads. If the live load can not exceed three times the dead load, determine the absolute maximum moment over the first interior support.

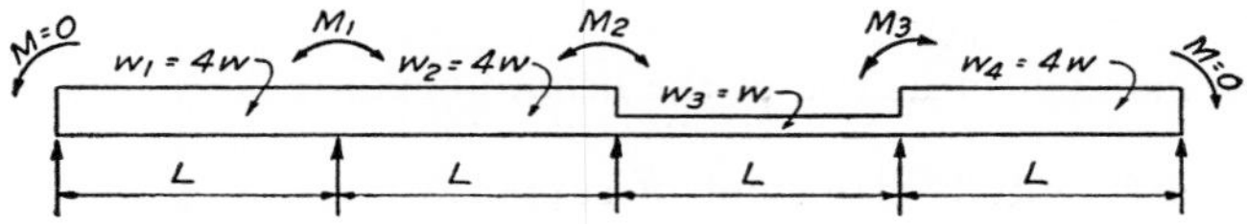

Solution:—The load arrangement for this moment to be a maximum should be as in the figure above, placing the live load on each side of the support and alternate spans each way from there.

Write the Three Moment Equations for spans 1-2, 2-3 and 3-4, simplifying each one as soon as written:—

$$0 + 2M_1(L + L) + M_2L = -\frac{4wL^3}{4} - \frac{4wL^3}{4}, \text{ so } 4M_1 + M_2 = -2wL^2 \quad (1)$$

$$M_1L + 2M_2(L + L) + M_3L = -\frac{4wL^3}{4} - \frac{wL^3}{4}, \text{ so } M_1 + 4M_2 + M_3 = -\frac{5wL^2}{4} \quad (2)$$

$$M_2L + 2M_3(L + L) + 0 = -\frac{wL^3}{4} - \frac{4wL^3}{4}, \text{ so } M_2 + 4M_3 = -\frac{5wL^2}{4} \quad (3)$$

$$4M_1 + 16M_2 + 4M_3 = -5wL^2 \quad (2)$$

$$M_2 + 4M_3 = -\frac{5wL^2}{4} \quad (3)$$

$$4M_1 + 15M_2 = -\frac{15wL^2}{4} \quad \text{(Combining (2) and (3) to eliminate } M_3) \quad (4)$$

$$60M_1 + 15M_2 = -30wL^2 \quad (1)$$

$$56M_1 = -\frac{105wL^2}{4} \quad \text{(Combining (4) and (1) to eliminate } M_2)$$

$$M_1 = -\frac{105wL^2}{224}, \text{ or } -\frac{105w_1L^2}{896}$$

* The equation $M_1 = -\frac{(4 + 0.579)wL^2}{4 \times 3.666}$ can be written without the need of setting down the Three Moment Equation.

CONTINUITY IN STRUCTURES

Observation—The continued application of the Theorem is here illustrated, and the simplicity of application to algebraic values shown.

These examples show how the Three Moment Equation can be used to solve for bending moments in continuous runs of beams. They could be extended indefinitely, as the theory of continuity is a subject in itself. If the moment over the first support is not zero, but is known by reason of a cantilevered end which produces a definite moment, that value (usually negative) can be substituted in the Three Moment Equation instead of zero.

The user is counselled to familiarize himself with this Equation and use it for cases that are outside the scope of these tables.

Moment Distribution

Moment Distribution is essentially a method of successive approximations and, when applied to continuous flexural members in a single line, is best understood as step (a) plus the repeated applications of steps (b) and (c) below:—

(a) Assume that all joints (supports) of the loaded run of beams are fixed, without rotation. The first step, then, is this:—

I—At each end of each span, compute the fixed end moment (F.E.M.) due to the loading of that span with joints assumed fixed.*

(b) For static equilibrium, the moment at the right end of the left span must equal that at the left end of the abutting right span, i.e., the moments acting on the joint must balance. The assumed fixed-end-moments will rarely be numerically equal and the second step is to relieve or "unlock" each of the joints, one at a time, and permit rotation until the moments on either side balance each other. The two meeting beams become resisting levers to take up the unbalanced moment in any joint, and will divide it in proportion to their relative stiffnesses as measured by the ratio I/L. This step is known as "distribution."

II—Having previously computed the relative stiffnesses ($K = I/L$) of the two beams, "distribute" the unbalanced moment at their junction in proportion to their stiffness.

(c) Since the adjoining beams described as resisting levers are considered artificially fixed at their far ends, it is impossible for them to receive a moment change at one end without inducing a moment at the other end, whose magnitude is a function of the shape of the beam. For a prismatic beam, this "carry-over" moment is one-half of the moment at the opposite end.

III—Carry over a portion (one-half for straight, prismatic beams) of the distributed moment to the opposite end of each beam.

---

* Values for a number of loading conditions are given in the tables on pages 4-9/12.

(d) Because step III was performed subsequently to and independently of step II, the induced moment in step III unbalances what was previously a balanced condition at the joint where the carry-over moment was added. Hence it is necessary to repeat steps II and III as often as desired to obtain closer and closer approximations of the true values. The steps can be stopped at any time, but only after a distribution and before a carry-over.

IV—Repeat steps II and III for closer approximations, stopping after a distribution of unbalanced moments.

Signs—It is customary to consider the moment applied to a supporting joint by a loaded beam as positive when it tends to cause clockwise rotation of the joint. (Thus, in the figure below, the F.E.M. at the right end of beam *ab*, usually designated as M_{ba}, is negative; that at the left end of beam *bc*, M_{bc}, is positive. The sign of the carry-over moment is the same as that of the distributed moment which causes it.

One variation of this procedure must be explained before illustrating with examples. In the case of a freely supported end, it is too tedious to assume that end fully fixed and then work it back to a free end by successive approximations, though that is quite possible. Less computing is done if the stiffness coefficient of an end (freely-supported) span is taken as $\frac{3}{4} I/L$, and if the moment at the free end is assumed zero (as it must be) and at the interior end as that of a beam supported on one end and fixed on the other $\left(-\frac{wL^2}{8}\right.$ for a uniform load).

Example—To verify the derivation in Example I, page 4-5, assume $w_1 = 4$ klf, $w_2 = 1$ klf, $L = 20$ ft, and $0.833L = 16.67$ ft, and compute the bending moment over the support by moment distribution.

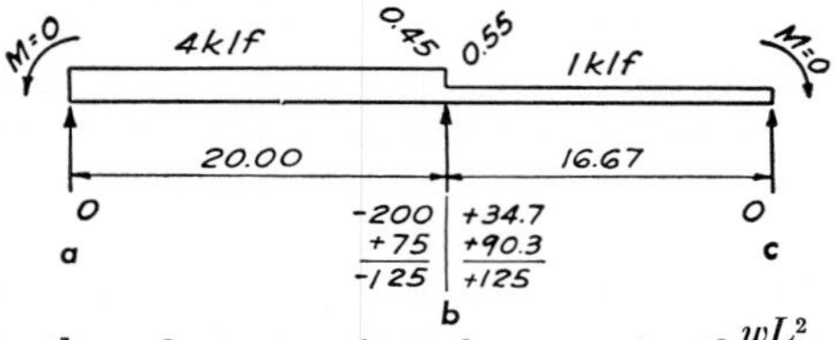

Solution:—Write the end moments in each span:—0 and $\frac{wL^2}{8} = -200$ kf for the left span, and $\frac{wL^2}{8} = +34.7$ kf for the right span. Determine the stiffnesses (I/L ratios) of the two spans. Since they have the same moment of inertia and similar end conditions and are each prismatic, their stiffnesses vary inversely as the spans, 1.0 for the left span and 1.2 for the right, so that the left span takes $\frac{1.0}{2.2}$, or 45 per cent of any unbalanced moment, and the right span takes $\frac{1.2}{2.2}$, or 55 per cent (written on the diagonal in the figure above).

The unbalanced moment is $-200 + 34.7 = -165.3$, so $+165.3$ is needed to resist this, of which 45 per cent, or 75.0, is provided by the beam in the left span and 55 per cent, or 90.3, by the beam in the right span. Because the beams were adjusted to a free outer end before starting, there is no carry-over and the work is complete. Adding the terms on each side of the support results in a negative moment of 125 ft-kips, in balance on either side of the support, and this compares with the value from Example I, page 4-5, which was $M_1 = -0.0782 w_1 L^2 = 125.1$ ft-kips.

COEFFICIENTS FOR MOMENTS IN BEAMS WITH FIXED ENDS (F.E.M.)

Moments In Beams Of Constant Section And With Fixed Ends

$$M = m \times W \times L$$

m = coefficient taken from diagram
W = total load on beam
L = length of beam
a = length in terms of L

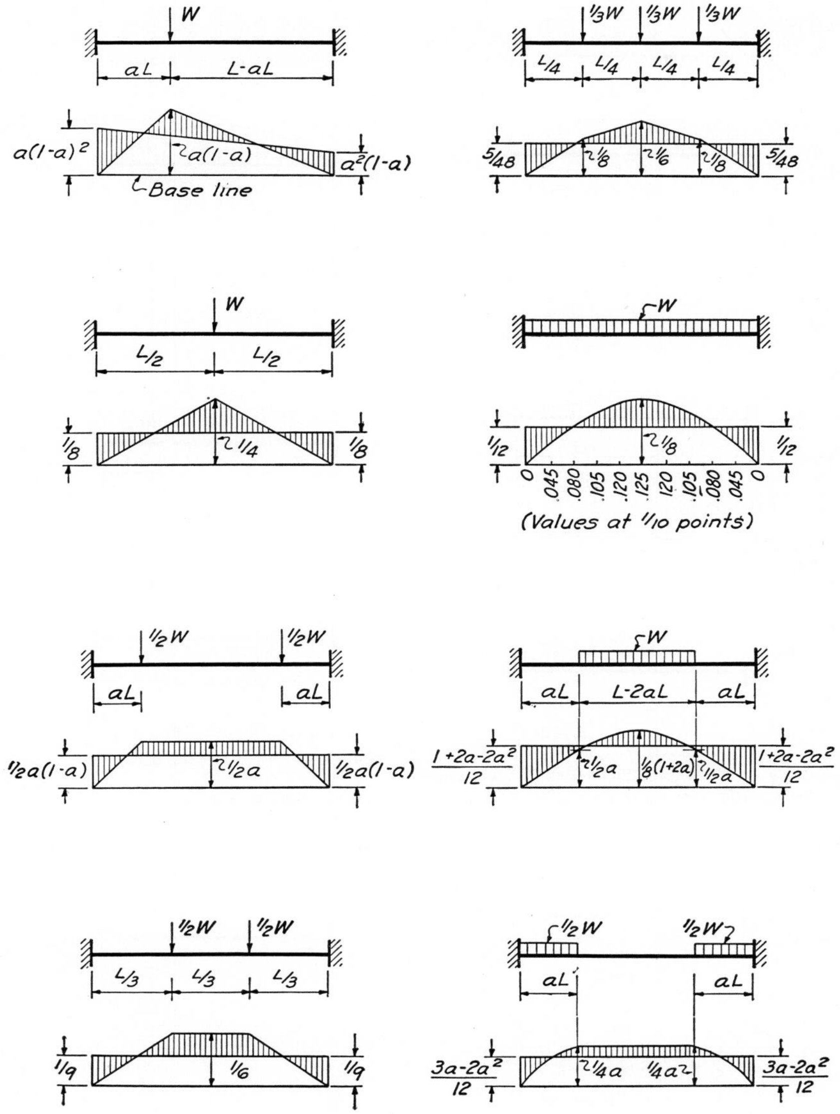

COEFFICIENTS FOR MOMENTS IN BEAMS WITH FIXED ENDS (F.E.M.)

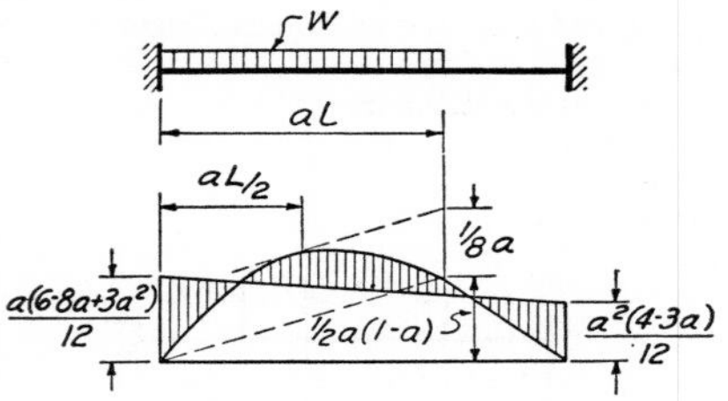

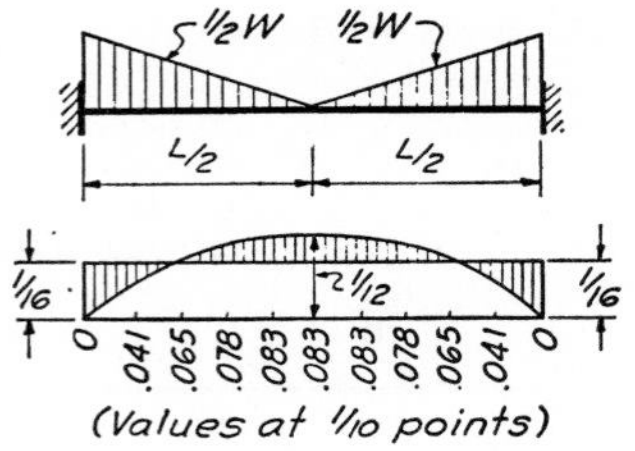

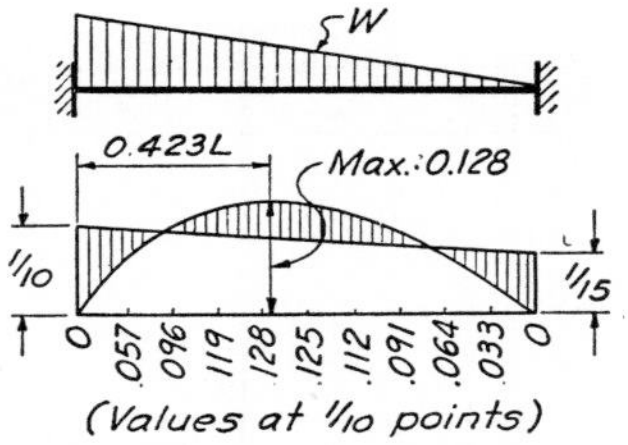

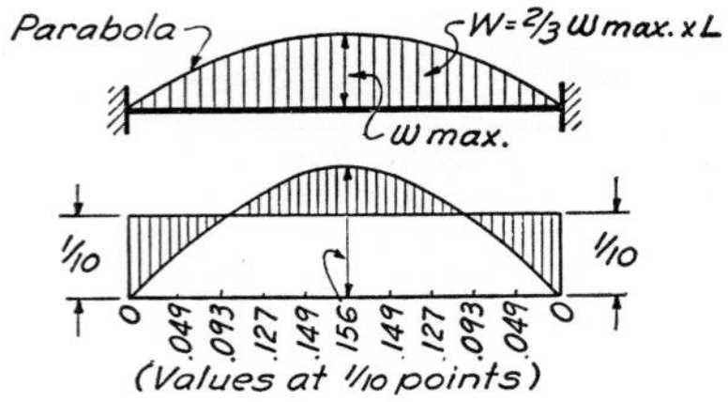

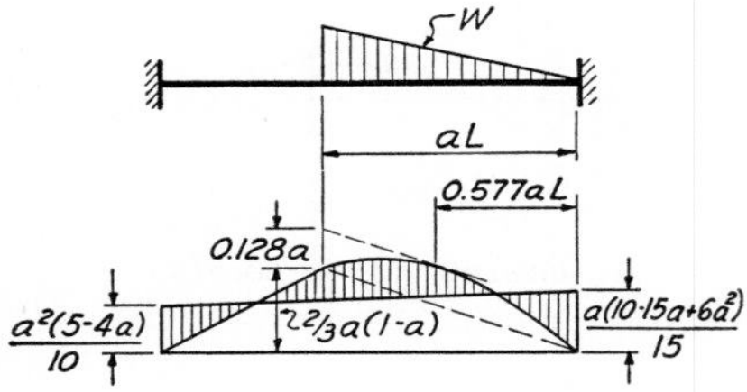

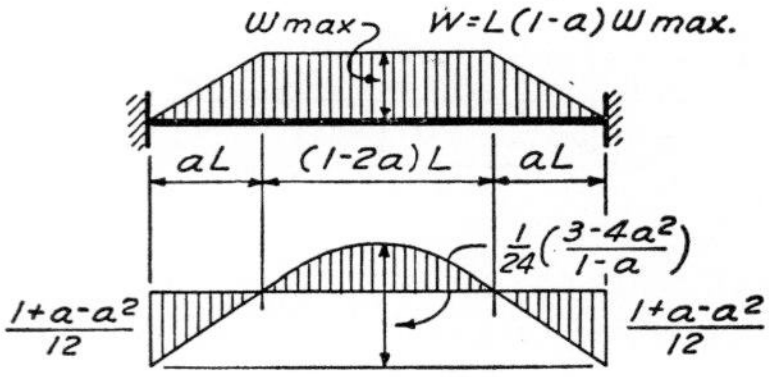

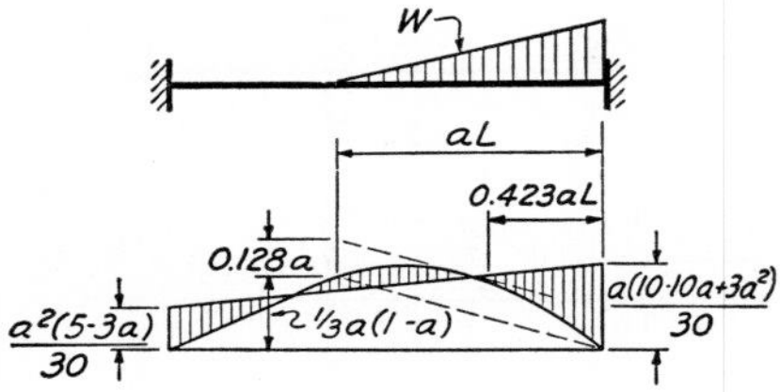

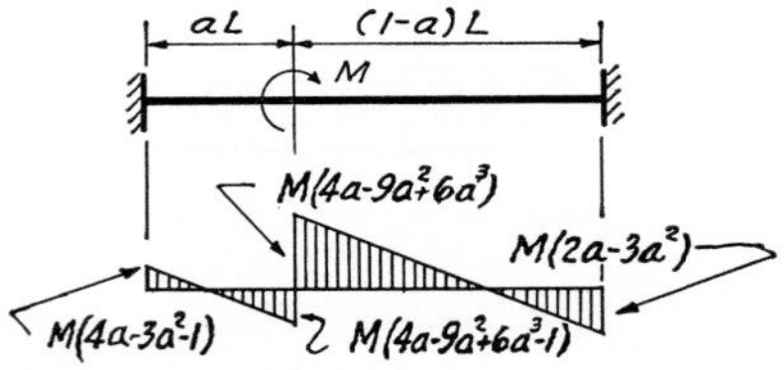

When M is clockwise as shown:
The two bending moments at M are always respectively — or + as shown.
Bending moment at left end is — for a>0<0.333 and + for a>0.333.
Bending moment at right end is + for a>0<0.667 and — for a>0.667.

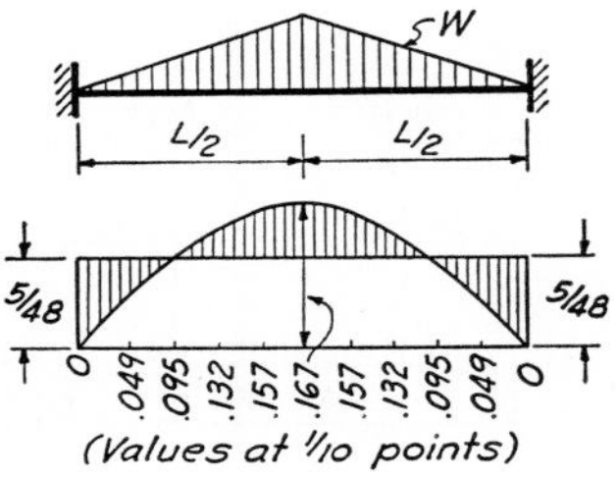

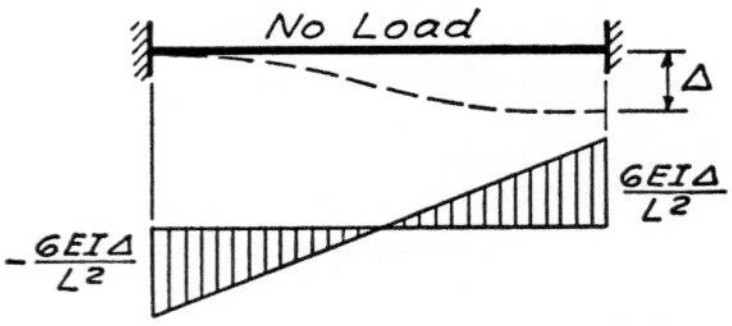

MOMENTS IN BEAMS OF CONSTANT CROSS-SECTION—ONE END FIXED

Moments In Beams Of Constant Section - One End Fixed, One End Free

$M = m \times W \times L$

m = coefficient taken from diagram
W = total load on beam
L = length of beam
a = length in terms of L

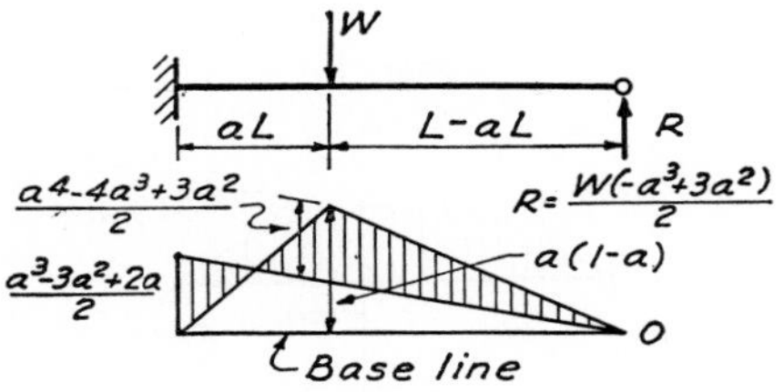

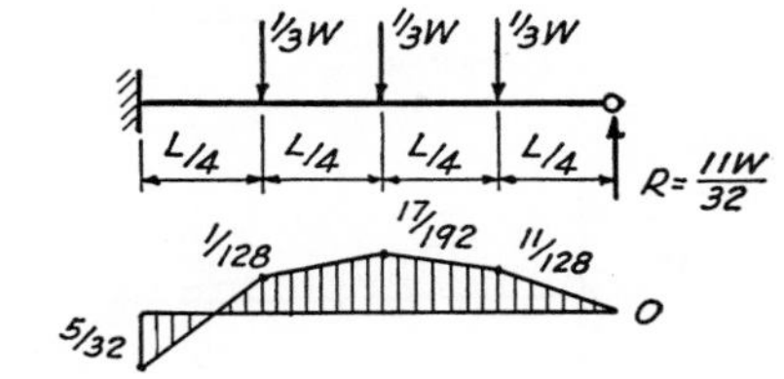

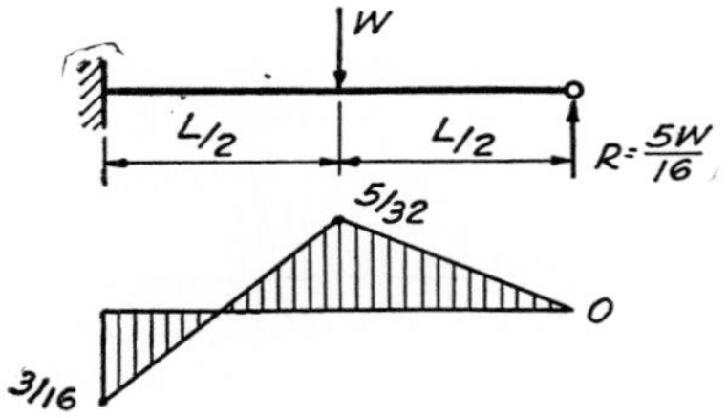

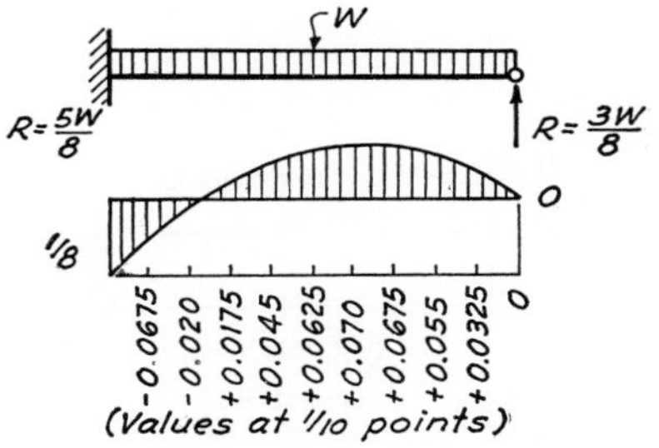

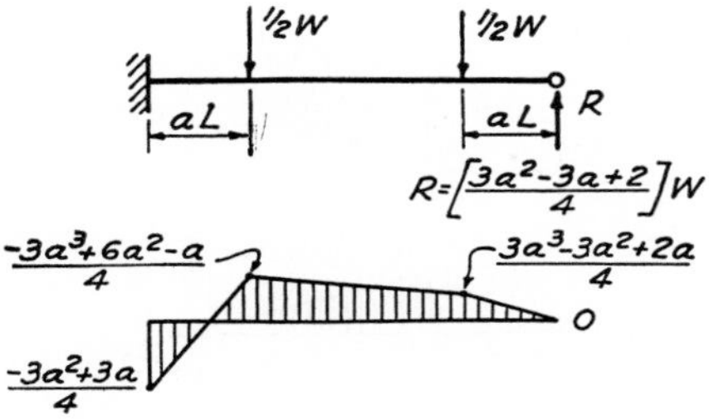

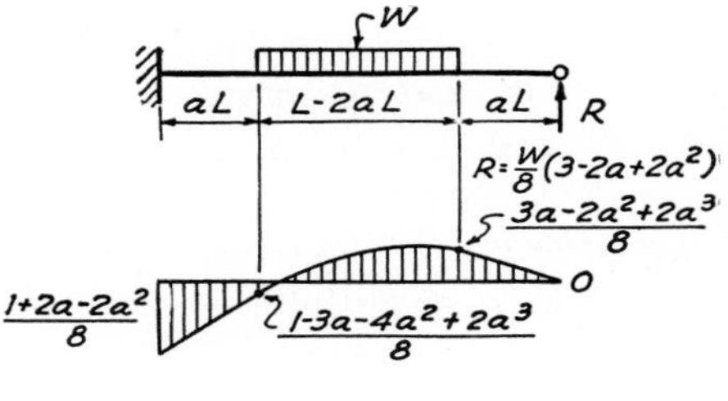

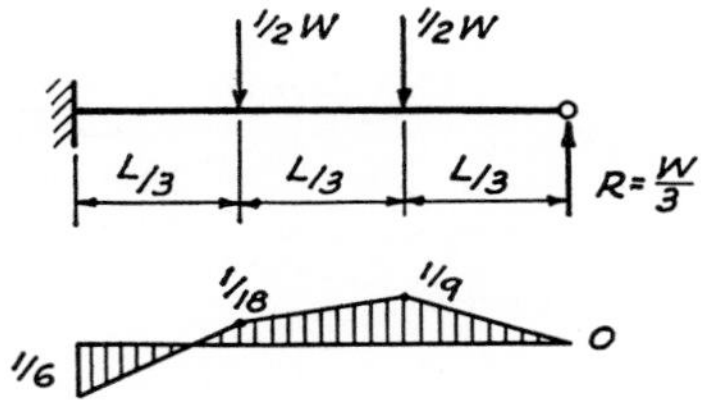

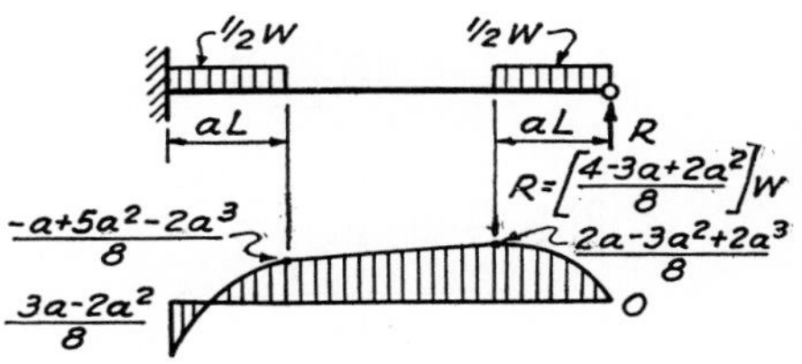

Moment M = m WL

MOMENTS IN BEAMS OF CONSTANT CROSS-SECTION—ONE END FIXED

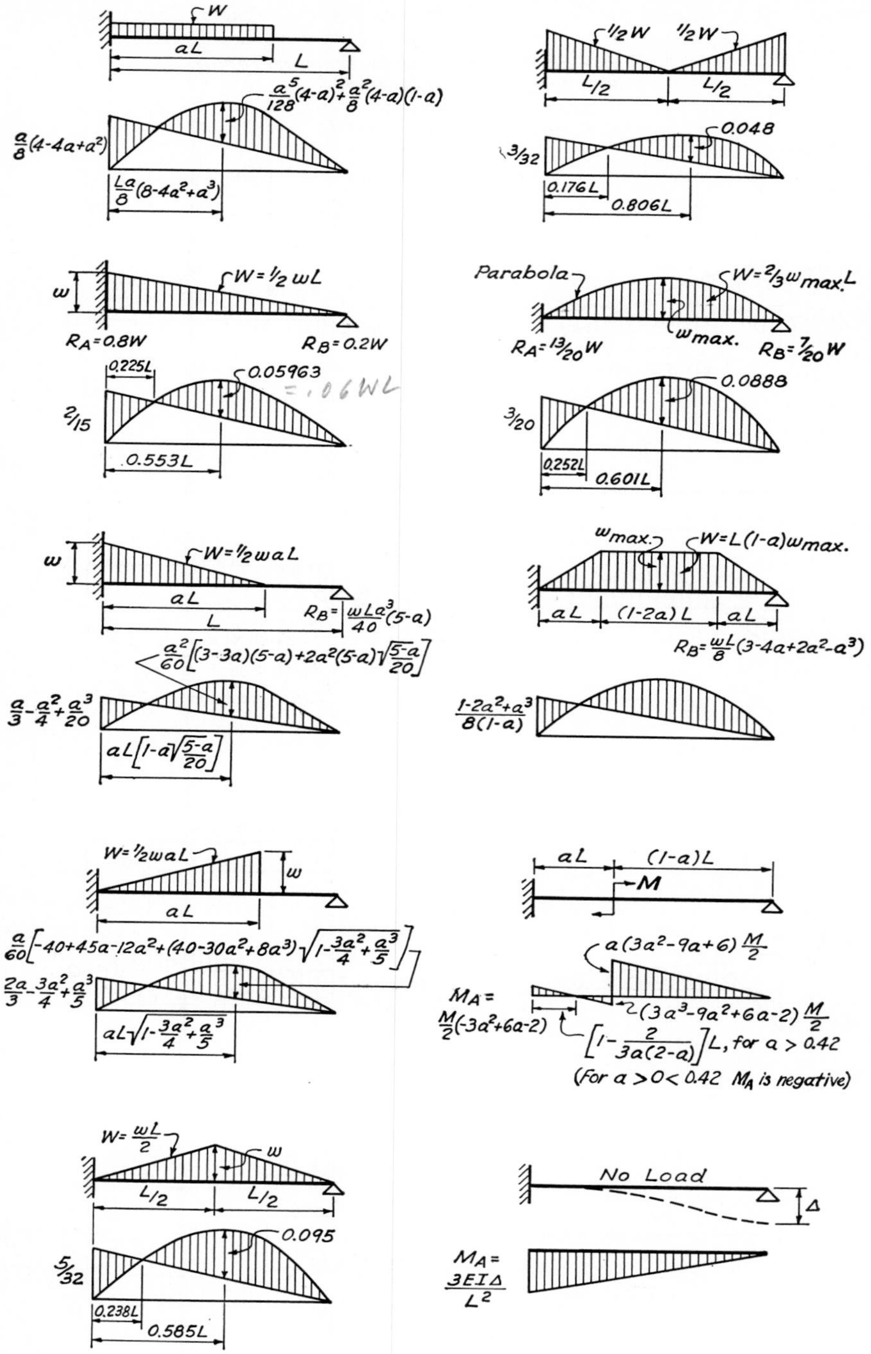

CONTINUITY IN STRUCTURES

Observation—With moment distribution it is almost impossible to work with algebraic terms, but the successive steps make the use of numerical values quite simple. A clear mental picture of each step is possible, such as *moment at the free end*, *fixed end moment*, *stiffness of members*, *participation in unbalanced moment*, *distribution of moment*, and *carry-over*. Quick, practical results are available to the designer, carried to such degree of precision as he desires.

Example—To verify the value of negative moment over the first interior support for Example II, page 4-6, assume $w_1 = w_2 = w_4 = 4$ klf, $w_3 = 1$ klf, and $L = 20$ ft, and determine the bending moment over the first interior support.

Solution:—The moments (kf) at the outer ends as given on line (1), figure below, are 0; at the other supports in order, $\frac{wL^2}{8} = -200$; $\frac{wL^2}{12} = +133.3$, -133.3, $+33.3$, -33.3; and $\frac{wL^2}{8} = +200$. The stiffnesses of the four spans, taking the free-end spans as $\frac{3}{4}I/L$, are 0.75, 1.00, 1.00 and 0.75. The distribution factors at each joint work out:—0, $\frac{0.75}{1.75} = 0.43$, $\frac{1.00}{1.75} = 0.57$, $\frac{1.00}{2.00} = 0.50$, 0.50 and, again, 0.57, 0.43, 0.

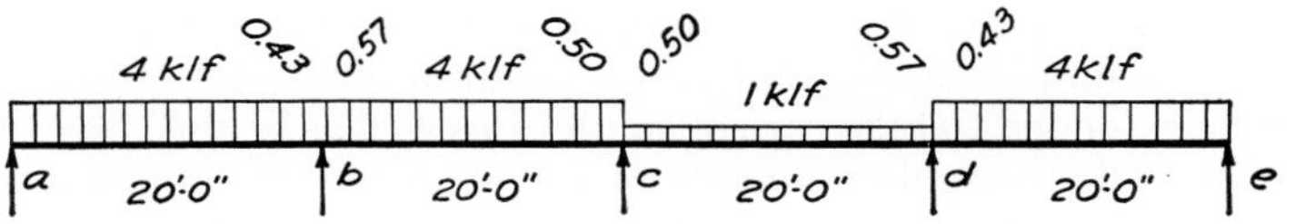

	ab	ba	bc	cb	cd	dc	de	ed	
(1)	0	-200	+133.3	-133.3	+33.3	-33.3	+200	0	FEM
(2)	0	+28.6	+38.1	+50.0	+50.0	-95.4	-71.3	0	Dist.
(3)	—	(-171.4)	(+171.4)	(-83.3)	(+83.3)	(-128.7)	(+128.7)	—	Σ
(4)	0	0	+25.0	+19.1	-47.7	+25.0	0	0	C.O.
(5)	0	-10.7	-14.3	+14.3	+14.3	-14.3	-10.7	0	Dist.
(6)	—	(-182.1)	(+182.1)	(-49.9)	(+49.9)	(-118.0)	(+118.0)	—	Σ
(7)	0	0	+7.2	-7.2	-7.2	+7.2	0	0	C.O.
(8)	0	-3.1	-4.1	+7.2	+7.2	-4.1	-3.1	0	Dist.
(9)	0	-185.2	+185.2	-49.9	+49.9	-114.9	+114.9	0	Σ

The unbalanced moment over the first interior support of -66.7 is "distributed" as 28.6 and 38.1 on line (2); and moments at other supports as indicated on the same line of figures. Now all of the joints are "in balance," and a fair approximation of a result can be had from the next line of figures enclosed in parentheses on line (3). However, the individual beams are not in equilibrium because of the induced moments on their other ends, and it is necessary to "carry over" one-half of these moments as shown below the parentheses on line (4).

Repeating the "distribution" of these smaller, unbalanced moments gives the values on line (5). Should work be stopped at this point, the final values would be as shown in parentheses on line (6).

For comparison, compute the value from the result of Example II, page 4-6, as $M_1 = -\frac{105 w_1 L^2}{896} = 187.5$ ft-kips. Thus it is seen that, with two cycles of distribution, a fairly good approximation is developing. Lines (7) and (8) repeat another cycle. It is felt that, in view of the many assumptions inherent in continuous structures, the value of 185.2 ft-kips (Line 9) is closely enough in agreement with the 187.5 ft-kips from Example II. The user may go through other cycles of distribution and carry-over to see how the value gradually approaches the theoretical one.

The summations here shown in parentheses are not recorded in practical computations and are included here to illustrate the increasing precision, cycle by cycle.

CONTINUITY IN STRUCTURES

Observation—Fairly reliable values can be obtained after a couple of cycles. The carry-overs show the degree of precision in each cycle and the work may be stopped when these CO values seem negligible. The computer has a clear picture of the action of the structure and the meaning of each step as he goes along—in fact, if he does not have such a clear picture, he should stop and get it.

For design purposes, it is usually sufficient to determine with reasonable accuracy the moment at a certain point for a maximum loading condition. Many methods have been proposed for shortening the computations. (As always, understand the method before trying simplifications.) For a workable result the effect of a load in the first span only of the figure on page 4-13 can be approximated as D_{bc} ($FEM_{ba} - \frac{1}{2}D_{ab}\ FEM_{ab}$) and of a load in the second span only as $D_{ba}(-FEM_{bc} + \frac{1}{2}D_{cb}\ FEM_{cb})$, where D is the distribution factor. Applied to this problem:

$$\text{1st Span } 0.57(-200 - 0 \times 0) = -114.0 \text{ kf}$$

$$\text{2nd Span } 0.43\left(-133.3 - \frac{0.50 \times 133.3}{2}\right) = -\ 71.6$$

$$-185.6 \text{ kf}$$

The examples shown are not complicated and present the Three Moment Equation as a simpler device than it works out in practice. Moment Distribution can be extended to take care of columns as well as beams, and to take care of members with variable moments of inertia (such as haunched beams and arched beams of various shapes). Each is a helpful tool in its place and each should be thoroughly understood by a designer of concrete structures.

To illustrate the application of Moment Distribution to a simple bent which is symmetrical in its framing and symmetrical in its loading (thus preventing sidesway or lurch), the following example is given. For more complicated frames, for frames with unsymmetrical loading or unsymmetrical members, for frames with varying moments of inertia or for frames undergoing horizontal loads, consult any good text on Moment Distribution.

Example—For the three-legged symmetrical bent illustrated in the figure below with pin-connected column bases and a symmetrical load of 2 kips per running foot, the moments of inertia of the columns being as 1 and 2 and that of the beams as 3, compute the negative moments at the tops of the three columns.

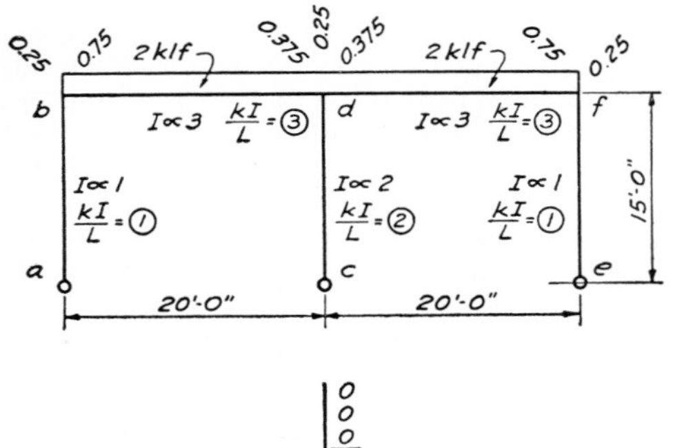

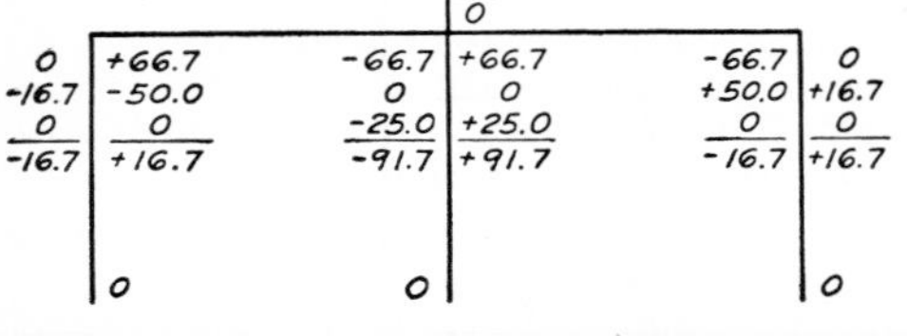

Solution:—Since the columns are pin-connected at the base, take $\frac{3}{4}\frac{I}{L}$, but for the beams use $\frac{I}{L}$ to obtain the following:—

$$\frac{3}{4}\frac{I_{ab}}{L} = \frac{3}{4}\frac{I_{ef}}{L} = \frac{3}{4}\frac{1}{15} = 0.05, \text{ varies as } 1$$

$$\frac{3}{4}\frac{I_{cd}}{L} = \frac{3}{4}\frac{2}{15} = 0.10, \text{ varies as } 2$$

$$\frac{I_{bd}}{L} = \frac{I_{df}}{L} = \frac{3}{20} = 0.15, \text{ varies as } 3$$

The distribution at joints b and f will then be $\frac{1}{1+3}$, or 0.25, in the column and $\frac{3}{1+3}$, or 0.75, in the beam. At joint d the distribution to the column will be $\frac{2}{3+2+3}$, or 0.25; and to each beam, $\frac{3}{3+2+3}$, or 0.375.

In the figure on page 4-14, the *FEM*'s are computed as $\frac{2 \times 20 \times 20}{12} = 66.7$. One distribution is made as noted and one carry-over. The results are totalled to give the moments desired. Note that the figures outside of the outer legs represent the column moments; those inside the outer legs, the beam moments. At joint *d* the two lower computations represent the beam moments and the upper one the column moment.

Sidesway

A structure unsymmetrical in its framing or unsymmetrical in its loading will be subjected to sidesway or lurch, so joint moments computed for rotation only must be corrected for translation. Often the simplest procedure is to solve first for rotation, see what horizontal force would be required to prevent sidesway, and then correct the values for the effect of a negative force of this amount.

Example I—For a two-legged symmetrical framed bent with hinged columns and unsymmetrical load as shown in (a), determine the corner moments M_A and M_B.

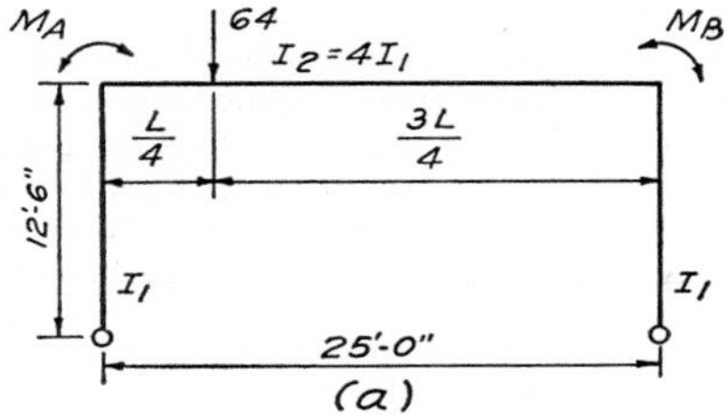

(a)

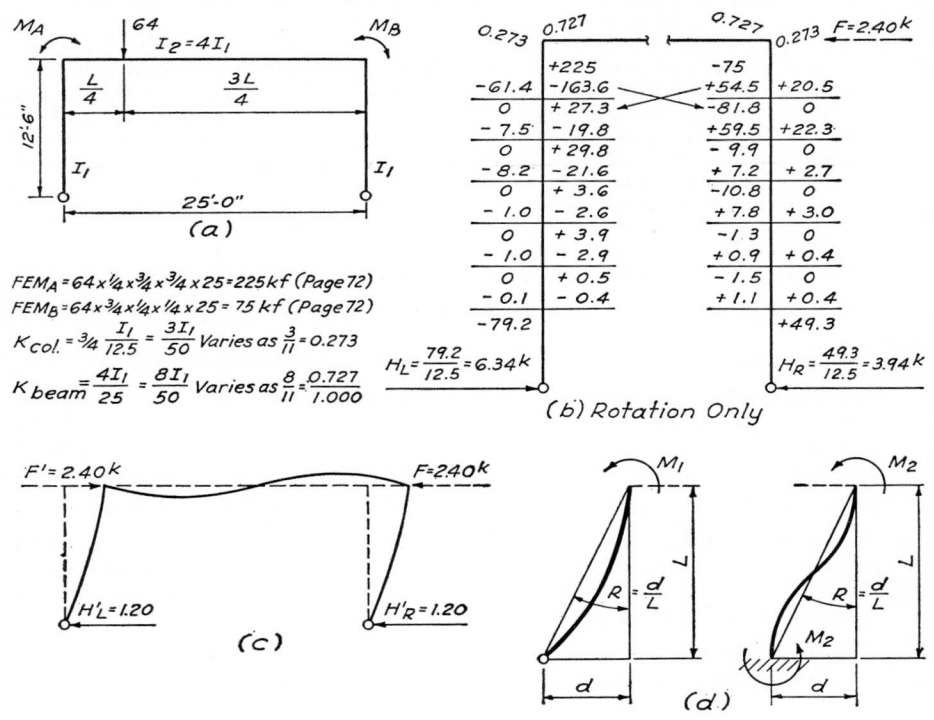

$FEM_A = 64 \times \frac{1}{4} \times \frac{3}{4} \times \frac{3}{4} \times 25 = 225 kf$ (Page 72)

$FEM_B = 64 \times \frac{3}{4} \times \frac{1}{4} \times \frac{1}{4} \times 25 = 75 kf$ (Page 72)

$K_{col.} = \frac{3}{4}\,\frac{I_1}{12.5} = \frac{3I_1}{50}$ Varies as $\frac{3}{11} = 0.273$

$K_{beam} = \frac{4I_1}{25} = \frac{8I_1}{50}$ Varies as $\frac{8}{11} = \frac{0.727}{1.000}$

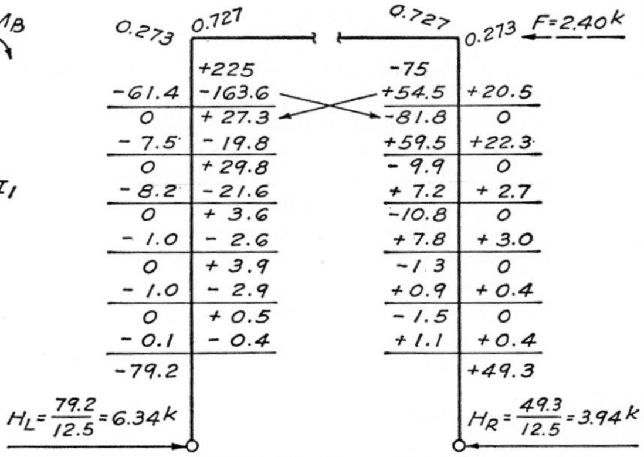

(b) Rotation Only

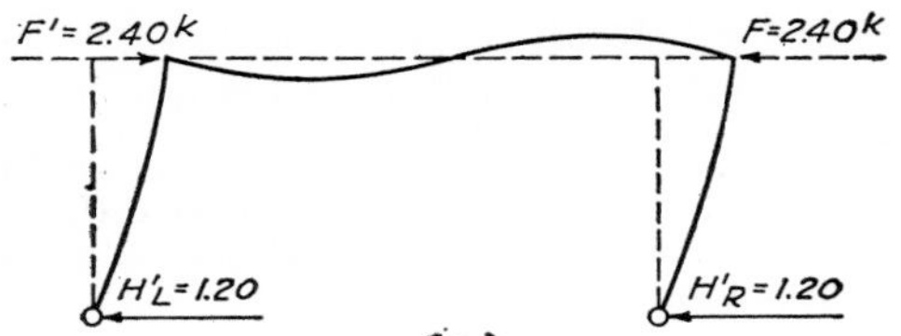

(c)

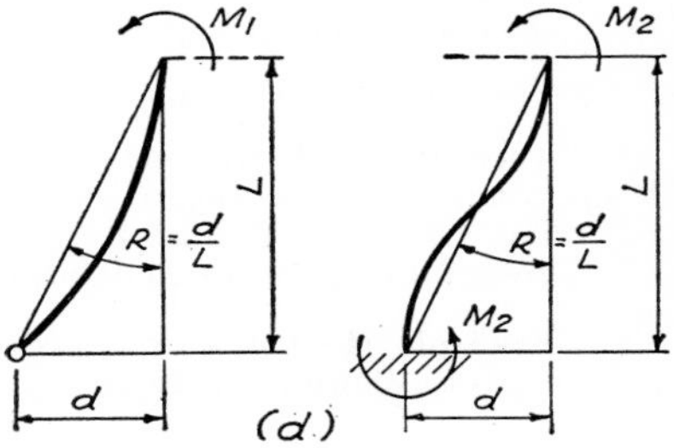

(d)

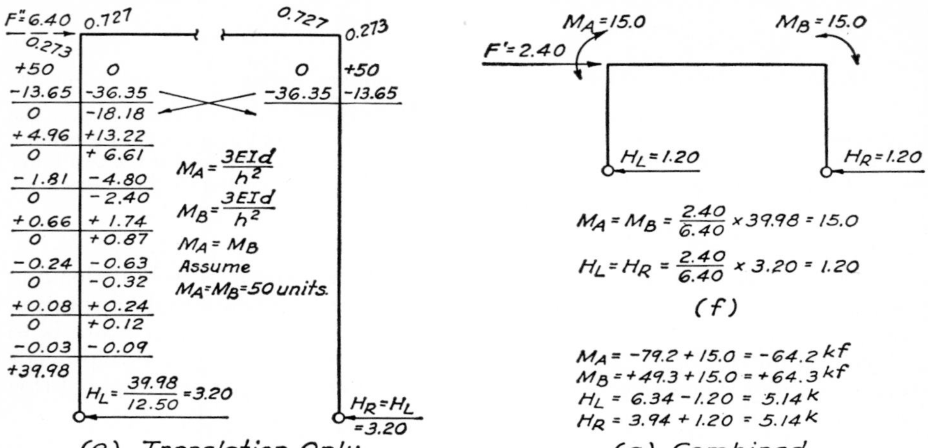

(e) Translation Only (f) (g) Combined

The fixed end moments in the beam and the stiffness ratios are first determined, as on (a). Then in (b) a moment distribution is made, resulting in corner moments of -79.2 and $+49.3$ *kf*, respectively. From these, the horizontal reactions at the bottoms of the columns are computed as 6.34 and 3.94, respectively. Since these are not equal to each other, a horizontal force ($F = 2.40$ kips), shown dotted on (*b*), would be required to restore equilibrium. This means that while the bent would deflect as shown by heavy lines in (c), the distribution has assumed the presence of a nonexistent force $F = 2.40$ kips, holding the two upper corners directly over the bases of the columns, so it is necessary to add the effects of a force $F' = 2.40$ kips in the opposite direction, i.e., determine the corner moments that it develops and combine them with those obtained in (b). While this is relatively simple for this bent, a procedure will be followed in (e) that can be applied to more complicated bents. As shown in (d), a member free on one end and fixed at the other, if offset a certain distance, *d*, develops a moment at the attached end of $M_1 = \frac{3EIR}{L} = \frac{3EId}{L^2}$, while one fixed at both ends develops a moment $M_2 = \frac{6EIR}{L} = \frac{6EId}{L^2}$. To determine the effects of a horizontal force, in (e), for equal horizontal offsets at the top of each column (i.e., no change in length of the connecting beam), express the corner moments at the tops of the columns in terms of such offset (for example, assume here a value for *Ed* of, say, 100 units); distribute the moments and compute the horizontal forces to find $F'' = 6.40$ kips; then, as in (f), the moments and shears for a force $F' = 2.40$ kips will be $\frac{2.40}{6.40}$ of those shown on (e). Then (b) and (f) are combined for the final moments, as tabulated in (g). For such a symmetrical case, this second distribution could be done mentally by making $H_L = H_R = F'/2 = 1.20$, and $M_A = M_B = 1.20 \times 12.5 = 15.0$, but the full explanation is given for convenience in discussing the next example.

Example II—For a two-legged unsymmetrically framed bent with unsymmetrical loads as shown in (a) in the figure, determine the corner moments M_A, M_B and M_C.

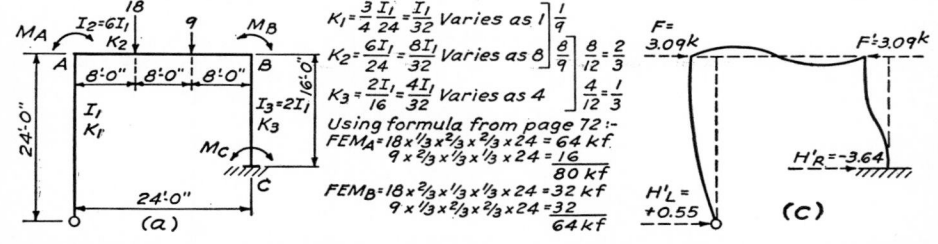

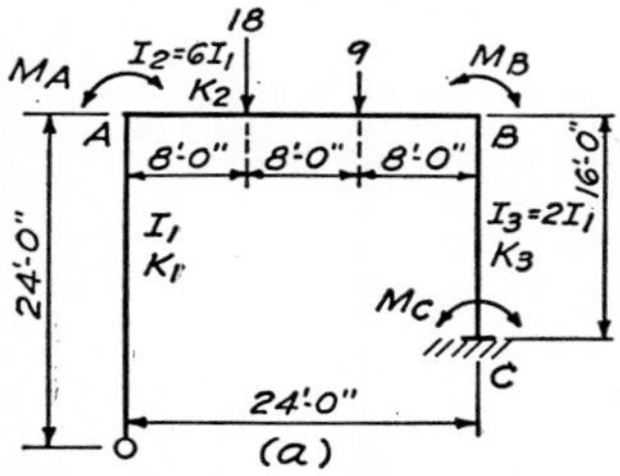

(a)

$K_1 = \frac{3}{4}\frac{I_1}{24} = \frac{I_1}{32}$ Varies as 1 $\quad \frac{1}{9}$

$K_2 = \frac{6I_1}{24} = \frac{8I_1}{32}$ Varies as 8 $\quad \frac{8}{9} \quad \frac{8}{12} = \frac{2}{3}$

$K_3 = \frac{2I_1}{16} = \frac{4I_1}{32}$ Varies as 4 $\quad \frac{4}{12} = \frac{1}{3}$

Using formula from page 72:-

$FEM_A = 18 \times \frac{1}{3} \times \frac{2}{3} \times \frac{2}{3} \times 24 = 64$ kf
$9 \times \frac{2}{3} \times \frac{1}{3} \times \frac{1}{3} \times 24 = 16$
80 kf

$FEM_B = 18 \times \frac{2}{3} \times \frac{1}{3} \times \frac{1}{3} \times 24 = 32$ kf
$9 \times \frac{1}{3} \times \frac{2}{3} \times \frac{2}{3} \times 24 = 32$
64 kf

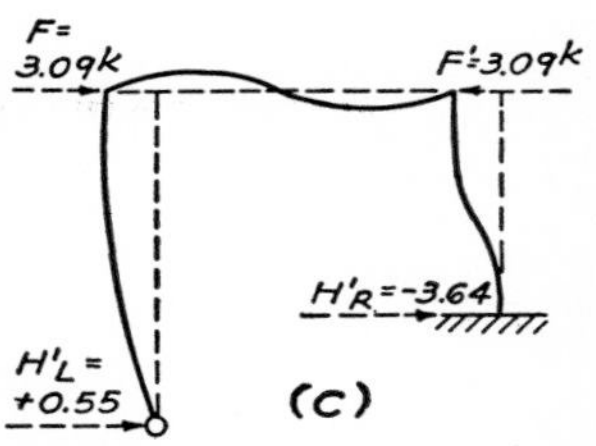

(c)

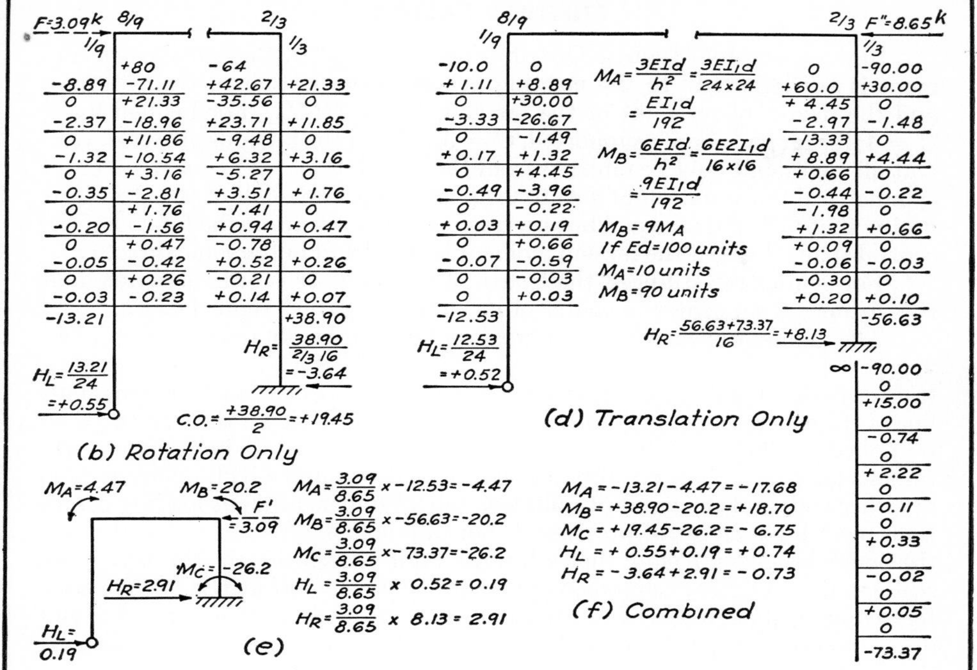

The stiffness ratios and the fixed end moments in the beam are first determined in (a). Then a moment distribution is made in (b), resulting in corner moments at the tops of the columns of -13.21 and $+38.90$ *kf*, respectively. Then the horizontal reactions at the feet of the columns are computed, realizing that the carry-over moment at the foot of the fixed base column will be exactly half the moment at the top of the same column, and, therefore, the horizontal reaction is obtained by dividing the corner moment by two-thirds the height of the column. This gives reactions of 0.55 and 3.64, and since these are not equal to each other, a horizontal force of $F = 3.09$ kips would be required to restore equilibrium, as shown dotted in (b). Again, this means that while the bent would deflect as indicated by the heavy lines in (c), the distribution has assumed the presence of a nonexistent force of $F = 3.09$ kips, holding the two upper corners directly over the bases of the columns. It becomes necessary to add the effects of a force $F' = 3.09$ kips in the opposite direction, i.e., determine the corner moments induced by this lateral force and combine them with those obtained in (b). As shown in the preceding example, the moments at the tops of the two columns for the same horizontal offset are in the ratio 1:9 as computed on (d). Assuming an indefinite displacement represented by $Ed = 100$ units would induce corner moments of 10 and 90 *kf*, respectively. A distribution gives corner moments at the tops of the columns of -12.53 and -56.63 and at the bottom of the fixed base column of -73.37 with horizontal reactions of $+0.52$ and $+8.13$, requiring a horizontal force $F'' = 8.65$ kips for equilibrium. Since 3.09 is all that is required, all values are reduced in the proportion 3.09/8.65 and recorded on (e). Finally, at (f), the values are combined for the final moments and horizontal reactions.

Observation—It is not possible to go much further into moment distribution in a handbook. These examples merely illustrate the possibilities of applying the method to framed bents.

Slender Columns

See page 11-5 for description of slender columns.

STIFFNESS FACTOR

In designing by Moment Distribution (pp. 4-7/17), the unbalanced moment is "distributed" to the meeting beams in proportion to their stiffness and the degree of restraint of the far end, $CK = CI/L$. For far end fixed, $C = 4$; for far end simply supported, $C = 3$. When the far ends are fixed, $C = 4$ at all times and may be omitted from the calculation. When a structure is symmetrical both in itself and as to load, work with one-half of the structure, noting that $C = 2$ if an equal but reversed moment occurs at the far end of the central span, $C = 6$ if the far end moment is equal and in the same direction.

For computing stiffness, the length of the member is ordinarily taken as the distance from center to center of its supports, rather than the clear span.

The moment of inertia of the cross section can be obtained in one of two ways:—

(a) For preliminary computations, use the moment of inertia of the gross outline of the concrete section, omitting the reinforcing steel. If the same method is applied to all of the members, this is fairly reasonable. In an ordinary continuous tee-beam, there is a tee section near midspan and a rectangular section at either end, and the point of inflection moves under different loading conditions, so a high degree of precision is not obtainable.

(b) Some designers, feeling that a heavily reinforced beam should have more stiffness than a lightly reinforced one, take the moment of inertia of the transformed area, though there is a question whether this is any more precise, and it can be done only after considerable preliminary designing to establish all the needed data.

For the "I" of a rectangular section reinforced on both faces, good illustrations are shown in the examples on pages 11-8 and 11-96.

For a rectangular section with reinforcement on one side only, "I" would be computed in the same manner except that certain terms would drop out.

The moment of inertia of a tee-beam is difficult to appraise properly, because, being an integral part of a floor system, there is a question of how much slab should be included as a tee, e.g., the same as recommended for stress computations (ACI 318-63-906); also because the portions of the beam undergoing negative bending are rectangular; and also because of the bending up of longitudinal bars. The designer may compute "I" either for a homogeneous concrete tee section or for the transformed area. Since the stiffnesses must be available before frame analysis can be started and the design can not be completed without assuming stiffnesses, it is best, in preliminary work and work where extreme precision can not be expected, to take the "I" of a tee-beam as about 2 to 2.25 times that of the stem only. The chart can be used for a slightly more precise value.

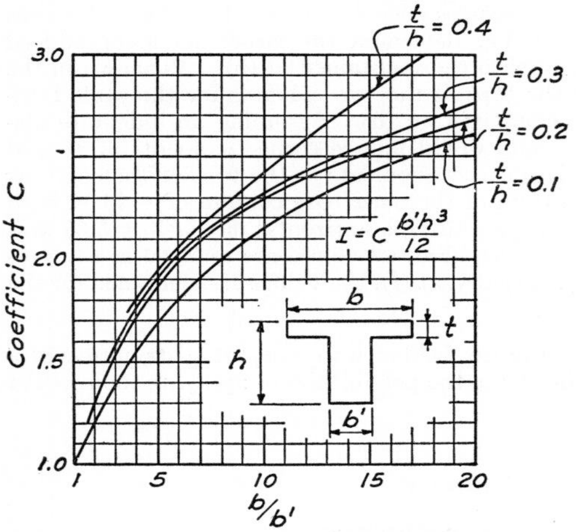

MOMENT OF INERTIA OF TEE BEAMS

BENDING OF BEAM BARS

Often for simplicity in placing, some of the tension bars in beams, slabs or joists are bent or "trussed" from the bottom in the central part of a span to the top at either support, and extended into the adjoining spans. Enough steel must be in the bottom at all points to provide resisting moment at least equal to the positive bending moment at that point under any position of the assumed load, and enough must be in the top to take care of the negative bending moment except that loose top bars can be added to make up any deficiency.

In a **single span** simply supported and uniformly loaded, the moment curve is parabolic (figure below) and bottom steel can be bent up just outside of the moment curve as shown in the figure and computed as follows (**L** being the span):—

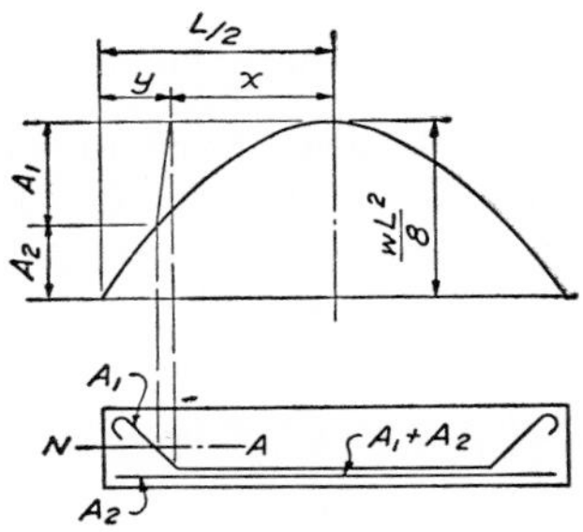

$$x^2 : \left(\frac{L}{2}\right)^2 = \frac{A_1}{A_1 + A_2}$$

For determining bend-up point of any percentage of tension bars:

$$x = \frac{L}{2}\sqrt{\frac{A_1}{A_1 + A_2}}$$

If $A_1 = A_2$, $x = 0.353L$

$y = 0.147L = L/7$ closely.

For **interior spans** of continuous beams of approximately equal spans and uniformly loaded, ACI 904(c) establishes coefficients for positive and negative moment that give moment curves about as shown in the figure below, making it possible to compute bending points about as follows (**L** being the span):—

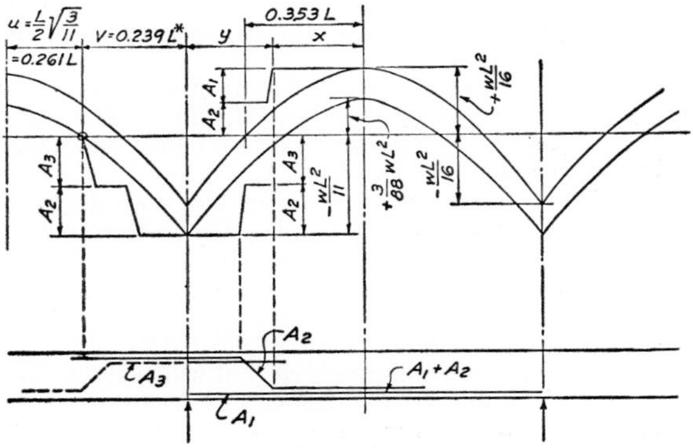

$$x^2 : (0.353L)^2 = \frac{A_1}{A_1 + A_2}$$

For determining bend-up point of any percentage of tension bars:

$$x = 0.353L\sqrt{\frac{A_1}{A_1 + A_2}}$$

If $A_1 = A_2$, $x = 0.250L$

$y = 0.250L = L/4$

For the extension of truss bars into the adjoining span, if $A_3 = A_2$, each being proportional to $\frac{1}{2}\frac{wL^2}{11}$, $u = \frac{L}{2}\sqrt{\frac{3}{11}} = 0.261L$, and $v = 0.239L = L/4$ closely.*

For **end spans** of continuous beams uniformly loaded, the moment parabolas are no longer symmetrical. If l is the span and

* ACI 918 requires that one-third of the bars be carried beyond this point of inflection L/16, d.

BENDING OF BEAM BARS

$M = wl^2/11$, zero shear is $l\sqrt{2/11}$, or $0.426l$ from the free end. Then, $x = 0.426l\sqrt{\frac{A_1}{A_1 + A_2}}$. If $A_1 = A_2$, $y = 0.125l$, or $l/8$ from the free end; and from the continuous end $y \gtrless l\,(1.0 - 0.426 - 0.301) = 0.273l$, or $3/11l$, slightly greater than $l/4$. Because of the many variables, y is often made $l/7$ from the free end and $l/5$ from the continuous end, leaving $0.657l$ horizontal near the middle of the span.

When A_1 and A_2 are not approximately equal or when the loads or spans vary considerably, values can be computed as shown or scaled from a fairly accurately sketched set of moment curves.

The curves on page 4-21 are helpful. For a single span, the percentage, $\frac{A_1}{A_1 + A_2}$, can be read downwards from the vertex, and the location of the bend-up points in percentages of l are horizontally opposite. For end spans, the upper curve is drawn for $M = +wl^2/11$ and the lower one for $M = -wl^2/10$, so that all the bend-up and bend-down points are read in percentages of l. For continuous spans, the curves are drawn for $M = +wl^2/16$ and $M = -wl^2/11$, respectively.

Example I—If a beam on a single span of 20 ft is reinforced with 6-#8 bars, 3 straight and 3 trussed, how should they be bent up?
Solution—Refer to upper diagram on page 4-21. Bend the first bar according to the ratio obtained by dividing the number of bent bars between center of span and point in question to the total steel area, in this case $1{:}6 = 1/6 = 0.167$, so $y = 0.30l$ from either end. The second bar is bent up for 2/6 or 0.333, where $y = 0.21l$. The third bar is bent for 3/6 or 0.50, where $y = 0.147l$.
Example II—If the beam in Example I were the end span of a continuous beam, how should the bars be bent up? Assume top steel consists of 3-#8 bars bent up in this span plus 3-#8 bars from adjoining span plus 1-#7 added straight top bar and determine bend-down points.
Solution—Refer to center diagram on page 4-21 using $wl^2/11$ curve for maximum positive moment. Bend up first bar ($1/6 = 0.167$) at $y = 0.26l$ and $0.60l$ from free end; second bar ($2/6 = 0.333$) at $y = 0.17l$ and $0.68l$ from free end; and third bar ($3/6 = 0.50$) at $y = 0.12l$ and $0.73l$ from free end.
For bending down bars, use the negative moment curve, $-wl^2/10$, and, since the bars differ in size, proportion by areas instead of number of bars. The #7 top bar is $0.60/5.34 = 0.113A_s$ and must extend $0.02l = 0.4$ ft beyond the face of the support, but at least $29D^2$ or 12 in. = 2.25 ft for bond, and as much more as required for practical placement. The three truss bars represent, respectively, $1.39/5.34 = 0.26A_s$, $2.18/5.34 = 0.408A_s$ and $2.97/5.34 = 0.557A_s$ and cannot bend down within $0.045l = 0.9$ ft, $0.075l = 1.5$ ft, and $0.10l = 2.0$ ft of the face of the support, each of which can be increased as necessary to produce a 45° slope from the corresponding bend-up point. The bars from the adjacent span represent $3.76/5.34 = 0.705A_s$, $4.55/5.34 = 0.853A_s$, and $5.34/5.34 = 1.0A_s$ and must extend at least $0.13l = 2.6$ ft, $0.17l = 3.4$ ft, and $0.20l = 4.0$ ft into this span, plus at least 12 diameters = 1.0 ft for anchorage. Often all three bars would be carried to $l/4 = 5.0$ ft, or even a little beyond that to be sure of covering the entire negative zone.

The tables on page 4-22 are helpful in detailing bent bars in terms of the clear span l.

BENDING OF BEAM BARS

DIAGRAMS FOR DETERMINING BEND POINTS
For explanation see pages 4-19 and 4-20.

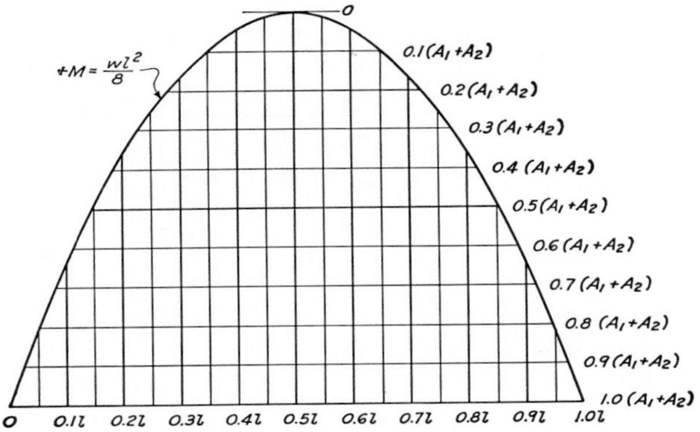

SINGLE SPAN

Use dotted curve for designs with end restraint, $+\text{M} = \frac{wl^2}{14}$

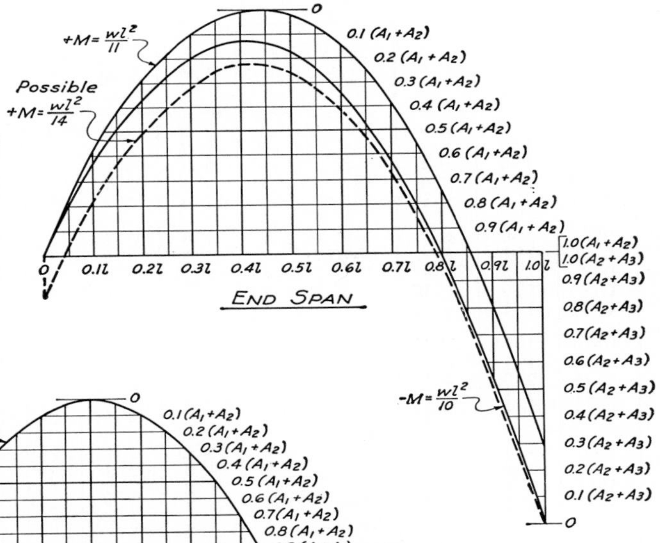

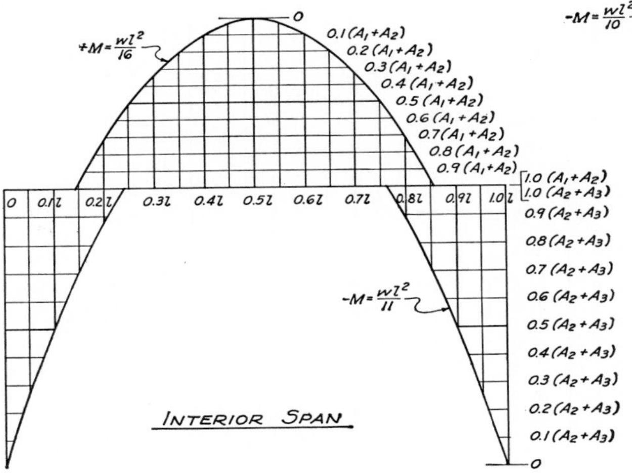

BENDING OF TRUSS BARS

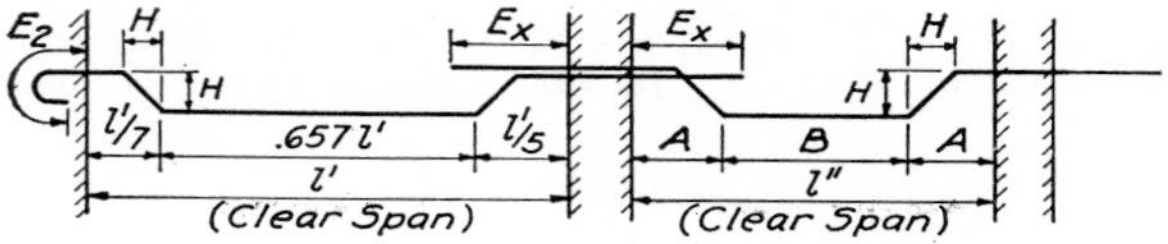

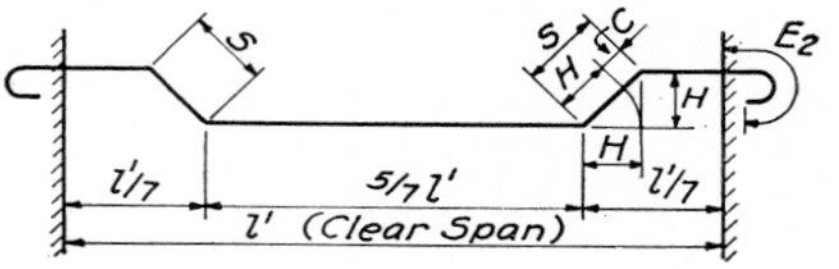

E_2 = 6 in. for #3 bars; 10 in. for #4 bars; $21D^2$ for #5 and larger, ($29D^2$ for #5 and larger, when $d > 12$ in.) (obtained by straight embedment if possible, hooked if necessary).

For slant, S, and increment, $I = 2C$, see page 2-22.

$E_x = 0.3l'$ or $0.3l''$ whichever is greater

	PERCENTAGES OF SPAN LENGTH										
l' = Span	$l'/16$	$l/7$	$0.15l'$	$l'/6 = 0.167l'$	$l'/5 = 0.20l'$	$l'/4$	$l'/3 = 0.33l'$	$l' - l'/4 - l'/4 = l'/2$	$l' - l'/5 - l'/5 = 0.60l'$	$l' - l'/7 - l'/5 = 0.657l'$	$l' - l'/7 - l'/7 = 5/7l'$
8′-0	0′-6	1′-2	1′-2	1′-4	1′-7	2′-0	2′-8	4′-0	4′-10	5′-3	5′-9
8′-6	0′-6	1′-3	1′-3	1′-5	1′-9	2′-2	2′-10	4′-3	5′-1	5′-7	6′-1
9′-0	0′-7	1′-4	1′-4	1′-6	1′-10	2′-3	3′-0	4′-6	5′-5	5′-11	6′-5
9′-6	0′-7	1′-5	1′-5	1′-7	1′-11	2′-5	3′-2	4′-9	5′-8	6′-3	6′-9
10′-0	0′-8	1′-5	1′-6	1′-8	2′-0	2′-6	3′-4	5′-0	6′-0	6′-7	7′-2
10′-6	0′-8	1′-6	1′-7	1′-9	2′-1	2′-8	3′-6	5′-3	6′-4	6′-11	7′-6
11′-0	0′-8	1′-7	1′-8	1′-10	2′-2	2′-9	3′-8	5′-6	6′-7	7′-3	7′-10
11′-6	0′-9	1′-8	1′-9	1′-11	2′-4	2′-11	3′-10	5′-9	6′-11	7′-7	8′-3
12′-0	0′-9	1′-9	1′-10	2′-0	2′-5	3′-0	4′-0	6′-0	7′-2	7′-11	8′-7
12′-6	0′-9	1′-10	1′-11	2′-1	2′-6	3′-2	4′-2	6′-3	7′-6	8′-2	8′-11
13′-0	0′-10	1′-11	1′-11	2′-2	2′-7	3′-3	4′-3	6′-6	7′-10	8′-6	9′-3
13′-6	0′-10	1′-11	2′-0	2′-3	2′-8	3′-5	4′-5	6′-9	8′-1	8′-11	9′-8
14′-0	0′-11	2′-0	2′-1	2′-4	2′-10	3′-6	4′-7	7′-0	8′-5	9′-2	10′-0
14′-6	0′-11	2′-1	2′-2	2′-5	2′-11	3′-8	4′-9	7′-3	8′-8	9′-6	10′-4
15′-0	0′-11	2′-2	2′-3	2′-6	3′-0	3′-9	4′-11	7′-6	9′-0	9′-10	10′-9
15′-6	1′-0	2′-3	2′-4	2′-7	3′-1	3′-11	5′-1	7′-9	9′-4	10′-2	11′-1
16′-0	1′-0	2′-4	2′-5	2′-8	3′-2	4′-0	5′-3	8′-0	9′-7	10′-6	11′-5
16′-6	1′-0	2′-4	2′-6	2′-9	3′-4	4′-2	5′-5	8′-3	9′-11	10′-10	11′-10
17′-0	1′-1	2′-5	2′-7	2′-10	3′-5	4′-3	5′-7	8′-6	10′-2	11′-2	12′-2
17′-6	1′-1	2′-6	2′-8	2′-11	3′-6	4′-5	5′-9	8′-9	10′-6	11′-6	12′-6
18′-0	1′-2	2′-7	2′-8	3′-0	3′-7	4′-6	5′-11	9′-0	10′-10	11′-10	12′-10
18′-6	1′-2	2′-8	2′-9	3′-1	3′-9	4′-8	6′-1	9′-3	11′-1	12′-2	13′-3
19′-0	1′-2	2′-9	2′-10	3′-2	3′-10	4′-9	6′-3	9′-6	11′-5	12′-6	13′-7
19′-6	1′-3	2′-9	2′-11	3′-3	3′-11	4′-11	6′-5	9′-9	11′-8	12′-10	13′-11
20′-0	1′-3	2′-11	3′-0	3′-4	4′-0	5′-0	6′-7	10′-0	12′-0	13′-2	14′-3
21′-0	1′-4	3′-0	3′-2	3′-6	4′-2	5′-3	6′-11	10′-6	12′-7	13′-10	15′-0
22′-0	1′-5	3′-2	3′-4	3′-8	4′-5	5′-6	7′-3	11′-0	13′-2	14′-5	15′-9
23′-0	1′-5	3′-3	3′-5	3′-10	4′-7	5′-9	7′-7	11′-6	13′-10	15′-1	16′-5
24′-0	1′-6	3′-5	3′-7	4′-0	4′-10	6′-0	7′-11	12′-0	14′-5	15′-9	17′-2
25′-0	1′-7	3′-7	3′-9	4′-2	5′-0	6′-3	8′-3	12′-6	15′-0	16′-5	17′-10
26′-0	1′-8	3′-9	3′-11	4′-4	5′-2	6′-6	8′-7	13′-0	15′-7	17′-1	18′-7
27′-0	1′-8	3′-10	4′-1	4′-6	5′-5	6′-9	8′-11	13′-6	16′-2	17′-9	19′-4
28′-0	1′-9	4′-0	4′-2	4′-8	5′-7	7′-0	9′-3	14′-0	16′-10	18′-5	20′-0
29′-0	1′-10	4′-2	4′-4	4′-10	5′-10	7′-3	9′-7	14′-6	17′-5	19′-1	20′-9
30′-0	1′-11	4′-4	4′-6	5′-0	6′-0	7′-6	9′-11	15′-0	18′-0	19′-9	21′-5

STIRRUPS IN CONCRETE BEAMS

Stirrups, in this handbook, are designed to satisfy all of a number of criteria as follows:—

1. The maximum diameter of stirrup shall be that which can be anchored within the half-depth of beam (see page 4-27) or the allowable stress in the stirrups shall be limited to that developed by the available anchorage. (ACI 919(a))

2. Stirrup spacing, except within distance d from the face of the support, shall be such that each stirrup is located near the centroid of equal portions of the "excess shear prism." (ACI 1202(a))

3. The "excess shear prism" has ordinates equal to $v - v_c$ where $v = \frac{V}{bd}$ and $v_c = 1.1\sqrt{f'_c}$ or, if a more detailed analysis is to be made, $\sqrt{f'_c} + 1300 \frac{p_w Vd}{M}$. (ACI 1201)

4. Within distance d from the face of the support the size and spacing of stirrups shall duplicate that required at distance d, at which point shear is to be considered maximum. (ACI 1202(a))

5. Stirrup spacing shall be continued beyond the point at which concrete alone can carry the shear a sufficient amount to reinforce the web to a distance d. (ACI 1202(a))

6. The maximum spacing of stirrups shall be $\frac{d}{2}$ when $v < 3\sqrt{f'_c}$, and $\frac{d}{4}$ when $v \gtrless 3\sqrt{f'_c} < 5\sqrt{f'_c}$. (ACI 1206(a))

7. Wherever any web reinforcement is required, it shall not be less than $A_v = 0.0015b's$. (ACI 1206(b))

8. While steel of 60,000 psi grade is permitted by Code to be stressed 24,000 psi in stirrups, the tables in this handbook are based upon a working stress, f_v, of 20,000 psi.

9. For purely construction reasons, this handbook has set a minimum spacing of stirrups of 3 inches.

To apply these criteria: the vertical component of the diagonal tension in any distance, s, along the neutral plane of the beam is equal to the total horizontal shear, $vb's$, * within that distance. The volume of the shear prism is proportional to the total diagonal tension in one end of the beam. The volume which represents the magnitude of the force carried by concrete lies between a plane which is distance v_c from the neutral plane and the neutral plane itself. The reinforcement within a distance d from the face of the support shall be the same as that computed at a distance d. The force which is to be carried by the first portion of the stirrups to be considered is represented by the volume of the prism between v_c and the exterior surface of the shear diagram in one direction and outside of distance d from the support in the other. This volume is shown stippled in all the examples which follow. The area, A_v, of stirrups required to account for this portion of the prism is this force divided by the allowable (or developed) stirrup stress, f_v.

---

* In a beam of rectangular cross section, $b' = b$. In beams of T or L section, b' is the width of stem.

Note: #3 is the minimum size deformed bar. It is recommended as the minimum size stirrup for general use. Even where #2 (an obsolete designation for plain ¼″ ϕ) with special anchorage would satisfy design requirements, over-all economy will usually be achieved by use of #3 stirrups.

STIRRUPS IN CONCRETE BEAMS

The second portion of stirrups, viz. that required within distance d from the face of the support, is simply made equal in size and spacing to what is required at distance d, even though the computed intensity of shear will probably be greater in that distance. For the third portion of stirrups, minimum stirrups are provided to reinforce for a distance d beyond the excess shear prism towards the center of the span.

For computing the spacing of stirrups within the excess shear prism, one can disregard that portion of the total shear prism that lies between a distance v_c from the neutral plane and the neutral plane itself, also that portion of the prism that lies within distance d from the face of the support. In selecting stirrups, the size must be small enough to permit complete development within the half-depth of beam (or the working stress must be appropriately reduced). The volume of the excess shear prism divided by the proper stress gives the stirrup area, A_v. Dividing A_v by the area of the number of legs of the selected size of stirrups gives the number of stirrups required for the excess shear prism alone. The spacing should be such as will locate a stirrup near the centroid of each approximately equal partial volume of the excess shear prism according to the number of stirrups and, in addition, the spacing shall not exceed $d/2$ for $v \leq 3\sqrt{f'_c}$ (or $d/4$ for $v > 3\sqrt{f'_c}$), and shall produce an effective area of stirrup that exceeds $0.0015b's$.

The problem resolves itself mainly into simple procedures for locating stirrups at the centers of these partial volumes. This can be done by tables (p. 4-33), by approximate computations, or by a specialized slide rule method, all of which are illustrated in the following examples.

Example 1—Stationary Uniform Load; Triangular Shear Diagram. Determine the size and spacing of stirrups in an 8 × 12 in. (d = 9.7 in.) simple rectangular beam, uniformly loaded, neglecting the effect of any bent-up tension bars (f'_c = 3750 psi, $f_v \leq$ 20,000 psi).*

Solution—Page 4-25 shows the load diagram (a) which produces an external shear diagram (b), a shear-intensity diagram (c), with a longitudinal shear prism as shown in (d). Values are given at distance d from the support as well as at the support. (Note that j is not used in determining the average shear intensity, $v = \frac{V}{b'd}$.) In (e) the longitudinal shear prism is cut off on the bottom for a height, v_c, and at the support for a length, d. Compute $v_c = 1.1\sqrt{f'_c}$, which, for 3750 psi concrete, equals 67.4 psi and the height of the excess shear prism, 89.6 psi. The stippled portion shows the "excess" shear that is to be carried by web reinforcement—in this case stirrups—at a stress of 20,000 psi, or whatever can be developed in the half-depth of beam. Taking a standard hook as developing 10,000 psi in the stirrup (ACI 919(a)1) the computations in (f) show that only 16,020 psi can be developed in #2 plain round hooked stirrups. (See also table on page 4-27.)

The computations in (e) show that 7-#2 plain round stirrups are required to account for the volume of the triangular excess shear prism itself. Although bent-up longitudinal steel might account for a portion of this prism, it is usually best and economical to disregard the contribution of the bent-up bars † because the designer can not usually foresee just what zone will be covered by the central three-quarters of the sloping portion of the bars. At best, the truss bars would replace only one or two stirrups. For the case of heavy girders, see Example 5.

The next step is to divide the triangular excess shear diagram into seven approximately equal parts and locate a stirrup near the centroid of each.

* A shallow beam was arbitrarily chosen to illustrate stirrup anchorage more clearly.
† See pages 4-19 and 4-20 for bending of bars.

STIRRUPS IN CONCRETE BEAMS

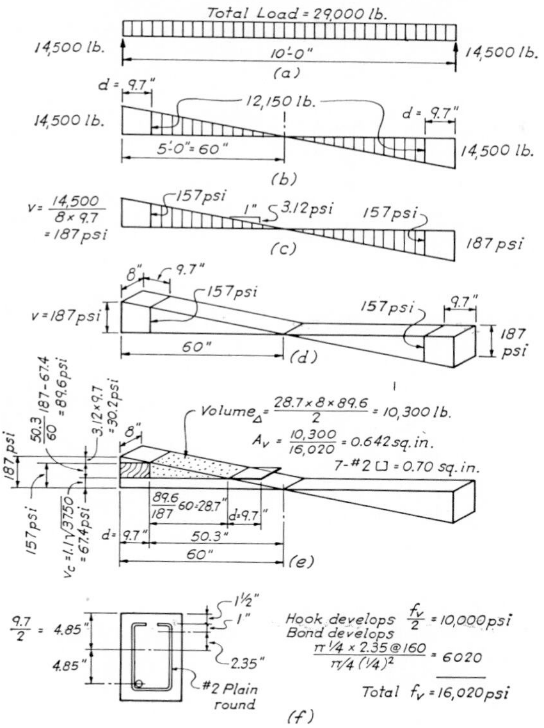

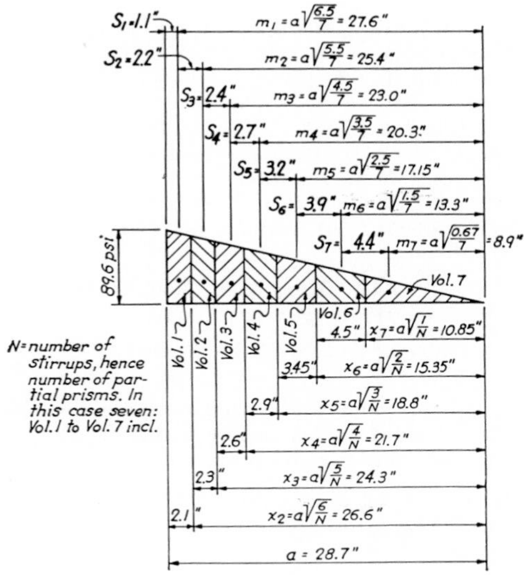

(g)

(continued on page 4-26)

STIRRUPS IN CONCRETE BEAMS

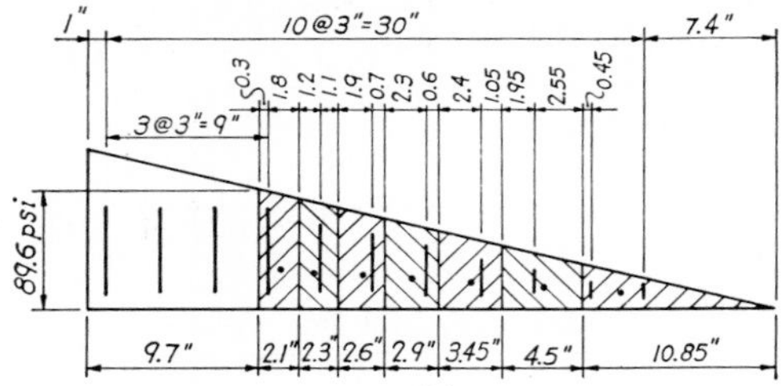

(h)

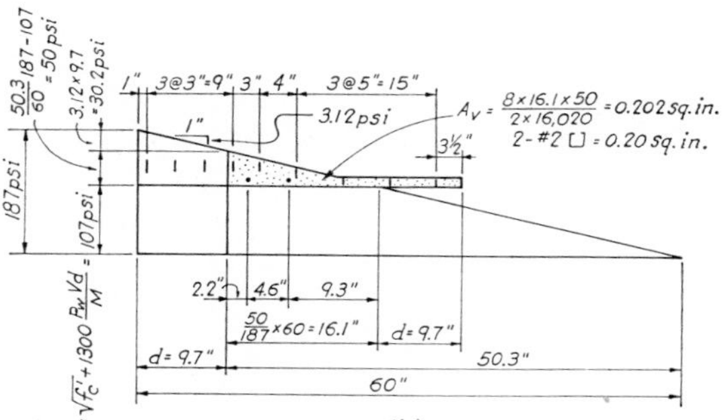

(k)

Scheme I. Using the table on page 4-33 with "*a*" = 28.7 in. for seven stirrups, read 1 @ 0.036*a*, 3 @ 0.08*a*, 2 @ 0.13*a*, and 1 @ 0.20*a*. Multiplying by "*a*," the spacings from distance *d* become 1, 2¼, 2¼, 2¼, 3¾, 3¾, and 5¾ in. These can be compared with those obtained by other schemes and the entire example will be summarized after the other schemes are explained.

Scheme II. A cut-and-try solution can be carried out on a slide rule. The slope of the shear diagram is easily established as 3.12 psi per inch of span. Also, 1-#2 two-legged stirrup at 16,020 psi accounts for 2 × 0.05 × 16020 = 1602 lb of excess shear. Starting with $v - v_c$ = 89.6 psi on an 8 in. beam width the excess shear per inch of span is 8 × 89.6 = 717 lb, so the required spacing is 1602/717 = 2.24 in. Thus the first stirrup is 1.12 in. from *d* and the next 2.24 in. Since the shear drops off 3.12 psi/in., at 3.36 in. the intensity is 717 − 8 × 3.36 × 3.12 = 633 and the spacing becomes 1602/633 = 2.53 in. At 5.89 in., the intensity is 571 pli and the spacing, 2.80 in.; at 8.69 in., 501, with a spacing of 3.20. This can be tabulated:—

Distance	—	1.12	3.36	5.89	8.69	11.89	15.70	20.64	28.66
$v - v_c$	—	717	633	571	501	421	325	202	—
Spacing	1.12	2.24	2.53	2.80	3.20	3.81	4.94	8.02	—

Since stirrups probably cannot be located much more precisely than to the nearest inch, such elaborate cut-and-try may not be justified. One might compute at distance *d* and halfway out distance *a* and prorate by eye.

However, the process just illustrated can be formalized into a procedure where the complete list of spacings can be read at one setting of a slide rule that has contiguous B and D scales.

Scheme III takes a little time to understand at first, but, once mastered, stirrups can be spaced almost automatically and at one setting of a slide rule.

STIRRUPS IN CONCRETE BEAMS

MAXIMUM DEVELOPABLE STRESSES IN STIRRUPS

$f'_c = 3750$ psi $\quad f_s = 20{,}000$ psi

Minimum embedment for full stress = 24 diameters.

Stirrups with Hooks as shown

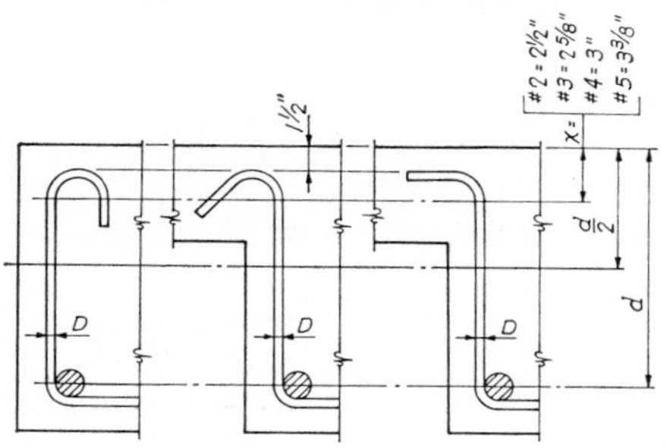

$\#2 - d = 5 + \frac{f_v - 10000}{1280};\ f_v = 10000 + 1280(d - 5)$

$\#3 - d = 5\tfrac{1}{4} + \frac{f_v - 10000}{2667};\ f_v = 10000 + 2667(d - 5\tfrac{1}{4})$

$\#4 - d = 6 + \frac{f_v - 10000}{2000};\ f_v = 10000 + 2000(d - 6)$

$\#5 - d = 6\tfrac{3}{4} + \frac{f_v - 10000}{1504};\ f_v = 10000 + 1504(d - 6\tfrac{3}{4})$

Stirrups without Hooks *

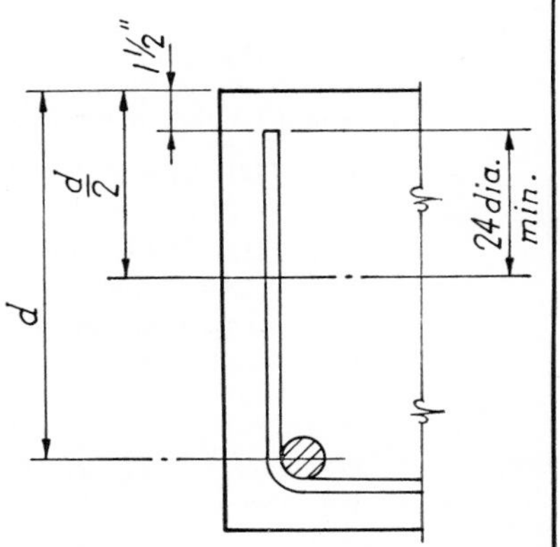

$\#3 - f_v = 5330\left(\frac{d}{2} - 1\tfrac{1}{2}\right)$

$\#4 - f_v = 4000\left(\frac{d}{2} - 1\tfrac{1}{2}\right)$

$\#5 - f_v = 3008\left(\frac{d}{2} - 1\tfrac{1}{2}\right)$

	Developable stress, f_v				Developable stress, f_v *		
	Plain	Deformed			Deformed		
Depth, d	#2	#3	#4	#5	#3	#4	#5
	$u = 160$	$u = 500$	$u = 500$	$u = 470$	$u = 500$	$u = 500$	$u = 470$
8	13,840	17,360	14,000	11,880			
9	15,120	20,000	16,000	13,380			
10	16,400	20,000	18,000	14,890			
11	17,680	20,000	20,000	16,400	8800		
12	18,960	20,000	20,000	17,900	10,000		
13	20,000	20,000	20,000	19,400	11,100	8300	
14	20,000	20,000	20,000	20,000	12,200	9100	
15	20,000	20,000	20,000	20,000	13,300	10,000	8000
16	20,000	20,000	20,000	20,000	14,400	10,800	8600
17	20,000	20,000	20,000	20,000	15,500	11,600	9300
	Minimum Depth to Develop $f_v = 20{,}000$ psi						
d	12.8	9″	11″	13.4″	21″	27″	33″

* ACI 919(a)4 requires embedment above or below the middepth, d/2, of the beam on the compression side.

STIRRUPS IN CONCRETE BEAMS

In figure (g) the triangular portion of the excess shear prism (representing that portion of the vertical component of the diagonal tension which must be carried by stirrups) is shown divided into seven equal parts, each representing the load on one stirrup. If these triangular prisms are to have volumes in the ratios 1, 2, 3, etc., their bases, called x_7, x_6, x_5, etc., must be in the ratios $\sqrt{\frac{1}{N}}, \sqrt{\frac{2}{N}}, \sqrt{\frac{3}{N}}$, etc. of a. The stirrups should be placed at the centroids of these volumes. It is entirely within the range of desired precision to consider that the upper set of dimensions (m values which place a stirrup at mid-length of all but the triangle at the vertex) locates these points. The subtractions indicated in the figure give the required spacings. The operation is carried through easily on a slide rule, using scratch paper for subtraction if it cannot be done mentally. The method is as follows:—

SET THE CROSS-HAIR AT THE VALUE OF a = 28.7 in. (figure (g)) *ON THE D SCALE.*

SET THE VALUE OF N ON THE B SCALE AT THE CROSS-HAIR. The index is now at the value of x_7 on the D scale.

SET THE CROSS-HAIR AT THE VALUE OF (N – ½) *ON THE B SCALE.* The cross-hair then indicates the value of m_1 on the D scale. The difference between a and m_1 is s_1, the distance of the first stirrup from a distance d from the support.

SET THE CROSS-HAIR AT THE VALUE OF (N – 1½) *ON THE B SCALE.* The cross-hair then indicates the value of m_2 on the D scale; $m_1 - m_2$ gives the distance between the first two stirrups, s_2.

CONTINUE THUS WITH (N – 2½), (N – 3½), *ETC. TO A SETTING FOR THE CROSS-HAIR ON THE B SCALE OF* (N – 5½). This gives the *m values* in the figure, and the differences between successive m values are the spacings, s.

FINALLY, SET THE CROSS-HAIR AT 0.67 *TO MULTIPLY THE VALUE OF* x_7 *BY* ⅔ *TO GET* m_7 at the centroid of the triangle. Subtracting $m_6 - m_7$ equals s_7.

To recap—Match a on the D scale to N on the B scale and at N – ½, N – 1½, N – 2½, etc., on B, read the spacings on D. Thus s_1 through s_7 are 1.1, 2.2, 2.4, 2.7, 3.2, 3.9, and 4.4 in., respectively.

Summary.* By whichever scheme is preferred, the spacings are, closely enough, 1, 3, 3, 3, 3, 4, and 4 in. Since v = 157 psi is less than $3\sqrt{f'_c}$ = 183 psi, a spacing of $d/2$ = 4.85 in. is allowable and no respacing is necessary to meet this provision.

The number of stirrups required from face of support through distance d = $\frac{9.7 \times 8 \times 89.6}{1602}$ = 4.34 stirrups whose spacing can be 1 in. plus 3 spaces @ 3 in., to be followed by the spacings s_1 through s_7, inclusive, arranged as developed on (h), page 4-26, as 7 @ 3 in. This takes care of spacing from face of support to a point 31 in. from the face of the support.

---

* ACI 1201(c) permits v_c to be assumed as $1.1\sqrt{f'_c}$. ACI 1201(d) permits computing the allowable v_c from $\sqrt{f'_c} + 1300\frac{p_w Vd}{M}$. This usually entails considerable work. In this example, one can compute $M_{c.l.}$ = 435,000 lb-in., M/bd^2 = 578, requiring compressive reinforcement and an A_s of approximately 2.14 sq in. so p_w is about 0.0276. The maximum value of v_c is $1.75\sqrt{f'_c}$ or 107 psi. At 1′-0″ from the face of the support V_1 = 11,600 lb, M_1 = 156,000 lb-in. and the allowable v_c is 107 psi. At 2′-0″ from the support V_2 = 8,700 lb, M_2 = 278,000 lb-in. and v_c is 107 psi. At 3′-0″, V_3 = 5,800 lb, M_3 = 365,000 lb-in., and v_c is 107 psi. Thus computation shows that if all the tension bars are anchored into the supports, v_c could be taken as 107 psi instead of 67.4 psi with the results shown in figure (k), page 4-26, viz. 9-#2 stirrups spaced 1″ + 4 @ 3″ + 4″ + 3 @ 5″.

STIRRUPS IN CONCRETE BEAMS

There remains 7.4 in. of the triangle and 9.7 in., the distance d from the vertex of the excess shear prism, or 17.1 in., to fill at 4.85 or, more practically, 4½ in. spacings, say 5 @ 4½ in. This means a total of 16 stirrups spaced 1″ + 10 @ 3″ + 5 @ 4½″.

Since #2 plain round stirrups provide poor anchorage, deformed #3 stirrups might appear better, but there must still be half a dozen or more minimum spaces of 3 in.

Finally, to keep $A_v \gtrless 0.0015b's$ requires a maximum stirrup spacing of $s = \frac{2 \times 0.05}{0.0015 \times 8} = 8.33$ in., which is not a determining factor in this example.

Example 2—Movable Live Loads. If the load and span remain the same as in Example 1, but two-thirds of the total load is live load capable of being removed, design the stirrups.

Solution—The figure below shows that the maximum live shear at any point becomes $V = w_L x^2/2L$. At midspan $V = w_L L/8$, or exactly one-quarter of the live end shear. The dead shear diagram is shown at (c) on the figure. The total external shear diagram (live plus dead) is shown in (d) with practically 31 psi at midspan. The inclined surface is here taken as a plane, though actually it is concave, this assumption being somewhat on the conservative side. Compute the value of $a = 44.5$ in. based upon a v_c of 67.4 psi. Then $A_v = 0.81$ sq in. This area might be made with 4-#3 stirrups as computed, if the spacings work out within the maximum allowable.

With $v = 158$ the shear is less than $v = 3\sqrt{f'_c} = 183$ psi so a maximum spacing of $d/2 = 4.85$ in. is allowed. For distance d from the face of the support $A_v = \frac{9.7 \times 8 \times 90.6}{20{,}000} = 0.35$ sq in.; 2-#3 U-shaped stirrups = 0.44 sq in. and they would be spaced 2.43, 4.85, and 2.43 in. In addition, stirrups would be spaced at 4.85 in. c/c from the last stirrup near the vertex of the triangle to cover a distance d from the vertex towards midspan. However, with only 5.8 in. left, this means #3 stirrups as shown on (d), viz. 2″ + 11 @ 5″ + 3″.

The requirement of $0.0015b's$ can be met with a spacing of $\frac{0.22}{0.0015 \times 8} = 18.4$ in., which is not a determining factor in this case.

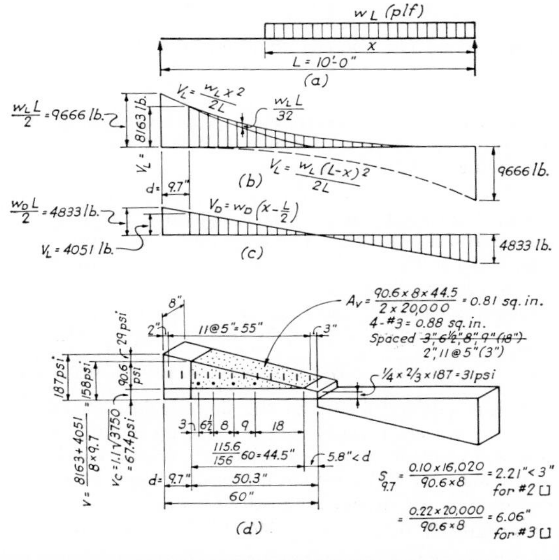

STIRRUPS IN CONCRETE BEAMS

Example 3—Center Concentrated Load; Rectangular Shear Prism. Given a center-concentrated load as shown in the figure below and neglecting the dead weight of the beam, compute the number of stirrups and their spacing.

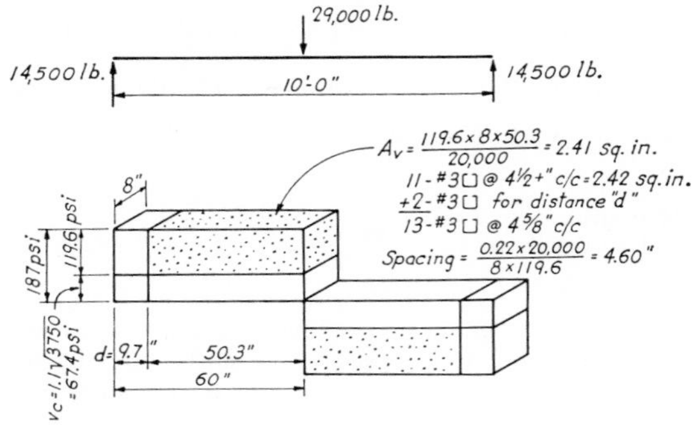

Solution—A_v is computed on the figure as 2.41 sq in., requiring 11-#3 stirrups at approximately $4\frac{1}{2}$ + in. spacing to provide 2.42 sq in. in a distance of 50.3 in., neglecting temporarily $d = 9.7$ in. For the distance d, 2-#3 stirrups at about the same spacing will fill the 9.7 in. Dividing the 60 in. half-span by 13 stirrups gives an average spacing of $60/13 = 4.62$ in. or say $4\frac{5}{8}$ in. with a half space at either end.

The shear, $v = 187$ psi, exceeds $3\sqrt{3750} = 183$ psi by 4 psi. According to ACI 1206(a), the spacing shall not exceed $d/4 = 2.43$ in. This illustrates the ever recurring problem of just what should a designer do? If his estimates of load are high, his methods conservative, and his assumed strength of concrete low, he has some slack. On the other hand, if the reverse is true, he is already over the limit. (Read the fly-leaf comments on "Precision.")

For future use, a second method is illustrated—that of dividing the capacity of a stirrup by the longitudinal shear per running inch of beam. Each stirrup accounts for $2 \times 0.11 \times 20{,}000 = 4400$ lb of excess longitudinal shear. The excess longitudinal shear is $8 \times 119.6 = 956.8$ pli. The spacing becomes $4400/956.8 = 4.60$ or $4\frac{5}{8}$ in.

If one cares to compute p_w, V, and M at successive sections, the formula $v_c = \sqrt{f'_c} + 1300\,\frac{p_w V d}{M}$ may be used and v_c might increase. Since, however, the spacing already computed exceeds $d/4$, there is no advantage in computing a greater allowable spacing.

Example 4—Uniform-plus-concentrated Load; Trapezoidal Shear Prism. Design stirrups for the combination of concentrated and uniform loads shown in the figure on page 4-31 for an 8×12 in. beam.

Solution—The shear prism on page 4-31 is shown with distance d from the face of the support neglected temporarily. The area and make-up of web reinforcement are shown on the diagram. The problem is to space 8 stirrups at the centers of equal portions of the trapezoidal shear prism whose base is 50.3 in. It is possible to work out a formula for doing this, but a cut-and-try solution is quicker and easier to apply. Each stirrup accounts for $2 \times 0.11 \times 20{,}000 = 4400$ lb of longitudinal shear, or since 1.76 sq in. were provided where 1.73 were required, use $\frac{1.73}{1.76} \times 4400 = 4320$ lb. This slight reduction will simply make the final results check a little more closely. In an 8 in. wide beam, the shear resistance of a stirrup is equivalent to $4320/8 = 540$ lb per inch of thickness of beam stem. At distance d from the face of the support, the excess longitudinal shear is 108.7 psi, so a stirrup should be one-half of $540/108.7$ or $2\frac{1}{2}$ in. from distance d. Starting, then, at $2\frac{1}{2}$ in. from distance d, the longitudinal shear is 105.9 psi, requiring a spacing of $540/105.9 = 5.11$ in., or a half-space of $2\frac{1}{2}$ in.

STIRRUPS IN CONCRETE BEAMS

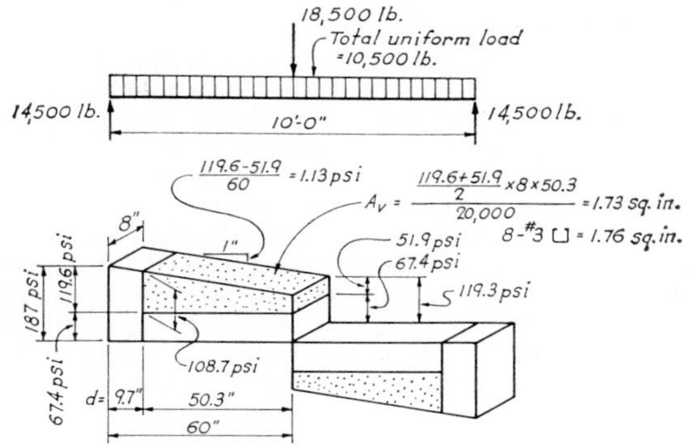

The next stirrup will be about 7½ in. from d where $v - v_c = 99.7$ psi with a spacing of 549/99.7 = 5.42 in. Although spacings are already excessive, this could be carried through:—

Stirrup Number	1	2	3	4	5	6	7	8	(to c.l.)
Distance from d	2½	7½	13½	19½	25½	32	39½	47½	2¾
Longitudinal shear, psi	105.9	99.7	93.5	87	79.5	73	64	55	
Spacings	2½	5	6	6	6	6½	7½	8	2¾

Since $v - v_c = 108.7$ is less than $3\sqrt{f'_c} = 183$, the maximum spacing is $d/2 = 9.7/2 = 4.85$, or 4½ in., and the final solution will be 2″ + 12 @ 4½″ + 4″.

Example 5—Girders Using Bent-up Bars and Stirrups for Web Reinforcement. Design web reinforcement for a heavy rectangular reinforced concrete girder 14 × 33

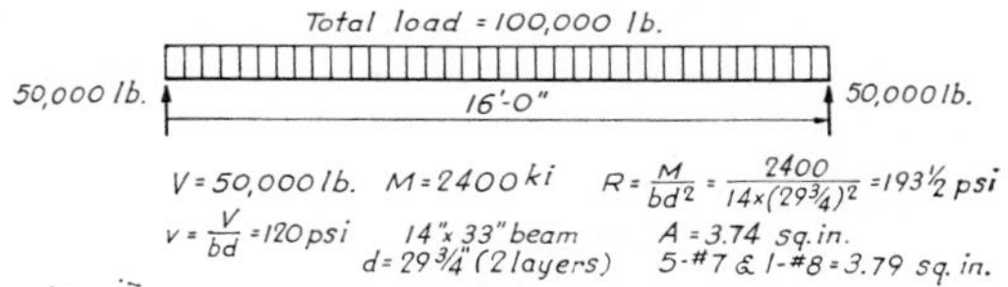

(a)

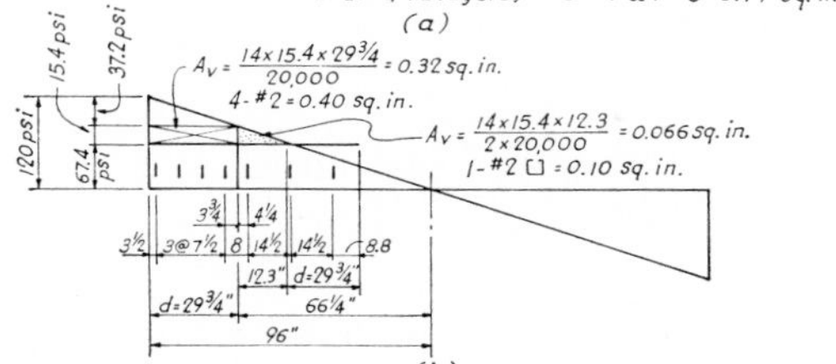

(b)

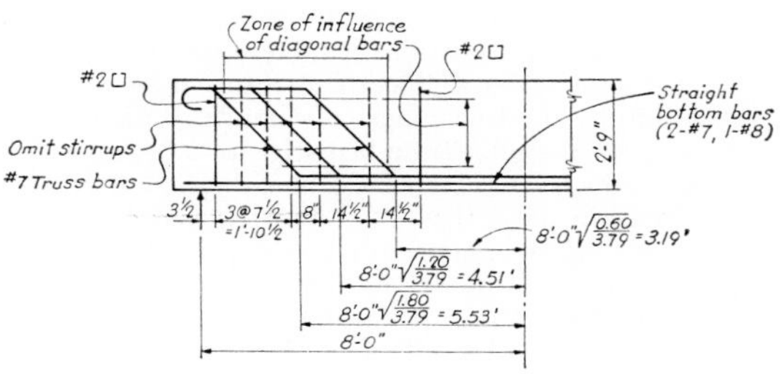

(c)

STIRRUPS IN CONCRETE BEAMS

in. (d = 29¾ in., two layers of steel) carrying 100,000 lb on a span of 16 ft, using truss bars where possible to eliminate stirrups.

Solution—This procedure is practical only on heavy girders where it is deemed advisable to detail the girder to scale rather than tabulate it in a schedule. The figure on page 4-31 in (a) shows an elevation of the girder, computation of $R = M/bd^2$ and the design of the tension reinforcement; while (b) shows the intensity of shear diagram. In (c), an elevation of the girder is drawn to scale, and, for a parabolic moment curve, the points at which individual tension bars can be bent up are calculated and shown. The zone through which the sloping portion of the truss bars may be considered effective, viz. ¾ of the slope length, ACI 1204(a), is indicated for each bar. In (d), the excess shear prism is shown and stirrups are designed as in Example 1 to account for this entire volume. Then, by scale or computation, those stirrups which fall within the effective zone of any inclined bar are automatically eliminated. A quick check shows that the truss bar affords more effective area than the stirrup it replaces.

Example 6—To illustrate the most common type of problem, design stirrups at f_v = 20,000 psi for the 8 × 22 in. stem of the T-beam shown below with a live load of 1.0 klf, a dead load of 1.33 klf, f'_c = 3750 psi.

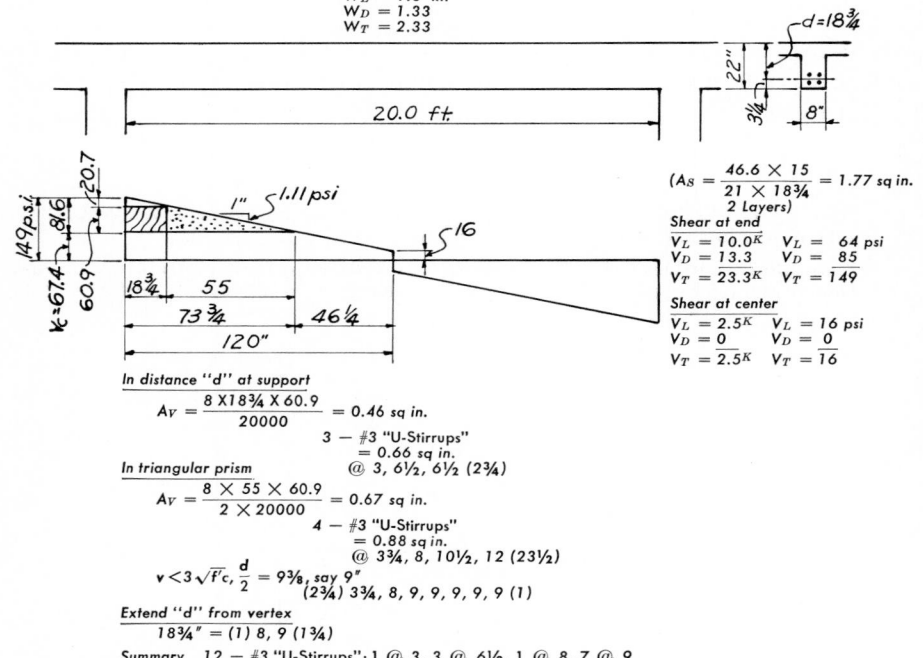

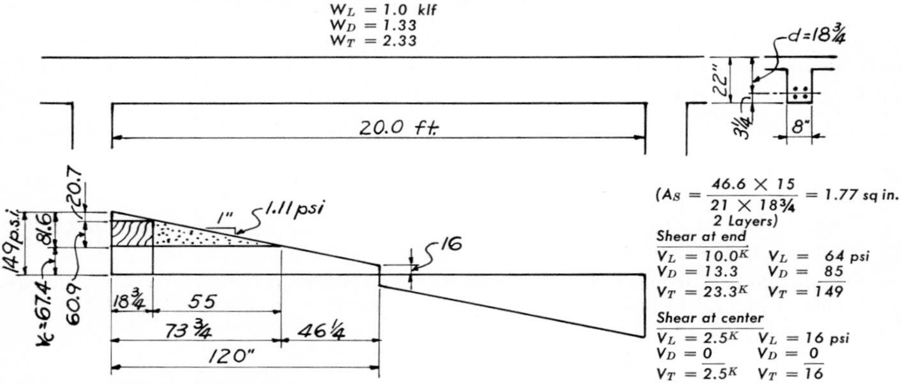

In distance "d" at support

$$A_V = \frac{8 \times 18\frac{3}{4} \times 60.9}{20000} = 0.46 \text{ sq in.}$$

3 — #3 "U-Stirrups" = 0.66 sq in. @ 3, 6½, 6½ (2¾)

In triangular prism

$$A_V = \frac{8 \times 55 \times 60.9}{2 \times 20000} = 0.67 \text{ sq in.}$$

4 — #3 "U-Stirrups" = 0.88 sq in. @ 3¾, 8, 10½, 12 (23½)

$v < 3\sqrt{f'_c}$, $\frac{d}{2}$ = 9⅜, say 9"
(2¾) 3¾, 8, 9, 9, 9, 9, 9 (1)

Extend "d" from vertex
18¾" = (1) 8, 9 (1¾)

Summary, 12 — #3 "U-Stirrups"; 1 @ 3, 3 @ 6½, 1 @ 8, 7 @ 9

Solution—The total solution can be worked out with no other computations than are given on the figure. Compute A_s to determine that positive steel will be in two layers with d = 18¾ in. Compute total shears and shear intensities at end, midspan, and distance d from the support as well as the distance a beyond which stirrups are not required. Compute number and spacings of stirrups in distance d from the support. (Space in parentheses is the distance from last stirrup to distance d.) Compute number and spacings of stirrups in triangular excess shear prism, viz. 4 @ 3¾, 8, 10½, and 12 in. (again the spacing in parentheses is from the last stirrup to the vertex of the excess shear prism). Compute maximum spacing as $d/2$ and respace the stirrups within the triangle to suit this limitation. (Again, the figure in parentheses is from last stirrup to vertex of the prism.) Compute spacings at $d/2$ to extend distance d beyond the vertex towards midspan. (Only 1¾ in. remains from last stirrup to end of space, but with one less stirrup this would be 10¾ in.) Combine the three parts into the summary of all stirrups required by these assumptions.

TABLE OF STIRRUP SPACINGS WITH TRIANGULAR SHEAR VARIATION.

Number of Stirrups at One End	Distance First Stirrup to Face of Support	Spacing, Center to Center, of Stirrups, in Terms of a									
		1st Group		2nd Group		3rd Group		4th Group		5th Group	
		No.	Spacing	No.	Spacing	No.	Spacing	No.	Spacing	No.	Spacing
20	0.013 a	8	0.03 a	7	0.04 a	2	0.06 a	1	0.08 a	1	0.11 a
19	0.013 a	7	0.03 a	6	0.04 a	3	0.06 a	1	0.08 a	1	0.12 a
18	0.014 a	6	0.03 a	5	0.04 a	4	0.06 a	1	0.08 a	1	0.12 a
17	0.015 a	5	0.03 a	5	0.04 a	4	0.06 a	1	0.09 a	1	0.13 a
16	0.016 a	3	0.03 a	5	0.04 a	5	0.06 a	1	0.09 a	1	0.13 a
15	0.017 a	2	0.03 a	5	0.04 a	4	0.06 a	2	0.08 a	1	0.14 a
14	0.018 a	5	0.04 a	4	0.05 a	2	0.08 a	1	0.09 a	1	0.14 a
13	0.019 a	4	0.04 a	3	0.05 a	3	0.08 a	1	0.09 a	1	0.14 a
12	0.021 a	6	0.05 a	3	0.07 a	1	0.12 a	1	0.15 a		
11	0.023 a	5	0.05 a	3	0.08 a	1	0.12 a	1	0.15 a		
10	0.025 a	3	0.05 a	4	0.08 a	1	0.12 a	1	0.16 a		
9	0.028 a	3	0.06 a	3	0.09 a	1	0.12 a	1	0.17 a		
8	0.032 a	2	0.07 a	3	0.09 a	1	0.13 a	1	0.18 a		
7	0.036 a	3	0.08 a	2	0.13 a	1	0.20 a				
6	0.04 a	3	0.10 a	1	0.15 a	1	0.22 a				
5	0.05 a	2	0.12 a	1	0.16 a	1	0.23 a				
4	0.07 a	2	0.16 a	1	0.26 a						
3	0.09 a	1	0.21 a	1	0.30 a						
2	0.13 a	1	0.37 a								
1	0.29 a										

Stirrups are to be supplied from face of support to distance *d* at spacing required at distance *d*.

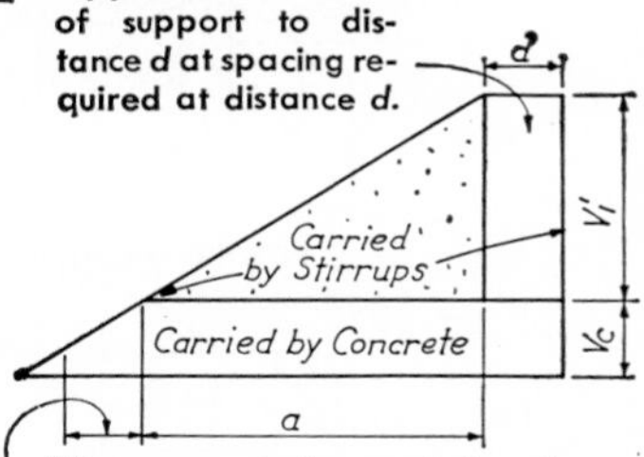

Stirrups are to be carried on for a distance "d" (one beam depth).

See explanation on pages 4-23 to 4-32.

MAXIMUM STIRRUP SPACING (U-SHAPED) FROM $A_v = 0.0015b's$.							
Stirrup size	Width of beam stem, b' (in.)						
	6	8	10	12	14	16	18
#2	11	8	6½	5½	4½	4	3½
#3		18	14	12	10	9	8
#4			26	22	19	16	14

PROPERTIES OF PARABOLA

TO DRAW A SYMMETRICAL PARABOLA

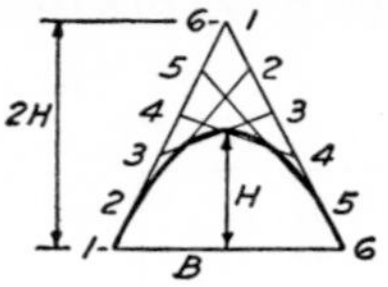

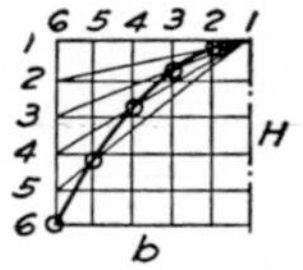

Method I

1. Given Base B, Height H.
2. Construct isosocles triangle, Base B, Height 2H.
3. Divide each equal leg into same number of equal parts.
4. Connect as shown.
5. These connecting lines are tangent to inscribed parabola.

Method II

1. Given half-base b, Height H.
2. Divide inclosing rectangle with same number of vertical and radiating lines.
3. Intersections of similarly numbered verticals and rays are points on the curve.

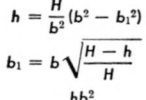

AREAS AND CENTROIDS OF PARABOLIC FIGURES

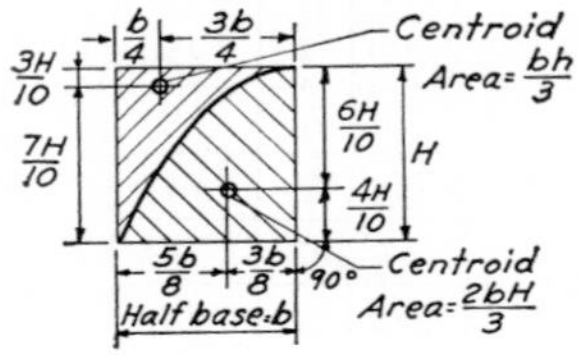

PARABOLIC SEGMENT

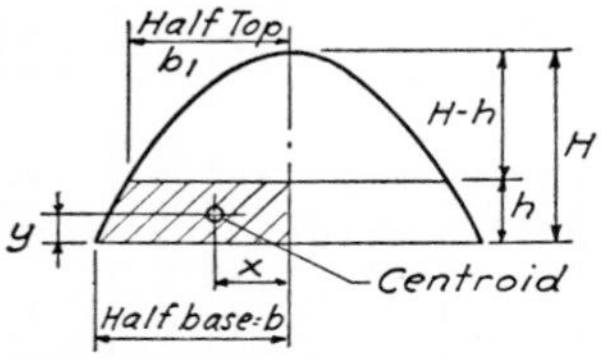

$$h = \frac{H}{b^2}(b^2 - b_1^2)$$

$$b_1 = b\sqrt{\frac{H-h}{H}}$$

$$H = \frac{hb^2}{b^2 - b_1^2}$$

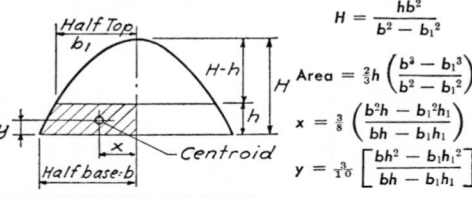

$$\text{Area} = \tfrac{2}{3}h\left(\frac{b^3 - b_1^3}{b^2 - b_1^2}\right)$$

$$x = \tfrac{3}{8}\left(\frac{b^2h - b_1^2h_1}{bh - b_1h_1}\right)$$

$$y = \tfrac{3}{10}\left[\frac{bh^2 - b_1h_1^2}{bh - b_1h_1}\right]$$

AREA BETWEEN PARABOLIC CURVE AND SECANT

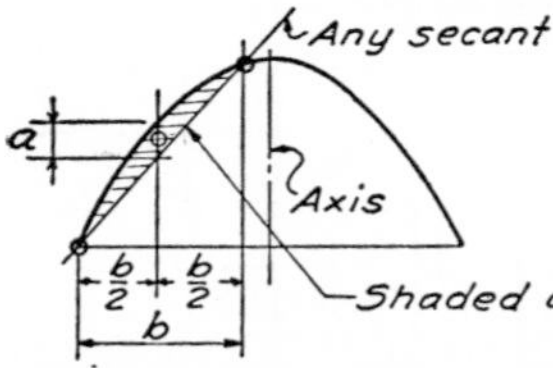

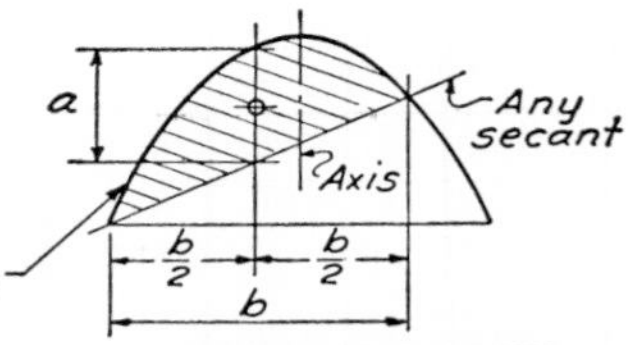

AREA BETWEEN PARABOLIC CURVE AND TANGENT

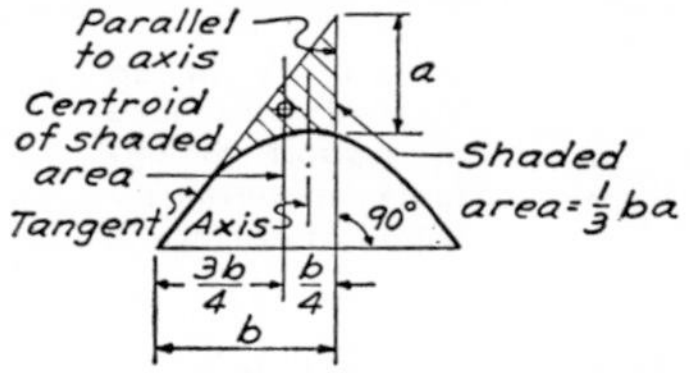

INTERMEDIATE ORDINATES

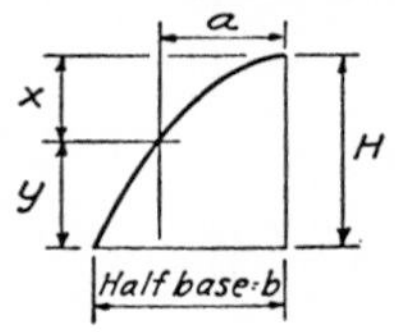

$$x = H\frac{a^2}{b^2}$$

$$y = H - x$$

POSITIVE MOMENT CONSISTENT WITH GIVEN NEGATIVE VALUES AT ENDS

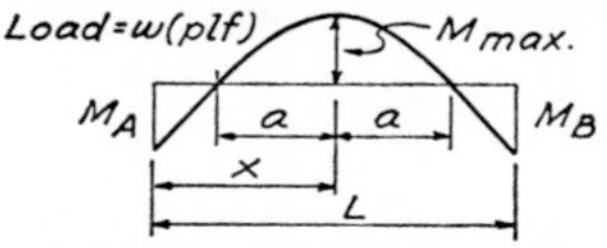

For algebraic consistency, call counter-clockwise exterior end moments positive

$$X = \frac{L}{2} + \frac{M_B + M_A}{wL}$$

$$+M_{max} = \frac{wL^2}{8} + \frac{M_B - M_A}{2} + \frac{(M_A + M_B)^2}{2wL^2}$$

$$a = \sqrt{\frac{L^2}{4} + \frac{M_B - M_A}{w} + \frac{(M_A + M_B)^2}{w^2L^2}}$$

ABSCISSA FOR GIVEN ORDINATE; RELATION POSITIVE AND NEGATIVE MOMENTS

For Given Positive Moment $k = \sqrt{\frac{2}{\alpha}}$ and $-M = (\frac{1}{2} - k)wL^2$

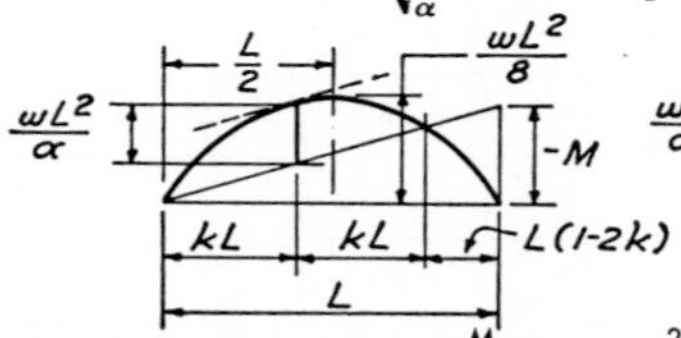

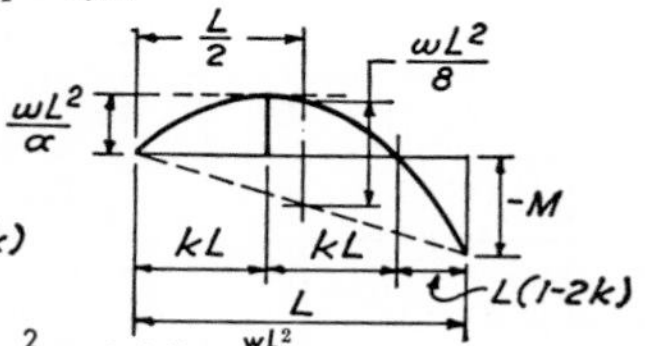

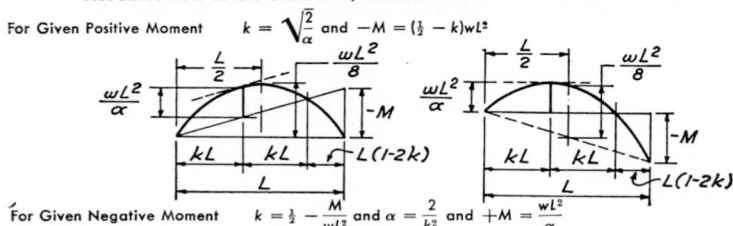

For Given Negative Moment $k = \frac{1}{2} - \frac{M}{wL^2}$ and $\alpha = \frac{2}{k^2}$ and $+M = \frac{wL^2}{\alpha}$

PROPERTIES OF SECTIONS

Section	Area	Axis to Extreme Fiber	Moment of Inertia	Radius of Gyration	Section Modulus
	A	x	I	$r = \sqrt{I \div A}$	$S = I \div x$
	sq. in.	in.	in.⁴	in.	in.³
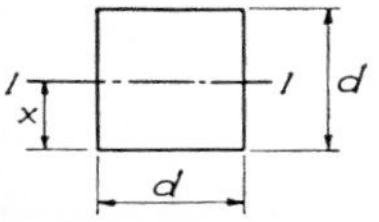	d^2	$\frac{d}{2}$	$\frac{d^4}{12}$	$\frac{d}{\sqrt{12}} = 0.2887d$	$\frac{d^3}{6}$
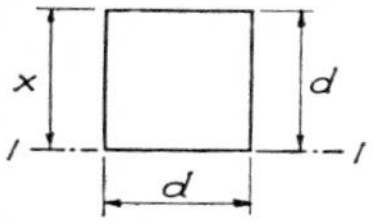	d^2	d	$\frac{d^4}{3}$	$\frac{d}{\sqrt{3}} = 0.5773d$	$\frac{d^3}{3}$
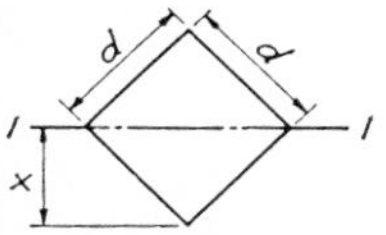	d^2	$\frac{d}{\sqrt{2}} = 0.7071d$	$\frac{d^4}{12}$	$\frac{d}{\sqrt{12}} = 0.2887d$	$\frac{d^3}{6\sqrt{2}} = 0.1179d^3$
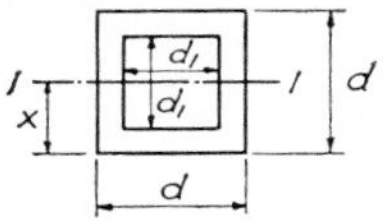	$d^2 - d_1^2$	$\frac{d}{2}$	$\frac{d^4 - d_1^4}{12}$	$\sqrt{\frac{d^2 + d_1^2}{12}}$; $\sqrt{\frac{1}{12}} = 0.2887$	$\frac{d^4 - d_1^4}{6d}$
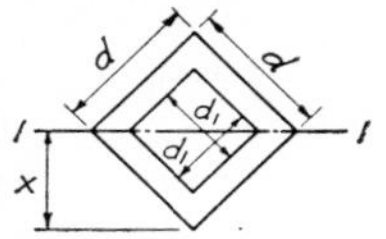	$d^2 - d_1^2$	$\frac{d}{\sqrt{2}} = 0.7071d$	$\frac{d^4 - d_1^4}{12}$	$\sqrt{\frac{d^2 + d_1^2}{12}}$; $\sqrt{\frac{1}{12}} = 0.2887$	$\frac{d^4 - d_1^4}{6d\sqrt{2}}$; $\frac{1}{6\sqrt{2}} = 0.1179$
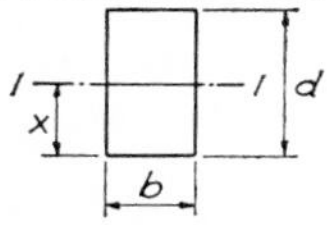	bd	$\frac{d}{2}$	$\frac{bd^3}{12}$	$\frac{d}{\sqrt{12}} = 0.2887d$	$\frac{bd^2}{6}$
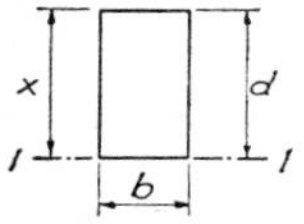	bd	d	$\frac{bd^3}{3}$	$\frac{d}{\sqrt{3}} = 0.5773d$	$\frac{bd^2}{3}$
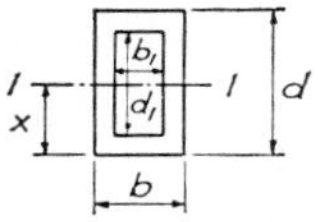	$bd - b_1d_1$	$\frac{d}{2}$	$\frac{bd^3 - b_1d_1^3}{12}$	$\sqrt{\frac{bd^3 - b_1d_1^3}{12(bd - b_1d_1)}}$	$\frac{bd^3 - b_1d_1^3}{6d}$
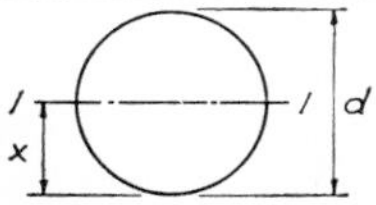	$\frac{\pi d^2}{4} = 0.7854d^2$	$\frac{d}{2}$	$\frac{\pi d^4}{64} = 0.0491d^4$	$\frac{d}{4}$	$\frac{\pi d^3}{32} = 0.0982d^3$
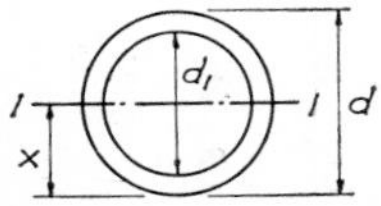	$\frac{\pi(d^2 - d_1^2)}{4}$; $\frac{\pi}{4} = 0.7854$	$\frac{d}{2}$	$\frac{\pi(d^4 - d_1^4)}{64}$; $\frac{\pi}{64} = 0.0491$	$\frac{\sqrt{d^2 + d_1^2}}{4}$	$\frac{\pi(d^4 - d_1^4)}{32d}$; $\frac{\pi}{32} = 0.0982$

PROPERTIES OF SECTIONS

Section	Area	Axis to Extreme Fiber	Moment of Inertia	Radius of Gyration	Section Modulus
	A	x	I	$r = \sqrt{I \div A}$	$S = I \div x$
	sq in.	in.	in.⁴	in.	in.³
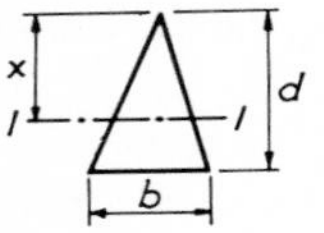	$\frac{bd}{2}$	$\frac{2d}{3}$	$\frac{bd^3}{36}$	$\frac{d}{\sqrt{18}} =$ 0.2357d	$\frac{bd^2}{24}$
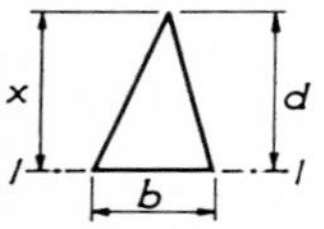	$\frac{bd}{2}$	d	$\frac{bd^3}{12}$	$\frac{d}{\sqrt{6}} =$ 0.4082d	$\frac{bd^2}{12}$
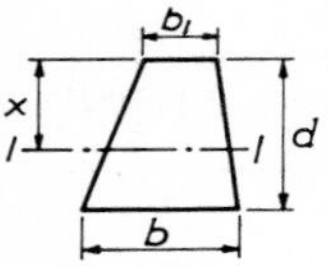	$\frac{(b+b_1)d}{2}$	$\frac{d(2b+b_1)}{3(b+b_1)}$	$\frac{d^3(b^2+4bb_1+b_1^2)}{36(b+b_1)}$	$\frac{d\sqrt{2(b^2+4bb_1+b_1^2)}}{6(b+b_1)}$	$\frac{d^2(b^2+4bb_1+b_1^2)}{12(2b+b_1)}$
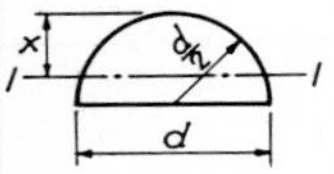	$\frac{\pi d^2}{8} =$ 0.3927d^2	$\frac{d}{2}\left(1-\frac{4}{3\pi}\right) =$ 0.2878d	$\frac{d^4}{16}\left(\frac{\pi}{8}-\frac{8}{9\pi}\right) =$ 0.00686d^4	$\frac{d\sqrt{9\pi^2-64}}{12\pi} =$ 0.1322d	$\frac{d^3(9\pi^2-64)}{192(3\pi-4)} =$ 0.0238d^3
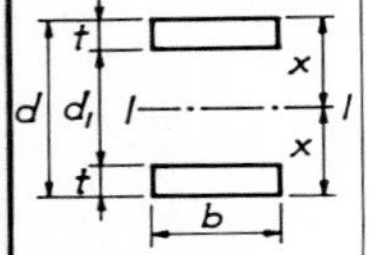	$b(d-d_1) = 2bt$	$\frac{d}{2}$	$\frac{b(d^3-d_1^3)}{12}$	$\sqrt{\frac{d^3-d_1^3}{12(d-d_1)}}$	$\frac{b(d^3-d_1^3)}{6d}$
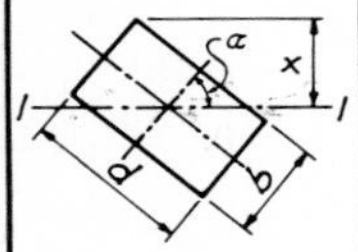	bd	$\frac{b\sin\alpha + d\cos\alpha}{2}$	$\frac{bd(b^2\sin^2\alpha + d^2\cos^2\alpha)}{12}$	$\sqrt{\frac{b^2\sin^2\alpha + d^2\cos^2\alpha}{12}}$	$\frac{bd(b^2\sin^2\alpha + d^2\cos^2\alpha)}{6(b\sin\alpha + d\cos\alpha)}$
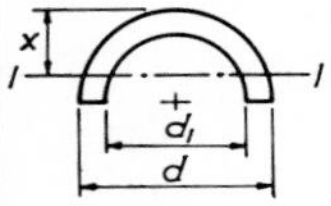	$\frac{\pi(d^2-d_1^2)}{8}$	$\frac{d}{2} - \frac{2(d^3-d_1^3)}{3\pi(d^2-d_1^2)}$ When d′ = d $x = d\left(\frac{\pi-2}{2\pi}\right)$	$\frac{0.1098}{16}(d^4-d_1^4) - \frac{0.283d^2d_1^2(d-d_1)}{16(d+d_1)}$	$\sqrt{\frac{8I}{\pi(d^2-d_1^2)}}$	$\frac{I}{x}$
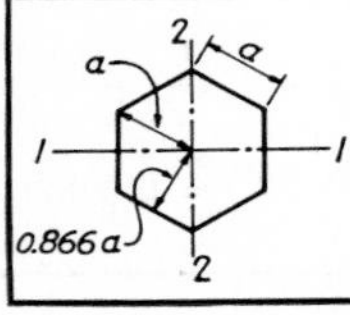	$\frac{3\sqrt{3}}{2}a^2 =$ 2.598a^2	$x_1 = a$ $x_2 = \frac{\sqrt{3}}{2}a$	$I_1 = I_2$ $\frac{5\sqrt{3}}{16}a^4 =$ 0.5413a^4	$a\sqrt{\frac{5}{24}} =$ 0.456a	$S_1 = \frac{5\sqrt{3}}{16}a^3$ $S_2 = \frac{5}{8}a^3$

Design Data, Weights, Loads, Design Notes, Hints
Section 5

DEAD WEIGHTS OF FLOORS, CEILINGS AND ROOFS, IN POUNDS PER SQUARE FOOT

	Weight (psf)
FLOORINGS:—	
Cement finish, per inch of thickness	12
Cinder concrete fill, per inch of thickness	8
3″ creosoted wood blocks on ½″ mortar base	21
2″ creosoted wood blocks on ½″ mortar base	17
3″ creosoted wood blocks on ⅛″ mastic bed	12
2″ creosoted wood blocks on ⅛″ mastic bed	9
⅞″ hardwood floor on sleepers clipped to concrete without fill	5
1½″ terrazzo floor finish directly on slab	19
1½″ terrazzo floor finish on 1″ mortar bed	30
1″ terrazzo finish on 2″ concrete bed	38
¾″ ceramic or quarry tile on ½″ mortar bed	16
¾″ ceramic or quarry tile on 1″ mortar bed	22
¼″ linoleum or asphalt tile directly on concrete	1
¼″ linoleum or asphalt tile on 1″ mortar bed	12
¾″ mastic floor	9
Hardwood flooring, ⅞″ thick	4
Subflooring (soft wood), ¾″ thick	2½
Gypsum slab, per inch of thickness	6
Asphalt mastic finish ("black top") 1½ in. thick	18
CEILINGS:—	
¾″ plaster directly on concrete, blocks or tile	5
¾″ plaster on metal lath furring	8
¾″ gypsum plaster on metal lath and channel suspended ceiling construction	10
Plaster on rock lath and channel ceiling construction	6
Acoustical fiber tile directly on concrete blocks or tile	1
Acoustical fiber tile on rock lath and channel ceiling construction	5
Acoustical fiber tile on suspended wood furring strips	3
ROOFS:—	
Five-ply felt and gravel (or slag)	6½
Three-ply felt and gravel (or slag)	5½
Five-ply felt composition roof, no gravel	4
Three-ply felt composition roof, no gravel	3
Asphalt strip shingles	3
Cement tile	16
Slate, ¼″ thick	9½
Slate, ½″ thick	19
Sheathing, ¾″ thick, Yellow Pine	3½
Sheathing, ¾″ thick, Spruce or Hemlock	2½
Skylight with galvanized iron frame, ¼″ wire glass	7
Gypsum, per inch of thickness	4
Poured gypsum on steel rails, per inch of thickness	5
Light-weight fill or insulation, porous glass, vermiculite, etc., per inch of thickness	1 to 2
Light-weight fill or insulation, cinder concrete, per inch of thickness	8
Spanish tile (laid)	9 to 12
Shingle-type clay tile	12 to 14
Metal deck (20 gauge)	2¼
Metal deck (18 gauge)	3
Corrugated metal (20 gauge)	1½
Flat cement tile, per inch of thickness	13
Wood fiber plank without subpurlins	3
Add for subpurlins	1 to 2
Rigid insulation board ½″ thick	1¼

(For weights of concrete joists, see pages 7-11 ff.)

Portland cement may be shipped in bulk or in sacks weighing 94 lb per sack, ordinarily considered 1 cu ft (4 sacks = 376 lb are referred to as a barrel).

DEAD WEIGHTS OF WALLS AND PARTITIONS, IN POUNDS PER SQUARE FOOT

	Weight (psf)		
	Un-plastered	One Side Plastered	Both Sides Plastered
WALLS:—			
4″ brick wall	40	45	50
9″ brick wall	80	85	90
13″ brick wall	120	125	130
17″ brick wall	160	165	170
21″ brick wall	205	210	215
25″ brick wall	245	250	255
4″ concrete block (130 pcf, 1-in. shell)	27	32	37
4″ concrete block (115 pcf, 1-in. shell)	24	29	34
4″ concrete block (95 pcf, 1-in. shell)	20	25	30
6″ concrete block (130 pcf, 1-in. shell)	33	38	43
6″ concrete block (115 pcf, 1-in. shell)	29	34	39
6″ concrete block (95 pcf, 1-in. shell)	24	29	34
8″ concrete block (130 pcf, 1-in. shell)	37	42	47
8″ concrete block (115 pcf, 1-in. shell)	32	35	42
8″ concrete block (95 pcf, 1-in. shell)	27	32	37
12″ concrete block (130 pcf, 1¼-in. shell)	60	65	70
12″ concrete block (115 pcf, 1¼-in. shell)	52	57	62
12″ concrete block (95 pcf, 1¼-in. shell)	44	49	54
4″ brick veneer over any of the above back-ups add	40	40	—
4″ concrete "brick-size" masonry (130 pcf)	36	41	46
4″ concrete "brick-size" masonry (115 pcf)	31	36	41
4″ concrete "brick-size" masonry (95 pcf)	26	31	36
4″ terra cotta tile	25	30	35
8″ terra cotta tile	33	38	43
12″ terra cotta tile	45	50	55
4″ glass block	20	—	—
Windows, glass, frame and sash	8	—	—
Porcelain enamel on sheet steel	3	—	—
Structural glass, per inch of thickness	15	—	—
4″ stone	55	—	—
Asbestos hardboard (corrugated), per ¼″ of thickness	3	—	—
4″ brickwork with 4″ hollow tile backing	60	65	—
4″ brickwork with 8″ hollow tile backing	75	80	—
PARTITIONS:—			
3″ clay tile	17	22	27
4″ clay tile	18	23	28
6″ clay tile	25	30	35
8″ clay tile	31	36	41
10″ clay tile	35	40	45
3″ gypsum block	10	15	20
4″ gypsum block	13	18	23
5″ gypsum block	16	21	26
6″ gypsum block	17	22	27
2″ solid plaster	—	—	20
2 x 4 studs, or metal studs, lath and ¾″ plaster	—	—	18
Steel partitions	4	—	—
½″ plaster on gypsum block or clay tile	—	4	8

Partitions are sometimes arbitrarily allowed for as 12, 15, 20, or 25 psf of floor area, which, at best, is not very precise. It is better to take off and weigh the partitions in a panel or two for any building of importance.

Dry wall - 2 x 4 studs plaster board, 5/8" plaster both side 16 #/□'

DEAD WEIGHTS OF MASONRY, IN POUNDS PER CUBIC FOOT

MASONRY:—	*Weight (pcf)*
Cinder concrete fill	60
Concrete, cinder	100
Concrete, slag	130
Concrete, stone	144
Concrete, reinforced stone	150
Brick masonry, soft	110
Brick masonry, common	125
Brick masonry, pressed	140
Dry rubble masonry, sandstone, bluestone	110
Dry rubble masonry, limestone, marble	125
Dry rubble masonry, granite, gneiss	130
Mortar rubble masonry, sandstone, bluestone	130
Mortar rubble masonry, limestone, marble	150
Mortar rubble masonry, granite, gneiss	155
Ashlar sandstone, bluestone	140
Ashlar limestone, marble	160
Ashlar granite, gneiss	165

BEARING CAPACITIES OF SOILS

Presumptive Surface Bearing Values of Foundation Materials

	Class of material	*Tons per square foot*
1	Massive crystalline bed rock including granite, diorite, gneiss, trap rock, hard limestone and dolomite	100
2	Foliated rock including bedded limestone, schist and slate in sound condition	40
3	Sedimentary rock including hard shales, sandstones, and thoroughly cemented conglomerates	25
4	Soft or broken bed rock (excluding shale), and soft limestone	10
5	Compacted, partially cemented gravels, and sand and hard-pan overlying rock	10
6	Gravel and sand-gravel mixtures	6
7	Loose gravel, hard dry clay, compact coarse sand, and soft shales	4
8	Loose, coarse sand and sand-gravel mixtures and compact fine sand (confined)	3
9	Loose medium sand (confined), stiff clay	2
10	Soft broken shale, soft clay	1.5

CAPACITY OF MASONRY WALL TO SUPPORT BEARING PLATES

	Allowable Bearing (psi)
3000 psi concrete *	750
2000 psi concrete *	500
1500 psi concrete *	375
Hard-burned common brick in cement mortar	200
Soft common brick in cement mortar	150
Hard-burned common brick in lime mortar	150
Soft common brick in lime mortar	120
Load-bearing back-up tile (cells vertical) †	150
Concrete blocks ‡ in cement mortar	150
Cinder blocks ‡ in cement mortar	120
Stone masonry in cement mortar	250

* Values given are for full area loaded and may be increased to a maximum 50% greater if load covers one-third or less of the area; other values interpolated.

† Non-load-bearing tile or tile with cells horizontal are not desirable materials for supporting loads.

‡ Meeting ASTM C90-52; increase 75% if solid units.

STRENGTH OF MATERIALS
Building Materials

Material	Average Ultimate Stress (psi) Compression	Average Ultimate Stress (psi) Tension	Average Ultimate Stress (psi) Bending	Safe Working Stress (psi) Compression	Safe Working Stress (psi) Bearing	Safe Working Stress (psi) Shearing	Modulus of Elasticity (psi)
Masonry, granite	......	......	......	420	600		
Masonry, limestone, bluestone	......	......	......	350	500		
Masonry, sandstone	......	......	......	280	400		
Masonry, rubble	......	......	......	140	250		
Masonry, brick, common	10000	200	600				
Ropes, cast steel hoisting	......	80000					
Ropes, standing, derrick	......	70000					
Ropes, manila	......	8000					
Stone, bluestone	12000	1200	2500	1200	1200	200	7,000,000
Stone, granite, gneiss	12000	1200	1600	1200	1200	200	7,000,000
Stone, limestone, marble	8000	800	1500	800	800	150	7,000,000
Stone, sandstone	5000	150	1200	500	500	150	3,000,000
Stone, slate	10000	3000	5000	1000	1000	175	14,000,000

BUILDING CODE UNIFORMLY DISTRIBUTED MINIMUM LIVE LOADS (PSF)

Occupancy	Codes								
	Basic Building Code BOCA 1960 Amend. 1963	Am. Std. Bldg. Code 1955 Nat. Bureau Stds. A58.1	Nat. Bd. of Fire Underwriters 1955	Internat'l* Conference Bldg. Officials Unif. Bldg. Code 1964	New York 1957	Chicago 1956	Philadelphia	Detroit	Southern Building Code Congress Southern Std. Bldg. Code 1954
Dwellings, apartment and tenement houses, hotels, hospitals and places of detention:									
Dwellings, private rooms and apartments	40 [30]	40	40 [30]	40	40 [11]	40	40	40	40 [43]
Public corridors, lobbies and dining rooms	100 [29]	100	100 [29]	100	100	75	100	100 [29]	100
School buildings:									
Class rooms and rooms for similar use	60 [27]	40	40	40	60 [12]	40	50 [25]	50 [25]	40
Corridors and public parts of the building	100	100	100	100	100	100	100	100	100
Theaters, assembly halls etc.:									
Auditoriums with fixed seats	60	60	60	50	75 [13]	60	60 [26]	60	50
Lobbies, passageways, gymnasiums, grandstands, stages and auditoriums or places of assemblage without fixed seats	100 [8]	100	100 [8]	100 [8]	100	100	100	100 [8]	100 [8]
Stage floor	150	150	150	125		150		150	150
Office building:									
Office space	50 [2,3]	80	80	50 [2,3]	50 [11]	50 [21,3]	60	50	50
Corridors					50				
Corridors and other public places	100	100	80	100	100 [42]	100	100	100	100
Workshops, factories and mercantile establishments:									
Manufacturing—light	125 *	125	125 [2]	75	120	100 [41]	120 [28]	125	100
Manufacturing—heavy	*			125	120 [41]	100 [41]	200 [28]		150
Storage—light	125	125	125 [2]	125	120	100 [41]	120-150 [28]	125	125
Storage—heavy	250	250	250 [2]	250	120 [41]	100 [41]	200 [28]	250	250
Stores—retail	75 [20]	100 [52]	75 [2]	75	75 [15]	100 [41]	100 [28]	75 [20]	75
Stores—wholesale	125	125	125 [2]	100	75 [15]	100 [41]	100 [28]	125	100
Garages:									
All types of vehicles	175 [16]		100-200 [45]	100 [9]	175 [14]	100 [9]	100 [4]	175	120 [9]
Passenger cars only	75 [16] †	100	100 [2]	50 [9]	75 [17]	50 [23]	75	80	75
Libraries:									
Stack rooms in schools	150	150	150	125	120			150	
Reading rooms		60	60	60		60		60	
All stairs and fire escapes, except in private residences	100 [47]	100	100 [48]	100	100	100	100	100	100
Roofs (flat)	20 [49]		20	20 [5]	40	25	30	30	20
Sidewalks	250 [4]	250 [33]	250 [4]	250	300 [18]		150 [31]	250	200 [4]
Wind	Min 15 [10]		15-40 [50]	15-100 [1]	0-20 [19]	20 [24]	15-25 [32]	20 [10]	10-40 [51]

BUILDING CODE UNIFORMLY DISTRIBUTED MINIMUM LIVE LOADS (PSF)

Notes:

[1] Varies with area, height and form factor.
[2] Or 2000 lb on any space 2½ feet square.
[3] Where partitions are subject to change add 20 psf to all other loads.
[4] Or 8000 lb concentrated.
[5] If area is 200 to 600 sf use 16 psf, over 600 sf, 12 psf. (Snow load to be used if greater)
[7] 60 for library reading rooms and 125 for stackrooms.
[8] 150 for armories.
[9] Or concentrated rear wheel of loaded truck in any position.
[10] 15 psf up to 50 ft, 20 psf up to 100 ft, increase 0.025 psf for each foot above 100 ft.
[11] Including corridors.
[12] For rooms with fixed seats or, by special permission, other small rooms. 120 for library stackrooms.
[13] 60 for churches.
[14] 6000 lb concentrated. Trucking space 100% max. wheel load, 12,000 lb conc. min., 175 psf on floor construction, 125 psf on beams and girders.
[15] 100 for entire first floor.
[16] Or 2000 lb concentrated. Trucking space, 150% max. wheel load; 175 psf on floor construction, 120 psf on beams and girders.
[17] Or 2000 lb concentrated.
[18] Or 12,000 lb concentrated for driveways over sidewalks.
[19] 20 psf from top down to 100 ft level, zero below; 30 psf on tanks, stacks and exposed structures.
[20] 100 psf on floor at grade, upper floors 75 psf.
[21] Or 2000 lb concentrated on any space 2½ feet square.
[22] Or 3000 lb concentrated on any space 4 feet square.
[23] 100 on first floor and alternate of 2000 lb on area 2½ feet square.
[24] 20 for buildings less than 300 ft high; add 0.025 psf per ft above 300 ft.
[25] Only school class rooms with fixed seats. (Removable seats 100 psf)
[26] Churches only.
[27] Fixed seats, 60 psf; removable seats, 100 psf.
[28] Every floor beam 4000 lb concentrated.
[29] Corridors in hotels, hospitals and multifamily dwellings (except corridors serving public rooms in hotels), 60 psf; corridors in one and two family dwellings 40 psf.
[30] On first floor, 40 psf; upper floors, 30 psf.
[31] Interior courts, sidewalks, etc., not accessible to a driveway.
[32] 15 psf up to 50 ft high, 20 psf from 50 to 200 ft, 25 psf over 200 ft high. Roofs over 30°, 20 psf on windward side, 10 psf on leeward.
[33] Subject to trucking.
[41] The minimum for storage or manufacturing is 120 psf (100 psf, Chicago), but floors must be designed for any heavier loads contemplated and for any concentrations.
[42] Including entire first floor but not including corridors on floors used for offices.
[43] 30 for one-story, one and two family dwellings.
[44] 10 for portions below 40 ft and 20 for portions above 40 ft.
[45] 150 psf for passenger cars; trucks-150 psf (3 to 10 tons incl. load), 200 psf (over 10 tons incl. load); concentrated load-150 per cent max. wheel load for passenger cars, 125 per cent max. axle load for trucks.
[46] 75 psf for open parking decks.
[47] 40 psf for one and two family dwellings; 300 lb concentrated load at center of any stair tread.
[48] 300 lb on 2½ ft square at any location.
[49] Not less than 30 psf when subject to snow loads.
[50] 15 psf for building height $<$ 30 ft; increase to 40 psf for building height $\geqq$ 1200 ft.
[51] 10 psf for portions below 30 ft; 40 psf for portions above 400 ft in Southern Inland Regions. Varies from 25 to 50 psf for Southern Coastal Regions.
[52] First floor 100, upper floors 75.

This table is indicative of required uniformly distributed live loads in a general way. For specific projects the applicable codes should be carefully studied for special provisions.

* Not less than actual loads.
† 50 psf where not accessible to wheel loads.

RECOMMENDED LIVE LOADS FOR STORAGE WAREHOUSES

U. S. Department of Commerce, National Bureau of Standards

Material	Weight per Cubic Ft of Space (lb)	Ht of Pile (ft)	Weight per Sq Ft of Floor (lb)	Recmd. Live Load (psf)
Building Materials				
Asbestos	50	6	300	
Bricks, Building	45	6	270	
Bricks, Fire Clay	75	6	450	
Cement, Natural	59	6	354	
Cement, Portland	72-105	6	432-630	300
Gypsum	50	6	300	to
Lime and plaster	53	5	265	400
Tiles	50	6	300	
Woods, Bulk	45	6	270	
Drugs, Paints, Oils, etc.				
Alum, pearl, in barrels	33	6	198	
Bleaching powder in hogsheads	31	3½	102	
Blue vitriol, in barrels	45	5	226	
Glycerine, in cases	52	6	312	
Linseed oil, in barrels	36	6	216	
Linseed oil, in iron drums	45	4	180	
Logwood extract, in boxes	70	5	350	
Rosin, in barrels	48	6	288	200
Shellac, Gum	38	6	228	to
Soaps	50	6	300	300
Soda ash, in hogsheads	62	2¾	167	
Soda, Caustic, in iron drums	88	3⅜	294	
Soda, Silicate, in barrels	53	6	318	
Sulphuric acid	60	1⅝	100	
Toilet articles	35	6	210	
Varnishes	55	6	330	
White lead paste, in cans	174	3½	610	
White lead, dry	86	4¾	408	
Red lead and Litharge, dry	132	3¾	495	

Material	Weight per Cubic Ft of Space (lb)	Ht of Pile (ft)	Weight per Sq Ft of Floor (lb)	Recmd. Live Load (psf)
Dry Goods, Cotton, Wool, etc.				
Burlap, in bales	43	6	258	
Carpets and rugs	30	6	180	
Coir Yarn, in bales	33	8	264	
Cotton, in bales, American	30	8	240	
Cotton, in bales, Foreign	40	8	320	
Cotton bleached goods in cases	28	8	224	
Cotton Flannel, in cases	12	8	96	
Cotton Sheeting, in cases	23	8	184	
Cotton Yarn, in cases	25	8	200	
Excelsior, compressed	19	8	152	200
Hemp, Italian, compressed	22	8	176	to 250
Hemp, Manila, compressed	30	8	240	
Jute, compressed	41	8	328	
Linen Damask, in cases	50	5	250	
Linen Goods, in cases	30	8	240	
Linen Towels, in cases	40	6	240	
Silk and Silk Goods	45	8	360	
Sisal, compressed	21	8	168	
Tow, compressed	29	8	232	
Wool, in bales, compressed	48			
Wool, in bales, not compressed	13	8	104	
Wool, Worsteds, in cases	27	8	216	

RECOMMENDED LIVE LOADS FOR STORAGE WAREHOUSES

U. S. Department of Commerce, National Bureau of Standards

Material	Weight per Cubic Ft of Space (lb)	Ht of Pile (ft)	Weight per Sq Ft of Floor (lb)	Recmd. Live Load (psf)
Groceries, Wines, Liquors, etc.				
Beans, in bags	40	8	320	
Beverages	40	8	320	
Canned Goods, in cases	58	6	348	
Cereals	45	8	360	
Cocoa	35	8	280	
Coffee, Roasted, in bags	33	8	264	
Coffee, Green, in bags	39	8	312	
Dates, in cases	55	6	330	
Figs, in cases	74	5	370	
Flour, in barrels	40	5	200	250
Fruits, Fresh	35	8	280	to
Meat and Meat Products	45	6	270	300
Milk, Condensed	50	6	300	
Molasses, in barrels	48	5	240	
Rice, in bags	58	6	348	
Sal Soda, in barrels	46	5	230	
Salt, in bags	70	5	350	
Soap Powder, in cases	38	8	304	
Starch, in barrels	25	6	150	
Sugar, in barrels	43	5	215	
Sugar, in cases	51	6	306	
Tea, in chests	25	8	200	
Wines and Liquors, in barrels	38	6	228	

Material	Weight per Cubic Ft of Space (lb)	Ht of Pile (ft)	Weight per Sq Ft of Floor (lb)	Recmd. Live Load (psf)
Hardware, Etc.				
Automobile Parts	40	8	320	
Chain	100	6	600	
Cutlery	45	8	360	
Door Checks	45	6	270	
Electrical Goods and Machinery	40	8	320	
Hinges	64	6	384	
Locks, in cases, packed	31	6	186	
Machinery, Light	20	8	160	
Plumbing, Fixtures	30	8	240	300
Plumbing, Supplies	55	6	330	to
Sash Fasteners	48	6	288	400
Screws	101	6	606	
Shafting steel	125			
Sheet Tin, in boxes	278	2	556	
Tools, Small, Metal	75	6	450	
Wire Cables, on reels			425	
Wire, Insulated Copper in coils	63	5	315	
Wire, Galvanized iron, in coils	74	4½	333	
Wire, Magnet, on spools	75	6	450	
Miscellaneous				
Automobile tires	30	6	180	
Automobiles, uncrated	8		64	
Books (solidly packed)	65	6	390	
Furniture	20			
Glass and Chinaware, in crates	40	8	320	
Hides and Leather, in bales	20	8	160	
Leather and Leather goods	40	8	320	
Paper, Newspaper, and Strawboards	35	6	210	
Paper, Writing and Calendared	60	6	360	
Rope, in coils	32	6	192	
Rubber, Crude	50	8	400	
Tobacco, bales	35	8	280	

FIRE RESISTIVE RATINGS OF CONCRETE CONSTRUCTION

The fire rating is the time, in hours, which a given member or construction will withstand the standard fire in accordance with the "Standard Methods of Fire Tests of Building Construction and Materials," ASTM E119. The following conditions determine the end point of the test and the rating is established by the first end point reached.

Bearing walls and floors must support their design load throughout the test and must not allow the passage of flames or hot gases sufficient to ignite cotton waste held on the surface. An end point is reached when the specimen fails to support its load or when the temperature on the surface away from the fire rises an average of 250°F or 325°F at any one point. In practically all tests of concrete walls or floors the controlling end point has been this temperature rise on the unexposed surface.

The end point for columns, beams and girders is the time at which the member will no longer carry its design load.

FLOORS

Type	Description	Rating
Reinforced Concrete Slab	4½″ thick—¾″ protection reinforcement—expanded slag aggregate	4 hr.
	5″ thick—¾″ protection reinforcement—expanded shale aggregate	4 hr.
	6″ thick—1″ protection reinforcement—air cooled slag aggregate	4 hr.
	6½″ thick—1″ protection reinforcement—other aggregates	4 hr.
	4½″ thick—¾″ protection reinforcement—expanded shale aggregate	3 hr.
	5½″ thick—1″ protection reinforcement—other aggregates	3 hr.
	6″ thick with electrical raceways and junction boxes—¾″ protection reinforcement	3 hr.
	4″ thick—¾″ protection reinforcement—expanded shale or slag	2 hr.
	4½″ thick—¾″ protection reinforcement	2 hr.
	3″ thick—¾″ protection reinforcement	1 hr.
Reinforced Concrete Joist	3″ top slab *—¾″ protection reinforcement—ceiling 1″ vermiculite-gypsum or perlite-gypsum plaster on metal lath	4 hr.
	2″ top slab *—¾″ protection reinforcement—ceiling ¾″ vermiculite-gypsum or perlite-gypsum plaster on metal lath	3 hr.
	3″ top slab—¾″ protection reinforcement	1 hr.
	*—Increase slab thickness 2″ where electrical raceways and junction boxes occur.	
Reinforced Concrete Joists with Concrete Block or Tile Fillers	4″ lightweight aggregate concrete block with 2″ concrete topping—¾″ protection reinforcement	3 hr.
	6″ clay tile with 2″ concrete topping—⅝″ sand-gypsum plaster	3 hr.
	4″ clay tile with 1½″ concrete topping—⅝″ sand-gypsum plaster	2 hr.

FIRE RESISTIVE RATINGS OF CONCRETE CONSTRUCTION

CONCRETE WALLS

Type	Description	Rating
Reinforced Concrete Walls	5″ thick—¾″ protection reinforcement—expanded shale or slag	4 hr.
	6½″ thick—1″ protection reinforcement—other aggregates	4 hr.
	4½″ thick—¾″ protection reinforcement—expanded shale or slag	3 hr.
	5½″ thick—1″ protection reinforcement—other aggregates	3 hr.
	4″ thick—¾″ protection reinforcement—expanded shale or slag	2 hr.
	4½″ thick—¾″ protection reinforcement—other aggregates	2 hr.
	3″ thick—¾″ protection reinforcement	1 hr.
	Note: portland cement stucco or plaster or gypsum plaster may be substituted for an equivalent thickness of concrete.	

HOLLOW CONCRETE MASONRY WALLS

Type	Description	Minimum Equivalent Thickness Inches,* for Ratings of			
		4 hr.	3 hr.	2 hr.	1 hr.
Hollow Concrete Masonry Units	Coarse aggregate, expanded slag, or pumice...	4.7	4.0	3.2	2.1
	Coarse aggregate, expanded clay or shale.....	5.7	4.8	3.8	2.6
	Coarse aggregate, limestone, cinders or unexpanded slag..........................	5.9	5.0	4.0	2.7
	Coarse aggregate, calcareous gravel..........	6.2	5.3	4.2	2.8
	Coarse aggregate, siliceous gravel............	6.7	5.7	4.5	3.0

* Equivalent thickness is the average thickness of the solid material in the wall. It may be found by taking the total volume of a wall unit, subtracting the volume of core spaces, dividing this by the area of the face of the unit. Where walls are plastered or faced with brick the thickness of plaster or brick may be included in determining the equivalent thickness.

Where combustible members are framed into the wall, the wall must be of such thickness or be so constructed that the thickness of solid material between the end of each member and the opposite face of the wall, or between members set in from opposite sides, will be not less than 93% of the thickness shown in the table.

COLUMNS, BEAMS, GIRDERS AND TRUSSES

Type	Protection of Reinforcement	Rating
Reinforced Concrete Columns	1½″ concrete—coarse aggregate limestone, calcareous gravel, trap rock or blast furnace slag—12″ or larger column	4 hr.
	2″ concrete—coarse aggregate granite, sandstone, or siliceous gravel—16″ or larger column	4 hr.
	1½″ concrete—coarse aggregate granite, sandstone or siliceous gravel—16″ or larger column	3 hr.
Reinforced Concrete Beams, Girders and Trusses	1½″ concrete	4 hr.
	1″ concrete	1 hr.

VOLUME OF CONCRETE IN COLUMNS

Round Columns and Caps

Column		Vol Shaft	Volume of Cap outside of Shaft (cu ft)					
Diam (in.)	Area (sq in.)	Per Vert Ft (cu ft)	Diameter of Cap = D 6′-0	5′-6	5′-0	4′-6	4′-0	3′-6
12	113	.79	29.62	22.75	17.02	12.31	8.54	5.61
14	154	1.07	28.88	22.09	16.43	11.79	8.09	5.23
16	201	1.40	28.07	21.35	15.77	11.22	7.60	4.82
18	255	1.77	27.17	20.55	15.06	10.60	7.08	4.38
20	314	2.18	26.20	19.69	14.30	9.95	6.52	3.94
22	380	2.64	25.17	18.77	13.50	9.26	5.95	3.48
24	452	3.14	24.09	17.81	12.66	8.55	5.37	3.02
26	531	3.69	22.95	16.81	11.80	7.82	4.78	2.56
28	616	4.28	21.77	15.78	10.92	7.09	4.19	2.12
30	707	4.91	20.56	14.73	10.02	6.35	3.61	1.70
32	804	5.59	19.32	13.66	9.12	5.62	3.04	1.31
34	908	6.31	18.06	12.58	8.22	4.90	2.51	.95
36	1018	7.07	16.79	11.50	7.33	4.20	2.00	....
38	1134	7.88	15.51	10.42	6.46	3.53	1.53	....
40	1257	8.73	14.23	9.36	5.61	2.89	1.10	....

To obtain the volume of column and cap:—

1. Multiply Dimension "H" in feet by "Volume of Shaft" (Col. 3).
2. From "Dia. of Column" and "Dia. of Cap" find volume of cap.
3. The sum of Items 1 and 2 equal the volume of one column.

Formula for Volume of Cap outside of Shaft:—

$$V = \frac{\pi}{1728}\left[1\tfrac{1}{2}(R^2 - r^2) + \tfrac{1}{3}(R^3 - r^3) - r^2(R - r)\right]$$

V = Volume of Cap in cu ft. R = Radius of cap in in.
r = Radius of Shaft in in.

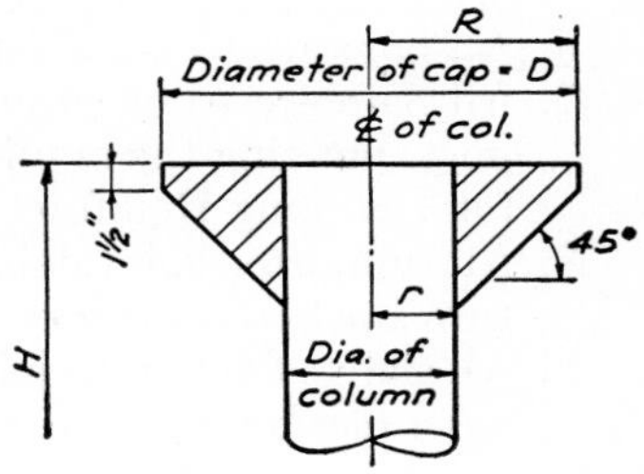

Square Columns

Column Size (in.)	Volume in Cubic Feet Per Vert Ft	Column Size (in.)	Volume in Cubic Feet Per Vert Ft
10 x 10	.70	25 x 25	4.34
11 x 11	.84	26 x 26	4.69
12 x 12	1.00	27 x 27	5.06
13 x 13	1.17	28 x 28	5.44
14 x 14	1.36	29 x 29	5.84
15 x 15	1.56	30 x 30	6.25
16 x 16	1.78	31 x 31	6.67
17 x 17	2.01	32 x 32	7.11
18 x 18	2.25	33 x 33	7.56
19 x 19	2.51	34 x 34	8.03
20 x 20	2.78	35 x 35	8.51
21 x 21	3.06	36 x 36	9.00
22 x 22	3.36	37 x 37	9.51
23 x 23	3.67	38 x 38	10.03
24 x 24	4.00	39 x 39	10.56
		40 x 40	11.11

GENERAL SUGGESTIONS FOR DRAWINGS OF REINFORCED CONCRETE STRUCTURES

All laps, strengths, dimensions, etc., are illustrative only. Desired values should be inserted by designer.

The following list of suggestions outlines a number of important items which should be covered on design drawings by details, or, for overlooked cases by notes. Numerical values and sizes given are not intended to represent a standard practice but merely to illustrate that the designer should specify clearly his individual preference or need.

1. All detailing and fabrication of reinforcing bars, unless otherwise noted, must follow the ACI "Manual of Standard Practice for Detailing Reinforced Concrete Structures (ACI 315-latest)."
2. All placing of reinforcing bars in the forms shall follow recommended practice in the book "Placing Reinforcing Bars."
3. All concrete not otherwise specified to be stone, gravel or slag concrete to test ____ psi in standard 6 x 12 in. cylinders at 28 days.
4. Not less than ____ sacks of cement shall be used per cubic yard of concrete regardless of the strength obtained, not over ____ gallons of water per sack of cement, and not over 4 in. slump.
5. Reinforcing bars (*except for those columns using* Grade 75) are to be 60,000 psi yield strength, deformed, billet steel; or 60,000 psi rail steel; or 60,000 psi axle steel meeting ASTM (*latest*) Specifications.
6. All bars are to have deformations meeting ASTM Specifications.
7. All bars are to be supported in the forms and spaced with wire bar supports meeting the requirements of the ACI "Manual of Standard Practice for Detailing Reinforced Concrete Structures (ACI 315-latest)."
8. All supported solid slabs † (unless otherwise specified) shall have temperature steel consisting of (*designer should state his requirements*).
9. All slabs of concrete joist construction † (unless otherwise specified) shall have (*designer should here state the size and spacing of temperature bars or the gauge and mesh of welded wire fabric that he wants*).
10. All concrete slabs on the ground † that are not otherwise provided for shall have temperature reinforcement consisting of (*designer supply size and spacing of bars or gauge and mesh of welded wire fabric*).
11. Welded wire fabric must have end laps of one full mesh plus 2 in. between cross wires and edge laps obtained by overlapping longitudinal selvage wires 2 in. and wiring all laps securely together. Welded wire fabric should extend into supporting beams and walls for anchorage unless an expansion joint is called for.
12. Reinforce all walls (unless otherwise specified) with #4 bars @ 12 in. c/c horizontal and vertical located at the center of the wall. (*Designer should show wall reinforcement on the drawings and use this note only for miscellaneous minor walls.*)
13. Lap all splices as specifically called for, but at least 36 bar diameters (12 in. minimum) for tension or 24 for compression, unless otherwise called for.

---

† Designer should clearly specify any other places to be reinforced with welded wire fabric or temperature bars.

GENERAL SUGGESTIONS FOR DRAWINGS OF REINFORCED CONCRETE STRUCTURES

14. Provide at least two #4 bars in top of wall footing under door and other openings, 4′-0″ longer than the opening.
15. Provide dowels in wall footings equivalent in size and number to vertical steel extending 24 bar dia. into footing and 24 bar dia. into wall. (*Designer should check that this can be done.*)
16. All areaways (unless otherwise specified) are to be doweled to main building with #4 bars @ 1′-0″ c/c, hooked or embedded 24 bar diameters into wall.
17. Lintels over all openings in interior partitions not otherwise covered are to be of precast concrete with thickness equal to the wall thickness. Depth shall be 8 in. for spans up to 6′-0″, reinforced with 1-#4 bar for each 4 in. of wall thickness.
18. Removable steel forms for concrete joist construction shall be at least 16 gauge, smooth, not corrugated, 20 or 30 in. wide, with narrow widths where required and with ends tapered where called for at a standard taper of 2 in. or 2½ in. each side in 3′-0″.
19. Unless otherwise shown, form around all openings, vents, etc. with double joists and headers if complete information on location is provided to supplier by the time placing drawings of form layouts are approved.
20. Structural concrete over forms of concrete joist construction is to be a minimum of 2½ in. thick, but not less than what is called for in the schedules.
21. Designer should indicate all special framings in concrete joist construction, including double or extra heavy joists under partitions,* distribution ribs, special spacings under batteries of toilets, and so on. Quite a few suggestions appear in the safe load tables on the succeeding pages.
22. Joists up to 8 in. wide parallel and adjacent to walls or beams need no reinforcement, providing they are integral with a bearing of concrete on the beam or wall. If independent of the wall or beam, they should have one full set of joist bars. When integral parallel joists are more than 8 in. in width, use one full set of joist bars.
23. Submit placing drawings for reinforcing steel and placing drawings for forms in concrete joist construction to the engineer in triplicate and obtain approval before fabricating.
24. Designer should indicate, either on standard diagrams under the schedules or in notes, the bending of bars, amount of cover above top bars and under bottom bars, amount of lap of bottom bars at interior support, clear distance between outside of concrete and stirrup leg, amount of embedment at walls, cover over column bars, amount of lap at various kinds of splices and anchorages, and any other pertinent information.†
25. In masonry bearing walls, no chases, risers, conduits or toothing of masonry shall occur within 1′-6″ of center-line of beam bearing or concentration.

---

* Note that a heavier joist each side of a partition, possibly with thickened concrete over a line of shallower pans, interferes less with vertical stands of piping in partitions than does an extra wide joist directly underneath the partition.

† Many designers allow a stated tonnage of bars to be used as directed in the field for special conditions.

GENERAL SUGGESTIONS FOR DRAWINGS OF REINFORCED CONCRETE STRUCTURES

26. Brick pilasters in backup walls where required for bearing are to be bonded into adjoining masonry.
27. All non-reentrant corners of concrete columns and beams exposed inside the structure are to have a ¾ in. x 45° chamfer.
28. When foundation walls span from basement to first floor, both basement floor slab and first floor slab shall be in place before any backfill is placed.
29. In two-way solid slabs, place short-span bars in the bottom layer.
30. Reinforced concrete beams are to have 8 in. bearing on walls, unless otherwise noted.
31. Solid slabs are to have at least 4 in. bearing on masonry walls, unless otherwise noted.
32. Where concrete beams frame into structural steel and no other detail is shown, structural steel fabricator shall provide at least two ¾ in. round anchor bolts with double nuts through the web or flanges of supporting steelwork, in addition to seat angles.
33. Provide two #3 stirrup tie bars in top of all concrete beams that have stirrups and do not have other top steel available for holding stirrups.
34. All reinforcing bars shall be securely wired together in the forms as called for in the book "Placing Reinforcing Bars" by CRSI.
35. Shoring under forms shall not be removed until the concrete it supports is capable of supporting itself and all superimposed loads.

11 STEPS TO A SUCCESSFUL DESIGN

1. Study the framework of the building as a whole.
2. Prepare alternative freehand sketches, comparing all likely methods of framing.
3. Establish column centers to come in partitions, to clear door and window openings, and to provide spacings of from 14 to 15 feet up to 25 to 30 feet.
4. Select rough preliminary sizes either from this handbook or by that rule of thumb which suggests making beam depth one inch per foot of span and width one-half of that—varying for unusual loads.
5. Make quantity surveys and cost comparisons from sketches of Step 2. This can be done quickly and roughly and still with a fair degree of accuracy.
6. Select that compromise which achieves the best balance between low cost of the building and minimum interference with desired facilities.
7. Preliminary framing sketches, made freehand on thin paper, can be printed and distributed to architects, mechanical engineers, and others to establish the general program and eliminate unnecessary changes on finished drawings.
8. Develop a sense of comparative values. A stair header has relatively little effect on the overall cost, but a whole line of spandrel beams on many stories can become a large item.
9. In planning the building visualize how forms would be constructed. For economy, keep beams and columns simple, without haunches, brackets, widened ends or offsets. Standardize concrete sizes for maximum reuse of forms.
10. Design the structure sufficiently strong to permit early stripping of forms for reuse, perhaps when concrete reaches 70% of design strength.
11. Select a beam size suitable for the average load and span, using same breadth-width combination for as many load-span combinations as possible, varying reinforcement only; select steel form depth and use repeatedly from basement to roof regardless of load; use one or two column sizes per floor and use same size for three or four consecutive stories or full height, and then reduce by several inches off one dimension of the column, next time off the other dimension.

(The following suggestions adapted from "A Manual of Standard Practice for Reinforced Concrete Construction," 1965, of the Concrete Reinforcing Steel Institute will repay careful reading.)

STANDARD DETAILS OF DESIGN

A few brief suggestions regarding standard practice may assist the designer in giving his clients the most economical and satisfactory structure that can be designed.

It is recognized that absolute uniformity is neither possible nor desirable. It is felt, however, that while completed structures may differ widely from each other, the application of the principle of standardization in methods, and in the design of the individual parts of the various structures will result in economy of time and cost.

No attempt will be made to cover all the items in a building. However, a few basic principles are proposed.

Design. It is recommended that standard methods of design be followed, as given in the "Building Code Requirements for Reinforced Concrete (ACI 318)," published by the American Concrete Institute, except where unusual conditions require departure from this practice.

Code of Standard Practice. It is recommended that the designer examine the Code of Standard Practice of the Concrete Reinforcing Steel Institute so as to be familiar with the practices and customs current in the industry. It will rarely be found necessary to vary from the principles incorporated in this Code.

Sizes of Bars and Spirals. It is recommended that the standard sizes of bars and spirals as specified in the Code of Standard Practice, in accordance with Simplified Practice Recommendations of the United States Department of Commerce, be observed. (See pages 2-3, 11-212 and 11-213.)

This gives the designer a sufficient range of sizes from which to select the steel areas. The number of different sizes used in any one structure should be held to a minimum.

Grade of Steel. Deformed reinforcing bars are available in yield strengths of 40,000, 50,000, 60,000, and 75,000 psi and in billet, rail, and axle steel. For maximum economy, the use of 60,000 psi steel should be considered. The special Grade 75 is available only in sizes #11, #14, and #18.

Length of Bars. It is recommended that as few different lengths as possible be used. This expedites shipment of steel and greatly simplifies storing and handling in the field. Lengths should be given to the nearest inch only, and, where practicable, to the nearest 3 in. Where it is important that the length called for be exact, a note to this effect should appear opposite the item on the bar list.

Beams and Girders. As far as practicable, the spacing, widths and depths of beams and girders should be uniform throughout the structure. Consideration should be given the relative costs of steel, concrete and form work when determining their width and depth.

Flat Slabs. Where flat slab design is used, the dimensions of the column capital and the size of the dropped panel should be unchanged throughout the building. It is recommended that the diameter of the column capital equal $.225l$ and the length of the dropped panel equal $.33l$.

Height of Stories. It is recommended that as many stories as possible in a building be of the same height. Where this is not possible, the lower stories should have the greater height.

Columns. Exterior columns should be the same width for the entire height of the structure. The space between columns should be of such size that an opening can be made to accommodate standard sizes of steel window sash.

The cross-sectional area of exterior columns should remain constant for at least two stories. Where the required area may be decreased, the change should be made in thickness only, the outside surface and the width of the column remaining constant, the inside surface only being set back.

Freestanding interior columns may be circular in cross-section. The diameter should be in even inches and changes should be made by intervals of two inches. Interior columns should be as small as is consistent with the structural requirements, and as far as practicable, the diameters of all columns should be constant throughout a single story.

The spacing of columns from center to center should be uniform. Column reinforcement should generally be of as large bars as is consistent with good practice.

Continuous spiral hooping should be used in preference to isolated hoops. Column steel should be spliced as dimensioned by the designer to insure tensile and compression capacities required in his analysis. It is particularly important to specify amount of laps and to dimension desired arrangement for staggering the splices. Where welding is used, specifications for the bars must include weldability requirements for the welding method specified.

Footings. Where considerable variations exist in the depths to which different footings must be carried, a pedestal or pier on top of the footing may be used to reach the level at which the columns start. The connection of columns to the footing or pedestal should be made with dowels of the same size and number as the vertical bars in the column above. If footing depth is insufficient to develop the dowels, an additional quantity of smaller dowels should be used to transmit the entire stress in the steel by bond.

The number of different sizes of footings should be reduced to a minimum.

Forms. Building designs must be carried out so as to provide the maximum amount of repetition with the use of the minimum amount of forms. Owing to the constantly increasing cost, and to the decreasing quantity available, the conservation of form lumber requires attention.

It will often be found that steel forms will cost less than lumber when used throughout a season or when leased for each individual structure.

The greater uniformity of work built with steel forms will recommend their use to the average engineer.

Fabrication of Reinforcing Steel. It is recommended that all reinforcing steel be shop fabricated and so specified, as operations can be performed with greater accuracy by the special machinery in the shop.

SAFE LOAD TABLES

One Way Solid Slabs
Explanation; Examples; Load Tables

Stair Slabs
Explanation; Examples; Load Tables

Section 6

ONE-WAY SOLID SLABS

This section presents load capacity tables for uniform depth solid concrete slabs reinforced for flexure in one direction and only for temperature and shrinkage in the other direction. The tabulated safe superimposed load capacities were obtained as the least value determined by shear, bond, positive or negative flexure. Such tabulated capacities must be equal to or greater than the sum of live, wind, earthquake, superimposed dead and similar effects.

GENERAL DESIGN CONSIDERATIONS

Moments are computed from the empirical coefficients of ACI 904,* as an elastic beam free to rotate on unyielding supports, using $wL'^2/11$ for positive moment in end spans, $wL'^2/16$ for continuous interior spans, and $wL'^2/8$ in single spans, assuming little or no restraint at discontinuous ends. (See sketches on pages 6-7 and 6-12.)

ACI 904 limits the use of empirical moment coefficients to ratios of live load to dead load of not more than three. Since part of the superimposed load may be dead load, the ratio of live to dead load may vary in each instance. Superimposed loads are tabulated well above three times the dead weight of the slab itself (to 600 psf).

Detail sketches show where bars are cut off, anchored, extended, and bent up all in accordance with current standard practices and the "Manual of Standard Practice for Detailing Reinforced concrete Structures," ACI 315-65. These practices have worked satisfactorily for many years for normal load and span ratios. The designer must be on the alert for any necessary modifications when the conditions of an individual design require them. He should, for example, eliminate truss bars if moment reversal can occur or if fatigue is a problem; and extend some top bars to be continuous throughout the span if ratio of live to dead load materially exceeds three.

Balanced reinforcement in a singly reinforced concrete member is 0.00959 for a concrete strength of $f'_c = 3000$ psi and a steel of $f_s = 24$ ksi. The percentages of reinforcement in the tables at mid-span and over the supports where slabs are continuous are limited to $p \leq 0.00833$. Limiting the maximum steel ratio in these tables to $p \leq 0.00833$, the moment of inertia of the gross concrete section can be used in deflection computations. In no case is compression in the concrete a determining factor, and compressive reinforcement is not required.

SCOPE OF LOAD TABLES

These tables for one-way solid slabs give the *safe superimposed load capacity*, in pounds per square foot (with the dead weight of the floor system itself deducted). One set of stresses is used: normal weight concrete with $f'_c = 3000$ psi and deformed bars meeting ASTM Grade 60 with $f_s = 24{,}000$ psi.

---

* References to the ACI Building Code, ACI 318-63, are given as "ACI-" followed by the number of the section in the text on solid slabs.

Three cases of end restraint are considered: (1) single spans simply supported, (2) end spans free on one end and continuous on the other, (3) interior spans continuous on both ends.

Slabs are tabulated for various ratios of reinforcement: single spans for (1) the minimum recommended (by CRSI) for practicable use in monolithic construction,* (2) a medium range $p \approx 0.005$, and (3) the maximum recommended, $p \leq 0.0083$; end and interior spans for (1) minimum recommended and (2) $p \leq 0.00833$. The recommended minimum reinforcement is a variable percentage since for adequate rigidity of top bars under ordinary construction traffic in monolithic construction minimum size #4 bars at maximum spacing of 12 are recommended. For thin slabs this practical minimum is well within code limits, i.e., $A_s = 0.0018bt$ spaced at 18 inches or $3t$ maximum. An exception is made for thin single span slabs where cross traffic is not expected. The recommended maximum reinforcement ratio, $p \leq 0.00833$, is the maximum for which the code permits use of the gross section moment of inertia in deflection computations. The limit of $p \leq 0.00833$ controls top reinforcement at continuous supports. The ratios of moment coefficients prescribed result in bottom reinforcement for end spans $p \approx 0.075$ and interior spans $p \approx 0.0057$ for a balanced design with top reinforcement, $p \leq 0.00833$.

Temperature reinforcement in structural floor and roof slabs is tabulated for deformed bars meeting ASTM specifications with $f_y = 60{,}000$ psi. The required lap at splices is 36 bar diameters.

Tabulated load capacities are for *net* safe superimposed loads. Total safe load was calculated and reduced by slab weight at 150 pcf.

BASIS FOR DESIGN

Flexural design is based on moment coefficients per ACI 904. (Pages 6-7, 6-12.) Allowable shear was calculated in accordance with ACI 1201. Both "short" (Eq. 12-1) and "long" (Eq. 12-2) formulas were compared and the larger value was used. Anchorage bond has been computed in accordance with ACI 1301 applied to bars bent and anchored in accordance with recommended bending detail sketches preceding each type of load table. Using gross moment of inertia, elastic deflections for all full tabulated superimposed loads are less than $L/360$. Thus none of the designs need be investigated for any live load deflection. Creep deflections will vary according to proportion of the superimposed design loads of long duration. Where long time deflection limits of the code apply, e.g., slabs supporting or attached to brittle partitions, the user must compute long time deflection. See page 6-6.

ASSUMPTIONS IN DESIGN

It was assumed that end restraint at free ends is negligible in effect on the positive moment. Top bars tabulated in Single Span tables provide at least ⅓ of the area tabulated for bottom steel but not less than #3 in size nor at

* In all cases, equal or greater than the minimum prescribed in ACI 911(b).

spacings more than 12 inches. This top steel is sufficient for ends supported by monolithic beams or girders, where code moment coefficient = $1/24\ wL'^2$ applies, as well as the ordinary incidental restraint when end bearing is provided by masonry walls.

For interior spans, top steel at continuous supports is assumed to include bent up truss bars from the adjoining span equal in size and area to those in the span considered. This condition will, of course, fit the typical case of equal depth slabs for equal spans equally loaded and will always be safe where adjoining span provides more steel. In order to fit unequal spans, provide the top steel area tabulated for the longer span. The difference between areas of truss bent bars from each adjacent span can be provided as straight top bars extending approximately ⅓ the longer span on both sides of the support.

For end spans top steel at the continuous interior supports is assumed to include the truss bars tabulated for an interior span of the *same slab thickness.* This condition will fit the typical practical situation. Where slabs of varying thickness are used for special load-span conditions, the tabulated top steel area must be provided using added straight top bars for any deficiency.

USE OF LOAD TABLES

Single Span Example 1—Prepare a working stress design for a single span solid slab floor to span 12′-8″ clear between masonry bearing walls for the following superimposed loads. Space permits a 6½ in. depth.

Live Load................................	100 psf
Floor finish.............................	24 psf
Ceiling..................................	8 psf
Total	132 psf

Solution:
Since clear span is 12′-8″ and a minimum bearing width of 4 inches is recommended, span c.-c. bearings for design is 12′-8″ + 2″ + 2″ = 13′-0″.
Try each load table beginning with minimum reinforcement to determine if the 6½ in. depth is feasible.
See page 6-8: $w =$ 0 psf capacity < 132
See page 6-9: $w =$ 65 psf capacity < 132
See page 6-10: $w =$ 149 psf capacity > 132
Use design from page 6-10:

t = 6½″ Bottom bar #5 @ 7″
Top bar #4 @ 12″
Temperature bars #4 @ 17″

Recommended Details for bar length, etc., are shown in sketch on page 6-7.

Single Span Example 2—Prepare a minimum depth roof slab design for a single clear span of 20 ft. between supporting monolithic beams for the following superimposed loads:

Live load, w_L = 30 psf
Roofing material, w_D = 15 psf

Total Superimposed Load *
w = 45 psf

Solution: See page 6-10 for maximum reinforcement tabulated (minimum depth). Select an 8″ slab; w = 47 psf capacity

Bottom bars	#5 @ 6″
Top bars	#4 @ 11″
Temperature bars	#4 @ 13″

* Note: Total load superimposed on the supporting beams is the sum of the slab weight 100 + 45 psf = 145 psf times half span 10 ft. = 1450 plf.

Single Span Example 3—Repeat requirements of example 1, $L = 13'\text{-}0''$; $w_D = 32$ psf, $w_L = 100$ psf and $w = 132$ psf, with the additional serviceability requirement that rigid partitions are to be attached to the bottom of the slab so that the design must meet the ACI 909 deflection limit of $L/360$ for the sum of elastic live load deflection plus creep deflection.

The computed long time deflection occurring after installation of partitions plus the computed elastic deflection due to service live load is limited by code to $\leq L/360$. For *all* designs tabulated the sum of the elastic deflection due to superimposed service live load plus the long time deflection due to slab weight is less than $L/360$. If part of the superimposed service load will remain in place it must be treated as a long time load for which additional deflection is double the immediate elastic deflections.

The tabulated load capacities above the zigzag line in the table on page 6-10 may include 30 psf or more long time superimposed service load. In this example, since long time service load is only 32 psf, any design capacity above the zigzag line adequate for strength will automatically satisfy long time deflection serviceability requirements.

Solution—Accumulate total superimposed load

Long-time load,	$w_D =$	32 psf
Live load,	$w_L =$	100 psf
Total superimposed load,	$w =$	132 psf

Select: 6½″ slab Bottom bars #5 @ 7 — Capacity $w = 149$ psf
Top bars #4 @ 12
Temp. bars #4 @ 17

For cases where a larger portion of the superimposed load than 30 psf remains in place a long time, a conservative short cut procedure will avoid need for actual deflection computations. Note that the creep factor is 2.0 for the additional long time deflection, ACI 909.

a. Multiply the semi-permanent superimposed service loads in excess of 30 psf times 2.0.
b. Add to the result of step (a), 30 psf plus service live load.
c. Select design from above the zigzag line in the load tables. The design will satisfy long time deflection serviceability requirements.

Note: If a large percentage of the superimposed load is a long time load, a complete deflection computation using formulas below may permit use of a thinner slab. The short cut procedure becomes increasingly conservative as designs selected in step c are located further above the zigzag line.

SERVICEABILITY DESIGN

Service live load limited by deflection not to exceed L/360.

Equate $L/360$ to $k\dfrac{wL^4}{EI}$ and solve for $w_{max.}$ in terms of (t/L). For all steel ratios $p \leq 0.00833$, use gross moment of inertia. For a 12 in. width $I = \dfrac{12t^3}{12} = t^3$.

Maximum w	*Type of Restraint*	*k*
$w_{max.} = 5{,}000(t/L)^3$	Single Span (simply supported)	5/384
$w_{max.} = 7{,}650(t/L)^3$	End Span (one free end)	3.25/384
$w_{max.} = 12{,}400(t/L)^3$	Interior Span	2/384

Load Controlled by Long-time Deflection Limit L/360

$w_{max.} = w_L + 2.0w_D$

w_L = service live load
w_D = service dead load
$= 25t$

$w_{max.}$ = Safe superimposed load + 2.0 × slab weight

		Service Live Load
Single Span:	$w_{max.} = 5{,}000(t/L)^3$	$w_L = 5{,}000(t/L)^3 - 25t$
End Span:	$w_{max.} = 7{,}650(t/L)^3$	$w_L = 7{,}650(t/L)^3 - 25t$
Interior Span:	$w_{max.} = 12{,}400(t/L)^3$	$w_L = 12{,}400(t/L)^3 - 25t$

Maximum safe superimposed load capacity limited by creep + live load deflection $\leq L/360$ when 30 psf of service live load is a long time load, i.e., partitions, ceilings, floor finish, etc.

Single Spans

$w_{max.} = 5{,}000(t/L)^3$

t = thickness, in.
L = span, ft.

Let w_s = safe superimposed load including 30 psf long-time load
$w_{max.} = (w_s - 30) + 2(w_D + 30)$.
Solving for $w_s = 5{,}000(t/L)^3 - 25t - 30$

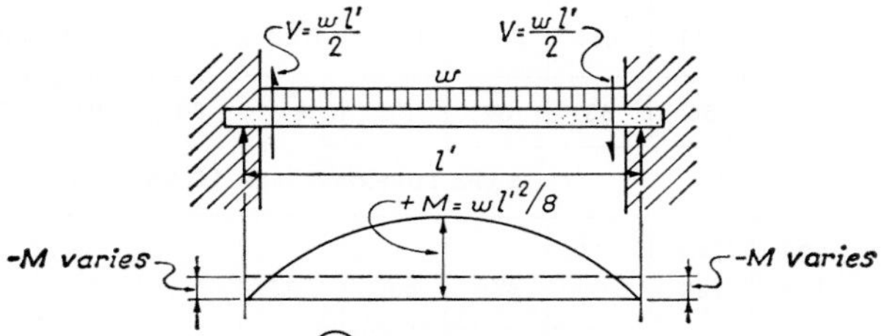

(1) SINGLE SPAN

Design Moments and Shears

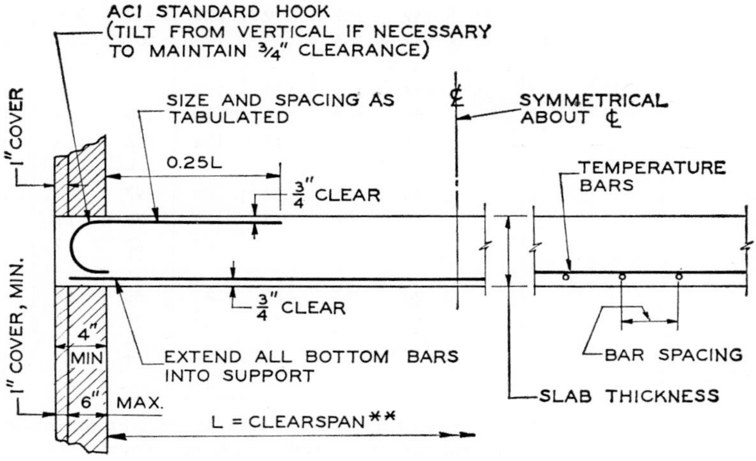

**SPAN FOR DESIGN C/C BEARINGS

Solid Concrete Slabs—Single Spans
(Simple spans simply supported)

SOLID ONE-WAY SLABS SINGLE SPAN

Recommended Min. Reinforcement
$p \geq 0.0018bt$*

$f'_c = 3{,}000$ psi $f_s = 24{,}000$ psi

For explanation and examples on use of this table, see page 6-5.

Thickness (in.)	4	4½	5	5½	6	6½	7	7½	8	8½	9
Bottom Bar Spacing (in.)	#3 12	#3 12	#3 12	#4 12	#4 12	#4 12	#4 12	#4 12	#4 12	#4 12	#4 12
Top Bar Spacing (in.)	#3 12	#3 12	#3 12	#4 12	#4 12	#4 12	#4 12	#4 12	#4 12	#4 12	#4 12
Temperature Bar Spacing (in.)	#3 15	#3 13	#3 12	#4 18	#4 18	#4 17	#4 15	#4 15	#4 13	#4 13	#4 12
Areas of Steel, Bot. in.^{2}/ft.	0.11	0.11	0.11	0.20	0.20	0.20	0.20	0.20	0.20	0.20	0.20
Slab Weight (psf)	50	56	63	69	75	81	88	94	100	106	113
SPAN	**SAFE SUPERIMPOSED LOAD (psf)**										
4′-0″	204	240	275								
4′-6″	154	182	209	478	533	587					
5′-0″	118	139	160	380	424	468	511	555	599		
5′-6″	90	107	124	307	342	378	413	449	484	520	555
6′-0″	69	82	95	250	279	308	337	366	395	425	454
6′-6″	52	62	73	205	229	253	277	301	325	350	374
7′-0″	38	47	55	169	189	209	229	249	269	290	310
7′-6″	27	34	40	139	156	173	190	207	224	241	257
8′-0″		23	28	115	129	143	158	172	186	200	214
8′-6″				95	107	119	130	142	154	166	178
9′-0″				78	88	98	108	118	128	138	148
9′-6″				63	71	80	88	97	105	114	122
10′-0″				51	58	65	72	79	86	93	100
10′-6″				40	46	51	57	63	69	75	81
11′-0″				30	35	40	45	50	54	59	64
11′-6″				22	26	30	34	38	42	45	49
12′-0″						21	24	27	30	33	36
12′-6″									20	23	25

* The minimum reinforcement recommended by CRSI is based on the practical consideration of rigidity against displacement under normal construction traffic. Although variable, the resulting percentage of steel $p \geq 0.0018bt$, the minimum prescribed by ACI 911(*b*).

SOLID ONE-WAY SLABS
SINGLE SPAN

$f'_c = 3{,}000$ psi
$f_s = 24{,}000$ psi

$p \simeq 0.005$

For explanation and examples on use of this table, see page 6-5.

Thickness (in.)	4	4½	5	5½	6	6½	7	7½	8	8½	9	9½	10
Bottom Bar	#4	#4	#4	#4	#4	#5	#5	#5	#6	#6	#6	#6	#6
Spacing (in.)	12	11	10	9	8	11	10	9	12	12	11	10	10
Top Bar	#3	#3	#3	#4	#4	#4	#4	#4	#4	#4	#4	#4	#4
Spacing (in.)	12	12	12	12	12	12	12	12	12	12	12	12	12
Temperature Bar	#3	#3	#3	#4	#4	#4	#4	#4	#4	#4	#4	#5	#5
Spacing (in.)	15	13	12	18	18	17	15	14	13	13	12	18	17
Areas of Steel, Bot. in.^{2}/ft.	0.200	0.218	0.240	0.267	0.300	0.338	0.372	0.413	0.440	0.440	0.480	0.528	0.528
Slab Weight (psf)	50	56	63	69	75	81	88	94	100	106	113	119	125
SPAN	**SAFE SUPERIMPOSED LOAD (psf)**												
4′-0″	403	521											
4′-6″	314	408	521										
5′-0″	249	325	417	530									
5′-6″	200	262	338	432	551								
6′-0″	162	214	277	356	456	570							
6′-6″	132	176	229	296	381	478	584						
7′-0″	108	145	191	248	321	404	496						
7′-6″	88	120	159	209	272	344	423	522	600				
8′-0″	72	99	133	176	231	294	364	450	518	557			
8′-6″	59	82	112	149	198	253	314	390	450	484	575		
9′-0″	47	68	94	126	169	218	272	340	393	422	504		
9′-6″	38	55	78	107	145	188	237	297	344	370	442	530	563
10′-0″	29	45	65	90	124	163	206	260	302	325	390	469	498
10′-6″	22	36	53	76	106	141	179	228	266	286	345	416	442
11′-0″		28	43	63	90	122	156	200	234	252	305	370	393
11′-6″		21	34	53	77	105	136	176	206	222	271	329	350
12′-0″			27	43	65	90	118	154	182	196	240	294	312
12′-6″			20	34	54	77	103	135	160	173	213	262	279
13′-0″				27	44	65	89	118	141	153	189	234	249
13′-6″				20	36	55	76	103	124	134	168	209	222
14′-0″					28	45	65	90	109	118	148	187	199
14′-6″					21	37	55	78	95	103	131	166	177
15′-0″						29	45	67	82	89	115	148	158
15′-6″						22	37	57	71	77	101	131	140
16′-0″							30	47	61	66	88	116	124
16′-6″							23	39	51	56	77	102	109
17′-0″								32	43	47	66	90	96
17′-6″								25	35	38	56	78	84
18′-0″									27	30	47	68	73
18′-6″									21	23	38	58	62
19′-0″											31	49	53
20′-0″											24	40	44

SOLID ONE-WAY SLABS SINGLE SPAN

$f'_c = 3{,}000$ psi
$f_s = 24{,}000$ psi

$p \leq 0.00833$

For explanation and examples on use of this table, see page 6-5.

Thickness (in.)	4	4½	5	5½	6	6½	7	7½	8	8½	9	9½	10
Bottom Bar	#4	#4	#4	#4	#4	#5	#5	#5	#5	#5	#6	#7	#7
Spacing (in.)	8	7	6	6	5	7	7	6	6	5	7	9	8
Top Bar	#3	#3	#3	#4	#4	#4	#4	#4	#4	#4	#4	#4	#4
Spacing (in.)	12	12	12	12	12	12	12	12	11	10	9	9	8
Temperature Bar	#3	#3	#3	#4	#4	#4	#4	#4	#4	#4	#4	#5	#5
Spacing (in.)	15	13	12	18	18	17	15	14	13	13	12	18	7
Areas of Steel, Bot. in.²/ft.	0.300	0.343	0.400	0.400	0.480	0.531	0.531	0.620	0.620	0.744	0.754	0.800	0.900
Slab Weight (psf)	50	56	63	69	75	81	88	94	100	106	113	119	125
SPAN	**SAFE SUPERIMPOSED LOAD (psf)**												
5′-0″	399	543											
5′-6″	325	444											
6′-0″	268	368	504	568									
6′-6″	223	308	424	478									
7′-0″	187	260	360	406	559								
7′-6″	158	221	307	348	480	587							
8′-0″	134	189	264	299	416	509	558						
8′-6″	113	162	228	258	361	444	487						
9′-0″	96	139	198	224	316	390	427	557					
9′-6″	82	120	172	195	277	343	376	492	531				
10′-0″	69	103	150	170	244	303	332	437	472				
10′-6″	58	89	131	149	215	268	294	389	420	563			
11′-0″	49	76	114	130	190	238	261	347	375	505	544		
11′-6″	41	65	99	113	168	211	232	311	336	455	490	555	
12′-0″	34	55	86	99	149	188	207	279	301	410	442	502	
12′-6″	27	47	75	86	132	168	184	250	271	371	399	454	559
13′-0″	21	39	65	75	116	149	164	225	243	335	362	412	508
13′-6″		32	56	64	103	133	146	202	219	304	328	374	463
14′-0″		26	48	55	90	118	130	182	197	276	298	341	423
14′-6″		21	40	47	79	105	116	163	177	251	271	310	387
15′-0″			34	40	70	93	103	147	159	228	246	283	354
15′-6″			28	33	61	82	91	132	143	207	224	258	324
16′-0″			22	27	52	72	80	118	129	188	203	235	297
16′-6″				21	45	63	70	106	115	171	185	214	272
17′-0″					38	55	61	94	103	155	168	195	250
17′-6″					32	47	53	84	92	140	152	178	229
18′-0″					26	40	45	74	81	127	138	162	210
18′-6″					21	34	38	66	72	115	125	147	192
19′-0″						38	32	57	63	104	113	134	176
19′-6″						23	26	50	55	93	102	121	161
20′-0″							20	43	47	83	91	109	147

USE OF LOAD TABLES FOR END SPAN & INTERIOR SPAN

End Span and Interior Span Example 1. Select a solid slab design for a floor supported by monolithic beams at (clear) spacings of 14 ft. Superimposed loads are: live load = 100 psf; ceiling construction = 10 psf; floor finish = 10 psf. No masonry partitions will be supported nor attached to the slab.

Live load = 100 psf
Dead load 10 + 10 = 20
Superimposed w = 120 psf

For equal loads and spans, end span is most critical for thickness (shear is 1.15 times that in interior spans) and so select end span design first, if it is desired to use the same depth of slab throughout.

See table for **End Span** minimum depth tabulated, page 6-14. Select thickness 6″; capacity furnished $w = 131$ psf > 120

Bottom straight bars, #4 } Alternated at a spacing of 7 in.
Truss bent bars, #5 }
Temperature bars #4 @ 18
Top bars at free end #4 @ 9 (Provide end hooks; see sketch on page 6-12 for details of bending, anchorage, etc.)

Interior Spans

See table on page 6-16 for minimum depth. Check capacity for 5½″ depth (determined from end span). $t = 6''$ capacity furnished $w = 128 > 120$

Select reinforcement:
Bottom straight bars, #4 } Alternated at a spacing of 9 in.
Truss bent bars, #5 }
Temperature bars, #4 @ 18″

Check that truss bent bars from interior span provide balance of steel area tabulated at first interior support for end span:

End span truss bars #5 @ 14 $\quad A_s = \dfrac{0.31 \times 12}{14} = 0.266$

Interior span truss bars #5 @ 18, $\quad A_s = \dfrac{0.31 \times 12}{18} = 0.206$

Total Top $A_s = 0.472$ in.²/ft.

Top A_s tabulated for end span, page 6-14, $A = 0.472$ in.²/ft.

This last step is required only when spans or loads vary and designs are selected with varying steel.

End Span and Interior Span Example 2: Add to the design requirements of Example 1 the serviceability requirement that partitions likely to be damaged by large deflections are to be supported. Estimated additional equivalent uniform load for partitions is 20 psf. Augmented superimposed loads become:

Live Load = 100
Dead loads 20 + 20 = 40
Superimposed w = 140 psf

Again, end span deflection with equal spans and loads will be critical since the deflection coefficient is 3.25 for end spans and 2 for interior spans. See table page 6-6.

Try table for minimum depth, page 6-14. A 6½ in. thick slab will satisfy strength (safety) requirement—capacity = 179 psf on span of 14 ft. Note that the capacity 179 psf lies well above zigzag line at which 30 psf semi-permanent live load produces long time deflection $\leq L/360$. Since the semi-permanent portion in this case is only 40 psf, it may be assumed that this design is satisfactory. (If the amount of superimposed semi-permanent load were much greater, it would be desirable to check the thickness selected by the appropriate formula, page 6-7 or to utilize the short cut procedure, page 6-6.)

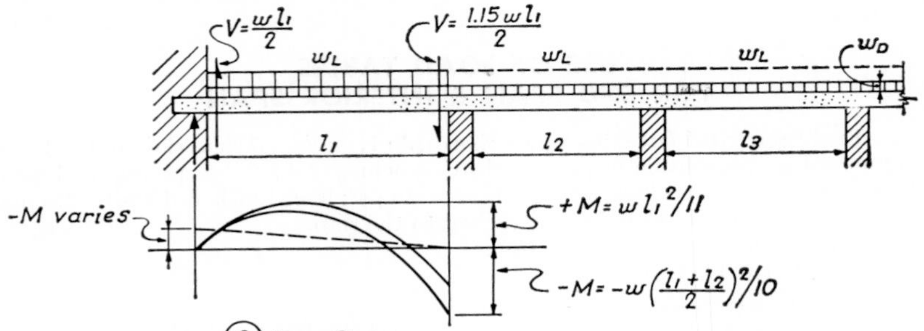

(2) END SPAN

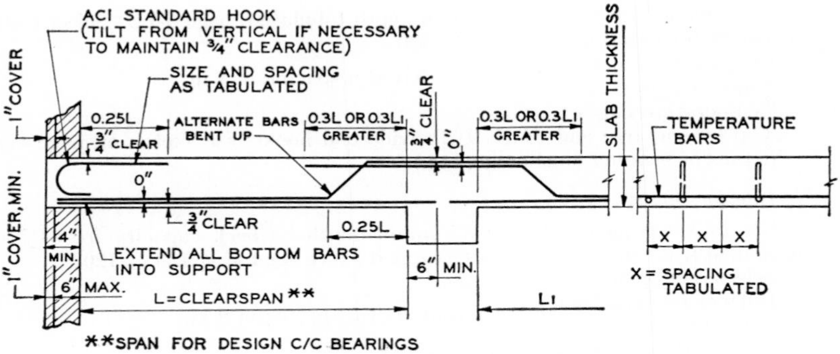

Solid Concrete Slab—End Spans

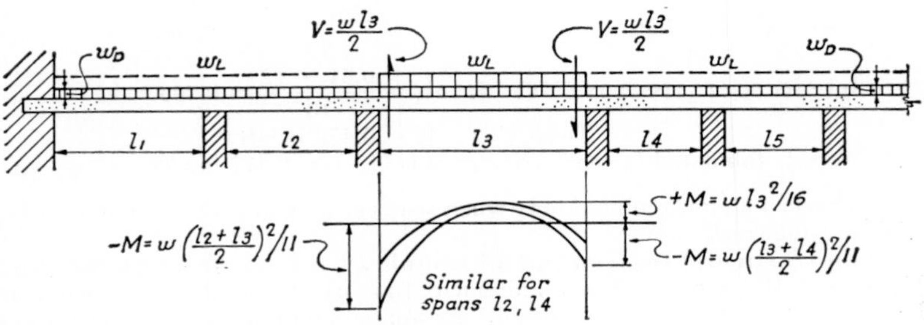

(3) INTERIOR SPANS

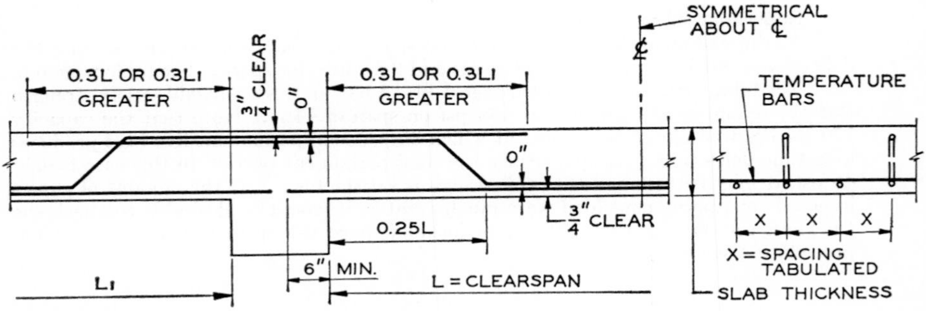

Solid Concrete Slabs—Interior Spans

SOLID ONE-WAY SLABS
END SPAN

Recommended Min. Reinforcement
$p \geq 0.0018bt$*

$f'_c = 3{,}000$ psi $f_s = 24{,}000$ psi

For explanation and examples on use of this table, see page 6-11.

Thickness (in.)	4	4½	5	5½	6	6½	7	7½	8	8½	9
Bottom Bar	#3	#3	#3	#3	#3	#3	#3	#4	#4	#4	#4
Truss Bar	#4	#4	#4	#4	#4	#4	#4	#4	#4	#4	#4
Spacing (in.)	12	12	12	12	12	12	12	12	12	12	12
Top Bar Free End	#4	#4	#4	#4	#4	#4	#4	#4	#4	#4	#4
Spacing (in.)	12	12	12	12	12	12	12	12	12	12	12
Temperature Bar	#3	#3	#3	#4	#4	#4	#4	#4	#4	#4	#4
Spacing (in.)	15	13	12	18	18	17	15	14	13	13	12
Areas of Steel (in.²/ft.) Top Int.	0.200	0.200	0.200	0.200	0.200	0.200	0.200	0.200	0.200	0.200	0.200
Areas of Steel (in.²/ft.) Bot.	0.155	0.155	0.155	0.155	0.155	0.155	0.155	0.200	0.200	0.200	0.200
Slab Weight (psf)	50	56	63	69	75	81	88	94	100	106	113
SPAN	**SAFE SUPERIMPOSED LOAD (psf)**										
4′-0″	473	554									
4′-6″	367	430	493	556							
5′-0″	290	340	391	441	492	542	593				
5′-6″	232	273	314	355	396	437	478				
6′-0″	188	222	256	289	323	356	390	574			
6′-6″	154	182	210	237	265	293	321	477	515	553	590
7′-0″	126	150	173	196	219	242	266	400	432	464	496
7′-6″	104	124	143	163	182	202	221	338	365	392	419
8′-0″	86	102	119	135	152	168	184	287	310	333	356
8′-6″	70	84	98	112	126	140	154	244	264	283	303
9′-0″	58	69	81	93	105	116	128	208	225	242	259
9′-6″	47	57	67	77	87	96	106	178	192	207	221
10′-0″	37	46	54	63	71	79	88	151	164	177	189
10′-6″	29	36	43	51	58	65	72	129	140	151	162
11′-0″	22	28	34	40	46	52	58	91	99	107	115
11′-6″		21	26	31	36	41	45	75	82	89	96
12′-0″				23	27	31	35	62	67	73	79
12′-6″						22	25	50	54	59	64
13′-0″								39	43	47	51
13′-6″								29	33	36	39
14′-0″								21	23	26	29

* The minimum reinforcement recommended by CRSI is based on the practical consideration of rigidity against displacement under normal construction traffic. Although variable, the resulting percentage of steel $p \geq 0.0018bt$, the minimum prescribed by ACI 911(*b*). #4 @ 12″ is considered to provide a practicable minimum rigidity for top steel.

SOLID ONE-WAY SLABS END SPAN

$f'_c = 3{,}000$ psi
$f_s = 24{,}000$ psi

Bottom Steel $p \sim 0.0075$
Top Steel $p \leq 0.00833$

For explanation and examples on use of this table, see page 6-11.

Thickness (in.)	4	4½	5	5½	6	6½	7	7½	8	8½	9	9½	10
Bottom Bar	#4	#4	#4	#4	#4	#4	#4	#5	#5	#5	#5	#5	#5
Truss Bar	#5	#5	#5	#5	#5	#5	#5	#6	#6	#6	#6	#6	#6
Spacing (in.)	11	10	9	8	7	6	6	8	7	7	6	6	5
Top Bar Free End	#4	#4	#4	#4	#4	#5	#5	#6	#6	#6	#6	#6	#6
Spacing (in.)	12	12	12	10	9	12	12	16	14	14	12	12	10
Temperature Bar	#3	#3	#3	#4	#4	#4	#4	#4	#4	#4	#4	#5	#5
Spacing (in.)	15	13	12	18	18	17	15	14	13	13	12	18	17
Area of Steel (in.²/ft.) Top Int.	0.302	0.329	0.362	0.418	0.472	0.542	0.576	0.594	0.670	0.670	0.770	0.770	0.905
Area of Steel (in.²/ft.) Bot.	0.278	0.306	0.340	0.382	0.437	0.510	0.510	0.562	0.643	0.643	0.750	0.750	0.900
Slab Weight (psf)	50	56	63	69	75	81	88	94	100	106	113	119	125
SPAN	**SAFE SUPERIMPOSED LOAD (psf)**												
4′-6″	683												
5′-0″	548												
5′-6″	447	583											
6′-0″	369	484											
6′-6″	309	406	525										
7′-0″	260	343	446	576									
7′-6″	221	293	382	495									
8′-0″	189	251	329	428	557								
8′-6″	162	217	285	372	486								
9′-0″	139	188	248	325	426	563							
9′-6″	120	163	217	286	376	498	545						
10′-0″	104	142	190	252	332	442	484	583					
10′-6″	90	124	167	222	295	394	432	521					
11′-0″	76	104	140	195	257	338	386	445	556	597			
11′-6″	65	91	123	173	229	303	347	400	501	538			
12′-0″	56	79	108	154	204	272	312	360	453	486			
12′-6″	48	68	95	136	183	245	281	325	410	441	558	595	
13′-0″	41	59	83	121	163	220	253	294	372	400	508	541	
13′-6″	34	51	72	107	146	199	229	266	338	363	464	494	
14′-0″	28	43	63	95	131	179	207	241	307	331	424	451	585
14′-6″	23	37	55	84	117	162	187	218	280	301	388	413	538
15′-0″		31	47	74	105	146	169	198	255	275	355	379	495
15′-6″		25	40	65	93	132	153	180	233	251	326	347	456
16′-0″		20	34	57	83	119	138	163	213	229	299	319	420
16′-6″			28	49	74	107	125	148	194	209	275	293	388
17′-0″			23	43	65	96	113	134	177	191	252	269	359
17′-6″				36	57	86	102	121	162	175	232	248	332
18′-0″				31	50	77	91	110	148	159	213	228	307
18′-6″				25	43	69	82	99	134	145	196	209	284
19′-0″				21	37	61	73	89	122	132	180	193	263
19′-6″					32	54	65	80	111	120	165	177	243
20′-0″					26	47	57	71	101	109	152	162	225

SOLID ONE-WAY SLABS INTERIOR SPAN

$f'_c = 3{,}000$ psi
$f_s = 24{,}000$ psi

Minimum Recommended Reinforcement * > 0.0018*bt*

For explanation and examples on use of this table, see page 6-11.

Thickness	4	4½	5	5½	6	6½	7	7½	8	8½	9
Bottom Bar	#3	#3	#3	#3	#3	#3	#3	#4	#4	#4	#4
Truss Bar	#4	#4	#4	#4	#4	#4	#4	#4	#4	#4	#4
Spacing (in.)	12	12	12	12	12	12	12	12	12	12	12
Temperature Bar	#3	#3	#3	#4	#4	#4	#4	#4	#4	#4	#4
Spacing in.	15	13	12	18	18	17	15	14	13	13	12
Areas of Steel — Top, in.²/ft.	0.200	0.200	0.200	0.200	0.200	0.200	0.200	0.200	0.200	0.200	0.200
Areas of Steel — Bot. in.²/ft.	0.155	0.155	0.155	0.155	0.155	0.155	0.155	0.200	0.200	0.200	0.200
Slab Weight (psf)	50	56	63	69	75	81	88	94	100	106	113
SPAN	**SAFE SUPERIMPOSED LOAD (psf)**										
4'-6"	581										
5'-0"	461	540									
5'-6"	372	436	501	565							
6'-0"	305	358	411	464	516	569					
6'-6"	252	296	341	385	429	473	517	561			
7'-0"	210	248	285	322	359	397	434	471	508	546	583
7'-6"	177	208	240	272	303	335	367	398	430	462	493
8'-0"	149	176	203	230	257	285	312	339	366	393	420
8'-6"	126	150	173	196	219	243	266	289	312	336	359
9'-0"	107	127	147	168	188	208	228	248	268	288	308
9'-6"	91	109	126	143	161	178	195	213	230	247	265
10'-0"	77	92	107	123	138	153	168	183	198	213	228
10'-6"	65	79	92	105	118	131	144	157	170	183	196
11'-0"	46	56	66	76	86	96	106	116	126	135	145
11'-6"	38	47	55	64	72	81	89	98	106	115	123
12'-0"	31	38	46	53	60	67	75	82	89	97	104
12'-6"	25	31	37	43	50	56	62	68	75	81	87
13'-0"		24	29	35	40	45	51	56	61	67	72
13'-6"			23	27	32	36	41	45	50	54	59
14'-0"				20	24	28	32	35	39	43	46
14'-6"						20	23	27	30	33	36
15'-0"									21	23	26

* The minimum reinforcement recommended by CRSI is based on the practical consideration of rigidity against displacement under normal construction traffic. Although variable, the resulting percentage of steel $p \geq 0.0018bt$, the minimum prescribed by ACI 911(*b*). #4 @ 12" is considered to provide a practicable minimum rigidity for top steel.

SOLID ONE-WAY SLABS INTERIOR SPAN

$f'_c = 3{,}000$ psi
$f_s = 24{,}000$ psi

Bottom Steel $p \sim 0.0057$
Top Steel $p \leq 0.00833$

For explanation and examples on use of this table, see page 6-5.

Thickness (in.)	4	4½	5	5½	6	6½	7	7½	8	8½	9	9½	10
Bottom Bar	#3	#4	#4	#4	#4	#4	#4	#5	#5	#5	#5	#5	#5
Truss Bar *	#4	#5	#5	#5	#5	#5	#5	#6	#6	#6	#6	#6	#6
Spacing (in.)	9	13	12	10	9	8	7	10	9	9	8	8	7
Temperature Bar	#3	#3	#3	#4	#4	#4	#4	#4	#4	#4	#4	#5	#5
Spacing (in.)	15	13	12	18	18	17	15	14	13	13	12	18	17
Areas of Steel (in.²/ft.) Top **	0.267	0.286	0.310	0.372	0.413	0.465	0.531	0.528	0.587	0.587	0.660	0.660	0.754
Areas of Steel (in.²/ft.) Bot.	0.207	0.235	0.255	0.306	0.340	0.383	0.437	0.450	0.500	0.500	0.563	0.563	0.643
Slab Weight (psf)	50	56	63	69	75	81	88	94	100	106	113	119	125
SPAN	**SAFE SUPERIMPOSED LOAD (psf)**												
5′-0″	631												
5′-6″	513												
6′-0″	423	526											
6′-6″	353	439	553										
7′-0″	297	371	468										
7′-6″	253	316	399	556									
8′-0″	216	271	343	480	604								
8′-6″	185	233	297	418	526								
9′-0″	160	202	258	365	461	583							
9′-6″	138	176	225	321	406	515							
10′-0″	120	153	197	283	359	457	584						
10′-6″	104	133	173	250	319	407	522	556					
11′-0″	79	102	134	197	254	326	421	449	551	592			
11′-6″	68	89	117	175	226	292	378	403	495	532			
12′-0″	58	77	103	155	201	261	340	362	447	480	592		
12′-6″	50	66	90	137	180	234	307	327	404	434	537	572	
13′-0″	42	57	78	122	160	211	277	295	366	393	488	520	
13′-6″	35	49	68	108	143	189	250	267	332	357	444	473	592
14′-0″	29	41	59	95	128	170	226	241	302	324	405	432	542
14′-6″	24	35	50	84	114	153	205	219	274	295	370	394	496
15′-0″		29	43	74	102	138	186	198	250	269	338	361	456
15′-6″		23	36	65	90	124	169	179	227	245	310	330	419
16′-0″			30	57	80	111	153	163	207	223	284	303	385
16′-6″			25	49	71	100	138	147	189	204	260	277	355
17′-0″			20	42	62	89	125	133	172	186	238	254	327
17′-6″				36	55	80	113	120	157	169	219	233	302
18′-0″				30	48	71	102	109	143	154	200	214	278
18′-6″				25	41	63	92	98	130	140	184	196	257
19′-0″				20	35	55	83	88	118	127	168	180	237
19′-6″					29	48	74	79	107	116	154	165	218
20′-0″					24	42	66	70	96	105	141	151	201

MANUAL CALCULATION

Example 1. Single Span—Derive the load capacity value tabulated for an 6 in. solid slab with recommended minimum reinforcement on a single clear span of 10 ft. See page 6-8. $w_s = 58$ psf. Note that most formulas in the ACI Code are best for review not direct design, hence the review approach in this example is convenient.
Total load = safe superimposed load plus slab weight.
Total load = 58 + 75 = 133 psf.

Flexure. Positive moment only need be checked.

Required capacity $= +M_u = WL^3/8$ Span $L = 10'-4''$ c.c. bearing

$$\text{Required } M_u = \frac{0.133 \times 10.3 \times 10.3}{8} \times 12 = 21.2 \text{ in. kip per foot}$$

Capacity furnished $M = A_s f_s jd$

Use $j = 0.88$ #4 @ 12, $A_s = 0.200$ in.²/ft.

$d = 6 - 0.75 - \frac{1}{2} \times \frac{1}{2} = 5$ in.

$M = 0.200 \times 24 \times 0.88 \times 5 = 21.2''k/\text{ft.}$ Positive Moment Controls

$$\text{Capacity furnished } w = \frac{8 \times 21.2}{10.3 \times 10.3} \times \frac{1}{12} = 133 \text{ psf}$$

Safe superimposed load = 133 − 75 = 58 psf

Check Shear Capacity.

$$\left.\begin{aligned} \text{Allowable } v_c &= 1.1\sqrt{f'_c} = 60.4 \text{ psi} \\ v_c &= \left(\sqrt{f'_c} + 1300 p_w \frac{Vd}{M}\right) \end{aligned}\right\} \text{Whichever is greater}$$

At critical section, d from face of support, $\frac{Vd}{M} = \frac{L/2 - d}{L/2 - d/2}$ for uniform load

$\frac{Vd}{M} > 1$ Use $\frac{Vd}{M} = 1$

$$v_c = \sqrt{3000} + 1300 \times \frac{0.2}{5 \times 12} \times 1) = 59.2 \text{ psi} < 60.4 \text{ psi}$$

Shear capacity at critical section
$V = 0.0604 \times 12 \times 5 = 3.62$ kips per 12″ width
$V = WL/2 - Wd$

$$W = \frac{V}{L/2 - d} = \frac{3.62}{5.15 - 7/12} = 0.79 \text{ ksf} > 0.133$$

Check Anchorage Bond. Anchorage bond capacity increases linearly and stress in the bars increases with moment in proportion to the square of the distance. A critical section is developed intermediate between center of bearing where stress in bar is zero and center of span where bar is fully developed. Embedment past center of bearing, $e = 1$ in. The #4 bottom bar requires 12 in. embedment to develop full $f_s = 24$ ksi at $0.80u$; it is necessary to check that the critical section either lies past 11 in. from the center of bearing or if not that stress at the critical section is developed.

The critical section for anchorage bond at a free end lies at a distance $x_{cr.}$ from the face of the support:

$$\begin{aligned} e + x_{cr.} &= \sqrt{eL + e^2} \\ &= 0.995 \text{ ft} \\ &= 12 \text{ in.} \end{aligned}$$

$e = 1$ in. $= .0833$ ft.
$L = 10.3$ ft.
See page 6-19 for derivation of $x_{cr.}$

Example 2. End Span—Derive the load capacity tabulated for an 8 in. slab with maximum percentage of reinforcement on a 20 ft. span. See load table on page 6-14. Tabulated safe superimposed load capacity, w = 101 psf.
Total capacity w = 101 psf + 100 = 201 psf
Steel Areas: Top at first interior support, 0.670 in.²/ft
Bottom at midspan, 0.643 in.²/ft.
(Top steel area assumes #6 @ 14 in. truss bars from end span and #6 @ 18 truss bars from interior span. See Interior Span table, 8 in. slab, page 6-16.)
Flexure Positive Moment $+ M_u = 1/11WL^2$

$$\text{Required } + M_u = \frac{0.201 \times 20 \times 20}{11} \times 12 = 88.0 \text{ kip-in./ft.}$$

Capacity furnished $+ M = A_s f_s jd$
$d = 8 - 0.75 - 0.35 = 6.90$ in.
$+ M = 0.643 \times 24 \times 0.88 \times 6.90 = 93.8$ kip-in./ft. > 88.0

Flexure Negative Moment $- M = 1/10WL^2$ *
Required $- M_u = 11/10 \times 88.0 = 97.0$ kip-in./ft.
$A_s = 0.670$ in.² $d = 8.00 - 0.75 - 0.38 = 6.87$ in.

Capacity furnished $- M_u = 0.670 \times 24 \times 0.88 \times 6.87 = 97.0$ kip-in./ft.*
Shear $v_c = 1.1 \sqrt{f'_c} = 60.4$ psi Since negative moment was critical use of long formula for shear is probably unnecessary.

At distance d from face of support $V = 1.15 \dfrac{wL}{2} - wd = w(0.575L - d)$

$$\text{Required } V = 0.201 \left(11.5 - \frac{6.87}{12}\right) = 0.201 \times 10.93 = 2.20 \text{ kip/ft.}$$

Shear capacity furnished $V = 0.0604 \times 12 \times 6.87 = 4.97$ kip/ft. > 2.20

Bond—Bottom bars at bend up need not be checked as stress approaches zero here. Bottom bars are not bent up at free end and so a double area is available and will not be critical.
Anchorage at bend down point for top bars. See Fig. page 6-12.
Available length $= 0.3L - 0.25L + t - 2 \times 0.75$
$= 0.05 \times 20 \times 12 + 8.0 - 1.5$
$= 18.5$ in.
Embedment required for full development, $f_s = 24$ ksi, on #6 bars at $0.80U$ = 18.3 in. < 18.5 in. and so no further check of flexural bond is required.
Capacity was controlled by flexure at interior support negative moment.*

* For clear spans over 10 ft., use moment coefficient 1/10; for clear spans 10 ft. or less, use 1/12.

ANCHORAGE BOND STRESS AT SIMPLE END SUPPORTS—UNIFORM LOAD

1301(c) ". . . . flexural bond stress need not be considered . . . in those cases of tension where anchorage bond is less than 0.8 of the permissible."

1301(b) ". . . . the calculated tension . . . in any bar at any section must be developed . . . by proper embedment length . . . . Anchorage or development bond stress, u, shall be computed as the bar forces, divided by the product of Σo times the embedment length."

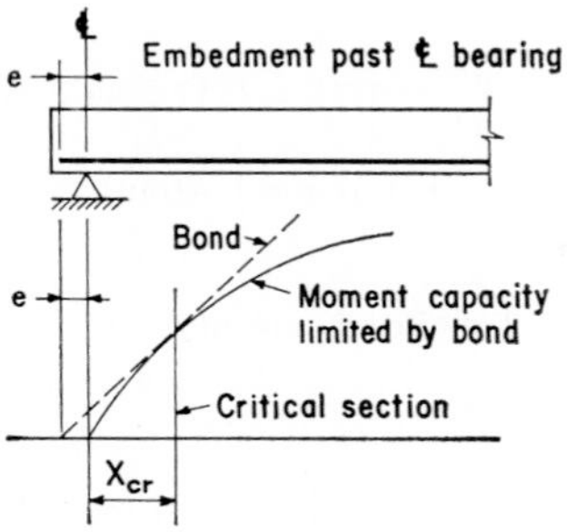

Let u = allowable bond stress, psi
x = distance from center support to a section, feet
e = embedment length beyond center support, feet
w = uniform load
Σo = sum of perimeters of bars so embedded, in.
jd = $\frac{7}{8}d$, in.
l = span, feet

$$0.8u = \frac{12M}{\Sigma ojd(x+e)(12)}$$

Note $M = \frac{1}{2}w \times (l - x)$ foot pounds x and e in feet.

$$0.8u = \frac{wx(l-x)}{(2)\Sigma ojd(x+e)}$$

Solving for w, limited by bond

$$W = \frac{1.6u_u\Sigma ojd(x+e)}{x(l-x)}$$

For limiting w,

$$\frac{dw}{dx} = 0 = 1.6u_u\Sigma ojd\,\frac{x(l-x)-(x+e)(l-2x)}{x^2(l-x)^2}$$

The factor $x(l-x) - (x+e)(l-2x) = 0$

Simplifying, $x_{cr} = \sqrt{le + e^2} - e$

Substitute this value of x_{cr} back into the formula for w to obtain the load, w, limited by bond.

End Span:

Similarly, for end spans, the distance to critical section x_{cr}. becomes:

$$x_{cr} = \sqrt{0.85le + e^2} - e.$$

MANUAL CALCULATION

Example 3. Interior Span—Derive the ultimate load capacity tabulated for an 8 in. slab with minimum reinforcement on a 15 ft. span. See page 6-15. Tabulated capacity = 21 psf.
Total ultimate capacity, w = 21 psf + 100 psf = 121 psf

Flexure Positive moment $+M = 1/16wL^2$

$$\text{Required } +M = \frac{0.121 \times 15 \times 15}{16} = 1.71 \text{ ft. kips/ft.}$$

Capacity furnished $+M = A_s f_s jd$

$$A_s = 0.200 \text{ in.}^2/\text{ft.} \qquad d = 8 - 0.75 - \frac{0.5}{2} = 7''$$

$$+M_u = \frac{0.2 \times 24 \times 0.88 \times 7}{12} = 2.47 \text{ ft.-kips/ft.}$$

$$\text{Negative Moment Required } -M = \frac{1}{11}wL^2 {}^* = \frac{16}{11} \times 1.71 = 2.47 \text{ ft.-kip/ft.}$$

Capacity furnished = 2.47 ft. kip/ft. (Same A_s top and bottom)
Load capacity furnished

$$w = \frac{11 \times 2.47}{15 \times 15} = 121 \text{ psf} = \text{Tabulated capacity}$$

Negative moment Controls.

$$\textbf{Shear:} \text{ Shear capacity required, } V = 0.121 \times \left(\frac{15}{2} - \frac{7}{12}\right) = 0.837 \text{ kips/ft.}$$

Shear capacity furnished $V_c = v_c bd$

$$\left.\begin{aligned} v_c &= 1.1\sqrt{f'_c} = 60.4 \text{ psi} \\ v_c &= \sqrt{f'_c} + 1300\, p_w \frac{Vd}{M} \end{aligned}\right\} \text{whichever is greater}$$

$$V_c = 0.0604 \times 12 \times 7 = 5.07 \text{ kips/ft.} > 0.837$$

Bond: Not critical. See page 6-18.

---

* For clear spans over 10 ft., use moment coefficient 1/11; for clear spans 10 ft. or less, use 1/12.

* Shear and bond are seldom critical in the economical range of spans for solid one-way slabs. The flexural capacity is very insensitive to concrete strength f'_c for the low steel ratios tabulated herein. A user wishing to use these tables with any f'_c need only check that span length is sufficient so that shear and bond are not critical.

STAIR SLABS—SINGLE SPANS

There are many possible combinations of rise and run, surface finishes and landing arrangements.

Risers and runs vary from 6-on-12 to 8-on-9. Surfaces vary from troweling alundum grits into the finished concrete to adding asphalt tile or linoleum, and on up to 1½ or 2 inches of terrazzo, stone or marble.

Landings may be a part of the floor construction (Type I) or an integral portion of the bottom of the stair (Type II) or built integrally at the top of the flight (Type III). Landing slabs might have their thickness reduced below that of the flight, being at a point where the bending moment is less. This refinement is only occasionally used and must be checked for strength. For Type II, the reinforcing steel is bent around the corner as in the diagram. For Type III, the bars should be bent and lapped around the re-entrant corner as shown, otherwise they would pull out. They are lapped a minimum of 36 bar diameters past each other, or as required by design considerations, and anchored in the top part of the slab. Landings are sometimes spanned crosswise of the flight to shorten the span of the stair slab.

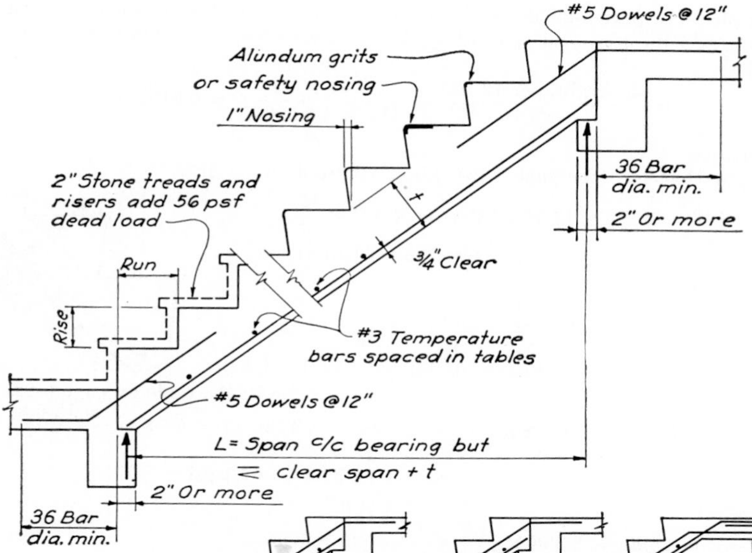

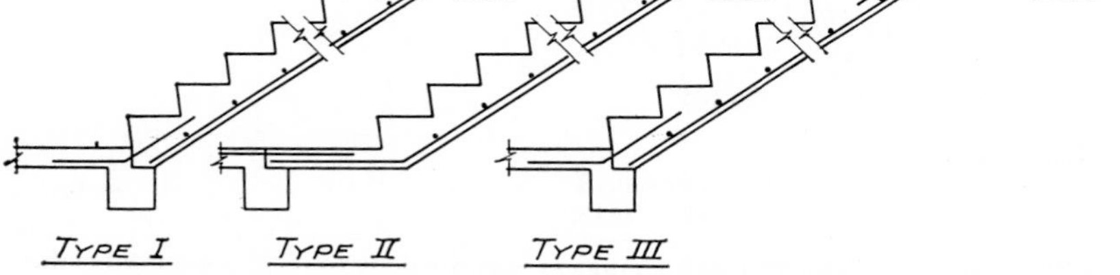

STAIR SLABS—SINGLE SPANS

Stair slabs are properly designed as horizontal spans, using the horizontally-projected load per square foot, the horizontal projection of the clear span and the inclined depth from the heel of the step to the soffit of the stair slab. Stairs are usually poured after the main structure, resting in pockets in the supporting beams and doweled to them. While the dowels might develop restraint, it is customary to design stair slabs as single spans without continuity.

Safe carrying capacities were obtained by computing the least safe total load as determined by shear or bond or flexure, and by deducting the weight of the slab itself (including the triangular step) to obtain the safe superimposed load. The tabulated capacity includes live load, finishes, ceilings, balustrades, partitions and everything but the dead weight of the structural concrete. Live loads are usually from 75 to 100 psf and, on main staircases, as much as 125 psf.

Tables are included for stair slabs on spans from 5 to 14 feet (7 to 18 risers), with rise-to-run ratios of 8-to-9 and 7-to-10½, for one set of stresses, viz., f_s = 24,000 psi, f_c = 1688 psi, and for the one case of single spans, as continuity is ordinarily not a factor in stair design.

For convenience, these tables may be entered in two ways:—(1) the horizontal projection L may be used directly; (2) if only the story height is known, it can be subdivided into a number of equal risers and the number of risers used for entering the table.

Example—For page 6-22, determine the capacity of a 6-inch stair slab reinforced with #6 bars, 8½ in. c/c, on a span of 12′-0″ (corresponding to about 16 risers of 8-on-9 steps).

$$p = \frac{A_s \text{ (sq in. per 12 in.)}}{db} = \frac{0.44 \times 12}{8\frac{1}{2} \times 4.88 \times 12} = 0.0106$$

Solution:-

Resisting Moment: (See page 3-15), Max. Allowable R_s = 225.7

$$M = Rbd^2 = 225.7 \times 12 \times 4.88^2 = w \times 12^2 \times \frac{12}{8}$$

$$w = 296 \text{ psf (total)}$$

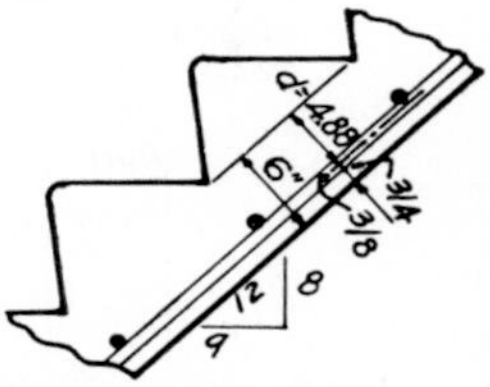

Deduct weight of slab:—

$$6 \times \frac{12}{9} @ 12\frac{1}{2} = 100$$

$$4 \times 12\frac{1}{2} = 50^* \quad 150 \text{ psf (dead weight)}$$

146 psf (as given in the table on page 6-22)

Shear (at distance d from support)—$V = bdv_c = 4.88 \times 12 \times 67.4 = \dfrac{w(12-0.8)}{2}$

$$v_c = 1.1\sqrt{3750} = 67.4 \text{ psi}$$

$$w = 705 \text{ psf}$$

Bond—$V = \Sigma ojdu = 2.356 \times \dfrac{12}{8\frac{1}{2}} \times \dfrac{7}{8} \times 4.88 \times 393 = \dfrac{w\,12}{2}$

$$u = \frac{4.8\sqrt{3750}}{0.75} = 393 \text{ psi}$$

$$w = 928 \text{ psf} > 296 \text{ psf}$$

Temperature Bars

$A_s = 0.0018 \times 6.00 \times 12 = 0.13$

#3 @ 10 = 0.132

* The series of 8″ steps (8 × 9 triangles) is equivalent to a 4″ horizontal slab.

RISE AND RUN OF STAIRS

Many rules have been proposed for the proper relation of rise to run, such as, rise + run = 17, rise × run = 75, and 2 × rise + run = 25; but a somewhat more comfortable stair results from the values in the following table:—

Rise	Run	Rise	Run	Rise	Run
6	12⅝	7	10¾	Following Are	
6⅛	12⅜	7⅛	10⅝	Extra Steep	
6¼	12⅛	7¼	10⅜	7⅞	9½
6⅜	11⅞	7⅜	10¼	8	9¼
6½	11⅝	7½	10	8⅛	9⅛
6⅝	11½	7⅝	9⅞	8¼	9
6¾	11¼	7¾	9⅝	8⅜	8¾
6⅞	11			8½	8⅝

Stairs are usually limited to not less than 3 rises (because of the danger of tripping on one or two steps) and not more than about 18 rises in one flight between landings. The table below gives the vertical height for any number of rises and can be used for the length of run by taking one less run than the number of rises in the flight:—

TOTAL HEIGHT (OR LENGTH) (FT AND IN.)

Rise or Run (in.)	Number of Rises (or Runs)															
	3	4	5	6	7	8	9	10	11	12	13	14	15	16	17	18
6	1-6	2-0	2-6	3-0	3-6	4-0	4-6	5-0	5-6	6-0	6-6	7-0	7-6	8-0	8-6	9-0
6¼	1-6¾	2-1	2-7¼	3-1½	3-7¾	4-2	4-8¼	5-2½	5-8¾	6-3	6-9¼	7-3½	7-9¾	8-4	8-10¼	9-4½
6½	1-7½	2-2	2-8½	3-3	3-9½	4-4	4-10½	5-5	5-11½	6-6	7-0½	7-7	8-1½	8-8	9-2½	9-9
6¾	1-8¼	2-3	2-9¾	3-4½	3-11¼	4-6	5-0¾	5-7½	6-2¼	6-9	7-3¾	7-10½	8-5¼	9-0	9-6¾	10-1½
7	1-9	2-4	2-11	3-6	4-1	4-8	5-3	5-10	6-5	7-0	7-7	8-2	8-9	9-4	9-11	10-6
7¼	1-9¾	2-5	3-0¼	3-7½	4-2¾	4-10	5-5¼	6-0½	6-7¾	7-3	7-10¼	8-5½	9-0¾	9-8	10-3¼	10-10½
7½	1-10½	2-6	3-1½	3-9	4-4½	5-0	5-7½	6-3	6-10½	7-6	8-1½	8-9	9-4½	10-0	10-7½	11-3
7¾	1-11¼	2-7	3-2¾	3-10½	4-6¼	5-2	5-9¾	6-5½	7-1¼	7-9	8-4¾	9-0½	9-8¼	10-4	10-11¾	11-7½
8	2-0	2-8	3-4	4-0	4-8	5-4	6-0	6-8	7-4	8-0	8-8	9-4	10-0	10-8	11-4	12-0
8¼	2-0¾	2-9	3-5¼	4-1½	4-9¾	5-6	6-2¼	6-10½	7-6¾	8-3	8-11¼	9-7½	10-3¾	11-0	11-8¼	12-4½
8½	2-1½	2-10	3-6½	4-3	4-11½	5-8	6-4½	7-1	7-9½	8-6	9-2½	9-11	10-7½	11-4	12-0½	12-9
8¾	2-2¼	2-11	3-7¾	4-4½	5-1¼	5-10	6-6¾	7-3½	8-0¼	8-9	9-5¾	10-2½	10-11¼	11-8	12-4¾	13-1½
9	2-3	3-0	3-9	4-6	5-3	6-0	6-9	7-6	8-3	9-0	9-9	10-6	11-3	12-0	12-9	13-6
9¼	2-3¾	3-1	3-10¼	4-7½	5-4¾	6-2	6-11¼	7-8½	8-5¾	9-3	10-0¼	10-9½	11-6¾	12-4	13-1¼	13-10½
9½	2-4½	3-2	3-11½	4-9	5-6½	6-4	7-1½	7-11	8-8½	9-6	10-3½	11-1	11-10½	12-8	13-5½	14-3
9¾	2-5¼	3-3	4-0¾	4-10½	5-8¼	6-6	7-3¾	8-1½	8-11¼	9-9	10-6¾	11-4½	12-2¼	13-0	13-9¾	14-7½
10	2-6	3-4	4-2	5-0	5-10	6-8	7-6	8-4	9-2	10-0	10-10	11-8	12-6	13-4	14-2	15-0
10¼	2-6¾	3-5	4-3¼	5-1½	5-11¾	6-10	7-8¼	8-6½	9-4¾	10-3	11-1¼	11-11½	12-9¾	13-8	14-6¼	15-4½
10½	2-7½	3-6	4-4½	5-3	6-1½	7-0	7-10½	8-9	9-7½	10-6	11-4½	12-3	13-1½	14-0	14-10½	15-9
10¾	2-8¼	3-7	4-5¾	5-4½	6-3¼	7-2	8-0¾	8-11½	9-10¼	10-9	11-7¾	12-6½	13-5¼	14-4	15-2¾	16-1½
11	2-9	3-8	4-7	5-6	6-5	7-4	8-3	9-2	10-1	11-0	11-11	12-10	13-9	14-8	15-7	16-6
11¼	2-9¾	3-9	4-8¼	5-7½	6-6¾	7-6	8-5¼	9-4½	10-3¾	11-3	12-2¼	13-1½	14-0¾	15-0	15-11¼	16-10½
11½	2-10½	3-10	4-9½	5-9	6-8½	7-8	8-7½	9-7	10-6½	11-6	12-5½	13-5	14-4½	15-4	16-3½	17-3
11¾	2-11¼	3-11	4-10¾	5-10½	6-10¼	7-10	8-9¾	9-9½	10-9¼	11-9	12-8¾	13-8½	14-8¼	15-8	16-7¾	17-7½
12	3-0	4-0	5-0	6-0	7-0	8-0	9-0	10-0	11-0	12-0	13-0	14-0	15-0	16-0	17-0	18-0

STAIR SLABS—SINGLE SPANS
9 in. Run, 8 in. Rise

For description of use of table, see page 6-21.

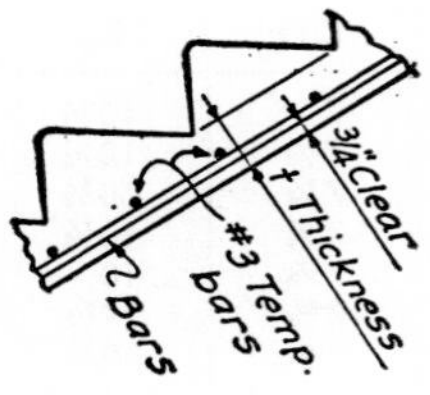

Approx. Balanced Reinforcement ($p = 0.0129$)

$f_s = 24{,}000$ psi $\quad f_c = 1688$ psi $\quad v_c = 67.4$ psi $\quad u = \dfrac{4.8\sqrt{f'_c}}{D}$

Safe superimposed load in pounds per square foot includes weight of any plastered ceiling, finished treads and finished risers (Weight of *all* concrete of stair slab and steps has already been deducted.)

	Slab Thickness (t) (in.)	3"	3½"	4"	4½"	5"	5½"	6"	6½"	7"
	Bars	#3	#4	#4	#5	#5	#6	#6	#6	#6
	Spacing (in.)	5"	6½"	6"	7½"	7½"	8½"	8½"	7½"	7"
	Spacing of #3 Temp. Bars	15"	15"	15"	14"	13"	12"	11"	10"	9½"
	Weight of Concrete (psf hor. projection)	101	109	117	125	134	142	150	158	167
Approx. No. of Risers*	Span (L) horizontal	Safe Superimposed Load (psf)								
7	5′-0	189								
7	5′-6	138								
8	6′-0	100	252							
8	6′-6	71	199							
9	7′-0	47	156	226						
10	7′-6		122	182						
10	8′-0		94	146	258					
11	8′-6		71	115	214					
12	9′-0			91	177	212				
12	9′-6			69	146	176				
13	10′-0				120	146				
14	10′-6				97	120	203	236		
14	11′-0				78	96	173	202		
15	11′-6					77	146	173		
16	12′-0					59	123	146	208	
16	12′-6						102	122	178	227
17	13′-0						83	102	154	197
18	13′-6						67	84	130	171
18	14′-0							68	110	147

* The rise of stairs may vary from about 6 in. to 8 in. and the run from about 11 in. to 9 in.

STAIR SLABS—SINGLE SPANS
10½ in. Run, 7 in. Rise

For description of use of table, see page 6-21.

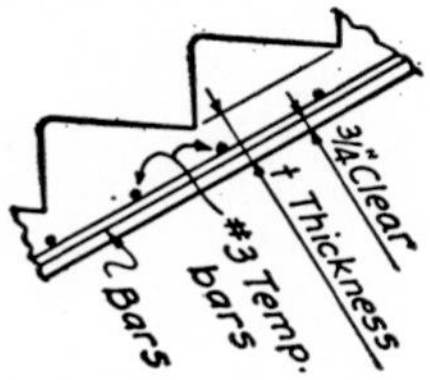

Approx. Balanced Reinforcement ($p = 0.0129$)

$f_s = 24{,}000$ psi $f_c = 1688$ psi $v_c = 67.4$ psi $u = \dfrac{4.8\sqrt{f'_c}}{D}$

Safe superimposed load in pounds per square foot includes weight of any plastered ceiling, finished treads and finished risers. (Weight of all concrete of stair slab and steps has already been deducted.)

	Slab thickness (t) (in.)	3"	3½"	4"	4½"	5"	5½"	6"	6½"	7"
	Bars	#3	#4	#4	#5	#5	#6	#6	#6	#6
	Spacing (in.)	5"	6½"	6"	7½"	7½"	8½"	8½"	7½"	7"
	Spacing of #3 Temp. Bars	15"	15"	15"	14"	13"	12"	11"	10"	9½"
	Weight of Concrete (psf hor. projection)	91	98	105	112	120	128	135	142	150
Approx. No. of Risers*	Span (L) horizontal	Safe Superimposed Load (psf)								
5	5'-0	199								
6	5'-6	148								
6	6'-0	110	263							
7	6'-6	81	210							
8	7'-0	57	167	237						
8	7'-6	38	133	193						
9	8'-0		105	157	271					
9	8'-6		83	127	227					
10	9'-0		62	102	191	226				
10	9'-6			81	160	192				
11	10'-0			63	133	162				
12	10'-6				110	135	215	251		
12	11'-0					113	185	217		
13	11'-6					94	159	188		
14	12'-0					75	134	161	224	
14	12'-6					60	114	137	195	244
15	13'-0						96	117	170	214
15	13'-6						80	99	147	188
16	14'-0						65	83	126	164
16	14'-6							68	108	143
17	15'-0								92	124
18	15'-6									106

* The rise of stairs may vary from about 6 in. to 8 in. and the run from about 11 in. to 9 in.

SAFE LOAD TABLES

Concrete Joists

Section 7

CONCRETE JOIST CONSTRUCTION

Concrete joist construction consists of narrow ribs or joists and a top slab of concrete, the whole formed by creating longitudinal void spaces by means of permanent or removable forms of steel or removable forms of wood or other material. Joist widths vary from 4 to 7 or 8 inches. Standard forms for the void spaces are usually 20 in. or 30 in. wide and have a depth of 6, 8, 10, 12, 14, 16 or 20 in. The top slab is usually 2, 2½, 3 or 4½ in. thick, but not less than 1/12 of the clear distance between ribs.

The following tables give the safe superimposed load in pounds per square foot (psf), i.e., the total carrying capacity as determined by the least of various factors such as shear, bond or flexure, with only the dead weight of the concrete deducted. Thus the safe superimposed load includes live load, partition allowance, floor finishes, fills, ceilings and everything but the dead weight of the concrete construction.

Since the tables are rather elaborate, a general outline of what is covered may be helpful. The tables are divided into three sections:—(1) single spans, (2) end spans, and (3) interior spans. Each of these sections has a short explanation, schedule of limitations, sketch of the recommended requirements and an illustrative example. Each section is subdivided into two parts, the first for 20-in. wide forms and the second for 30-in. wide forms. Within each such section, the tables are divided by depth of form and thicknesses of top slab.

All tables are based upon the recommendations of the "Building Code Requirements for Reinforced Concrete (ACI 318-63)," and in the case of end spans the positive moment is here taken as $wl'^2/11$, i.e., without restraint at the outer end. Bond and diagonal tension values are based upon deformed bars conforming to ASTM. Attention is directed to the fact that plain bars or deformed bars not meeting ASTM cannot be used with these tables.

The arrangement of bars and chairs, and the bending, spacing, lapping and embedment of bars are all in accordance with "Manual of Standard Practice for Detailing Reinforced Concrete Structures (ACI 315)."

The load capacities apply for the particular conditions described, but there are so many variables in loads, stiffnesses, continuity and in the quality of materials that the services of a structural engineer are recommended for final designs.

TEMPERATURE REINFORCEMENT

Temperature reinforcement in the concrete top slab over forms and in a direction normal to the span of the joists shall be of bars or welded wire fabric at least equal in area to the values in the following table and increased where necessary for flexure, giving due consideration to concentrated loads:

CONCRETE JOIST CONSTRUCTION

Thickness of Top Slab	Grade 40 Bars	Grade 60 Bars	Welded Wire Fabric†
2½ in.	#3 @ 12	#3 @ 12	4 × 12 − 9/12
3 in.	#3 @ 15	#3 @ 15	4 × 12 − 8/12
4½ in.	#3 @ 12	#3 @ 13½	4 × 12 − 5/10
	All tied with ¼″ϕ @ 4′-2″c/c		

† Spacing and wire size normal to joists. Max. spacing parallel to joists is 12 in.

TAPERED ENDS

Conforming to U. S. Department of Commerce Simplified Practice Recommendation R87-32, tapered end forms are available which increase the effective joist width 2 in. on each side for 20 in. wide forms and 2½ in. on each side for 30 in. wide forms in a distance of 3 ft from the end. Above and to the right of the zigzag line in the tables, tapered ends must be used or the tabulated values proportionately reduced. Below and to the left of these lines, square (nontapered) ends are adequate. In computing these tables, whenever adding tapered ends increased the capacity by ten per cent or more, tapered ends were used, otherwise not. Hence, immediately below and to the left of the zigzag lines, slight increases in capacity may result with tapered ends.

For computing shear, the width of joist is that at mid-height of form.

CONTROL OF DEFLECTIONS

The majority of spans used in concrete joist construction do not require special consideration of deflections. It is recommended that the maximum span for floor construction, particularly where partitions extend parallel to the joists, should be limited to 24 times the total depth of construction (t), the same value being used in the tables for single, end, and interior conditions. This limitation is indicated by a horizontal line across each table. ACI 909 requires that deflections of spans exceeding certain span-depth ratios must be computed and controlled. For roofs, or where time-sagging is not important, the designer may find that span/depth ratios may exceed 24 without requiring any special provisions to reduce deflection due to creep. However, longer spans, i.e., beyond 24 times the depth of the construction, may require special consideration. It is practical to construct spans with l/t exceeding 24 and still keep deflections within Code limits. Cambering or the use of compressive reinforcement, or both, may be necessary. Compressive reinforcement substantially reduces the creep of the concrete, as is illustrated on pages 3-18 and 3-19. ACI 318-63 recommends that long-time additional deflections be assumed as 0.8 of the immediate elastic deflection when the compressive reinforcement is equal to the tensile, but must be taken as two times if no compressive reinforcement is provided. Cambering top and bottom surfaces is desirable on the longer spans to compensate for calculated deflections.

CONCRETE JOIST CONSTRUCTION

DEFORMATION WITH TIME

It is recommended that the maximum span for floor construction, particularly where partitions extend parallel to the joists, should be limited to 24 times total depth of construction (t). This limitation is indicated by a horizontal line across each table. This ratio is retained for single, end and interior conditions. For roofs, or where time-sagging is not important, span/depth ratios may exceed 24, if desired. ACI 909 requires checking of deflections in all cases where the span/depth ratio exceeds the values in Table ACI 909(b).

DISTRIBUTING RIBS

For floor construction, use distributing ribs with at least 1-#4 bar top and 1-#4 bar bottom as follows:—

One near the center of spans from 20 ft to 30 ft and
two near the third points of spans over 30 ft.

STRESSES

As noted at the beginning of each set of tables, steel of 60,000 psi grade is stressed to 24,000 psi. Where it is necessary to use some other stress, vary the steel areas in direct proportion. Concrete is assumed to test 3,750 psi. If weaker concrete is used, the capacity will be reduced for shear and bond.

UNEQUAL CONTINUOUS SPANS

Bending moments are computed from the clear span for positive moment in continuous spans and from the average of the two adjacent clear spans for negative moment. The assumptions are made that the larger of two adjacent spans does not exceed the shorter by more than 20 per cent and that the unit live load does not exceed three times the unit dead load. For cases outside of these limitations, the moments must be corrected by more accurate methods (see pages 4-3 to 4-17).

The values tabulated under End Spans apply accurately only when there are two additional approximately equal spans continuous with the one under consideration. If there is only one adjacent span, the negative moment should be $wl'^2/9$ instead of $wl'^2/10$, and those values that are governed by negative moment would be reduced accordingly. Values obtained from positive moment would not change.

The values tabulated under Interior Spans apply accurately only when there are two additional approximately equal spans continuous with each end of the one under consideration. If either end is continuous with an end span, the negative moment should be $wl'^2/10$ instead of $wl'^2/11$ and the safe load as governed by negative moment should be reduced accordingly. Values obtained from positive moment would not change. This condition can also be checked by reference to the same data in the tables for End Spans.

LIVE LOAD LIMITATIONS

ACI 318-63-904(c) establishes moment factors for cases where the unit live load does not exceed three times the unit dead load. If the ratio is greater,

CONCRETE JOIST CONSTRUCTION—SINGLE SPAN

the effect of unbalanced panel loads may require more accurate analysis (see pages 4-3 to 4-17).

The dead load in such analyses includes not only the weight of the concrete slab (which is here deducted from the total load to obtain the safe superimposed load), but any ceilings, floor finishes, partitions, and similar immovable features. Hence it is not practicable to indicate in these tables the points where the unit live load is exactly equal to three times the unit dead load. The safe superimposed loads have been tabulated to values somewhat above 400 psf and then stopped. The user is cautioned to check the ratio of live to dead loads in the higher capacities.

Example I—Determine the safe carrying capacity on spans of 12 and 18 ft of 6-in. deep forms plus 2½ in. of top slab with 5 in. wide joists at 25 in. centers and reinforced with 1-#7 bottom bar and 1-#7 truss bar. Dead weight of construction is 48 psf.*

$$f'_c = 3750 \text{ psi}, f_c = 1688, f_s = 24{,}000 \text{ psi}, n = \frac{29{,}000{,}000}{(145)^{1.5}33\sqrt{3750}} = 8.22$$

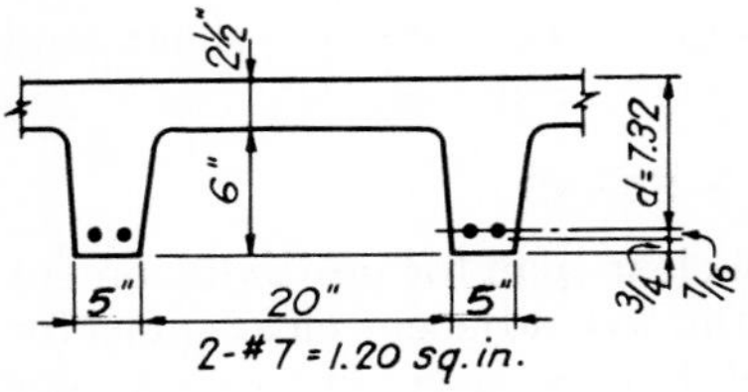

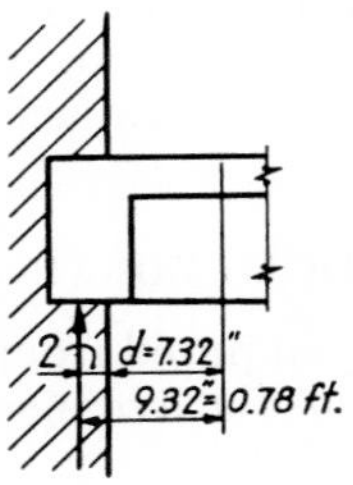

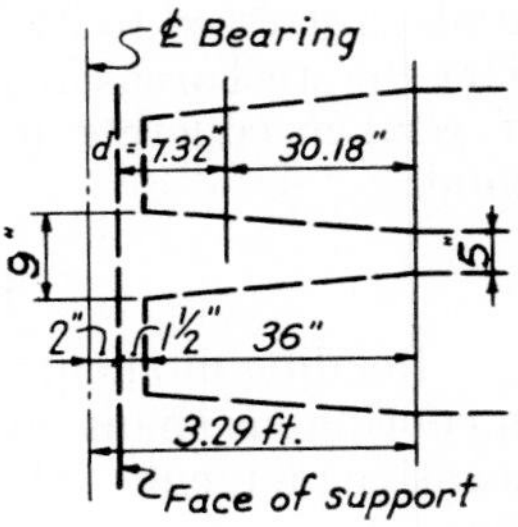

Solution (Live load capacity determined by:)

Shear

$$V = v_c bd \qquad v_c = 1.2\sqrt{3750} = 73.5 \quad \text{Av. } b = 5 + 6/12 = 5.50 \text{ in.}$$
$$= 73.5 \times 5.50 \times 7.32 = 2965 \text{ lb}$$
$$= 2.08\,\frac{w(L - 1.56)}{2} \{\text{at } 2'' + (d = 7.32'') = 0.78 \text{ ft from c.l. of bearing}\}$$
$$\text{For } L = 12 \text{ ft}, w = \frac{2850}{L - 1.56} = 273 - 48 = 225 \text{ psf}$$
$$\text{For } L = 18 \text{ ft}, w = \frac{2850}{L - 1.56} = 173 - 48 = 125 \text{ psf}$$

Bond

$$V = u\Sigma ojd \quad u \text{ (on 1-\#7 bottom bar)} = \frac{4.8\sqrt{3750}}{0.875} = 336 < 500 \text{ psi}$$
$$= 336 \times 2.749 \times 7/8 \times 7.32 = 5920 \text{ lb}$$
$$= 2.08\,\frac{wL}{2}$$
$$\text{For } L = 12 \text{ ft}, w = \frac{5690}{L} = 474 - 48 = 426 \text{ psf}$$
$$\text{For } L = 18 \text{ ft}, w = \frac{5690}{L} = 316 - 48 = 268 \text{ psf}$$

---

* Dead weight is computed:— 2½ in. top slab 31 psf

$$\text{Joist } \frac{5 + 6.0}{2} \times \frac{6 \times 150}{2.08 \times 144} = \frac{17 \text{ psf}}{48 \text{ psf}}$$

CONCRETE JOIST CONSTRUCTION—SINGLE SPAN

Positive Moment $A_s = 1.20$ sq in. $p = \frac{1.20}{25 \times 7.32} = 0.00656$(so N.A. is probably in $2\frac{1}{2}''$ flange)

$$pn = 0.0542$$
$$k = \sqrt{0.1084 + 0.00293} - 0.0542 = 0.334 - 0.054 = 0.280$$
$$j = 0.907 \qquad kd = 2.05 \text{ in.} < 2.50 \text{ in.}$$
$$M = 1.20 \times 24000 \times 0.907 \times 7.32 = 191{,}500 \text{ lb-in.}$$
$$= \frac{2.08wL^2 12}{8}$$

For $L = 12$ ft, $w = \frac{61{,}300}{L^2} = 426 - 48 =$ **378 psf**

For $L = 18$ ft, $w = \frac{61{,}300}{L^2} = 189 - 48 =$ **141 psf**

Tapered Ends For $L = 12$ ft, For $L = 18$ ft: Shear-capacity < Moment-capacity so increase shear capacity with tapered ends

$b = 5.50 + \frac{30.18}{36} 4 = 8.85$ in. (see cut page 7-6)

$$V = 73.5 \times 8.85 \times 7.32 = 4770 \text{ lb}$$

$= 2.08 \frac{w(L - 1.56)}{2}$ at d + 2″ = 0.78 ft from c.l. of bearing.

For $L = 12$ ft, $w = \frac{4590}{L - 1.56} = 439 - 48 = 391$ psf > 378 psf

For $L = 18$ ft, $w = \frac{4590}{L - 1.56} = 279 - 48 = 231$ psf > 141 psf

Root of Taper $V = 2965 \text{ lb} = \frac{2.08w(L - 6.58)}{2}$; $6.58 = 2 \times 3.29$ (see cut page 7-6)

For $L = 12$ ft, $w = \frac{2850}{L - 6.58} = 526 - 48 = 478$ psf > 378 psf

For $L = 18$ ft, $w = \frac{2850}{L - 6.58} = 249 - 48 = 201$ psf > 141 psf

Deflection $E_c = (145)^{1.5}\, 33\sqrt{3750} = 3{,}530{,}000$ psi

$pf_y = 0.00656 \times 60{,}000 = 394 < 500$ so use gross section

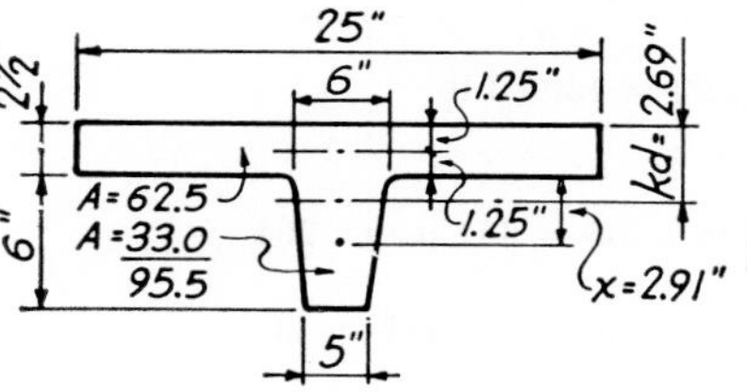

$$x = \frac{h}{3}\left(\frac{a + 2b}{a + b}\right) = \frac{6}{3}\left(\frac{6 + 10}{6 + 5}\right) = 2.91 \text{ in.}$$

$$kd = 1.25 + \frac{33.0}{95.5}(1.25 + 2.91) = 2.69 \text{ in.}$$

$$I_c = 62.5\left(\frac{2\frac{1}{2}^2}{12} + \overline{1.44}^2\right) = 162 \text{ in.}^4$$

$$30\left(\frac{6^2}{12} + \overline{2.81}^2\right) = 327$$

$$3\left(\frac{6^2}{36} + \overline{1.81}^2\right) = \underline{13}$$

$$502 \text{ in.}^4$$

$$\Delta = \frac{wL^4}{76.8EI}$$

$$\Delta_{12} = \frac{2.08 \times 378 \times \overline{12}^4 \times 1728}{76.8 \times 3{,}530{,}000 \times 502} = 0.207'' < \left(\frac{L}{180} = 0.80''\right) < \left(\frac{L}{360} = 0.40''\right)$$

$$\Delta_{18} = \frac{2.08 \times 141 \times \overline{18}^4 \times 1728}{76.8 \times 3{,}530{,}000 \times 502} = 0.39'' < \left(\frac{L}{180} = 1.20''\right) < \left(\frac{L}{360} = 0.60''\right)$$

Summary—On a span of 18 ft the capacity is limited to 141 psf by tension in the reinforcing steel resisting positive moment, the compression in the concrete is less than the allowable (since $p = 0.00656$), and the bond (with a capacity of 268 psf is adequate). The shear on a nontapered end (125 psf) requires a tapered end (231 psf) with a value at the root of the taper of 201 psf.

CONCRETE JOIST CONSTRUCTION—SINGLE SPAN

On a span of 12 ft the capacity by moment is 378 psf, the bond at 426 psf is more than adequate, but a tapered end (391 psf) is required as a nontapered end (225 psf) would be overstressed in diagonal tension. The value at the root of the taper (478 psf) is also sufficient.

It is only by comparing the various capacities from all the criteria that the allowable superimposed load can be determined. This must then be checked for meeting the deflection requirements.

Example II—To illustrate T-beam design of joists, determine the safe carrying capacity on spans of 24 and 36 ft of 16 in. deep forms plus 2½ in. of top slab with 6 in. wide joists at 26 in. centers and reinforced with 1-#8 straight bottom bar and 1-#7 truss bar.

$f'_c = 3750$ psi; $f_s = 24{,}000$ psi; $n = 8.22$; Dead weight $= 31 + \dfrac{7.33 \times 16 \times 150}{144 \times 2.17} = 88$ psf

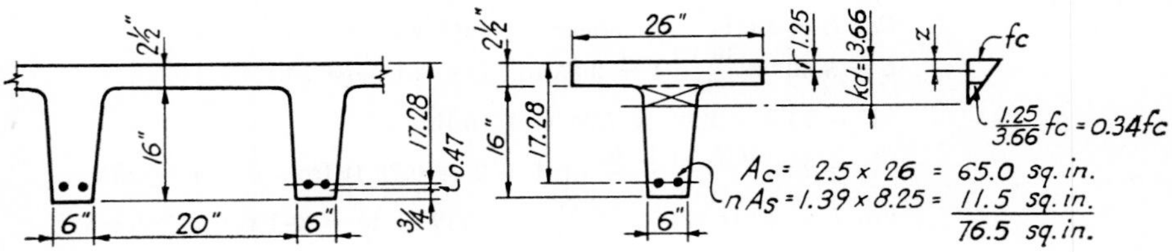

Shear

$V = 73.5 \times 7.33 \times 17.28 = 9300$ lb $\qquad b = 6 + {}^{16}\!/_{12} = 7.33$

$= 2.17w\left(\dfrac{L - 3.22}{2}\right) \quad 2 \times 1.61 = 3.22$ ft

For $L = 24$, $w = \dfrac{8650}{L - 3.22} = 416 - 88 = 328$ psf > 204

For $L = 36$, $w = \dfrac{8650}{L - 3.22} = 264 - 88 = 175$ psf > 43

} No tap. end req'd.

Bond

$V = \Sigma o u j d \qquad u = \dfrac{4.8\sqrt{3750}}{1.0} = 294$ psi

$= 294 \times 3.142 \times \frac{7}{8} \times 17.28 = 13{,}960$ lb

$= 2.17\,\dfrac{wL}{2}$

For $L = 24$, $w = \dfrac{12950}{L} = 539 - 88 = 451$ psf > 204

For $L = 36$, $w = \dfrac{12950}{L} = 360 - 88 = 272$ psf > 43

Positive Moment $\quad A_s = 1.39$ sq in. $\quad p = \dfrac{1.39}{26 \times 17.28} = 0.0031 \quad pn = 0.0256$

N.A. is probably below 2½" slab.

Taking moments about slab center and neglecting any small compression in the stem:

$kd = 1.25 + \dfrac{11.5 \times 16.03}{76.5} = 3.66$ in. > 2.5 in.

$k = \dfrac{3.66}{17.28} = 0.212$

$z =$ c. of g. of trapezoid $= \dfrac{h}{3}\left(\dfrac{a + 2b}{a + b}\right) = \dfrac{2.5}{3}\left(\dfrac{1 + 0.68}{1 + 0.34}\right) = 1.03$ in.

CONCRETE JOIST CONSTRUCTION—SINGLE SPAN

$jd = 17.28 - 1.03 = 16.25$ in.

Moment capacity $= 24000 \times 1.39 \times 16.25 = 544{,}000$ lb-in.

$$= 2.17 \frac{wL^2 12}{8}$$

$$\text{For } L = 24,\ w = \frac{167{,}000}{L^2} = 292 - 88 = \mathbf{204\ psf}$$

$$\text{For } L = 36,\ w = \frac{167{,}000}{L^2} = 131 - 88 = \mathbf{43\ psf}$$

Live Load Deflection

$$\Delta = \frac{wL^4}{76.8EI} \qquad E = 145^{1.5} 33 \sqrt{3750} = 3{,}530{,}000 \text{ psi}$$

$pf_y = 0.0031 \times 60{,}000 = 186 < 500$ so use gross section

$$x = \frac{h}{3}\left(\frac{a + 2b}{a + b}\right) = \frac{16}{3}\left(\frac{8.67 + 12}{8.67 + 6}\right) = 7.52 \text{ in.}$$

$$kd = 1.25 + \frac{117.3}{182.3}(1.25 + 7.52) = 6.89 \text{ in.}$$

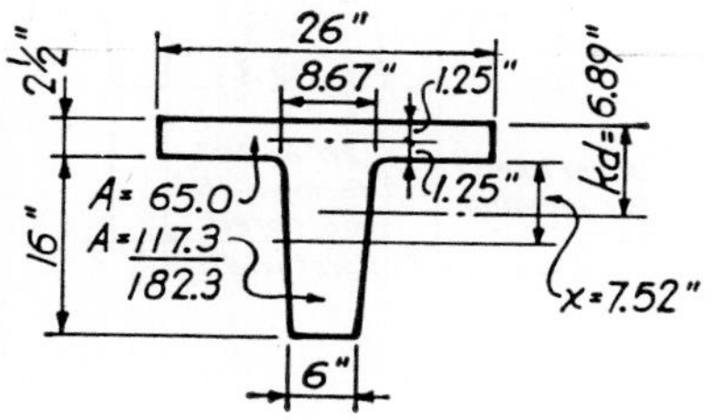

$$I_c = 65\left(\frac{\overline{2\frac{1}{2}}^2}{12} + \overline{5.64}^2\right) = 2100 \text{ in.}^4$$

$$96\left(\frac{\overline{16}^2}{12} + \overline{3.61}^2\right) = 3300$$

$$21.3\left(\frac{\overline{2 \times 16}^2}{36} + \overline{0.94}^2\right) = \underline{322}$$

$$5722 \text{ in.}^4$$

$$\Delta_{24} = \frac{2.17 \times 204 \times \overline{24}^4 \times 1728}{76.8 \times 3{,}530{,}000 \times 5722} = 0.164'' < \frac{L}{180} < \frac{L}{360}$$

$$\Delta_{36} = \frac{2.17 \times 43 \times \overline{36}^4 \times 1728}{76.8 \times 3{,}530{,}000 \times 5722} = 0.174'' < \frac{L}{180} < \frac{L}{360}$$

MAXIMUM SIZE BARS IN JOISTS

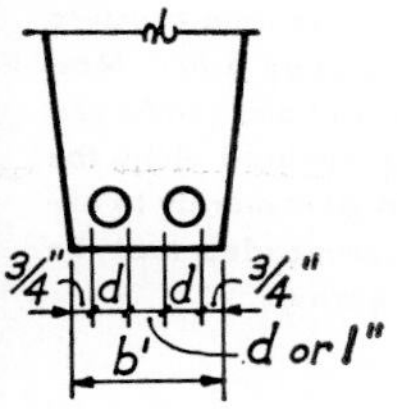

b′ (in.)	Max. size equal dia. bars
4	#6
5	#9
6 and wider	#11

CONCRETE JOIST CONSTRUCTION—SINGLE SPAN

The general description of concrete joist construction on pages 7-3 to 7-5 should be read in connection with these explanations.

Tables on pages 7-11 to 7-31, inclusive, give the safe superimposed loads on single (noncontinuous) spans of concrete joist construction. For continuous spans, see the tables on pages 7-38 to 7-83.

The arrangement of joists and of reinforcing bars should be as shown on the figure below:—

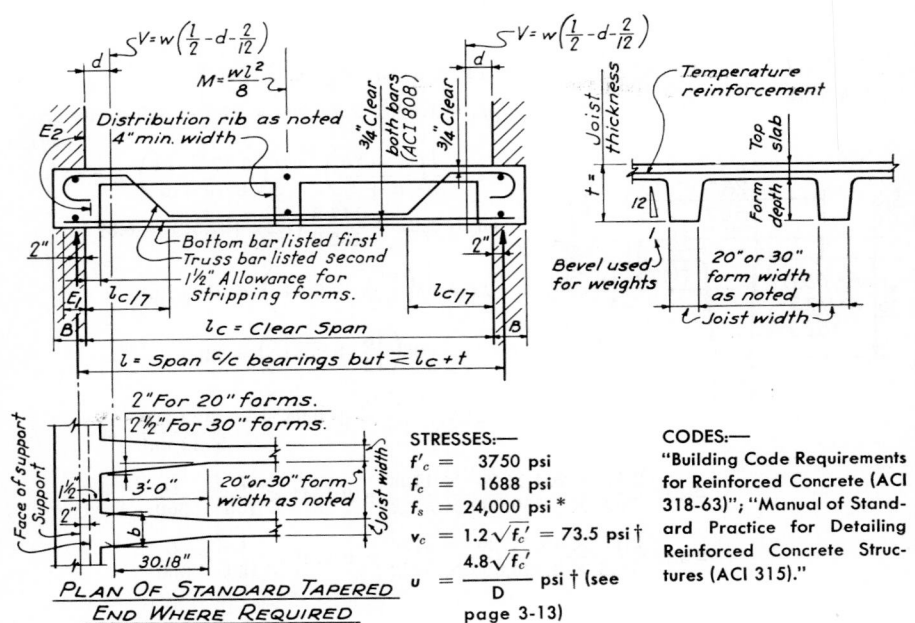

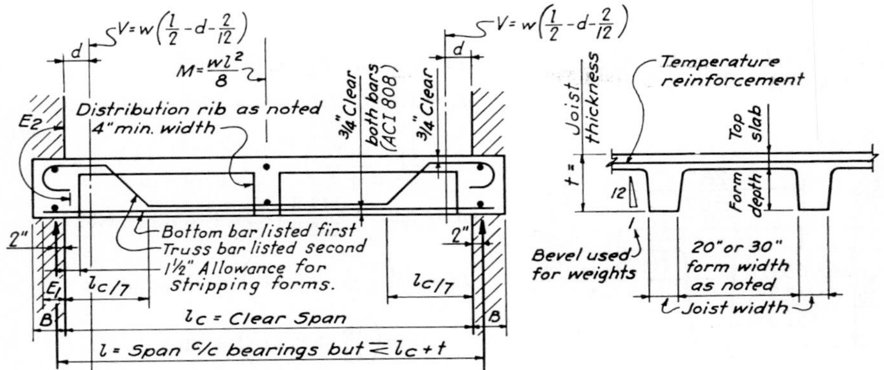

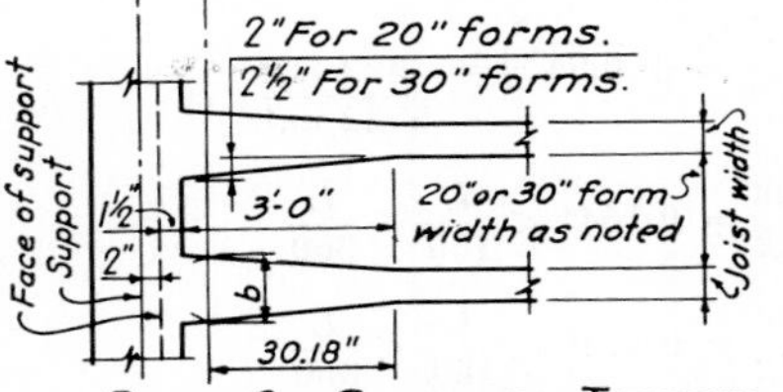

PLAN OF STANDARD TAPERED END WHERE REQUIRED

STRESSES:—

f'_c = 3750 psi

f_c = 1688 psi

f_s = 24,000 psi *

$v_c = 1.2\sqrt{f_c'} = 73.5$ psi †

$u = \dfrac{4.8\sqrt{f_c'}}{D}$ psi † (see page 3-13)

CODES:—

"Building Code Requirements for Reinforced Concrete (ACI 318-63)"; "Manual of Standard Practice for Detailing Reinforced Concrete Structures (ACI 315)."

E_1 = 6 in. minimum for bottom bars (straight if possible, bent if necessary).

E_2 = anchorage length computed from allowable anchorage bond stress, page 3-13, often requiring a semicircular hook.

B = ordinarily 4 in. minimum (or preferably 6 in.) and sufficient in any case to keep the bearing pressure on the wall within the allowable for the material of which the wall is made (see page 5-6). Most designers prefer to have a continuous distribution rib of concrete bearing on the wall and reinforced with at least 1-#4 bar top and 1-#4 bar bottom whenever it is desired to spread the load along the wall bearing. When providing bearing on existing masonry walls, it is often sufficient merely to extend the joist stems into individual pockets cut into the wall, but it is then recommended that the stiffening rib be placed between the joists parallel and adjacent to the wall bearing.

Almost all usual combinations of form depth, top slab and joist reinforcement are presented herewith. To show how the tables for single spans were computed and to permit extension beyond the scope of the tables if required, illustrative examples were shown on pages 7-6 to 7-9, incl.

* Flexural value is based upon using bars of ASTM A61 or A432 grade (f_y = 60,000 psi).

† Bond and diagonal tension values are based upon deformed bars meeting ASTM A305. Plain round bars or deformed bars not meeting ASTM A305 will not give sufficient bond resistance.

CONCRETE JOIST CONSTRUCTION
SINGLE SPAN—20 INCH WIDE FORMS
Safe Superimposed Load (psf)

For limitations and explanation of use of tables, see pages 7-3 to 7-5.

Depth: 6″ FORMS + 2½″ CONCRETE

Joists	4″ Joists @ 24″ c/c Wt 45 psf					5″ Joists @ 25″ c/c Wt 48 psf							
Bottom Bar / Truss Bar	#4 / #4	#5 / #4	#5 / #5	#6 / #5	#6 / #6	#4 / #4	#5 / #4	#5 / #5	#6 / #5	#6 / #6	#7 / #6	#7 / #7	#8 / #7
Length of Span in Feet													
8	309	399				293	380						
9	235	306	379			222	290	360	438				
10	182	226	299	364	432	171	226	278	346	411			
11	143	190	239	293	349	133	179	226	278	332	394	427	
12	113	153	194	239	286	104	143	182	211	271	323	378	
13	89	124	153	197	238	82	115	148	186	224	269	315	338
14	71	100	131	164	199	64	93	121	154	187	225	265	307
15	56	82	108	137	167	50	75	100	128	152	190	225	263
16	44	67	90	110	142	38	60	82	107	132	162	192	226
17	34	54	74	97	121		48	67	89	112	138	165	195
18		43	62	82	103		38	55	75	95	114	141	169
19		34	51	69	83			45	62	80	101	123	146
20			41	58	75			36	52	68	87	106	128
21			33	48	64				42	57	74	89	111

Depth: 6″ FORMS + 3″ CONCRETE

Joists	4″ Joists @ 24″ c/c Wt 52 psf					5″ Joists @ 25″ c/c Wt 54 psf							
Bottom Bar / Truss Bar	#4 / #4	#5 / #4	#5 / #5	#6 / #5	#6 / #6	#4 / #4	#5 / #4	#5 / #5	#6 / #5	#6 / #6	#7 / #6	#7 / #7	#8 / #7
Length of Span in Feet													
9	248	324	402			234	307	382					
10	191	241	316	387		180	239	297	368	438			
11	149	200	253	311	371	139	188	239	295	352	419		
12	117	160	204	253	304	109	150	192	225	288	344	402	
13	93	129	162	208	251	85	120	156	196	237	285	335	359
14	73	104	137	173	210	66	96	127	162	197	239	281	325
15	57	85	113	144	176	51	77	104	134	161	201	238	280
16	44	68	93	115	149	38	61	85	111	139	170	203	239
17	33	55	77	101	126		48	69	93	117	145	174	206
18		43	63	85	107		37	56	77	99	120	149	178
19		34	51	71	86			45	64	83	105	129	154
20			41	59	77			35	52	70	90	111	134
21			33	49	65				43	58	77	93	117
22				40	55				34	49	65	83	102

Values below horizontal line are for spans in excess of 24 *t*.
Above and to the right of the zigzag line, tapered ends are required.

CONCRETE JOIST CONSTRUCTION
SINGLE SPAN—20 INCH WIDE FORMS
Safe Superimposed Load (psf)

For limitations and explanation of use of tables, see pages 7-3 to 7-5.

Depth: 6″ FORMS + 4½″ CONCRETE

Joists	4″ Joists @ 24″ c/c Wt 71 psf					5″ Joists @ 25″ c/c Wt 73 psf							
Bottom Bar / Truss Bar	#4 / #4	#5 / #4	#5 / #5	#6 / #5	#6 / #6	#4 / #4	#5 / #4	#5 / #5	#6 / #5	#6 / #6	#7 / #6	#7 / #7	#8 / #7
Length of Span in Feet													
9	287	379				271	359	422					
10	220	289	370			206	278	351	432				
11	170	231	294	364	436	158	217	277	345	415			
12	132	183	216	295	356	122	171	222	268	337	405		
13	102	146	190	241	293	93	135	178	227	277	335	394	422
14	79	117	155	199	243	70	107	144	186	211	279	330	380
15	60	93	126	164	203	52	84	116	153	189	234	279	329
16	44	73	103	132	170	37	65	94	126	159	197	236	280
17	31	57	83	113	143		50	75	103	132	152	201	240
18		43	67	93	120		37	59	84	110	138	172	207
19		32	53	77	96			46	69	92	119	147	178
20			41	62	84			35	55	76	100	114	154
21			31	50	70				43	62	85	105	133
22				40	58				33	51	71	92	115
23				30	47					40	59	78	99
24					38					31	48	66	79
25											39	55	73

Depth: 8″ FORMS + 2½″ CONCRETE

Joists	4″ Joists @ 24″ c/c Wt 51 psf					5″ Joists @ 25″ c/c Wt 54 psf							
Bottom Bar / Truss Bar	#4 / #4	#5 / #4	#5 / #5	#6 / #5	#6 / #6	#5 / #4	#5 / #5	#6 / #5	#6 / #6	#7 / #6	#7 / #7	#8 / #7	#8 / #8
Length of Span in Feet													
10	239	308	389			296	369						
11	189	250	313	383		235	296	363	433				
12	151	202	235	314	375	189	240	286	355	423			
13	121	165	209	260	312	154	197	245	295	353	413	440	
14	98	136	174	218	262	125	162	204	229	297	349	398	
15	79	112	145	167	222	102	135	171	207	252	297	347	352
16	63	92	122	151	189	84	112	144	177	215	255	299	307
17	50	76	102	132	162	68	93	122	151	170	219	258	271
18	39	62	86	112	139	55	77	103	129	156	190	225	242
19	30	51	72	96	115	44	64	87	110	137	165	196	218
20		41	60	81	103	35	53	73	94	119	133	172	197
21		33	50	69	89		43	61	81	103	123	151	178
22			41	59	77		34	51	69	89	110	133	157
23			33	49	66			43	58	77	96	117	140
24				41	57			35	49	66	84	98	124
25				34	48				41	57	73	91	110

Values below horizontal line are for spans in excess of 24 t.
Above and to the right of the zigzag line, tapered ends are required.

CONCRETE JOIST CONSTRUCTION
SINGLE SPAN—20 INCH WIDE FORMS
Safe Superimposed Load (psf)

For limitations and explanation of use of tables, see pages 7-3 to 7-5.

Depth: 8″ FORMS + 3″ CONCRETE

Joists	4″ Joists @ 24″ c/c Wt 57 psf					5″ Joists @ 25″ c/c Wt 60 psf							
Bottom Bar	#4	#5	#5	#6	#6	#5	#5	#6	#6	#7	#7	#8	#8
Truss Bar	#4	#4	#5	#5	#6	#4	#5	#5	#6	#6	#7	#7	#8
Length of Span in Feet													
10	248	325	407			309	386						
11	195	260	327	401		245	309	380					
12	155	210	247	328	392	197	250	301	372	444			
13	124	171	218	271	326	159	204	256	308	369	433		
14	99	140	180	226	273	129	168	212	240	310	365	417	
15	79	114	150	174	231	105	139	177	216	263	310	363	367
16	63	94	125	157	196	85	115	149	183	224	266	312	320
17	50	77	104	136	168	69	95	125	156	177	229	270	283
18	38	62	87	115	143	55	78	105	133	162	198	234	252
19		50	73	97	119	43	64	88	113	142	171	204	226
20		40	60	83	106	33	52	74	96	122	137	179	205
21		31	49	70	91		42	62	82	105	127	157	185
22			40	59	78		33	51	69	91	113	138	163
23			32	49	66			42	58	78	98	121	144
24				40	56			34	49	67	85	100	128
25				33	48				40	57	74	93	113
26					40				33	48	64	82	100

Depth: 8″ FORMS + 4½″ CONCRETE

Joists	4″ Joists @ 24″ c/c Wt 76 psf					5″ Joists @ 25″ c/c Wt 79 psf							
Bottom Bar	#4	#5	#5	#6	#6	#5	#5	#6	#6	#7	#7	#8	#8
Truss Bar	#4	#4	#5	#5	#6	#4	#5	#5	#6	#6	#7	#7	#8
Length of Span in Feet													
11	216	291	368			274	348	399					
12	170	233	283	370	444	218	280	349	421				
13	134	188	242	304	368	174	227	287	348	419			
14	105	152	199	252	307	140	185	237	275	351	414		
15	82	123	164	196	258	112	151	196	242	296	351	413	415
16	63	99	135	176	218	89	124	163	203	251	299	354	361
17	48	79	111	147	184	70	101	136	171	200	256	305	317
18	35	63	91	124	143	54	82	113	145	182	220	263	282
19		49	74	103	130	41	65	93	122	155	190	228	252
20		37	60	86	113		52	77	103	133	152	199	227
21			47	71	96		40	63	86	113	140	173	205
22			37	58	80			50	71	96	122	151	181
23				47	67			39	59	82	105	132	159
24				37	56			30	48	69	90	109	140
25					46				38	57	77	100	123
26					37					47	66	86	108
27										38	55	74	86
28										30	46	64	80

Values below horizontal line are for spans in excess of 24 t.
Above and to the right of the zigzag line, tapered ends are required.

CONCRETE JOIST CONSTRUCTION
SINGLE SPAN—20 INCH WIDE FORMS
Safe Superimposed Load (psf)

For limitations and explanation of use of tables, see pages 7-3 to 7-5.

Depth: 10″ FORMS + 2½″ CONCRETE

Joists	4″ Joists @ 24″ c/c Wt 57 psf					5″ Joists @ 25″ c/c Wt 61 psf							
Bottom Bar / Truss Bar	#4 / #4	#5 / #4	#5 / #5	#6 / #5	#6 / #6	#5 / #5	#6 / #5	#6 / #6	#7 / #6	#7 / #7	#8 / #7	#8 / #8	#9 / #8
Length of Span in Feet 13	152	206	261	323	386	245	305	365	437				
14	124	170	218	271	326	203	254	292	369	432			
15	101	141	182	214	277	169	214	260	314	369	432	433	
16	82	118	154	194	236	142	181	221	268	317	372	378	
17	66	98	130	166	203	119	154	189	218	274	323	335	333
18	53	81	110	142	162	100	131	162	200	238	282	300	298
19	42	67	93	122	149	83	111	140	173	208	247	270	268
20	33	55	79	105	131	69	95	120	151	170	217	245	243
21		45	66	90	114	58	80	104	131	158	191	223	222
22		36	55	77	99	47	68	89	114	140	169	199	203
23			46	66	86	38	57	77	100	123	150	177	187
24			38	56	74	30	48	66	87	108	127	158	173
25			30	47	64		39	56	75	95	118	141	160
26				39	55		32	47	65	83	104	126	148
27				33	47			39	56	73	92	104	134
28					40			33	48	64	82	97	120
29					34				41	56	72	90	108

Depth: 10″ FORMS + 3″ CONCRETE

Joists	4″ Joists @ 24″ c/c Wt 63 psf					5″ Joists @ 25″ c/c Wt 67 psf							
Bottom Bar / Truss Bar	#4 / #4	#5 / #4	#5 / #5	#6 / #5	#6 / #6	#5 / #5	#6 / #5	#6 / #6	#7 / #6	#7 / #7	#8 / #7	#8 / #8	#9 / #8
Length of Span in Feet 13	156	212	269	334	400	253	315	379					
14	126	174	224	280	337	209	263	304	382	448			
15	102	144	187	222	286	174	220	268	325	382	447	448	
16	82	119	157	200	244	145	186	228	277	328	385	392	
17	66	99	132	170	209	121	157	194	226	283	334	347	
18	52	81	111	145	167	101	133	166	206	246	291	309	
19	40	67	94	124	153	84	113	143	178	214	254	279	
20	30	54	78	106	134	69	96	122	154	176	223	252	
21		44	66	90	116	57	81	105	134	162	196	230	
22		34	54	77	100	46	68	90	116	143	173	204	209
23			44	65	86	36	56	77	101	125	153	182	192
24			36	55	74		47	65	87	110	129	161	177
25				46	64		38	55	75	96	120	144	163
26				38	54		30	46	65	84	106	128	151
27				31	46			38	55	73	93	106	136
28					38			31	47	63	82	99	122
29					32				39	55	72	90	109
30									32	47	63	80	98

Values below horizontal line are for spans in excess of 24 t.
Above and to the right of the zigzag line, tapered ends are required.

CONCRETE JOIST CONSTRUCTION
SINGLE SPAN—20 INCH WIDE FORMS
Safe Superimposed Load (psf)

For limitations and explanation of use of tables, see pages 7-3 to 7-5.

Depth: 10″ FORMS + 4½″ CONCRETE

Joists	4″ Joists @ 24″ c/c Wt 82 psf					5″ Joists @ 25″ c/c Wt 86 psf							
Bottom Bar / Truss Bar	#4 / #4	#5 / #4	#5 / #5	#6 / #5	#6 / #6	#5 / #5	#6 / #5	#6 / #6	#7 / #6	#7 / #7	#8 / #7	#8 / #8	#9 / #8
Length of Span in Feet													
15	104	152	201	246	313	186	239	294	358	423			
16	82	124	167	216	265	154	200	248	304	362	427	432	
17	64	101	139	182	226	127	168	210	250	311	369	381	
18	48	82	115	154	182	104	141	179	223	268	320	339	
19	35	65	95	130	165	85	118	152	192	232	279	304	
20		51	78	110	141	68	98	129	165	192	243	275	
21		39	64	92	121	54	81	109	142	175	213	249	
22			51	77	103	42	67	92	122	152	187	222	226
23			40	64	87	31	54	77	104	132	150	196	207
24			30	52	74		43	64	89	115	139	173	190
25				42	62		33	53	76	99	126	153	175
26				32	51			42	64	85	110	135	161
27					42			33	53	73	96	111	144
28					33				43	62	84	103	128
29									35	52	72	93	114
30										43	62	81	101
31										35	53	71	83

Depth: 12″ FORMS + 2½″ CONCRETE

Joists	4″ Joists @ 24″ c/c Wt 63 psf				5″ Joists @ 25″ c/c Wt 67 psf						6″ Joists @ 26″ c/c Wt 72 psf			
Bottom Bar / Truss Bar	#5 / #4	#5 / #5	#6 / #5	#6 / #6	#6 / #6	#7 / #6	#7 / #7	#8 / #7	#8 / #8	#9 / #8	#9 / #8	#9 / #9	#10 / #9	#10 / #10
Length of Span in Feet														
17	119	157	200	244	228	268	329	388	398					
18	100	134	172	200	196	241	287	339	357		415			
19	83	114	148	183	169	209	251	298	322		375			
20	69	97	128	160	146	183	209	262	292		333	341		
21	57	82	110	139	127	159	193	232	267		295	312		
22	47	69	95	121	110	139	170	205	242	243	263	287		
23	38	58	82	106	95	122	150	167	216	224	234	264		
24	30	49	70	92	82	107	133	156	193	207	210	242	243	
25		40	60	80	70	93	117	144	172	192	173	217	226	
26		32	51	70	60	81	103	128	154	179	163	196	210	
27			43	60	51	71	91	114	129	164	151	176	197	
28			35	52	43	61	80	102	121	148	135	159	184	
29				44	35	52	70	90	111	133	122	136	171	172
30				37		45	61	80	100	120	109	129	155	162
31				31		38	53	71	89	100	98	117	141	152
32						31	46	63	80	95	87	106	128	144
33							39	55	71	88	78	95	108	135

Values below horizontal line are for spans in excess of 24 t.
Above and to the right of the zigzag line, tapered ends are required.

CONCRETE JOIST CONSTRUCTION
SINGLE SPAN—20 INCH WIDE FORMS
Safe Superimposed Load (psf)

For limitations and explanation of use of tables, see pages 7-3 to 7-5.

Depth: 12″ FORMS + 3″ CONCRETE

Joists	4″ Joists @ 24″ c/c Wt 69 psf				5″ Joists @ 25″ c/c Wt 74 psf						6″ Joists @ 26″ c/c Wt 78 psf		
Bottom Bar	#5	#5	#6	#6	#6	#7	#7	#8	#8	#9	#9	#9	#10
Truss Bar	#4	#5	#5	#6	#6	#6	#7	#7	#8	#8	#8	#9	#9
Length of Span in Feet													
17	120	160	204	250	233	276	338	398	410				
18	100	135	175	205	200	246	294	347	367		427		
19	83	114	150	187	172	214	256	304	330		385	386	
20	68	97	129	162	148	186	215	268	300		340	350	
21	56	81	111	141	128	162	197	236	273		301	320	
22	45	68	95	122	110	141	173	209	246	249	268	294	
23	35	57	81	106	95	123	152	171	219	229	238	271	
24		47	69	92	81	107	134	159	195	212	213	246	249
25		38	58	80	69	93	118	146	174	196	177	221	231
26		30	49	69	59	81	103	129	156	182	166	198	215
27			41	59	49	70	91	115	131	165	152	178	201
28			33	50	41	60	79	102	123	149	136	147	188
29				42	33	51	69	90	111	134	122	139	172
30				35		43	60	79	99	120	109	130	156
31						36	52	70	88	101	97	117	141
32							44	61	79	95	87	105	128
33							37	53	70	87	77	94	109

Depth: 12″ FORMS + 4½″ CONCRETE

Joists	4″ Joists @ 24″ c/c Wt 88 psf				5″ Joists @ 25″ c/c Wt 93 psf						6″ Joists @ 26″ c/c Wt 97 psf		
Bottom Bar	#5	#5	#6	#6	#6	#7	#7	#8	#8	#9	#9	#9	#10
Truss Bar	#4	#5	#5	#6	#6	#6	#7	#7	#8	#8	#8	#9	#9
Length of Span in Feet													
19	81	116	156	197	181	228	253	329	356		418		
20	65	97	133	169	155	197	233	288	322		368	379	
21	51	80	112	146	132	170	209	253	293		325	345	
22	39	65	95	125	112	147	182	222	263	266	288	316	
23		52	80	107	95	127	159	183	233	244	255	291	
24		41	66	92	80	109	139	170	207	224	277	263	267
25		31	54	78	67	94	121	152	184	207	190	235	247
26			44	65	55	80	105	134	163	192	178	210	229
27			34	55	45	67	91	118	137	174	160	188	213
28				45	35	56	78	103	128	155	142	156	198
29				36		47	67	90	114	139	126	146	181
30						38	57	78	100	124	111	135	163
31						30	47	68	88	103	98	120	147
32							39	58	77	97	87	107	120
33							31	49	67	87	76	95	113
34								41	58	76	66	84	106
35								34	50	67	57	74	95

Values below horizontal line are for spans in excess of 24 t.
Above and to the right of the zigzag line, tapered ends are required.

CONCRETE JOIST CONSTRUCTION
SINGLE SPAN—20 INCH WIDE FORMS
Safe Superimposed Load (psf)

For limitations and explanation of use of tables, see pages 7-3 to 7-5.

Depth	14″ FORMS + 2½″ CONCRETE											
Joists	5″ Joists @ 25″ c/c Wt 75 psf							6″ Joists @ 26″ c/c Wt 80 psf				
Bottom Bar	#6	#6	#7	#7	#8	#8	#9	#8	#9	#9	#10	#10
Truss Bar	#5	#6	#6	#7	#7	#8	#8	#8	#8	#9	#9	#10
Length of Span in Feet												
20	137	172	215	250	308	339		338	390	396		
21	117	149	188	227	272	310		272	346	362		
22	101	130	165	201	242	284		253	309	333		
23	86	113	145	177	200	254	261	236	276	307		
24	73	97	127	157	187	227	242	211	247	285		
25	62	84	111	139	171	204	224	188	207	256	263	
26	51	72	97	123	152	183	209	168	194	231	246	
27	42	62	85	109	136	154	194	150	179	209	229	
28	34	52	74	96	121	145	175	134	161	172	215	
29		44	64	85	108	133	159	120	145	163	202	
30		36	55	74	96	119	143	107	130	154	184	190
31			47	65	86	107	121	95	117	140	167	179
32			40	57	76	96	114	85	105	126	152	168
33			33	49	67	86	106	75	94	114	129	159
34				42	59	77	96	66	84	103	123	150
35				35	52	68	86	58	75	93	115	137
36				30	45	61	77	51	67	84	104	126
37					39	54	69	44	59	75	95	105

Depth	14″ FORMS + 3″ CONCRETE											
Joists	5″ Joists @ 25″ c/c Wt 81 psf							6″ Joists @ 26″ c/c Wt 86 psf				
Bottom Bar	#6	#6	#7	#7	#8	#8	#9	#8	#9	#9	#10	#10
Truss Bar	#5	#6	#6	#7	#7	#8	#8	#8	#8	#9	#9	#10
Length of Span in Feet												
21	118	151	190	230	276	316		279	352	370		
22	100	130	166	203	245	288	289	260	313	340		
23	85	113	145	179	204	257	266	239	279	314		
24	72	97	127	158	190	229	246	213	250	288	289	
25	60	83	111	139	172	205	228	190	211	259	269	
26	50	71	97	123	153	184	212	169	198	233	250	
27	40	60	84	108	136	156	195	151	180	210	234	
28	32	50	73	95	121	147	176	134	161	175	219	
29		42	62	83	107	132	159	119	145	165	203	205
30		34	53	73	95	118	143	106	130	154	185	192
31			45	63	84	106	122	94	116	139	168	181
32			37	54	74	95	115	83	104	126	152	170
33			30	46	65	84	105	73	93	113	131	161
34				39	57	75	94	64	83	102	124	150
35				33	49	66	84	56	73	91	114	137
36					42	58	75	48	65	82	103	125
37					36	51	67	41	57	73	93	106

Values below horizontal line are for spans in excess of 24 f.
Above and to the right of the zigzag line, tapered ends are required.

CONCRETE JOIST CONSTRUCTION
SINGLE SPAN—20 INCH WIDE FORMS
Safe Superimposed Load (psf)

For limitations and explanation of use of tables, see pages 7-3 to 7-5.

Depth: 14″ FORMS + 4½″ CONCRETE

Joists	5″ Joists @ 25″ c/c Wt 100 psf							6″ Joists @ 26″ c/c Wt 105 psf					
Bottom Bar	#6	#6	#7	#7	#7	#8	#9	#8	#9	#9	#10	#10	#11
Truss Bar	#5	#6	#6	#7	#7	#8	#8	#8	#8	#9	#9	#10	#10
Length of Span in Feet													
23	83	113	149	186	217	270	281	252	296	334			
24	68	96	129	163	201	241	259	223	241	304	307		
25	55	81	111	142	178	214	239	198	225	273	284		
26	44	67	96	124	157	175	222	175	209	244	264		
27	34	56	82	108	139	163	203	155	187	219	246		
28		45	69	94	122	151	182	137	166	185	229		
29		35	58	81	107	134	163	121	148	174	211	214	
30			48	69	94	119	133	106	132	158	191	201	
31			39	59	82	105	125	93	117	142	172	188	
32			30	49	71	93	116	81	104	127	144	177	
33				41	61	82	104	70	91	113	135	166	
34				33	52	71	92	60	80	101	126	152	155
35					43	62	82	51	70	89	113	138	146
36					36	53	72	43	61	79	101	113	138
37						45	63	35	52	69	91	107	130
38						38	54		44	60	81	101	122
39						31	47		37	52	71	91	111
40							40		30	45	63	82	101

Depth: 16″ FORMS + 2½″ CONCRETE

Joists	6″ Joists @ 26″ c/c Wt 88 psf							7″ Joists @ 27″ c/c Wt 93 psf					
Bottom Bar	#6	#7	#7	#8	#8	#9	#9	#9	#9	#10	#10	#11	#11
Truss Bar	#6	#6	#7	#7	#8	#8	#9	#8	#9	#9	#10	#10	#11
Length of Span in Feet													
24	100	133	166	204	243	285	325	266	294	358	368		
25	86	116	146	181	217	241	295	238	276	323	343		
26	73	100	129	161	194	227	266	213	248	292	320		
27	61	87	113	143	174	207	241	191	224	243	300		
28	51	75	99	127	156	186	201	171	202	230	278	280	
29	42	64	87	113	139	168	190	154	182	217	253	263	
30	34	54	75	100	125	151	179	138	164	197	231	248	
31		45	65	88	111	136	162	123	148	179	195	234	
32		37	56	77	99	123	147	110	133	162	185	221	
33		30	47	68	88	110	133	98	120	147	175	204	209
34			40	59	78	99	120	87	108	133	160	187	198
35			33	51	69	89	109	77	97	121	146	158	188
36				43	61	79	98	68	86	109	133	150	178
37				36	53	70	88	59	77	98	121	143	168
38				30	46	62	79	52	68	89	110	132	154
39					39	55	71	45	60	80	100	120	130
40					33	48	63	38	53	71	90	110	124
41						41	56	32	46	63	82	100	118

Values below horizontal line are for spans in excess of 24 t.
Above and to the right of the zigzag line, tapered ends are required.

CONCRETE JOIST CONSTRUCTION
SINGLE SPAN—20 INCH WIDE FORMS
Safe Superimposed Load (psf)

For limitations and explanation of use of tables, see pages 7-3 to 7-5.

Depth: 16″ FORMS + 3″ CONCRETE

Joists	6″ Joists @ 26″ c/c Wt 94 psf							7″ Joists @ 27″ c/c Wt 99 psf					
Bottom Bar	#6	#7	#7	#8	#8	#9	#9	#9	#9	#10	#10	#11	#11
Truss Bar	#6	#6	#7	#7	#8	#8	#9	#8	#9	#9	#10	#10	#11
Length of Span in Feet													
25	85	115	146	182	218	246	298	239	278	326	349		
26	71	99	128	161	195	231	268	214	250	294	326		
27	59	85	112	143	174	208	242	191	225	248	305		
28	49	73	98	126	155	187	204	171	202	234	280	285	
29	39	62	85	111	139	168	193	153	182	218	255	267	
30	31	52	73	98	124	151	179	137	164	197	232	252	
31		43	63	86	110	135	162	122	147	178	198	237	
32		35	53	75	98	121	146	109	132	162	188	223	224
33			45	65	86	109	132	96	119	146	175	204	212
34			37	56	76	97	119	85	106	132	159	187	200
35			30	48	67	87	107	75	95	119	145	159	190
36				40	58	77	96	66	84	107	131	152	180
37				33	50	68	86	57	75	97	119	143	167
38					43	60	77	49	66	87	108	130	153
39					36	52	68	42	58	77	98	119	131
40					30	45	61	35	50	69	88	108	124
41						38	53		43	61	79	98	118
42						32	46		36	53	71	89	108

Depth: 16″ FORMS + 4½″ CONCRETE

Joists	6″ Joists @ 26″ c/c Wt 113 psf							7″ Joists @ 27″ c/c Wt 118 psf					
Bottom Bar	#6	#7	#7	#8	#8	#9	#9	#9	#9	#10	#10	#11	#11
Truss Bar	#6	#6	#7	#7	#8	#8	#9	#8	#9	#9	#10	#10	#11
Length of Span in Feet													
27	54	83	111	144	178	214	229	197	232	264	320		
28	43	69	96	127	158	191	215	175	208	248	290	299	
29	33	57	82	111	140	171	202	155	186	224	262	280	
30		46	69	96	123	152	182	138	166	201	220	263	
31		36	58	83	108	136	163	122	148	181	208	248	
32			48	71	95	121	147	107	132	163	195	228	233
33			38	60	83	107	131	94	117	147	177	207	220
34			30	51	72	94	117	82	104	131	160	175	207
35				42	62	83	105	71	92	118	144	165	196
36				33	52	72	93	61	80	105	130	156	183
37					44	63	82	51	70	93	117	142	167
38					36	54	72	43	60	82	105	128	141
39						45	63	35	52	72	94	116	134
40						38	54		43	63	84	105	126
41						31	46		36	55	74	94	115
42							39			47	65	84	104
43							32			39	57	75	94
44										32	49	67	85

Values below horizontal line are for spans in excess of 24 t.
Above and to the right of the zigzag line, tapered ends are required.

CONCRETE JOIST CONSTRUCTION
SINGLE SPAN—20 INCH WIDE FORMS
Safe Superimposed Load (psf)

For limitations and explanation of use of tables, see pages 7-3 to 7-5.

Depth	20″ FORMS + 2½″ CONCRETE										
Joists	7″ Joists @ 27″ c/c Wt 112 psf							8″ @ 28″ c/c Wt 118 psf			
Bottom Bar Truss Bar	#7 #6	#7 #7	#8 #7	#8 #8	#9 #8	#9 #9	#10 #9	#10 #9	#10 #10	#11 #10	#11 #11
Length of Span in Feet											
31	48	72	99	127	158	189	227	210	248	282	327
32	38	61	87	113	141	170	207	190	226	263	301
33	30	51	75	100	126	154	188	172	205	240	254
34		41	64	88	113	139	171	155	187	220	242
35		33	55	77	100	125	155	140	170	201	230
36			46	67	89	112	141	126	154	184	214
37			37	57	78	100	127	113	140	168	197
38			30	49	69	89	115	101	127	153	181
39				41	60	79	104	90	115	140	166
40				33	51	70	93	80	103	127	152
41					44	62	84	71	93	116	139
42					37	54	75	62	83	105	127
43					30	46	66	54	74	95	116
44						39	58	47	66	85	106
45						33	51	40	58	77	96
46							44	33	50	68	87
47							38		43	61	79

Depth	20″ FORMS + 3″ CONCRETE											
Joists	7″ Joists @ 27″ c/c Wt 118 psf								8″ @ 28″ c/c Wt 124 psf			
Bottom Bar Truss Bar	#6 #6	#7 #6	#7 #7	#8 #7	#8 #8	#9 #8	#9 #9	#10 #9	#10 #9	#10 #10	#11 #10	#11 #11
Length of Span in Feet												
31		45	69	97	126	156	188	227	209	248	286	330
32		35	58	84	111	140	169	206	189	225	263	302
33			48	72	97	124	152	187	170	205	240	258
34			38	61	85	111	137	169	153	186	219	245
35			30	51	74	98	123	153	138	168	200	233
36				42	64	86	110	139	124	153	183	213
37				34	54	76	98	125	111	138	166	196
38					45	66	87	113	99	125	152	179
39					37	57	76	101	88	112	138	164
40					30	48	67	91	78	101	125	150
41						40	58	81	68	90	113	137
42						33	50	72	59	80	102	125
43							43	63	51	71	92	114
44							36	55	43	62	82	103
45								48	36	54	74	93
46								41		47	65	84
47								34		40	57	76

Values below horizontal line are for spans in excess of 24 t.
Above and to the right of the zigzag line, tapered ends are required.

CONCRETE JOIST CONSTRUCTION
SINGLE SPAN—20 INCH WIDE FORMS
Safe Superimposed Load (psf)

For limitations and explanation of use of tables, see pages 7-3 to 7-5.

Depth: 20″ FORMS + 4½″ CONCRETE

Joists	7″ Joists @ 27″ c/c Wt 137 psf					8″ Joists @ 28″ c/c Wt 143 psf							
Bottom Bar	#8	#8	#9	#9	#10	#8	#8	#9	#9	#10	#10	#11	#11
Truss Bar	#7	#8	#8	#9	#9	#7	#8	#8	#9	#9	#10	#10	#11
Length of Span in Feet													
32	79	107	137	168	206	66	93	122	151	188	226	266	285
33	66	93	121	150	186	54	79	106	134	169	205	242	270
34	55	80	106	133	167	43	66	92	118	151	185	220	255
35	44	68	93	118	151	32	55	79	104	135	166	199	233
36	35	57	81	105	135		44	67	91	120	150	181	213
37		47	69	92	121		35	56	78	106	134	164	194
38		37	59	80	108			46	67	93	120	148	177
39			49	70	95			37	57	82	107	134	161
40			40	60	84				47	71	95	120	146
41			32	50	74				38	61	84	108	132
42				42	64				30	51	73	96	120
43				34	55					43	64	85	108
44					47					35	55	75	97
45					39						46	66	86
46					31						38	57	77
47											31	49	68
48												41	59

CONCRETE JOIST CONSTRUCTION
SINGLE SPAN—30 INCH WIDE FORMS
Safe Superimposed Load (psf)

For limitations and explanation of use of tables, see pages 7-3 to 7-5.

Depth: 6″ FORMS + 2½″ CONCRETE

Joists	4″ Joists @ 34″ c/c Wt 41 psf					5″ Joists @ 35″ c/c Wt 43 psf				6″ Joists @ 36″ c/c Wt 45 psf			
Bottom Bar	#4	#5	#5	#6	#6	#6	#7	#7	#8	#7	#8	#8	#9
Truss Bar	#4	#4	#5	#5	#6	#6	#6	#7	#7	#7	#7	#8	#8
Length of Span in Feet													
9	159	210	262	320	380	367	408			394			
10	121	151	204	251	300	289	344	363		350			
11	93	127	162	201	241	232	277	324		312			
12	72	100	130	162	196	188	226	265	290	255	282		
13	55	79	99	132	161	154	186	220	257	211	247	257	
14	42	63	85	109	133	127	155	184	216	176	207	235	
15	31	50	68	89	111	100	129	155	182	148	175	203	214
16		39	55	69	93	87	109	131	155	124	148	173	189
17		30	44	61	78	72	91	111	133	99	126	149	166
18			35	50	65	60	73	95	114	89	108	128	147
19				41	50	50	65	81	98	76	92	110	128

Values below horizontal line are for spans in excess of 24 t.

Above and to the right of the zigzag line, tapered ends are required.

CONCRETE JOIST CONSTRUCTION
SINGLE SPAN—30 INCH WIDE FORMS
Safe Superimposed Load (psf)

For limitations and explanation of use of tables, see pages 7-3 to 7-5.

Depth	6″ FORMS + 3″ CONCRETE												
Joists	4″ Joists @ 34″ c/c Wt 47 psf					5″ Joists @ 35″ c/c Wt 49 psf						6″ Joists @ 36″ c/c Wt 50 psf	
Bottom Bar / Truss Bar	#4 / #4	#5 / #4	#5 / #5	#6 / #5	#6 / #6	#5 / #5	#6 / #5	#6 / #6	#7 / #6	#7 / #7	#8 / #7	#8 / #7	#8 / #8
Length of Span in Feet													
9	166	221	277	339	403	266	327	389	433				
10	126	160	215	266	318	202	255	306	365	385			
11	96	132	170	212	255	162	203	245	293	344			
12	73	104	135	170	207	128	150	198	239	281	307	298	
13	55	82	104	138	169	102	131	161	196	232	272	262	271
14	41	64	87	113	140	82	107	133	163	194	228	219	248
15	30	50	70	92	116	65	87	105	135	163	193	184	215
16		38	56	71	96	51	70	90	113	137	163	156	183
17			44	62	80	40	57	74	95	116	139	133	156
18			34	50	66	30	46	61	75	98	119	113	134
19				40	50		36	50	66	83	102	96	115
20				32	45			40	55	70	87	77	99
21					36			32	45	56	75	70	85
22									37	50	64	59	73

Depth	6″ FORMS + 4½″ CONCRETE												
Joists	4″ Joists @ 34″ c/c Wt 66 psf					5″ Joists @ 35″ c/c Wt 68 psf						6″ Joists @ 36″ c/c Wt 69 psf	
Bottom Bar / Truss Bar	#4 / #4	#5 / #4	#5 / #5	#6 / #5	#6 / #6	#5 / #5	#6 / #5	#6 / #6	#7 / #6	#7 / #7	#8 / #7	#8 / #7	#8 / #8
Length of Span in Feet													
9	189	254	321	397		286	382						
10	141	188	248	309	372	238	297	358	429				
11	105	149	194	244	296	185	234	284	343	403			
12	78	115	153	195	238	145	176	228	278	329	359	347	
13	57	88	118	157	194	113	149	185	227	270	317	307	315
14	40	67	95	126	158	89	119	150	186	224	263	255	288
15		50	74	102	129	69	95	119	154	186	223	213	250
16		36	58	77	106	52	76	99	127	156	188	179	212
17			44	65	86	39	59	80	105	130	159	151	180
18			32	51	70		46	65	83	109	135	127	153
19				39	52		34	51	71	91	114	107	130
20					45			40	58	76	96	85	111
21					34			30	46	59	81	76	94
22									36	51	68	63	80
23										41	57	52	63
24										32	47	42	56
25											36	33	47

Values below horizontal line are for spans in excess of 24 t.
Above and to the right of the zigzag line, tapered ends are required.

CONCRETE JOIST CONSTRUCTION
SINGLE SPAN—30 INCH WIDE FORMS
Safe Superimposed Load (psf)

For limitations and explanation of use of tables, see pages 7-3 to 7-5.

Depth: 8″ FORMS + 2½″ CONCRETE

Joists	4″ Joists @ 34″ c/c Wt 45 psf					5″ Joists @ 35″ c/c Wt 48 psf						6″ Joists @ 36″ c/c Wt 50 psf		
Bottom Bar	#4	#5	#5	#6	#6	#6	#7	#7	#8	#8	#9	#8	#9	#9
Truss Bar	#4	#4	#5	#5	#6	#6	#6	#7	#7	#8	#8	#8	#8	#9
Length of Span in Feet														
10	161	209	269	330	392	378	449					450		
11	126	169	214	265	316	304	363	423				404		
12	98	135	173	215	259	248	297	349	379			367		
13	77	109	138	177	214	205	247	290	337			335		
14	61	88	115	147	179	155	206	244	283			307		
15	47	71	95	122	150	139	174	206	242			270	281	
16	36	57	78	98	126	119	147	176	208	211		231	249	
17		45	64	85	107	100	125	150	179	185		199	220	
18		36	52	71	91	85	103	129	154	164		173	196	
19			43	59	73	71	91	111	134	147		150	174	175
20			34	49	65	60	77	96	116	132	131	130	152	158
21				41	55	50	66	79	101	120	118	114	133	144
22				33	46	41	56	71	88	106	108	99	117	131
23					38	34	47	61	77	93	98	83	103	120
24					32		40	52	61	81	90	76	91	106
25							33	45	56	71	82	66	80	94
26								38	50	63	75	57	65	83

Depth: 8″ FORMS + 3″ CONCRETE

Joists	4″ Joists @ 34″ c/c Wt 51 psf					5″ Joists @ 35″ c/c Wt 54 psf						6″ Joists @ 36″ c/c Wt 56 psf		
Bottom Bar	#4	#5	#5	#6	#6	#6	#7	#7	#8	#8	#9	#8	#9	#9
Truss Bar	#4	#4	#5	#5	#6	#6	#6	#7	#7	#8	#8	#8	#8	#9
Length of Span in Feet														
10	166	219	279	344	410	395								
11	129	175	222	276	330	317	380	442				423		
12	100	139	164	224	270	258	311	364	396			383		
13	78	111	144	183	222	212	257	303	352			349		
14	60	89	118	151	185	161	214	254	295			321		
15	46	71	96	125	154	144	180	214	252			282	293	
16	34	56	79	100	130	122	152	182	216	219		241	259	
17		44	64	86	109	102	128	155	185	192		207	228	
18		34	52	72	92	86	106	133	160	170		179	203	
19			41	59	73	72	92	114	138	151		155	180	181
20			32	48	65	59	78	98	119	136		135	157	163
21				39	54	49	66	80	103	123		117	137	148
22				31	45	40	56	72	90	108	110	102	120	135
23					37	32	46	61	77	95	100	84	106	123
24					30		38	52	61	83	91	77	92	109
25							31	44	56	72	83	66	81	96

Values below horizontal line are for spans in excess of 24 t.
Above and to the right of the zigzag line, tapered ends are required.

CONCRETE JOIST CONSTRUCTION
SINGLE SPAN—30 INCH WIDE FORMS
Safe Superimposed Load (psf)

For limitations and explanation of use of tables, see pages 7-3 to 7-5.

Depth: 8″ FORMS + 4½″ CONCRETE

Joists	4″ Joists @ 34″ c/c Wt 70 psf					5″ Joists @ 35″ c/c Wt 73 psf						6″ Joists @ 36″ c/c Wt 75 psf		
Bottom Bar	#4	#5	#5	#6	#6	#6	#7	#7	#8	#8	#9	#8	#9	#9
Truss Bar	#4	#4	#5	#5	#6	#6	#6	#7	#7	#8	#8	#8	#8	#9
Length of Span in Feet														
10	181	246	312	387		447								
11	138	192	246	308	372	357	430							
12	105	150	184	248	301	289	350	412	448			432		
13	79	118	157	201	247	236	288	341	396			393		
14	59	92	126	164	203	181	238	284	330			360		
15	43	72	101	134	168	159	198	238	281			317	329	
16		55	81	108	140	132	166	201	241	242		270	290	
17		41	64	89	116	109	127	170	205	211		231	254	
18			49	72	96	89	114	144	175	186		198	224	
19			37	58	76	73	97	122	150	165		170	200	
20				46	65	59	81	103	129	147		147	173	179
21				35	53	47	67	84	110	131		126	150	161
22					42	36	55	73	94	116	117	109	131	146
23					32		44	61	80	100	105	89	113	132
24							35	50	62	86	95	80	98	117
25								41	56	74	86	68	85	102
26								32	47	63	78	57	68	89
27									39	53	68	48	62	77

Depth: 10″ FORMS + 2½″ CONCRETE

Joists	4″ Joists @ 34″ c/c Wt 49 psf					5″ Joists @ 35″ c/c Wt 52 psf						6″ Joists @ 36″ c/c Wt 54 psf		
Bottom Bar	#4	#5	#5	#6	#6	#6	#7	#7	#8	#8	#9	#9	#9	#10
Truss Bar	#4	#4	#5	#5	#6	#6	#6	#7	#7	#8	#8	#8	#9	#9
Length of Span in Feet														
14	79	113	146	185	224	200	258	304	350					
15	63	92	121	142	189	179	218	258	300			348		
16	49	75	101	128	160	151	186	221	260	262		309		
17	38	61	84	110	136	128	147	190	225	231		273		
18		49	70	93	116	109	134	164	195	205		244		
19		39	58	78	96	92	117	142	170	184		219		
20		31	47	66	85	79	100	113	148	166		192	198	
21			38	55	73	66	86	104	130	151		170	180	
22			31	46	62	56	74	93	114	135	136	150	165	
23				38	53	47	64	81	100	120	125	132	151	
24				31	45	39	54	70	82	106	115	117	137	
25					37	32	46	60	76	93	106	104	122	128
26					31		39	52	67	83	97	87	109	118
27							32	45	58	73	88	81	97	110
28								38	51	61	78	72	86	102
29								32	44	56	69	63	71	93

Values below horizontal line are for spans in excess of 24 t.
Above and to the right of the zigzag line, tapered ends are required.

CONCRETE JOIST CONSTRUCTION
SINGLE SPAN—30 INCH WIDE FORMS
Safe Superimposed Load (psf)

For limitations and explanation of use of tables, see pages 7-3 to 7-5.

Depth: 10″ FORMS + 3″ CONCRETE

Joists	4″ Joists @ 34″ c/c Wt 56 psf					5″ Joists @ 35″ c/c Wt 58 psf						6″ Joists @ 36″ c/c Wt 61 psf		
Bottom Bar	#4	#5	#5	#6	#6	#6	#7	#7	#8	#8	#9	#9	#9	#10
Truss Bar	#4	#4	#5	#5	#6	#6	#6	#7	#7	#8	#8	#8	#9	#9
Length of Span in Feet														
14	79	114	149	189	230	207	266	314	362					
15	62	92	123	146	193	183	224	266	310			360		
16	48	74	101	131	163	154	190	227	269	270		319		
17	36	60	84	111	139	130	151	195	231	237		281		
18		47	69	93	118	110	137	167	200	211		251		
19		37	56	78	97	93	118	144	174	189		225		
20			45	65	85	78	101	115	151	170		198	203	
21			36	54	72	66	87	106	132	154		174	185	
22				44	61	55	74	93	115	138		153	169	
23				36	51	45	63	81	101	121	127	135	154	
24					43	37	53	69	82	107	116	119	139	141
25					35	30	44	59	76	94	106	105	124	130
26							37	51	66	83	98	88	110	120
27							30	43	57	72	88	82	97	111
28								36	49	60	78	72	86	103
29								30	42	55	69	63	71	93
30									36	48	61	55	66	83

Depth: 10″ FORMS + 4½″ CONCRETE

Joists	4″ Joists @ 34″ c/c Wt 74 psf					5″ Joists @ 35″ c/c Wt 77 psf						6″ Joists @ 36″ c/c Wt 79 psf		
Bottom Bar	#4	#5	#5	#6	#6	#6	#7	#7	#8	#8	#9	#9	#9	#10
Truss Bar	#4	#4	#5	#5	#6	#6	#6	#7	#7	#8	#8	#8	#9	#9
Length of Span in Feet														
14	78	117	157	202	249	229	290	344	397			430		
15	58	93	127	158	207	197	243	290	338			396		
16	43	73	103	138	173	164	204	246	293			349		
17	30	56	83	114	145	136	163	209	251	257		307		
18		42	66	94	112	114	146	179	216	227		272		
19		31	52	77	101	94	123	153	186	202		243		
20			40	62	85	78	104	121	161	181		214	219	
21			30	50	70	64	87	111	139	163		187	198	
22				39	58	51	73	95	120	146		163	180	
23				30	47	40	60	80	103	127	132	143	164	
24					37	31	49	68	84	110	120	125	148	
25							39	57	76	96	109	109	130	136
26							31	47	65	83	100	90	114	125
27								38	54	71	89	82	100	115
28								30	45	58	78	71	88	106
29									37	52	68	61	71	96
30									30	44	58	52	66	84

Values below horizontal line are for spans in excess of 24 t.
Above and to the right of the zigzag line, tapered ends are required.

CONCRETE JOIST CONSTRUCTION
SINGLE SPAN—30 INCH WIDE FORMS
Safe Superimposed Load (psf)

For limitations and explanation of use of tables, see pages 7-3 to 7-5.

Depth: 12″ FORMS + 2½″ CONCRETE

Joists	4″ Joists @ 34″ c/c Wt 53 psf					5″ Joists @ 35″ c/c Wt 57 psf						6″ Joists @ 36″ c/c Wt 61 psf		
Bottom Bar	#4	#5	#5	#6	#6	#6	#7	#7	#8	#8	#9	#9	#9	#10
Truss Bar	#4	#4	#5	#5	#6	#6	#6	#7	#7	#8	#8	#8	#9	#9
Length of Span in Feet														
16	63	93	123	158	193	183	224	266	312			368		
17	50	76	103	134	165	156	183	229	271	276		326		
18	39	62	86	114	132	133	165	198	236	246		291		
19		51	72	97	121	114	143	172	206	221		262		
20		41	60	82	105	97	123	141	180	200		233	238	
21		32	50	70	90	83	107	130	158	182		206	217	
22			41	59	78	71	92	114	139	165		183	199	
23			33	50	67	60	80	100	123	147	151	162	183	
24				41	57	51	69	87	103	130	139	144	167	
25				34	49	42	59	76	95	116	129	117	150	155
26					41	35	50	66	84	103	119	109	134	144
27					34		43	57	74	83	109	101	120	134
28							36	49	65	78	98	90	107	124
29							30	42	57	72	87	80	90	116
30								36	49	63	78	71	84	104
31								30	43	56	69	63	77	94
32									37	49	59	55	68	84

Depth: 12″ FORMS + 3″ CONCRETE

Joists	4″ Joists @ 34″ c/c Wt 60 psf					5″ Joists @ 35″ c/c Wt 63 psf						6″ Joists @ 36″ c/c Wt 67 psf		
Bottom Bar	#4	#5	#5	#6	#6	#6	#7	#7	#8	#8	#9	#9	#9	#10
Truss Bar	#4	#4	#5	#5	#6	#6	#6	#7	#7	#8	#8	#8	#9	#9
Length of Span in Feet														
17	47	75	103	135	168	158	187	234	278	282		335		
18	36	61	86	114	134	134	168	202	241	251		299		
19		49	71	97	122	114	144	175	210	226		268		
20		38	58	82	105	97	124	143	183	204		238	243	
21			48	69	90	82	107	132	161	185		210	221	
22			38	57	77	69	92	115	141	168		186	202	
23			30	47	65	58	79	100	124	148	153	164	186	
24				39	55	49	67	87	104	131	141	146	169	170
25				31	46	40	57	75	95	116	130	118	151	157
26					38	32	48	65	83	103	120	110	135	145
27					31		40	56	73	83	109	101	120	135
28							33	47	63	77	97	90	107	125
29								40	55	70	87	79	90	116
30								33	47	62	77	70	84	104
31									40	54	68	61	75	93
32									34	47	58	53	67	83
33										40	53	46	59	69

Values below horizontal line are for spans in excess of 24 t.
Above and to the right of the zigzag line, tapered ends are required.

CONCRETE JOIST CONSTRUCTION
SINGLE SPAN—30 INCH WIDE FORMS
Safe Superimposed Load (psf)

For limitations and explanation of use of tables, see pages 7-3 to 7-5.

Depth: 12″ FORMS + 4½″ CONCRETE

Joists	4″ @ 34″ c/c Wt 78 psf		5″ Joists @ 35″ c/c Wt 82 psf							6″ Joists @ 36″ c/c Wt 86 psf				
Bottom Bar / Truss Bar	#6 / #5	#6 / #6	#6 / #5	#6 / #6	#7 / #6	#7 / #7	#8 / #7	#8 / #8	#9 / #8	#8 / #8	#9 / #8	#9 / #9	#10 / #9	#10 / #10
Length of Span in Feet														
19	96	125	87	116	149	183	222	239		250	287			
20	79	105	71	96	127	151	193	214		217	254	259		
21	64	88	57	80	108	136	168	194		189	223	234		
22	52	74	45	66	91	116	146	175		156	196	213		
23	41	61	34	54	76	100	126	154	159	144	172	195		
24	31	50		43	64	85	106	135	145	126	151	178		
25		40		33	52	72	95	118	132	109	122	157	163	
26		31			42	61	82	103	121	95	113	139	150	
27					34	51	70	82	111	82	102	123	139	
28						41	59	76	97	70	89	109	128	
29						33	50	67	85	60	77	90	118	
30							41	57	74	50	67	84	105	110
31							34	49	65	42	57	73	93	102
32								41	54	34	49	64	82	95
33								34	48		41	55	66	88
34									40		34	47	62	80

Depth: 14″ FORMS + 2½″ CONCRETE

Joists	5″ Joists @ 35″ c/c Wt 62 psf					6″ Joists @ 36″ c/c Wt 65 psf				7″ Joists @ 37″ c/c Wt 69 psf			
Bottom Bar / Truss Bar	#7 / #6	#7 / #7	#8 / #7	#8 / #8	#9 / #8	#9 / #8	#9 / #9	#10 / #9	#10 / #10	#9 / #9	#10 / #9	#10 / #10	#11 / #10
Length of Span in Feet													
20	146	170	213	234		275	277			300	318		
21	127	155	187	213		243	253			266	291		
22	110	136	165	195		216	232			236	267		
23	96	119	134	174	178	192	214			210	246		
24	83	104	125	154	164	171	197			176	220	228	
25	72	91	114	138	152	141	178	182		165	197	211	
26	62	80	101	123	140	132	159	169		150	177	197	
27	53	70	89	101	130	122	143	157		134	160	184	
28	45	61	79	95	117	109	129	147		120	136	168	
29	38	52	69	87	105	97	109	137		107	128	152	160
30	31	45	61	77	94	86	103	125	129	96	116	138	150
31		38	53	68	78	77	93	113	121	85	105	114	141
32		32	46	60	73	68	83	102	113	76	94	107	132
33			40	53	67	60	74	85	106	67	84	102	121
34			34	47	60	53	66	80	100	59	76	92	110
35				41	53	46	59	75	91	52	67	83	100
36				35	47	40	52	67	83	46	60	75	85
37				30	41	35	46	60	75	39	53	67	81

Values below horizontal line are for spans in excess of 24 t.
Above and to the right of the zigzag line, tapered ends are required.

CONCRETE JOIST CONSTRUCTION
SINGLE SPAN—30 INCH WIDE FORMS
Safe Superimposed Load (psf)

For limitations and explanation of use of tables, see pages 7-3 to 7-5.

14″ FORMS + 3″ CONCRETE

Depth	14″ FORMS + 3″ CONCRETE											
Joists	5″ Joists @ 35″ c/c Wt 68 psf					6″ Joists @ 36″ c/c Wt 71 psf				7″ Joists @ 37″ c/c Wt 75 psf		
Bottom Bar	#7	#7	#8	#8	#9	#9	#9	#10	#10	#9	#10	#10
Truss Bar	#6	#7	#7	#8	#8	#8	#9	#9	#10	#9	#9	#10
Length of Span in Feet												
21	127	156	189	216		246	257			269	296	
22	110	136	166	197		218	236			239	272	
23	95	119	135	175	180	194	217			212	248	250
24	82	104	126	155	165	172	200			179	222	231
25	70	90	114	138	152	142	179	184		167	199	215
26	60	79	100	122	141	133	160	171		150	178	199
27	51	68	88	101	130	121	143	159		134	146	186
28	42	59	77	95	117	108	117	148		119	137	169
29	35	50	68	85	104	96	109	138		106	129	152
30		42	59	75	93	85	102	124	129	94	115	138
31		36	51	66	77	75	91	112	121	84	103	114
32			44	58	72	66	82	101	113	74	93	108
33			37	51	65	58	72	84	106	65	83	101
34			31	44	58	50	64	79	99	57	74	91
35				38	51	44	57	73	89	50	65	81
36				32	44	37	50	65	81	43	58	73
37					38	32	43	58	66	37	51	65

14″ FORMS + 4½″ CONCRETE

Depth	14″ FORMS + 4½″ CONCRETE													
Joists	5″ Joists @ 35″ c/c Wt 87 psf						6″ Joists @ 36″ c/c Wt 90 psf				7″ Joists @ 37″ c/c Wt 94 psf		
Bottom Bar	#7	#7	#8	#8	#9	#9	#9	#9	#10	#10	#10	#10	#11
Truss Bar	#6	#7	#7	#8	#8	#9	#8	#9	#9	#10	#9	#10	#10
Length of Span in Feet													
23	92	119	139	180	185		201	226			262		
24	78	102	128	159	169		178	208			233	243	
25	65	88	113	140	155		147	185	190		207	224	
26	54	75	98	123	143		137	164	176		185	208	
27	44	63	85	101	131		122	146	162		151	193	
28	35	53	73	94	116		107	118	151		142	174	178
29		43	63	82	103	112	94	110	140		130	156	166
30		35	53	71	90	103	82	101	125	130	116	140	155
31			44	61	73	96	71	89	111	121	103	116	144
32			36	52	68	87	61	78	99	113	91	109	133
33				44	60	76	52	68	83	105	80	99	119
34				37	52	67	44	59	77	97	70	88	107
35				30	44	53	37	51	68	86	61	78	89
36					37	49	30	43	60	77	52	69	83
37					30	44		36	52	62	45	60	76
38						37		30	45	58	37	52	67
39						31			38	52	31	45	59

Values below horizontal line are for spans in excess of 24 f.
Above and to the right of the zigzag line, tapered ends are required.

CONCRETE JOIST CONSTRUCTION
SINGLE SPAN—30 INCH WIDE FORMS
Safe Superimposed Load (psf)

For limitations and explanation of use of tables, see pages 7-3 to 7-5.

Depth: 16″ FORMS + 2½″ CONCRETE

Joists	6″ Joists @ 36″ c/c Wt 72 psf						7″ Joists @ 37″ c/c Wt 76 psf				8″ @ 38″ c/c Wt 80 psf	
Bottom Bar / Truss Bar	#7 / #6	#7 / #7	#8 / #7	#8 / #8	#9 / #8	#9 / #9	#9 / #9	#10 / #9	#10 / #10	#11 / #10	#11 / #10	#11 / #11
Length of Span in Feet 25	76	98	123	149	166	206	193	228	242		270	
26	65	85	109	133	155	185	174	206	225		254	
27	55	74	96	118	142	166	156	169	211		235	
28	46	64	84	105	127	137	140	160	195		213	222
29	38	55	74	93	113	129	125	150	177	184	193	209
30	31	46	64	82	101	121	112	136	161	173	161	196
31		39	56	72	91	109	100	123	134	162	153	183
32		32	48	64	81	98	89	111	127	153	144	167
33			41	56	72	88	80	99	120	141	131	153
34			34	48	63	79	71	89	109	128	119	130
35				42	56	71	63	80	98	107	108	123
36				36	49	63	55	72	89	101	98	116
37				30	43	56	48	64	80	96	89	105
38					37	49	42	57	72	88	80	96
39					31	43	36	50	65	80	72	87
40						38	31	44	58	72	64	79
41						32		38	52	65	58	71
42								33	46	59	51	64

Depth: 16″ FORMS + 3″ CONCRETE

Joists	6″ Joists @ 36″ c/c Wt 78 psf						7″ Joists @ 37″ c/c Wt 83 psf						8″ @ 38″ c/c Wt 87 psf	
Bottom Bar / Truss Bar	#7 / #6	#7 / #7	#8 / #7	#8 / #8	#9 / #8	#9 / #9	#8 / #8	#9 / #8	#9 / #9	#10 / #9	#10 / #10	#11 / #10	#10 / #10	#11 / #10
Length of Span in Feet 25	74	97	122	149	167	206	139	166	194	230	245		253	274
26	63	83	107	132	157	185	122	148	174	206	228		208	258
27	53	72	94	117	141	166	107	131	155	171	213		196	236
28	44	61	82	103	126	138	94	116	139	161	196	198	184	213
29	35	52	71	91	112	129	82	103	124	150	177	185	166	193
30		44	62	80	100	120	72	91	111	135	160	174	150	163
31		36	53	70	89	107	62	80	98	121	135	163	135	154
32			45	61	78	96	53	70	87	109	127	154	122	144
33			38	53	69	86	45	61	77	98	118	140	109	130
34			31	45	61	76	38	53	68	87	107	127	98	118
35				39	53	68	31	45	60	78	96	107	88	106
36				32	46	60		39	52	69	87	101	78	96
37					39	53		32	45	61	78	95	70	86
38					33	46			39	54	69	86	62	77
39						40			33	47	62	77	54	69
40						34				41	55	69	47	62
41										35	48	62	41	55

Values below horizontal line are for spans in excess of 24 *t*.
Above and to the right of the zigzag line, tapered ends are required.

CONCRETE JOIST CONSTRUCTION
SINGLE SPAN—30 INCH WIDE FORMS
Safe Superimposed Load (psf)

For limitations and explanation of use of tables, see pages 7-3 to 7-5.

Depth: 16″ FORMS + 4½″ CONCRETE

Joists	6″ Joists @ 36″ c/c Wt 97 psf						7″ Joists @ 37″ c/c Wt 101 psf				8″ Joists @ 38″ c/c Wt 105 psf	
Bottom Bar	#7	#7	#8	#8	#9	#9	#9	#10	#10	#11	#11	#11
Truss Bar	#6	#7	#7	#8	#8	#9	#9	#9	#10	#10	#10	#11
Length of Span in Feet												
27	46	67	91	115	141	168	157	178	220	218	243	250
28	36	55	78	101	125	140	139	166	200	203	219	234
29		45	66	87	110	131	123	151	180	190	197	218
30		36	56	75	97	118	109	135	161	177	168	204
31			46	65	85	105	95	120	137	166	159	186
32			37	55	74	93	84	106	129	154	144	168
33			30	46	64	81	73	94	116	139	129	141
34				38	54	71	63	83	104	125	116	133
35				30	46	62	54	73	93	106	103	124
36					38	53	45	63	82	100	92	111
37					31	45	38	55	72	91	82	100
38						38	31	47	64	81	72	89
39						32		40	55	72	63	80
40								33	48	63	55	71
41									41	55	48	62

Depth: 20″ FORMS + 2½″ CONCRETE

Joists	7″ Joists @ 37″ c/c Wt 90 psf						8″ Joists @ 38″ c/c Wt 95 psf				9″ Joists @ 39″ c/c Wt 101 psf	
Bottom Bar	#7	#8	#8	#9	#9	#10	#10	#10	#11	#11	#11	#11
Truss Bar	#7	#7	#8	#8	#9	#9	#9	#10	#10	#11	#10	#11
Length of Span in Feet												
28	74	99	124	151	179	209	201	235	271	279	257	263
29	63	86	110	135	161	193	181	213	247	262	233	249
30	53	75	97	120	145	175	163	193	211	247	212	235
31	44	65	85	107	130	158	147	175	200	233	192	222
32	36	55	75	95	116	143	132	159	186	214	174	202
33		47	65	84	104	129	119	144	169	179	158	184
34		39	56	74	93	117	106	130	154	170	143	168
35		32	48	65	83	105	95	117	140	162	130	153
36			41	57	74	95	85	106	128	150	117	139
37			34	49	65	85	76	95	116	137	106	127
38				42	57	76	67	86	105	125	96	115
39				36	50	68	59	77	95	114	86	104
40				30	43	60	51	68	86	104	77	94
41					37	53	44	61	77	95	68	85
42					31	46	38	53	69	86	61	77
43						40	32	47	62	78	53	69
44						35		40	55	70	47	61
45								35	49	63	40	54

Values below horizontal line are for spans in excess of 24 t.
Above and to the right of the zigzag line, tapered ends are required.

CONCRETE JOIST CONSTRUCTION
SINGLE SPAN—30 INCH WIDE FORMS
Safe Superimposed Load (psf)

For limitations and explanation of use of tables, see pages 7-3 to 7-5.

Depth: 20″ FORMS + 3″ CONCRETE

Joists	7″ Joists @ 37″ c/c Wt 96 psf					8″ Joists @ 38″ c/c Wt 101 psf				9″ Joists @ 39″ c/c Wt 107 psf				
Bottom Bar	#8	#8	#9	#9	#10	#10	#10	#11	#11	#9	#10	#10	#11	#11
Truss Bar	#7	#8	#8	#9	#9	#9	#10	#10	#11	#9	#9	#10	#10	#11
Length of Span in Feet														
27	111	138	168	198	224	222	255	299	301	174	210	246	283	
28	97	122	150	178	211	200	235	271	282	154	188	222	257	267
29	84	108	133	159	192	180	212	226	265	137	168	200	233	252
30	72	94	118	143	173	162	192	213	249	121	150	180	211	238
31	62	82	105	128	156	145	174	201	234	107	134	162	191	221
32	52	72	93	114	141	130	157	185	214	94	120	146	173	201
33	43	62	82	102	127	116	142	168	181	82	106	131	156	183
34	35	53	71	90	114	104	128	152	171	72	94	117	141	166
35		45	62	80	103	93	115	138	162	62	83	105	128	151
36		37	54	71	92	82	103	125	148	53	73	94	115	137
37		30	46	62	82	73	93	113	135	45	64	83	103	124
38			39	54	73	64	83	102	123	37	55	73	93	113
39			32	46	64	55	74	92	112	30	47	65	83	102
40				39	57	48	65	83	101		40	56	74	92
41				33	49	41	57	74	92		33	49	65	82
42					43	34	50	66	83			41	57	74
43					36		43	58	74			35	50	65

Depth: 20″ FORMS + 4½″ CONCRETE

Joists	7″ Joists @ 37″ c/c Wt 115 psf				8″ Joists @ 38″ c/c Wt 120 psf					9″ Joists @ 39″ c/c Wt 126 psf	
Bottom Bar	#8	#9	#9	#10	#9	#10	#10	#11	#11	#11	#11
Truss Bar	#8	#8	#9	#9	#9	#9	#10	#10	#11	#10	#11
Length of Span in Feet											
27	136	167	199	232	186	225	264	305	310	290	297
28	119	148	177	214	165	201	237	275	290	261	279
29	103	130	158	192	146	179	213	233	272	235	262
30	89	114	140	172	129	160	192	220	255	212	245
31	76	100	124	154	113	142	172	203	235	191	222
32	65	87	110	138	99	127	154	184	195	171	201
33	54	75	96	123	86	112	138	166	184	154	181
34	45	64	84	109	74	99	124	149	174	138	164
35	36	54	73	97	64	87	110	134	159	123	148
36		45	63	85	54	76	98	121	144	110	133
37		37	54	75	45	65	86	108	130	98	120
38			45	65	36	56	76	96	117	86	107
39			37	56		47	66	86	106	76	95
40			30	48		39	57	76	95	66	85
41				40		32	49	66	85	57	75
42				33			41	58	75	49	66
43							34	50	66	41	57

Values below horizontal line are for spans in excess of 24 t.
Above and to the right of the zigzag line, tapered ends are required.

CONCRETE JOIST CONSTRUCTION—END SPAN

Read the general explanation of the arrangement of tables for Concrete Joist Construction on pages 7-3 to 7-5 before using these tables for end spans. The details of temperature reinforcement, tapered end forms, distribution ribs, and especially the type of deformed bars all apply equally well here.

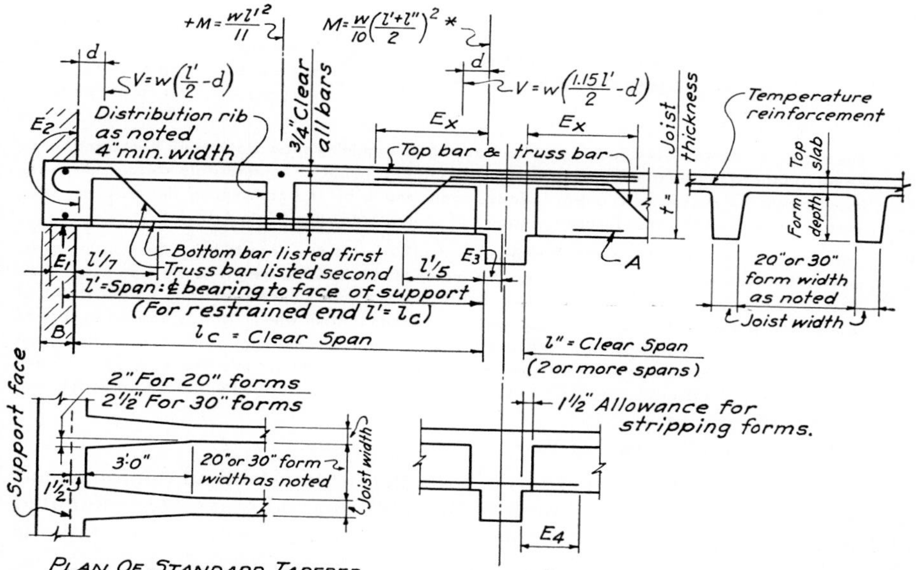

PLAN OF STANDARD TAPERED END WHERE REQUIRED

STRESSES:—

f'_c = 3750 psi
f_c = 1688 psi
f_s = 24,000 psi †
$v_c = 1.2\sqrt{f'_c}$ = 73.5 psi ‡
$u = \dfrac{4.8\sqrt{f'_c}}{D}$ = (See Table on page 3-13) ‡

CODES:— "Building Code Requirements for Reinforced Concrete (ACI 318-63)"; "Manual of Standard Practice for Detailing Reinforced Concrete Structures (ACI 315)."

E_1 = 6 in. minimum for bottom bars (straight if possible, bent if necessary).
E_2 = 6 in. for #3 bars, 10 in. for #4 bars; $21D^2$ for #5 and larger, ($29D^2$ for #5 and larger when d > 12 in.), (obtained by straight embedment if possible, hooked if necessary).

---

* These tables provide for a negative moment $M = \frac{w}{10}\left(\frac{l' + l''}{2}\right)^2$ at the continuous end, which is applicable when there is *more than one* additional span beyond the interior support. In the case of a structure only two spans wide, this negative moment should be $M = wl'^2/9$. This would require increasing the total negative reinforcement by approximately 10 per cent, which is best done by increasing the extra top bar. It is also recommended that the bottom bars be extended distance E_4 in this case.

† Based upon deformed bars of ASTM A61 or A432 grade (f_y = 60,000 psi).

‡ Bond and diagonal tension values are based upon deformed bars meeting ASTM A305 or A408. Plain round bars or deformed bars not meeting ASTM A305 or A408 will not give sufficient bond resistance.

CONCRETE JOIST CONSTRUCTION—END SPAN

E_3 = bottom bar to extend 6 in. into the support except when values in the load tables are printed in boldface type.

E_4 = When the values in the load tables are printed in boldface type, bottom bar should extend not less than 6 in. for #3 and #4 bars or $21D^2$ for #5 and larger nor less than $l''/10$ * past the far face of the support.

E_x = not less than $\left\{ \begin{array}{l} l'/4 \\ l''/4 \\ \text{6 in. past bend-down point for \#3 bars, 10 in. for \#4 and} \\ 21D^2 \text{ for \#5 and larger } (29D^2 \text{ for \#5 and larger when} \\ d > 12 \text{ in.)} \end{array} \right\}$ whichever is greatest.

(ACI 918(e) requires top bars to extend to $l'/16$, d, or the depth of the member past point of inflection.)

The top bar in the table is scheduled on the basis of the adjoining span providing a bent bar of area equal to that of the bent bar in the span under consideration; any considerable variation in negative moment by reason of changes in load, span length, or end restraint of the adjacent span must be worked out by the general principles of continuity (pages 4-3 to 4-17, incl.).

B = ordinarily 4 in. minimum (or preferably 6 in.) and sufficient in any case to keep the bearing pressure on the wall within the allowable for the material of which the wall is made (see page 5-6). Most designers prefer to have a continuous distribution rib of concrete bearing on the wall and reinforced with at least one #4 bar top and one #4 bar bottom whenever it is desired to spread the load along the wall bearing. When providing bearing on existing masonry work, it is often sufficient merely to extend the joist stems into individual pockets cut into the wall, but it is then recommended that the stiffening rib be placed between the joists parallel and adjacent to the wall bearing.

A = bottom bar in adjoining span, not shown.

Almost all usual combinations of form depth, top slab and reinforcement are presented herewith. To show how the tables for end spans were computed and to permit extension of the tables if required, an illustrative example is shown:—

Example—Determine the safe carrying capacity on spans of 16 and 21 feet of 8 in. deep forms plus 2½ in. of top slab with 5 in. wide joists at 25 in. centers and reinforced with one #6 bottom bar and one #6 truss bar as shown on page 7-39 with $f'_c = 3750$ psi and $f_s = 24{,}000$ psi.

Solution: Dead weight of slab = 54 psf (computed as on page 7-5)

Shear Max. allowable $V = v_c bd$ $v_c = 1.2\sqrt{3750} = 73.5$psi $d = 9.38$ in. (see cut on next page) Av. $b = 5 + 8/12 = 5.67$

$$V = 73.5 \times 5.67 \times 9.38 = 3910 \text{ lb}$$

$$= 2.08\frac{w(1.15L - 1.56)\dagger}{2} \quad \text{(at distance "d" from support)}$$

$$\text{For } L = 16,\ w = \frac{3910}{1.04 \times (1.15L - 1.56)} = 223 - 54 = 169 \text{ psf}$$

$$\text{For } L = 21,\ w = \frac{3910}{1.04 \times (1.15L - 1.56)} = 166 - 54 = 112 \text{ psf}$$

---

* Embedment of bottom bar at interior support is determined by the fact that the bottom bar is required for compressive reinforcement. The exact length varies. The maximum is that which will develop the full compression in the bar at the higher unit stress permitted by the ACI Code (24,000 psi) (ACI 318-63, Sect. 1102(c) and which will at the same time extend the needed distance across the moment curve. The capacity of the joist may be determined by shear, bond or flexure. The recommendation for E_4 will cover the worst condition. The user may at his option work out the needs of any particular problem (see page 7-62).

† Shear is increased at the continuous end as per ACI Code 904(c). 1.56 = 2d

CONCRETE JOIST CONSTRUCTION—END SPAN

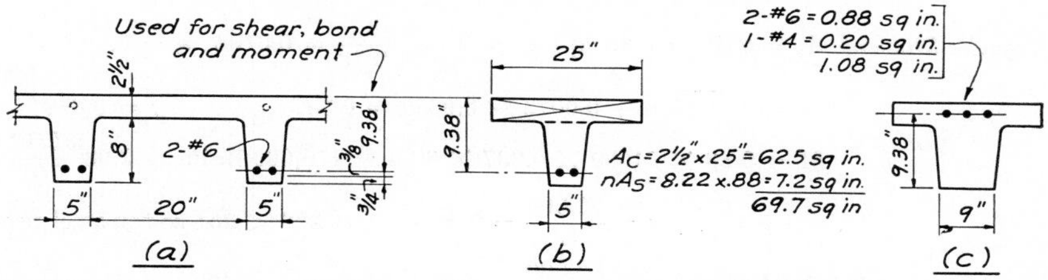

Bond Max. allowable $V = u\Sigma o jd$ $\quad u = \dfrac{4.8\sqrt{3750}}{0.75} = 392 < 500$ psi (page 3-13)

$V = 392 \times 2.356 \times \frac{7}{8} \times 9.38 = 7580$ lb (one #6 bottom at free end)

$= 2.08\frac{wL}{2}$ (at free end)

For $L = 16$, $w = \dfrac{7580}{1.04L} = 455 - 54 = 401$ psf

For $L = 21$, $w = \dfrac{7580}{1.04L} = 347 - 54 = 293$ psf

Positive Moment $A_s = 2\text{-}\#6 = 0.88$ sq in. (with $t = 2.5$ in. N.A. is probably in flange)

$p = \dfrac{0.88}{25 \times 9.38} = 0.00375$

$n = \dfrac{29{,}000{,}000}{(145)^{1.5}33\sqrt{3750}} = 8.22$* $\qquad pn = 0.0308$

$k = \sqrt{0.0616 + 0.00095} - 0.0308 = 0.25 - 0.0308 = 0.219$

$j = 0.927$ $\qquad kd = 2.05$ in. < 2.5 in.

Max. pos. moment $M = A_s f_s jd = 0.88 \times 24{,}000 \times 0.927 \times 9.38 = 183{,}000$ lb-in.

$= 2.08\dfrac{wL^2 \times 12}{11}$

For $L = 16$, $w = \dfrac{80{,}600}{L^2} = 315 - 54 = 261$ psf

For $L = 21$, $w = \dfrac{80{,}600}{L^2} = 183 - 54 =$ **129** psi } In table on page 7-39

Tapered Ends Since w from $+M$ exceeds w from V by more than 10%, use tapered end forms (page 7-4). At distance d, $b = 5.67 + \dfrac{28.12}{36}4 = 8.80$ in. (Similar to figure on page 7-6)

$V = v_c bd = 73.5 \times 8.80 \times 9.38 = 6060$ lb

$= 2.08 \times \dfrac{w(1.15L - 1.56)}{2}$ $\qquad (1.56 = 2d)$

For $L = 16$, $w = \dfrac{5830}{(1.15L - 1.56)} = 347 - 54 = 293$ psf > 255 psf

For $L = 21$, $w = \dfrac{5830}{(1.15L - 1.56)} = 257 - 54 = 203$ psf > 129 psf

Root of Taper $V = 3910$ lb $= 2.08\dfrac{w(1.15L - 6.25)}{2}$

For $L = 16$, $w = \dfrac{3760}{1.15L - 6.25} = 309 - 54 =$ **255 psf**

For $L = 21$, $w = \dfrac{3760}{1.15L - 6.25} = 209 - 54 = 155$ psf > 129 psf

* See page 3-5.

CONCRETE JOIST CONSTRUCTION—END SPAN

Negative Moment $A_s = 2\text{-}\#6 = 0.88$ sq in. $p = \dfrac{0.88}{9 \times 9.38} = 0.0104$ $n = 8.22$ *

$pn = 0.0855$

$k = \sqrt{0.1710 + 0.0073} - 0.0855 = 0.337$ $j = 0.887$

$M = 0.88 \times 24000 \times 0.887 \times 9.38 = 176{,}000$ lb-in. $= 2.08\dfrac{wL^2 12}{10}$

For $L = 16$, $w = \dfrac{70{,}500}{L^2} = 276 - 54 = 222 < 261$ so top steel needed

For $L = 21$, $w = \dfrac{70{,}500}{L^2} = 160 - 54 = 106 < 129$ so top steel needed

Negative Moment with additional top bar

Add 1-#4 top bar to 2-#6 truss bars over support

$A_s = 0.88 + 0.20 = 1.08$ sq in.

$p = \dfrac{1.08}{9 \times 9.38} = 0.0128 < (0.0129 = p_b)$

(for "balanced" reinforcement $k = \dfrac{1}{1 + \dfrac{24000}{8.25 \times 1688}} = 0.367$)

$p_b = \dfrac{1688 \times 0.367}{2 \times 24000} = 0.0129$ $pn = 0.0128 \times 8\frac{1}{4} = 0.105$ *

$k = \sqrt{0.210 + 0.0110} - 0.105 = 0.470 - 0.105 = 0.365$ $j = 0.878$

$M = 1.08 \times 24000 \times 0.878 \times 9.38 = 213{,}400$ lb-in. $= 2.08\dfrac{wL^2 12}{10}$

For $L = 16$, $w = \dfrac{85{,}400}{L^2} = 334 - 54 = 280 > 255$

For $L = 21$, $w = \dfrac{85{,}400}{L^2} = 194 - 54 = 140 > 129$

Minimum Bars $p = \dfrac{200}{(f_y = 60{,}000)} = 0.00333$ $A_s = 0.00333 \times 5.67 \times 9.38 = \mathbf{0.178}$

2-#3 = 0.22 would provide enough.

Live Load Deflection

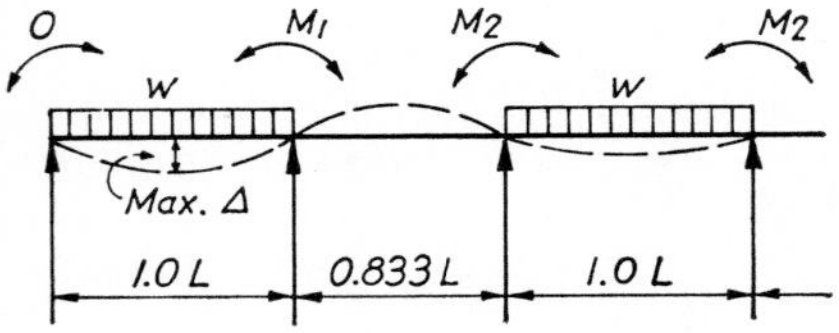

Determine M_1 for critical load pattern ($= M_B$ in formula for deflection):

$$0 + 2M_1(1.833L) + M_2(0.833L) = -\frac{wL^3}{4}$$

$$M_1(0.833L) + 2M_2(1.833L) + M_2L = -\frac{wL^3}{4}$$

$$3.667M_1 + 0.833M_2 = -\frac{wL^2}{4}$$

$$0.833M_1 + 4.667M_2 = -\frac{wL^2}{4}$$

$$20.55M_1 + 4.667M_2 = -1.40wL^2$$

$$M_1 = -\frac{1.15wL^2}{19.72} = -0.0583wL^2$$

$$x = (0.5 - 0.0583)L = 0.4417L$$

$E_c = (145)^{1.5}\,33\sqrt{3750} = 3{,}530{,}000$ psi

$$+M = \frac{(0.4417)^2}{2}wL^2 = \frac{wL^2}{10.27}$$

* See page 3-5.

CONCRETE JOIST CONSTRUCTION—END SPAN

Since $p = \dfrac{0.88}{5.67 \times 9.38} = 0.0166$, $pf_y = 0.0166 \times 60{,}000 =$ 996 > 500 so use moment of inertia of transformed section.*

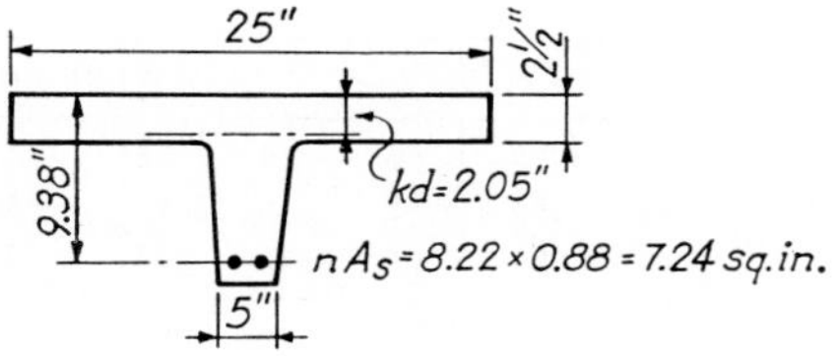

$$I = \frac{25 \times (2.05)^3}{3} = 71.6 \text{ in.}^4$$

$$7.24 \times (7.33)^2 = \underline{388.}$$

$$460.$$

$$\Delta \doteq \frac{5}{384}\frac{wL^4}{EI} - \frac{M_BL^2}{16EI}, \text{where } M_B = M_1 = -0.0583wL^2,$$

$$\Delta \doteq \frac{wL^4}{EI}(0.01303 - 0.00365) = 0.00938\frac{wL^4}{EI}$$

When $\Delta = 16$, $w = 255$

$$\Delta_{16} = 0.00938\frac{2.08 \times 255 \times (16)^4 \times 1728}{3{,}530{,}000 \times 460} = 0.345 \text{ in.} < \frac{L}{180} < \frac{L}{360}$$

When $\Delta = 21$, $w = 129$

$$\Delta_{21} = 0.00938\frac{2.08 \times 129 \times (21)^4 \times 1728}{3{,}530{,}000 \times 460} = 0.52 \text{ in.} < \frac{L}{180} < \frac{L}{360}$$

Summary. The safe superimposed capacity on a 16-ft span, as determined by positive moment, is 261 psf, which is more than 10% greater than the 169 psf determined by shear on a square end. A tapered end at 293 psf is more than ample, and the capacity of 255 psf at the root of the taper is determining. Bond at the free end provides a capacity of 401 psf, which is more than required. Negative moment with only the truss bars would be the determining factor at 222 psf, but a #4 added top bar raises this to 280 psf. Deflection is checked as shown.

For a 21-ft span, positive moment establishes a capacity of 129 psf, which exceeds that of shear on a square end (112 psf), by more than 10%, so tapered ends are used (203 psf), and the shear at the root of the taper is adequate at 155 psf. Bond at 293 psf is not a factor. Negative moment with only the truss bars is insufficient at 106 psf, but with an added #4 top bar, the resulting 140 psf is adequate. Again deflection is checked.

---

* ACI 909(c) permits using the average moment of inertia of end and mid-span. Compute I:—

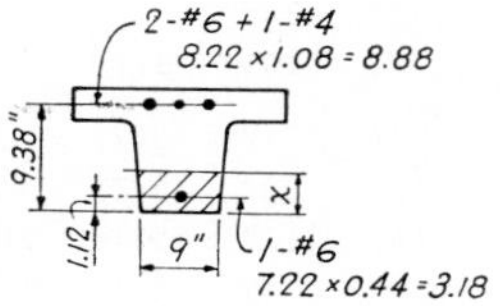

$$(9x + 8.88 + 3.18)x = 8.88 \times 9.38 + 3.18 \times 1.12 + 9x\frac{x}{2}$$

$$4.5x^2 + 12.06x = 86.76 \qquad x = 3.05''$$

$$I = 8.88 \times 6.33^2 = 358 \text{ in.}^4$$

$$3.18 \times 1.93^2 = 12$$

$$\tfrac{1}{3} \times 9 \times 3.05^3 = \underline{85}$$

$$455$$

$AvI = \dfrac{460 + 455}{2} = 458$ in.[4] which happens to be so close to the 460 used as to make recomputation of deflection unnecessary.

CONCRETE JOIST CONSTRUCTION
END SPAN—20 INCH WIDE FORMS
Safe Superimposed Load (psf)

For limitations and explanation of use of tables, see pages 7-33 to 7-37.

Depth: 6″ FORMS + 2½″ CONCRETE

Joists	4″ Joists @ 24″ c/c					Wt 45 psf	5″ Joists @ 25″ c/c					Wt 48 psf
Bottom Bar	#4	#5	#5	#6	#6	#6	#5	#5	#6	#6	#6	#7
Truss Bar	#4	#4	#5	#5	#5	#6	#4	#5	#5	#5	#6	#6
Top Bar	#4	#4	#4	#4	#5	#4	#4	#4	#4	#5	#4	#5
Span l′ in Ft												
8	441											
9	340	436					416					
10	267	346	381				328	407	410			
11	213	278	337				263	328	363			
12	156	227	283	299			214	268	308	325		
13	**139**	187	235	**270**			**167**	221	256	273	**293**	
14	**114**	155	196	**229**			**145**	185	214	229	**267**	
15	**94**	129	165	**194**	**198**		**120**	155	180	193	**233**	**235**
16	**77**	**101**	140	**165**	**173**		**100**	**123**	153	164	**199**	**206**
17	**63**	**91**	119	**141**	**150**	**153**	**83**	**110**	130	140	**171**	**183**
18	**52**	**76**	101	**121**	**129**	**136**	**69**	**93**	**102**	120	**148**	**163**
19	**42**	**64**	86	**104**	**111**	**122**	**57**	**79**	**93**	103	**128**	**147**
20	**33**	**53**	**70**	**90**	**96**	**110**	**47**	**67**	**80**	**86**	**111**	**133**
21		**44**	**63**	**77**	**83**	**99**	**38**	**56**	**68**	**76**	**96**	**119**

Depth: 6″ FORMS + 3″ CONCRETE

Joists	4″ Joists @ 24″ c/c					Wt 52 psf	5″ Joists @ 25″ c/c					Wt 54 psf
Bottom Bar	#4	#5	#5	#6	#6	#6	#5	#5	#6	#6	#6	#7
Truss Bar	#4	#4	#5	#5	#5	#6	#4	#5	#5	#5	#6	#6
Top Bar	#4	#4	#4	#4	#5	#4	#4	#4	#4	#5	#4	#5
Span l′ in Ft												
9	360						442					
10	282	367	405				348	432	436			
11	224	295	358				279	348	386			
12	165	239	300				226	284	327	345		
13	**146**	197	248	**285**			**177**	234	271	289	311	
14	**119**	163	207	**242**			**152**	195	227	242	**282**	
15	**97**	135	174	**205**	208		**126**	163	191	204	**247**	
16	**79**	**105**	147	**174**	**182**		**104**	**130**	161	173	**211**	**218**
17	**65**	**94**	124	**149**	**158**	160	**86**	**115**	137	147	**181**	**192**
18	**52**	**78**	105	**127**	**135**	**142**	**71**	**97**	**107**	126	**155**	**172**
19	**42**	**65**	89	**109**	**116**	**127**	**58**	**82**	**98**	107	**134**	**154**
20	**33**	**54**	**72**	**93**	**100**	**114**	**48**	**68**	**84**	**89**	**116**	**139**
21		**44**	**64**	**80**	**86**	**103**	**38**	**57**	**71**	**78**	**100**	**125**
22		**36**	**54**	**68**	**74**	**93**	**30**	**47**	**60**	**67**	**87**	**110**

Tabulated values in boldface type require embedment E_4 explained on page 7-34.
Above and to the right of the zigzag line, tapered ends are required.

CONCRETE JOIST CONSTRUCTION
END SPAN—20 INCH WIDE FORMS
Safe Superimposed Load (psf)

For limitations and explanation of use of tables, see pages 7-33 to 7-37.

Depth: 6″ FORMS + 4½″ CONCRETE

Joists	4″ Joists @ 24″ c/c, Wt 71 psf						5″ Joists @ 25″ c/c Wt 73 psf		
Bottom Bar	#4	#5	#5	#6	#6	#6	#6	#7	#7
Truss Bar	#4	#4	#5	#5	#5	#6	#6	#6	#7
Top Bar	#4	#4	#4	#4	#5	#4	#4	#5	#4
Span l′ in Ft									
9	421								
10	328	430							
11	259	344	419				455		
12	194	278	350	369			404		
13	166	227	288	331			363		
14	134	186	239	279			328		
15	108	153	199	234	240		288		
16	86	**120**	167	197	208		245	251	
17	69	**104**	140	167	181	182	209	221	
18	54	**85**	118	142	154	161	178	197	
19	41	**70**	98	120	131	143	153	**176**	
20	31	**56**	**79**	102	111	128	131	**158**	
21		**45**	**68**	86	95	114	112	**142**	
22		**35**	**56**	72	80	**103**	96	**124**	**129**
23			**45**	**57**	68	**90**	**77**	**107**	**117**
24			**36**	**51**	**52**	**77**	**69**	**93**	**106**
25				**41**	**47**	**66**	**58**	**80**	**97**

Depth: 8″ FORMS + 2½″ CONCRETE

Joists	4″ Joists @ 24″ c/c, Wt 51 psf						5″ Joists @ 25″ c/c Wt 54 psf			
Bottom Bar	#4	#5	#5	#6	#6	#6	#6	#6	#7	#7
Truss Bar	#4	#4	#5	#5	#5	#6	#5	#6	#6	#7
Top Bar	#4	#4	#4	#4	#5	#4	#5	#4	#5	#4
Span l′ in Ft										
10	347	449								
11	278	363	448							
12	219	297	369	398			428	432		
13	185	246	307	353	359		357	389		
14	153	205	258	298	306		300	354		
15	127	**157**	218	253	265		255	306	317	
16	105	**143**	186	216	232	233	218	255	279	
17	88	**123**	159	186	200	207	187	227	249	
18	73	**104**	137	161	173	185	161	197	**223**	
19	60	**89**	**110**	139	150	167	**134**	171	**201**	
20	50	**75**	**101**	121	130	151	**120**	149	**183**	
21	40	**64**	**87**	105	114	137	**104**	129	**161**	**167**
22	32	**54**	**75**	**85**	99	**124**	**90**	**107**	**142**	**153**
23		**45**	**64**	**79**	79	**109**	**78**	**99**	**125**	**141**
24		**37**	**55**	**70**	**73**	**96**	**68**	**88**	**111**	**130**
25		**30**	**47**	**60**	**66**	**85**	**58**	**77**	**98**	**120**

Tabulated values in boldface type require embedment E_4 explained on page 7-34.
Above and to the right of the zigzag line, tapered ends are required.

CONCRETE JOIST CONSTRUCTION
END SPAN—20 INCH WIDE FORMS
Safe Superimposed Load (psf)

For limitations and explanation of use of tables, see pages 7-33 to 7-37.

Depth: 8″ FORMS + 3″ CONCRETE

Joists	4″ Joists @ 24″ c/c					Wt 57 psf	5″ Joists @ 25″ c/c			Wt 60 psf
Bottom Bar	#4	#5	#5	#6	#6	#6	#6	#6	#7	#7
Truss Bar	#4	#4	#5	#5	#5	#6	#5	#6	#6	#7
Top Bar	#4	#4	#4	#4	#5	#4	#5	#4	#5	#4
Span l′ in Ft										
11	290	379								
12	229	310	386	416			448			
13	192	256	321	370	374		373	407		
14	158	213	269	311	319		314	370		
15	130	**163**	227	264	276		266	320	331	
16	108	**148**	193	225	241		227	274	291	
17	89	**126**	164	193	207	214	194	236	259	
18	73	**107**	141	166	179	191	167	204	232	
19	60	**90**	**113**	144	155	172	**139**	177	**209**	
20	49	**76**	**103**	124	134	156	**124**	154	**189**	
21	39	**64**	**89**	107	117	141	**107**	135	**167**	**173**
22	31	**53**	**76**	**87**	101	128	**92**	**110**	**147**	**158**
23		**44**	**65**	**80**	**80**	112	**79**	**102**	**129**	**145**
24		**36**	**55**	**70**	**74**	98	**68**	**89**	**114**	**134**
25			**46**	**61**	**66**	86	**58**	**78**	**100**	**123**
26			**38**	**52**	**57**	76	**49**	**67**	**81**	**110**

Depth: 8″ FORMS + 4½″ CONCRETE

Joists	4″ Joists @ 24″ c/c					Wt 76 psf	5″ Joists @ 25″ c/c				Wt 79 psf
Bottom Bar	#4	#5	#5	#6	#6	#6	#6	#6	#7	#7	#8
Truss Bar	#4	#4	#5	#5	#5	#6	#5	#6	#6	#7	#7
Top Bar	#4	#4	#4	#4	#5	#4	#5	#4	#5	#4	#6
Span l′ in Ft											
12	261	348	436								
13	211	286	361	420			423				
14	172	236	301	352	358		354	417			
15	141	183	253	297	308		299	361	373		
16	115	**164**	213	252	269		253	308	327		
17	93	**137**	181	215	230	237	215	264	289		
18	75	**114**	153	184	198	211	**169**	228	258		
19	60	**95**	**123**	157	170	189	**154**	196	232		
20	47	**78**	**110**	135	146	169	**134**	170	208		
21	36	**64**	**93**	115	126	153	**115**	147	182	190	
22		**52**	**78**	**93**	108	138	**98**	**120**	159	173	
23		**41**	**65**	**85**	**85**	120	**83**	**110**	139	158	
24		**32**	**54**	**73**	**78**	104	**70**	**94**	121	145	
25			**44**	**62**	**67**	90	**58**	**81**	106	**133**	
26			**35**	**51**	**56**	78	**48**	**69**	**86**	**119**	**121**
27				**42**	**47**	67	**39**	**58**	**80**	**105**	**112**
28				**34**	**38**	**54**	**31**	**49**	**70**	**92**	**103**
29					**31**	**48**		**40**	**60**	**81**	**95**

Tabulated values in boldface type require embedment E_4 explained on page 7-34.
Above and to the right of the zigzag line, tapered ends are required.

CONCRETE JOIST CONSTRUCTION
END SPAN—20 INCH WIDE FORMS
Safe Superimposed Load (psf)

For limitations and explanation of use of tables, see pages 7-33 to 7-37.

Depth: 10″ FORMS + 2½″ CONCRETE

Joists	4″ Joists @ 24″ c/c					Wt 57 psf	5″ Joists @ 25″ c/c				Wt 61 psf
Bottom Bar	#4	#5	#5	#6	#6	#6	#6	#6	#7	#7	#8
Truss Bar	#4	#4	#5	#5	#5	#6	#5	#6	#6	#7	#7
Top Bar	#4	#4	#4	#4	#5	#4	#5	#4	#5	#4	#6
Span l′ in Ft											
15	159	202	271	316	327		316	379	397		
16	133	182	232	271	288		271	326	350		
17	112	155	199	234	249	256	233	282	312		
18	94	132	172	202	216	230	190	245	281		
19	78	113	142	176	188	207	175	214	254		
20	65	97	129	153	165	188	152	188	226	231	
21	54	83	112	134	144	172	133	151	200	212	
22	45	70	97	111	127	157	116	141	177	194	
23	36	60	84	103	103	139	101	128	157	179	
24		50	72	92	96	123	88	112	139	166	
25		42	62	80	86	109	76	99	114	153	
26		35	54	70	75	97	66	87	107	137	142
27			46	61	65	78	57	76	99	123	132
28			39	53	57	73	49	67	88	110	124
29			32	45	49	67	42	58	78	98	116
30				39	43	59	35	51	69	83	108
31				33	36	52		44	61	78	99

Depth: 10″ FORMS + 3″ CONCRETE

Joists	4″ Joists @ 24″ c/c					Wt 63 psf	5″ Joists @ 25″ c/c				Wt 67 psf
Bottom Bar	#4	#5	#5	#6	#6	#6	#6	#6	#7	#7	#8
Truss Bar	#4	#4	#5	#5	#5	#6	#5	#6	#6	#7	#7
Top Bar	#4	#4	#4	#4	#5	#4	#5	#4	#5	#4	#6
Span l′ in Ft											
16	136	185	239	280	297		280	338	362		
17	113	157	205	241	257	264	241	292	323		
18	94	133	176	208	222	236	197	253	290		
19	78	113	145	181	193	213	180	221	262		
20	65	96	131	157	169	193	156	193	233	238	
21	53	82	113	137	147	176	135	155	206	218	
22	43	69	98	113	129	160	117	144	182	200	
23	34	58	84	105	105	142	102	130	161	184	
24		48	72	93	97	125	88	114	142	170	
25		40	62	81	86	111	76	100	116	156	
26		32	52	70	75	98	66	88	108	140	145
27			44	60	65	78	56	76	100	125	135
28			37	52	56	73	48	67	89	112	126
29			30	44	48	66	40	58	78	100	117
30				37	41	58	33	50	69	84	110
31				31	34	51		42	60	79	100
32						44		36	53	70	90

Tabulated values in boldface type require embedment E_4 explained on page 7-34.
Above and to the right of the zigzag line, tapered ends are required.

CONCRETE JOIST CONSTRUCTION
END SPAN—20 INCH WIDE FORMS
Safe Superimposed Load (psf)

For limitations and explanation of use of tables, see pages 7-33 to 7-37.

Depth	10″ FORMS + 4½″ CONCRETE										
Joists	4″ Joists @ 24″ c/c Wt 82 psf						5″ Joists @ 25″ c/c Wt 86 psf				
Bottom Bar	#4	#5	#5	#6	#6	#6	#6	#6	#7	#7	#8
Truss Bar	#4	#4	#5	#5	#5	#6	#5	#6	#6	#7	#7
Top Bar	#4	#4	#4	#4	#5	#4	#5	#4	#5	#4	#6
Span l′ in Ft 18	96	141	171	226	241	255	216	277	317		
19	78	118	156	195	208	229	**193**	240	285		
20	63	99	**137**	168	180	207	**166**	208	255	258	
21	50	83	**117**	145	156	187	**143**	**168**	224	235	
22	38	68	**100**	**120**	135	170	**123**	**156**	197	215	
23		56	**85**	**110**	**110**	150	**106**	**137**	173	197	
24		45	**71**	**95**	**101**	131	**90**	**119**	152	181	
25		35	**59**	**82**	**87**	115	**77**	**103**	**123**	167	
26			**49**	**69**	**74**	100	**65**	**89**	**114**	149	154
27			**40**	**59**	**63**	**80**	**54**	**77**	**104**	132	142
28			**31**	**49**	**53**	**73**	**44**	**66**	**91**	117	132
29				**40**	**44**	**65**	**36**	**55**	**79**	103	122
30				**32**	**36**	**55**		**46**	**68**	**86**	**114**
31						**47**		**38**	**59**	**80**	**104**
32						**39**		**31**	**50**	**70**	**92**
33						**32**			**42**	**61**	**82**
34									**35**	**52**	**72**

Depth	12″ FORMS + 2½″ CONCRETE												
Joists	4″ Joists @ 24″ c/c Wt 63 psf						5″ Joists @ 25″ c/c Wt 67 psf					6″ @ 26″ Wt 72 psf	
Bottom Bar	#4	#5	#5	#6	#6	#6	#6	#6	#7	#7	#8	#8	#9
Truss Bar	#4	#4	#5	#5	#5	#6	#5	#6	#6	#7	#7	#8	#8
Top Bar	#4	#4	#4	#4	#5	#4	#5	#4	#5	#4	#6	#5	#7
Span l′ in Ft 19	96	137	175	213	227	247	**211**	257	303			353	
20	81	117	**156**	186	199	225	**184**	226	273	276		322	
21	68	101	**136**	**149**	174	206	**161**	**186**	241	253		296	
22	56	86	**118**	**138**	154	189	**141**	**173**	214	233		273	
23	46	74	**103**	**128**	**128**	168	**123**	**155**	190	215		252	
24	38	63	**90**	**113**	**119**	150	**108**	**137**	169	199		234	
25	30	53	**78**	**100**	**105**	133	**94**	**121**	**141**	185		218	
26		45	**67**	**88**	**93**	118	**82**	**107**	**132**	167	171	203	
27		37	**58**	**77**	**81**	**98**	**71**	**94**	**122**	150	160	**190**	
28		30	**50**	**67**	**71**	**92**	**62**	**83**	**109**	135	149	**178**	
29			**42**	**59**	**63**	**83**	**53**	**73**	**97**	121	140	**164**	**166**
30			**35**	**51**	**54**	**74**	**45**	**64**	**86**	**104**	**131**	**149**	**156**
31				**44**	**47**	**65**	**38**	**56**	**76**	**98**	**122**	**135**	**147**
32				**37**	**40**	**57**	**32**	**48**	**68**	**88**	**111**	**111**	**139**
33				**31**	**34**	**50**		**41**	**60**	**79**	**100**	**105**	**131**
34						**44**		**35**	**53**	**70**	**90**	**100**	**122**
35						**38**		**30**	**46**	**63**	**77**	**91**	**111**

Tabulated values in boldface type require embedment E_4 explained on page 7-34.
Above and to the right of the zigzag line, tapered ends are required.

CONCRETE JOIST CONSTRUCTION
END SPAN—20 INCH WIDE FORMS
Safe Superimposed Load (psf)

For limitations and explanation of use of tables, see pages 7-33 to 7-37.

Depth: 12" FORMS + 3" CONCRETE

Joists	4" Joists @ 24" c/c, Wt 69 psf						5" Joists @ 25" c/c, Wt 74 psf				6" Joists @ 26" c/c, Wt 78 psf		
Bottom Bar	#4	#5	#5	#6	#6	#6	#6	#7	#7	#8	#8	#8	#9
Truss Bar	#4	#4	#5	#5	#5	#6	#6	#6	#7	#7	#7	#8	#8
Top Bar	#4	#4	#4	#4	#5	#4	#4	#5	#4	#6	#6	#5	#7
Span l' in Ft													
19	96	138	179	217	232	253	264	311			363		
20	80	118	158	190	203	230	231	280	283		331		
21	67	101	137	**151**	178	210	**190**	247	259		304		
22	55	86	119	**140**	156	192	**177**	219	238		280		
23	44	73	103	**130**	**130**	171	**157**	194	219		258		
24	35	62	89	**114**	**120**	152	**139**	173	203		236	239	
25		52	77	**100**	**106**	134	**122**	**143**	188		212	223	
26		43	66	**88**	**93**	119	**107**	**134**	169	174	190	208	
27		35	56	**76**	**81**	**98**	**94**	**123**	152	162	171	194	
28			48	**66**	**71**	**92**	**83**	**109**	136	151	**142**	**182**	
29			40	**57**	**61**	**83**	**72**	**97**	**111**	142	**134**	**166**	**169**
30			33	**49**	**53**	**73**	**63**	**86**	**104**	133	**124**	**150**	**159**
31				**42**	**45**	**64**	**54**	**76**	**98**	**123**	**111**	**136**	**149**
32				**35**	**38**	**56**	**47**	**67**	**87**	**111**	**100**	**113**	**141**
33					**32**	**49**	**40**	**59**	**78**	**100**	**89**	**106**	**132**
34						**42**	**33**	**51**	**69**	**90**	**80**	**100**	**122**
35						**36**		**44**	**61**	**77**	**71**	**90**	**111**

Depth: 12" FORMS + 4½" CONCRETE

Joists	4" Joists @ 24" c/c, Wt 88 psf						5" Joists @ 25" c/c, Wt 93 psf					6" @ 26", Wt 97 psf	
Bottom Bar	#4	#5	#5	#6	#6	#6	#6	#6	#7	#7	#8	#8	#9
Truss Bar	#4	#4	#5	#5	#5	#6	#5	#6	#6	#7	#7	#8	#8
Top Bar	#4	#4	#4	#4	#5	#4	#5	#4	#5	#4	#6	#5	#7
Span l' in Ft													
20	78	121	165	201	214	244	198	247	302			357	
21	63	102	142	**160**	187	221	171	204	266	277		327	
22	50	85	121	**147**	162	202	148	**188**	234	253		300	
23	38	71	104	**135**	**136**	179	128	**165**	207	233		277	
24		58	88	**117**	**123**	158	110	**144**	182	215		256	
25		47	75	**101**	**107**	139	95	**126**	**151**	198		237	
26		37	63	**87**	**92**	122	81	**109**	**141**	178	183	220	
27			52	**75**	**79**	**100**	68	**95**	**126**	159	170	205	
28			42	**63**	**68**	**93**	57	**82**	**111**	141	158	191	
29			34	**53**	**57**	**81**	47	**70**	**98**	**115**	147	175	
30				**44**	**48**	**70**	38	**60**	**85**	**107**	137	158	166
31				**36**	**40**	**61**	30	**50**	**74**	**99**	126	142	156
32					**32**	**52**		**42**	**64**	**87**	113	**117**	146
33						**43**		**34**	**55**	**76**	101	**110**	**137**
34						**36**			**47**	**67**	90	**102**	**126**
35									**39**	**58**	**76**	**91**	**114**
36									**32**	**50**	**71**	**81**	**102**
37										**42**	**62**	**71**	**85**

Tabulated values in boldface type require embedment E_4 explained on page 7-34.
Above and to the right of the zigzag line, tapered ends are required.

CONCRETE JOIST CONSTRUCTION
END SPAN—20 INCH WIDE FORMS
Safe Superimposed Load (psf)

For limitations and explanation of use of tables, see pages 7-33 to 7-37.

Depth: 14″ FORMS + 2½″ CONCRETE

Joists	5″ Joists @ 25″ c/c					Wt 75 psf	6″ Joists @ 26″ c/c Wt 80 psf				7″ @ 27″ c/c Wt 85 psf	
Bottom Bar	#6	#6	#7	#7	#8	#8	#8	#8	#9	#9	#9	#10
Truss Bar	#5	#6	#6	#7	#7	#8	#7	#8	#8	#9	#9	#9
Top Bar	#5	#4	#5	#4	#6	#5	#6	#5	#7	#5	#5	#7
Span l′ in Ft												
22	165	**206**	251	270			317				359	
23	145	**182**	224	250			293				333	
24	127	**161**	200	232			272				309	
25	112	**143**	**168**	216			244	254			288	
26	98	**127**	**158**	196	200		220	237			270	
27	85	**112**	**144**	177	187		199	222			253	
28	74	**99**	**129**	159	175		**166**	208			237	
29	64	**88**	**115**	**132**	164		**157**	194	194	194	223	
30	55	**77**	**103**	**124**	154		**146**	176	183	183	**210**	
31	47	**68**	**92**	**117**	145		**132**	160	172	172	**199**	
32	40	**59**	**82**	**105**	132	136	**119**	**133**	163	163	**188**	
33	33	**51**	**72**	**94**	120	129	**107**	**126**	**154**	154	**172**	**176**
34		**44**	**64**	**85**	**99**	121	**97**	**120**	**145**	**145**	**157**	**167**
35		**37**	**56**	**76**	**93**	115	**87**	**109**	**132**	**138**	**132**	**159**
36		**31**	**49**	**68**	**88**	**108**	**78**	**99**	**121**	**130**	**126**	**150**
37			**43**	**60**	**80**	**101**	**70**	**89**	**102**	**124**	**120**	**143**
38			**37**	**53**	**72**	**92**	**62**	**81**	**97**	**117**	**109**	**134**
39			**31**	**47**	**65**	**84**	**55**	**73**	**92**	**111**	**100**	**108**

Depth: 14″ FORMS + 3″ CONCRETE

Joists	5″ Joists @ 25″ c/c					Wt 81 psf	6″ Joists @ 26″ c/c Wt 86 psf				7″ @ 27″ c/c Wt 91 psf	
Bottom Bar	#6	#6	#7	#7	#8	#8	#8	#8	#9	#9	#9	#10
Truss Bar	#5	#6	#6	#7	#7	#8	#7	#8	#8	#9	#9	#9
Top Bar	#5	#4	#5	#4	#6	#5	#6	#5	#7	#5	#5	#7
Span l′ in Ft												
22	167	209	256	276			324				367	
23	146	184	228	255			299				340	
24	128	163	203	236			276	278			316	
25	112	144	**171**	219			248	258			295	
26	98	127	**160**	198	203		223	241			275	
27	85	112	**145**	178	189		201	226			258	
28	73	99	**129**	160	177		**169**	211			242	
29	63	87	**115**	**133**	166		**160**	196			227	
30	54	76	**102**	**125**	155		**147**	177	185		214	
31	45	66	**91**	**116**	145	146	**132**	161	175		**202**	
32	38	57	**81**	**104**	132	137	**119**	**135**	165		**189**	
33	31	49	**71**	**93**	119	129	**107**	**128**	155		**172**	**179**
34		42	**62**	**83**	**99**	122	**96**	**120**	**145**	147	**157**	**169**
35		35	**54**	**74**	**93**	115	**86**	**108**	**132**	**139**	**134**	**160**
36			**47**	**66**	**87**	108	**76**	**98**	**120**	**131**	**127**	**152**
37			**40**	**58**	**79**	100	**68**	**88**	**102**	**124**	**119**	**144**
38			**34**	**51**	**70**	90	**60**	**79**	**97**	**118**	**108**	**133**
39				**45**	**63**	82	**53**	**71**	**90**	**110**	**99**	**108**

Tabulated values in boldface type require embedment E_4 explained on page 7-34.
Above and to the right of the zigzag line, tapered ends are required.

CONCRETE JOIST CONSTRUCTION
END SPAN—20 INCH WIDE FORMS
Safe Superimposed Load (psf)

For limitations and explanation of use of tables, see pages 7-33 to 7-37.

Depth: 14″ FORMS + 4½″ CONCRETE

Joists	5″ Joists @ 25″ c/c					Wt 100 psf	6″ Joists @ 26″ c/c Wt 105 psf				7″ @ 27″ c/c Wt 110 psf	
Bottom Bar	#6	#6	#7	#7	#8	#8	#8	#8	#9	#9	#9	#10
Truss Bar	#5	#6	#6	#7	#7	#8	#7	#8	#8	#9	#9	#9
Top Bar	#5	#4	#5	#4	#6	#5	#6	#5	#7	#5	#5	#7
Span l′ in Ft												
24	130	168	213	247			293	294			337	
25	112	147	**180**	229			262	273			313	
26	96	129	**168**	207	211		234	254			292	
27	82	113	**149**	185	197		210	237			273	
28	70	98	**131**	165	183		**178**	221			255	
29	59	85	**116**	**137**	171		**167**	204	206		239	
30	48	73	**102**	**129**	160		**151**	184	193		225	
31	39	62	**89**	**117**	149		**135**	166	181		211	
32	31	52	**78**	**104**	134	140	**120**	**140**	170		197	198
33		43	**68**	**92**	120	131	**107**	**132**	160		179	187
34		35	**58**	**81**	**99**	123	**95**	**121**	148	151	162	176
35			**49**	**71**	**93**	115	**84**	**108**	134	142	**138**	**166**
36			**41**	**62**	**85**	108	**74**	**97**	121	134	**131**	**157**
37			**34**	**53**	**76**	98	**64**	**86**	**103**	126	**120**	**148**
38				**46**	**67**	88	**56**	**77**	**98**	**119**	**109**	**135**
39				**38**	**58**	**72**	**48**	**68**	**88**	**110**	**98**	**110**
40				**32**	**51**	**67**	**40**	**59**	**79**	**99**	**88**	**105**
41					**44**	**62**	**34**	**51**	**70**	**82**	**78**	**99**

Depth: 16″ FORMS + 2½″ CONCRETE

Joists	6″ Joists @ 26″ c/c							Wt 88 psf	7″ Joists @ 27″ c/c Wt 93 psf				8″ @ 28″ c/c Wt 98 psf	
Bottom Bar	#6	#7	#7	#8	#8	#9	#9	#9	#9	#9	#10	#10	#10	#10
Truss Bar	#6	#6	#7	#7	#8	#8	#8	#9	#8	#9	#9	#10	#10	#10
Top Bar	#4	#5	#4	#6	#5	#6	#7	#5	#7	#5	#7	#5	#5	#6
Span l′ in Ft														
26	132	163	**209**	253	270				307				342	
27	116	145	**187**	229	253				288				320	
28	102	129	**168**	**194**	238				269	271			301	
29	90	115	**151**	**183**	223				245	255			284	
30	78	101	**136**	**169**	203	209			223	240			268	
31	68	90	**122**	**153**	185	197			**189**	227			253	
32	58	79	**109**	**138**	**156**	186			**179**	213	214		240	
33	50	69	**97**	**125**	**148**	174	176		**169**	195	202		**227**	
34	42	60	**87**	**113**	**140**	159	167		**154**	178	192		**216**	
35	35	52	**77**	**102**	**127**	**132**	154	158	**140**	**154**	**182**		**205**	
36		44	**68**	**91**	**115**	**126**	141	150	**127**	**147**	**173**		**195**	
37		37	**60**	**82**	**105**	**120**	**120**	142	**116**	**140**	**164**		**157**	**185**
38		31	**52**	**73**	**95**	**114**	**114**	**135**	**105**	**128**	**156**		**150**	**170**
39			**45**	**65**	**86**	**107**	**107**	**128**	**95**	**117**	**126**	**149**	**143**	**143**
40			**39**	**58**	**77**	**98**	**98**	**119**	**86**	**106**	**120**	**141**	**137**	**137**
41			**33**	**51**	**69**	**89**	**89**	**98**	**77**	**97**	**115**	**135**	**131**	**131**
42				**45**	**62**	**81**	**81**	**93**	**70**	**88**	**110**	**129**	**120**	**122**

Tabulated values in boldface type require embedment E_4 explained on page 7-34.
Above and to the right of the zigzag line, tapered ends are required.

CONCRETE JOIST CONSTRUCTION
END SPAN—20 INCH WIDE FORMS
Safe Superimposed Load (psf)

For limitations and explanation of use of tables, see pages 7-33 to 7-37.

Depth: 16″ FORMS + 3″ CONCRETE

Joists	6″ Joists @ 26″ c/c Wt 94 psf					7″ Joists @ 27″ c/c Wt 99 psf					8″ Joists @ 28″ c/c Wt 104 psf			
Bottom Bar	#6	#7	#7	#8	#8	#8	#9	#9	#10	#10	#10	#10	#10	#11
Truss Bar	#6	#6	#7	#7	#8	#8	#8	#9	#9	#10	#9	#10	#10	#10
Top Bar	#4	#5	#4	#6	#5	#5	#7	#5	#7	#5	#7	#5	#6	#7
Span l′ in Ft														
26	132	165	**210**	256	274	283	313				348			
27	116	146	**188**	230	257	**241**	293				327			
28	101	130	**169**	**197**	241	**228**	272	275			307			
29	88	115	**151**	**186**	225	**208**	247	259			289			
30	77	101	**135**	**169**	204	**188**	224	244			273			
31	66	89	**121**	**153**	185	**170**	**192**	230			257			
32	56	78	**108**	**138**	**157**	**154**	**182**	216			236	**244**		
33	47	68	**96**	**124**	**149**	**139**	**169**	198	205		216	**231**		
34	39	58	**85**	**112**	**139**	**125**	**153**	181	194		**185**	**219**		
35	32	50	**75**	**100**	**126**	**113**	**139**	**156**	184		**176**	**208**		
36		42	**66**	**90**	**114**	**101**	**126**	**148**	174		**167**	**197**		
37		35	**58**	**80**	**103**	**91**	**114**	**139**	166		**155**	**159**	**185**	
38			**50**	**71**	**93**	**81**	**103**	**127**	155	**157**	**141**	**152**	**170**	**177**
39			**43**	**63**	**84**	**72**	**93**	**115**	**127**	**150**	**129**	**145**	**145**	**169**
40			**36**	**55**	**75**	**64**	**84**	**105**	**121**	**142**	**118**	**138**	**138**	**161**
41			**30**	**48**	**67**	**56**	**75**	**95**	**115**	**135**	**107**	**132**	**132**	**131**
42				**42**	**59**	**49**	**67**	**86**	109	**129**	**97**	**121**	**121**	**125**
43				**36**	**53**	**42**	**60**	**78**	**100**	**105**	**88**	**111**	**111**	**119**

Depth: 16″ FORMS + 4½″ CONCRETE

Joists	6″ Joists @ 26″ c/c Wt 113 psf					7″ Joists @ 27″ c/c Wt 118 psf					8″ Joists @ 28″ c/c Wt 123 psf			
Bottom Bar	#6	#7	#7	#8	#8	#8	#9	#9	#10	#10	#10	#10	#10	#11
Truss Bar	#6	#6	#7	#7	#8	#8	#8	#9	#9	#10	#9	#10	#10	#10
Top Bar	#4	#5	#4	#6	#5	#5	#7	#5	#7	#5	#7	#5	#6	#7
Span l′ in Ft														
27	116	149	192	**220**	268	**255**	308				345			
28	100	131	171	**207**	251	**240**	284	289			324			
29	86	115	152	**193**	233	**216**	257	271			304			
30	73	100	**135**	**173**	211	**194**	**213**	255			286			
31	61	87	119	**155**	190	**174**	**201**	240			270			
32	51	75	105	**139**	**163**	**157**	**190**	225			248	255		
33	41	**64**	93	**124**	**154**	**140**	**172**	204	212		226	241		
34	**33**	**54**	81	**111**	**140**	**126**	**155**	**170**	200		**193**	228		
35		**44**	70	**98**	**126**	**112**	**140**	**161**	189		**183**	216		
36		36	60	**87**	**113**	**100**	**126**	**153**	179		**172**	198	204	
37			51	**76**	**101**	**88**	**113**	**139**	169		**156**	**166**	188	193
38			43	**67**	**90**	**78**	**102**	**126**	155	161	**142**	**157**	**157**	**183**
39			35	**58**	**80**	**68**	**91**	**114**	**129**	152	**129**	**150**	**150**	**174**
40				**50**	**71**	**59**	**81**	**103**	**123**	**144**	**117**	**142**	**142**	**165**
41				**42**	**62**	**51**	**71**	**92**	**117**	**137**	**105**	**131**	**131**	**134**
42				**35**	**54**	**43**	**62**	**82**	**107**	**130**	**95**	**119**	**119**	**128**
43					**46**	**36**	**54**	**73**	**97**	**105**	**85**	**108**	**108**	**122**
44					**39**		**47**	**65**	**87**	**100**	**76**	**98**	**98**	**116**

Tabulated values in boldface type require embedment E_4 explained on page 7-34.
Above and to the right of the zigzag line, tapered ends are required.

CONCRETE JOIST CONSTRUCTION
END SPAN—20 INCH WIDE FORMS
Safe Superimposed Load (psf)

For limitations and explanation of use of tables, see pages 7-33 to 7-37.

Depth	20″ FORMS + 2½″ CONCRETE												
Joists	7″ Joists @ 27″ c/c						Wt 112 psf		8″ Joists @ 28″ c/c			Wt 118 psf	
Bottom Bar	#7	#7	#8	#8	#9	#9	#10	#10	#10	#10	#10	#11	#11
Truss Bar	#6	#7	#7	#8	#8	#9	#9	#10	#9	#10	#10	#10	#11
Top Bar	#5	#4	#6	#5	#7	#5	#7	#6	#7	#5	#6	#8	#6
Span l′ in Ft													
32	90	123	160	196	**232**	268			294	299			
33	78	109	144	178	**214**	247	253		**247**	284			
34	67	96	129	161	**196**	**210**	240		**235**	269			
35	57	85	116	146	**179**	**200**	228		**224**	256			
36	48	74	103	132	**163**	**190**	216		**213**	238	243		
37	40	65	92	119	**148**	**178**	206		**198**	**204**	232		
38	32	56	82	107	**135**	**164**	191	196	**182**	**194**	215	220	
39		47	72	97	**123**	**150**	**164**	187	**167**	**186**	**186**	210	
40		40	63	86	**111**	**137**	**156**	178	**153**	**178**	**178**	200	
41		33	55	77	**101**	**125**	**149**	170	**140**	**168**	**170**	191	
42			47	68	**91**	**114**	**143**	162	**128**	**155**	**157**	**182**	
43			40	60	**82**	**104**	**132**	154	**117**	**142**	**145**	**173**	
44			33	53	**73**	**94**	**121**	145	**107**	**131**	**133**	**148**	**167**
45				46	**65**	**86**	**111**	**124**	**97**	**120**	**122**	**141**	**160**
46				39	**58**	**77**	**101**	**119**	**88**	**110**	**112**	**135**	**153**
47				33	**51**	**69**	**93**	**114**	**80**	**101**	**102**	**126**	**130**
48					**44**	**62**	**84**	**107**	**72**	**92**	**94**	**116**	**124**
49					**38**	**55**	**76**	**98**	**64**	**83**	**85**	**107**	**119**

Depth	20″ FORMS + 3″ CONCRETE												
Joists	7″ Joists @ 27″ c/c						Wt 118 psf		8″ Joists @ 28″ c/c			Wt 124 psf	
Bottom Bar	#7	#7	#8	#8	#9	#9	#10	#10	#10	#10	#10	#11	#11
Truss Bar	#6	#7	#7	#8	#8	#9	#9	#10	#9	#10	#10	#10	#11
Top Bar	#5	#4	#6	#5	#7	#5	#7	#6	#7	#5	#6	#8	#6
Span l′ in Ft													
33	76	108	142	177	**214**	250	255		**250**	287			
34	65	95	127	160	**195**	**212**	242		**238**	272			
35	55	84	114	144	**178**	**202**	229		**227**	259			
36	46	73	101	130	**162**	**192**	218		**215**	241	246		
37	37	63	90	117	**147**	**177**	207		**198**	**206**	234		
38	30	53	79	105	**133**	**162**	192	197	**181**	**196**	217	222	
39		45	69	94	**121**	**148**	**165**	187	**166**	**188**	**188**	211	
40		37	60	84	**109**	**135**	**157**	179	**152**	**179**	**179**	201	
41		30	52	74	**98**	**123**	**150**	170	**139**	**169**	**169**	192	
42			44	65	**88**	**112**	**141**	162	**126**	**155**	**155**	183	
43			37	57	**79**	**102**	**130**	155	**115**	**143**	**143**	**172**	175
44			30	49	**70**	**92**	**119**	146	**104**	**131**	**131**	**148**	**167**
45				42	**62**	**83**	**108**	**124**	**95**	**120**	**120**	**142**	**160**
46				35	**55**	**74**	**99**	**119**	**85**	**110**	**110**	**135**	**153**
47					**48**	**66**	**90**	**113**	**77**	**100**	**100**	**124**	**130**
48					**41**	**59**	**81**	**104**	**69**	**91**	**91**	**114**	**124**
49					**35**	**52**	**73**	**96**	**61**	**82**	**82**	**105**	**119**

Tabulated values in boldface type require embedment E_4 explained on page 7-34.
Above and to the right of the zigzag line, tapered ends are required.

CONCRETE JOIST CONSTRUCTION
END SPAN—20 INCH WIDE FORMS
Safe Superimposed Load (psf)

For limitations and explanation of use of tables, see pages 7-33 to 7-37.

Depth	20″ FORMS + 4½″ CONCRETE											
Joists	7″ Joists @ 27″ c/c, Wt 137 psf							8″ Joists @ 28″ c/c, Wt 143 psf				
Bottom Bar	#7	#8	#8	#9	#9	#10	#10	#10	#10	#10	#11	#11
Truss Bar	#7	#7	#8	#8	#9	#9	#10	#9	#10	#10	#10	#11
Top Bar	#4	#6	#5	#7	#5	#7	#6	#7	#5	#6	#8	#6
Span l′ in Ft												
35	79	111	143	177	**208**	235		**236**	267			
36	67	97	128	160	**194**	223		**217**	249	253		
37	57	85	114	145	**176**	211		**198**	**213**	237	239	
38	47	74	101	130	**160**	196	200	**180**	**203**	**203**	227	
39	38	63	89	117	**145**	**168**	190	**164**	**193**	**193**	216	
40		54	78	105	**132**	**160**	181	**149**	**183**	**183**	206	
41		45	68	93	**119**	**151**	172	**135**	**167**	**167**	196	
42		36	59	83	**107**	**138**	163	**122**	**153**	**153**	184	187
43			50	73	**96**	**125**	155	**110**	**139**	**139**	**158**	178
44			42	64	**86**	**114**	**131**	**99**	**127**	**127**	**151**	169
45			34	55	**76**	**103**	**124**	**89**	**115**	**115**	**143**	161
46				47	**67**	**93**	**118**	**79**	**104**	**104**	**130**	**154**
47				39	**59**	**83**	**108**	**70**	**94**	**94**	**119**	**131**
48				32	**51**	**74**	**98**	**61**	**84**	**84**	**109**	**125**
49					**44**	**66**	**89**	**53**	**75**	**75**	**99**	**119**
50					**37**	**58**	**80**	**46**	**67**	**67**	**89**	**112**
51					**30**	**51**	**72**	**39**	**59**	**59**	**80**	**102**

CONCRETE JOIST CONSTRUCTION
END SPAN—30 INCH WIDE FORMS
Safe Superimposed Load (psf)

For limitations and explanation of use of tables, see pages 7-33 to 7-37.

Depth	6″ FORMS + 2½″ CONCRETE								
Joists	4″ Joists @ 34″ c/c, Wt 41 psf					5″ Joists @ 35″ c/c, Wt 43 psf			6″ @ 36″ c/c, Wt 45 psf
Bottom Bar	#4	#5	#5	#6	#6	#6	#6	#7	#8
Truss Bar	#4	#4	#5	#5	#6	#5	#6	#6	#7
Top Bar	#4	#4	#4	#5	#4	#5	#4	#5	#6
Span l′ in Ft									
9	233	303	335			361			380
10	181	238	292			315			332
11	143	190	238	255		278			294
12	113	153	193	220		229	248		262
13	**89**	124	159	181		189	**221**		236
14	**73**	102	131	153		157	**187**		**215**
15	**58**	83	109	131		131	**160**		**186**
16	**46**	68	91	113		110	**136**	**139**	**162**
17	**36**	**55**	76	98	99	93	**115**	**122**	**143**
18		**45**	64	83	87	78	**98**	**108**	**127**
19		**37**	53	71	**77**	66	**84**	**96**	**114**
20			**40**	60	**69**	**53**	**72**	**86**	**102**

Tabulated values in boldface type require embedment E_4 explained on page 7-34.
Above and to the right of the zigzag line, tapered ends are required.

CONCRETE JOIST CONSTRUCTION
END SPAN—30 INCH WIDE FORMS
Safe Superimposed Load (psf)

For limitations and explanation of use of tables, see pages 7-33 to 7-37.

Depth: 6″ FORMS + 3″ CONCRETE

Joists	4″ Joists @ 34″ c/c Wt 47 psf					5″ Joists @ 35″ c/c Wt 49 psf				6″ @ 36″ c/c Wt 50 psf	
Bottom Bar	#4	#5	#5	#6	#6	#6	#6	#7	#7	#7	#7
Truss Bar	#4	#4	#5	#5	#6	#5	#6	#6	#7	#6	#7
Top Bar	#4	#4	#4	#5	#4	#5	#4	#5	#4	#5	#4
Span l′ in Ft											
9	246	321	355			383				409	
10	190	251	309			334				357	
11	149	199	251	270		294				315	
12	118	160	203	232		242	262			281	
13	**93**	130	166	190		199	233			252	
14	**74**	105	137	160		165	197			**229**	
15	**59**	86	114	136		137	168			**194**	**197**
16	**46**	70	94	118		115	142	145		**165**	**172**
17	**36**	**56**	78	102		96	120	**127**		**140**	**151**
18		**45**	65	86	90	81	102	**112**		**120**	**134**
19		**36**	53	73	79	67	87	**100**		**102**	**120**
20			**40**	61	70	**53**	74	**89**		**87**	**107**
21			**35**	51	**62**	**46**	62	**79**	**80**	**75**	**94**
22				42	**55**	**38**	53	**68**	**71**	**64**	**81**

Depth: 6″ FORMS + 4½″ CONCRETE

Joists	4″ Joists @ 34″ c/c Wt 66 psf						5″ Joists @ 35″ c/c Wt 68 psf				6″ Joists @ 36″ c/c Wt 69 psf		
Bottom Bar	#4	#5	#5	#6	#6	#6	#6	#6	#7	#7	#7	#7	#8
Truss Bar	#4	#4	#5	#5	#5	#6	#5	#6	#6	#7	#6	#7	#7
Top Bar	#4	#4	#4	#4	#5	#4	#5	#4	#5	#4	#5	#4	#6
Span l′ in Ft													
9	284	374	417										
10	218	291	360				392				421		
11	169	229	291	312			343				369		
12	121	182	234	266			280	304			327		
13	102	146	190	217			229	268			293		
14	79	117	155	181			188	225			264		
15	61	93	126	150	153		156	192			222	227	
16	46	**68**	103	124	131		129	162			187	197	
17	33	**58**	84	103	113		106	135	142		158	172	
18		**45**	68	85	94	97	88	114	125		133	151	
19		**34**	55	69	78	85	72	95	110		113	134	
20			**39**	56	64	74	**56**	80	97		95	**120**	
21			**33**	45	52	65	**47**	66	85		80	**105**	
22				35	42	56	**37**	54	72	76	67	**89**	**95**
23					33	49		44	60	**68**	**52**	**76**	**85**
24						40		**34**	50	**60**	**46**	**64**	**76**
25						31			41	**53**	**37**	**54**	**69**

Tabulated values in boldface type require embedment E_4 explained on page 7-34.
Above and to the right of the zigzag line, tapered ends are required.

CONCRETE JOIST CONSTRUCTION
END SPAN—30 INCH WIDE FORMS
Safe Superimposed Load (psf)

For limitations and explanation of use of tables, see pages 7-33 to 7-37.

Depth	8″ FORMS + 2½″ CONCRETE										
Joists	4″ Joists @ 34″ c/c Wt 45 psf					5″ Joists @ 35″ c/c Wt 48 psf				6″ Joists @ 36″ Wt 50 psf	
Bottom Bar	#4	#5	#5	#6	#6	#6	#6	#7	#7	#7	#8
Truss Bar	#4	#4	#5	#5	#6	#5	#6	#6	#7	#7	#7
Top Bar	#4	#4	#4	#5	#4	#5	#4	#5	#4	#4	#6
Span l′ in Ft											
11	189	250	311			366	370			396	
12	145	203	254	294		300	330			353	
13	123	166	210	244		249	297			318	
14	100	137	175	207		208	251			289	
15	81	114	147	178		176	213	218		254	
16	66	**92**	124	156		149	181	191		223	
17	54	**79**	105	134	137	126	155	169		197	
18	43	**66**	89	115	122	108	134	150		176	
19	34	**54**	**68**	98	109	**87**	115	135		**159**	
20		**45**	**62**	84	97	**78**	99	121		**142**	
21		**37**	**53**	72	88	**67**	86	105	110	**124**	**129**
22			**45**	62	80	**57**	**68**	92	**100**	**109**	**118**
23			**37**	53	69	**48**	**62**	80	**92**	**95**	**108**
24			**31**	**43**	60	**40**	**55**	70	**84**	**83**	**99**
25				**38**	52	**34**	**47**	60	**77**	**73**	**91**

Depth	8″ FORMS + 3″ CONCRETE											
Joists	4″ Joists @ 34″ c/c Wt 51 psf					5″ Joists @ 35″ c/c Wt 54 psf				6″ Joists @ 36″ Wt 56 psf		
Bottom Bar	#4	#5	#5	#6	#6	#6	#6	#7	#7	#7	#7	#8
Truss Bar	#4	#4	#5	#5	#6	#5	#6	#6	#7	#6	#7	#7
Top Bar	#4	#4	#4	#5	#4	#5	#4	#5	#4	#5	#4	#6
Span l′ in Ft												
11	196	259	324			383	387			415		
12	151	210	265			313	345			369		
13	126	172	218	254		259	310			332		
14	102	141	181	214		216	261			297	301	
15	82	116	151	184		182	221	226		252	264	
16	66	**94**	127	160		153	188	197		215	231	
17	53	**80**	107	137	141	130	160	174		184	205	
18	42	**66**	90	117	124	110	137	155		158	183	
19	32	**54**	**69**	100	111	**89**	118	139		136	164	
20		**44**	**62**	85	99	**79**	101	124	125	118	**146**	
21		**35**	**53**	73	89	**67**	87	108	113	102	**127**	133
22			**44**	62	80	**56**	**68**	93	102	**82**	**111**	**121**
23			**36**	52	70	**47**	**62**	81	**93**	**76**	**97**	**111**
24				**42**	60	**39**	**54**	70	**85**	**66**	**85**	**101**
25				**37**	51	**32**	**46**	60	**78**	**56**	**74**	**92**
26				**30**	44		**39**	**48**	**70**	**48**	**60**	**81**

Tabulated values in boldface type require embedment E_4 explained on page 7-34.
Above and to the right of the zigzag line, tapered ends are required.

CONCRETE JOIST CONSTRUCTION
END SPAN—30 INCH WIDE FORMS
Safe Superimposed Load (psf)

For limitations and explanation of use of tables, see pages 7-33 to 7-37.

Depth: 8″ FORMS + 4½″ CONCRETE

Joists	4″ Joists @ 34″ c/c			Wt 70 psf		5″ Joists @ 35″ c/c			Wt 73 psf		6″@36″c/c Wt 75 psf		
Bottom Bar	#4	#5	#5	#6	#6	#6	#6	#7	#7	#8	#7	#8	#8
Truss Bar	#4	#4	#5	#5	#6	#5	#6	#6	#7	#7	#7	#7	#8
Top Bar	#4	#4	#4	#5	#4	#5	#4	#5	#4	#6	#4	#6	#4
Span l′ in Ft													
12	168	232	295	342		352	388				418		
13	135	188	241	282		290	347				374		
14	107	152	199	236		240	292				337		
15	84	113	164	202		200	246	250			294		
16	66	**100**	136	174		167	207	218			257		
17	50	**81**	113	149	151	140	176	191			226		
18	38	**65**	93	125	133	117	149	169			201		
19		**52**	**71**	105	117	**95**	127	150			179		
20		**40**	**63**	88	104	**82**	107	134			160		
21		**30**	**51**	74	92	**68**	91	115	120		138	144	
22			**40**	61	82	**55**	**70**	99	108		119	130	
23			**31**	50	70	**45**	**63**	84	97		103	118	
24				**39**	59	**35**	**53**	72	88		89	107	
25				**32**	49		**43**	61	79		76	**98**	
26					40		**35**	51	71		**60**	**85**	**89**
27					32			**41**	61	64	**55**	**73**	**81**
28								**35**	51	58	**46**	**63**	**74**
29									43	**52**	**38**	**54**	**68**

Depth: 10″ FORMS + 2½″ CONCRETE

Joists	4″ Joists @ 34″ c/c			Wt 49 psf		5″ Joists @ 35″ c/c			Wt 52 psf	6″ @ 36″ Wt 54 psf	
Bottom Bar	#4	#5	#5	#6	#6	#6	#6	#7	#7	#8	#8
Truss Bar	#4	#4	#5	#5	#6	#5	#6	#6	#7	#7	#8
Top Bar	#4	#4	#4	#5	#4	#5	#4	#5	#4	#6	#5
Span l′ in Ft											
14	127	173	219	257		260	312	317		361	
15	104	133	185	222		220	265	275		321	
16	86	**120**	157	194		187	227	241		282	
17	71	**102**	133	169	172	160	195	214		251	
18	58	**86**	114	145	153	**127**	169	192		225	
19	47	**72**	**91**	126	137	**117**	146	173		203	
20	38	**60**	**83**	109	124	**101**	127	154	156	185	
21	30	**50**	**71**	94	112	**87**	110	135	142	168	
22		**41**	**60**	82	102	**75**	**92**	118	130	154	
23		**34**	**51**	71	90	**64**	**84**	104	119	142	
24			**43**	**59**	79	**55**	**73**	91	110	**131**	
25			**36**	**52**	69	**47**	**63**	80	101	**117**	121
26			**30**	**45**	60	**39**	**54**	**67**	91	**104**	**112**
27				**38**	52	**33**	**47**	**63**	80	**93**	**104**
28				**32**	**43**		**40**	**55**	71	**82**	**97**
29					**39**		**34**	**48**	63	**67**	**90**
30					**33**			**42**	**51**	**63**	**80**

Tabulated values in boldface type require embedment E_4 explained on page 7-34.
Above and to the right of the zigzag line, tapered ends are required.

CONCRETE JOIST CONSTRUCTION
END SPAN—30 INCH WIDE FORMS
Safe Superimposed Load (psf)

For limitations and explanation of use of tables, see pages 7-33 to 7-37.

Depth: 10″ FORMS + 3″ CONCRETE

Joists	4″ Joists @ 34″ c/c Wt 56 psf					5″ Joists @ 35″ c/c Wt 58 psf				6″ @ 36″ c/c Wt 61 psf		
Bottom Bar	#4	#5	#5	#6	#6	#6	#7	#7	#8	#8	#8	#9
Truss Bar	#4	#4	#5	#5	#6	#6	#6	#7	#7	#7	#8	#8
Top Bar	#4	#4	#4	#5	#4	#4	#5	#4	#6	#6	#5	#7
Span l′ in Ft												
15	105	136	189	228		274	283			331		
16	86	120	160	199		234	248			291		
17	70	100	135	173		200	220			258		
18	57	83	115	148	156	173	196			231		
19	45	69	**92**	127	139	149	177			209		
20	36	57	**83**	110	125	129	157	160		189		
21		47	**70**	95	113	112	137	145		172		
22		38	**59**	81	103	**93**	120	132		157		
23		30	**49**	70	91	**84**	105	121		145		
24			**41**	**58**	79	**72**	92	111		133		
25			**34**	**51**	68	**62**	80	102		119	123	
26				**43**	59	**53**	**67**	91	93	105	113	
27				**36**	51	**45**	**62**	80	86	93	**105**	
28				**30**	**41**	**38**	**54**	71	79	83	**98**	
29					**37**	**32**	**47**	62	73	**67**	**90**	
30					**31**		**40**	**49**	**68**	**62**	**81**	**84**
31							**34**	**46**	**62**	**56**	**72**	**78**

Depth: 10″ FORMS + 4½″ CONCRETE

Joists	4″ Joists @ 34″ c/c Wt 74 psf					5″ Joists @ 35″ c/c Wt 77 psf					6″@36″c/c Wt79 psf		
Bottom Bar	#4	#5	#5	#6	#6	#6	#6	#7	#7	#8	#8	#8	#9
Truss Bar	#4	#4	#5	#5	#6	#5	#6	#6	#7	#7	#7	#8	#8
Top Bar	#4	#4	#4	#5	#4	#5	#4	#5	#4	#6	#6	#5	#7
Span l′ in Ft													
17	68	102	141	184	186	174	216	237			281		
18	53	83	118	156	164	139	184	210			250		
19	40	67	94	133	146	**124**	158	188			225		
20		54	**82**	113	130	**105**	135	168	169		203		
21		42	**68**	96	116	**88**	116	145	152		184		
22		32	**55**	81	104	**74**	**95**	126	138		167		
23			**45**	**62**	91	**61**	**84**	109	125		152		
24			**35**	**55**	78	**50**	**71**	94	114		139		
25				**46**	66	**40**	**59**	80	104		124	128	
26				**37**	56	**31**	**49**	**66**	92	94	109	117	
27					47		**40**	**60**	80	86	95	108	
28					**36**		**32**	**50**	69	78	83	100	
29					**31**			**42**	59	72	**66**	92	
30								**34**	51	66	**61**	81	84
31									**42**	60	**54**	71	77
32									**35**	52	**45**	62	**71**
33										44	**38**	53	**66**

Tabulated values in boldface type require embedment E_4 explained on page 7-34.
Above and to the right of the zigzag line, tapered ends are required.

CONCRETE JOIST CONSTRUCTION
END SPAN—30 INCH WIDE FORMS
Safe Superimposed Load (psf)

For limitations and explanation of use of tables, see pages 7-33 to 7-37.

Depth: 12″ FORMS + 2½″ CONCRETE

Joists	4″ Joists @ 34″ c/c Wt 53 psf					5″ Joists @ 35″ c/c Wt 57 psf					6″ @ 36″ c/c Wt 61 psf	
Bottom Bar	#4	#5	#5	#6	#6	#6	#7	#7	#8	#8	#8	#9
Truss Bar	#4	#4	#5	#5	#6	#6	#6	#7	#7	#8	#8	#8
Top Bar	#4	#4	#4	#5	#4	#4	#5	#4	#6	#5	#5	#7
Span l′ in Ft												
18	73	103	138	176	184	204	230				273	
19	60	87	114	153	166	177	207				247	
20	49	74	**102**	133	150	154	187	188			224	
21	39	62	**88**	116	136	**124**	165	172			205	
22	31	52	**75**	101	124	**115**	145	157			188	
23		43	**65**	**82**	111	**103**	128	145			174	
24		35	**55**	**75**	98	**90**	113	133			161	
25			**47**	**66**	86	**79**	**92**	123			149	
26			**39**	**57**	76	**69**	**85**	112	113		138	
27			**33**	**49**	67	**60**	**79**	100	105		129	
28				**42**	**56**	**52**	**70**	89	98		120	
29				**36**	**51**	**44**	**61**	79	91		111	
30				**30**	**44**	**38**	**54**	**65**	85		100	104
31					**38**	**32**	**47**	**61**	79		90	98
32					**32**		**41**	**55**	71	74	81	**92**
33							**35**	**48**	64	69	**68**	**86**
34							**30**	**42**	57	65	**64**	**80**

Depth: 12″ FORMS + 3″ CONCRETE

Joists	4″ Joists @ 34″ c/c Wt 60 psf					5″ Joists @ 35″ c/c Wt 63 psf					6″ @ 36″ Wt 67 psf		
Bottom Bar	#4	#5	#5	#6	#6	#6	#7	#7	#8	#8	#8	#9	#9
Truss Bar	#4	#4	#5	#5	#6	#6	#6	#7	#7	#8	#8	#8	#9
Top Bar	#4	#4	#4	#5	#4	#4	#5	#4	#6	#5	#5	#7	#5
Span l′ in Ft													
19	58	87	115	155	168	180	211				252		
20	47	73	102	134	151	156	191				229		
21	37	61	87	116	137	**125**	167	174			209		
22		50	74	101	125	**116**	147	159			192		
23		**41**	63	**81**	112	**103**	129	146			176		
24		**33**	53	**75**	98	**90**	114	134			163		
25			44	**65**	86	**78**	**92**	124			151		
26			37	**56**	75	**67**	**85**	112			140		
27			30	**47**	65	**58**	**79**	99	105		130		
28				**40**	**54**	**50**	**69**	88	98		121		
29				**33**	**49**	**42**	**60**	78	91		112		
30					**42**	**35**	**52**	**64**	84		100	104	
31					**35**		**45**	**60**	78		90	98	
32					**30**		**38**	**53**	70	73	80	91	
33							**32**	**46**	62	68	**67**	**85**	
34								**40**	55	63	**63**	**79**	**80**
35								**34**	**44**	59	**56**	**71**	**75**

Tabulated values in boldface type require embedment E_4 explained on page 7-34.
Above and to the right of the zigzag line, tapered ends are required.

CONCRETE JOIST CONSTRUCTION
END SPAN—30 INCH WIDE FORMS
Safe Superimposed Load (psf)

For limitations and explanation of use of tables, see pages 7-33 to 7-37.

Depth	12″ FORMS + 4½″ CONCRETE											
Joists	4″ Joists @ 34″ c/c Wt 78 psf				5″ Joists @ 35″ c/c Wt 82 psf					6″ @ 36″ c/c Wt 86 psf		
Bottom Bar	#5	#5	#6	#6	#6	#7	#7	#8	#8	#8	#9	#9
Truss Bar	#4	#5	#5	#6	#6	#6	#7	#7	#8	#8	#8	#9
Top Bar	#4	#4	#5	#4	#4	#5	#4	#6	#5	#5	#7	#5
Span l′ in Ft												
21	56	85	117	140	130	175	182			221		
22	44	71	100	126	**120**	153	165			202		
23	34	58	**80**	112	**103**	133	151			185		
24		47	**72**	97	**89**	116	138			169		
25		38	**60**	83	**75**	**92**	126			156		
26			**50**	71	**64**	**85**	113			144		
27			**41**	61	**53**	**76**	99	105		133		
28			**33**	**49**	**44**	**65**	87	97		123		
29				**42**	**36**	**55**	76	89		113		
30				**35**		**46**	**61**	82		101	105	
31						**38**	**56**	76		89	97	
32						**31**	**48**	67	69	78	90	
33							**40**	58	64	**64**	84	
34							**33**	50	59	**59**	78	
35								43	54	**52**	68	72
36								**35**	49	**44**	60	67
37								**30**	44	**38**	53	**62**
38									38	**31**	**43**	**58**

Depth	14″ FORMS + 2½″ CONCRETE											
Joists	5″ Joists @ 35″ c/c Wt 62 psf					6″ Joists @ 36″ c/c Wt 65 psf				7″ @ 37″ Wt 69 psf		
Bottom Bar	#6	#7	#7	#8	#8	#8	#8	#9	#9	#9	#9	#10
Truss Bar	#6	#6	#7	#7	#8	#7	#8	#8	#9	#8	#9	#9
Top Bar	#4	#5	#4	#6	#5	#6	#5	#7	#4	#7	#5	#7
Span l′ in Ft												
21	150	195	201			240				275		
22	**139**	172	184			220				254		
23	**123**	152	170			203				234		
24	**108**	135	157			188				217		
25	**95**	**111**	145			169	175			202		
26	**83**	**104**	133			152	163			189		
27	**72**	**95**	119	125		136	152			176		
28	**63**	**84**	106	116		**112**	142			163	165	
29	**55**	**75**	95	108		**105**	133			148	155	
30	**47**	**66**	**80**	101		**98**	120	124		134	145	
31	**40**	**58**	**75**	95		**88**	108	116		**110**	137	
32	**34**	**50**	**67**	86	89	**78**	97	109		**104**	127	128
33		**44**	**59**	77	83	**70**	**83**	102		**98**	116	120
34		**38**	**52**	69	78	**62**	**78**	96		**89**	105	**114**
35		**32**	**46**	**58**	73	**55**	**71**	88	91	**80**	83	**107**
36			**40**	**54**	69	**48**	**63**	79	**86**	**72**	83	**101**
37			**35**	**49**	64	**42**	**57**	72	**81**	**65**	79	**96**
38			**30**	**43**	57	**37**	**50**	**61**	**76**	**58**	72	**90**

Tabulated values in boldface type require embedment E_4 explained on page 7-34.
Above and to the right of the zigzag line, tapered ends are required.

CONCRETE JOIST CONSTRUCTION
END SPAN—30 INCH WIDE FORMS
Safe Superimposed Load (psf)

For limitations and explanation of use of tables, see pages 7-33 to 7-37.

Depth: 14″ FORMS + 3″ CONCRETE

Joists	5″ Joists @ 35″ c/c			Wt 68 psf		6″ Joists @ 36″ c/c			Wt 71 psf		7″ @ 37″ c/c		Wt 75 psf
Bottom Bar	#6	#7	#7	#8	#8	#8	#8	#9	#9	#9	#9	#9	#10
Truss Bar	#6	#6	#7	#7	#8	#7	#8	#8	#9	#9	#8	#9	#9
Top Bar	#4	#5	#4	#6	#5	#6	#5	#7	#4	#5	#7	#5	#7
Span l′ in Ft													
22	**140**	174	186			224					258		
23	**123**	153	171			206					238		
24	**107**	135	158			190					221		
25	**94**	**112**	146			171	176				205		
26	**82**	**104**	133	134		153	164				191		
27	**71**	**94**	119	125		136	153				178		
28	**61**	**83**	106	116		**112**	142				164	167	
29	**53**	**73**	94	108		**105**	133				148	156	
30	**45**	**64**	**79**	101		**97**	119	124			134	146	
31	**38**	**56**	**74**	94		**87**	107	116			**110**	137	
32	**31**	**48**	**65**	85	88	**77**	96	109			**104**	128	
33		**41**	**57**	76	82	**68**	**82**	102			**98**	116	121
34		**35**	**50**	68	76	**60**	**77**	96			**88**	105	114
35			**44**	**56**	71	**53**	**69**	86	90		**79**	**88**	**107**
36			**38**	**52**	67	**46**	**61**	78	85		**70**	**83**	**101**
37			**32**	**47**	62	**40**	**54**	**64**	77	80	**62**	**78**	**95**
38				**41**	55	**34**	**48**	**60**	70	**75**	**55**	**70**	**88**

Depth: 14″ FORMS + 4½″ CONCRETE

Joists	5″ Joists @ 35″ c/c			Wt 87 psf		6″ Joists @ 36″ c/c			Wt 90 psf	7″ @ 37″ c/c	Wt 94 psf
Bottom Bar	#6	#7	#7	#8	#8	#8	#9	#9	#10	#10	#10
Truss Bar	#6	#6	#7	#7	#8	#8	#8	#9	#9	#9	#10
Top Bar	#4	#5	#4	#6	#5	#5	#7	#5	#7	#7	#5
Span l′ in Ft											
23	123	157	176			214				249	
24	106	137	161			197				230	
25	91	**113**	148			182				212	
26	78	**104**	134			168				197	
27	66	**92**	118	125		156				183	
28	55	**80**	104	115		145				170	
29	46	**68**	91	106		134				159	
30	37	**58**	**76**	98		120	124			148	
31	30	**49**	**69**	91		107	116			139	
32		**41**	**60**	82	84	95	108			130	
33		**34**	**51**	72	78	**80**	100			121	
34			**43**	63	72	**74**	93			114	
35			**36**	**51**	66	**65**	84	87		106	
36			**30**	**47**	61	**56**	74	81		100	
37				**40**	56	**48**	66	76		93	
38				**33**	49	**41**	**55**	71		83	**88**
39					42	**35**	**50**	65		75	**82**

Tabulated values in boldface type require embedment E_4 explained on page 7-34.
Above and to the right of the zigzag line, tapered ends are required.

CONCRETE JOIST CONSTRUCTION
END SPAN—30 INCH WIDE FORMS
Safe Superimposed Load (psf)

For limitations and explanation of use of tables, see pages 7-33 to 7-37.

Depth: 16″ FORMS + 2½″ CONCRETE

Joists	6″ Joists @ 36″ c/c						Wt 72 psf	7″ @ 37″ c/c			Wt 76 psf	8″@38″ c/c Wt 80 psf		
Bottom Bar	#6	#7	#7	#8	#9	#9	#9	#9	#9	#10	#10	#9	#10	#10
Truss Bar	#6	#6	#7	#7	#8	#8	#9	#8	#9	#9	#10	#9	#9	#10
Top Bar	#4	#5	#4	#6	#6	#7	#5	#7	#5	#7	#5	#5	#7	#5
Span l′ in Ft 25	101	124	**160**	196	199			232				262		
26	88	109	**143**	176	186			216				245		
27	76	96	**128**	158	173			202				227		
28	66	85	**114**	**132**	162			189				206	214	
29	57	74	**101**	**124**	152			171				187	201	
30	49	65	**90**	**114**	143			155	167			**157**	189	
31	41	56	**80**	**103**	134			**130**	157			**149**	179	
32	34	48	**71**	**92**	126			**123**	148			**141**	164	169
33		41	**62**	**82**	118	119	119	**115**	135			**128**	150	159
34		35	**55**	**74**	107	112	112	**104**	123	132		**116**	**126**	151
35			**48**	**65**	97	103	106	**94**	**104**	124		**105**	**119**	143
36			**41**	**58**	**82**	94	100	**85**	**99**	118		**95**	**114**	131
37			**35**	**51**	**78**	**78**	94	**77**	**94**	111		**86**	**107**	119
38			**30**	**45**	**74**	**74**	89	**69**	**85**	101	106	**77**	**97**	**103**
39				**39**	**69**	**69**	83	**62**	**77**	93	**100**	**69**	**88**	**98**
40				**34**	**63**	**63**	76	**55**	**70**	**79**	**95**	**62**	**80**	**93**
41					**56**	**56**	**62**	**49**	**63**	**75**	**90**	**55**	**73**	**88**

Depth: 16″ FORMS + 3″ CONCRETE

Joists	6″ Joists @ 36″ c/c						Wt 78 psf	7″ @ 37″ c/c			Wt 83 psf	8″@38″c/c Wt 87 psf		
Bottom Bar	#6	#7	#7	#8	#9	#9	#9	#9	#9	#10	#10	#10	#10	#11
Truss Bar	#6	#6	#7	#7	#8	#8	#9	#8	#9	#9	#10	#10	#10	#10
Top Bar	#4	#5	#4	#6	#6	#7	#5	#7	#5	#7	#5	#5	#6	#7
Span l′ in Ft 26	87	109	**143**	176	187			218				247		
27	75	95	**127**	158	174			204				231		
28	64	83	**113**	**132**	163			190	191			216		
29	55	73	**100**	**124**	152			172	179			203		
30	46	63	**89**	**113**	143			155	168			191		
31	38	54	**78**	**101**	134			**130**	158			180		
32	31	46	**69**	**90**	126			**123**	149			170		
33		39	**60**	**80**	118			**114**	135	139		160		
34		32	**52**	**71**	107	111		**103**	123	132		151		
35			**45**	**63**	97	101	105	**93**	**104**	124		143		
36			**38**	**55**	**81**	92	99	**83**	**98**	117		131	136	
37			**32**	**48**	**77**	**77**	93	**74**	**92**	111		119	**127**	128
38				**42**	**72**	**72**	88	**66**	**83**	101	105	**102**	**116**	**121**
39				**36**	**67**	**67**	82	**59**	**75**	92	99	**97**	**97**	**115**
40				**30**	**60**	**60**	74	**52**	**67**	**78**	**94**	**92**	**92**	**109**
41					**53**	**53**	67	**46**	**60**	**74**	**89**	**87**	**88**	**103**
42					**47**	**47**	**57**	**40**	**54**	**70**	**84**	**79**	**80**	**82**

Tabulated values in boldface type require embedment E_4 explained on page 7-34.
Above and to the right of the zigzag line, tapered ends are required.

CONCRETE JOIST CONSTRUCTION
END SPAN—30 INCH WIDE FORMS
Safe Superimposed Load (psf)

For limitations and explanation of use of tables, see pages 7-33 to 7-37.

Depth: 16″ FORMS + 4½″ CONCRETE

Joists	6″ Joists @ 36″ c/c, Wt 97 psf							7″ Joists @ 37″ c/c, Wt 101 psf				8″ Joists @ 38″ c/c, Wt 105 psf		
Bottom Bar	#7	#7	#8	#8	#9	#9	#9	#9	#9	#10	#10	#10	#10	#11
Truss Bar	#6	#7	#7	#8	#8	#8	#9	#8	#9	#9	#10	#10	#10	#10
Top Bar	#5	#4	#6	#5	#6	#7	#5	#7	#5	#7	#5	#5	#6	#7
Span l′ in Ft														
28	79	108	**134**	166				195	196			224		
29	68	95	**125**	154				175	183			210		
30	57	82	**112**	139	143			157	171			196		
31	47	71	**99**	124	134			**132**	160			184		
32	39	61	**87**	**102**	125			**124**	150			173		
33	31	52	**76**	**96**	117			**113**	136	140		163		
34		43	**66**	**87**	105	109		**101**	123	131		153		
35		35	**57**	**77**	94	99	102	**89**	**103**	123		144		
36			**49**	**68**	**78**	88	95	**79**	**97**	116		132	136	
37			**41**	**59**	**73**	**73**	89	**70**	**89**	109		120	127	128
38			**34**	**51**	**68**	**68**	83	**61**	**79**	99	102	**101**	115	120
39				**44**	**61**	**61**	78	**53**	**70**	89	96	**96**	**96**	114
40				**37**	**53**	**53**	69	**45**	**62**	**75**	91	**90**	**90**	105
41				**31**	**46**	**46**	61	**38**	**54**	**70**	85	**84**	**84**	95
42					**40**	**40**	**51**	**32**	**47**	**65**	78	**75**	**75**	**80**
43					**34**	**34**	**47**		**40**	**58**	70	**67**	**67**	**75**
44							**42**		**34**	**51**	**58**	**60**	**60**	**71**
45							**36**			**44**	**54**	**52**	**52**	**67**

Depth: 20″ FORMS + 2½″ CONCRETE

Joists	7″ Joists @ 37″ c/c, Wt 90 psf							8″ Joists @ 38″ c/c, Wt 95 psf					9″ @ 39″ c/c, Wt 101 psf	
Bottom Bar	#7	#8	#8	#9	#9	#10	#10	#10	#10	#10	#11	#11	#11	#11
Truss Bar	#7	#7	#8	#8	#9	#9	#10	#9	#10	#10	#10	#11	#10	#11
Top Bar	#4	#6	#5	#7	#5	#7	#6	#7	#5	#6	#8	#6	#8	#6
Span l′ in Ft														
32	81	108	135	**161**	187			210	212				230	
33	71	96	122	**149**	173	176		192	201				220	
34	62	86	110	**135**	**145**	167		**165**	190				211	
35	54	76	99	**123**	**137**	158		**157**	181				201	
36	46	67	89	**111**	**130**	149		**149**	168	171			191	
37	39	59	79	**100**	**122**	142		**138**	**142**	163			182	
38	32	51	70	**91**	**111**	132	135	**127**	**135**	152	154		167	173
39		44	62	**82**	**101**	**111**	128	**115**	**129**	**129**	146		**145**	165
40		38	55	**73**	**92**	**106**	121	**105**	**123**	**123**	139		**138**	157
41		32	48	**66**	**83**	**101**	115	**96**	**116**	**117**	133		**130**	**132**
42			42	**58**	**75**	**96**	110	**87**	**106**	**108**	126		**120**	**126**
43			36	**52**	**68**	**88**	104	**79**	**97**	**99**	119	120	**110**	**120**
44			30	**45**	**61**	**80**	99	**71**	**88**	**90**	**101**	115	**100**	**115**
45				**40**	**54**	**73**	**83**	**64**	**80**	**82**	**96**	109	**92**	**110**
46				**34**	**48**	**66**	**79**	**57**	**73**	**75**	**92**	**104**	**84**	**102**
47					**43**	**59**	**75**	**51**	**66**	**68**	**85**	**87**	**76**	**94**
48					**37**	**53**	**70**	**45**	**59**	**61**	**78**	**83**	**69**	**86**
49					**32**	**48**	**64**	**39**	**53**	**55**	**71**	**80**	**62**	**78**

Tabulated values in boldface type require embedment E_4 explained on page 7-34.
Above and to the right of the zigzag line, tapered ends are required.

CONCRETE JOIST CONSTRUCTION
END SPAN—30 INCH WIDE FORMS
Safe Superimposed Load (psf)

For limitations and explanation of use of tables, see pages 7-33 to 7-37.

20″ FORMS + 3″ CONCRETE

Depth / Joists	7″ Joists @ 37″ c/c					Wt 96 psf	8″ @ 38″ c/c		Wt 101 psf		9″ @ 39″ c/c		Wt 107 psf
Bottom Bar	#8	#8	#9	#9	#10	#10	#10	#10	#11	#11	#11	#11	#11
Truss Bar	#7	#8	#8	#9	#9	#10	#9	#10	#10	#11	#10	#11	#11
Top Bar	#6	#5	#7	#5	#7	#6	#7	#6	#8	#6	#8	#5	#6
Span l′ in Ft													
33	95	120	**147**	174	176		193	202			222		
34	84	108	**133**	**145**	167		**166**	191			212		
35	74	96	**120**	**137**	157		**157**	181			202		
36	65	86	**109**	**130**	149		**149**	172			192		
37	56	76	**98**	**120**	141		**137**	163			181	182	
38	48	68	**88**	**109**	131	134	**124**	151	154		**152**	173	
39	41	59	**79**	**99**	**110**	127	**113**	**128**	146		**145**	161	165
40	35	52	**70**	**89**	**105**	120	**103**	**122**	139		**138**	**138**	157
41		45	**62**	**80**	**99**	114	**93**	**115**	132		**128**	**132**	145
42		38	**55**	**72**	**94**	108	**84**	**105**	126		**117**	**125**	**125**
43		32	**48**	**65**	**85**	103	**76**	**96**	117	119	**107**	**120**	**120**
44			**42**	**58**	**77**	97	**68**	**87**	**100**	114	**98**	**113**	**114**
45			**36**	**51**	**70**	**81**	**60**	**79**	**95**	108	**89**	**103**	**108**
46			**30**	**45**	**63**	**77**	**54**	**72**	**90**	103	**81**	**95**	**99**
47				**39**	**56**	**73**	**47**	**64**	**82**	**86**	**73**	**86**	**91**
48				**33**	**50**	**67**	**41**	**58**	**75**	**82**	**66**	**78**	**83**
49					**44**	**60**	**36**	**51**	**68**	**78**	**59**	**71**	**75**
50					**39**	**54**	**30**	**45**	**61**	**74**	**52**	**64**	**68**

20″ FORMS + 4½″ CONCRETE

Depth / Joists	7″ Joists @ 37″ c/c				Wt 115 psf	8″ @ 38″ c/c		Wt 120 psf	9″ @ 39″ c/c	Wt 126 psf
Bottom Bar	#8	#9	#9	#10	#10	#10	#11	#11	#11	#11
Truss Bar	#8	#8	#9	#9	#10	#10	#10	#11	#10	#11
Top Bar	#5	#7	#5	#7	#6	#6	#8	#6	#8	#6
Span l′ in Ft										
34	103	130	**145**	166		193			216	
35	91	117	**137**	157		182			205	
36	80	104	**129**	148		172			194	
37	70	93	**116**	139		162			180	184
38	60	82	**104**	129	131	**135**	153		**154**	174
39	52	72	**93**	**108**	124	**128**	145		**146**	165
40	44	63	**83**	**102**	117	**121**	137		**136**	157
41	36	55	**74**	**96**	110	**110**	130		**124**	145
42		47	**65**	**87**	104	**100**	123		**112**	**125**
43		40	**57**	**78**	98	**90**	**102**	116	**102**	**119**
44		33	**49**	**70**	91	**81**	**97**	110	**92**	**113**
45			**42**	**62**	**76**	**72**	**92**	104	**82**	**103**
46			**36**	**54**	**72**	**64**	**83**	99	**74**	**93**
47				**47**	**66**	**56**	**75**	90	**65**	**84**
48				**41**	**58**	**49**	**67**	**77**	**58**	**75**
49				**35**	**52**	**42**	**59**	**73**	**50**	**68**
50					**45**	**36**	**53**	**69**	**44**	**60**
51					**39**	**30**	**46**	**62**	**37**	**53**
52					**33**		**40**	**55**	**31**	**46**

Tabulated values in boldface type require embedment E_4 explained on page 7-34.
Above and to the right of the zigzag line, tapered ends are required.

CONCRETE JOIST CONSTRUCTION—INTERIOR SPAN

Read the general explanation of the arrangement of tables for Concrete Joist Construction on pages 7-3 to 7-5 before using these tables for interior spans. The details of temperature reinforcement, tapered end forms, distribution ribs, and especially the type of deformed bars all apply equally well here.

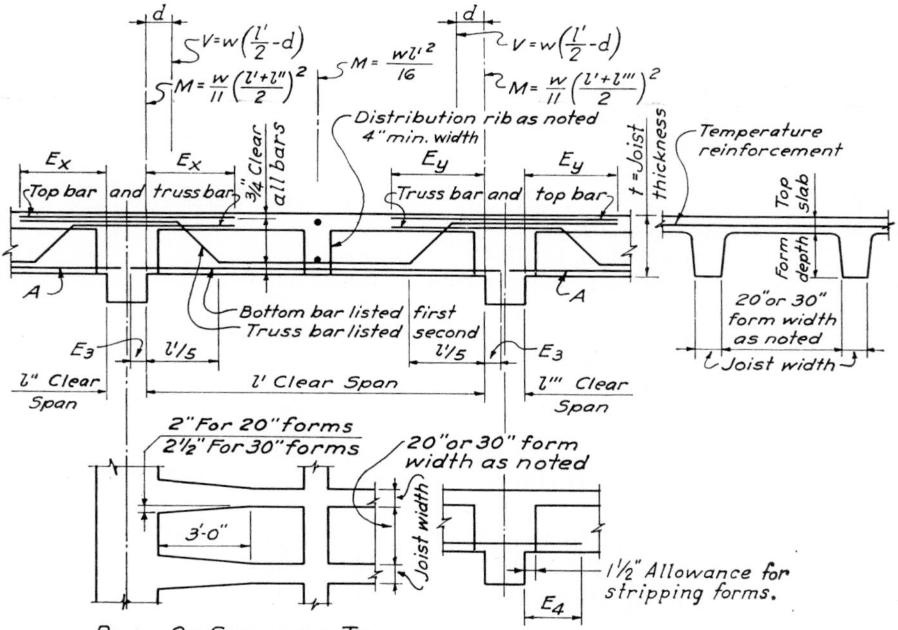

PLAN OF STANDARD TAPERED END WHERE REQUIRED

STRESSES:—

$f'_c = 3750$ psi

$f_c = 1688$ psi

$f_s = 24{,}000$ psi *

$v_c = 1.2\sqrt{f'_c} = 73.5$ psi †

$u = \dfrac{4.8\sqrt{f'_c}}{D}$ = (See Table on page 3-13)†

CODES:— "Building Code Requirements for Reinforced Concrete (ACI 318-63)"; "Manual of Standard Practice for Detailing Reinforced Concrete Structures (ACI 315)."

E_3 = bottom bar to extend 6 in. into the support except when values in the load tables are printed in boldface type (straight if possible, bent if necessary).

E_4 = When the values in the load tables are printed in boldface type, bottom bar should extend not less than 6 in. for #3 bars, 8 in. for #4 bars or $21D^2$ for #5 and larger nor less than $l'''/10$ past the far face of the support. Embedment of bottom bar at interior support is determined by the fact that the bottom bar is required for compressive reinforcement. The exact length varies. The maximum is that which will develop the full compression in the bar at the highest unit stress permitted by the ACI Code (24,000 psi) and which will at the same time extend the needed distance across the moment curve. The capacity of the joist may be determined by shear, bond or flexure. The

* Using ASTM A61 or A432 bars (f_y = 60,000 psi)

† Bond and diagonal tension values are based upon deformed bars meeting ASTM A305 or A408. Plain round bars or deformed bars not meeting ASTM A305 or A408 will not give sufficient bond resistance.

CONCRETE JOIST CONSTRUCTION—INTERIOR SPAN

recommendation for E_4 will cover the worst condition. The user may at his option work out the needs of any particular problem (see pages 7-61, 7-62).

E_x = not less than { $l'/4$; $l''/4$; 6 in. past bend-down point for #3 bars, 10 in. for #4 bars, and $21D^2$ for #5 and larger ($29D^2$ for #5 and larger when $d > 12$ in.). } whichever is greatest.

(ACI 918(e) requires top bars to extend to $l'/16$, or the effective depth of the member past point of inflection.)

E_y = not less than { $l'/4$; $l'''/4$; 6 in. past bend-down point for #3 bars, 10 in. for #4 bars, and $21D^2$ for #5 and larger ($29D^2$ for #5 and larger when $d > 12$ in.). } whichever is greatest.

The top bar in the table is scheduled on the basis of the adjoining span providing a bent bar of area equal to that of the bent bar in the span under consideration; any considerable variation in negative moment by reason of changes in load, span length, or end restraint of the adjacent span must be worked out by the general principles of continuity (pages 4-3 to 4-18, incl.).

A = bottom bar in adjoining span.

Almost all usual combinations of form depth, top slab and reinforcement are presented herewith. To show how the tables for interior spans were computed and to permit extension of the tables if required, an illustrative example is shown:—

Example—Determine the safe carrying capacity on spans of 18 and 26 ft. of 10 in. deep forms plus 3 in. of top slab with 5 in. joists at 25 in. centers and reinforced with one #7 bottom bar, one #7 truss bar and one #7 top bar (see page 7-66), with $f'_c = 3750$ psi, $f_s = 24{,}000$ psi, $n = 8.25$, $d = 11.82$ in., $b = 5 + 10/12 = 5.83$ in., dead weight = 67 (computed as on page 7-7).

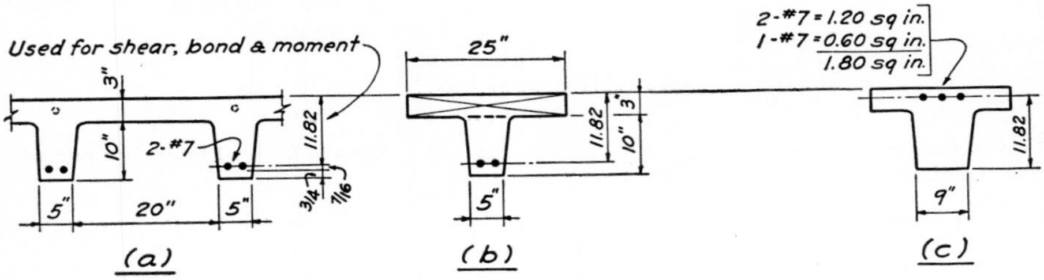

Solution

Shear

$$V = v_c bd = 73.5 \times 5.83 \times 11.82 = 5070 \qquad v_c = 1.2\sqrt{3750} = 73.5$$

$$= 2.08\frac{w(L - 1.97)}{2} \text{ at distance, } d, \text{ from support}$$

$$\text{For } L = 18,\ w = \frac{4870}{L - 1.97} = 304 - 67 = 238 \text{ psf}$$

$$\text{For } L = 26,\ w = \frac{4870}{L - 1.97} = 202 - 67 = 135 \text{ psf}$$

CONCRETE JOIST CONSTRUCTION—INTERIOR SPAN

Bond $V = u\Sigma ojd;\ u = \dfrac{4.8 \times \sqrt{3750}}{0.875} = 336 < 500$

$= 336 \times 2.749 \times 7/8 \times 11.82 = 9560$ lb (on one #7 bottom bar at point of inflection)

$= \dfrac{2.08wL \times 0.70\ *}{2}$

For $L = 18,\ w = \dfrac{13{,}120}{L} = 728 - 67 = 661$ psf

For $L = 26,\ w = \dfrac{13{,}120}{L} = 504 - 67 = 437$ psf

Positive Moment $A_s = 2\text{-}\#7 = 1.20$ sq in. (With $t = 3''$, N.A. is probably in flange)

$p = \dfrac{1.20}{25 \times 11.82} = 0.00406 \quad pn = 0.0335$

$k = \sqrt{0.0670 + 0.00112} - 0.0335 = 0.2615 - 0.0335 = 0.228$

$kd = 2.70$ in. < 3 in. $\quad j = 0.924$

$M = A_s f_s jd = 1.20 \times 24{,}000 \times 0.924 \times 11.82 = 315{,}000$ lb-in.

$= 2.08\dfrac{wL^2 12}{16}$

For $L = 18,\ w = \dfrac{202{,}000}{L^2} = 623 - 67 = 556$ psf

For $L = 26,\ w = \dfrac{202{,}000}{L^2} = 299 - 67 = 232$ psf

Tapered End Since w from positive moment is greater than from shear, use tapered ends. $b = 5.83 + \dfrac{25.68}{36}4 = 8.69$ in.

$V = 73.5 \times 8.69 \times 11.82 = 7570 \text{ lb} = \dfrac{2.08w(L - 1.97)}{2}$

For $L = 18,\ w = \dfrac{7280}{L - 1.97} = 454 - 67 = 387$ psf

For $L = 26,\ w = \dfrac{7280}{L - 1.97} = 303 - 67 = 236$ psf

Root of taper $5070 = 2.08\,w\dfrac{(L - 6.25)^{\dagger}}{2}$

For $L = 18,\ w = \dfrac{4870}{L - 6.25} = 415 - 67 = $ **348** psf

For $L = 26,\ w = \dfrac{4870}{L - 6.25} = 247 - 67 = $ **180** psf

(as given in table on page 7-66)

* 0.70 is a factor to represent the shear at the point of inflection where the bond on the bottom bar is a maximum, see figure below.

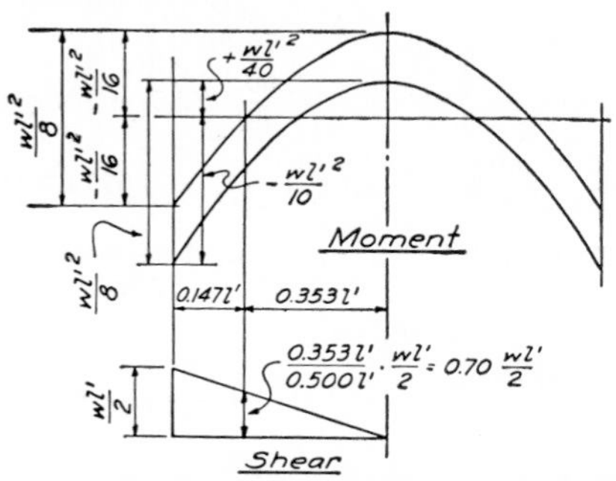

† The value 6.25 comes from the fact that the end of the form is about 1½ in. ± from the beam side and each tapered end is 3'-0" long so the total distance is 2(3.00 + 0.125 ±) = say 6.25.

CONCRETE JOIST CONSTRUCTION—INTERIOR SPAN

Negative Moment $k_{bal.} = \dfrac{1}{1 + \dfrac{24000}{8.25 \times 1688}} = 0.367 \quad p_{bal.} = \dfrac{1688 \times 0.367}{2 \times 24{,}000} = 0.0129$

$j_{bal.} = 0.878$

$R_c = \frac{1}{2} \times 1688 \times 0.367 \times 0.878 = 272$

$p = \dfrac{3 \times 0.60}{9 \times 11.82} = 0.0169 > p_{bal.}$, concrete governs

$M_c = 272 \times 9 \times \overline{11.82}^2 = 342{,}000 \text{ lb-in.} = 2.08\dfrac{wL^2 12}{11}$

For $L = 18,\ w = \dfrac{151{,}000}{L^2} = 465 - 67 = 398 \text{ psf} > 348 \text{ psf}$

For $L = 26,\ w = \dfrac{151{,}000}{L^2} = 223 - 67 = 156 \text{ psf} < 180 \text{ psf}$

Negative Moment with 1-#7 top added, and 2-#7 bottom overlapped

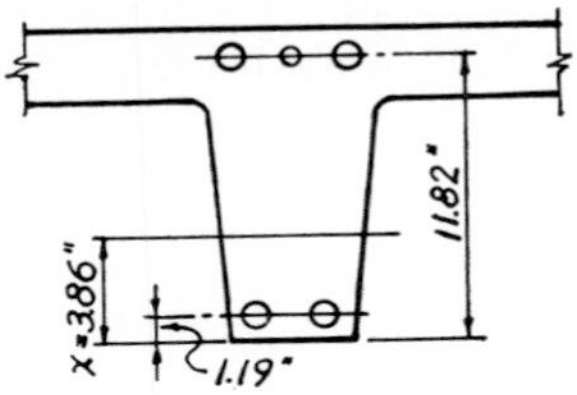

$$\begin{aligned} 14.85 \times 11.82 &= 175.5 \\ 18.6 \times 1.19 &= 22.2 \\ 9x \cdot \frac{x}{2} &= 4.5x^2 \\ \hline 33.45 + 9x \cdot (x) &= 197.7 + 4.5x^2 \\ x(9x + 33.45) &= 4.5x^2 + 197.7 \\ 4.5x^2 + 33.45x &= 197.7 \\ x^2 + 7.43x + (3.76)^2 &= 43.9 + 14.1 \\ x = -3.76 \pm \sqrt{58.0} &= 3.86 \end{aligned}$$

$(2 \times 8.25 - 1)1.20 = 18.6$ sq in.

$C_c = 9 \times 3.86 \times \dfrac{1688}{2} = 29{,}400 \times 2.57 = 75{,}600$

$C_s = 18.6 \times \dfrac{2.67}{3.86} 1688 = \dfrac{21{,}700}{51{,}100} \times 2.67 = \dfrac{57{,}900}{)133{,}500}$

$2.61\ (+\ 7.96) = 10.57$ in.

$T_s = 14.85 \times \dfrac{7.96}{3.86} 1688 = 51{,}700$
$\quad = 3 \times 0.60 \times 24{,}000 = 43{,}200$

$M = 43{,}200 \times 10.57 = 457{,}000 \text{ lb-in.} = 2.08\dfrac{wL^2 12}{11}$

For $L = 18$, no compressive steel needed

For $L = 26,\ w = \dfrac{202{,}000}{L^2} = 299 - 67 = 233 > 180$

(Since min. safe load is determined by shear capacity at root of taper which varies linearly with span, this is about lightest top bar to produce equivalent moment capacity on longest spans.)

Deflection. Assume max. deflection occurs at mid-span with same load pattern as produces max. positive moment, and using min. live load from root of taper

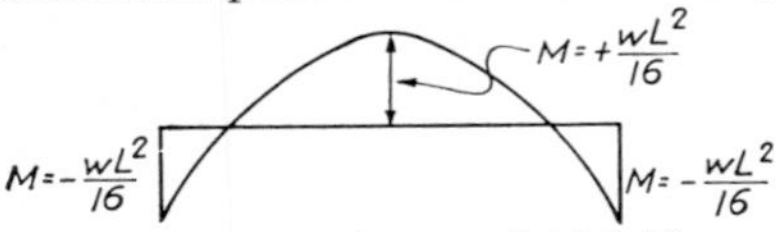

$$\Delta = \frac{wL^4}{76.8EI} - \frac{ML^2}{8EI} = \frac{wL^4}{EI}\left(\frac{1728}{76.8} - \frac{1728}{16 \times 8}\right) = \frac{wL^4}{EI}(22.5 - 13.5) = \frac{9wL^4}{EI}$$

Since $p_w = \dfrac{A_s}{b'd} = \dfrac{2 \times 0.60}{5.83 \times 11.82} = 0.0174,\ pf_y = 0.0174 \times 60{,}000 = 1042$ is greater than 500, the moment of inertia of the transformed section shall be used in computing deflections.

$E_c = (145)^{1.5} 33\sqrt{3750} = 3{,}540{,}000$ psi

At support: — $I = 1163$ in.^{4}

Mean $I = \dfrac{(1163 + 987)}{2} = 1075$

At mid-span: —

$I = 25 \times \dfrac{(2.70)^3}{3} = 164.1$

$8.25 \times 1.20 \times (9.12)^2 = 823.$

$987.$

$$\Delta_{18} = 9\frac{2.08 \times 348 \times \overline{18}^4}{3{,}540{,}000 \times 1075} = 0.180'' < \frac{L}{180} = 1.2'' < \frac{L}{360} = 0.60''$$

$$\Delta_{26} = 9\frac{2.08 \times 180 \times \overline{26}^4}{3{,}540{,}000 \times 1075} = 0.405'' < \frac{L}{180} = 1.77'' < \frac{L}{360} = 0.88''$$

CONCRETE JOIST CONSTRUCTION
INTERIOR SPAN—20 INCH WIDE FORMS
Safe Superimposed Load (psf)

For limitations and explanation of use of tables, see pages 7-59 to 7-62.

Depth: 6″ FORMS + 2½″ CONCRETE

Joists	4″ Joists @ 24″ c/c, Wt 45 psf				5″ Joists @ 25″ c/c, Wt 48 psf	6″ Joists @ 26″ c/c, Wt 50 psf	
Bottom Bar	#4	#4	#5	#5	#6	#6	#7
Truss Bar	#4	#5	#5	#6	#6	#7	#7
Top Bar	#4	#4	#5	#5	#6	#6	#7
Span l′ in Ft: 10	396	445					
11	320	395			424		
12	261	350	354		381	405	
13	216	292	320		344	366	
14	180	245	273		314	334	
15	151	208	237		280	306	
16	124	177	208		247	282	
17	106	152	184		220	251	
18	90	131	162	163	197	226	
19	76	113	141	147	178	204	
20	64	98	123	133	161	186	
21	54	69	107	121	147	170	
22	45	59	94	111	135	156	
23	38	50	82	101	122	138	144
24	31	43	72	93	108	123	133

Depth: 6″ FORMS + 3″ CONCRETE

Joists	4″ @ Joists 24″ c/c, Wt 52 psf				5″ Joists @ 25″ c/c, Wt 54 psf					6″ Joists @ 26″ c/c, Wt 56 psf		
Bottom Bar	#4	#4	#5	#5	#4	#5	#5	#6	#6	#6	#6	#7
Truss Bar	#4	#5	#5	#6	#5	#5	#6	#6	#7	#6	#7	#7
Top Bar	#4	#4	#5	#5	#4	#5	#5	#6	#6	#6	#6	#7
Span l′ in Ft: 10	421											
11	339	419			429							
12	277	371	375		352	408				435		
13	228	309	339		292	356	365			393		
14	190	259	288		245	300	332			357		
15	159	219	250		207	254	296			327		
16	130	187	219		175	217	261			301		
17	111	160	194		144	186	232			265		
18	93	137	171		127	160	207			231	238	
19	79	118	148	154	109	139	180	187		201	215	
20	66	101	129	139	93	112	157	170		176	196	
21	55	76	112	126	80	102	138	154		155	179	
22	46	65	98	115	68	88	121	141		136	164	
23	38	55	85	105	58	76	106	129		120	151	
24	30	46	74	96	49	65	93	114	118	93	136	139
25		39	55	89	41	56	63	101	109	81	121	129
26		32	47	79	34	48	55	89	101	71	108	120

Tabulated values in boldface type require embedment E_4 explained on page 7-59.
Above and to the right of the zigzag line, tapered ends are required.

CONCRETE JOIST CONSTRUCTION
INTERIOR SPAN—20 INCH WIDE FORMS
Safe Superimposed Load (psf)

For limitations and explanation of use of tables, see pages 7-59 to 7-62.

Depth: 6″ FORMS + 4½″ CONCRETE

Joists	4″ Joists @ 24″ c/c Wt 71 psf				5″ Joists @ 25″ c/c Wt 73 psf				6″ Joists @ 26″ c/c Wt 75 psf			
Bottom Bar	#4	#4	#5	#5	#5	#5	#6	#6	#5	#5	#6	#6
Truss Bar	#4	#5	#5	#6	#5	#6	#6	#7	#5	#6	#6	#7
Top Bar	#4	#4	#5	#5	#5	#5	#6	#6	#5	#5	#6	#6
Span l′ in Ft												
11	398											
12	323	435	438									
13	265	361	394		415	428			396			
14	219	302	334		348	388			332	419		
15	**166**	254	288		294	345			280	358	382	
16	**149**	215	252		250	302			**215**	305	**351**	
17	**125**	182	222		213	**268**			**197**	262	**312**	
18	**104**	155	194	195	182	**239**			**172**	226	**272**	
19	**87**	132	167	175	157	**208**	**214**		**147**	195	**236**	**249**
20	**72**	113	144	157	**128**	**181**	**194**		**125**	169	**206**	**226**
21	**59**	**92**	124	142	**115**	**157**	**176**		**107**	**140**	**180**	**205**
22	**47**	**81**	107	**128**	**99**	**137**	**160**		**91**	**127**	**158**	**188**
23	**37**	**69**	92	**117**	**84**	**119**	**146**		**77**	**110**	**138**	**172**
24		**57**	79	**106**	**72**	**104**	**130**	**133**	**65**	**95**	**111**	**156**
25		**48**	**65**	**97**	**61**	**83**	**115**	**122**	**54**	**82**	**103**	**138**
26		**39**	**58**	**86**	**51**	**71**	**101**	**112**	**44**	**70**	**91**	**122**
27		**31**	**49**	**75**	**42**	**61**	**88**	**103**	**36**	**60**	**79**	**108**

Depth: 8″ FORMS + 2½″ CONCRETE

Joists	4″ Joists @ 24″ c/c Wt 51 psf					5″ Joists @ 25″ c/c Wt 54 psf			6″ Joists @ 26″ c/c Wt 57 psf		
Bottom Bar	#4	#4	#5	#5	#6	#5	#6	#6	#6	#6	#7
Truss Bar	#4	#5	#5	#6	#6	#6	#6	#7	#6	#7	#7
Top Bar	#4	#4	#5	#5	#6	#5	#6	#6	#6	#6	#7
Span l′ in Ft											
12	342										
13	284	380	423								
14	238	321	368			415			**445**		
15	**193**	273	320			376			**408**		
16	**169**	234	282			332			**376**		
17	**144**	201	245	250		296			**331**	**336**	
18	**123**	174	213	224		**258**	**266**		**289**	**303**	
19	**106**	151	186	203		**226**	**241**		**254**	**275**	
20	**91**	**126**	163	184		**199**	**220**		**224**	**251**	
21	**77**	**115**	143	**168**		**176**	**201**		**198**	**230**	
22	**66**	**100**	126	**155**		**155**	**185**		**175**	**212**	
23	**56**	**88**	**102**	**142**		**138**	**166**	**170**	**142**	**194**	**196**
24	**48**	**76**	**95**	**132**		**114**	**149**	**157**	**133**	**174**	**182**
25	**40**	**67**	**87**	**118**	**122**	**101**	**133**	**146**	**121**	**156**	**169**
26	**33**	**58**	**77**	**105**	**113**	**89**	**119**	**136**	**108**	**140**	**158**
27		**50**	**67**	**94**	**105**	**79**	**95**	**127**	**96**	**126**	**147**
28		**43**	**59**	**84**	**98**	**70**	**88**	**119**	**86**	**96**	**135**

Tabulated values in boldface type require embedment E_4 explained on page 7-59.
Above and to the right of the zigzag line, tapered ends are required.

CONCRETE JOIST CONSTRUCTION
INTERIOR SPAN—20 INCH WIDE FORMS
Safe Superimposed Load (psf)

For limitations and explanation of use of tables, see pages 7-59 to 7-62.

Depth: 8″ FORMS + 3″ CONCRETE

Joists	4″ Joists @ 24″ c/c			Wt 57 psf		5″ Joists @ 25″ c/c Wt 60 psf			6″ Joists @ 26″ c/c Wt 63 psf		
Bottom Bar	#4	#4	#5	#5	#6	#5	#6	#6	#6	#6	#7
Truss Bar	#4	#5	#5	#6	#6	#6	#6	#7	#6	#7	#7
Top Bar	#4	#4	#5	#5	#6	#5	#6	#6	#6	#6	#7
Span l′ in Ft											
13	297	397	442								
14	248	335	384			434					
15	**202**	284	334			392			427		
16	**176**	243	294			346			**393**		
17	**149**	209	255	259		**309**			**347**	351	
18	**127**	181	221	233		**269**	277		**303**	**316**	
19	**108**	156	193	210		**235**	**251**		**266**	**286**	
20	**92**	**130**	169	191		**207**	**228**		**234**	**261**	
21	**79**	**118**	148	174		**182**	**209**		**206**	**239**	
22	**67**	**102**	130	**159**		**161**	**192**		**183**	**220**	
23	**56**	**89**	**104**	**147**		**142**	**173**		**148**	**202**	**203**
24	**47**	**77**	**97**	**135**		**118**	**154**	**162**	**138**	**180**	**188**
25	**39**	**67**	**89**	**121**	**125**	**108**	**137**	**151**	**126**	**161**	**175**
26	**32**	**58**	**78**	**108**	**116**	**96**	**123**	**140**	**112**	**145**	**163**
27		**49**	**68**	**96**	**108**	**84**	**97**	**130**	**99**	**130**	**152**
28		**42**	**59**	**85**	**100**	**74**	**91**	**122**	**88**	**103**	**141**

Depth: 8″ FORMS + 4½″ CONCRETE

Joists	4″ Joists @ 24″ c/c			Wt 76 psf		5″ Joists @ 25″ c/c Wt 79 psf			6″ Joists @ 26″ c/c Wt 82 psf		
Bottom Bar	#4	#4	#5	#5	#6	#5	#6	#6	#6	#6	#7
Truss Bar	#4	#5	#5	#6	#6	#6	#6	#7	#6	#7	#7
Top Bar	#4	#4	#5	#5	#6	#5	#6	#6	#6	#6	#7
Span l′ in Ft											
13	334	449									
14	253	377	432								
15	**228**	319	375			**443**					
16	**195**	271	329			390			**444**		
17	**164**	232	286	289		346			386	396	
18	**138**	199	247	258		302	310		336	356	
19	**117**	**156**	214	232		264	280		293	322	
20	**98**	**143**	186	210		230	254		257	292	
21	**82**	**127**	162	191		202	232		226	**267**	
22	**68**	**109**	141	174		177	**212**		198	**245**	
23	**56**	**93**	**112**	159		155	**193**		**164**	**225**	**226**
24	**46**	**80**	**104**	146		**129**	**171**	178	**153**	**201**	**209**
25	**36**	**68**	**94**	131	134	**120**	**151**	**164**	**138**	**179**	**193**
26		**57**	**81**	115	124	**105**	**134**	**152**	**122**	**159**	**179**
27		**48**	**70**	102	**114**	**92**	**104**	**141**	**107**	**142**	**167**
28		**39**	**60**	89	**106**	**80**	**97**	**131**	**94**	**116**	**156**
29		**31**	**51**	78	**98**	**69**	**91**	**122**	**82**	**109**	**140**

Tabulated values in boldface type require embedment E_4 explained on page 7-59.
Above and to the right of the zigzag line, tapered ends are required.

CONCRETE JOIST CONSTRUCTION
INTERIOR SPAN—20 INCH WIDE FORMS
Safe Superimposed Load (psf)

For limitations and explanation of use of tables, see pages 7-59 to 7-62.

Depth: 10″ FORMS + 2½″ CONCRETE

Joists	4″ Joists @ 24″ c/c, Wt 57 psf					5″ Joists @ 25″ c/c, Wt 61 psf				6″ Joists @ 26″ c/c, Wt 64 psf			
Bottom Bar	#4	#4	#5	#5	#6	#5	#6	#6	#7	#6	#6	#7	#7
Truss Bar	#4	#5	#5	#6	#6	#6	#6	#7	#7	#6	#7	#7	#8
Top Bar	#4	#4	#5	#5	#6	#5	#6	#6	#7	#6	#6	#7	#6
Span l′ in Ft 17	183	251	305	321		366	377			403	425		
18	157	218	266	289		320	339			353	384		
19	135	183	233	262		281	308			310	349		
20	117	166	205	239		248	282			274	319		
21	101	145	181	219		220	258			243	293		
22	87	128	147	201		195	236			200	270		
23	75	112	138	186		163	211	219		187	243	251	
24	64	98	127	167	173	153	189	203		174	218	233	
25	55	86	113	149	160	138	169	189		155	196	217	
26	47	76	100	134	150	123	135	177		139	176	203	
27	39	66	89	120	140	110	128	165		124	146	190	
28	33	58	79	100	131	98	120	155		111	138	173	177
29		50	70	92	121	87	109	140	146	100	129	157	167
30		43	61	83	110	78	98	127	137	89	117	143	157
31		37	54	74	99	69	88	116	129	79	105	118	148
32		31	47	66	79	61	79	94	122	71	95	112	138

Depth: 10″ FORMS + 3″ CONCRETE

Joists	4″ Joists @ 24″ c/c, Wt 63 psf					5″ Joists @ 25″ c/c, Wt 67 psf				6″ Joists @ 26″ c/c, Wt 70 psf			
Bottom Bar	#4	#4	#5	#5	#6	#5	#6	#6	#7	#6	#6	#7	#7
Truss Bar	#4	#5	#5	#6	#6	#6	#6	#7	#7	#6	#7	#7	#8
Top Bar	#4	#4	#5	#5	#6	#5	#6	#6	#7	#6	#6	#7	#6
Span l′ in Ft 17	180	258	315	331		379	390			419	441		
18	154	204	275	298		331	351			366	397		
19	132	188	240	270		291	318			322	361		
20	113	170	211	246		256	290			284	330		
21	97	148	186	225		226	265			251	303		
22	83	130	151	207		200	236	244	244	206	279		
23	71	113	141	191		168	210	225	225	193	251	258	
24	60	99	129	171	177	157	188	209	209	179	224	240	
25	50	87	115	153	164	141	168	194	194	160	202	224	
26	42	75	101	137	152	125	138	181	180	142	181	209	
27	34	66	89	122	142	111	130	169	169	127	150	195	
28		57	79	101	133	99	123	159	159	113	142	178	182
29		49	69	95	123	88	111	143	149	101	132	162	171
30		41	61	86	111	78	100	130	140	90	119	146	161
31		35	53	77	100	69	89	117	131	80	107	120	152
32			46	68	79	60	80	97	124	71	96	114	141
33			40	61	75	53	71	89	117	62	86	108	129

Tabulated values in boldface type require embedment E_4 explained on page 7-59.
Above and to the right of the zigzag line, tapered ends are required.

CONCRETE JOIST CONSTRUCTION
INTERIOR SPAN—20 INCH WIDE FORMS
Safe Superimposed Load (psf)

For limitations and explanation of use of tables, see pages 7-59 to 7-62.

Depth: 10″ FORMS + 4½″ CONCRETE

Joists	4″ Joists @ 24″ c/c Wt 82 psf					5″ @ 25″ Wt 86 psf				6″ @ 26″ Wt 89 psf			
Bottom Bar	#4	#4	#5	#5	#6	#5	#6	#6	#7	#6	#6	#7	#7
Truss Bar	#4	#5	#5	#6	#6	#6	#6	#7	#7	#6	#7	#7	#8
Top Bar	#4	#4	#5	#5	#6	#5	#6	#6	#7	#6	#6	#7	#6
Span l′ in Ft													
18	164	224	301	325		365	385			406	439		
19	139	206	262	293		319	349			355	397		
20	118	181	229	266		280	317			312	362		
21	100	157	200	243		246	290			275	332		
22	84	136	162	222		217	258	265		227	305		
23	70	118	151	204		182	229	244		212	274	282	
24	58	102	137	183	188	169	204	226		194	245	261	
25	47	88	120	162	174	149	181	209		172	219	242	
26	37	75	105	144	161	132	148	194		153	196	226	
27		64	91	128	150	116	139	181		135	162	211	
28		54	79	105	139	102	131	169		120	153	193	
29		45	69	98	124	89	117	153	158	106	140	174	183
30		37	59	89	111	78	104	137	148	93	126	157	172
31			50	78	99	68	92	123	138	82	112	128	162
32			42	68	80	59	81	101	130	71	100	121	152
33			35	59	75	50	71	95	122	62	89	114	138
34				51	70	42	62	88	114	53	79	102	125

Depth: 12″ FORMS + 2½″ CONCRETE

Joists	4″ Joists @ 24″ c/c Wt 63 psf					5″ @ 25″ Wt 67 psf				6″ @ 26″ Wt 72 psf		
Bottom Bar	#4	#4	#5	#5	#6	#5	#6	#6	#7	#6	#6	#7
Truss Bar	#4	#5	#5	#6	#6	#6	#6	#7	#7	#6	#7	#7
Top Bar	#4	#4	#5	#5	#6	#5	#6	#6	#7	#6	#6	#7
Span l′ in Ft												
20	136	200	247	296		297	346			329	390	
21	118	175	202	272		264	309	317		269	359	
22	102	154	189	251		221	276	292		251	325	332
23	88	136	174	225	232	207	247	271		236	291	308
24	76	120	155	201	216	186	221	252		211	262	286
25	65	106	138	181	201	167	183	235		189	236	267
26	56	93	123	162	188	149	173	220		170	196	250
27	47	82	110	137	174	134	163	206		152	185	231
28	40	72	98	130	157	120	149	188	194	137	174	210
29	33	63	87	119	142	107	134	170	182	123	157	191
30		55	77	107	129	96	121	155	172	110	142	158
31		48	69	96	110	86	109	130	162	99	129	150
32		41	61	87	104	76	99	124	153	88	117	143
33		35	53	78	99	68	89	117	144	79	106	131
34			47	70	90	60	80	106	132	70	95	119
35			41	62	82	53	72	96	106	62	86	108
36			35	56	74	46	64	88	101	55	78	99

Tabulated values in boldface type require embedment E_4 explained on page 7-59.
Above and to the right of the zigzag line, tapered ends are required.

CONCRETE JOIST CONSTRUCTION
INTERIOR SPAN—20 INCH WIDE FORMS
Safe Superimposed Load (psf)

For limitations and explanation of use of tables, see pages 7-59 to 7-62.

12″ FORMS + 3″ CONCRETE

Depth / Joists	4″ Joists @ 24″ c/c Wt 69 psf					5″ @ 25″ Wt 74 psf				6″ @ 26″ Wt 78 psf			
Bottom Bar	#4	#4	#5	#5	#6	#5	#6	#6	#7	#6	#6	#7	#7
Truss Bar	#4	#5	#5	#6	#6	#6	#6	#7	#7	#6	#7	#7	#8
Top Bar	#4	#4	#5	#5	#6	#5	#6	#6	#7	#6	#6	#7	#6
Span l′ in Ft													
20	138	**204**	253	304		305	356			339	401		
21	119	**178**	**207**	279		270	318	325		**277**	369		
22	102	**157**	**193**	257		**227**	283	300		**259**	334	341	
23	88	**138**	**177**	229	237	**212**	253	277		**242**	299	316	
24	75	**121**	**158**	205	220	**190**	226	258		**216**	269	294	
25	64	**106**	**140**	184	205	**170**	**187**	240		**193**	242	274	
26	54	**93**	**124**	165	191	**151**	**176**	224		**173**	**201**	**256**	
27	45	**81**	**110**	**140**	177	**135**	**166**	210		**155**	**190**	**237**	**239**
28	38	**71**	**98**	**132**	160	**121**	**151**	191	197	**139**	**177**	**215**	**224**
29	30	**62**	**87**	**119**	144	**108**	**136**	173	**185**	**124**	**160**	**195**	**211**
30		**53**	**77**	**107**	130	**96**	**123**	157	**175**	**111**	**145**	**161**	**199**
31		**46**	**68**	**96**	**111**	**85**	**110**	**132**	**165**	**99**	**131**	**153**	**188**
32		**39**	**59**	**86**	**105**	**76**	**99**	**125**	**155**	**89**	**118**	**145**	**172**
33		**32**	**52**	**77**	**99**	**67**	**89**	**118**	**146**	**79**	**106**	**133**	**137**
34			**45**	**69**	**90**	**59**	**80**	**107**	**133**	**70**	**96**	**121**	**130**
35			**39**	**61**	**81**	**51**	**71**	**97**	**107**	**62**	**86**	**110**	**124**

12″ FORMS + 4½″ CONCRETE

Depth / Joists	4″ Joists @ 24″ c/c Wt 88 psf					5″ @ 25″ Wt 93 psf				6″ @ 26″ Wt 97 psf			
Bottom Bar	#4	#4	#5	#5	#6	#5	#6	#6	#7	#6	#6	#7	#7
Truss Bar	#4	#5	#5	#6	#6	#6	#6	#7	#7	#6	#7	#7	#8
Top Bar	#4	#4	#5	#5	#6	#5	#6	#6	#7	#6	#6	#7	#6
Span l′ in Ft													
21	122	**187**	**223**	298		290	344	350		**302**	399		
22	103	**163**	**207**	274		**245**	305	322		**282**	362	368	
23	87	**142**	**187**	244	252	**227**	272	297		**261**	323	340	
24	73	**123**	**165**	217	233	**201**	242	275		**232**	289	316	
25	61	**107**	**145**	194	216	**178**	**200**	256		**206**	259	294	
26	50	**93**	**128**	173	201	**158**	**188**	238		**183**	**216**	271	273
27	40	**80**	**112**	**146**	186	**140**	**177**	223		**163**	**203**	245	255
28	31	**68**	**99**	**137**	167	**124**	**159**	203	208	**145**	**187**	221	239
29		**58**	**86**	**122**	150	**109**	**142**	183	195	**129**	**168**	200	224
30		**48**	**75**	**109**	135	**96**	**127**	165	183	**114**	**151**	**171**	**211**
31		**40**	**65**	**96**	**114**	**85**	**113**	**138**	172	**101**	**136**	**162**	**199**
32		**32**	**56**	**85**	**107**	**74**	**100**	**130**	**162**	**89**	**121**	**153**	**183**
33			**47**	**75**	**101**	**64**	**89**	**121**	**152**	**78**	**109**	**139**	**144**
34			**39**	**66**	**90**	**55**	**79**	**109**	**138**	**68**	**97**	**125**	**136**
35			**32**	**57**	**80**	**47**	**69**	**97**	**110**	**59**	**86**	**113**	**129**
36				**49**	**71**	**40**	**61**	**87**	**104**	**51**	**76**	**102**	**123**

Tabulated values in boldface type require embedment E_4 explained on page 7-59.
Above and to the right of the zigzag line, tapered ends are required.

CONCRETE JOIST CONSTRUCTION
INTERIOR SPAN—20 INCH WIDE FORMS
Safe Superimposed Load (psf)

For limitations and explanation of use of tables, see pages 7-59 to 7-62.

Depth: 14″ FORMS + 2½″ CONCRETE

Joists	5″ Joists @ 25″ c/c Wt 75 psf						6″ @ 26″ Wt 80 psf				7″ @ 27″ Wt 85 psf		
Bottom Bar	#5	#5	#6	#6	#7	#7	#7	#7	#7	#8	#7	#8	#8
Truss Bar	#5	#6	#6	#7	#7	#8	#7	#8	#8	#8	#8	#8	#9
Top Bar	#5	#5	#6	#6	#7	#6	#7	#6	#7	#8	#7	#8	#8
Span l′ in Ft													
21	230	**290**	361	379			427				470		
22	204	**272**	322	351			395				435		
23	180	**244**	289	325			367				404		
24	159	**218**	**240**	303			342				376		
25	141	**196**	**226**	283			318				352		
26	125	**175**	**213**	265			288	298			330		
27	111	**157**	**195**	242	249		261	280			305	310	
28	98	**141**	**176**	220	234		238	264			278	**292**	
29	86	**127**	**159**	201	220		**204**	**249**			253	**276**	
30	76	**114**	**144**	**170**	208		**194**	**235**			**214**	**261**	
31	67	**102**	**130**	**162**	**197**		**184**	**218**	**222**		**204**	**247**	
32	58	**91**	**118**	**152**	**186**		**170**	**174**	**208**	**211**	**193**	**230**	**233**
33	50	**81**	**106**	**138**	**170**	**176**	**155**	**166**	**191**	**200**	**177**	**185**	**221**
34	43	**72**	**96**	**126**	**139**	**167**	**142**	**158**	**176**	**190**	**162**	**177**	**210**
35	37	**64**	**86**	**115**	**133**	**158**	**129**	**151**	**151**	**181**	**148**	**169**	**200**
36	31	**57**	**78**	**105**	**127**	**151**	**118**	**140**	**144**	**172**	**136**	**161**	**190**
37		**50**	**70**	**95**	**120**	**143**	**108**	**129**	**136**	**164**	**124**	**151**	**181**

Depth: 14″ FORMS + 3″ CONCRETE

Joists	5″ Joists @ 25″ c/c Wt 81 psf						6″ @ 26″ Wt 86 psf			7″ @ 27″ Wt 91 psf			
Bottom Bar	#5	#5	#6	#6	#7	#7	#7	#7	#7	#7	#7	#7	#8
Truss Bar	#5	#6	#6	#7	#7	#8	#7	#8	#8	#7	#8	#8	#8
Top Bar	#5	#5	#6	#6	#7	#6	#7	#6	#7	#7	#6	#7	#8
Span l′ in Ft													
22	207	**278**	330	358			405			423	446		
23	183	**249**	295	332			376			379	414		
24	161	**222**	**245**	309			350			341	385		
25	143	**198**	**230**	288			325			**289**	351	360	
26	126	**178**	**217**	270			294	304		**273**	318	337	
27	111	**159**	**198**	246	253		267	286		**258**	289	310	317
28	98	**142**	**178**	224	238		242	269		**234**	**243**	282	298
29	86	**127**	**161**	203	224		**208**	253		**212**	**231**	257	**281**
30	75	**114**	**145**	**173**	211		**198**	232	239	**193**	**219**	**219**	**266**
31	65	**102**	**131**	**164**	196	198	**188**	212	**226**	**175**	**205**	**208**	**252**
32	56	**91**	**118**	**153**	179	188	**172**	**177**	**211**	**159**	**187**	**195**	**233**
33	48	**80**	**106**	**139**	164	**178**	**157**	**169**	**193**	**144**	**170**	**179**	**189**
34	41	**71**	**96**	**126**	**141**	**168**	**143**	**161**	**177**	**131**	**155**	**163**	**180**
35	34	**63**	**86**	**115**	**134**	**160**	**130**	**153**	**153**	**118**	**142**	**149**	**172**
36		**55**	**77**	**104**	**128**	**152**	**119**	**142**	**146**	**107**	**129**	**136**	**164**
37		**48**	**69**	**95**	**120**	**144**	**108**	**130**	**137**	**97**	**118**	**124**	**152**

Tabulated values in boldface type require embedment E_4 explained on page 7-59.
Above and to the right of the zigzag line, tapered ends are required.

CONCRETE JOIST CONSTRUCTION
INTERIOR SPAN—20 INCH WIDE FORMS
Safe Superimposed Load (psf)

For limitations and explanation of use of tables, see pages 7-59 to 7-62.

Depth: 14″ FORMS + 4½″ CONCRETE

Joists	5″ Joists @ 25″ c/c Wt 100 psf						6″ @ 26″ Wt 105 psf			7″ @ 27″ Wt 110 psf			
Bottom Bar	#5	#5	#6	#6	#7	#7	#7	#7	#8	#7	#7	#8	#8
Truss Bar	#5	#6	#6	#7	#7	#8	#8	#8	#8	#8	#8	#8	#9
Top Bar	#5	#5	#6	#6	#7	#6	#6	#7	#8	#6	#7	#8	#8
Span l′ in Ft													
24	167	**233**	**262**	328			371			412			
25	146	**207**	**245**	305			346			377	385		
26	128	**184**	**231**	285			323			341	360		
27	112	**164**	**207**	260	266		303			308	331	337	
28	97	**146**	**186**	235	250		284			**260**	300	317	
29	84	**129**	**167**	213	234		267			**246**	273	298	
30	72	**114**	**149**	**181**	221		245	252		**233**	**233**	281	
31	61	**101**	**134**	**171**	206		223	237		**216**	**221**	260	264
32	52	**89**	**120**	**157**	187	195	**186**	221	224	**196**	**205**	237	250
33	43	**78**	**107**	**142**	170	184	**177**	202	212	**178**	**186**	**199**	237
34	35	**68**	**95**	**128**	**145**	174	**168**	**168**	**201**	**162**	**169**	**190**	**224**
35		**58**	**84**	**116**	**138**	164	**160**	**160**	**190**	**147**	**154**	**180**	**213**
36		**50**	**74**	**104**	**131**	**156**	**146**	**152**	**180**	**133**	**140**	**172**	**202**
37		**42**	**65**	**93**	**122**	**147**	**133**	**140**	**171**	**120**	**127**	**157**	**190**
38		**35**	**57**	**83**	**110**	**117**	**121**	**127**	**137**	**108**	**115**	**144**	**175**
39			**49**	**74**	**100**	**111**	**110**	**116**	**131**	**97**	**103**	**131**	**148**
40			**42**	**66**	**90**	**106**	**99**	**105**	**124**	**87**	**93**	**119**	**141**
41			**35**	**58**	**81**	**100**	**89**	**95**	**118**	**78**	**83**	**108**	**134**

Depth: 16″ FORMS + 2½″ CONCRETE

Joists	6″ Joists @ 26″ c/c Wt 88 psf						7″ @ 27″ Wt 93 psf			8″ @ 28″ Wt 98 psf			
Bottom Bar	#5	#6	#6	#7	#7	#8	#7	#8	#8	#7	#8	#8	#9
Truss Bar	#6	#6	#7	#7	#8	#8	#8	#8	#9	#8	#8	#9	#9
Top Bar	#5	#6	#6	#7	#7	#8	#7	#8	#8	#7	#8	#8	#9
Span l′ in Ft													
25	207	242	**304**	364	372		410			400	446		
26	185	218	**286**	330	349		384	385		**343**	409	416	
27	165	195	**259**	300	328		350	362		**325**	372	392	
28	148	176	**235**	**258**	309		319	341		**300**	**308**	369	
29	132	158	**213**	**245**	292		**269**	322		**273**	**293**	349	
30	118	142	**194**	**232**	276		**256**	300	304	**249**	**279**	330	
31	105	128	**176**	**215**	261		**243**	275	288	**227**	**265**	**313**	
32	93	115	**160**	**196**	240	248	**223**	**232**	273	**207**	**247**	**291**	**297**
33	83	103	**145**	**179**	220	**236**	**204**	**221**	**259**	**189**	**227**	**268**	**283**
34	73	92	**132**	**164**	**190**	**224**	**187**	**211**	**247**	**173**	**208**	**229**	**269**
35	64	82	**120**	**150**	**182**	**213**	**171**	**202**	**235**	**157**	**191**	**219**	**256**
36	56	73	**108**	**137**	**172**	**203**	**157**	**190**	**224**	**144**	**175**	**210**	**244**
37	48	64	**98**	**125**	**158**	**166**	**144**	**175**	**209**	**131**	**161**	**194**	**201**
38	41	56	**89**	**114**	**145**	**159**	**132**	**161**	**176**	**119**	**147**	**179**	**192**
39	35	49	**80**	**104**	**134**	**152**	**121**	**148**	**169**	**108**	**135**	**165**	**184**
40		43	**72**	**95**	**123**	**146**	**110**	**136**	**162**	**98**	**124**	**152**	**177**
41		37	**64**	**86**	**113**	**139**	**100**	**126**	**154**	**89**	**113**	**140**	**167**

Tabulated values in boldface type require embedment E_4 explained on page 7-59.
Above and to the right of the zigzag line, tapered ends are required.

CONCRETE JOIST CONSTRUCTION
INTERIOR SPAN—20 INCH WIDE FORMS
Safe Superimposed Load (psf)

For limitations and explanation of use of tables, see pages 7-59 to 7-62.

Depth: 16″ FORMS + 3″ CONCRETE

Joists	6″ Joists @ 26″ c/c Wt 94 psf						7″ @ 27″ Wt 99 psf			8″ @ 28″ Wt 104 psf			
Bottom Bar	#5	#6	#6	#7	#7	#8	#7	#8	#8	#7	#8	#8	#9
Truss Bar	#6	#6	#7	#7	#8	#8	#8	#8	#9	#8	#8	#9	#9
Top Bar	#5	#6	#6	#7	#7	#8	#7	#8	#8	#7	#8	#8	#9
Span l′ in Ft													
26	187	221	**290**	337	356		390	393		**352**	418	425	
27	167	198	**262**	306	334		354	369		**333**	380	400	
28	149	178	**237**	**263**	315		323	348		**303**	**316**	377	
29	132	159	**215**	**249**	297		**275**	328		**276**	**300**	356	
30	118	143	**195**	**237**	280		**261**	306	309	**251**	**285**	337	
31	104	128	**177**	**217**	264	265	**246**	281	293	**229**	**271**	**319**	
32	92	115	**160**	**198**	242	252	**225**	**236**	277	**209**	**250**	**294**	**303**
33	81	102	**145**	**181**	**203**	239	**205**	**225**	263	**190**	**229**	**271**	**287**
34	71	91	**132**	**165**	**193**	**227**	**188**	**215**	**250**	**173**	**210**	**234**	**273**
35	62	81	**119**	**151**	**184**	**216**	**172**	**205**	**238**	**158**	**192**	**223**	**260**
36	54	71	**108**	**137**	**172**	**206**	**157**	**191**	**227**	**144**	**176**	**211**	**247**
37	46	63	**97**	**125**	**158**	**168**	**144**	**176**	**210**	**130**	**161**	**195**	**204**
38	39	55	**87**	**114**	**145**	**161**	**131**	**162**	**178**	**118**	**148**	**179**	**195**
39	32	47	**78**	**104**	**133**	**154**	**120**	**149**	**171**	**107**	**135**	**165**	**187**
40		41	**70**	**94**	**122**	**147**	**109**	**137**	**163**	**97**	**124**	**152**	**179**
41		34	**62**	**85**	**112**	**139**	**99**	**125**	**153**	**87**	**113**	**140**	**168**

Depth: 16″ FORMS + 4½″ CONCRETE

Joists	6″ Joists @ 26″ c/c Wt 113 psf						7″ @ 27″ Wt 118 psf				8″ @ 28″ Wt 123 psf		
Bottom Bar	#5	#6	#6	#7	#7	#8	#7	#8	#8	#9	#8	#9	#9
Truss Bar	#6	#6	#7	#7	#8	#8	#8	#8	#9	#9	#9	#9	#10
Top Bar	#5	#6	#6	#7	#7	#8	#7	#8	#8	#9	#8	#9	#9
Span l′ in Ft													
27	171	205	**275**	**295**			375	390			424		
28	151	183	**248**	**278**			340	367			399		
29	133	164	**224**	**263**	312		**292**	346			376		
30	118	146	**202**	**248**	294		**277**	324	325		356		
31	103	129	**182**	**225**	276		**257**	296	307		336		
32	90	115	**164**	**205**	252	262	**234**	**249**	291		309	319	
33	78	101	**148**	**186**	**212**	249	**213**	**237**	276		**259**	302	
34	67	89	**133**	**169**	**202**	236	**194**	**226**	262		**247**	287	
35	57	78	**119**	**153**	**192**	223	**177**	**215**	249		**235**	273	
36	48	68	**107**	**139**	**176**	205	**161**	**197**	**236**		**219**	**257**	258
37	40	58	**95**	**126**	**161**	**174**	**146**	**180**	**217**	**225**	**201**	**214**	**246**
38	32	50	**85**	**113**	**147**	**166**	**132**	**165**	**186**	**214**	**184**	**205**	**235**
39		42	**75**	**102**	**134**	**158**	**120**	**151**	**177**	**204**	**169**	**196**	**224**
40		34	**66**	**92**	**122**	**151**	**108**	**138**	**169**	**195**	**155**	**186**	**214**
41			**57**	**82**	**111**	**140**	**98**	**126**	**156**	**162**	**141**	**171**	**204**
42			**49**	**73**	**100**	**128**	**88**	**114**	**143**	**155**	**129**	**157**	**192**
43			**42**	**65**	**91**	**117**	**78**	**104**	**131**	**148**	**118**	**145**	**163**
44			**35**	**57**	**82**	**107**	**70**	**94**	**120**	**141**	**107**	**133**	**156**

Tabulated values in boldface type require embedment E_4 explained on page 7-59.
Above and to the right of the zigzag line, tapered ends are required.

CONCRETE JOIST CONSTRUCTION
INTERIOR SPAN—20 INCH WIDE FORMS
Safe Superimposed Load (psf)

For limitations and explanation of use of tables, see pages 7-59 to 7-62.

20″ FORMS + 2½″ CONCRETE

Depth / Joists	7″ Joists @ 27″ c/c Wt 112 psf							8″ @ 28″ Wt 118 psf			9″ @ 29″ Wt 123 psf		
Bottom Bar	#6	#6	#7	#7	#8	#8	#9	#8	#9	#9	#9	#9	#10
Truss Bar	#6	#7	#7	#8	#8	#9	#9	#9	#9	#10	#9	#10	#10
Top Bar	#6	#6	#7	#7	#8	#8	#9	#8	#9	#9	#9	#9	#10
Span l′ in Ft													
32	133	185	214	**281**	**314**	357		**339**	387		**363**	412	
33	118	167	195	**258**	**300**	340		**324**	368		**347**	392	
34	105	151	178	**237**	**282**	324		**309**	343	349	**331**	374	
35	93	137	162	**217**	**260**	308		**288**	**296**	333	**313**	357	
36	82	123	147	**200**	**240**	**261**	295	**266**	**283**	318	**289**	**341**	
37	72	111	133	**183**	**222**	**250**	282	**246**	**271**	304	**267**	**290**	326
38	63	100	121	**168**	**204**	**240**	**269**	**227**	**260**	291	**247**	**278**	**312**
39	54	89	109	**154**	**189**	**228**	**230**	**210**	**246**	**278**	**229**	**266**	**299**
40	46	79	98	**141**	**174**	**211**	**221**	**194**	**228**	**267**	**211**	**256**	**256**
41	39	70	88	**129**	**160**	**196**	**212**	**179**	**212**	**256**	**195**	**238**	**246**
42	32	62	79	**118**	**148**	**182**	**203**	**165**	**197**	**220**	**181**	**221**	**236**
43		54	70	**107**	**136**	**168**	**196**	**153**	**182**	**211**	**167**	**205**	**227**
44		47	62	**98**	**125**	**156**	**185**	**141**	**169**	**203**	**154**	**191**	**219**
45		40	55	**89**	**115**	**144**	**172**	**129**	**156**	**193**	**142**	**177**	**210**
46		34	48	**80**	**105**	**133**	**160**	**119**	**145**	**180**	**131**	**164**	**196**
47			41	**72**	**96**	**123**	**149**	**109**	**134**	**168**	**120**	**152**	**183**
48			35	**65**	**88**	**114**	**138**	**100**	**124**	**156**	**110**	**141**	**170**

20″ FORMS + 3″ CONCRETE

Depth / Joists	7″ Joists @ 27″ c/c Wt 118 psf							8″ @ 28″ Wt 124 psf			9″ @ 29″ Wt 129 psf		
Bottom Bar	#6	#6	#7	#7	#8	#8	#9	#8	#9	#9	#9	#9	#10
Truss Bar	#6	#7	#7	#8	#8	#9	#9	#9	#9	#10	#9	#10	#10
Top Bar	#6	#6	#7	#7	#8	#8	#9	#8	#9	#9	#9	#9	#10
Span l′ in Ft													
34	105	151	179	**237**	**285**	328		**314**	348	354	**337**	380	
35	92	136	162	**217**	**262**	310	313	**289**	**301**	338	**316**	362	
36	81	122	147	**199**	**241**	**265**	298	**267**	**288**	322	**292**	346	
37	70	109	133	**182**	**222**	**253**	285	**246**	**275**	308	**269**	**294**	330
38	61	98	120	**167**	**205**	**243**	272	**227**	**264**	294	**249**	**282**	**316**
39	52	87	108	**153**	**189**	**228**	**233**	**210**	**248**	**282**	**230**	**270**	**302**
40	44	77	97	**140**	**174**	**211**	**223**	**193**	**230**	**270**	**212**	**256**	**260**
41	36	68	87	**127**	**160**	**195**	**214**	**178**	**213**	**256**	**196**	**238**	**249**
42		59	78	**116**	**147**	**180**	**205**	**164**	**197**	**223**	**181**	**221**	**240**
43		51	69	**105**	**135**	**167**	**197**	**151**	**183**	**214**	**167**	**205**	**230**
44		44	61	**96**	**124**	**154**	**186**	**139**	**169**	**206**	**154**	**190**	**221**
45		37	53	**86**	**113**	**142**	**172**	**128**	**156**	**192**	**141**	**176**	**212**
46		30	46	**78**	**104**	**131**	**160**	**117**	**144**	**179**	**130**	**163**	**197**
47			39	**70**	**94**	**121**	**148**	**107**	**133**	**166**	**119**	**151**	**184**
48			33	**62**	**86**	**111**	**138**	**98**	**123**	**154**	**109**	**140**	**171**
49				**55**	**78**	**102**	**127**	**89**	**113**	**143**	**100**	**129**	**159**
50				**48**	**70**	**94**	**118**	**80**	**104**	**133**	**91**	**119**	**148**

Tabulated values in boldface type require embedment E_4 explained on page 7-59.
Above and to the right of the zigzag line, tapered ends are required.

CONCRETE JOIST CONSTRUCTION
INTERIOR SPAN—20 INCH WIDE FORMS
Safe Superimposed Load (psf)

For limitations and explanation of use of tables, see pages 7-59 to 7-62.

Depth: 20″ FORMS + 4½″ CONCRETE

Joists	7″ Joists @ 27″ c/c Wt 137 psf							8″ @ 28″ Wt 143 psf			9″ @ 29″ Wt 148 psf		
Bottom Bar	#6	#6	#7	#7	#8	#8	#9	#8	#9	#9	#9	#9	#10
Truss Bar	#6	#7	#7	#8	#8	#9	#9	#9	#9	#10	#9	#10	#10
Top Bar	#6	#6	#7	#7	#8	#8	#9	#8	#9	#9	#9	#9	#10
Span l′ in Ft													
34	102	151	182	242	292	341		323	364	369	352	397	
35	89	135	164	221	268	318	324	297	315	351	324	378	
36	77	120	148	202	246	276	309	273	301	335	299	355	360
37	66	107	133	184	226	264	294	251	288	319	275	309	344
38	55	94	119	167	207	250	281	231	273	305	253	295	329
39	46	83	106	152	190	230	241	212	252	291	233	281	314
40	37	72	95	138	174	213	231	195	233	279	215	260	271
41		62	84	125	159	196	221	179	215	241	197	241	260
42		53	73	113	146	180	212	164	198	231	181	223	249
43		45	64	102	133	166	200	150	183	221	166	206	239
44		37	55	91	121	153	185	137	168	207	152	190	229
45			47	81	110	140	171	125	155	192	139	176	213
46			39	72	99	128	158	114	142	178	127	162	197
47			32	64	90	117	146	103	130	165	116	149	183
48				56	80	107	134	93	119	152	105	137	169
49				48	72	97	124	84	109	140	95	126	157
50				41	64	88	113	75	99	129	86	115	145
51				34	56	80	104	67	90	119	77	105	134

CONCRETE JOIST CONSTRUCTION
INTERIOR SPAN—30 INCH WIDE FORMS
Safe Superimposed Load (psf)

For limitations and explanation of use of tables, see pages 7-59 to 7-62.

Depth: 6″ FORMS + 2½″ CONCRETE

Joists	4″ Joists @ 34″ c/c Wt 41 psf				5″ @ 35″ Wt 43 psf			6″ @ 36″ Wt 45 psf		
Bottom Bar	#4	#4	#5	#5	#5	#5	#6	#5	#6	#6
Truss Bar	#4	#5	#5	#6	#5	#6	#6	#6	#6	#7
Top Bar	#4	#4	#5	#5	#5	#5	#6	#5	#6	#6
Span l′ in Ft										
10	272	342			372					
11	218	294	303		329			351		
12	177	241	262		277	292		315		
13	145	199	217		229	261		283		
14	119	166	184		192	222		238	258	
15	99	140	158		162	191		202	225	
16	78	118	138		137	168		172	197	
17	66	100	121		117	148		147	172	
18	54	85	106		100	132		127	149	
19	44	72	91	95	85	115	118	109	129	139
20	36	61	78	85	68	100	107	94	112	126
21		40	67	76	57	87	96	67	98	114

Tabulated values in boldface type require embedment E_4 explained on page 7-59.
Above and to the right of the zigzag line, tapered ends are required.

CONCRETE JOIST CONSTRUCTION
INTERIOR SPAN—30 INCH WIDE FORMS
Safe Superimposed Load (psf)

For limitations and explanation of use of tables, see pages 7-59 to 7-62.

Depth: 6″ FORMS + 3″ CONCRETE

Joists	4″ Joists @ 34″ c/c Wt 47 psf			5″ @ 35″ Wt 49 psf		6″ @ 36″ Wt 50 psf			
Bottom Bar	#4	#4	#5	#5	#6	#5	#5	#6	#6
Truss Bar	#4	#5	#5	#6	#6	#5	#6	#6	#7
Top Bar	#4	#4	#5	#5	#6	#5	#5	#6	#6
Span l′ in Ft									
10	288	362		391		425			
11	230	311	320	346		347	373		
12	186	254	276	309		284	333		
13	152	210	228	275		234	**300**	301	
14	124	174	193	233		195	**251**	**273**	
15	102	146	165	**201**		164	**213**	**237**	
16	**81**	123	144	**176**		138	**181**	**207**	
17	**67**	103	126	**155**		**111**	**155**	**182**	
18	**55**	87	**110**	**138**		**97**	**132**	**157**	**162**
19	**45**	73	**94**	**120**	**123**	**82**	**114**	**136**	**145**
20	**36**	62	**81**	**104**	**111**	**69**	**98**	**118**	**131**
21		**43**	**69**	**89**	**100**	**58**	**73**	**102**	**119**
22		**35**	**59**	**77**	**90**	**48**	**62**	**89**	**108**
23			**50**	**67**	**82**	**40**	**53**	**77**	**99**
24			**42**	**57**	**71**	**33**	**44**	**57**	**90**
25				**49**	**62**		**37**	**49**	**79**
26					**53**		**30**	**41**	**69**

Depth: 6″ FORMS + 4½″ CONCRETE

Joists	4″ Joists @ 34″ c/c Wt 66 psf				5″ @ 35″ Wt 68 psf				6″ @ 36″ Wt 69 psf				
Bottom Bar	#4	#4	#5	#5	#4	#5	#5	#6	#4	#5	#5	#6	#6
Truss Bar	#4	#5	#5	#6	#5	#5	#6	#6	#5	#5	#6	#6	#7
Top Bar	#4	#4	#5	#5	#4	#5	#5	#6	#4	#5	#5	#6	#6
Span l′ in Ft													
11	266	362	372		349	408			336	408	438		
12	214	294	319		282	343	359		271	332	390		
13	172	241	262		231	282	319		221	273	350		
14	140	199	220		190	234	269		**174**	226	293	316	
15	113	165	187		157	196	231		**149**	188	246	273	
16	**89**	137	161		130	164	200		**123**	157	208	238	
17	**72**	114	140		**103**	138	175		**101**	**127**	177	208	
18	**58**	95	122		**89**	116	155		**83**	**109**	150	178	184
19	**45**	79	103	107	**73**	97	135	138	**67**	**91**	128	153	165
20	**34**	65	86	95	**59**	**76**	115	123	**54**	**75**	109	131	**148**
21		**49**	72	84	**48**	**67**	98	**110**	**43**	**62**	**86**	113	**133**
22		**42**	60	74	**37**	**55**	84	**99**	**33**	**50**	**78**	97	**120**
23		**33**	50	66		**45**	71	**89**		**40**	**66**	83	**109**
24			40	59		**36**	60	**78**		**31**	**55**	**65**	**99**
25			**30**	**52**			50	**67**			**45**	**59**	**86**
26				**46**			**35**	**57**			**37**	**50**	**75**

Tabulated values in boldface type require embedment E_4 explained on page 7-59.
Above and to the right of the zigzag line, tapered ends are required.

CONCRETE JOIST CONSTRUCTION
INTERIOR SPAN—30 INCH WIDE FORMS
Safe Superimposed Load (psf)

For limitations and explanation of use of tables, see pages 7-59 to 7-62.

Depth	8" FORMS+2½" CONCRETE										
Joists	4" Joists @ 34" c/c Wt 45 psf				5" @ 35" Wt 48 psf			6" @ 36" Wt 50 psf			
Bottom Bar	#4	#4	#5	#5	#5	#5	#6	#5	#5	#6	#6
Truss Bar	#4	#5	#5	#6	#5	#6	#6	#5	#6	#6	#7
Top Bar	#4	#4	#5	#5	#5	#5	#6	#5	#5	#6	#6
Span l' in Ft											
12	234	315	353		363	387		351	417		
13	193	262	294		302	349		292	370	376	
14	160	220	251		254	299		245	312	342	
15	**127**	186	217		216	260		207	265	301	
16	**110**	158	190		184	228		**165**	227	263	
17	**93**	135	165	167	158	203		**149**	196	227	234
18	**78**	115	142	149	136	178	181	**128**	169	197	210
19	**66**	99	123	134	**108**	155	164	**110**	147	172	**190**
20	**55**	**80**	107	121	**100**	135	**148**	**94**	**117**	151	**173**
21	**46**	**73**	93	110	**87**	118	**135**	**81**	**109**	132	**158**
22	**38**	**63**	81	100	**75**	104	**124**	**70**	**97**	116	**144**
23	**31**	**54**	70	**92**	**65**	91	**111**	**60**	**85**	**94**	**133**
24		**46**	**58**	**84**	**56**	**73**	**98**	**51**	**74**	**88**	**119**
25		**39**	**52**	**76**	**48**	**63**	**86**	**43**	**64**	**79**	**106**
26		**32**	**45**	**67**	**40**	**55**	**76**	**36**	**56**	**70**	**94**
27			**39**	**58**	**34**	**48**	**67**	**30**	**48**	**61**	**84**

Depth	8" FORMS+3" CONCRETE										
Joists	4" Joists @ 34" c/c Wt 51 psf				5" @ 35" Wt 54 psf			6" @ 36" Wt 56 psf			
Bottom Bar	#4	#4	#5	#5	#5	#5	#6	#5	#5	#6	#6
Truss Bar	#4	#5	#5	#6	#5	#6	#6	#5	#6	#6	#7
Top Bar	#4	#4	#5	#5	#5	#5	#6	#5	#5	#6	#6
Span l' in Ft											
12	243	328	368		380	404		367	436		
13	200	272	306		316	364		305	386	393	
14	165	228	260		265	311		255	326	357	
15	**132**	192	225		224	270		215	277	314	
16	**113**	163	197		191	237		**172**	237	274	
17	**94**	138	170	172	163	210		**155**	203	237	243
18	**79**	118	147	153	140	184	188	**132**	175	205	218
19	**66**	101	126	137	**111**	160	169	**113**	152	179	197
20	**54**	**81**	109	124	**102**	139	153	**97**	**121**	156	**178**
21	**45**	**73**	94	112	**88**	121	**139**	**83**	**112**	136	**163**
22	**36**	**63**	82	102	**76**	106	**127**	**70**	**99**	119	**149**
23		**53**	70	93	**65**	92	**114**	**60**	**86**	**96**	**137**
24		**45**	**58**	85	**55**	**74**	**100**	**50**	**75**	**90**	**122**
25		**37**	**52**	**76**	**47**	**67**	**88**	**42**	**65**	**81**	**108**
26		**31**	**44**	**67**	**39**	**58**	**77**	**35**	**56**	**70**	**96**
27			**37**	**58**	**33**	**50**	**68**		**48**	**61**	**85**

Tabulated values in boldface type require embedment E_4 explained on page 7-59.
Above and to the right of the zigzag line, tapered ends are required.

CONCRETE JOIST CONSTRUCTION
INTERIOR SPAN—30 INCH WIDE FORMS
Safe Superimposed Load (psf)

For limitations and explanation of use of tables, see pages 7-59 to 7-62.

Depth: 8″ FORMS + 4½″ CONCRETE

Joists	4″ Joists @ 34″ c/c Wt 70 psf					5″ @ 35″ Wt 73 psf				6″ @ 36″ Wt 75 psf			
Bottom Bar	#4	#4	#5	#5	#6	#5	#5	#6	#6	#5	#5	#6	#6
Truss Bar	#4	#5	#5	#6	#6	#5	#6	#6	#7	#5	#6	#6	#7
Top Bar	#4	#4	#5	#5	#6	#5	#5	#6	#6	#5	#5	#6	#6
Span 1′ in Ft													
13	221	304	342			356	409			344	437	444	
14	181	253	289			297	349			286	367	401	
15	**145**	211	248			250	301			240	310	352	
16	**121**	178	216			211	263			**192**	264	308	
17	**100**	149	187	188		179	232			**170**	225	265	271
18	**81**	126	160	166	166	152	203	206		**144**	193	229	242
19	**66**	106	136	148	148	**121**	175	184		**122**	166	198	217
20	**53**	**85**	116	132	132	**110**	151	166		**103**	**132**	171	196
21	**42**	**74**	99	119	119	**93**	130	150		**87**	**122**	149	178
22	**32**	**62**	84	107	107	**78**	112	136		**72**	**105**	129	162
23		**51**	71	96	96	**66**	97	118	122	**60**	**90**	**103**	148
24		**41**	**57**	87	87	**55**	**76**	103	111	**49**	**77**	**95**	**132**
25		**32**	**50**	78	79	**45**	**70**	89	102	**40**	**65**	**85**	**116**
26			**41**	67	71	**36**	**61**	77	**93**	**31**	**55**	**73**	**101**
27			**33**	57	65		**51**	67	**85**		**45**	**62**	**89**
28				48	58		**42**	**54**	**78**		**37**	**53**	**77**
29				40	53		**35**	**49**	**71**		**30**	**44**	**63**

Depth: 10″ FORMS + 2½″ CONCRETE

Joists	4″ Joists @ 34″ c/c Wt 49 psf					5″ @ 35″ Wt 52 psf				6″ @ 36″ Wt 54 psf			
Bottom Bar	#4	#4	#5	#5	#6	#5	#5	#6	#6	#5	#6	#6	#7
Truss Bar	#4	#5	#5	#6	#6	#5	#6	#6	#7	#6	#6	#7	#7
Top Bar	#4	#4	#5	#5	#6	#5	#5	#6	#6	#5	#6	#6	#7
Span 1′ in Ft													
16	**141**	198	241	245		231	292			283	328	335	
17	**120**	170	208	217		199	256	260		245	284	299	
18	**102**	146	180	195		**158**	223	234		212	248	269	
19	**86**	**120**	157	176		**146**	195	211		**169**	217	243	
20	**73**	**109**	137	160		**129**	171	192		**157**	191	222	
21	**62**	**95**	120	145		**113**	150	176		**142**	168	203	
22	**52**	**82**	105	133		**98**	132	156	160	**124**	**136**	187	
23	**44**	**71**	**88**	122		**85**	**108**	138	148	**109**	**127**	**169**	172
24	**36**	**61**	**81**	110	113	**74**	**100**	123	136	**96**	**117**	**151**	160
25	**30**	**53**	**71**	98	104	**65**	**91**	109	126	**84**	**104**	**135**	**148**
26		**45**	**62**	87	97	**56**	**80**	97	**118**	**74**	**92**	**121**	**138**
27		**38**	**54**	77	90	**48**	**71**	**82**	**109**	**65**	**81**	**108**	**129**
28		**32**	**47**	68	**83**	**41**	**62**	**77**	**102**	**56**	**72**	**91**	**117**
29			**40**	**56**	**77**	**35**	**54**	**69**	**93**	**49**	**63**	**85**	**105**
30			**34**	**49**	**69**		**48**	**61**	**84**	**42**	**56**	**76**	**95**

Tabulated values in boldface type require embedment E_4 explained on page 7-59.
Above and to the right of the zigzag line, tapered ends are required.

CONCRETE JOIST CONSTRUCTION
INTERIOR SPAN—30 INCH WIDE FORMS
Safe Superimposed Load (psf)

For limitations and explanation of use of tables, see pages 7-59 to 7-62.

Depth: 10″ FORMS + 3″ CONCRETE

Joists	4″ Joists @ 34″ c/c Wt 56 psf					5″ @ 35″ Wt 58 psf				6″ @ 36″ Wt 61 psf			
Bottom Bar	#4	#4	#5	#5	#6	#5	#5	#6	#6	#5	#6	#6	#7
Truss Bar	#4	#5	#5	#6	#6	#5	#6	#6	#7	#6	#6	#7	#7
Top Bar	#4	#4	#5	#5	#6	#5	#5	#6	#6	#5	#6	#6	#7
Span 1′ in Ft													
16	138	203	248	251		238	301			292	340	346	
17	116	173	213	223		204	263	268		252	294	308	
18	98	149	184	199		**162**	229	240		218	256	277	
19	82	**122**	160	180		**149**	200	217		**174**	223	250	
20	69	**110**	139	163		**132**	175	197		**161**	196	228	
21	58	**95**	121	148		**114**	153	180		**145**	172	208	
22	48	**82**	106	135		**99**	134	159	164	**126**	**139**	191	
23	39	**70**	**89**	124		**86**	**109**	141	150	**111**	**129**	173	176
24	31	**60**	**81**	111	114	**74**	**102**	125	139	**97**	**119**	154	163
25		**51**	**70**	98	105	**64**	**91**	111	128	**84**	**105**	137	**151**
26		**43**	**61**	87	97	**55**	**80**	98	119	**74**	**93**	122	**141**
27		**36**	**52**	77	90	**47**	**70**	**83**	**110**	**64**	**82**	109	**131**
28		**30**	**45**	68	83	**39**	**61**	**77**	**103**	**55**	**72**	**92**	**119**
29			**38**	**56**	73	**33**	**53**	**69**	**94**	**47**	**63**	**87**	**107**
30			**32**	**50**	65		**46**	**61**	**84**	**40**	**55**	**77**	**96**

Depth: 10″ FORMS + 4½″ CONCRETE

Joists	4″ Joists @ 34″ c/c Wt 74 psf					5″ @ 35″ Wt 77 psf				6″ @ 36″ Wt 79 psf			
Bottom Bar	#4	#4	#5	#5	#6	#5	#5	#6	#6	#5	#6	#6	#7
Truss Bar	#4	#5	#5	#6	#6	#5	#6	#6	#7	#6	#6	#7	#7
Top Bar	#4	#4	#5	#5	#6	#5	#5	#6	#6	#5	#6	#6	#7
Span 1′ in Ft													
16	145	218	269	272		258	328			320	374	379	
17	121	184	230	240		220	287	291		274	323	337	
18	100	157	198	213		**176**	248	260		236	280	301	
19	82	**129**	170	191		**161**	215	233		**189**	243	272	
20	67	**113**	146	172		**139**	186	211		**174**	212	246	
21	54	**96**	126	155		**119**	162	192		**153**	185	224	
22	43	**81**	109	141		**102**	141	170	173	**132**	**149**	205	
23	33	**68**	**90**	128		**87**	**114**	149	159	**115**	**138**	185	188
24		**57**	**80**	115	117	**73**	**106**	131	145	**99**	**125**	164	173
25		**47**	**68**	100	107	**62**	**92**	115	134	**85**	**109**	145	160
26		**38**	**58**	87	98	**52**	**80**	100	123	**73**	**95**	128	148
27		**30**	**48**	76	90	**42**	**68**	**84**	114	**62**	**83**	113	134
28			**40**	65	82	**34**	**58**	**78**	105	**52**	**71**	**95**	119
29			**32**	**53**	72		**49**	**68**	95	**43**	**61**	**88**	106
30				**47**	63		**41**	**58**	84	**35**	**52**	**77**	94
31				**40**	54		**34**	**50**	74		**44**	**67**	**77**
32				**33**	46			**42**	65		**36**	**58**	**72**

Tabulated values in boldface type require embedment E_4 explained on page 7-59.
Above and to the right of the zigzag line, tapered ends are required.

CONCRETE JOIST CONSTRUCTION
INTERIOR SPAN—30 INCH WIDE FORMS
Safe Superimposed Load (psf)

For limitations and explanation of use of tables, see pages 7-59 to 7-62.

12″ FORMS + 2½″ CONCRETE

Depth / Joists	4″ Joists @ 34″ c/c Wt 53 psf					5″ @ 35″ Wt 57 psf				6″ @ 36″ Wt 61 psf			
Bottom Bar	#4	#4	#5	#5	#6	#5	#5	#6	#6	#6	#6	#7	#7
Truss Bar	#4	#5	#5	#6	#6	#5	#6	#6	#7	#6	#7	#7	#8
Top Bar	#4	#4	#5	#5	#6	#5	#5	#6	#6	#6	#6	#7	#6
Span l′ in Ft 18	120	**169**	218	243		**202**	267	289		298	330		
19	102	**153**	190	220		**181**	234	262		262	299		
20	87	**133**	166	200		**158**	206	239		231	273		
21	74	**116**	**134**	183		**138**	182	213	217	**185**	251		
22	63	**101**	**124**	168		**121**	**149**	189	200	**173**	229	231	
23	53	**88**	**114**	151	155	**106**	**139**	169	185	**162**	204	214	
24	45	**77**	**100**	135	143	**93**	**126**	150	171	**144**	183	198	
25	37	**67**	**88**	120	133	**81**	**112**	**122**	159	**128**	164	185	
26	30	**58**	**78**	107	124	**71**	**99**	**115**	148	**114**	147	170	
27		**50**	**68**	**88**	114	**62**	**88**	**108**	138	**101**	**125**	153	160
28		**43**	**60**	**83**	103	**54**	**78**	**98**	127	**90**	**118**	138	150
29		**36**	**52**	**76**	92	**46**	**69**	**87**	115	**80**	**107**	125	**141**
30		**30**	**46**	**67**	83	**39**	**61**	**78**	103	**71**	**96**	**105**	**132**
31			**39**	**60**	**69**	**33**	**53**	**69**	93	**63**	**86**	**100**	**125**
32			**34**	**53**	**64**		**47**	**62**	**80**	**55**	**77**	**94**	**114**
33				**47**	**61**		**40**	**55**	**75**	**48**	**69**	**86**	**103**
34				**41**	**55**		**35**	**48**	**68**	**42**	**62**	**77**	**84**

12″ FORMS + 3″ CONCRETE

Depth / Joists	4″ Joists @ 34″ c/c Wt 60 psf					5″ @ 35″ Wt 63 psf				6″ @ 36″ Wt 67psf			
Bottom Bar	#4	#4	#5	#5	#6	#5	#6	#6	#7	#6	#6	#7	#7
Truss Bar	#4	#5	#5	#6	#6	#6	#6	#7	#7	#6	#7	#7	#8
Top Bar	#4	#4	#5	#5	#6	#5	#6	#6	#7	#6	#6	#7	#6
Span l′ in Ft 19	102	**155**	193	224		239	267			268	307		
20	86	**134**	169	204		210	243			236	280		
21	73	**116**	**135**	186		185	218	222		**190**	256		
22	61	**101**	**126**	170		**151**	193	204		**177**	234	236	
23	51	**87**	**114**	153	157	**141**	171	188		**165**	208	218	
24	42	**76**	**100**	136	145	**127**	152	174		**146**	186	202	
25	34	**65**	**88**	121	134	**112**	**123**	161		**130**	166	188	
26		**56**	**77**	107	124	**99**	**115**	150		**115**	149	173	174
27		**47**	**67**	**88**	115	**87**	**108**	140		**102**	**127**	156	162
28		**40**	**58**	**82**	103	**77**	**98**	128	130	**90**	**119**	140	152
29		**33**	**50**	**75**	92	**67**	**87**	115	122	**80**	**107**	126	142
30			**43**	**66**	82	**59**	**77**	104	114	**70**	**96**	**106**	**134**
31			**37**	**58**	**67**	**51**	**68**	93	107	**62**	**86**	**100**	**126**
32			**31**	**51**	**63**	**44**	**60**	**79**	**101**	**54**	**76**	**95**	**115**
33				**44**	**59**	**38**	**53**	**74**	**94**	**47**	**68**	**86**	**104**
34				**39**	**53**	**32**	**46**	**67**	**85**	**40**	**60**	**77**	**84**

Tabulated values in boldface type require embedment E_4 explained on page 7-59.
Above and to the right of the zigzag line, tapered ends are required.

CONCRETE JOIST CONSTRUCTION
INTERIOR SPAN—30 INCH WIDE FORMS
Safe Superimposed Load (psf)

For limitations and explanation of use of tables, see pages 7-59 to 7-62.

Depth: 12″ FORMS + 4½″ CONCRETE

Joists	4″ Joists @ 34″ c/c Wt 78 psf					5″ Joists @ 35″ c/c Wt 82 psf					6″ @ 36″ Wt 86 psf		
Bottom Bar	#4	#4	#5	#5	#6	#5	#5	#6	#6	#7	#6	#7	#7
Truss Bar	#4	#5	#5	#6	#6	#5	#6	#6	#7	#7	#7	#7	#8
Top Bar	#4	#4	#5	#5	#6	#5	#5	#6	#6	#7	#6	#7	#6
Span l′ in Ft													
20	85	**137**	176	214		159	222	258			299		
21	70	**117**	**141**	194		137	194	231	234		273		
22	57	**100**	**130**	177		117	**159**	204	214		249	250	
23	45	**85**	**116**	158	162	101	**148**	180	197		221	230	
24	36	**72**	**100**	139	148	86	**130**	158	181		196	213	
25		**60**	**86**	122	136	73	**113**	**127**	167		174	197	
26		**50**	**74**	107	126	61	**99**	**119**	155		**141**	182	
27		**41**	**63**	**87**	116	51	**86**	**110**	143		**132**	163	169
28		**33**	**53**	**81**	103	42	**74**	**98**	131	133	**122**	146	157
29			**45**	**71**	91	34	**64**	**86**	117	124	**108**	130	147
30			**37**	**62**	80		**54**	**75**	104	115	**96**	**108**	137
31			**30**	**53**	**64**		**46**	**65**	92	107	**84**	**102**	124
32				**45**	**59**		**38**	**56**	**77**	99	**74**	**95**	111
33				**38**	**55**		**31**	**48**	**72**	89	**65**	**85**	100
34				**31**	**47**			**41**	**63**	79	**56**	**75**	**83**
35					**40**			**34**	**55**	70	**48**	**66**	**78**
36					**34**				**48**	59	**41**	**58**	**73**

Depth: 14″ FORMS + 2½″ CONCRETE

Joists	5″ Joists @ 35″ c/c Wt 62 psf					6″ @ 36″ Wt 65 psf				7″ @ 37″ Wt 69 psf			
Bottom Bar	#5	#5	#6	#6	#7	#6	#7	#7	#7	#7	#7	#7	#8
Truss Bar	#5	#6	#6	#7	#7	#7	#7	#8	#8	#7	#8	#8	#8
Top Bar	#5	#5	#6	#6	#7	#6	#7	#6	#7	#7	#6	#7	#8
Span l′ in Ft													
22	137	**185**	223	242		268	277			294	309		
23	120	**167**	199	224		239	257			263	286		
24	105	**149**	**162**	208		215	238			236	266		
25	92	**132**	**152**	193		193	222			**197**	243	249	
26	81	**118**	**143**	180		**165**	201	207		**186**	220	233	
27	70	**105**	**130**	166	169	**156**	181	194		**176**	199	216	218
28	61	**93**	**117**	150	158	**141**	164	182		**159**	**165**	196	205
29	53	**83**	**105**	136	149	**127**	**139**	171		**144**	**156**	178	193
30	46	**73**	**94**	**113**	140	**114**	**131**	157	161	**130**	**148**	**148**	182
31	39	**65**	**84**	**107**	130	**103**	**125**	143	152	**117**	**138**	**141**	**172**
32	33	**57**	**75**	**101**	119	**93**	**114**	130	143	**106**	**126**	**133**	**160**
33		**50**	**67**	**91**	108	**83**	**104**	**111**	131	**96**	**114**	**122**	**147**
34		**44**	**60**	**82**	**91**	**75**	**94**	**106**	119	**86**	**104**	**111**	**121**
35		**38**	**53**	**74**	**86**	**67**	**85**	**101**	**101**	**77**	**94**	**101**	**115**
36		**33**	**47**	**67**	**82**	**60**	**77**	**93**	**96**	**69**	**85**	**92**	**109**
37			**41**	**60**	**77**	**53**	**69**	**84**	**91**	**62**	**77**	**83**	**102**

Tabulated values in boldface type require embedment E_4 explained on page 7-59.
Above and to the right of the zigzag line, tapered ends are required.

CONCRETE JOIST CONSTRUCTION
INTERIOR SPAN—30 INCH WIDE FORMS
Safe Superimposed Load (psf)

For limitations and explanation of use of tables, see pages 7-59 to 7-62.

Depth: 14″ FORMS + 3″ CONCRETE

Joists	5″ Joists @ 35″ c/c Wt 68 psf						6″ @ 36″ Wt 71 psf				7″ @ 37″ Wt 75 psf				
Bottom Bar	#5	#5	#6	#6	#7		#6	#7	#7	#7	#7	#7	#7	#8	#8
Truss Bar	#5	#6	#6	#7	#7		#7	#7	#8	#8	#7	#8	#8	#8	#9
Top Bar	#5	#5	#6	#6	#7		#6	#7	#6	#7	#7	#6	#7	#8	#8
Span l′ in Ft															
22	137	**188**	227	245			273	282			300	315			
23	120	**169**	202	227			244	261			268	292			
24	105	**150**	**164**	210			218	242			240	271			
25	91	**133**	**154**	195			**178**	226			**201**	248	253		
26	79	**118**	**145**	182			**167**	204	210		**189**	224	236		
27	69	**104**	**131**	168	170		**157**	184	196		**179**	202	219	221	
28	59	**92**	**117**	151	159		**141**	166	184		**161**	**168**	198	208	
29	51	**82**	**104**	136	149		**127**	**140**	173		**145**	**158**	180	195	
30	43	**72**	**93**	**113**	140		**114**	**132**	158	162	**131**	**150**	**150**	184	
31	36	**63**	**83**	**107**	131		**102**	**125**	144	153	**118**	**139**	**142**	170	173
32	30	**55**	**74**	**100**	119	124	**92**	**114**	131	144	**106**	**126**	**135**	155	163
33		**48**	**66**	**90**	108	116	**82**	**103**	**112**	131	**95**	**114**	**122**	141	154
34		**41**	**58**	**81**	**90**	110	**73**	**93**	**106**	119	**85**	**103**	**111**	**121**	**146**
35		**35**	**51**	**73**	**85**	104	**65**	**84**	**100**	**100**	**76**	**93**	**100**	**115**	**138**
36		**30**	**44**	**65**	**81**	96	**58**	**76**	**92**	**95**	**68**	**84**	**91**	**110**	**131**
37			**38**	**58**	**75**	87	**51**	**68**	**83**	**90**	**61**	**76**	**82**	**102**	**124**
38			**33**	**52**	**68**	79	**45**	**61**	**75**	**82**	**54**	**68**	**74**	**93**	**114**

Depth: 14″ FORMS + 4½″ CONCRETE

Joists	5″ Joists @ 35″ c/c Wt 87 psf						6″ @ 36″ Wt 90 psf				7″ @ 37″ Wt 94 psf			
Bottom Bar	#5	#5	#6	#6	#7	#7	#6	#7	#7	#7	#7	#7	#8	#8
Truss Bar	#5	#6	#6	#7	#7	#8	#7	#7	#8	#8	#8	#8	#8	#9
Top Bar	#5	#5	#6	#6	#7	#6	#6	#7	#6	#7	#6	#7	#8	#8
Span l′ in Ft														
24	104	**153**	**171**	218			228	254			286			
25	89	**134**	**160**	202			**186**	236			262	266		
26	76	**117**	**149**	188			**174**	213	218		235	248		
27	64	**103**	**132**	172	175		**162**	191	203		212	230	231	
28	54	**90**	**117**	154	163		**144**	171	190		**175**	207	217	
29	44	**78**	**103**	138	152		**128**	**144**	178		**165**	187	203	
30	36	**67**	**91**	**114**	142		**114**	**136**	163		**155**	**155**	191	
31		**58**	**80**	**107**	132		**101**	**128**	147	156	**143**	**147**	176	178
32		**49**	**70**	**98**	119	123	**89**	**115**	133	147	**128**	**137**	159	168
33		**41**	**60**	**87**	107	116	**79**	**103**	**112**	133	**115**	**123**	144	158
34		**34**	**52**	**77**	**88**	108	**69**	**92**	**106**	120	**103**	**111**	**124**	149
35			**44**	**68**	**83**	102	**60**	**81**	**100**	**100**	**92**	**99**	**117**	140
36			**37**	**60**	**78**	94	**52**	**72**	**90**	**94**	**82**	**89**	**111**	**133**
37			**31**	**52**	**72**	85	**45**	**63**	**81**	**87**	**73**	**79**	**101**	**125**
38				**45**	**63**	76	**38**	**56**	**72**	**78**	**64**	**70**	**91**	**115**
39				**39**	**56**	**64**	**31**	**48**	**64**	**70**	**56**	**62**	**82**	**104**
40				**32**	**49**	**60**		**42**	**56**	**62**	**49**	**54**	**73**	**88**

Tabulated values in boldface type require embedment E_4 explained on page 7-59.
Above and to the right of the zigzag line, tapered ends are required.

CONCRETE JOIST CONSTRUCTION
INTERIOR SPAN—30 INCH WIDE FORMS
Safe Superimposed Load (psf)

For limitations and explanation of use of tables, see pages 7-59 to 7-62.

Depth: 16″ FORMS + 2½″ CONCRETE

Joists	6″ Joists @ 36″ c/c Wt 72 psf					7″ @ 37″ Wt 76 psf			8″ @ 38″ Wt 80 psf		
Bottom Bar	#6	#6	#7	#7	#8	#7	#8	#8	#8	#8	#9
Truss Bar	#6	#7	#7	#8	#8	#8	#8	#9	#8	#9	#9
Top Bar	#6	#6	#7	#7	#8	#7	#8	#8	#8	#8	#9
Span l′ in Ft											
25	166	**211**	256			291			320		
26	149	**199**	231			273			295	299	
27	133	**180**	210			248	256		267	281	
28	118	**162**	**178**			226	241		243	264	
29	106	**147**	**168**	202		**188**	227		**208**	249	
30	94	**133**	**159**	191		**178**	212	213	**197**	235	
31	84	**120**	**147**	180		**169**	194	202	**187**	223	
32	74	**108**	**133**	166	171	**155**	177	191	**174**	208	211
33	66	**97**	**121**	152	162	**142**	**153**	181	**159**	191	200
34	58	**88**	**110**	**129**	153	**129**	**146**	172	**145**	**161**	**190**
35	51	**79**	**100**	**123**	145	**118**	**139**	**163**	**133**	**153**	**181**
36	44	**71**	**91**	**116**	133	**107**	**130**	**155**	**121**	**146**	**172**
37	38	**63**	**82**	**106**	**112**	**97**	**119**	**145**	**110**	**136**	**140**
38	32	**56**	**74**	**97**	**106**	**89**	**109**	**134**	**101**	**124**	**134**
39		**50**	**67**	**89**	**101**	**80**	**100**	**115**	**92**	**114**	**128**
40		**44**	**60**	**81**	**97**	**73**	**91**	**110**	**83**	**105**	**122**
41		**38**	**54**	**74**	**92**	**66**	**83**	**104**	**75**	**96**	**115**

Depth: 16″ FORMS + 3″ CONCRETE

Joists	6″ Joists @ 36″ c/c Wt 78 psf					7″ @ 37″ Wt 83 psf			8″ Joists @ 38″ c/c Wt 87 psf				
Bottom Bar	#6	#6	#7	#7	#8	#7	#8	#8	#7	#8	#8	#9	#9
Truss Bar	#6	#7	#7	#8	#8	#8	#8	#9	#8	#8	#9	#9	#10
Top Bar	#6	#6	#7	#7	#8	#7	#8	#8	#7	#8	#8	#9	#9
Span l′ in Ft													
26	149	**202**	235	247		277			**249**	300	304		
27	133	**181**	212	231		251	259		**236**	272	285		
28	118	**163**	**180**	217		228	244		**216**	247	268		
29	105	**147**	**170**	204		**190**	230		**196**	**211**	253		
30	93	**132**	**161**	192		**180**	215	216	**177**	**200**	238		
31	82	**119**	**147**	182		**171**	196	204	**161**	**190**	225		
32	73	**107**	**133**	166	172	**156**	179	193	**146**	**176**	209	213	
33	64	**96**	**121**	152	162	**142**	**154**	182	**132**	**160**	191	202	
34	56	**86**	**109**	**129**	154	**129**	**147**	173	**119**	**146**	**162**	192	
35	48	**77**	**99**	**123**	146	**117**	**140**	164	**108**	**133**	**155**	**182**	
36	41	**69**	**89**	**115**	134	**106**	**130**	**156**	**97**	**121**	**147**	**173**	
37	35	**61**	**81**	**105**	**111**	**96**	**119**	**145**	**88**	**110**	**135**	**141**	**164**
38		**54**	**72**	**96**	**106**	**87**	**109**	**133**	**79**	**100**	**124**	**134**	**156**
39		**47**	**65**	**87**	**101**	**79**	**99**	**115**	**71**	**91**	**113**	**128**	**149**
40		**41**	**58**	**79**	**96**	**71**	**90**	**109**	**63**	**82**	**103**	**123**	**142**
41		**36**	**51**	**71**	**91**	**63**	**82**	**103**	**56**	**74**	**94**	**115**	**135**
42		**30**	**45**	**65**	**83**	**57**	**74**	**94**	**49**	**67**	**86**	**105**	**129**

Tabulated values in boldface type require embedment E_4 explained on page 7-59.
Above and to the right of the zigzag line, tapered ends are required.

CONCRETE JOIST CONSTRUCTION
INTERIOR SPAN—30 INCH WIDE FORMS
Safe Superimposed Load (psf)

For limitations and explanation of use of tables, see pages 7-59 to 7-62.

16″ FORMS + 4½″ CONCRETE

Depth	6″ Joists @ 36″ c/c Wt 97 psf					7″ @ 37″ Wt 101 psf			8″ Joists @ 38″ c/c Wt 105 psf				
Bottom Bar	#6	#6	#7	#7	#8	#8	#8	#9	#7	#8	#8	#9	#9
Truss Bar	#6	#7	#7	#8	#8	#8	#9	#9	#8	#8	#9	#9	#10
Top Bar	#6	#6	#7	#7	#8	#8	#8	#9	#7	#8	#8	#9	#9
Span l′ in Ft													
29	103	**148**	**175**	210		238			**202**	**221**	263		
30	90	**132**	**165**	197		223			**182**	**209**	248		
31	78	**118**	**149**	185		203	209		**164**	**198**	233		
32	68	**105**	**134**	169	174	184	198		**147**	**180**	216	220	
33	58	**93**	**120**	153	164	**158**	186		**133**	**164**	197	208	
34	49	**82**	**108**	**130**	155	**150**	176		**119**	**148**	**167**	197	
35	41	**72**	**96**	**123**	146	**142**	167		**106**	**134**	**159**	185	
36	34	**63**	**86**	**114**	134	**131**	158		**95**	**121**	**149**	170	176
37		**55**	**76**	**103**	122	**119**	146	149	**85**	**109**	**136**	**144**	167
38		**47**	**67**	**92**	**105**	**107**	133	142	**75**	**98**	**123**	**136**	158
39		**40**	**59**	**83**	**99**	**97**	**114**	134	**66**	**88**	**112**	**130**	150
40		**33**	**52**	**74**	**94**	**87**	**109**	**127**	**58**	**79**	**101**	**123**	**143**
41			**45**	**66**	**87**	**78**	**101**	**121**	**50**	**70**	**92**	**114**	**136**
42			**38**	**59**	**79**	**70**	**91**	**98**	**43**	**62**	**82**	**103**	**129**
43			**32**	**52**	**71**	**62**	**83**	**93**	**36**	**54**	**74**	**94**	**119**
44				**45**	**63**	**55**	**74**	**88**	**30**	**47**	**66**	**85**	**101**
45				**39**	**56**	**48**	**67**	**84**		**41**	**59**	**77**	**96**

20″ FORMS + 2½″ CONCRETE

Depth	7″ Joists @ 37″ c/c Wt 90 psf					8″ @ 38″ Wt 95 psf				9″ Joists @ 39″ c/c Wt 101 psf				
Bottom Bar	#7	#7	#8	#8	#9	#8	#9	#9	#10	#8	#9	#9	#10	#10
Truss Bar	#7	#8	#8	#9	#9	#9	#9	#10	#10	#9	#9	#10	#10	#11
Top Bar	#7	#7	#8	#8	#9	#8	#9	#9	#10	#8	#9	#9	#10	#10
Span l′ in Ft														
34	121	**165**	**198**	228		**220**	246	249		**210**	**239**	270		
35	110	**151**	**182**	217		**205**	**210**	237		**193**	**225**	257		
36	99	**138**	**167**	201	207	**189**	**201**	226		**177**	**207**	246		
37	89	**126**	**153**	**174**	197	**174**	**192**	216		**162**	**191**	229	234	
38	80	**115**	**141**	**167**	188	**160**	**184**	206		**149**	**176**	**199**	224	
39	71	**105**	**129**	**159**	176	**147**	**173**	197		**137**	**162**	**190**	214	
40	63	**95**	**119**	**146**	**153**	**135**	**160**	188		**125**	**149**	**182**	**205**	
41	56	**86**	**109**	**135**	**146**	**124**	**148**	**180**		**114**	**137**	**169**	**175**	195
42	49	**78**	**99**	**125**	**140**	**114**	**137**	**154**	**173**	**104**	**126**	**157**	**168**	**187**
43	43	**71**	**91**	**115**	**134**	**105**	**126**	**148**	**166**	**95**	**116**	**145**	**161**	**179**
44	37	**63**	**83**	**106**	**127**	**96**	**116**	**142**	**159**	**87**	**107**	**134**	**155**	**172**
45	32	**57**	**75**	**97**	**117**	**88**	**107**	**135**	**136**	**78**	**98**	**124**	**148**	**165**
46		**51**	**68**	**89**	**109**	**80**	**99**	**125**	**131**	**71**	**89**	**115**	**138**	**159**
47		**45**	**62**	**82**	**100**	**73**	**91**	**116**	**126**	**64**	**81**	**106**	**128**	**137**
48		**39**	**56**	**75**	**93**	**66**	**83**	**107**	**121**	**57**	**74**	**97**	**119**	**131**
49		**34**	**50**	**68**	**85**	**59**	**76**	**99**	**116**	**51**	**67**	**90**	**110**	**126**

Tabulated values in boldface type require embedment E_4 explained on page 7-59.
Above and to the right of the zigzag line, tapered ends are required.

CONCRETE JOIST CONSTRUCTION
INTERIOR SPAN—30 INCH WIDE FORMS
Safe Superimposed Load (psf)

For limitations and explanation of use of tables, see pages 7-59 to 7-62.

Depth: 20″ FORMS + 3″ CONCRETE

Joists	7″ Joists @ 37″ c/c Wt 96 psf				8″ Joists @ 38″ c/c Wt 101 psf					9″ @ 39″ Wt 107 psf			
Bottom Bar	#7	#8	#8	#9	#8	#8	#9	#9	#10	#9	#9	#10	#10
Truss Bar	#8	#8	#9	#9	#8	#9	#9	#10	#10	#9	#10	#10	#11
Top Bar	#7	#8	#8	#9	#8	#8	#9	#9	#10	#9	#9	#10	#10
Span l′ in Ft													
34	164	199	229		186	222	249	251		241	273		
35	150	182	218		170	205	212	239		226	260		
36	136	167	183	208	156	188	202	228		208	248		
37	124	153	175	198	142	173	193	217		192	209	236	
38	113	140	167	189	130	159	185	207		177	200	226	
39	102	129	157	176	118	146	174	198		162	192	216	
40	93	118	145	153	107	134	160	189		149	182	203	205
41	84	107	133	146	97	122	148	180	181	137	168	176	196
42	75	98	123	140	88	112	136	154	173	126	155	169	188
43	68	89	113	134	80	102	126	148	166	115	144	162	180
44	60	81	103	126	72	93	115	142	159	106	133	155	172
45	54	73	95	116	64	85	106	133	136	96	122	148	165
46	47	66	87	107	57	77	97	123	130	88	112	138	159
47	41	59	79	99	51	70	89	113	125	80	103	128	137
48	36	53	72	91	45	63	81	105	120	72	95	118	131
49	31	47	65	84	39	56	74	96	115	65	87	109	126

Depth: 20″ FORMS + 4½″ CONCRETE

Joists	7″ Joists @ 37″ c/c Wt 115 psf				8″ @ 38″ Wt 120 psf				9″ @ 39″ Wt 126 psf				
Bottom Bar	#7	#8	#8	#9	#8	#9	#9	#10	#8	#9	#9	#10	#10
Truss Bar	#8	#8	#9	#9	#9	#9	#10	#10	#9	#9	#10	#10	#11
Top Bar	#7	#8	#8	#9	#8	#9	#9	#10	#8	#9	#9	#10	#10
Span l′ in Ft													
36	134	167	187	210	189	207	232		177	211	253	254	
37	121	152	178	200	173	198	221		161	193	215	242	
38	109	139	169	190	158	188	210		146	177	206	230	
39	98	126	156	178	144	174	200		133	162	196	219	
40	88	114	143	154	131	159	191		120	148	182	208	
41	78	103	130	146	119	146	180	182	109	135	168	179	199
42	69	93	119	140	108	134	155	174	98	123	154	171	190
43	61	84	108	133	98	122	149	166	88	112	141	164	182
44	53	75	98	122	88	112	141	158	79	101	130	157	173
45	46	67	89	112	79	102	129	136	70	91	119	146	166
46	39	59	81	103	71	92	119	130	62	82	108	135	159
47	33	52	73	94	63	83	109	124	54	74	99	124	137
48		45	65	85	56	75	100	119	47	66	90	114	131
49		39	58	77	49	67	91	113	40	58	81	104	125
50		33	51	70	42	60	83	106	34	51	73	95	119
51			45	63	36	53	75	97		44	66	87	109

Tabulated values in boldface type require embedment E_4 explained on page 7-59.
Above and to the right of the zigzag line, tapered ends are required.

SAFE LOAD TABLES
Flat Slabs
Section 8

TWO-WAY FLAT SLABS—SQUARE PANELS WITH DROP PANELS

For two-way dome or waffle slabs, see Section 9.

Tables are presented for the slab thickness, width and thickness of drop panel, minimum size of column capital, strips of reinforcing bars, weight of steel and volume of concrete per square foot of floor area on spans of 15 to 40 ft by one-foot intervals, for safe superimposed loads of 50, 100, 150, 200, 250, 300, 400 and 500 psf for typical square interior panels with drop panels, column capitals,* and minimum column size meeting ACI Chap. 21 empirical method and for similar strips perpendicular to the wall for exterior square panels that are built integrally with a spandrel beam or concrete wall.†

All tables are based upon the recommendations of the "Building Code Requirements for Reinforced Concrete (ACI 318-63)," using one set of fiber stresses, viz., $f'_c = 3750$ psi and $f_s = 24{,}000$ psi, and are based upon using deformed bars meeting the requirements of ASTM for Grade 60 bars.

As shown on page 8-4, the two-way slab is divided into two bands or strips of reinforcement, one over the columns and extending a quarter panel each side of the center-line, known as a "column strip," and one a half-panel wide between two column strips, known as a "middle strip." A second set of column and middle strips runs at right angles to the first, which explains the designation "two-way" slab. Each strip in these tables has straight bars in the bottom and truss bars that are in the bottom at midspan and in the top over the supports, and each strip may, in addition, have supplementary separate top bars when required. The structure must have at least three consecutive panels in a row in each direction to come within the ACI Code values for moments; if the building is narrower, a special analysis must be made which will have the effect of increasing the reinforcement. The successive spans must be of such lengths that they do not differ by more than twenty per cent of the longer span.

While values have been computed only for square panels, it is possible to estimate values for a rectangular panel fairly accurately by using the long side for one set of strips and the short side for the other. The ACI Code limits the ratio of long to short side to 1.33.

For exterior panels, it is possible to take the strips that are continuous, i.e., parallel to the discontinuous edge, from the table for Typical Interior Panels. The strips that are noncontinuous, i.e., perpendicular to the discontinuous edge, are given by the table for Strips Perpendicular to an Exterior Wall, provided that the exterior edge of the panel frames into a concrete column or concrete bearing wall integral with the slab. If the slab simply rests upon a masonry wall without any edge restraint, then the slab and drop panel thicknesses must be increased 15 per cent and the bars in the strips perpendicular to the exterior wall must be changed as follows from the values in the tables for Typical Exterior Panels:—

Positive steel in column strip:—Increase 50%.
Negative steel in column strip at wall:—Decrease to 17% of tabulated value.
Negative steel in column strip over first interior column:—Increase 30%.

---

* Column capitals are here arbitrarily taken as 22½ per cent of the panel length. Minimum column size must meet ACI Eq. (21-1).

† Connection between slab and column should be developed for moment due to unbalanced loads (see "Transfer of Bending Moment between Flat Plate Floor and Column" —Joseph DiStasio, Sr. and M. P. Van Buren, ACI Journal, Vol. 32, September, 1960).

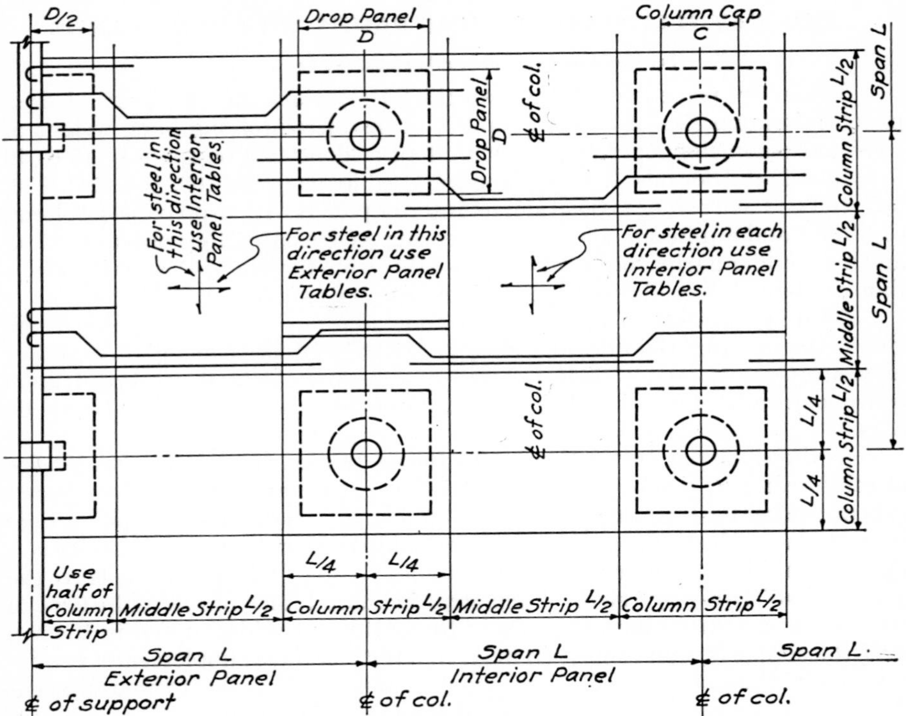

TYPICAL PLAN

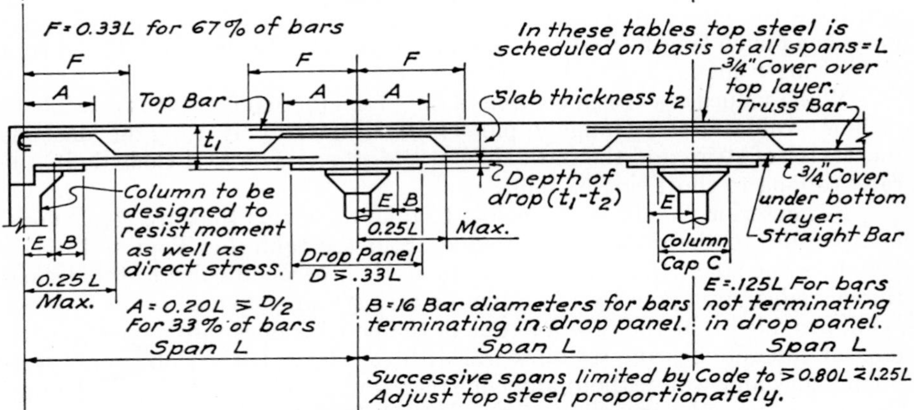

TYPICAL SECTION – COLUMN STRIP

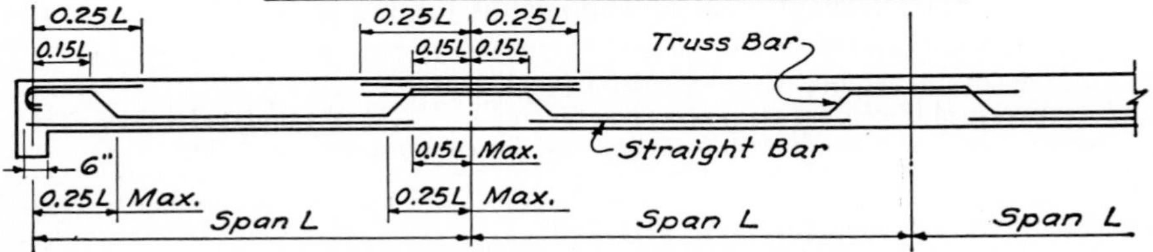

TYPICAL BENDING – MIDDLE STRIP

Straight top bars over other interior supports may be required in the middle strip for unequal loads and/or spans.

TWO-WAY FLAT SLABS—SQUARE PANELS WITH DROP PANELS

Positive steel in middle strip:—Increase 30%.
Negative steel in middle strip at exterior wall:—Decrease to 30% of tabulated value.
Negative steel in middle strip at first interior row of columns:—Increase 30%.

For corner panels which are discontinuous on two edges, both sets of strips should be taken from the tables for Typical Exterior Panels; if both discontinuous edges rest upon masonry walls, the corrections above shall apply for both sets of strips.

The concrete quantities given per square foot of floor area include all structural concrete in slab and drop panel but do not include any material in the column capital, column, nor any floor finish above the structural slab. Note that the "safe superimposed load" represents live load, floor finishes, partition allowance, and everything except the weight of the concrete. For a table of quantities in columns and column capitals, see page 5-13.

The weight of steel is the average weight in pounds per sq ft of all bars in the slab but not including bars in beams, columns, walls or footings.

The effective depth of slab is computed on the basis of an allowance of ¾ in. cover over the bars in all cases, and, where bars cross each other, by an allowance of one bar diameter plus 0.03 in. for deformations.

While the scope of these tables is adequate for most purposes, it is not practicable to present all possible combinations. For those who wish to extend beyond the coverage of the tables as well as for those who wish to know how they were computed, the following examples will be instructive:—

Example—For the table on page 8-10, design a two-way typical interior flat slab panel 20′-0″ square for a safe superimposed load of 250 psf. Stresses:—$f_c = 1688$ psi, $f_s = 24{,}000$ psi. See ACI Code Art. 2102 and 2104.

Column Cap:—Size of cap is determined by keeping stresses around periphery within the allowable,* but 22½ per cent of the panel length (or 4′-6″ for this case) is often used and will be tried here. Caps are often made in multiples of 6 in. to suit the standard steel forms available.

Drop Panel:—Size of panel is determined by keeping stresses around periphery within the allowable, but should be at least 0.33 of the panel length in the parallel direction.* (8′-3″ will be assumed here.)

Slab Thickness:—Slab thickness, t_2, shall not be less than $L/40$, which equals 6 in., nor less than $t_2 = 0.024\,L\left(1-\frac{2c}{3L}\right)\sqrt{\frac{w'}{f'_c/2000}} + 1$, where c = diameter of column cap in feet, L = span in feet, and w' = uniform dead plus live load, psf, so

$$t_2 = 0.024 \times 20\left(1 - \frac{2 \times 4.5}{3 \times 20}\right)\sqrt{\frac{331}{3750/2000}} + 1'' = 6.43 \text{ in.,}$$

and shall be sufficient to keep bending and shearing stresses within Code limits. For the present, 6½ in. will be assumed.

Drop Panel Thickness:—ACI 318 requires the total thickness in drop panel to be at least $t_1 = 0.028\,L\left(1-\frac{2c}{3L}\right)\sqrt{\frac{w'}{f'_c/2000}} + 1\tfrac{1}{2}'' = 0.028 \times 20\left(1-\frac{2\times 4.5}{3\times 20}\right)\sqrt{\frac{331}{3750/2000}}$ $+ 1\tfrac{1}{2}'' = 7.83$ in., and not greater than $1.5t_2$ which is 9¾ in. and is used here.

* The 1963 ACI Code is considerably less fixed in the proportions of the parts than early codes, giving the designer more latitude in selecting outlines, but requiring that the conditions around the periphery of cap or drop and at all critical sections be within Code limits for stresses.

TWO-WAY FLAT SLABS—SQUARE PANELS WITH DROP PANELS

Total Bending Moment:—$M_o = 0.09\ WLF\left(1 - \frac{2c}{3L}\right)^2$, where $F = 1.15 - \frac{c}{L}$, but $\ngtr 1.00$.

Superimposed load	$= 20 \times 20 \times 250$	$= 100{,}000$ lb
Slab	$= 20 \times 20 \times 0.54 \times 150$	$= 33{,}600$ lb
Drop	$= 8.25 \times 8.25 \times 0.27 \times 150 =$	2,760 lb
		136,360 lb

$$F = 1.15 - \frac{4.5}{20} = 0.925 \text{ but must be } \ngtr 1.00.$$

$$M_o = 0.09 \times 136{,}360 \times 20 \times 12 \times 1.00\left(1 - \frac{2 \times 4.5}{3 \times 20}\right)^2 = 2{,}128{,}000 \text{ lb-in.}$$

Column Strip:—Positive moment $= 0.20\ M_o = 425{,}600$ lb-in.
$d = 6.5 - 0.75 - 0.32 = 5.43$ in. Take $b = \frac{3}{4} \times$ panel width (ACI 2102(c)1):—

$$A_s = \frac{M}{jf_sd} = \frac{425{,}600}{\frac{7}{8} \times 24{,}000 \times 5.43} = 3.73 \text{ sq in. } 12\text{-}\#5 \text{ bars} = 3.72 \text{ sq in.} \begin{cases} 6 \text{ Straight} \\ 6 \text{ Truss} \end{cases}$$

$$R = \frac{M}{bd^2} = \frac{425{,}600}{\frac{3}{4} \times 120 \times 5.43 \times 5.43} = 161 < 271, \text{ so } f_c < 1688 \text{ psi}$$

Negative moment (computed for a series of equal spans as explained on page 8-3) $= 0.50\ M_o = 1{,}064{,}000$ lb-in.
$d^* = 6.5 + 3.25 - 0.75 - 0.63 - 0.03 - 0.31 = 8.03$ in.
Take $b = \frac{3}{4} \times$ drop width (ACI 2102(c)1):—

$$A_s = \frac{M}{jf_sd} = \frac{1{,}064{,}000}{\frac{7}{8} \times 24{,}000 \times 8.03} = 6.30 \text{ sq in.}\dagger$$

2×6-#5 truss bars	=	3.72 sq in.
8-#5 top bars	=	2.48 sq in.
		6.20 sq in.

$$R = \frac{M}{bd^2} = \frac{1{,}064{,}000}{\frac{3}{4} \times 99 \times 8.03 \times 8.03} = 222 < 271, \text{ so } f_c < 1688 \text{ psi}$$

Middle Strip:—Positive moment $= 0.15\ M_o = 319{,}000$ lb-in.
$d = 6.5 - 0.75 - 0.63 - 0.03 - 0.31 = 4.78$, since the bars in the middle strip in one direction must rest on top of those at right angles, thus reducing the effective depth.

$$A_s = \frac{319{,}000}{\frac{7}{8} \times 24{,}000 \times 4.78} = 3.18 \text{ sq in.}\ddagger \quad 10\text{-}\#5 \text{ bars} = 3.10 \text{ sq in.} \begin{cases} 5 \text{ Straight} \\ 5 \text{ Truss} \end{cases}$$

Since the negative moment has the same numerical value and since the bars are all in one layer at the top and have a better moment arm, it is unnecessary to recompute the moment here; simply bend up one-half or slightly over one-half of the bars in this strip.

Shear around Column Cap:—This is figured on a vertical section around a circle with a radius that is larger than the cap radius by one-half the thickness of slab and drop panel less 1½ in. (ACI 2102(c)2):—

$$v = \frac{V}{bd} = \frac{(20 \times 20 - \pi \times 2.59 \times 2.59) \times 341}{2 \times \pi \times 31\frac{1}{8} \times 8.03} = 82 \text{ psi} < (2\sqrt{3750} = 122) \text{ psi}$$

* This equals slab thickness plus drop thickness less fireproofing less top layer of bars (as lower layer has less moment arm) less 0.03 for deformations and less half the diameter of the lower layer of top bars.

† The area provided is about 1½ per cent less than the computed area assuming $j = \frac{7}{8}$. However, since $p = 0.00785$, based on three-fourths of the width of drop panel, $j = 0.90$ (page 3-15) and $A_s = 6.13$ sq in., so that the proposed steel is sufficiently close to the requirements.

‡ Checking again, $p = 0.0054$, $j = 0.915$, $A_s = 3.04$ sq in., so that the 3.10 sq in. furnished is sufficient.

TWO-WAY FLAT SLABS—SQUARE PANELS WITH DROP PANELS

Shear around Drop Panel:—This is figured on a vertical section around a square, each side of which lies at a distance beyond the drop panel equal to one-half the slab thickness less 1½ in. (ACI 2102(c)2):—

$$v = \frac{V}{b_o d} = \frac{(20 \times 20 - 8.67 \times 8.67) \times 341}{4 \times 104 \times 5.43} = 49 \text{ psi} < (2\sqrt{3750}) = 122.5 \text{ psi}$$

It is impracticable to present a full study of flat slabs in a manual such as this or to tabulate more than a few typical cases. The negative moment and top steel in these tables is computed for a series of equal spans. In those cases where the adjoining span is longer or shorter than the span under consideration, adjustment must be made in the amount of top steel. Rectangular panels, openings through slabs, spans varying more than 20 per cent, panels with marginal beams or with interior beams, and many similar variations require special treatment best undertaken by a structural engineer.

TWO-WAY FLAT SLAB FLOORS, SQUARE PANELS—INTERIOR PANELS

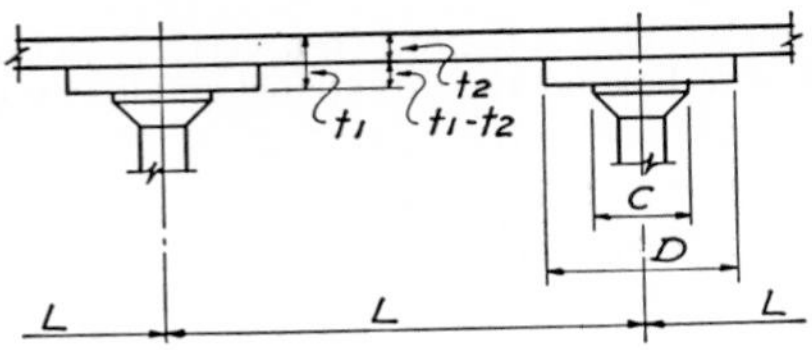

For general instructions and notes on the use of this table, see pages 8-3 to 8-7 incl.

Span / Drop / Cap	Safe Super-imposed Load (psf)	Slab Thickness t_2 (in.)	Drop Panel Thickness (t_1-t_2) (in.)	Each Column Strip: Straight Quant.	Straight Bar No.	Straight Length	Trussed Quant.	Trussed Bar No.	Trussed Length
L = 15′-0	50	4½	2¼	6	#3	10′-9	4	#3	25′-3
	100	4½	2¼	5	#3	10′-9	5	#3	25′-3
	150	4½	2¼	6	#3	10′-9	7	#3	25′-3
D = 6′-0	200	4¾	2¼	8	#3	10′-9	8	#3	25′-3
	250	5	2¼	5	#4	10′-9	5	#4	25′-3
	300	5½	2½	5	#4	10′-9	5	#4	25′-3
C = 3′-6	400	6	2¾	4	#5	10′-9	4	#5	25′-3
	500	6½	3	4	#5	10′-9	5	#5	25′-3
L = 16′-0	50	5	2¼	6	#3	11′-6	4	#3	27′-0
	100	5	2¼	5	#3	11′-6	6	#3	27′-0
	150	5	2¼	7	#3	11′-6	8	#3	27′-0
D = 6′-3	200	5	2¼	5	#4	11′-6	5	#4	27′-0
	250	5½	2½	5	#4	11′-6	6	#4	27′-0
	300	5¾	2¾	6	#4	11′-6	6	#4	27′-0
C = 3′-6	400	6½	3	4	#5	11′-6	5	#5	27′-0
	500	7	3¼	5	#5	11′-6	5	#5	27′-0
L = 17′-0	50	5¼	2½	5	#3	12′-3	5	#3	28′-6
	100	5¼	2½	6	#3	12′-3	7	#3	28′-6
	150	5¼	2½	8	#3	12′-3	8	#3	28′-6
D = 6′-6	200	5¼	2½	6	#4	12′-3	6	#4	28′-6
	250	5¾	2½	6	#4	12′-3	6	#4	28′-9
	300	6	2¾	4	#5	12′-3	5	#5	28′-9
C = 4′-0	400	6¾	3	5	#5	12′-3	5	#5	28′-9
	500	7¼	3½	4	#6	12′-6	4	#6	28′-9
L = 18′-0	50	5½	2½	5	#3	12′-3	6	#3	30′-3
	100	5½	2½	7	#3	12′-3	8	#3	30′-3
	150	5½	2½	5	#4	12′-3	6	#4	30′-3
D = 7′-6	200	5½	2½	6	#4	12′-3	7	#4	30′-3
	250	6	2¾	5	#5	12′-3	5	#5	30′-3
	300	6½	3	5	#5	12′-3	5	#5	30′-3
C = 4′-0	400	7	3¼	4	#6	12′-6	5	#6	30′-6
	500	7¾	3¾	4	#6	12′-6	5	#6	30′-6

TWO-WAY FLAT SLAB FLOORS, SQUARE PANELS—INTERIOR PANELS

f_s = 24,000 psi
f_c = 1,688 psi
v_c = 122.5 psi

Each Column Strip			Each Middle Strip						Weight of Steel (psf)	Average Cubic Feet of Concrete Per Square Foot of Floor*
Top			Straight			Trussed				
Quant.	Bar No.	Length	Quant.	Bar No.	Length	Quant.	Bar No.	Length		
4	#3	10′-0	5	#3	10′-6	5	#3	22′-9	1.24	.405
7	#3	10′-0	5	#3	10′-6	5	#3	22′-9	1.39	.405
8	#3	10′-0	5	#3	10′-6	6	#3	22′-9	1.70	.405
10	#3	10′-0	6	#3	10′-6	7	#3	22′-9	2.04	.426
7	#4	10′-0	4	#4	10′-6	5	#4	22′-9	2.41	.447
8	#4	10′-0	4	#4	10′-6	5	#4	23′-0	2.47	.492
6	#5	10′-0	5	#4	10′-6	5	#4	23′-0	2.88	.537
5	#5	10′-0	4	#5	10′-6	4	#5	23′-0	3.27	.582
6	#3	10′-9	5	#3	11′-3	5	#3	24′-3	1.23	.445
8	#3	10′-9	5	#3	11′-3	5	#3	24′-3	1.42	.445
10	#3	10′-9	6	#3	11′-3	6	#3	24′-3	1.81	.445
8	#4	10′-9	7	#3	11′-3	8	#3	24′-3	2.25	.445
7	#4	10′-9	5	#4	11′-3	5	#4	24′-6	2.47	.490
9	#4	10′-9	5	#4	11′-3	5	#4	24′-6	2.64	.514
6	#5	10′-9	4	#5	11′-3	4	#5	24′-6	3.16	.580
8	#5	10′-9	4	#5	11′-3	5	#5	24′-6	3.63	.625
5	#3	11′-3	5	#3	12′-0	5	#3	26′-0	1.17	.468
7	#3	11′-3	5	#3	12′-0	6	#3	26′-0	1.48	.468
12	#3	11′-3	7	#3	12′-0	7	#3	26′-0	1.89	.468
8	#4	11′-3	5	#4	12′-0	5	#4	26′-0	2.42	.468
10	#4	11′-3	5	#4	12′-0	6	#4	26′-0	2.65	.510
6	#5	11′-3	6	#4	12′-0	6	#4	26′-0	2.93	.534
8	#5	11′-3	4	#5	12′-0	5	#5	26′-0	3.41	.599
6	#6	11′-3	5	#5	12′-0	5	#5	26′-0	3.78	.647
6	#3	12′-0	5	#3	12′-9	5	#3	27′-6	1.20	.495
9	#3	12′-0	6	#3	12′-9	6	#3	27′-6	1.57	.495
7	#4	12′-0	8	#3	12′-9	8	#3	27′-6	2.10	.495
9	#4	12′-0	5	#4	12′-9	6	#4	27′-6	2.57	.495
7	#5	12′-0	6	#4	12′-9	6	#4	27′-6	2.91	.540
8	#5	12′-0	4	#5	12′-9	5	#5	27′-6	3.20	.585
5	#6	12′-0	5	#5	12′-9	5	#5	27′-6	3.73	.630
6	#6	12′-0	4	#6	12′-9	4	#6	27′-6	4.04	.700

* These cubic foot quantities include drop panel but not column capital.

TWO-WAY FLAT SLAB FLOORS, SQUARE PANELS—INTERIOR PANELS

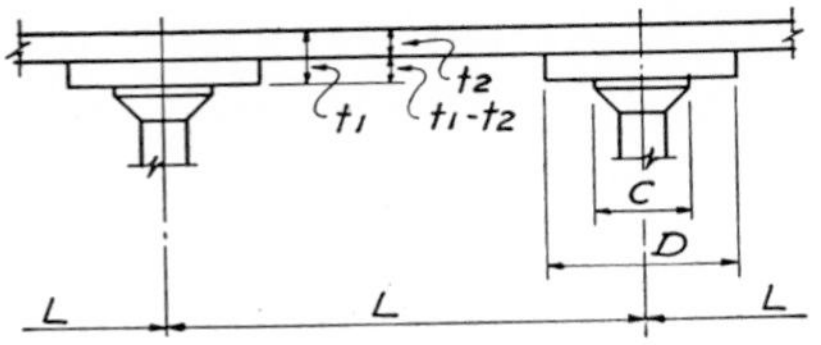

For general instructions and notes on the use of this table, see pages 8-3 to 8-7 incl.

Span / Drop / Cap	Safe Super-imposed Load (psf)	Slab Thickness t_2 (in.)	Drop Panel Thickness (t_1-t_2) (in.)	Each Column Strip: Straight Quant.	Straight Bar No.	Straight Length	Trussed Quant.	Trussed Bar No.	Trussed Length
L = 19′-0	50	5¾	2¾	6	#3	13′-3	6	#3	32′-0
	100	5¾	2¾	8	#3	13′-3	8	#3	32′-0
	150	5¾	2¾	6	#4	13′-3	6	#4	32′-0
D = 7′-6	200	5¾	2¾	5	#5	13′-3	5	#5	32′-0
	250	6¼	2¾	5	#5	13′-3	6	#5	32′-0
	300	6¾	3	5	#5	13′-3	6	#5	32′-0
C = 4′-6	400	7½	3½	4	#6	13′-6	5	#6	32′-0
	500	8	3¾	5	#6	13′-6	5	#6	32′-0
L = 20′-0	50	6	3	7	#3	13′-6	7	#3	33′-9
	100	6	3	5	#4	13′-6	6	#4	33′-9
	150	6	3	7	#4	13′-6	7	#4	33′-9
D = 8′-3	200	6	3	5	#5	13′-6	6	#5	33′-9
	250	6½	3¼	6	#5	13′-6	6	#5	33′-9
	300	7	3¼	4	#6	13′-9	5	#6	33′-9
C = 4′-6	400	7¾	3½	5	#6	13′-9	5	#6	33′-9
	500	8½	4	5	#6	13′-9	6	#6	33′-9
L = 21′-0	50	6½	3	7	#3	14′-6	8	#3	35′-3
	100	6½	3	6	#4	14′-6	6	#4	35′-3
	150	6½	3	5	#5	14′-6	5	#5	35′-3
D = 8′-3	200	6½	3	6	#5	14′-6	6	#5	35′-3
	250	7	3¼	5	#6	14′-9	5	#6	35′-3
	300	7½	3½	5	#6	14′-9	5	#6	35′-6
C = 4′-6	400	8¼	4	6	#6	14′-9	6	#6	35′-6
	500	9	4½	6	#6	14′-9	7	#6	35′-6
L = 22′-0	50	6¾	3¼	5	#4	14′-9	5	#4	37′-0
	100	6¾	3¼	6	#4	14′-9	7	#4	37′-0
	150	6¾	3¼	5	#5	14′-9	6	#5	37′-0
D = 9′-0	200	6¾	3¼	6	#5	14′-9	7	#5	37′-0
	250	7¼	3¼	5	#6	15′-0	5	#6	37′-0
	300	7¼	3½	5	#6	15′-0	6	#6	37′-0
C = 5′-0	400	8½	4	6	#6	15′-0	7	#6	37′-3
	500	9¼	4½	7	#6	15′-0	7	#6	37′-3

TWO-WAY FLAT SLAB FLOORS, SQUARE PANELS—INTERIOR PANELS

$f_s = 24{,}000$ psi
$f_c = 1{,}688$ psi
$v_c = 122.5$ psi

Each Column Strip			Each Middle Strip						Weight of Steel (psf)	Average Cubic Feet of Concrete Per Square Foot of Floor *
Top			Straight			Trussed				
Quant.	Bar No.	Length	Quant.	Bar No.	Length	Quant.	Bar No.	Length		
8	#3	12′-9	5	#3	13′-6	6	#3	29′-0	1.28	.515
12	#3	12′-9	6	#3	13′-6	7	#3	29′-0	1.66	.515
8	#4	12′-9	5	#4	13′-6	5	#4	29′-0	2.17	.515
7	#5	12′-9	6	#4	13′-6	6	#4	29′-0	2.77	.515
7	#5	12′-9	6	#4	13′-6	7	#4	29′-0	3.06	.557
8	#5	12′-9	5	#5	13′-6	5	#5	29′-0	3.31	.601
6	#6	12′-9	4	#6	13′-6	4	#6	29′-0	3.83	.670
8	#6	12′-9	4	#6	13′-6	5	#6	29′-0	4.39	.715
9	#3	13′-3	6	#3	14′-0	6	#3	30′-6	1.35	.543
6	#4	13′-3	7	#3	14′-0	8	#3	30′-6	1.81	.543
9	#4	13′-3	6	#4	14′-0	6	#4	30′-6	2.40	.543
7	#5	13′-3	5	#5	14′-0	5	#5	30′-6	3.05	.543
8	#5	13′-3	5	#5	14′-0	5	#5	30′-6	3.20	.588
6	#6	13′-3	5	#5	14′-0	6	#5	30′-6	3.60	.629
9	#6	13′-3	4	#6	14′-0	5	#6	30′-6	4.25	.695
8	#6	13′-3	5	#6	14′-0	5	#6	30′-6	4.51	.765
10	#3	14′-0	7	#3	14′-9	7	#3	32′-0	1.45	.580
8	#4	14′-0	5	#4	14′-9	5	#4	32′-0	1.95	.580
7	#5	14′-0	6	#4	14′-9	6	#4	32′-0	2.49	.580
9	#5	14′-0	5	#5	14′-9	5	#5	32′-0	3.12	.580
7	#6	14′-0	5	#5	14′-9	6	#5	32′-0	3.63	.625
8	#6	14′-0	4	#6	14′-9	5	#6	32′-0	3.97	.670
8	#6	14′-0	5	#6	14′-9	5	#6	32′-0	4.41	.739
8	#6	14′-0	5	#6	14′-9	6	#6	32′-3	4.88	.805
6	#4	14′-9	7	#3	15′-6	8	#3	33′-6	1.55	.608
8	#4	14′-9	5	#4	15′-6	6	#4	33′-6	2.06	.608
7	#5	14′-9	7	#4	15′-6	7	#4	33′-6	2.67	.608
9	#5	14′-9	5	#5	15′-6	6	#5	33′-6	3.28	.608
8	#6	14′-9	6	#5	15′-6	6	#5	33′-6	3.62	.649
8	#6	14′-9	4	#6	15′-6	5	#6	33′-6	4.00	.695
8	#6	14′-9	5	#6	15′-6	6	#6	33′-6	4.64	.764
10	#6	14′-9	6	#6	15′-6	6	#6	33′-9	5.02	.834

* These cubic foot quantities include drop panel but not column capital.

TWO-WAY FLAT SLAB FLOORS, SQUARE PANELS—INTERIOR PANELS

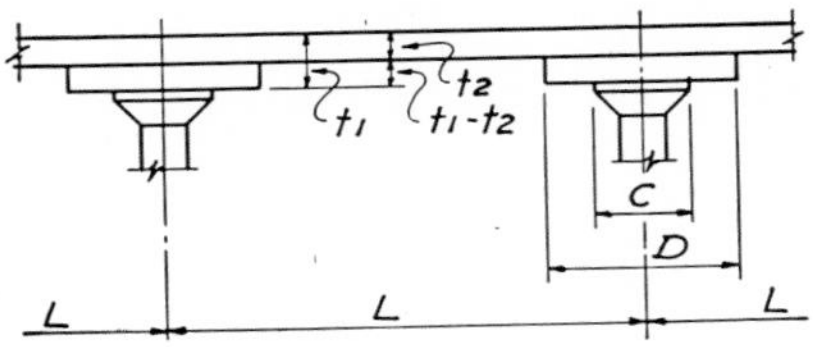

For general instructions and notes on the use of this table, see pages 8-3 to 8-7 incl.

Span / Drop / Cap	Safe Super-imposed Load (psf)	Slab Thickness t_2 (in.)	Drop Panel Thickness (t_1-t_2) (in.)	Each Column Strip: Straight Quant.	Straight Bar No.	Straight Length	Trussed Quant.	Trussed Bar No.	Trussed Length
L = 23′-0	50	7	3¼	5	#4	15′-6	6	#4	38′-9
	100	7	3¼	5	#5	15′-6	5	#5	38′-9
	150	7	3¼	6	#5	15′-6	6	#5	38′-9
D = 9′-3	200	7	3¼	5	#6	15′-9	6	#6	38′-9
	250	7½	3½	6	#6	15′-9	6	#6	38′-9
	300	8	3¾	6	#6	15′-9	6	#6	38′-9
C = 5′-0	400	9	4¼	7	#6	15′-9	7	#6	38′-9
	500	9¾	4¾	5	#7	16′-3	6	#7	38′-9
L = 24′-0	50	7¼	3½	6	#4	16′-6	6	#4	40′-3
	100	7¼	3½	5	#5	16′-6	5	#5	40′-3
	150	7¼	3½	6	#5	16′-6	7	#5	40′-3
D = 9′-3	200	7¼	3½	5	#6	16′-9	6	#6	40′-3
	250	7¾	3¾	6	#6	16′-9	7	#6	40′-6
	300	8¼	4	6	#6	16′-9	7	#6	40′-6
C = 5′-6	400	9¼	4½	7	#6	16′-9	8	#6	40′-6
	500	10	5	6	#7	17′-3	6	#7	40′-6
L = 25′-0	50	7½	3¾	6	#4	16′-9	7	#4	42′-0
	100	7½	3¾	6	#5	16′-9	6	#5	42′-0
	150	7½	3¾	7	#5	16′-9	8	#5	42′-0
D = 10′-0	200	7½	3¾	6	#6	17′-0	7	#6	42′-0
	250	8¼	3¾	7	#6	17′-0	7	#6	42′-0
	300	8¾	4½	7	#6	17′-0	8	#6	42′-3
C = 5′-6	400	9¾	4¾	6	#7	17′-6	6	#7	42′-3
	500	10½	5½	7	#7	17′-6	7	#7	42′-3
L = 26′-0	50	8	3¾	7	#4	17′-3	7	#4	43′-9
	100	8	3¾	6	#5	17′-3	6	#5	43′-9
	150	8	3¾	7	#5	17′-3	8	#5	43′-9
D = 10′-6	200	8	3¾	6	#6	17′-6	7	#6	43′-9
	250	8½	4	7	#6	17′-6	8	#6	43′-9
	300	9	4¼	8	#6	17′-6	8	#6	43′-9
C = 6′-0	400	10	4¾	6	#7	18′-0	7	#7	43′-9
	500	11	5¼	7	#7	18′-0	7	#7	44′-0

TWO-WAY FLAT SLAB FLOORS, SQUARE PANELS—INTERIOR PANELS

f_s = 24,000 psi
f_c = 1,688 psi
v_c = 122.5 psi

Each Column Strip			Each Middle Strip						Weight of Steel (psf)	Average Cubic Feet of Concrete Per Square Foot of Floor *
Top			Straight			Trussed				
Quant.	Bar No.	Length	Quant.	Bar No.	Length	Quant.	Bar No.	Length		
7	#4	15′-3	8	#3	16′-3	8	#3	35′-0	1.64	.627
7	#5	15′-3	6	#4	16′-3	6	#4	35′-0	2.27	.627
9	#5	15′-3	5	#5	16′-3	5	#5	35′-0	2.84	.627
7	#6	15′-3	6	#5	16′-3	6	#5	35′-0	3.59	.627
8	#6	15′-3	5	#6	16′-3	5	#6	35′-0	4.01	.672
10	#6	15′-3	5	#6	16′-3	6	#6	35′-0	4.38	.717
10	#6	15′-3	6	#6	16′-3	6	#6	35′-3	4.79	.807
8	#7	15′-3	5	#7	16′-3	5	#7	35′-3	5.36	.877
8	#4	16′-0	5	#4	17′-0	5	#4	36′-6	1.71	.647
8	#5	16′-0	6	#4	17′-0	7	#4	36′-6	2.32	.647
9	#5	16′-0	5	#5	17′-0	6	#5	36′-6	3.00	.647
8	#6	16′-0	5	#6	17′-0	5	#6	36′-6	3.76	.647
8	#6	16′-0	5	#6	17′-0	6	#6	36′-6	4.26	.692
9	#6	16′-0	5	#6	17′-0	6	#6	36′-6	4.34	.737
10	#6	16′-0	6	#6	17′-0	6	#6	36′-9	4.82	.827
9	#7	16′-0	5	#7	17′-0	5	#7	36′-9	5.38	.895
8	#4	16′-6	5	#4	17′-6	6	#4	38′-0	1.80	.675
8	#5	16′-6	5	#5	17′-6	5	#5	38′-0	2.55	.675
9	#5	16′-6	6	#5	17′-6	6	#5	38′-0	3.12	.675
8	#6	16′-6	5	#6	17′-6	6	#6	38′-0	4.06	.675
10	#6	16′-6	5	#6	17′-6	6	#6	38′-0	4.30	.738
9	#6	16′-6	6	#6	17′-6	6	#6	38′-3	4.52	.786
9	#7	16′-6	5	#7	17′-6	5	#7	38′-3	5.14	.876
9	#7	16′-6	5	#7	17′-6	6	#7	38′-3	5.78	.945
10	#4	17′-3	6	#4	18′-3	6	#4	39′-6	1.87	.718
9	#5	17′-3	5	#5	18′-3	5	#5	39′-6	2.51	.718
11	#5	17′-3	6	#5	18′-3	7	#5	39′-6	3.24	.718
9	#6	17′-3	5	#6	18′-3	6	#6	39′-6	3.98	.718
10	#6	17′-3	6	#6	18′-3	6	#6	39′-6	4.41	.763
12	#6	17′-3	6	#6	18′-3	7	#6	39′-9	4.83	.808
9	#7	17′-3	5	#7	18′-3	6	#7	39′-9	5.44	.898
11	#7	17′-3	6	#7	18′-3	6	#7	39′-9	5.88	.988

* These cubic foot quantities include drop panel but not column capital.

TWO-WAY FLAT SLAB FLOORS, SQUARE PANELS—INTERIOR PANELS

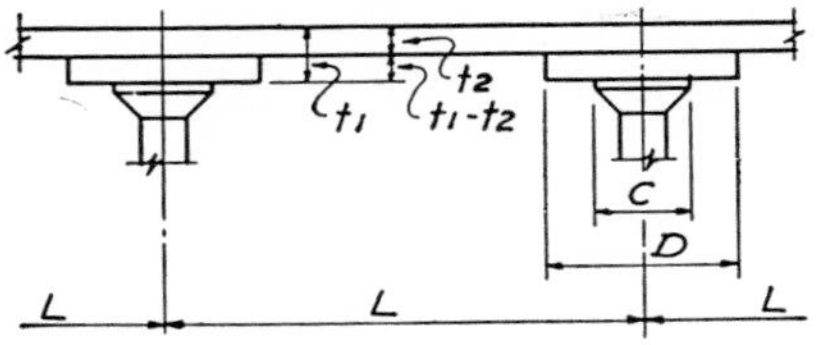

For general instructions and notes on the use of this table, see pages 8-3 to 8-7 incl.

Span / Drop / Cap	Safe Super-imposed Load (psf)	Slab Thickness t_2 (in.)	Drop Panel Thickness (t_1-t_2) (in.)	Each Column Strip: Straight Quant.	Straight Bar No.	Straight Length	Trussed Quant.	Trussed Bar No.	Trussed Length
L = 27′-0	50	8¼	4	8	#4	18′-0	8	#4	45′-6
	100	8¼	4	7	#5	18′-0	7	#5	45′-6
	150	8¼	4	6	#6	18′-3	6	#6	45′-6
D = 10′-9	200	8¼	4	7	#6	18′-3	8	#6	45′-6
	250	8¾	4¼	8	#6	18′-3	8	#6	45′-6
	300	9½	4½	6	#7	18′-9	7	#7	45′-6
C = 6′-0	400	10½	5	7	#7	18′-9	7	#7	45′-6
	500	11½	5½	8	#7	18′-9	8	#7	45′-9
L = 28′-0	50	8½	4	5	#5	18′-6	6	#5	47′-0
	100	8½	4	7	#5	18′-6	8	#5	47′-0
	150	8½	4	6	#6	18′-9	7	#6	47′-0
D = 11′-3	200	8½	4	8	#6	18′-9	8	#6	47′-0
	250	9	4½	8	#6	18′-9	9	#6	47′-0
	300	9¾	4¾	7	#7	19′-3	7	#7	47′-3
C = 6′-6	400	10¾	5¼	7	#7	19′-3	8	#7	47′-3
	500	11¾	5¾	8	#7	19′-3	9	#7	47′-3
L = 29′-0	50	8¾	4¼	6	#5	19′-0	7	#5	48′-9
	100	8¾	4¼	8	#5	19′-0	8	#5	48′-9
	150	8¾	4¼	7	#6	19′-3	7	#6	48′-9
D = 11′-9	200	8¾	4¼	8	#6	19′-3	9	#6	48′-9
	250	9½	4½	7	#7	19′-9	7	#7	48′-9
	300	10¼	4¾	7	#7	19′-9	8	#7	48′-9
C = 6′-6	400	11½	5½	8	#7	19′-9	9	#7	49′-0
	500	12¼	6	9	#7	19′-9	9	#7	49′-0
L = 30′-0	50	9	4½	7	#5	19′-3	7	#5	50′-6
	100	9	4½	9	#5	19′-3	9	#5	50′-6
	150	9	4½	7	#6	19′-6	8	#6	50′-6
D = 12′-6	200	9	4½	9	#6	19′-6	9	#6	50′-6
	250	9¾	4½	7	#7	20′-0	8	#7	50′-6
	300	10½	5	8	#7	20′-0	8	#7	50′-6
C = 7′-0	400	11½	5¾	9	#7	20′-0	9	#7	50′-6
	500	12½	6¼	9	#7	20′-0	10	#7	50′-9

TWO-WAY FLAT SLAB FLOORS, SQUARE PANELS—INTERIOR PANELS

f_s = 24,000 psi
f_c = 1,688 psi
v_c = 122.5 psi

Each Column Strip			Each Middle Strip						Weight of Steel (psf)	Average Cubic Feet of Concrete Per Square Foot of Floor *
Top			Straight			Trussed				
Quant.	Bar No.	Length	Quant.	Bar No.	Length	Quant.	Bar No.	Length		
11	#4	18′-0	6	#4	19′-0	7	#4	41′-0	2.03	.740
9	#5	18′-0	5	#5	19′-0	6	#5	41′-0	2.72	.740
9	#6	18′-0	5	#6	19′-0	5	#6	41′-0	3.49	.740
9	#6	18′-0	6	#6	19′-0	6	#6	41′-0	4.18	.740
12	#6	18′-0	7	#6	19′-0	7	#6	41′-3	4.73	.785
8	#7	18′-0	5	#7	19′-0	6	#7	41′-3	5.15	.851
11	#7	18′-0	6	#7	19′-0	6	#7	41′-3	5.66	.941
11	#7	18′-0	6	#7	19′-0	7	#7	41′-3	6.26	1.031
8	#5	18′-6	7	#4	19′-9	7	#4	42′-6	2.14	.762
10	#5	18′-6	6	#5	19′-9	6	#5	42′-6	2.84	.762
9	#6	18′-6	5	#6	19′-9	6	#6	42′-6	3.69	.762
11	#6	18′-6	6	#6	19′-9	7	#6	42′-6	4.40	.762
12	#6	18′-6	7	#6	19′-9	7	#6	42′-9	4.73	.811
10	#7	18′-6	5	#7	19′-9	6	#7	42′-9	5.25	.876
11	#7	18′-6	6	#7	19′-9	7	#7	42′-9	5.92	.966
11	#7	18′-6	7	#7	19′-9	7	#7	42′-9	6.37	1.057
8	#5	19′-3	5	#5	20′-6	5	#5	44′-3	2.32	.787
12	#5	19′-3	6	#5	20′-6	7	#5	44′-3	3.00	.787
11	#6	19′-3	6	#6	20′-6	6	#6	44′-3	3.85	.787
12	#6	19′-3	7	#6	20′-6	7	#6	44′-3	4.57	.787
10	#7	19′-3	6	#7	20′-6	6	#7	44′-3	5.16	.853
10	#7	19′-3	6	#7	20′-6	6	#7	44′-3	5.40	.919
11	#7	19′-3	7	#7	20′-6	7	#7	44′-3	6.15	1.013
13	#7	19′-3	7	#7	20′-6	8	#7	44′-3	6.65	1.103
9	#5	20′-0	5	#5	21′-0	6	#5	45′-9	2.44	.815
12	#5	20′-0	7	#5	21′-0	7	#5	45′-9	3.10	.815
10	#6	20′-0	6	#6	21′-0	7	#6	45′-9	3.97	.815
13	#6	20′-0	7	#6	21′-0	8	#6	45′-9	4.69	.815
10	#7	20′-0	6	#7	21′-0	6	#7	45′-9	5.21	.878
11	#7	20′-0	6	#7	21′-0	7	#7	45′-9	5.60	.947
12	#7	20′-0	7	#7	21′-0	8	#7	45′-9	6.31	1.042
13	#7	20′-0	8	#7	21′-0	8	#7	46′-0	6.75	1.132

* These cubic foot quantities include drop panel but not column capital.

TWO-WAY FLAT SLAB FLOORS, SQUARE PANELS—INTERIOR PANELS

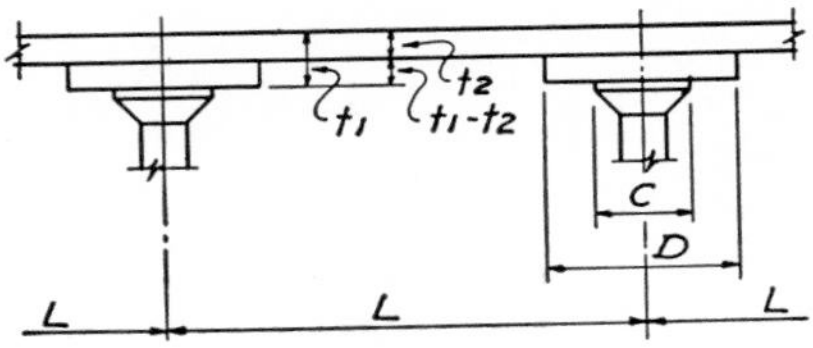

For general instructions and notes on the use of this table, see pages 8-3 to 8-7 incl.

Span / Drop / Cap	Safe Super-imposed Load (psf)	Slab Thickness t_2 (in.)	Drop Panel Thickness (t_1-t_2) (in.)	Each Column Strip: Straight Quant.	Straight Bar No.	Straight Length	Trussed Quant.	Trussed Bar No.	Trussed Length
L = 31′-0	50	9½	4½	7	#5	20′-0	8	#5	52′-3
	100	9½	4½	9	#5	20′-0	10	#5	52′-3
	150	9½	4½	8	#6	20′-3	9	#6	52′-3
D = 12′-9	200	9½	4½	7	#7	20′-9	8	#7	52′-3
	250	10¼	4¾	8	#7	20′-9	8	#7	52′-3
	300	10¾	5	8	#7	20′-9	9	#7	52′-3
C = 7′-0	400	12	5¾	9	#7	20′-9	10	#7	52′-3
	500	13¼	6¼	8	#8	21′-0	8	#8	52′-6
L = 32′-0	50	9¾	4¾	8	#5	20′-9	8	#5	53′-9
	100	9¾	4¾	7	#6	21′-0	8	#6	53′-9
	150	9¾	4¾	9	#6	21′-0	9	#6	53′-9
D = 13′-0	200	9¾	4¾	8	#7	21′-6	8	#7	53′-9
	250	10½	5	8	#7	21′-6	9	#7	53′-9
	300	11¼	5½	9	#7	21′-6	9	#7	54′-0
C = 7′-0	400	12½	6	10	#7	21′-6	10	#7	54′-0
	500	13¾	6½	8	#8	21′-9	9	#8	54′-0
L = 33′-0	50	10	4¾	8	#5	21′-3	9	#5	55′-6
	100	10	4¾	8	#6	21′-6	8	#6	55′-6
	150	10	4¾	9	#6	21′-6	10	#6	55′-6
D = 13′-6	200	10	4¾	8	#7	22′-0	9	#7	55′-6
	250	11	5¼	9	#7	22′-0	9	#7	55′-6
	300	11½	5¾	10	#7	22′-0	10	#7	55′-6
C = 7′-6	400	12¾	6¼	8	#8	22′-3	9	#8	55′-9
	500	14	6¾	9	#8	22′-3	9	#8	55′-9
L = 34′-0	50	10¼	5	9	#5	22′-0	10	#5	57′-3
	100	10¼	5	8	#6	22′-3	9	#6	57′-3
	150	10¼	5	10	#6	22′-3	11	#6	57′-3
D = 13′-9	200	10½	5	9	#7	22′-9	9	#7	57′-3
	250	11¼	5¼	9	#7	22′-9	10	#7	57′-3
	300	12	5¾	10	#7	22′-9	11	#7	57′-3
C = 7′-6	400	13¼	6½	9	#8	23′-0	9	#8	57′-6
	500	14½	7	9	#8	23′-0	10	#8	57′-6

TWO-WAY FLAT SLAB FLOORS, SQUARE PANELS—INTERIOR PANELS

On spans above 30 feet, deflection must be computed. Excessive deflections can be minimized with compressive reinforcement and by cambering the formwork.

f_s = 24,000 psi
f_c = 1,688 psi
v_c = 122.5 psi

Each Column Strip			Each Middle Strip						Weight of Steel (psf)	Average Cubic Feet of Concrete Per Square Foot of Floor *
Top			Straight			Trussed				
Quant.	Bar No.	Length	Quant.	Bar No.	Length	Quant.	Bar No.	Length		
9	#5	20′-6	6	#5	21′-9	6	#5	47′-3	2.52	.855
13	#5	20′-6	7	#5	21′-9	8	#5	47′-3	3.26	.855
11	#6	20′-6	7	#6	21′-9	7	#6	47′-3	4.20	.855
10	#7	20′-6	6	#7	21′-9	6	#7	47′-3	5.04	.855
12	#7	20′-6	6	#7	21′-9	7	#7	47′-3	5.50	.921
12	#7	20′-6	7	#7	21′-9	7	#7	47′-3	5.82	.966
13	#7	20′-6	8	#7	21′-9	8	#7	47′-3	6.51	1.081
12	#8	20′-6	6	#8	21′-9	7	#8	47′-6	7.21	1.192
12	#5	21′-3	6	#5	22′-6	7	#5	48′-9	2.71	.878
9	#6	21′-3	6	#6	22′-6	6	#6	48′-9	3.52	.878
13	#6	21′-3	7	#6	22′-6	8	#6	48′-9	4.40	.878
12	#7	21′-3	6	#7	22′-6	7	#7	48′-9	5.33	.878
12	#7	21′-3	7	#7	22′-6	7	#7	48′-9	5.63	.944
14	#7	21′-3	7	#7	22′-6	8	#7	48′-9	6.09	1.013
16	#7	21′-3	8	#7	22′-6	9	#7	49′-0	6.86	1.124
12	#8	21′-3	7	#8	22′-6	7	#8	49′-0	7.39	1.235
12	#5	22′-0	7	#5	23′-3	7	#5	50′-3	2.78	.900
11	#6	22′-0	6	#6	22′-3	7	#6	50′-3	3.73	.900
13	#6	22′-0	8	#6	23′-3	8	#6	50′-3	4.48	.900
12	#7	22′-0	7	#7	23′-3	7	#7	50′-3	5.47	.900
13	#7	22′-0	7	#7	23′-3	8	#7	50′-3	5.82	.990
13	#7	22′-0	8	#7	23′-3	8	#7	50′-3	6.20	1.039
11	#8	22′-0	7	#8	23′-3	7	#8	50′-6	7.06	1.150
14	#8	22′-0	7	#8	23′-3	8	#8	50′-6	7.74	1.261
12	#5	22′-6	7	#5	24′-0	8	#5	51′-9	2.93	.922
12	#6	22′-6	7	#6	24′-0	7	#6	51′-9	3.89	.922
14	#6	22′-6	8	#6	24′-0	9	#6	51′-9	4.75	.922
13	#7	22′-6	7	#7	24′-0	8	#7	51′-9	5.65	.943
14	#7	22′-6	8	#7	24′-0	8	#7	51′-9	6.01	1.009
14	#7	22′-6	8	#7	24′-0	9	#7	51′-9	6.48	1.078
13	#8	22′-6	7	#8	24′-0	8	#8	52′-0	7.40	1.193
14	#8	22′-6	8	#8	24′-0	8	#8	52′-0	7.88	1.304

* These cubic foot quantities include drop panel but not column capital.

TWO-WAY FLAT SLAB FLOORS, SQUARE PANELS—INTERIOR PANELS

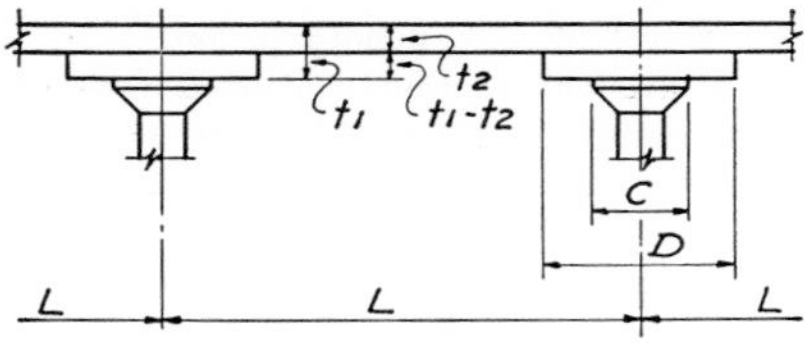

For general instructions and notes on the use of this table, see pages 8-3 to 8-7 incl.

Span / Drop / Cap	Safe Super-imposed Load (psf)	Slab Thickness t_2 (in.)	Drop Panel Thickness $(t_1 - t_2)$ (in.)	Each Column Strip — Straight: Quant.	Straight: Bar No.	Straight: Length	Trussed: Quant.	Trussed: Bar No.	Trussed: Length*
L = 35′-0	50	10½	5¼	10	#5	22′-9	10	#5	58′-9
	100	10½	5¼	9	#6	23′-0	9	#6	58′-9
	150	10½	5¼	11	#6	23′-0	11	#6	58′-9
D = 14′-0	200	10¾	5¼	9	#7	23′-6	10	#7	58′-9
	250	11½	5½	10	#7	23′-6	11	#7	59′-0
	300	12¼	6	11	#7	23′-6	11	#7	59′-0
C = 8′-0	400	13¾	6½	9	#8	23′-9	10	#8	59′-0
	500	14¾	7¼	10	#8	23′-9	11	#8	59′-3
L = 36′-0	50	11	5¼	11	#5	23′-6	11	#5	60′-6
	100	11	5¼	10	#6	23′-9	10	#6	60′-6
	150	11	5¼	8	#7	24′-3	9	#7	60′-6
D = 14′-3	200	11¼	5¼	10	#7	24′-3	10	#7	60′-6
	250	12	5¾	11	#7	24′-3	11	#7	60′-6
	300	12¾	6¼	9	#8	24′-6	9	#8	60′-9
C = 8′-0	400	14¼	6¾	10	#8	24′-6	10	#8	60′-9
	500	15½	7½	11	#8	24′-6	11	#8	60′-9
L = 37′-0	50	11¼	5½	8	#6	24′-3	9	#6	62′-3
	100	11¼	5½	10	#6	24′-3	11	#6	62′-3
	150	11¼	5½	9	#7	24′-9	10	#7	62′-3
D = 14′-9	200	11½	5½	10	#7	24′-9	11	#7	62′-3
	250	12¼	5¾	11	#7	24′-9	12	#7	62′-3
	300	13	6½	9	#8	25′-0	10	#8	62′-3
C = 8′-6	400	14½	7	10	#8	25′-0	11	#8	62′-6
	500	15¾	7½	11	#8	25′-0	12	#8	62′-6
L = 38′-0	50	11½	5½	9	#6	24′-9	9	#6	64′-0
	100	11½	5½	11	#6	24′-9	11	#6	64′-0
	150	11½	5½	10	#7	25′-3	10	#7	64′-0
D = 15′-3	200	11¾	5¾	11	#7	25′-3	12	#7	64′-0
	250	12¾	6¼	9	#8	25′-6	10	#8	64′-0
	300	13½	6½	10	#8	25′-6	10	#8	64′-0
C = 8′-6	400	15	7¼	11	#8	25′-6	11	#8	64′-3
	500	16¼	8	12	#8	25′-6	13	#8	64′-3

* Generally, bars in excess of 60 ft or so in length should be spliced for shipment.

TWO-WAY FLAT SLAB FLOORS, SQUARE PANELS—INTERIOR PANELS

On spans above 30 feet, deflection must be computed. Excessive deflections can be minimized with compressive reinforcement and by cambering the formwork.

$f_s = 24{,}000$ psi
$f_c = 1{,}688$ psi
$v_c = 122.5$ psi

Each Column Strip			Each Middle Strip						Weight of Steel (psf)	Average Cubic Feet of Concrete Per Square Foot of Floor *
Top			Straight			Trussed				
Quant.	Bar No.	Length	Quant.	Bar No.	Length	Quant.	Bar No.	Length		
14	#5	23′-3	8	#5	24′-6	8	#5	53′-3	3.01	.945
13	#6	23′-3	7	#6	24′-6	8	#6	53′-3	4.02	.945
16	#6	23′-3	9	#6	24′-6	9	#6	53′-3	4.84	.945
13	#7	23′-3	8	#7	24′-6	8	#7	53′-3	5.76	.966
14	#7	23′-3	8	#7	24′-6	9	#7	53′-3	6.30	1.032
16	#7	23′-3	9	#7	24′-6	9	#7	53′-3	6.62	1.101
13	#8	23′-3	7	#8	24′-6	8	#8	53′-6	7.44	1.233
14	#8	23′-3	8	#8	24′-6	9	#8	53′-6	8.26	1.326
15	#5	24′-0	8	#5	25′-3	9	#5	54′-9	3.19	.985
14	#6	24′-0	8	#6	25′-3	8	#6	54′-9	4.23	.985
13	#7	24′-0	7	#7	25′-3	7	#7	54′-9	5.09	.985
16	#7	24′-0	8	#7	25′-3	9	#7	54′-9	6.09	1.006
16	#7	24′-0	9	#7	25′-3	9	#7	54′-9	6.43	1.075
13	#8	24′-0	7	#8	25′-3	8	#8	55′-0	6.99	1.144
15	#8	24′-0	8	#8	25′-3	8	#8	55′-0	7.65	1.276
16	#8	24′-0	9	#8	25′-3	9	#8	55′-0	8.43	1.390
10	#6	24′-6	6	#6	26′-0	7	#6	56′-3	3.41	1.010
14	#6	24′-6	8	#6	26′-0	9	#6	56′-3	4.37	1.010
12	#7	24′-6	7	#7	26′-0	8	#7	56′-3	5.30	1.010
15	#7	24′-6	9	#7	26′-0	9	#7	56′-3	6.10	1.031
17	#7	24′-6	9	#7	26′-0	10	#7	56′-3	6.68	1.097
13	#8	24′-6	8	#8	26′-0	8	#8	56′-6	7.13	1.169
15	#8	24′-6	8	#8	26′-0	9	#8	56′-6	7.90	1.301
16	#8	24′-6	9	#8	26′-0	10	#8	56′-6	8.65	1.412
13	#6	25′-3	7	#6	26′-9	8	#6	57′-9	3.70	1.032
17	#6	25′-3	9	#6	26′-9	9	#6	57′-9	4.52	1.032
15	#7	25′-3	8	#7	26′-9	8	#7	57′-9	5.52	1.032
16	#7	25′-3	9	#7	26′-9	10	#7	57′-9	6.43	1.056
13	#8	25′-3	8	#8	26′-9	8	#8	58′-0	6.94	1.146
15	#8	25′-3	8	#8	26′-9	9	#8	58′-0	7.44	1.212
17	#8	25′-3	9	#8	26′-9	9	#8	58′-0	8.07	1.347
16	#8	25′-3	10	#8	26′-9	10	#8	58′-3	8.87	1.462

* These cubic foot quantities include drop panel but not column capital.

TWO-WAY FLAT SLAB FLOORS, SQUARE PANELS—INTERIOR PANELS

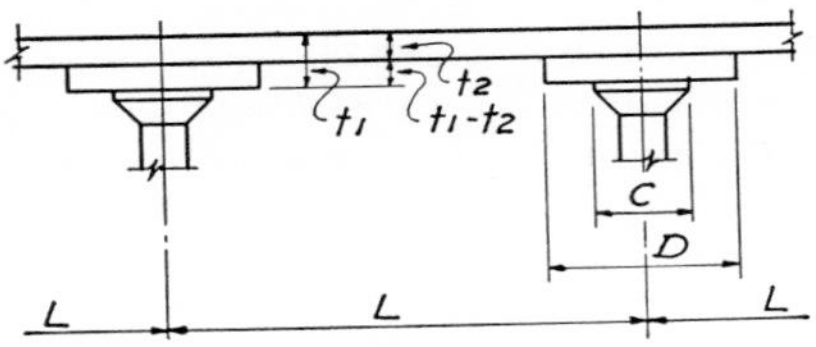

For general instructions and notes on the use of this table, see pages 8-3 to 8-7 incl.

Span / Drop / Cap	Safe Superimposed Load (psf)	Slab Thickness t_2 (in.)	Drop Panel Thickness (t_1-t_2) (in.)	Each Column Strip — Straight: Quant.	Straight: Bar No.	Straight: Length	Trussed: Quant.	Trussed: Bar No.	Trussed: Length*
L = 39′-0	50	11¾	5¾	9	#6	25′-3	10	#6	65′-6
	100	11¾	5¾	12	#6	25′-3	12	#6	65′-6
	150	11¾	5¾	10	#7	25′-9	11	#7	65′-6
D = 15′-9	200	12¼	5¾	12	#7	25′-9	12	#7	65′-6
	250	13	6¼	10	#8	26′-0	10	#8	65′-9
	300	13¾	6¾	10	#8	26′-0	11	#8	65′-9
C = 9′-0	400	15¼	7½	12	#8	26′-0	12	#8	65′-9
	500	16¾	8	10	#9	26′-6	10	#9	66′-0
L = 40′-0	50	12	6	10	#6	26′-0	11	#6	67′-3
	100	12	6	12	#6	26′-0	13	#6	67′-3
	150	12	6	11	#7	26′-6	12	#7	67′-3
D = 16′-0	200	12½	6	13	#7	26′-6	13	#7	67′-3
	250	13½	6½	10	#8	26′-9	11	#8	67′-3
	300	14¼	7	11	#8	26′-9	12	#8	67′-6
C = 9′-0	400	15¾	7¾	12	#8	26′-9	13	#8	67′-6
	500	17¼	8¼	11	#9	27′-3	11	#9	67′-6

* Generally, bars in excess of 60 ft or so in length should be spliced for shipment.

TWO-WAY FLAT SLAB FLOORS, SQUARE PANELS—INTERIOR PANELS

On spans above 30 feet, deflection must be computed. Excessive deflections can be minimized with compressive reinforcement and by cambering the formwork.

f_s = 24,000 psi
f_c = 1,688 psi
v_c = 122.5 psi

Each Column Strip			Each Middle Strip						Weight of Steel (psf)	Average Cubic Feet of Concrete Per Square Foot of Floor *
Top			Straight			Trussed				
Quant.	Bar No.	Length	Quant.	Bar No.	Length	Quant.	Bar No.	Length		
13	#6	25′-9	7	#6	27′-6	8	#6	59′-3	3.73	1.057
17	#6	25′-9	9	#6	27′-6	10	#6	59′-3	4.69	1.057
14	#7	25′-9	8	#7	27′-6	9	#7	59′-3	5.63	1.057
18	#7	25′-9	9	#7	27′-6	10	#7	59′-3	6.46	1.099
15	#8	25′-9	8	#8	27′-6	8	#8	59′-6	7.03	1.168
15	#8	25′-9	8	#8	27′-6	9	#8	59′-6	7.47	1.238
17	#8	25′-9	9	#8	27′-6	10	#8	59′-6	8.37	1.373
16	#9	25′-9	8	#9	27′-6	9	#9	59′-9	9.37	1.505
13	#6	26′-6	8	#6	28′-0	9	#6	60′-9	3.98	1.080
17	#6	26′-6	10	#6	28′-0	11	#6	60′-9	4.86	1.080
15	#7	26′-6	9	#7	28′-0	10	#7	60′-9	6.03	1.080
19	#7	26′-6	10	#7	28′-0	11	#7	61′-0	6.84	1.122
15	#8	26′-6	8	#8	28′-0	9	#8	61′-0	7.28	1.212
15	#8	26′-6	9	#8	28′-0	9	#8	61′-0	7.70	1.281
17	#8	26′-6	10	#8	28′-0	10	#8	61′-0	8.49	1.416
16	#9	26′-6	9	#9	28′-0	9	#9	61′-3	9.65	1.548

* These cubic foot quantities include drop panel but not column capital.

TWO-WAY FLAT SLAB FLOORS, SQUARE PANELS—BANDS PERPENDICULAR TO AN EXTERIOR WALL

For Bands Parallel to Walls or Not in End Spans, Use "Two-Way Flat Slab Floors, Square Panels—Interior Panels," Pages 8-8 to 8-21 incl.

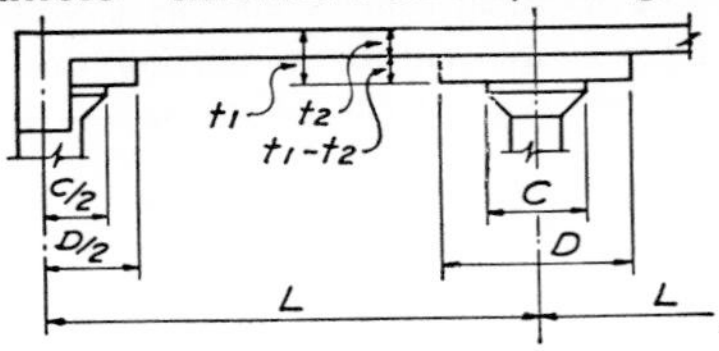

For general instructions and notes on the use of this table, see pages 8-3 to 8-7 incl.

Span / Drop / Cap	Safe Superimposed Load (psf)	Slab Thickness t_2 (in.)	Drop Panel Thickness (t_1-t_2) (in.)	Each Column Strip: Straight			Trussed			Top at Ext. Col.		
				Quant.	Bar No.	Length	Quant.	Bar No.	Length	Quant.	Bar No.	Length
L = 15′-0	50	4½	2¼	6	#3	10′-9	4	#3	21′-9	7	#3	6′-6
	100	4½	2¼	6	#3	10′-9	6	#3	21′-9	8	#3	6′-6
	150	4½	2¼	8	#3	10′-9	8	#3	21′-9	11	#3	6′-6
D = 6′-0	200	4¾	2¼	9	#3	10′-9	10	#3	21′-9	13	#3	6′-6
	250	5	2¼	6	#4	10′-9	6	#4	21′-9	9	#4	6′-6
	300	5½	2½	6	#4	10′-9	7	#4	21′-9	9	#4	6′-6
C = 3′-6	400	6	2¾	5	#5	10′-9	5	#5	22′-0	7	#5	6′-6
	500	6½	3	5	#5	10′-9	6	#5	22′-0	8	#5	6′-6
L = 16′-0	50	5	2¼	5	#3	11′-6	5	#3	23′-3	8	#3	7′-0
	100	5	2¼	7	#3	11′-6	7	#3	23′-3	10	#3	7′-0
	150	5	2¼	9	#3	11′-6	9	#3	23′-3	12	#3	7′-0
D = 6′-0	200	5	2¼	6	#4	11′-6	7	#4	23′-3	9	#4	7′-0
	250	5½	2½	6	#4	11′-6	7	#4	23′-3	9	#4	7′-0
	300	5¾	2¾	7	#4	11′-6	8	#4	23′-3	10	#4	7′-0
C = 3′-6	400	6½	3	5	#5	11′-6	6	#5	23′-3	8	#5	7′-0
	500	7	3¼	6	#5	11′-6	6	#5	23′-3	9	#5	7′-0
L = 17′-0	50	5¼	2½	5	#3	12′-3	6	#3	24′-6	9	#3	7′-3
	100	5¼	2½	7	#3	12′-3	8	#3	24′-6	10	#3	7′-3
	150	5¼	2½	10	#3	12′-3	10	#3	24′-6	13	#3	7′-3
D = 6′-6	200	5¼	2½	7	#4	12′-3	7	#4	24′-6	10	#4	7′-3
	250	5¾	2½	7	#4	12′-3	8	#4	24′-6	11	#4	7′-3
	300	6	2¾	5	#5	12′-3	6	#5	24′-6	8	#5	7′-3
C = 4′-0	400	6¾	3	6	#5	12′-3	6	#5	24′-6	9	#5	7′-3
	500	7¼	3½	5	#6	12′-6	5	#6	24′-9	7	#6	7′-3
L = 18′-0	50	5½	2½	6	#3	12′-3	7	#3	25′-9	9	#3	7′-6
	100	5½	2½	9	#3	12′-3	9	#3	25′-9	12	#3	7′-6
	150	5½	2½	6	#4	12′-3	7	#4	25′-9	9	#4	7′-6
D = 7′-6	200	5½	2½	8	#4	12′-3	8	#4	25′-9	11	#4	7′-6
	250	6	2¾	6	#5	12′-3	6	#5	26′-0	8	#5	7′-6
	300	6½	3	6	#5	12′-3	6	#5	26′-0	9	#5	7′-6
C = 4′-0	400	7	3¼	5	#6	12′-6	5	#6	26′-0	7	#6	7′-6
	500	7¾	3¾	5	#6	12′-6	6	#6	26′-0	8	#6	7′-6

TWO-WAY FLAT SLAB FLOORS, SQUARE PANELS— BANDS PERPENDICULAR TO AN EXTERIOR WALL

f_s = 24,000 psi
f_c = 1,688 psi
v_c = 122.5 psi

Each Column Strip			Each Middle Strip									Weight of Steel (psf)	Average Cubic Feet of Concrete Per Square Foot of Floor *
Top at Int. Col.			Top at Ext. Col.			Straight			Trussed				
Quant.	Bar No.	Length	Quant.	Bar No.	Length	Quant.	Bar No.	Length	Quant.	Bar No.	Length		
5	#3	10′-0	6	#3	5′-3	6	#3	12′-9	4	#3	20′-6	1.32	.405
8	#3	10′-0	6	#3	5′-3	6	#3	12′-9	6	#3	20′-6	1.57	.405
10	#3	10′-0	8	#3	5′-3	7	#3	12′-9	8	#3	20′-6	2.00	.405
11	#3	10′-0	9	#3	5′-3	8	#3	12′-9	9	#3	20′-6	2.34	.426
9	#4	10′-0	6	#4	5′-3	6	#4	12′-9	6	#4	20′-6	2.81	.447
8	#4	10′-0	6	#4	5′-3	6	#4	12′-9	6	#4	20′-9	2.86	.492
7	#5	10′-0	7	#4	5′-3	7	#4	12′-9	7	#4	20′-9	3.40	.537
6	#5	10′-0	5	#5	5′-3	5	#5	12′-9	5	#5	20′-9	3.80	.582
6	#3	10′-9	5	#3	5′-6	5	#3	13′-9	5	#3	21′-9	1.30	.445
9	#3	10′-9	7	#3	5′-6	6	#3	13′-9	7	#3	21′-9	1.65	.445
12	#3	10′-9	9	#3	5′-6	8	#3	13′-9	9	#3	21′-9	2.12	.445
8	#4	10′-9	10	#3	5′-6	10	#3	13′-9	10	#3	21′-9	2.61	.445
9	#4	10′-9	7	#4	5′-6	6	#4	13′-9	7	#4	22′-0	2.87	.490
10	#4	10′-9	7	#4	5′-6	7	#4	13′-9	7	#4	22′-0	3.11	.514
7	#5	10′-9	5	#5	5′-6	5	#5	13′-9	5	#5	22′-0	3.63	.580
9	#5	10′-9	6	#5	5′-6	5	#5	13′-9	6	#5	22′-0	4.09	.625
6	#3	11′-3	5	#3	5′-9	5	#3	14′-6	5	#3	23′-3	1.27	.468
9	#3	11′-3	7	#3	5′-9	7	#3	14′-6	7	#3	23′-3	1.68	.468
13	#3	11′-3	9	#3	5′-9	9	#3	14′-6	9	#3	23′-3	2.16	.468
9	#4	11′-3	7	#4	5′-9	6	#4	14′-6	7	#4	23′-3	2.77	.468
11	#4	11′-3	7	#4	5′-9	7	#4	14′-6	7	#4	23′-3	3.02	.510
8	#5	11′-3	8	#4	5′-9	7	#4	14′-6	8	#4	23′-3	3.40	.534
10	#5	11′-3	6	#5	5′-9	6	#5	14′-6	6	#5	23′-3	3.92	.599
7	#6	11′-3	7	#5	5′-9	6	#5	14′-6	7	#5	23′-3	4.40	.647
7	#3	12′-0	6	#3	6′-0	6	#3	15′-6	6	#3	24′-6	1.35	.495
12	#3	12′-0	8	#3	6′-0	8	#3	15′-6	8	#3	24′-6	1.82	.495
8	#4	12′-0	11	#3	6′-0	10	#3	15′-6	11	#3	24′-6	2.39	.495
11	#4	12′-0	8	#4	6′-0	7	#4	15′-6	8	#4	24′-6	2.97	.495
8	#5	12′-0	8	#4	6′-0	8	#4	15′-6	8	#4	24′-6	3.32	.540
9	#5	12′-0	6	#5	6′-0	6	#5	15′-6	6	#5	24′-6	3.64	.585
7	#6	12′-0	7	#5	6′-0	6	#5	15′-6	7	#5	24′-6	4.24	.630
7	#6	12′-0	6	#6	6′-0	5	#6	15′-6	6	#6	24′-6	4.74	.700

* These cubic foot quantities include drop panel but not column capital.

TWO-WAY FLAT SLAB FLOORS, SQUARE PANELS— BANDS PERPENDICULAR TO AN EXTERIOR WALL

For Bands Parallel to Walls or Not in End Spans, Use "Two-Way Flat Slab Floors, Square Panels—Interior Panels," Pages 8-8 to 8-21 incl.

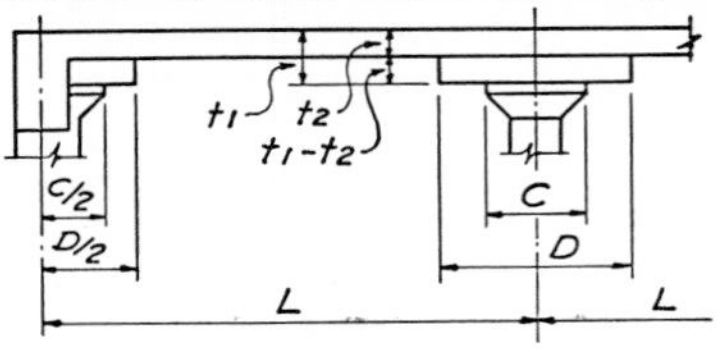

For general instructions and notes on the use of this table, see pages 8-3 to 8-7 incl.

Span / Drop / Cap	Safe Superimposed Load (psf)	Slab Thickness t_2 (in.)	Drop Panel Thickness (t_1-t_2) (in.)	Each Column Strip: Straight			Trussed			Top at Ext. Col.		
				Quant.	Bar No.	Length	Quant.	Bar No.	Length	Quant.	Bar No.	Length
L = 19′-0	50	5¾	2¾	7	#3	13′-3	7	#3	27′-3	10	#3	8′-0
	100	5¾	2¾	10	#3	13′-3	10	#3	27′-3	13	#3	8′-0
	150	5¾	2¾	7	#4	13′-3	7	#4	27′-3	10	#4	8′-0
D = 7′-6	200	5¾	2¾	6	#5	13′-3	6	#5	27′-3	8	#5	8′-0
	250	6¼	2¾	6	#5	13′-3	7	#5	27′-3	9	#5	8′-0
	300	6¾	3	6	#5	13′-3	7	#5	27′-3	10	#5	8′-0
C = 4′-6	400	7½	3½	5	#6	13′-6	6	#6	27′-3	8	#6	8′-0
	500	8	3¾	6	#6	13′-6	6	#6	27′-3	9	#6	8′-0
L = 20′-0	50	6	3	8	#3	13′-6	8	#3	28′-6	12	#3	8′-3
	100	6	3	6	#4	13′-6	7	#4	28′-6	9	#4	8′-3
	150	6	3	8	#4	13′-6	9	#4	28′-6	11	#4	8′-3
D = 8′-3	200	6	3	6	#5	13′-6	7	#5	28′-6	9	#5	8′-3
	250	6½	3¼	7	#5	13′-6	8	#5	28′-6	10	#5	8′-3
	300	7	3¼	5	#6	13′-9	6	#6	28′-6	8	#6	8′-3
C = 4′-6	400	7¾	3½	6	#6	13′-9	7	#6	28′-9	9	#6	8′-3
	500	8½	4	7	#6	13′-9	7	#6	28′-9	10	#6	8′-3
L = 21′-0	50	6½	3	9	#3	14′-6	9	#3	30′-0	13	#3	8′-6
	100	6½	3	7	#4	14′-6	7	#4	30′-0	10	#4	8′-6
	150	6½	3	6	#5	14′-6	6	#5	30′-0	9	#5	8′-6
D = 8′-3	200	6½	3	7	#5	14′-6	7	#5	30′-0	10	#5	8′-6
	250	7	3¼	5	#6	14′-9	6	#6	30′-0	8	#6	8′-6
	300	7½	3½	6	#6	14′-9	6	#6	30′-0	9	#6	8′-6
C = 4′-6	400	8¼	4	7	#6	14′-9	7	#6	30′-0	10	#6	8′-6
	500	9	4¼	7	#6	14′-9	8	#6	30′-0	11	#6	8′-6
L = 22′-0	50	6¾	3¼	5	#4	14′-9	6	#4	31′-3	8	#4	9′-0
	100	6¾	3¼	8	#4	14′-9	8	#4	31′-3	11	#4	9′-0
	150	6¾	3¼	6	#5	14′-9	7	#5	31′-3	9	#5	9′-0
D = 9′-0	200	6¾	3¼	8	#5	14′-9	8	#5	31′-3	11	#5	9′-0
	250	7¼	3¼	6	#6	15′-0	6	#6	31′-3	9	#6	9′-0
	300	7¾	3½	6	#6	15′-0	7	#6	31′-3	10	#6	9′-0
C = 5′-0	400	8½	4	7	#6	15′-0	8	#6	31′-3	11	#6	9′-0
	500	9¼	4½	8	#6	15′-0	9	#6	31′-6	12	#6	9′-0

TWO-WAY FLAT SLAB FLOORS, SQUARE PANELS—BANDS PERPENDICULAR TO AN EXTERIOR WALL

f_s = 24,000 psi
f_c = 1,688 psi
v_c = 122.5 psi

Each Column Strip			Each Middle Strip									Weight of Steel (psf)	Average Cubic Feet of Concrete Per Square Foot of Floor *
Top at Int. Col.			Top at Ext. Col.			Straight			Trussed				
Quant.	Bar No.	Length	Quant.	Bar No.	Length	Quant.	Bar No.	Length	Quant.	Bar No.	Length		
9	#3	12′-9	7	#3	6′-3	6	#3	16′-3	7	#3	25′-9	1.42	.515
13	#3	12′-9	9	#3	6′-3	9	#3	16′-3	9	#3	25′-9	1.91	.515
10	#4	12′-9	7	#4	6′-3	7	#4	16′-3	7	#4	25′-9	2.52	.515
8	#5	12′-9	9	#4	6′-3	8	#4	16′-3	9	#4	25′-9	3.21	.515
9	#5	12′-9	9	#4	6′-3	9	#4	16′-3	9	#4	25′-9	3.52	.557
9	#5	12′-9	7	#5	6′-3	6	#5	16′-3	7	#5	25′-9	3.78	.601
7	#6	12′-9	5	#6	6′-3	5	#6	16′-3	5	#6	25′-9	4.36	.670
9	#6	12′-9	6	#6	6′-3	6	#6	16′-3	6	#6	25′-9	4.98	.715
10	#3	13′-3	8	#3	6′-6	7	#3	17′-0	8	#3	27′-0	1.52	.543
7	#4	13′-3	11	#3	6′-6	10	#3	17′-0	11	#3	27′-0	2.09	.543
10	#4	13′-3	8	#4	6′-6	7	#4	17′-0	8	#4	27′-0	2.73	.543
8	#5	13′-3	7	#5	6′-6	6	#5	17′-0	7	#5	27′-0	3.49	.543
9	#5	13′-3	7	#5	6′-6	7	#5	17′-0	7	#5	27′-0	3.75	.588
7	#6	13′-3	8	#5	6′-6	7	#5	17′-0	8	#5	27′-0	4.16	.629
9	#6	13′-3	6	#6	6′-6	6	#6	17′-0	6	#6	27′-0	4.83	.695
9	#6	13′-3	7	#6	6′-6	6	#6	17′-0	7	#6	27′-0	5.19	.765
12	#3	14′-0	8	#3	6′-9	8	#3	18′-0	8	#3	28′-3	1.61	.580
10	#4	14′-0	7	#4	6′-9	6	#4	18′-0	7	#4	28′-3	2.24	.580
8	#5	14′-0	9	#4	6′-9	8	#4	18′-0	9	#4	28′-3	2.90	.580
11	#5	14′-0	7	#5	6′-9	7	#5	18′-0	7	#5	28′-3	3.59	.580
8	#6	14′-0	8	#5	6′-9	7	#5	18′-0	8	#5	28′-3	4.08	.625
9	#6	14′-0	6	#6	6′-9	6	#6	18′-0	6	#6	28′-3	4.48	.670
9	#6	14′-0	7	#6	6′-9	6	#6	18′-0	7	#6	28′-3	5.00	.739
10	#6	14′-0	7	#6	6′-9	7	#6	18′-0	7	#6	28′-6	5.48	.805
7	#4	14′-9	9	#3	7′-0	9	#3	18′-9	9	#3	29′-6	1.70	.608
10	#4	14′-9	7	#4	7′-0	7	#4	18′-9	7	#4	29′-6	2.33	.608
8	#5	14′-9	9	#4	7′-0	9	#4	18′-9	9	#4	29′-6	3.00	.608
10	#5	14′-9	8	#5	7′-0	7	#5	18′-9	8	#5	29′-6	3.73	.608
10	#6	14′-9	8	#5	7′-0	8	#5	18′-9	8	#5	29′-6	4.15	.649
9	#6	14′-9	7	#6	7′-0	6	#6	18′-9	7	#6	29′-6	4.61	.695
10	#6	14′-9	7	#6	7′-0	7	#6	18′-9	7	#6	29′-6	5.21	.764
11	#6	14′-9	8	#6	7′-0	7	#6	18′-9	8	#6	29′-9	5.69	.834

* These cubic foot quantities include drop panel but not column capital.

TWO-WAY FLAT SLAB FLOORS, SQUARE PANELS— BANDS PERPENDICULAR TO AN EXTERIOR WALL

For Bands Parallel to Walls or Not in End Spans, Use "Two-Way Flat Slab Floors, Square Panels—Interior Panels," Pages 8-8 to 8-21 incl.

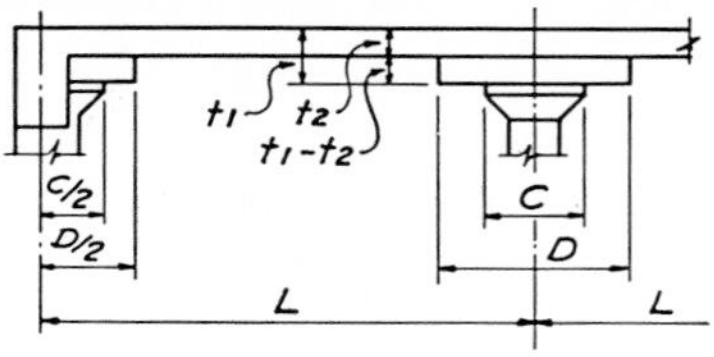

For general instructions and notes on the use of this table, see pages 8-3 to 8-7 incl.

Span / Drop / Cap	Safe Superimposed Load (psf)	Slab Thickness t_2 (in.)	Drop Panel Thickness (t_1-t_2) (in.)	Each Column Strip								
				Straight			Trussed			Top at Ext. Col.		
				Quant.	Bar No.	Length	Quant.	Bar No.	Length	Quant.	Bar No.	Length
L = 23′-0	50	7	3¼	6	#4	15′-6	7	#4	32′-6	9	#4	9′-3
	100	7	3¼	6	#5	15′-6	6	#5	32′-6	8	#5	9′-3
	150	7	3¼	7	#5	15′-6	8	#5	32′-6	10	#5	9′-3
D = 9′-3	200	7	3¼	6	#6	15′-9	7	#6	32′-6	9	#6	9′-3
	250	7½	3½	7	#6	15′-9	7	#6	32′-9	10	#6	9′-3
	300	8	3¾	7	#6	15′-9	8	#6	32′-9	11	#6	9′-3
C = 5′-0	400	9	4¼	8	#6	15′-9	9	#6	32′-9	12	#6	9′-3
	500	9¾	4¾	7	#7	16′-3	7	#7	32′-9	10	#7	9′-3
L = 24′-0	50	7¼	3½	7	#4	16′-6	7	#4	34′-0	10	#4	9′-6
	100	7¼	3½	6	#5	16′-6	7	#5	34′-0	9	#5	9′-6
	150	7¼	3½	8	#5	16′-6	8	#5	34′-0	11	#5	9′-6
D = 9′-3	200	7¼	3½	7	#6	16′-9	7	#6	34′-0	10	#6	9′-6
	250	7¾	3¾	7	#6	16′-9	8	#6	34′-0	11	#6	9′-6
	300	8¼	4	8	#6	16′-9	8	#6	34′-0	11	#6	9′-6
C = 5′-6	400	9¼	4½	9	#6	16′-9	9	#6	34′-0	13	#6	9′-6
	500	10	5	7	#7	17′-3	8	#7	34′-3	10	#7	9′-6
L = 25′-0	50	7½	3¾	8	#4	16′-9	8	#4	35′-3	11	#4	9′-9
	100	7½	3¾	7	#5	16′-9	7	#5	35′-3	10	#5	9′-9
	150	7½	3¾	9	#5	16′-9	9	#5	35′-3	12	#5	9′-9
D = 10′-0	200	7½	3¾	7	#6	17′-0	8	#6	35′-3	11	#6	9′-9
	250	8¼	3¾	8	#6	17′-0	8	#6	35′-3	12	#6	9′-9
	300	8¾	4¼	9	#6	17′-0	9	#6	35′-6	12	#6	9′-9
C = 5′-6	400	9¾	4¾	7	#7	17′-6	8	#7	35′-6	10	#7	9′-9
	500	10½	5¼	8	#7	17′-6	8	#7	35′-6	11	#7	9′-9
L = 26′-0	50	8	3¾	8	#4	17′-3	9	#4	36′-9	12	#4	10′-3
	100	8	3¾	7	#5	17′-3	8	#5	36′-9	10	#5	10′-3
	150	8	3¾	9	#5	17′-3	10	#5	36′-9	13	#5	10′-3
D = 10′-6	200	8	3¾	8	#6	17′-6	8	#6	36′-9	11	#6	10′-3
	250	8½	4	9	#6	17′-6	9	#6	36′-9	12	#6	10′-3
	300	9	4¼	9	#6	17′-6	10	#6	36′-9	13	#6	10′-3
C = 6′-0	400	10	4¾	8	#7	18′-0	8	#7	36′-9	11	#7	10′-3
	500	11	5¼	8	#7	18′-0	9	#7	36′-9	12	#7	10′-3

TWO-WAY FLAT SLAB FLOORS, SQUARE PANELS— BANDS PERPENDICULAR TO AN EXTERIOR WALL

f_s = 24,000 psi
f_c = 1,688 psi
v_c = 122.5 psi

Each Column Strip			Each Middle Strip									Weight of Steel (psf)	Average Cubic Feet of Concrete Per Square Foot of Floor *
Top at Int. Col.			Top at Ext. Col.			Straight			Trussed				
Quant.	Bar No.	Length	Quant.	Bar No.	Length	Quant.	Bar No.	Length	Quant.	Bar No.	Length		
8	#4	15′-3	11	#3	7′-3	10	#3	19′-9	11	#3	30′-9	1.85	.627
8	#5	15′-3	8	#4	7′-3	8	#4	19′-9	8	#4	30′-9	2.57	.627
10	#5	15′-3	7	#5	7′-3	7	#5	19′-9	7	#5	30′-9	3.29	.627
8	#6	15′-3	9	#5	7′-3	8	#5	19′-9	9	#5	30′-9	4.13	.627
10	#6	15′-3	7	#6	7′-3	6	#6	19′-9	7	#6	30′-9	4.58	.672
11	#6	15′-3	7	#6	7′-3	7	#6	19′-9	7	#6	30′-9	4.94	.717
11	#6	15′-3	8	#6	7′-3	7	#6	19′-9	8	#6	31′-0	5.43	.807
9	#7	15′-3	7	#7	7′-3	6	#7	19′-9	7	#7	31′-0	6.15	.877
9	#4	16′-0	7	#4	7′-6	6	#4	20′-6	7	#4	32′-0	1.93	.647
8	#5	16′-0	9	#4	7′-6	8	#4	20′-6	9	#4	32′-0	2.64	.647
10	#5	16′-0	8	#5	7′-6	7	#5	20′-6	8	#5	32′-0	3.41	.647
10	#6	16′-0	7	#6	7′-6	6	#6	20′-6	7	#6	32′-0	4.35	.647
10	#6	16′-0	7	#6	7′-6	7	#6	20′-6	7	#6	32′-0	4.76	.692
12	#6	16′-0	8	#6	7′-6	7	#6	20′-6	8	#6	32′-0	5.01	.737
12	#6	16′-0	9	#6	7′-6	8	#6	20′-6	9	#6	32′-3	5.57	.827
10	#7	16′-0	7	#7	7′-6	7	#7	20′-6	7	#7	32′-3	6.24	.895
10	#4	16′-6	8	#4	7′-9	7	#4	21′-3	8	#4	33′-3	2.08	.675
9	#5	16′-6	7	#5	7′-9	6	#5	21′-3	7	#5	33′-3	2.87	.675
11	#5	16′-6	8	#5	7′-9	8	#5	21′-3	8	#5	33′-3	3.55	.675
9	#6	16′-6	8	#6	7′-9	7	#6	21′-3	8	#6	33′-3	4.59	.675
12	#6	16′-6	8	#6	7′-9	7	#6	21′-3	8	#6	33′-3	4.86	.738
11	#6	16′-6	8	#6	7′-9	8	#6	21′-3	8	#6	33′-6	5.14	.786
10	#7	16′-6	7	#7	7′-9	7	#7	21′-3	7	#7	33′-6	5.95	.876
11	#7	16′-6	8	#7	7′-9	7	#7	21′-3	8	#7	33′-6	6.54	.945
11	#4	17′-3	8	#4	8′-0	7	#4	22′-3	8	#4	34′-6	2.11	.718
10	#5	17′-3	7	#5	8′-0	7	#5	22′-3	7	#5	34′-6	2.90	.718
12	#5	17′-3	9	#5	8′-0	8	#5	22′-3	9	#5	34′-6	3.67	.718
11	#6	17′-3	8	#6	8′-0	7	#6	22′-3	8	#6	34′-6	4.56	.718
12	#6	17′-3	8	#6	8′-0	8	#6	22′-3	8	#6	34′-6	4.98	.763
13	#6	17′-3	9	#6	8′-0	9	#6	22′-3	9	#6	34′-9	5.44	.808
11	#7	17′-3	8	#7	8′-0	7	#7	22′-3	8	#7	34′-9	6.23	.898
12	#7	17′-3	8	#7	8′-0	8	#7	22′-3	8	#7	34′-9	6.66	.988

* These cubic foot quantities include drop panel but not column capital.

TWO-WAY FLAT SLAB FLOORS, SQUARE PANELS— BANDS PERPENDICULAR TO AN EXTERIOR WALL

For Bands Parallel to Walls or Not in End Spans, Use "Two-Way Flat Slab Floors, Square Panels—Interior Panels," Pages 8-8 to 8-21 incl.

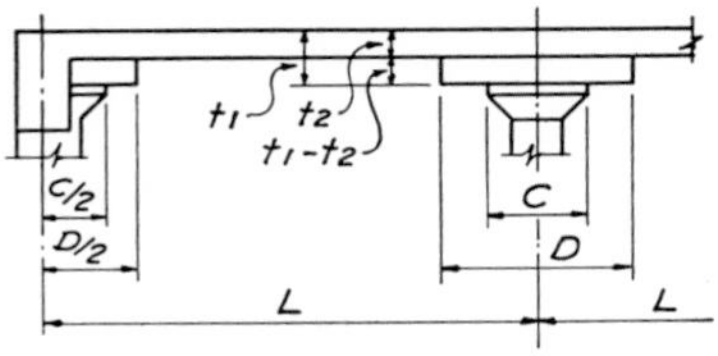

For general instructions and notes on the use of this table, see pages 8-3 to 8-7 incl.

Span / Drop / Cap	Safe Superimposed Load (psf)	Slab Thickness t_2 (in.)	Drop Panel Thickness (t_1-t_2) (in.)	Each Column Strip								
				Straight			Trussed			Top at Ext. Col.		
				Quant.	Bar No.	Length	Quant.	Bar No.	Length	Quant.	Bar No.	Length
L = 27′-0	50	8¼	4	9	#4	18′-0	10	#4	38′-0	13	#4	10′-6
	100	8¼	4	8	#5	18′-0	9	#5	38′-0	11	#5	10′-6
	150	8¼	4	7	#6	18′-3	8	#6	38′-0	10	#6	10′-6
	200	8¼	4	9	#6	18′-3	9	#6	38′-0	12	#6	10′-6
D = 10′-9	250	8¾	4¼	9	#6	18′-3	10	#6	38′-0	14	#6	10′-6
	300	9½	4½	7	#7	18′-9	8	#7	38′-0	11	#7	10′-6
C = 6′-0	400	10½	5	8	#7	18′-9	9	#7	38′-3	12	#7	10′-6
	500	11½	5½	9	#7	18′-9	10	#7	38′-3	13	#7	10′-6
L = 28′-0	50	8½	4	7	#5	18′-6	7	#5	39′-3	10	#5	10′-9
	100	8½	4	9	#5	18′-6	9	#5	39′-3	12	#5	10′-9
	150	8½	4	8	#6	18′-9	8	#6	39′-3	11	#6	10′-9
D = 11′-3	200	8½	4	9	#6	18′-9	10	#6	39′-3	13	#6	10′-9
	250	9	4½	10	#6	18′-9	11	#6	39′-6	14	#6	10′-9
	300	9¾	4¾	8	#7	19′-3	8	#7	39′-6	11	#7	10′-9
C = 6′-6	400	10¾	5¼	9	#7	19′-3	10	#7	39′-6	13	#7	10′-9
	500	11¾	5¾	10	#7	19′-3	10	#7	39′-6	14	#7	10′-9
L = 29′-0	50	8¾	4¼	7	#5	19′-0	8	#5	40′-9	10	#5	11′-3
	100	8¾	4¼	10	#5	19′-0	10	#5	40′-9	14	#5	11′-3
	150	8¾	4¼	8	#6	19′-3	9	#6	40′-9	12	#6	11′-3
D = 11′-9	200	8¾	4¼	10	#6	19′-3	11	#6	40′-9	14	#6	11′-3
	250	9½	4½	8	#7	19′-9	9	#7	40′-9	12	#7	11′-3
	300	10¼	4¾	9	#7	19′-9	9	#7	40′-9	13	#7	11′-3
C = 6′-6	400	11¼	5½	10	#7	19′-9	10	#7	40′-9	14	#7	11′-3
	500	12¼	6	11	#7	19′-9	11	#7	41′-0	15	#7	11′-3
L = 30′-0	50	9	4½	8	#5	19′-3	8	#5	42′-0	11	#5	11′-6
	100	9	4½	10	#5	19′-3	11	#5	42′-0	14	#5	11′-6
	150	9	4½	9	#6	19′-6	10	#6	42′-0	13	#6	11′-6
D = 12′-6	200	9	4½	11	#6	19′-6	11	#6	42′-0	15	#6	11′-6
	250	9¾	4½	9	#7	20′-0	9	#7	42′-0	13	#7	11′-6
	300	10½	5	9	#7	20′-0	10	#7	42′-3	13	#7	11′-6
C = 7′-0	400	11½	5¾	10	#7	20′-0	11	#7	42′-3	15	#7	11′-6
	500	12½	6¼	11	#7	20′-0	12	#7	42′-3	16	#7	11′-6

TWO-WAY FLAT SLAB FLOORS, SQUARE PANELS— BANDS PERPENDICULAR TO AN EXTERIOR WALL

f_s = 24,000 psi
f_c = 1,688 psi
v_c = 122.5 psi

Each Column Strip			Each Middle Strip									Weight of Steel (psf)	Average Cubic Feet of Concrete Per Square Foot of Floor *
Top at Int. Col.			Top at Ext. Col.			Straight			Trussed				
Quant.	Bar No.	Length	Quant.	Bar No.	Length	Quant.	Bar No.	Length	Quant.	Bar No.	Length		
12	#4	18′-0	9	#4	8′-3	8	#4	23′-0	9	#4	35′-9	2.28	.740
10	#5	18′-0	8	#5	8′-3	7	#5	23′-0	8	#5	35′-9	3.09	.740
10	#6	18′-0	7	#6	8′-3	7	#6	23′-0	7	#6	35′-9	4.02	.740
11	#6	18′-0	9	#6	8′-3	8	#6	23′-0	9	#6	35′-9	4.83	.740
13	#6	18′-0	9	#6	8′-3	9	#6	23′-0	9	#6	36′-0	5.30	.785
10	#7	18′-0	7	#7	8′-3	7	#7	23′-0	7	#7	36′-0	5.74	.851
12	#7	18′-0	8	#7	8′-3	8	#7	23′-0	8	#7	36′-0	6.41	.941
12	#7	18′-0	9	#7	8′-3	8	#7	23′-0	9	#7	36′-0	7.02	1.031
9	#5	18′-6	10	#4	8′-6	9	#4	24′-0	10	#4	37′-0	2.44	.762
12	#5	18′-6	8	#5	8′-6	8	#5	24′-0	8	#5	37′-0	3.19	.762
11	#6	18′-6	8	#6	8′-6	7	#6	24′-0	8	#6	37′-0	4.21	.762
13	#6	18′-6	9	#6	8′-6	9	#6	24′-0	9	#6	37′-0	5.00	.762
13	#6	18′-6	10	#6	8′-6	9	#6	24′-0	10	#6	37′-3	5.38	.811
12	#7	18′-6	8	#7	8′-6	7	#7	24′-0	8	#7	37′-3	5.89	.876
12	#7	18′-6	9	#7	8′-6	8	#7	24′-0	9	#7	37′-3	6.69	.966
13	#7	18′-6	9	#7	8′-6	9	#7	24′-0	9	#7	37′-3	7.11	1.057
9	#5	19′-3	7	#5	8′-9	7	#5	24′-9	7	#5	38′-6	2.61	.787
13	#5	19′-3	9	#5	8′-9	9	#5	24′-9	9	#5	38′-6	3.41	.787
12	#6	19′-3	8	#6	8′-9	8	#6	24′-9	8	#6	38′-6	4.35	.787
13	#6	19′-3	10	#6	8′-9	9	#6	24′-9	10	#6	38′-6	5.19	.787
11	#7	19′-3	8	#7	8′-9	8	#7	24′-9	8	#7	38′-6	5.86	.853
12	#7	19′-3	8	#7	8′-9	8	#7	24′-9	8	#7	37′-6	6.10	.919
13	#7	19′-3	9	#7	8′-9	9	#7	24′-9	9	#7	38′-6	6.85	1.013
15	#7	19′-3	10	#7	8′-9	10	#7	24′-9	10	#7	38′-6	7.51	1.103
11	#5	20′-0	8	#5	9′-0	7	#5	25′-6	8	#5	39′-9	2.74	.815
13	#5	20′-0	10	#5	9′-0	9	#5	25′-6	10	#5	39′-9	3.49	.815
12	#6	20′-0	9	#6	9′-0	8	#6	25′-6	9	#6	39′-9	4.54	.815
15	#6	20′-0	11	#6	9′-0	10	#6	25′-6	11	#6	39′-9	5.37	.815
12	#7	20′-0	9	#7	9′-0	8	#7	25′-6	9	#7	39′-9	5.99	.878
13	#7	20′-0	9	#7	9′-0	8	#7	25′-6	9	#7	39′-9	6.31	.947
14	#7	20′-0	10	#7	9′-0	10	#7	25′-6	10	#7	39′-9	7.11	1.042
15	#7	20′-0	11	#7	9′-0	10	#7	25′-6	11	#7	40′-0	7.63	1.132

* These cubic foot quantities include drop panel but not column capital.

TWO-WAY FLAT SLAB FLOORS, SQUARE PANELS— BANDS PERPENDICULAR TO AN EXTERIOR WALL

For Bands Parallel to Walls or Not in End Spans, Use "Two-Way Flat Slab Floors, Square Panels—Interior Panels," Pages 8-8 to 8-21 incl.

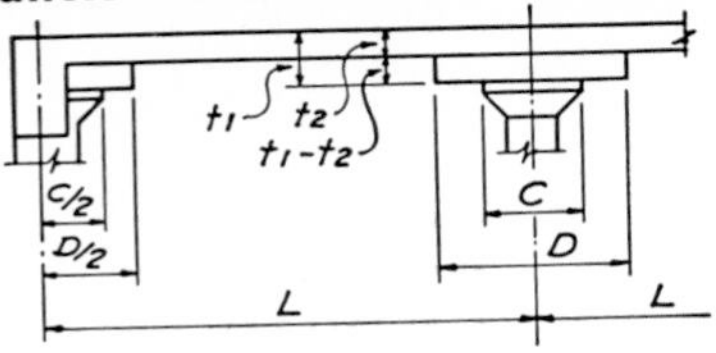

For general instructions and notes on the use of this table, see pages 8-3 to 8-7 incl.

Span / Drop / Cap	Safe Super-imposed Load (psf)	Slab Thickness t_2 (in.)	Drop Panel Thickness (t_1-t_2) (in.)	Each Column Strip: Straight			Trussed			Top at Ext. Col.		
				Quant.	Bar No.	Length	Quant.	Bar No.	Length	Quant.	Bar No.	Length
L = 31′-0	50	9½	4½	9	#5	20′-0	9	#5	43′-6	12	#5	11′-9
	100	9½	4½	11	#5	20′-0	12	#5	43′-6	16	#5	11′-9
	150	9½	4½	10	#6	20′-3	10	#6	43′-6	14	#6	11′-9
D = 12′-9	200	9½	4½	9	#7	20′-9	9	#7	43′-6	12	#7	11′-9
	250	10¼	4¾	9	#7	20′-9	10	#7	43′-6	14	#7	11′-9
	300	10¾	5	10	#7	20′-9	11	#7	43′-6	15	#7	11′-9
C = 7′-0	400	12	5¾	11	#7	20′-9	12	#7	43′-6	16	#7	11′-9
	500	13¼	6¼	9	#8	21′-0	10	#8	43′-9	13	#8	11′-9
L = 32′-0	50	9¾	4¾	9	#5	20′-9	10	#5	44′-9	13	#5	12′-3
	100	9¾	4¾	9	#6	21′-0	9	#6	44′-9	12	#6	12′-3
	150	9¾	4¾	11	#6	21′-0	11	#6	44′-9	15	#6	12′-3
D = 13′-0	200	9¾	4¾	9	#7	21′-6	10	#7	44′-9	13	#7	12′-3
	250	10½	5	10	#7	21′-6	11	#7	44′-9	15	#7	12′-3
	300	11¼	5½	11	#7	21′-6	11	#7	44′-9	15	#7	12′-3
C = 7′-0	400	12½	6	12	#7	21′-6	13	#7	45′-0	17	#7	12′-3
	500	13¾	6½	10	#8	21′-9	11	#8	45′-0	14	#8	12′-3
L = 33′-0	50	10	4¾	10	#5	21′-3	11	#5	46′-0	14	#5	12′-6
	100	10	4¾	9	#6	21′-6	10	#6	46′-0	13	#6	12′-6
	150	10	4¾	11	#6	21′-6	12	#6	46′-0	16	#6	12′-6
D = 13′-6	200	10	4¾	10	#7	22′-0	10	#7	46′-0	14	#7	12′-6
	250	11	5¼	11	#7	22′-0	11	#7	46′-3	15	#7	12′-6
	300	11½	5¾	12	#7	22′-0	12	#7	46′-3	16	#7	12′-6
C = 7′-6	400	12¾	6¼	10	#8	22′-3	10	#8	46′-3	14	#8	12′-6
	500	14	6¾	11	#8	22′-3	11	#8	46′-6	15	#8	12′-6
L = 34′-0	50	10¼	5	11	#5	22′-0	12	#5	47′-6	16	#5	12′-9
	100	10¼	5	10	#6	22′-3	11	#6	47′-6	14	#6	12′-9
	150	10¼	5	12	#6	22′-3	13	#6	47′-6	17	#6	12′-9
D = 13′-9	200	10½	5	11	#7	22′-9	11	#7	47′-6	15	#7	12′-9
	250	11¼	5¼	11	#7	22′-9	12	#7	47′-6	17	#7	12′-9
	300	12	5¾	12	#7	22′-9	13	#7	47′-6	17	#7	12′-9
C = 7′-6	400	13¼	6½	11	#8	23′-0	11	#8	47′-9	15	#8	12′-9
	500	14½	7	11	#8	23′-0	12	#8	47′-9	16	#8	12′-9

TWO-WAY FLAT SLAB FLOORS, SQUARE PANELS— BANDS PERPENDICULAR TO AN EXTERIOR WALL

On spans above 30 feet, deflection must be computed. Excessive deflections can be minimized with compressive reinforcement and by cambering the formwork.

f_s = 24,000 psi
f_c = 1,688 psi
v_c = 122.5 psi

Each Column Strip			Each Middle Strip									Weight of Steel (psf)	Average Cubic Feet of Concrete Per Square Foot of Floor*
Top at Int. Col.			Top at Ext. Col.			Straight			Trussed				
Quant.	Bar No.	Length	Quant.	Bar No.	Length	Quant.	Bar No.	Length	Quant.	Bar No.	Length		
11	#5	20′-6	8	#5	9′-3	8	#5	26′-6	8	#5	41′-0	2.84	.855
15	#5	20′-6	11	#5	9′-3	10	#5	26′-6	11	#5	41′-0	3.72	.855
13	#6	20′-6	9	#6	9′-3	9	#6	26′-6	9	#6	41′-0	4.67	.855
12	#7	20′-6	9	#7	9′-3	8	#7	26′-6	9	#7	41′-0	5.77	.855
13	#7	20′-6	9	#7	9′-3	9	#7	26′-6	9	#7	41′-0	6.20	.921
14	#7	20′-6	10	#7	9′-3	9	#7	26′-6	10	#7	41′-0	6.67	.966
15	#7	20′-6	11	#7	9′-3	10	#7	26′-6	11	#7	41′-0	7.36	1.081
13	#8	20′-6	9	#8	9′-3	8	#8	26′-6	9	#8	41′-3	8.02	1.192
13	#5	21′-3	9	#5	9′-6	9	#5	27′-3	9	#5	42′-3	3.04	.878
12	#6	21′-3	8	#6	9′-6	8	#6	27′-3	8	#6	42′-3	4.00	.878
15	#6	21′-3	10	#6	9′-6	10	#6	27′-3	10	#6	42′-3	4.95	.878
13	#7	21′-3	9	#7	9′-6	9	#7	27′-3	9	#7	42′-3	5.98	.878
14	#7	21′-3	10	#7	9′-6	9	#7	27′-3	10	#7	42′-3	6.46	.944
16	#7	21′-3	10	#7	9′-6	10	#7	27′-3	10	#7	42′-3	6.83	1.013
17	#7	21′-3	11	#7	9′-6	11	#7	27′-3	11	#7	42′-6	7.65	1.124
14	#8	21′-3	10	#8	9′-6	9	#8	27′-3	10	#8	42′-6	8.44	1.235
13	#5	22′-0	10	#5	9′-9	9	#5	28′-3	10	#5	43′-6	3.15	.900
13	#6	22′-0	9	#6	9′-9	8	#6	28′-3	9	#6	43′-6	4.19	.900
16	#6	22′-0	11	#6	9′-9	10	#6	28′-3	11	#6	43′-6	5.09	.900
14	#7	22′-0	10	#7	9′-9	9	#7	28′-3	10	#7	43′-6	6.15	.900
15	#7	22′-0	10	#7	9′-9	10	#7	28′-3	10	#7	43′-6	6.55	.990
16	#7	22′-0	11	#7	9′-9	11	#7	28′-3	11	#7	43′-6	7.09	1.039
14	#8	22′-0	10	#8	9′-9	9	#8	28′-3	10	#8	43′-9	8.03	1.150
15	#8	22′-0	10	#8	9′-9	10	#8	28′-3	10	#8	43′-9	8.62	1.261
14	#5	22′-6	10	#5	10′-0	10	#5	29′-0	10	#5	44′-9	3.30	.922
13	#6	22′-6	10	#6	10′-0	9	#6	29′-0	10	#6	44′-9	4.40	.922
16	#6	22′-6	12	#6	10′-0	11	#6	29′-0	12	#6	44′-9	5.34	.922
15	#7	22′-6	10	#7	10′-0	10	#7	29′-0	10	#7	44′-9	6.35	.943
16	#7	22′-6	11	#7	10′-0	11	#7	29′-0	11	#7	44′-9	6.83	1.009
17	#7	22′-6	12	#7	10′-0	11	#7	29′-0	12	#7	44′-9	7.32	1.078
15	#8	22′-6	10	#8	10′-0	10	#8	29′-0	10	#8	45′-0	8.32	1.193
16	#8	22′-6	11	#8	10′-0	10	#8	29′-0	11	#8	45′-0	8.86	1.304

* These cubic foot quantities include drop panel but not column capital.

TWO-WAY FLAT SLAB FLOORS, SQUARE PANELS—BANDS PERPENDICULAR TO AN EXTERIOR WALL

For Bands Parallel to Walls or Not in End Spans, Use "Two-Way Flat Slab Floors, Square Panels—Interior Panels," Pages 8-8 to 8-21 incl.

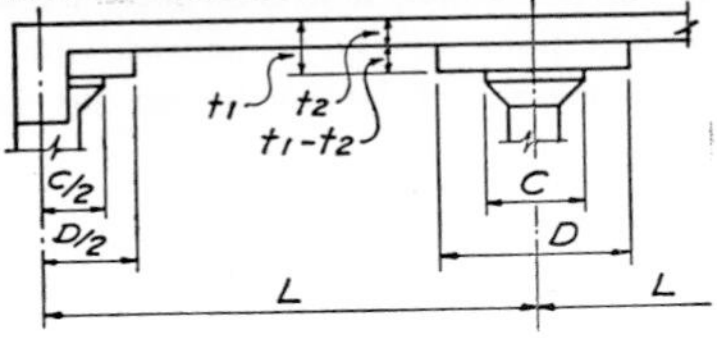

For general instructions and notes on the use of this table, see pages 8-3 to 8-7 incl.

Span / Drop / Cap	Safe Superimposed Load (psf)	Slab Thickness t_2 (in.)	Drop Panel Thickness (t_1-t_2) (in.)	Each Column Strip: Straight Quant.	Straight Bar No.	Straight Length	Trussed Quant.	Trussed Bar No.	Trussed Length	Top at Ext. Col. Quant.	Top at Ext. Col. Bar No.	Top at Ext. Col. Length
L = 35′-0	50	10½	5¼	12	#5	22′-9	12	#5	48′-9	16	#5	13′-3
	100	10½	5¼	11	#6	23′-0	11	#6	48′-9	15	#6	13′-3
	150	10½	5¼	13	#6	23′-0	14	#6	48′-9	18	#6	13′-3
D = 14′-0	200	10¾	5¼	11	#7	23′-6	12	#7	48′-9	16	#7	13′-3
	250	11½	5½	12	#7	23′-6	13	#7	48′-9	17	#7	13′-3
	300	12¼	6	13	#7	23′-6	14	#7	49′-0	18	#7	13′-3
C = 8′-0	400	13¾	6½	11	#8	23′-9	12	#8	49′-0	16	#8	13′-3
	500	14¾	7¼	12	#8	23′-9	13	#8	49′-0	17	#8	13′-3
L = 36′-0	50	11	5¼	13	#5	23′-6	13	#5	50′-3	18	#5	13′-6
	100	11	5¼	11	#6	23′-9	12	#6	50′-3	16	#6	13′-6
	150	11	5¼	10	#7	24′-3	11	#7	50′-3	15	#7	13′-6
D = 14′-3	200	11¼	5¼	12	#7	24′-3	12	#7	50′-3	17	#7	13′-6
	250	12	5¾	13	#7	24′-3	13	#7	50′-3	18	#7	13′-6
	300	12¾	6¼	11	#8	24′-6	11	#8	50′-3	15	#8	13′-6
C = 8′-0	400	14¼	6¾	12	#8	24′-6	12	#8	50′-6	17	#8	13′-6
	500	15½	7½	13	#8	24′-6	13	#8	50′-6	18	#8	13′-6
L = 37′-0	50	11¼	5½	10	#6	24′-3	10	#6	51′-6	14	#6	13′-9
	100	11¼	5½	12	#6	24′-3	13	#6	51′-6	17	#6	13′-9
	150	11¼	5½	11	#7	24′-9	11	#7	51′-6	15	#7	13′-9
D = 14′-9	200	11½	5½	13	#7	24′-9	13	#7	51′-6	18	#7	13′-9
	250	12¼	5¾	14	#7	24′-9	14	#7	51′-6	20	#7	13′-9
	300	13	6½	11	#8	25′-0	12	#8	51′-9	16	#8	13′-9
C = 8′-6	400	14½	7	12	#8	25′-0	13	#8	51′-9	18	#8	13′-9
	500	15¾	7½	14	#8	25′-0	14	#8	51′-9	19	#8	13′-9
L = 38′-0	50	11½	5½	11	#6	24′-9	11	#6	52′-9	15	#6	14′-3
	100	11½	5½	13	#6	24′-9	14	#6	52′-9	19	#6	14′-3
	150	11½	5½	12	#7	25′-3	12	#7	52′-9	17	#7	14′-3
D = 15′-3	200	11¾	5¾	14	#7	25′-3	14	#7	52′-9	19	#7	14′-3
	250	12¾	6¼	11	#8	25′-6	12	#8	53′-0	16	#8	14′-3
	300	13½	6½	12	#8	25′-6	12	#8	53′-0	17	#8	14′-3
C = 8′-6	400	15	7¼	13	#8	25′-6	14	#8	53′-0	19	#8	14′-3
	500	16¼	8	15	#8	25′-6	15	#8	53′-3	20	#8	14′-3

TWO-WAY FLAT SLAB FLOORS, SQUARE PANELS— BANDS PERPENDICULAR TO AN EXTERIOR WALL

On spans above 30 feet, deflection must be computed. Excessive deflections can be minimized with compressive reinforcement and by cambering the formwork.

f_s = 24,000 psi
f_c = 1,688 psi
v_c = 122.5 psi

Each Column Strip			Each Middle Strip									Weight of Steel (psf)	Average Cubic Feet of Concrete Per Square Foot of Floor *
Top at Int. Col.			Top at Ext. Col.			Straight			Trussed				
Quant.	Bar No.	Length	Quant.	Bar No.	Length	Quant.	Bar No.	Length	Quant.	Bar No.	Length		
16	#5	23′-3	11	#5	10′-3	11	#5	29′-9	11	#5	46′-0	3.40	.945
15	#6	23′-3	10	#6	10′-3	10	#6	29′-9	10	#6	46′-0	4.52	.945
17	#6	23′-3	12	#6	10′-3	12	#6	29′-9	12	#6	46′-0	5.44	.945
15	#7	23′-3	11	#7	10′-3	10	#7	29′-9	11	#7	46′-0	6.50	.966
16	#7	23′-3	12	#7	10′-3	11	#7	29′-9	12	#7	46′-0	7.07	1.032
18	#7	23′-3	12	#7	10′-3	12	#7	29′-9	12	#7	46′-0	7.47	1.101
15	#8	23′-3	11	#8	10′-3	10	#8	29′-9	11	#8	46′-3	8.47	1.233
16	#8	23′-3	11	#8	10′-3	11	#8	29′-9	11	#8	46′-3	9.15	1.326
18	#5	24′-0	12	#5	10′-6	11	#5	30′-9	12	#5	47′-3	3.60	.985
16	#6	24′-0	11	#6	10′-6	10	#6	30′-9	11	#6	47′-3	4.71	.985
14	#7	24′-0	10	#7	10′-6	9	#7	30′-9	10	#7	47′-3	5.75	.985
18	#7	24′-0	11	#7	10′-6	11	#7	30′-9	11	#7	47′-3	6.73	1.006
19	#7	24′-0	12	#7	10′-6	12	#7	30′-9	12	#7	47′-3	7.22	1.075
15	#8	24′-0	10	#8	10′-6	10	#8	30′-9	10	#8	47′-6	7.86	1.144
17	#8	24′-0	11	#8	10′-6	11	#8	30′-9	11	#8	47′-6	8.63	1.276
18	#8	24′-0	12	#8	10′-6	12	#8	30′-9	12	#8	47′-6	9.41	1.390
13	#6	24′-6	9	#6	10′-9	9	#6	31′-6	9	#6	48′-6	3.86	1.010
16	#6	24′-6	12	#6	10′-9	11	#6	31′-6	12	#6	48′-6	4.90	1.010
15	#7	24′-6	10	#7	10′-9	10	#7	31′-6	10	#7	48′-6	5.89	1.010
18	#7	24′-6	12	#7	10′-9	11	#7	31′-6	12	#7	48′-6	6.86	1.031
20	#7	24′-6	13	#7	10′-9	12	#7	31′-6	13	#7	48′-6	7.48	1.097
15	#8	24′-6	11	#8	10′-9	10	#8	31′-6	11	#8	48′-9	8.04	1.169
17	#8	24′-6	12	#8	10′-9	11	#8	31′-6	12	#8	48′-9	8.85	1.301
19	#8	24′-6	13	#8	10′-9	12	#8	31′-6	13	#8	48′-9	9.70	1.412
15	#6	25′-3	10	#6	11′-0	9	#6	32′-6	10	#6	49′-9	4.12	1.032
19	#6	25′-3	12	#6	11′-0	12	#6	32′-6	12	#6	49′-9	5.08	1.032
17	#7	25′-3	11	#7	11′-0	11	#7	32′-6	11	#7	49′-9	6.22	1.032
19	#7	25′-3	13	#7	11′-0	12	#7	32′-6	13	#7	49′-9	7.21	1.056
15	#8	25′-3	11	#8	11′-0	10	#8	32′-6	11	#8	50′-0	7.83	1.146
18	#8	25′-3	11	#8	11′-0	11	#8	32′-6	11	#8	50′-0	8.30	1.212
19	#8	25′-3	12	#8	11′-0	12	#8	32′-6	12	#8	50′-0	9.09	1.347
20	#8	25′-3	14	#8	11′-0	13	#8	32′-6	14	#8	50′-3	10.07	1.462

* These cubic foot quantities include drop panel but not column capital.

TWO-WAY FLAT SLAB FLOORS, SQUARE PANELS— BANDS PERPENDICULAR TO AN EXTERIOR WALL

For Bands Parallel to Walls or Not in End Spans, Use "Two-Way Flat Slab Floors, Square Panels—Interior Panels," Pages 8-8 to 8-21 incl.

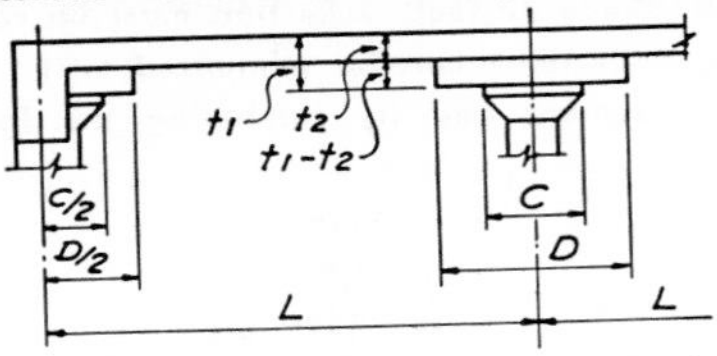

For general instructions and notes on the use of this table, see pages 8-3 to 8-7 incl.

Span / Drop / Cap	Safe Superimposed Load (psf)	Slab Thickness t_2 (in.)	Drop Panel Thickness (t_1-t_2) (in.)	Each Column Strip: Straight Quant.	Straight Bar No.	Straight Length	Trussed Quant.	Trussed Bar No.	Trussed Length	Top at Ext. Col. Quant.	Top at Ext. Col. Bar No.	Top at Ext. Col. Length
L = 39′-0	50	11¾	5¾	11	#6	25′-3	12	#6	54′-3	16	#6	14′-6
	100	11¾	5¾	14	#6	25′-3	15	#6	54′-3	20	#6	14′-6
	150	11¾	5¾	12	#7	25′-9	13	#7	54′-3	18	#7	14′-6
D = 15′-9	200	12¼	5¾	14	#7	25′-9	15	#7	54′-3	20	#7	14′-6
	250	13	6¼	12	#8	26′-0	12	#8	54′-3	17	#8	14′-6
	300	13¾	6¼	13	#8	26′-0	13	#8	54′-3	18	#8	14′-6
C = 9′-0	400	15¼	7½	14	#8	26′-0	15	#8	54′-6	20	#8	14′-6
	500	16¼	8	12	#9	26′-6	13	#9	54′-6	17	#9	14′-6
L = 40′-0	50	12	6	12	#6	26′-0	13	#6	55′-6	17	#6	14′-9
	100	12	6	15	#6	26′-0	16	#6	55′-6	21	#6	14′-9
	150	12	6	13	#7	26′-6	14	#7	55′-6	19	#7	14′-9
D = 16′-0	200	12½	6	15	#7	26′-6	16	#7	55′-6	21	#7	14′-9
	250	13½	6½	12	#8	26′-9	13	#8	55′-9	18	#8	14′-9
	300	14¼	7	13	#8	26′-9	14	#8	55′-9	19	#8	14′-9
C = 9′-0	400	15¾	7¾	15	#8	26′-9	15	#8	55′-9	21	#8	14′-9
	500	17¼	8¼	13	#9	27′-3	13	#9	56′-0	18	#9	14′-9

TWO-WAY FLAT SLAB FLOORS, SQUARE PANELS—BANDS PERPENDICULAR TO AN EXTERIOR WALL

On spans above 30 feet, deflection must be computed. Excessive deflections can be minimized with compressive reinforcement and by cambering the formwork.

f_s = 24,000 psi
f_c = 1,688 psi
v_c = 122.5 psi

Each Column Strip			Each Middle Strip									Weight of Steel (psf)	Average Cubic Feet of Concrete Per Square Foot of Floor *
Top at Int. Col.			Top at Ext. Col.			Straight			Trussed				
Quant.	Bar No.	Length	Quant.	Bar No.	Length	Quant.	Bar No.	Length	Quant.	Bar No.	Length		
15	#6	25′-9	11	#6	11′-3	10	#6	33′-3	11	#6	51′-0	4.23	1.057
19	#6	25′-9	13	#6	11′-3	13	#6	33′-3	13	#6	51′-0	5.28	1.057
17	#7	25′-9	12	#7	11′-3	11	#7	33′-3	12	#7	51′-0	6.37	1.057
20	#7	25′-9	13	#7	11′-3	13	#7	33′-3	13	#7	51′-0	7.25	1.099
17	#8	25′-9	11	#8	11′-3	11	#8	33′-3	11	#8	51′-3	7.92	1.168
18	#8	25′-9	12	#8	11′-3	11	#8	33′-3	12	#8	51′-3	8.46	1.238
19	#8	25′-9	13	#8	11′-3	13	#8	33′-3	13	#8	51′-3	9.43	1.373
17	#9	25′-9	11	#9	11′-3	11	#9	33′-3	11	#9	51′-6	10.41	1.505
15	#6	26′-6	11	#6	11′-6	11	#6	34′-0	11	#6	52′-3	4.42	1.080
20	#6	26′-6	14	#6	11′-6	14	#6	34′-0	14	#6	52′-3	5.49	1.080
18	#7	26′-6	13	#7	11′-6	12	#7	34′-0	13	#7	52′-3	6.74	1.080
21	#7	28′-6	14	#7	11′-6	14	#7	34′-0	14	#7	52′-6	7.60	1.122
17	#8	26′-6	12	#8	11′-6	11	#8	34′-0	12	#8	52′-6	8.15	1.212
18	#8	26′-6	13	#8	11′-6	12	#8	34′-0	13	#8	52′-6	8.73	1.281
21	#8	26′-6	14	#8	11′-6	13	#8	34′-0	14	#8	52′-6	9.61	1.416
19	#9	26′-6	12	#9	11′-6	12	#9	34′-0	12	#9	52′-9	10.82	1.548

* These cubic foot quantities include drop panel but not column capital.

SAFE LOAD TABLES

Waffle Flat Slabs

Section 9

WAFFLE FLAT SLABS—SQUARE PANELS

For Two-Way Flat Slabs see section 8.

Tables are presented for domes that meet U. S. Dept. of Commerce Simplified Practice Recommendation R265-63 viz. 30 in. x 30 in. square domes with 3-in. flanges (6 in. wide joist ribs at 36 in. centers) and 19 in. x 19 in. square domes with 2½-in. flanges (5 in. joist ribs at 24 in. centers) in standard depths of 8, 10, 12 and 14 in. and 6, 8, 10 and 12 in. respectively as well as 16 and 20 in. depths for 30 in. widths. Tables are given for both 3 in. and 4½ in. top slabs for the 30-in. domes and 2½ in. and 4½ in. for the 19-in. domes. Spans range from 21 ft to 51 ft for 30-in. domes and from 16 ft to 42 ft for 19-in., for safe superimposed loads of 50, through 300 psf, where applicable, both for typical square interior panels and for joists perpendicular to the wall for square exterior panels that are built integrally with exterior columns. Tables give total slab thickness, size of drop panel, column or column cap, reinforcing steel in each joist, and average weight of steel and volume of concrete per square foot of floor area. The tabulated values do not cover the entire range of loads and spans; heavier loads, thicker top slabs, longer spans can be taken care of by the procedures on pages 9-6 and 9-7, using, where necessary, the provisions illustrated on pages 9-8 and 9-9.

All tables are based upon the recommendations of the "Building Code Requirements for Reinforced Concrete (ACI 318-63)—Empirical Method (Section 2104)," using one set of fiber stresses, viz. $f'_c = 3750$ psi and $f_s = 24{,}000$ psi, and are based upon using deformed bars whose deformations meet the requirements of ASTM.

As shown on page 9-4, the waffle slab has rows of joists at right angles to each other, with domes omitted around the columns to form "drop panels," and either the columns are of sufficient size to keep the diagonal tension within allowable values or a flaring cap is provided. Shallower domes are sometimes used around the drop panel to provide sufficient cover for heavy top bars. Joists in each direction are divided into two bands or strips, one over the columns and extending a quarter panel width each side of the column center-line, designed to provide reinforcement for the column strip, and the other filling in between consecutive column strips and designed to provide reinforcement for the middle strip. A second set of similar strips of joists runs at right angles to the first. Each joist has a straight bottom bar and a truss bar which is in the bottom of the slab between column centers and bent up into the top of the slab on each column center-line. When shears exceed the relatively low values allowed for v_c, flat, zig-zag bent stirrups are added, usually just for the length of a single dome, but sometimes for two successive domes away from the drop panel. Additional straight bars are required both ways in the top of each drop panel. A layer of 6 x 6-#6/#6 welded wire fabric is recommended in the top slab over the domes in all cases, and this is to be increased or supplemented if unusually heavy concentrated loads are contemplated.

The structure must have **at least three consecutive panels in a row in each direction to come within the ACI Code values for empirical moments; if the building is narrower a special analysis must be made** which will have the effect of increasing the reinforcement. The successive **spans must be of such lengths that they do not differ by more than twenty per cent** of the longer span. An elastic analysis as outlined in ACI Chapter 21 can always be made.

30-In. Domes, 36-In. C/C
19-In. Domes, 24-In. C/C

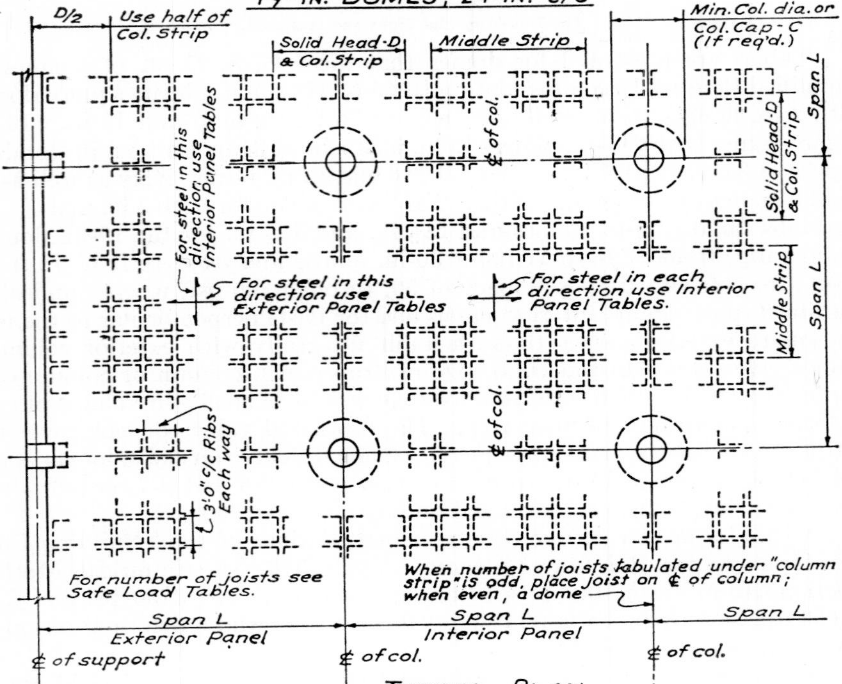

TYPICAL PLAN

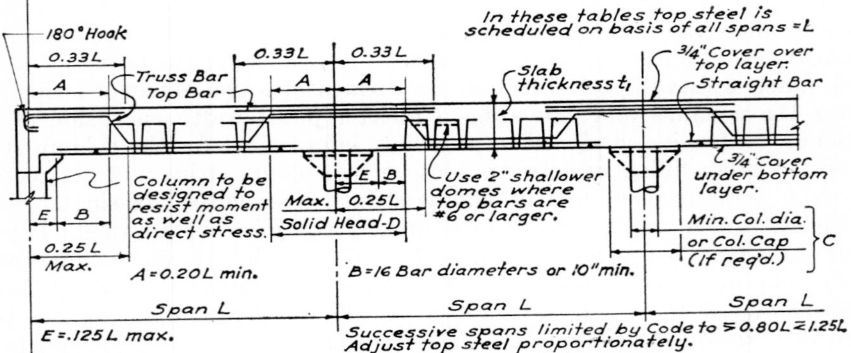

TYPICAL SECTION - COLUMN STRIP

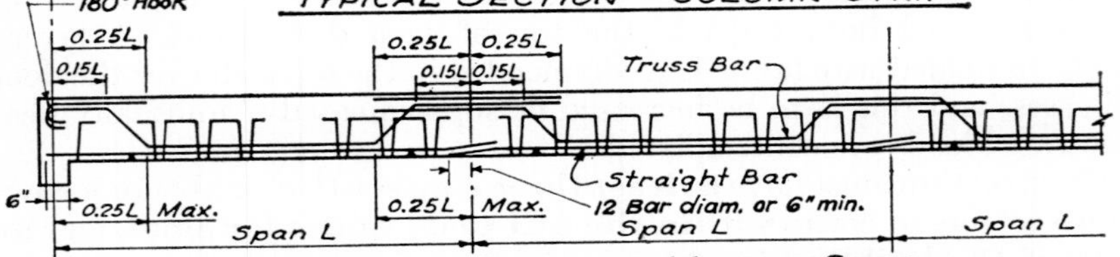

TYPICAL BENDING - MIDDLE STRIP

NOTE: Details illustrated are for Type "B" End Support only (ACI Table 2104 f)

For other types of end supports, see page 9-5.
Straight top bars over other interior supports may be required in the middle strip for unequal loads and/or spans.

WAFFLE FLAT SLABS—SQUARE PANELS

The panels tabulated are in multiples of 3 ft for 30-in. wide domes, or 2 ft for 19-in., so that joists space out exactly. There will be a joist or a row of domes on the column center according to whether the number of joists in the column strip is odd or even, arranged this way to provide the proper size of drop panel. Special filler size domes are available on a limited basis to fill out column spacings that are not multiples of 3 ft or 2 ft. This condition can also be handled by using wider joist ribs in the column strip.

Values have been given only for square panels. It is possible to estimate values for a rectangular panel, using the long side for one set of joists, the short side for the other. The ACI Code, Empirical Method, limits the ratio of long-to-short side to 1.33. The designer should sketch out the spacings for a typical panel and correlate with the column spacings as a part of the early planning.

For exterior panels, take joists that are continuous, i.e., parallel to discontinuous edge, from tables for Typical Interior Panels. Take strips that are noncontinuous, i.e., perpendicular to discontinuous edge, from tables for Strips Perpendicular to an Exterior Wall, provided exterior edge of panel frames into a concrete column or concrete bearing wall integral with slab. If slab simply rests upon a masonry wall without any edge restraint, then bars in joists perpendicular to exterior wall must be changed from values in tables for Typical Exterior Panels as follows:—

Positive steel in column strip:—Increase 50%.
Negative steel in column strip at wall:—Decrease to 17% of tabulated value.
Negative steel in column strip over first interior column:—Increase 30%.
Positive steel in middle strip:—Increase 30%.
Negative steel in middle strip at exterior wall:—Decrease to 30% of tabulated value.
Negative steel in middle strip at first interior row of columns:—Increase 30%.

For corner panels discontinuous on two edges, take both sets of strips from tables for Typical Exterior Panels. If both discontinuous edges rest upon masonry walls, above corrections shall apply to each set of strips.

To guard against excessive diagonal tension stresses in the slab around the column head, the tables give the "Min. Col. Cap" which is the minimum diameter of support (i.e., column or cap) that will keep $v_c \lesssim 2\sqrt{f'_c} = 2\sqrt{3750} = 122.5$ psi (ACI 1207(c)). For moderate loads and spans, such sizes are not excessive as column diameters, but for heavier loads on longer spans a conical cap seems desirable. These tables do not consider the use of any of the types of "shear head" reinforcement suggested to eliminate caps.

Min. Col. Dia. 12′0″ Story Height tabulates diameter for average minimum column stiffness above and below the slab as required by ACI 2104(a), assuming a 12 ft. story height.

The concrete quantities given per square foot of floor area include all structural concrete in slab and drop panel but do not include any material in the supporting beams, column capital, column, nor any floor finish above the structural slab. "Safe superimposed load" represents live load, floor finishes, partition allowance, and everything except the weight of the structural concrete. For a table of quantities in columns and column capitals, see page 5-13.

WAFFLE FLAT SLABS—SQUARE PANELS

The weight of steel is the average weight in pounds per square foot of all longitudinal straight, truss, and top bars in the slab including stirrups, but not welded wire fabric, nor bars in beams, columns, walls, or footings.

The effective depth of slab is computed on the basis of an allowance of ¾ inch cover over the bars in all cases, and, where bars cross each other, by an allowance of one bar diameter plus 0.12 in. for deformations, but the bars each way were finally selected to satisfy the greater of the steel requirements in the two directions.

The scope of these tables is adequate for most purposes. It is not practicable to cover all possible combinations. For those who wish to extend beyond the coverage of these tables as well as for those who wish to know how they were computed, the following example will be instructive:—

Example—For the table on page 9-20, design a two-way dome slab for a 30 ft square interior panel with 100 psf superimposed load, using a 14 + 3 slab (t_1 = 17 in.); stresses, f_c = 1688 psi, f_s = 24,000 psi, n = 8.2.

Lay out the domes as 10 rows of 10 domes less 4 x 4 for drop panel or 84 total, each of which displaces 980 lb of concrete (table on page 9-7).

$$30 \times 30 \ @ \begin{cases} 100 \quad \text{LL} \\ 212.5 \text{ for } 17'' \text{ slab} \\ 312.5 \end{cases} = 281{,}500 \text{ lb}$$

$$\text{Less 84 domes @ 980 lb} = \underline{82{,}300}$$

$$W = 199{,}200 \text{ lb}$$

Shear at Edge of Drop Panel: * There are 4 sides of 5 joists each or 20 joists to resist this shear. Average width of joist = 6 + 1.75 = 7.75 in.

Twenty joists @ 7.75 × 15.5 × 73.5 = 176,600 lb. The net shear is 199,200 − 12.5 × 12.5 @ 312.5 = 150,400 lb < 176,600, so stirrups are not required.

Shear around Column Head: *—Assume C = 18 in., then the diameter of the periphery is 33.5 in. = 2.79 ft. Load outside the periphery is $199{,}200 - \dfrac{\pi \times 2.79^2 \times 312.5}{4} = 197{,}300$ lb, and $v_c = \dfrac{197{,}300}{\pi \times 33.5 \times 15.5} = 121 < 122.5$ psi.

Bending Moment. Because the relative stiffnesses of joists and drop panel are about the same as in a standard two-way flat slab, coefficients will be taken from ACI Table 2104(f).

$$M_o = 0.09\,WFL\left(1 - \frac{2c}{3L}\right)^2, \text{ where } F = 1.15 - \frac{1.5}{30} = 1.10, \text{ so } M_o = 0.09 \times 199{,}200 \times 1.10 \times 30 \times 12\left(1 - \frac{2 \times 1.5}{3 \times 30}\right)^2 = 6{,}650{,}000 \text{ lb-in., which is subdivided:—}$$

	Column Strip		*Middle Strip*	
	Negative	*Positive*	*Negative*	*Positive*
Percentage of M_o	50	20	15	15
Moment kip—in.	3325	1330	998	998
d (in.)	15.0	15.88	15.94	15.19
A_s (sq. in.)	10.5	4.00	3.00	3.14

Positive Moment, Column Strip:—5 Joists @ 1-#6 straight and 1-#6 truss bar = 4.40 sq in. > 4.00.

Positive Moment, Middle Strip:—5 Joists @ 1-#5 straight and 1-#5 truss bar = 3.10 sq in. < 3.14.

---

*For methods of increasing shear capacity see pp. 9-8 and 9-9.

WAFFLE FLAT SLABS—SQUARE PANELS

For the entire width of panel, there is furnished 7.50 sq in. > 7.12 sq in. required.

Negative Moment, Column Strip:—

Truss bars = 2 × 5 @ 0.44 = 4.40 sq. in
Top bars = 14 @ 0.44 = 6.16

10.56 sq in. > 10.5 sq in.

Negative Moment, Middle Strip:—5 Joists @ 2 × 0.31 = 3.10 sq in. > 3.00 sq in. required. With $p = \frac{0.62}{6 \times 15.94} = 0.0065 < 0.0129$ it is unnecessary to check f_c.

Check Compression in Concrete of Drop Panel:—Use three-quarters of drop width = 112.5 in. (ACI 2102(c)1).

$$R = \frac{M}{bd^2} = \frac{3{,}325{,}000}{112.5 \times 15.0 \times 15.0} = 132 < 271, \text{ so } f_c < 1688 \text{ psi (page 3-15).}$$

Check Compression in Concrete at Ends of Joists at Edge of Drop Panel:—Neg. Mom. $-M$ = approx 260,000 on 5 joists so $R = \frac{260{,}000}{5 \times 6 \times 15.0 \times 15.0} = 38.6 < 271.$

Placing bars in two-way dome floor slabs can follow order on page 8-7.

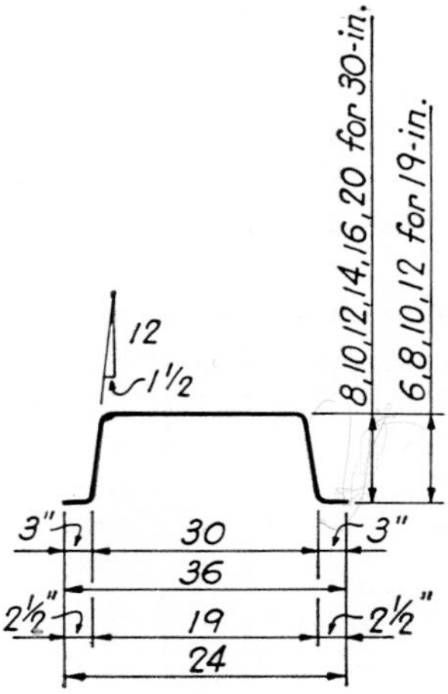

DOME DATA

Depth (in.)	Volume (cf per dome)	Weight of displaced concrete (lb per dome)	3″ top slab: Equiv. slab thickness (in.)	3″ top slab: Weight (psf)	4½″ top slab: Equiv. slab thickness (in.)	4½″ top slab: Weight (psf)
30-in. wide domes						
8	3.85	578	5.8	73	7.3	92
10	4.78	717	6.7	83	8.2	102
12	5.53	830	7.4	95	9.1	114
14	6.54	980	8.3	106	9.9	120
16	7.44	1116	9.1	114	10.6	133
20	9.16	1375	10.8	135	12.3	154
19-in. wide domes			2½″ top slab		4½″ top slab	
6	1.09	163	5.2	66	7.2	90
8	1.41	211	6.3	78	8.3	103
10	1.90	285	6.8	85	8.8	111
12	2.14	321	8.1	101	10.1	126

TYPICAL JOIST STIRRUP UNITS

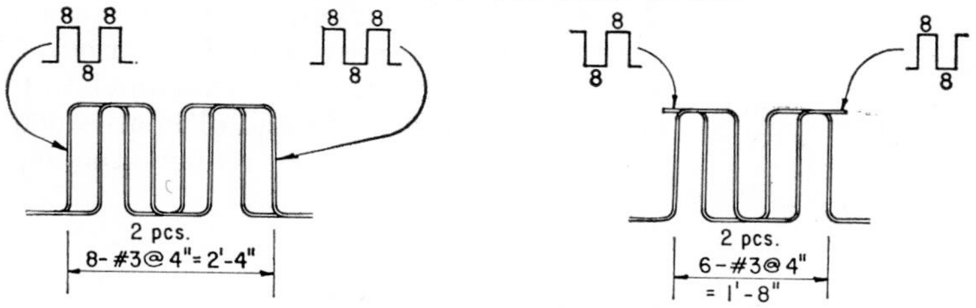

For use with 30 x 30 domes

For use with 19 x 19 domes

WAFFLE FLAT SLABS—SQUARE PANELS

The tables on pages 9-10 to 9-51 do not cover all loads and spans. They can be interpolated or reasonably extrapolated with good precision. The procedures on pages 9-6 and 9-7 can be used to design for heavier loads or longer spans.

In some cases, the layout on page 9-4 will not provide sufficient shear capacity. To keep the shear stresses within prescribed limits, the following procedures are suggested:

(1) Provide for **shear** (diagonal tension) **in the solid portion of the slab** over and around the column by using (a) a large column, (b) a column cap, (c) a thick top slab, (d) a thickened drop panel, or (e) some acceptable form of steel shear reinforcement between slab and column.

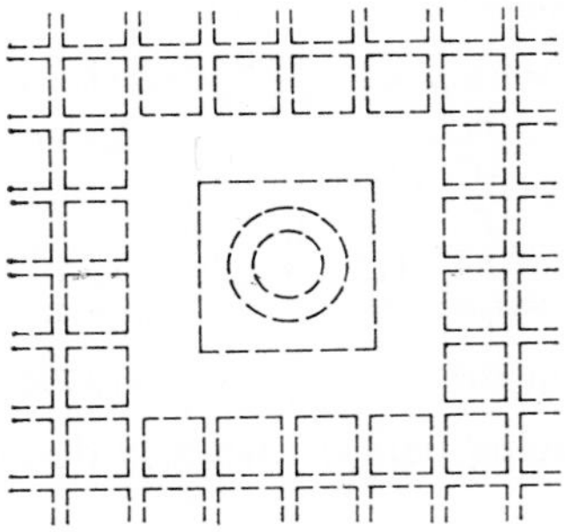

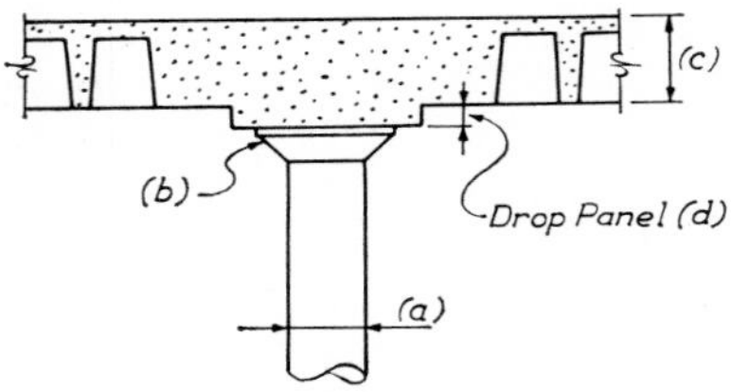

FIG. A

(2) Provide for **excess shear in the individual joists** around the periphery of the solid slab over the column by using shear reinforcement in each joist (page 9-7), or increase the width of joists using filler size dome forms around the solid portion as shown in Fig. B. It is often practicable also to provide wider joist ribs, extending from solid head to solid head, through the use of standard size dome forms which eliminates the need for the filler size dome forms.

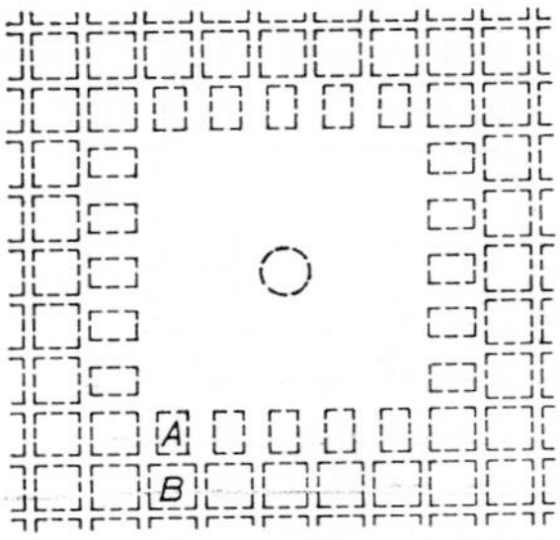

A = Special Dome Forms 20"×30"
B = Standard Dome Forms 30"×30"

FIG. B

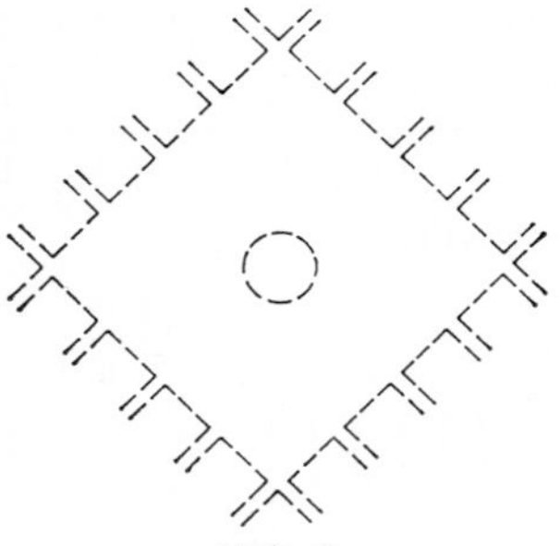

FIG. C

(3) In some cases diagonal solid slabs over the columns as shown in Fig. C and diagonal joists have been tried. They do not affect the shear too much but may increase stiffness and ultimate shear and by yield line theory reduce cracking due to negative moments.

WAFFLE FLAT SLABS—SQUARE PANELS

Applies to Safe Load Tables on Pages 9-10 to 9-51.

1. Bar lengths are scheduled as computed. For lengths in excess of around 60 ft, check availability of material and transportation facilities.

2. Refer to diagram on page 9-4. When number of joists in a column strip is odd, place a joist on column center-line; when even, center a row of domes on column center-line.

3. Centering system could be a solid deck to support the domes, but more likely a series of one-way soffit planks, the flanges of the domes forming the joist soffits both ways.

4. Bar supports are placed in ribs that extend in one direction as described for one-way joists on page 5-16; bars in the cross ribs rest on top of those previously placed at right angles.

5. The instructions for placing two-way flat slabs (page 8-7) should be read, but steel placement is much more like that of placing two layers of one-way joists at right angles to each other.

6. Interior panels are tabulated on even-numbered pages, from 9-10 ff. The weight of steel per square foot of floor is for an interior panel continuous on all four sides.

7. For strips that span onto walls or beams, the increased amount of steel per strip is tabulated on odd-numbered pages, from 9-11 ff, and the weight of steel per square foot of floor is for a side wall panel with bars continuous one way and increased in the other direction but cut off at the wall or beam.

8. A corner panel, semicontinuous in two directions, should be as much heavier than a slab described under #7 above as #7 is heavier than #6.

9. Only deformed bars with deformations meeting ASTM will provide the computed bond.

10. Panel capacities, where determined by shear around the column cap, may be increased by some of the devices shown on page 9-8.

11. Large deflections can be decreased by thickening the slab or by the use of compressive reinforcement.

12. Where story heights exceed 12 ft. or where slabs are stiffened only by columns underneath and not above, calculate minimum column diameter; do not use tabulated value.

13. Tables are based upon normal weight concrete (145 pcf). If lightweight aggregate is used, check both shear capacity and deflection.

14. For details of stirrups in joist ribs, see page 9-7.

WAFFLE FLAT SLABS—SQUARE PANELS—30-IN.-WIDE DOMES

For general instructions and notes on the use of this table, see pages 9-3 to 9-9 incl.

	Span Drop-D Form Depth plus Top Slab	Live Load (psf)	f_1 (in.)	Min. Col. Dia. 12′-0 Story Height (in.)	Min. Col. Cap. C (Shear) (in.)	Interior Square Panel Each Column Strip No. Jst.	Bars Trussed Straight	Bars Top **	Stirrups per Jst.*	Each Middle Strip No. Jst.	Bars Trussed Straight	Wt.† of Steel (psf)
1	L = 21′-0	50	11	13	12	3	#5 x 35′-7 #4 x 16′-2	1-#4 x 13′-11 7-#4 x 12′-8	—	4	#4 x 32′-2 #4 x 21′-8	1.61
2	D = 6′-6	100	11	16	12	3	#5 x 35′-7 #5 x 16′-2	3-#5 x 13′-11 7-#5 x 12′-8	2-#3	4	#4 x 32′-2 #4 x 21′-8	2.12
3	8 + 3	150	11	19	18	3	#6 x 35′-7 #5 x 16′-2	2-#5 x 13′-11 9-#5 x 12′-8	2-#3	4	#4 x 32′-2 #5 x 21′-10	2.55
4	L = 21′-0	50	13	13	12	3	#4 x 35′-8 #4 x 16′-2	2-#4 x 13′-11 7-#4 x 12′-8	—	4	#4 x 32′-4 #4 x 21′-8	1.48
5	D = 6′-6	100	13	16	12	3	#5 x 35′-8 #4 x 16′-2	3-#4 x 13′-11 9-#4 x 12′-8	2-#3	4	#4 x 32′-4 #4 x 21′-8	1.91
6	10 + 3	150	13	19	13	3	#6 x 35′-8 #4 x 16′-2	2-#4 x 13′-11 11-#4 x 12′-8	2-#3	4	#4 x 32′-4 #4 x 21′-8	2.17
7		200	13	20	18	3	#6 x 35′-8 #5 x 16′-2	3-#5 x 13′-11 8-#5 x 12′-8	2-#3	4	#5 x 32′-4 #4 x 21′-8	2.64
8		250	13	22	23	3	#6 x 35′-8 #6 x 16′-6	3-#6 x 13′-11 7-#6 x 12′-8	2-#3	4	#5 x 32′-4 #4 x 21′-8	2.96
9	L = 21′-0	50	15	13	12	3	#4 x 35′-10 #4 x 16′-2	2-#4 x 13′-11 6-#4 x 12′-8	—	4	#4 x 32′-6 #4 x 21′-8	1.44
10	D = 6′-6	100	15	16	12	3	#5 x 35′-10 #4 x 16′-2	2-#4 x 13′-11 7-#4 x 12′-8	—	4	#4 x 32′-6 #4 x 21′-8	1.66
11	12 + 3	150	15	19	12	3	#5 x 35′-10 #5 x 16′-2	2-#5 x 13′-11 7-#5 x 12′-8	2-#3	4	#4 x 32′-6 #4 x 21′-8	2.09
12		200	15	20	12	3	#6 x 35′-10 #5 x 16′-2	2-#5 x 13′-11 8-#5 x 12′-8	2-#3	4	#4 x 32′-6 #5 x 21′-10	2.52
13		250	15	22	17	3	#6 x 35′-10 #6 x 16′-6	2-#6 x 13′-11 7-#6 x 12′-8	2-#3	4	#5 x 32′-6 #4 x 21′-8	2.88
14		300	15	23	21	3	#6 x 35′-10 #6 x 16′-6	3-#6 x 13′-11 7-#6 x 12′-8	2-#3	4	#5 x 32′-6 #4 x 21′-8	2.98
15	L = 21′-0	50	17	13	12	3	#5 x 36′-0 #4 x 16′-2	— 5-#4 x 12′-8	—	4	#5 x 32′-7 #4 x 21′-8	1.73
16	D = 6′-6	100	17	16	12	3	#5 x 36′-0 #4 x 16′-2	1-#4 x 13′-11 7-#4 x 12′-8	—	4	#5 x 32′-7 #4 x 21′-8	1.85
17	14 + 3	150	17	19	12	3	#5 x 36′-0 #5 x 16′-2	2-#5 x 13′-11 6-#5 x 12′-8	2-#3	4	#5 x 32′-7 #4 x 21′-8	2.27
18		200	17	20	12	3	#5 x 36′-0 #5 x 16′-2	3-#5 x 13′-11 8-#5 x 12′-8	2-#3	4	#5 x 32′-7 #4 x 21′-8	2.45
19		250	17	22	12	3	#6 x 36′-0 #5 x 16′-2	2-#5 x 13′-11 9-#5 x 12′-8	2-#3	4	#5 x 32′-7 #4 x 21′-8	2.67
20		300	17	23	15	3	#6 x 36′-0 #6 x 16′-6	2-#6 x 13′-11 7-#6 x 12′-8	2-#3	4	#5 x 32′-7 #4 x 21′-8	2.90
21	L = 21′-0	50	19	13	12	3	#5 x 36′-1 #4 x 16′-2	— 5-#4 x 12′-8	—	4	#5 x 32′-9 #4 x 21′-8	1.73
22	D = 6′-6	100	19	16	12	3	#5 x 36′-1 #4 x 16′-2	1-#4 x 13′-11 6-#4 x 12′-8	—	4	#5 x 32′-9 #4 x 21′-8	1.81
23	16 + 3	150	19	18	12	3	#5 x 36′-1 #4 x 16′-2	2-#4 x 13′-11 8-#4 x 12′-8	—	4	#5 x 32′-9 #4 x 21′-8	1.93
24		200	19	20	12	3	#5 x 36′-1 #5 x 16′-2	2-#5 x 13′-11 7-#5 x 12′-8	2-#3	4	#5 x 32′-9 #4 x 21′-8	2.35
25		250	19	22	12	3	#6 x 36′-1 #5 x 16′-2	2-#5 x 13′-11 7-#5 x 12′-8	2-#3	4	#5 x 32′-9 #4 x 21′-8	2.57
26		300	19	23	12	3	#6 x 36′-1 #5 x 16′-2	3-#5 x 13′-11 8-#5 x 12′-8	2-#3	4	#5 x 32′-9 #4 x 21′-8	2.70
27	L = 21′-0	150	23	18	12	3	#5 x 36′-5 #5 x 16′-2	1-#5 x 13′-11 4-#5 x 12′-8	—	4	#5 x 33′-0 #5 x 21′-10	2.09
28	D = 6′-6	200	23	20	12	3	#5 x 36′-5 #5 x 16′-2	2-#5 x 13′-11 5-#5 x 12′-8	—	4	#5 x 33′-0 #5 x 21′-10	2.21
29	20 + 3	250	23	22	12	3	#5 x 36′-5 #5 x 16′-2	2-#5 x 13′-11 7-#5 x 12′-8	2-#3	4	#5 x 33′-0 #5 x 21′-10	2.53
30		300	23	23	12	3	#6 x 36′-5 #4 x 16′-2	2-#4 x 13′-11 11-#4 x 12′-8	2-#3	4	#5 x 33′-0 #5 x 21′-10	2.63

*,**,† For notes, see page 9-9.

WAFFLE FLAT SLABS—SQUARE PANELS—30-IN.-WIDE DOMES

For general instructions and notes on the use of this table, see pages 9-3 to 9-9 incl.

	Strips Perpendicular to an Exterior Wall									
	Column Strip					Middle Strip				
Av.‡ Cu. Ft. Conc. (psf)	Top Bars at Ext. Col.**	No. Jsts.	Bars Trussed Straight	Top Bars at First Int. Col.	Stirrups per Joist*	No. Jsts.	Bars Trussed Straight	Top Bars at Ext. Support	Wt.† of Steel (psf)	
0.510	4-#4 x 8′-6 5-#4 x 7′-10	3	#5 x 30′-2 #4 x 16′-2	2-#4 x 13′-11 8-#4 x 12′-8	—	4	#4 x 28′-5 #4 x 21′-4	1-#4 x 6′-9	1.65	1
0.510	4-#5 x 8′-6 4-#5 x 7′-10	3	#6 x 30′-2 #5 x 16′-2	3-#5 x 13′-11 7-#5 x 12′-8	2-#3	4	#4 x 28′-5 #5 x 21′-5	2-#4 x 6′-9	2.31	2
0.510	4-#6 x 8′-6 4-#6 x 7′-10	3	#6 x 30′-2 #6 x 16′-6	3-#5 x 13′-11 10-#5 x 12′-8	2-#3	4	#5 x 28′-5 #5 x 21′-5	1-#5 x 6′-9	2.76	3
0.581	4-#4 x 8′-6 4-#4 x 7′-10	3	#5 x 30′-3 #4 x 16′-2	3-#4 x 13′-11 7-#4 x 12′-8	—	4	#4 x 28′-7 #4 x 21′-4	1-#4 x 6′-9	1.57	4
0.581	4-#5 x 8′-6 4-#5 x 7′-10	3	#5 x 30′-3 #5 x 16′-2	3-#4 x 13′-11 11-#4 x 12′-8	2-#3	4	#4 x 28′-7 #5 x 21′-5	1-#4 x 6′-9	2.06	5
0.581	3-#6 x 8′-6 3-#6 x 7′-10	3	#6 x 30′-3 #6 x 16′-6	3-#4 x 13′-11 13-#4 x 12′-8	2-#3	4	#5 x 28′-7 #4 x 21′-4	1-#5 x 6′-9	2.41	6
0.581	5-#5 x 8′-6 5-#5 x 7′-10	3	#7 x 30′-3 #5 x 16′-2	4-#5 x 13′-11 9-#5 x 12′-8	2-#3	4	#5 x 28′-7 #5 x 21′-5	1-#5 x 6′-9	2.85	7
0.581	4-#6 x 8′-6 4-#6 x 7′-10	3	#7 x 30′-3 #6 x 16′-6	3-#6 x 13′-11 8-#6 x 12′-8	2-#3	4	#5 x 28′-7 #6 x 21′-6	2-#5 x 6′-9	3.29	8
0.654	4-#4 x 8′-6 4-#4 x 7′-10	3	#5 x 30′-5 #4 x 16′-2	3-#4 x 13′-11 6-#4 x 12′-8	—	4	#4 x 28′-9 #4 x 21′-4	1-#4 x 6′-9	1.54	9
0.654	3-#5 x 8′-6 3-#5 x 7′-10	3	#5 x 30′-5 #5 x 16′-2	3-#4 x 13′-11 9-#4 x 12′-8	—	4	#4 x 28′-9 #4 x 21′-4	1-#4 x 6′-9	1.74	10
0.654	4-#5 x 8′-6 4-#5 x 7′-10	3	#6 x 30′-5 #5 x 16′-2	3-#5 x 13′-11 7-#5 x 12′-8	2-#3	4	#4 x 28′-9 #5 x 21′-5	2-#4 x 6′-9	2.31	11
0.654	4-#6 x 8′-6 4-#6 x 7′-10	3	#6 x 30′-5 #6 x 16′-6	3-#5 x 13′-11 9-#5 x 12′-8	2-#3	4	#5 x 28′-9 #5 x 21′-5	1-#5 x 6′-9	2.76	12
0.654	4-#6 x 8′-6 4-#6 x 7′-10	3	#7 x 30′-5 #6 x 16′-6	3-#6 x 13′-11 6-#6 x 12′-8	2-#3	4	#5 x 28′-9 #5 x 21′-5	1-#5 x 6′-9	3.07	13
0.654	4-#6 x 8′-6 4-#6 x 7′-10	3	#7 x 30′-5 #6 x 16′-6	3-#6 x 13′-11 8-#6 x 12′-8	2-#3	4	#5 x 28′-9 #6 x 21′-6	2-#5 x 6′-9	3.31	14
0.729	4-#4 x 8′-6 4-#4 x 7′-10	3	#5 x 30′-6 #4 x 16′-2	1-#4 x 13′-11 5-#4 x 12′-8	—	4	#5 x 28′-10 #4 x 21′-4	1-#5 x 6′-9	1.78	15
0.729	4-#4 x 8′-6 5-#4 x 7′-10	3	#5 x 30′-6 #4 x 16′-2	2-#4 x 13′-11 8-#4 x 12′-8	—	4	#5 x 28′-10 #4 x 21′-4	1-#5 x 6′-9	1.89	16
0.729	4-#5 x 8′-6 4-#5 x 7′-10	3	#5 x 30′-6 #5 x 16′-2	3-#5 x 13′-11 7-#5 x 12′-8	2-#3	4	#5 x 28′-10 #4 x 21′-4	1-#5 x 6′-9	2.32	17
0.729	4-#5 x 8′-6 4-#5 x 7′-10	3	#6 x 30′-6 #5 x 16′-2	3-#5 x 13′-11 8-#5 x 12′-8	2-#3	4	#5 x 28′-10 #4 x 21′-4	1-#5 x 6′-9	2.52	18
0.729	4-#6 x 8′-6 4-#6 x 7′-10	3	#6 x 30′-6 #6 x 16′-6	3-#5 x 13′-11 10-#5 x 12′-8	2-#3	4	#5 x 28′-10 #5 x 21′-5	1-#5 x 6′-9	2.86	19
0.729	4-#6 x 8′-6 4-#6 x 7′-10	3	#7 x 30′-6 #6 x 16′-6	3-#6 x 13′-11 7-#6 x 12′-8	2-#3	4	#5 x 28′-10 #6 x 21′-6	1-#5 x 6′-9	3.20	20
0.806	3-#4 x 8′-6 3-#4 x 7′-10	3	#5 x 30′-8 #4 x 16′-2	— 5-#4 x 12′-8	—	4	#5 x 29′-0 #4 x 21′-4	1-#5 x 6′-9	1.75	21
0.806	4-#4 x 8′-6 4-#4 x 7′-10	3	#5 x 30′-8 #4 x 16′-2	2-#4 x 13′-11 7-#4 x 12′-8	—	4	#5 x 29′-0 #4 x 21′-4	1-#5 x 6′-9	1.85	22
0.806	3-#5 x 8′-6 4-#5 x 7′-10	3	#5 x 30′-8 #5 x 16′-2	3-#4 x 13′-11 10-#4 x 12′-8	—	4	#5 x 29′-0 #4 x 21′-4	1-#5 x 6′-9	2.03	23
0.806	4-#5 x 8′-6 4-#5 x 7′-10	3	#6 x 30′-8 #5 x 16′-2	3-#5 x 13′-11 7-#5 x 12′-8	2-#3	4	#5 x 29′-0 #4 x 21′-4	1-#5 x 6′-9	2.46	24
0.806	3-#6 x 8′-6 3-#6 x 7′-10	3	#6 x 30′-8 #6 x 16′-6	3-#5 x 13′-11 8-#5 x 12′-8	2-#3	4	#5 x 29′-0 #4 x 21′-4	1-#5 x 6′-9	2.66	25
0.806	5-#5 x 8′-6 5-#5 x 7′-10	3	#7 x 30′-8 #5 x 16′-2	4-#5 x 13′-11 8-#5 x 12′-8	2-#3	4	#5 x 29′-0 #5 x 21′-5	1-#5 x 6′-9	2.89	26
0.967	3-#5 x 8′-6 3-#5 x 7′-10	3	#5 x 30′-11 #5 x 16′-2	2-#5 x 13′-11 5-#5 x 12′-8	—	4	#5 x 29′-3 #5 x 21′-5	1-#5 x 6′-9	2.15	27
0.967	4-#5 x 8′-6 4-#5 x 7′-10	3	#5 x 30′-11 #5 x 16′-2	2-#5 x 13′-11 7-#5 x 12′-8	—	4	#5 x 29′-3 #5 x 21′-5	1-#5 x 6′-9	2.28	28
0.967	4-#5 x 8′-6 4-#5 x 7′-10	3	#6 x 30′-11 #5 x 16′-2	3-#5 x 13′-11 7-#5 x 12′-8	2-#3	4	#5 x 29′-3 #5 x 21′-5	1-#5 x 6′-9	2.65	29
0.967	3-#6 x 8′-6 3-#6 x 7′-10	3	#6 x 30′-11 #6 x 16′-6	3-#4 x 13′-11 13-#4 x 12′-8	2-#3	4	#5 x 29′-3 #5 x 21′-5	1-#5 x 6′-9	2.77	30

*,**,†,‡ For notes, see page 9-9.

WAFFLE FLAT SLABS—SQUARE PANELS—30-IN.-WIDE DOMES

For general instructions and notes on the use of this table, see pages 9-3 to 9-9 incl.

	Span Drop-D Form Depth plus Top Slab	Live Load (psf)	t_1 (in.)	Min. Col. Dia. 12'-0 Story Height (in.)	Min. Col. Cap. C (Shear) (in.)	Interior Square Panel: Each Column Strip: No. Jst.	Each Column Strip: Bars: Trussed Straight	Each Column Strip: Bars: Top **	Each Column Strip: Stirrups per Jst.*	Each Middle Strip: No. Jst.	Each Middle Strip: Bars: Trussed Straight	Wt.† of Steel (psf)
1	L = 21'-0	50	12½	13	12	3	#5 x 35'-8 #4 x 16'-2	1-#4 x 13'-11 7-#4 x 12'-8	—	4	#4 x 32'-4 #4 x 21'-8	1.62
2	D = 6'-6	100	12½	16	12	3	#5 x 35'-8 #5 x 16'-2	2-#5 x 13'-11 7-#5 x 12'-8	2-#3	4	#4 x 32'-4 #4 x 21'-8	2.07
3	8 + 4½	150	12½	19	15	3	#6 x 35'-8 #5 x 16'-2	2-#5 x 13'-11 8-#5 x 12'-8	2-#3	4	#4 x 32'-4 #5 x 21'-10	2.50
4		200	12½	20	20	3	#6 x 35'-8 #6 x 16'-6	2-#6 x 13'-11 7-#6 x 12'-8	2-#3	4	#5 x 32'-4 #4 x 21'-8	2.86
5	L = 21'-0	50	14½	13	12	3	#4 x 35'-10 #4 x 16'-2	2-#4 x 13'-11 7-#4 x 12'-8	—	4	#4 x 32'-5 #4 x 21'-8	1.48
6	D = 6'-6	100	14½	16	12	3	#5 x 35'-10 #4 x 16'-2	2-#4 x 13'-11 9-#4 x 12'-8	2-#3	4	#4 x 32'-5 #4 x 21'-8	1.88
7	10 + 4½	150	14½	19	12	3	#6 x 35'-10 #4 x 16'-2	2-#4 x 13'-11 10-#4 x 12'-8	2-#3	4	#4 x 32'-5 #4 x 21'-8	2.14
8		200	14½	20	14	3	#6 x 35'-10 #5 x 16'-2	2-#5 x 13'-11 9-#5 x 12'-8	2-#3	4	#5 x 32'-5 #4 x 21'-8	2.65
9		300	14½	23	23	3	#7 x 35'-10 #5 x 16'-2	2-#5 x 13'-11 10-#5 x 12'-8	2-#3	4	#5 x 32'-5 #5 x 21'-10	3.12
10	L = 21'-0	50	16½	13	12	3	#4 x 35'-11 #4 x 16'-2	2-#4 x 13'-11 6-#4 x 12'-8	—	4	#4 x 32'-7 #4 x 21'-8	1.45
11	D = 6'-6	100	16½	16	12	3	#5 x 35'-11 #4 x 16'-2	2-#4 x 13'-11 7-#4 x 12'-8	—	4	#4 x 32'-7 #4 x 21'-8	1.67
12	12 + 4½	150	16½	18	12	3	#5 x 35'-11 #5 x 16'-2	2-#5 x 13'-11 7-#5 x 12'-8	2-#3	4	#4 x 32'-7 #4 x 21'-8	2.10
13		200	16½	20	12	3	#6 x 35'-11 #5 x 16'-2	2-#5 x 13'-11 7-#5 x 12'-8	2-#3	4	#4 x 32'-7 #4 x 21'-8	2.33
14		300	16½	23	17	3	#6 x 35'-11 #6 x 16'-6	3-#6 x 13'-11 7-#6 x 12'-8	2-#3	4	#5 x 32'-7 #4 x 21'-8	2.99
15	L = 21'-0	50	18½	13	12	3	#5 x 36'-1 #4 x 16'-2	— 5-#4 x 12'-8	—	4	#5 x 32'-9 #4 x 21'-8	1.73
16	D = 6'-6	100	18½	16	12	3	#5 x 36'-1 #4 x 16'-2	1-#4 x 13'-11 7-#4 x 12'-8	—	4	#5 x 32'-9 #4 x 21'-8	1.85
17	14 + 4½	150	18½	18	12	3	#5 x 36'-1 #5 x 16'-2	2-#5 x 13'-11 6-#5 x 12'-8	—	4	#5 x 32'-9 #4 x 21'-8	2.11
18		200	18½	20	12	3	#5 x 36'-1 #5 x 16'-2	3-#5 x 13'-11 7-#5 x 12'-8	2-#3	4	#5 x 32'-9 #4 x 21'-8	2.41
19		300	18½	23	12	3	#6 x 36'-1 #6 x 16'-6	2-#6 x 13'-11 7-#6 x 12'-8	2-#3	4	#5 x 32'-9 #4 x 21'-8	2.92
20	L = 21'-0	50	20½	13	12	3	#5 x 36'-3 #4 x 16'-2	— 5-#4 x 12'-8	—	4	#5 x 32'-10 #4 x 21'-8	1.74
21	D = 6'-6	100	20½	16	12	3	#5 x 36'-3 #4 x 16'-2	1-#4 x 13'-11 6-#4 x 12'-8	—	4	#5 x 32'-10 #4 x 21'-8	1.82
22	16 + 4½	150	20½	18	12	3	#5 x 36'-3 #4 x 16'-2	2-#4 x 13'-11 8-#4 x 12'-8	—	4	#5 x 32'-10 #4 x 21'-8	1.94
23		200	20½	20	12	3	#5 x 36'-3 #5 x 16'-2	2-#5 x 13'-11 7-#5 x 12'-8	2-#3	4	#5 x 32'-10 #4 x 21'-8	2.36
24		300	20½	23	12	3	#6 x 36'-3 #5 x 16'-2	2-#5 x 13'-11 9-#5 x 12'-8	2-#3	4	#5 x 32'-10 #4 x 21'-8	2.71
25	L = 21'-0	50	24½	13	12	3	#6 x 36'-6 #5 x 16'-2	— 3-#5 x 12'-8	—	4	#6 x 33'-2 #5 x 21'-10	2.47
26	D = 6'-6	100	24½	16	12	3	#6 x 36'-6 #5 x 16'-2	— 4-#5 x 12'-8	—	4	#6 x 33'-2 #5 x 21'-10	2.53
27	20 + 4½	150	24½	18	12	3	#6 x 36'-6 #5 x 16'-2	— 4-#5 x 12'-8	—	4	#6 x 33'-2 #5 x 21'-10	2.53
28		200	24½	20	12	3	#6 x 36'-6 #5 x 16'-2	— 5-#5 x 12'-8	—	4	#6 x 33'-2 #5 x 21'-10	2.59
29		300	24½	23	12	3	#6 x 36'-6 #5 x 16'-2	2-#5 x 13'-11 6-#5 x 12'-8	2-#3	4	#6 x 33'-2 #5 x 21'-10	2.99

*,**,† For notes, see page 9-9.

WAFFLE FLAT SLABS—SQUARE PANELS—30-IN.-WIDE DOMES

For general instructions and notes on the use of this table, see pages 9-3 to 9-9 incl.

Av.‡ Cu. Ft. Conc. (psf)	Strips Perpendicular to an Exterior Wall								Wt.† of Steel (psf)	
	Column Strip					Middle Strip				
	Top Bars at Ext. Col.**	No. Jsts.	Bars: Trussed Straight	Top Bars at First Int. Col.	Stir-rups per Joist*	No. Jsts.	Bars: Trussed Straight	Top Bars at Ext. Support		
.635	4-#4 x 8′-6 5-#4 x 7′-10	3	#5 x 30′-3 #4 x 16′-2	2-#4 x 13′-11 8-#4 x 12′-8	—	4	#4 x 28′-7 #4 x 21′-4	1-#4 x 6′-9	1.65	1
.635	4-#5 x 8′-6 4-#5 x 7′-10	3	#6 x 30′-3 #5 x 16′-2	3-#5 x 13′-11 7-#5 x 12′-8	2-#3	4	#4 x 28′-7 #5 x 21′-5	2-#4 x 6′-9	2.29	2
.635	4-#6 x 8′-6 4-#6 x 7′-10	3	#6 x 30′-3 #6 x 16′-6	3-#5 x 13′-11 9-#5 x 12′-8	2-#3	4	#5 x 28′-7 #5 x 21′-5	1-#5 x 6′-9	2.73	3
.635	4-#6 x 8′-6 4-#6 x 7′-10	3	#7 x 30′-3 #6 x 16′-6	3-#6 x 13′-11 7-#6 x 12′-8	2-#3	4	#5 x 28′-7 #6 x 21′-6	1-#5 x 6′-9	3.15	4
.706	4-#4 x 8′-6 4-#4 x 7′-10	3	#5 x 30′-4 #4 x 16′-2	3-#4 x 13′-11 7-#4 x 12′-8	—	4	#4 x 28′-8 #4 x 21′-4	1-#4 x 6′-9	1.57	5
.706	4-#5 x 8′-6 4-#5 x 7′-10	3	#5 x 30′-4 #5 x 16′-2	3-#4 x 13′-11 11-#4 x 12′-8	2-#3	4	#4 x 28′-8 #4 x 21′-4	1-#4 x 6′-9	1.98	6
.706	3-#6 x 8′-6 3-#6 x 7′-10	3	#6 x 30′-4 #6 x 16′-6	3-#4 x 13′-11 12-#4 x 12′-8	2-#3	4	#4 x 28′-8 #5 x 21′-5	2-#4 x 6′-9	2.39	7
.706	5-#5 x 8′-6 5-#5 x 7′-10	3	#7 x 30′-4 #5 x 16′-2	3-#5 x 13′-11 9-#5 x 12′-8	2-#3	4	#5 x 28′-8 #5 x 21′-5	1-#5 x 6′-9	2.85	8
.706	3-#7 x 8′-6 3-#7 x 7′-10	3	#7 x 30′-4 #7 x 16′-10	3-#5 x 13′-11 12-#5 x 12′-8	2-#3	4	#5 x 28′-8 #6 x 21′-6	2-#5 x 6′-9	3.44	9
.779	4-#4 x 8′-6 4-#4 x 7′-10	3	#5 x 30′-6 #4 x 16′-2	3-#4 x 13′-11 6-#4 x 12′-8	—	4	#4 x 28′-10 #4 x 21′-4	1-#4 x 6′-9	1.55	10
.779	3-#5 x 8′-6 3-#5 x 7′-10	3	#5 x 30′-6 #5 x 16′-2	2-#4 x 13′-11 9-#4 x 12′-8	—	4	#4 x 28′-10 #4 x 21′-4	1-#4 x 6′-9	1.73	11
.779	4-#5 x 8′-6 4-#5 x 7′-10	3	#6 x 30′-6 #5 x 16′-2	3-#5 x 13′-11 6-#5 x 12′-8	2-#3	4	#4 x 28′-10 #5 x 21′-5	2-#4 x 6′-9	2.31	12
.779	3-#6 x 8′-6 3-#6 x 7′-10	3	#6 x 30′-6 #6 x 16′-6	3-#5 x 13′-11 8-#5 x 12′-8	2-#3	4	#5 x 28′-10 #5 x 21′-5	1-#5 x 6′-9	2.59	13
.779	4-#6 x 8′-6 4-#6 x 7′-10	3	#7 x 30′-6 #6 x 16′-6	3-#6 x 13′-11 8-#6 x 12′-8	2-#3	4	#5 x 28′-10 #6 x 21′-6	2-#5 x 6′-9	3.33	14
.854	4-#4 x 8′-6 4-#4 x 7′-10	3	#5 x 30′-8 #4 x 16′-2	1-#4 x 13′-11 5-#4 x 12′-8	—	4	#5 x 29′-0 #4 x 21′-4	1-#5 x 6′-9	1.78	15
.854	4-#4 x 8′-6 5-#4 x 7′-10	3	#5 x 30′-8 #4 x 16′-2	2-#4 x 13′-11 8-#4 x 12′-8	—	4	#5 x 29′-0 #4 x 21′-4	1-#5 x 6′-9	1.89	16
.854	4-#5 x 8′-6 4-#5 x 7′-10	3	#5 x 30′-8 #5 x 16′-2	2-#5 x 13′-11 7-#5 x 12′-8	—	4	#5 x 29′-0 #4 x 21′-4	1-#5 x 6′-9	2.15	17
.854	4-#5 x 8′-6 4-#5 x 7′-10	3	#6 x 30′-8 #5 x 16′-2	3-#5 x 13′-11 8-#5 x 12′-8	2-#3	4	#5 x 29′-0 #4 x 21′-4	1-#5 x 6′-9	2.51	18
.854	4-#6 x 8′-6 4-#6 x 7′-10	3	#7 x 30′-8 #6 x 16′-6	3-#6 x 13′-11 7-#6 x 12′-8	2-#3	4	#5 x 29′-0 #6 x 21′-6	1-#5 x 6′-9	3.21	19
.931	3-#4 x 8′-6 4-#4 x 7′-10	3	#5 x 30′-9 #4 x 16′-2	— 5-#4 x 12′-8	—	4	#5 x 29′-1 #4 x 21′-4	1-#5 x 6′-9	1.76	20
.931	4-#4 x 8′-6 4-#4 x 7′-10	3	#5 x 30′-9 #4 x 16′-2	2-#4 x 13′-11 7-#4 x 12′-8	—	4	#5 x 29′-1 #4 x 21′-4	1-#5 x 6′-9	1.86	21
.931	3-#5 x 8′-6 3-#5 x 7′-10	3	#5 x 30′-9 #5 x 16′-2	3-#4 x 13′-11 9-#4 x 12′-8	—	4	#5 x 29′-1 #4 x 21′-4	1-#5 x 6′-9	2.00	22
.931	4-#5 x 8′-6 4-#5 x 7′-10	3	#6 x 30′-9 #5 x 16′-2	3-#5 x 13′-11 6-#5 x 12′-8	2-#3	4	#5 x 29′-1 #4 x 21′-4	1-#5 x 6′-9	2.46	23
.931	4-#6 x 8′-6 4-#6 x 7′-10	3	#6 x 30′-9 #6 x 16′-6	3-#5 x 13′-11 10-#5 x 12′-8	2-#3	4	#5 x 29′-1 #5 x 21′-5	1-#5 x 6′-9	2.89	24
1.092	2-#5 x 8′-6 2-#5 x 7′-10	3	#6 x 31′-1 #5 x 16′-2	— 3-#5 x 12′-8	—	4	#6 x 29′-5 #5 x 21′-5	1-#6 x 6′-9	2.49	25
1.092	3-#5 x 8′-6 3-#5 x 7′-10	3	#6 x 31′-1 #5 x 16′-2	— 4-#5 x 12′-8	—	4	#6 x 29′-5 #5 x 21′-5	1-#6 x 6′-9	2.57	26
1.092	3-#5 x 8′-6 3-#5 x 7′-10	3	#6 x 31′-1 #5 x 16′-2	— 5-#5 x 12′-8	—	4	#6 x 29′-5 #5 x 21′-5	1-#6 x 6′-9	2.58	27
1.092	4-#5 x 8′-6 4-#5 x 7′-10	3	#6 x 31′-1 #5 x 16′-2	1-#5 x 13′-11 5-#5 x 12′-8	—	4	#6 x 29′-5 #5 x 21′-5	1-#6 x 6′-9	2.67	28
1.092	4-#5 x 8′-6 4-#5 x 7′-10	3	#6 x 31′-1 #5 x 16′-2	2-#5 x 13′-11 8-#5 x 12′-8	2-#3	4	#6 x 29′-5 #5 x 21′-5	1-#6 x 6′-9	3.03	29

*,**,†,‡ For notes, see page 9-9.

WAFFLE FLAT SLABS—SQUARE PANELS—30-IN.-WIDE DOMES

For general instructions and notes on the use of this table, see pages 9-3 to 9-9 incl.

	Span Drop-D Form Depth plus Top Slab	Live Load (psf)	t_1 (in.)	Min. Col. Dia. 12'-0 Story Height (in.)	Min. Col. Cap. C (Shear) (in.)	Interior Square Panel — Each Column Strip: No. Jst.	Each Column Strip — Bars: Trussed Straight	Each Column Strip — Bars: Top **	Each Column Strip — Bars: Stirrups per Jst.*	Each Middle Strip: No. Jst.	Each Middle Strip — Bars: Trussed Straight	Wt.† of Steel (psf)
1	L = 24'-0	50	11	15	12	4	#5 x 40'-6 #4 x 16'-2	3-#4 x 15'-11 11-#4 x 14'-5	—	4	#4 x 36'-8 #4 x 24'-8	1.78
2	D = 9'-6 8 + 3	100	11	18	19	4	#6 x 40'-6 #4 x 16'-2	3-#4 x 15'-11 15-#4 x 14'-5	2-#3	4	#5 x 36'-8 #5 x 24'-10	2.62
3	L = 24'-0	50	13	14	12	4	#5 x 40'-8 #4 x 16'-2	2-#4 x 15'-11 9-#4 x 14'-5	—	4	#4 x 36'-10 #4 x 24'-8	1.68
4	D = 9'-6	100	13	18	14	4	#5 x 40'-8 #5 x 16'-2	3-#5 x 15'-11 10-#5 x 14'-5	—	4	#5 x 36'-10 #4 x 24'-8	2.28
5	10 + 3	150	13	20	20	4	#6 x 40'-8 #5 x 16'-2	3-#5 x 15'-11 11-#5 x 14'-5	2-#3	4	#5 x 36'-10 #5 x 24'-10	2.86
6		200	13	22	27	4	#6 x 40'-8 #6 x 16'-6	3-#6 x 15'-11 9-#6 x 14'-5	2-#3	4	#5 x 36'-10 #6 x 25'-0	3.31
7	L = 24'-0	50	15	14	12	4	#4 x 40'-10 #4 x 16'-2	4-#4 x 15'-11 10-#4 x 14'-5	—	4	#4 x 37'-0 #4 x 24'-8	1.58
8	D = 9'-6	100	15	18	12	4	#5 x 40'-10 #5 x 16'-2	3-#5 x 15'-11 8-#5 x 14'-5	—	4	#5 x 37'-0 #4 x 24'-8	2.18
9	12 + 3	150	15	20	15	4	#6 x 40'-10 #5 x 16'-2	2-#5 x 15'-11 10-#5 x 14'-5	2-#3	4	#5 x 37'-0 #4 x 24'-8	2.63
10		200	15	22	21	4	#6 x 40'-10 #5 x 16'-2	3-#5 x 15'-11 12-#5 x 14'-5	2-#3	4	#5 x 37'-0 #5 x 24'-10	2.93
11		300	15	25	32	4	#7 x 40'-10 #5 x 16'-2	3-#5 x 15'-11 14-#5 x 14'-5	2-#3	4	#6 x 37'-0 #5 x 24'-10	3.58
12	L = 24'-0	50	17	14	12	4	#5 x 40'-11 #4 x 16'-2	1-#4 x 15'-11 7-#4 x 14'-5	—	4	#5 x 37'-1 #4 x 24'-8	1.78
13	D = 9'-6	100	17	18	12	4	#5 x 40'-11 #4 x 16'-2	3-#4 x 15'-11 11-#4 x 14'-5	—	4	#5 x 37'-1 #4 x 24'-8	1.99
14	14 + 3	150	17	20	12	4	#5 x 40'-11 #5 x 16'-2	3-#5 x 15'-11 11-#5 x 14'-5	—	4	#5 x 37'-1 #4 x 24'-8	2.34
15		200	17	22	16	4	#6 x 40'-11 #5 x 16'-2	3-#5 x 15'-11 10-#5 x 14'-5	2-#3	4	#5 x 37'-1 #5 x 24'-10	2.84
16		300	17	25	25	4	#6 x 40'-11 #6 x 16'-6	3-#6 x 15'-11 11-#6 x 14'-5	2-#3	4	#6 x 37'-1 #5 x 24'-10	3.57
17	L = 24'-0	50	19	15	12	4	#5 x 41'-1 #4 x 16'-2	1-#4 x 15'-11 7-#4 x 14'-5	—	4	#5 x 37'-3 #4 x 24'-8	1.78
18	D = 9'-6	100	19	18	12	4	#5 x 41'-1 #4 x 16'-2	2-#4 x 15'-11 11-#4 x 14'-5	—	4	#5 x 37'-3 #4 x 24'-8	1.96
19	16 + 3	150	19	20	12	4	#5 x 41'-1 #5 x 16'-2	3-#5 x 15'-11 9-#5 x 14'-5	—	4	#5 x 37'-3 #4 x 24'-8	2.24
20		200	19	22	12	4	#6 x 41'-1 #5 x 16'-2	2-#5 x 15'-11 10-#5 x 14'-5	—	4	#5 x 37'-3 #4 x 24'-8	2.50
21		300	19	25	20	4	#6 x 41'-1 #6 x 16'-6	3-#6 x 15'-11 9-#6 x 14'-5	2-#3	4	#6 x 37'-3 #4 x 24'-8	3.31
22	L = 24'-0	50	23	15	12	4	#5 x 41'-4 #5 x 16'-2	— 4-#5 x 14'-5	—	4	#5 x 37'-6 #5 x 24'-10	1.94
23	D = 9'-6	100	23	18	12	4	#5 x 41'-4 #5 x 16'-2	1-#5 x 15'-11 6-#5 x 14'-5	—	4	#5 x 37'-6 #5 x 24'-10	2.11
24	20 + 3	150	23	20	12	4	#5 x 41'-4 #5 x 16'-2	2-#5 x 15'-11 8-#5 x 14'-5	—	4	#5 x 37'-6 #5 x 24'-10	2.27
25		200	23	22	12	4	#5 x 41'-4 #5 x 16'-2	3-#5 x 15'-11 9-#5 x 14'-5	—	4	#5 x 37'-6 #5 x 24'-10	2.38
26		300	23	25	12	4	#6 x 41'-4 #5 x 16'-2	3-#5 x 15'-11 12-#5 x 14'-5	2-#3	4	#5 x 37'-6 #5 x 24'-10	3.00
27	L = 24'-0	50	12½	14	12	4	#5 x 40'-8 #4 x 16'-2	3-#4 x 15'-11 11-#4 x 14'-5	—	4	#4 x 36'-10 #4 x 24'-8	1.79
28	D = 9'-6	100	12½	18	17	4	#5 x 40'-8 #5 x 16'-2	4-#5 x 15'-11 10-#5 x 14'-5	2-#3	4	#5 x 36'-10 #4 x 24'-8	2.47
29	8 + 4½	150	12½	20	23	4	#6 x 40'-8 #5 x 16'-2	3-#5 x 15'-11 12-#5 x 14'-5	2-#3	4	#5 x 36'-10 #5 x 24'-10	2.90
30		200	12½	22	30	4	#6 x 40'-8 #6 x 16'-6	3-#6 x 15'-11 10-#6 x 14'-5	2-#3	4	#6 x 36'-10 #5 x 24'-10	3.45

*,**,† For notes, see page 9-9.

WAFFLE FLAT SLABS—SQUARE PANELS—30-IN.-WIDE DOMES

For general instructions and notes on the use of this table, see pages 9-3 to 9-9 incl.

Av.‡ Cu. Ft. Conc. (psf)	Strips Perpendicular to an Exterior Wall								Wt.† of Steel (psf)	
	Column Strip					Middle Strip				
	Top Bars at Ext. Col.**	No. Jsts.	Bars: Trussed / Straight	Top Bars at First Int. Col.	Stirrups per Joist *	No. Jsts.	Bars: Trussed / Straight	Top Bars at Ext. Support		
.536	5-#5 x 9'-6 5-#5 x 8'-9	4	#5 x 34'-1 #5 x 16'-2	4-#4 x 15'-11 14-#4 x 14'-5	—	4	#5 x 32'-2 #5 x 24'-5	1-#5 x 7'-6	2.04	1
.536	4-#6 x 9'-6 4-#6 x 8'-9	4	#6 x 34'-1 #6 x 16'-6	5-#4 x 15'-11 17-#4 x 14'-5	2-#3	4	#5 x 32'-2 #6 x 24'-6	2-#5 x 7'-6	2.87	2
.613	4-#5 x 9'-6 4-#5 x 8'-9	4	#5 x 34'-3 #5 x 16'-2	3-#4 x 15'-11 11-#4 x 14'-5	—	4	#4 x 32'-4 #5 x 24'-5	2-#4 x 7'-6	1.86	3
.613	5-#5 x 9'-6 5-#5 x 8'-9	4	#6 x 34'-3 #5 x 16'-2	4-#5 x 15'-11 10-#5 x 14'-5	—	4	#5 x 32'-4 #6 x 24'-6	1-#5 x 7'-6	2.51	4
.613	5-#6 x 9'-6 5-#6 x 8'-9	4	#6 x 34'-3 #6 x 16'-6	4-#5 x 15'-11 13-#5 x 14'-5	2-#3	4	#6 x 32'-4 #5 x 24'-5	1-#6 x 7'-6	3.08	5
.613	5-#6 x 9'-6 5-#6 x 8'-9	4	#7 x 34'-3 #6 x 16'-6	4-#6 x 15'-11 9-#6 x 14'-5	2-#3	4	#6 x 32'-4 #6 x 24'-6	1-#6 x 7'-6	3.54	6
.692	6-#4 x 9'-6 6-#4 x 8'-9	4	#5 x 34'-5 #4 x 16'-2	4-#4 x 15'-11 10-#4 x 14'-5	—	4	#4 x 32'-6 #5 x 24'-5	2-#4 x 7'-6	1.76	7
.692	7-#4 x 9'-6 8-#4 x 8'-9	4	#6 x 34'-5 #4 x 16'-2	3-#5 x 15'-11 9-#5 x 14'-5	—	4	#5 x 32'-6 #5 x 24'-5	1-#5 x 7'-6	2.31	8
.692	4-#6 x 9'-6 4-#6 x 8'-9	4	#6 x 34'-5 #6 x 16'-6	3-#5 x 15'-11 12-#5 x 14'-5	2-#3	4	#5 x 32'-6 #6 x 24'-6	2-#5 x 7'-6	2.91	9
.692	7-#5 x 9'-6 7-#5 x 8'-9	4	#7 x 34'-5 #5 x 16'-2	5-#5 x 15'-11 11-#5 x 14'-5	2-#3	4	#6 x 32'-6 #6 x 24'-6	1-#6 x 7'-6	3.26	10
.692	4-#7 x 9'-6 5-#7 x 8'-9	4	#7 x 34'-5 #7 x 16'-10	5-#5 x 15'-11 16-#5 x 14'-5	2-#3	4	#6 x 32'-6 #7 x 24'-7	2-#6 x 7'-6	4.00	11
.773	5-#4 x 9'-6 5-#4 x 8'-9	4	#5 x 34'-6 #4 x 16'-2	2-#4 x 15'-11 9-#4 x 14'-5	—	4	#5 x 32'-7 #4 x 24'-4	1-#5 x 7'-6	1.82	12
.773	5-#5 x 9'-6 5-#5 x 8'-9	4	#5 x 34'-6 #5 x 16'-2	4-#4 x 15'-11 13-#4 x 14'-5	—	4	#5 x 32'-7 #4 x 24'-4	1-#5 x 7'-6	2.07	13
.773	6-#5 x 9'-6 6-#5 x 8'-9	4	#6 x 34'-6 #5 x 16'-2	4-#5 x 15'-11 10-#5 x 14'-5	—	4	#5 x 32'-7 #6 x 24'-6	1-#5 x 7'-6	2.58	14
.773	5-#6 x 9'-6 5-#6 x 8'-9	4	#6 x 34'-6 #6 x 16'-6	4-#5 x 15'-11 13-#5 x 14'-5	2-#3	4	#5 x 32'-7 #6 x 24'-6	2-#5 x 7'-6	3.10	15
.773	6-#6 x 9'-6 6-#6 x 8'-9	4	#7 x 34'-6 #6 x 16'-6	4-#6 x 15'-11 11-#6 x 14'-5	2-#3	4	#6 x 32'-7 #7 x 24'-7	1-#6 x 7'-6	3.87	16
.856	5-#4 x 9'-6 5-#4 x 8'-9	4	#5 x 34'-8 #4 x 16'-2	1-#4 x 15'-11 9-#4 x 14'-5	—	4	#5 x 32'-9 #4 x 24'-4	1-#5 x 7'-6	1.81	17
.856	4-#5 x 9'-6 4-#5 x 8'-9	4	#5 x 34'-8 #5 x 16'-2	3-#4 x 15'-11 13-#4 x 14'-5	—	4	#5 x 32'-9 #4 x 24'-4	1-#5 x 7'-6	2.02	18
.856	5-#5 x 9'-6 5-#5 x 8'-9	4	#6 x 34'-8 #5 x 16'-2	4-#5 x 15'-11 9-#5 x 14'-5	—	4	#5 x 32'-9 #5 x 24'-5	1-#5 x 7'-6	2.41	19
.856	4-#6 x 9'-6 4-#6 x 8'-9	4	#6 x 34'-8 #6 x 16'-6	3-#5 x 15'-11 12-#5 x 14'-5	—	4	#5 x 32'-9 #6 x 24'-6	2-#5 x 7'-6	2.77	20
.856	5-#6 x 9'-6 5-#6 x 8'-9	4	#7 x 34'-8 #6 x 16'-6	4-#6 x 15'-11 10-#6 x 14'-5	2-#3	4	#6 x 32'-9 #6 x 24'-6	1-#6 x 7'-6	3.59	21
1.028	3-#5 x 9'-6 3-#5 x 8'-9	4	#5 x 34'-11 #5 x 16'-2	1-#5 x 15'-11 5-#5 x 14'-5	—	4	#5 x 33'-0 #5 x 24'-5	1-#5 x 7'-6	1.99	22
1.028	4-#5 x 9'-6 4-#5 x 8'-9	4	#5 x 34'-11 #5 x 16'-2	2-#5 x 15'-11 7-#5 x 14'-5	—	4	#5 x 33'-0 #5 x 24'-5	1-#5 x 7'-6	2.15	23
1.028	5-#5 x 9'-6 5-#5 x 8'-9	4	#5 x 34'-11 #5 x 16'-2	3-#5 x 15'-11 9-#5 x 14'-5	—	4	#5 x 33'-0 #5 x 24'-5	1-#5 x 7'-6	2.30	24
1.028	5-#5 x 9'-6 5-#5 x 8'-9	4	#6 x 34'-11 #5 x 16'-2	4-#5 x 15'-11 9-#5 x 14'-5	—	4	#5 x 33'-0 #5 x 24'-5	1-#5 x 7'-6	2.48	25
1.028	5-#6 x 9'-6 5-#6 x 8'-9	4	#6 x 34'-11 #6 x 16'-6	4-#5 x 15'-11 14-#5 x 14'-5	2-#3	4	#6 x 33'-0 #6 x 24'-6	1-#6 x 7'-6	3.29	26
.661	5-#5 x 9'-6 5-#5 x 8'-9	4	#5 x 34'-3 #5 x 16'-2	4-#4 x 15'-11 13-#4 x 14'-5	—	4	#5 x 32'-4 #4 x 24'-4	1-#5 x 7'-6	1.97	27
.661	6-#5 x 9'-6 6-#5 x 8'-9	4	#6 x 34'-3 #5 x 16'-2	4-#5 x 15'-11 11-#5 x 14'-5	2-#3	4	#5 x 32'-4 #6 x 24'-6	2-#5 x 7'-6	2.77	28
.661	7-#5 x 9'-6 7-#5 x 8'-9	4	#7 x 34'-3 #5 x 16'-2	5-#5 x 15'-11 11-#5 x 14'-5	2-#3	4	#6 x 32'-4 #6 x 24'-6	1-#6 x 7'-6	3.24	29
.661	5-#6 x 9'-6 6-#6 x 8'-9	4	#7 x 34'-3 #6 x 16'-6	4-#6 x 15'-11 11-#6 x 14'-5	2-#3	4	#6 x 32'-4 #7 x 24'-7	1-#6 x 7'-6	3.76	30

*,**,†,‡ For notes, see page 9-9.

WAFFLE FLAT SLABS—SQUARE PANELS—30-IN.-WIDE DOMES

For general instructions and notes on the use of this table, see pages 9-3 to 9-9 incl.

	Span Drop-D Form Depth plus Top Slab	Live Load (psf)	t_1 (in.)	Min. Col. Dia. 12′-0 Story Height (in.)	Min. Col. Cap. C (Shear) (in.)	Interior Square Panel: Each Column Strip: No. Jst.	Each Column Strip: Bars: Trussed Straight	Each Column Strip: Bars: Top **	Each Column Strip: Bars: Stirrups per Jst.*	Each Middle Strip: No. Jst.	Each Middle Strip: Bars: Trussed Straight	Wt.† of Steel (psf)
1	L = 24′-0	50	14½	14	12	4	#5 x 40′-9 #4 x 16′-2	2-#4 x 15′-11 9-#4 x 14′-5	—	4	#4 x 36′-11 #4 x 24′-8	1.69
2	D = 9′-6	100	14½	18	12	4	#5 x 40′-9 #5 x 16′-2	3-#5 x 15′-11 10-#5 x 14′-5	—	4	#5 x 36′-11 #4 x 24′-8	2.28
3	10 + 4½	150	14½	20	18	4	#6 x 40′-9 #5 x 16′-2	3-#5 x 15′-11 10-#5 x 14′-5	2-#3	4	#5 x 36′-11 #5 x 24′-10	2.82
4		200	14½	22	23	4	#6 x 40′-9 #6 x 16′-6	3-#6 x 15′-11 9-#6 x 14′-5	2-#3	4	#5 x 36′-11 #6 x 25′-0	3.32
5		300	14½	25	35	4	#7 x 40′-9 #6 x 16′-6	3-#6 x 15′-11 10-#6 x 14′-5	2-#3	4	#6 x 36′-11 #6 x 25′-0	3.94
6	L = 24′-0	50	16½	14	12	4	#5 x 40′-11 #4 x 16′-2	1-#4 x 15′-11 9-#4 x 14′-5	—	4	#4 x 37′-1 #4 x 24′-8	1.65
7	D = 9′-6	100	16½	18	12	4	#5 x 40′-11 #5 x 16′-2	2-#5 x 15′-11 9-#5 x 14′-5	—	4	#5 x 37′-1 #4 x 24′-8	2.18
8	12 + 4½	150	16½	20	13	4	#6 x 40′-11 #5 x 16′-2	2-#5 x 15′-11 9-#5 x 14′-5	2-#3	4	#5 x 37′-1 #4 x 24′-8	2.60
9		200	16½	22	18	4	#6 x 40′-11 #5 x 16′-2	3-#5 x 15′-11 11-#5 x 14′-5	2-#3	4	#5 x 37′-1 #5 x 24′-10	2.89
10		300	16½	25	28	4	#7 x 40′-11 #5 x 16′-2	3-#5 x 15′-11 13-#5 x 14′-5	2-#3	4	#6 x 37′-1 #5 x 24′-10	3.54
11	L = 24′-0	50	18½	15	12	4	#5 x 41′-1 #4 x 16′-2	1-#4 x 15′-11 8-#4 x 14′-5	—	4	#5 x 37′-3 #4 x 24′-8	1.82
12	D = 9′-6	100	18½	18	12	4	#5 x 41′-1 #4 x 16′-2	3-#4 x 15′-11 11-#4 x 14′-5	—	4	#5 x 37′-3 #4 x 24′-8	1.99
13	14 + 4½	150	18½	20	12	4	#5 x 41′-1 #5 x 16′-2	3-#5 x 15′-11 10-#5 x 14′-5	—	4	#5 x 37′-3 #4 x 24′-8	2.29
14		200	18½	22	13	4	#6 x 41′-1 #5 x 16′-2	3-#5 x 15′-11 10-#5 x 14′-5	2-#3	4	#5 x 37′-3 #5 x 24′-10	2.86
15		300	18½	25	22	4	#6 x 41′-1 #6 x 16′-6	3-#6 x 15′-11 10-#6 x 14′-5	2-#3	4	#6 x 37′-3 #5 x 24′-10	3.51
16	L = 24′-0	50	20½	15	12	4	#5 x 41′-2 #4 x 16′-2	1-#4 x 15′-11 7-#4 x 14′-5	—	4	#5 x 37′-4 #4 x 24′-8	1.79
17	D = 9′-6	100	20½	18	12	4	#5 x 41′-2 #4 x 16′-2	2-#4 x 15′-11 11-#4 x 14′-5	—	4	#5 x 37′-4 #4 x 24′-8	1.96
18	16 + 4½	150	20½	20	12	4	#5 x 41′-2 #5 x 16′-2	3-#5 x 15′-11 8-#5 x 14′-5	—	4	#5 x 37′-4 #4 x 24′-8	2.19
19		200	20½	22	12	4	#6 x 41′-2 #5 x 16′-2	2-#5 x 15′-11 9-#5 x 14′-5	—	4	#5 x 37′-4 #4 x 24′-8	2.45
20		300	20½	25	17	4	#6 x 41′-2 #6 x 16′-6	3-#6 x 15′-11 9-#6 x 14′-5	2-#3	4	#5 x 37′-4 #6 x 25′-0	3.38
21	L = 24′-0	50	24½	15	12	4	#6 x 41′-6 #5 x 16′-2	— 5-#5 x 14′-5	—	4	#6 x 37′-8 #5 x 24′-10	2.51
22	D = 9′-6	100	24½	18	12	4	#6 x 41′-6 #5 x 16′-2	— 5-#5 x 14′-5	—	4	#6 x 37′-8 #5 x 24′-10	2.51
23	20 + 4½	150	24½	20	12	4	#6 x 41′-6 #5 x 16′-2	— 6-#5 x 14′-5	—	4	#6 x 37′-8 #5 x 24′-10	2.56
24		200	24½	22	12	4	#6 x 41′-6 #5 x 16′-2	1-#5 x 15′-11 8-#5 x 14′-5	—	4	#6 x 37′-8 #5 x 24′-10	2.72
25		300	24½	25	12	4	#6 x 41′-6 #5 x 16′-2	3-#5 x 15′-11 11-#5 x 14′-5	2-#3	4	#6 x 37′-8 #5 x 24′-10	3.21
26	L = 27′-0	50	13	16	12	4	#5 x 45′-8 #5 x 19′-2	4-#5 x 17′-10 10-#5 x 16′-3	—	5	#4 x 41′-4 #4 x 27′-8	2.04
27	D = 9′-6 10 + 3	100	13	19	20	4	#6 x 45′-8 #6 x 19′-6	3-#6 x 17′-10 9-#6 x 16′-3	2-#3	5	#5 x 41′-4 #4 x 27′-8	2.85

*,**,† For notes, see page 9-9.

WAFFLE FLAT SLABS—SQUARE PANELS—30-IN.-WIDE DOMES

For general instructions and notes on the use of this table, see pages 9-3 to 9-9 incl.

Av.‡ Cu. Ft. Conc. (psf)	Strips Perpendicular to an Exterior Wall								Wt.† of Steel (psf)	
	Column Strip					Middle Strip				
	Top Bars at Ext. Col.**	No. Jsts.	Bars Trussed Straight	Top Bars at First Int. Col.	Stir-rups per Joist	No. Jsts.	Bars Trussed Straight	Top Bars at Ext. Support		
.738	4-#5 x 9′-6 4-#5 x 8′-9	4	#5 x 34′-4 #5 x 16′-2	3-#4 x 15′-11 11-#4 x 14′-5	—	4	#4 x 32′-5 #5 x 24′-5	2-#4 x 7′-6	1.86	1
.738	5-#5 x 9′-6 5-#5 x 8′-9	4	#6 x 34′-4 #5 x 16′-2	4-#5 x 15′-11 9-#5 x 14′-5	—	4	#5 x 32′-5 #6 x 24′-6	1-#5 x 7′-6	2.50	2
.738	5-#6 x 9′-6 5-#6 x 8′-9	4	#6 x 34′-4 #6 x 16′-6	4-#5 x 15′-11 12-#5 x 14′-5	2-#3	4	#5 x 32′-5 #6 x 24′-6	2-#5 x 7′-6	3.06	3
.738	5-#6 x 9′-6 5-#6 x 8′-9	4	#7 x 34′-4 #6 x 16′-6	4-#6 x 15′-11 9-#6 x 14′-5	2-#3	4	#6 x 32′-5 #6 x 24′-6	1-#6 x 7′-6	3.55	4
.738	5-#7 x 9′-6 5-#7 x 8′-9	4	#7 x 34′-4 #7 x 16′-10	4-#6 x 15′-11 12-#6 x 14′-5	2-#3	4	#6 x 32′-5 #7 x 24′-7	2-#6 x 7′-6	4.24	5
.817	6-#4 x 9′-6 6-#4 x 8′-9	4	#5 x 34′-6 #4 x 16′-2	2-#4 x 15′-11 10-#4 x 14′-5	—	4	#4 x 32′-7 #5 x 24′-5	2-#4 x 7′-6	1.78	6
.817	5-#5 x 9′-6 5-#5 x 8′-9	4	#6 x 34′-6 #5 x 16′-2	3-#5 x 15′-11 8-#5 x 14′-5	—	4	#5 x 32′-7 #5 x 24′-5	1-#5 x 7′-6	2.35	7
.817	4-#6 x 9′-6 4-#6 x 8′-9	4	#6 x 34′-6 #6 x 16′-6	3-#5 x 15′-11 11-#5 x 14′-5	2-#3	4	#5 x 32′-7 #6 x 24′-6	2-#5 x 7′-6	2.89	8
.817	7-#5 x 9′-6 7-#5 x 8′-9	4	#7 x 34′-6 #5 x 16′-2	4-#5 x 15′-11 12-#5 x 14′-5	2-#3	4	#6 x 32′-7 #6 x 24′-6	1-#6 x 7′-6	3.25	9
.817	4-#7 x 9′-6 4-#7 x 8′-9	4	#7 x 34′-6 #7 x 16′-10	4-#5 x 15′-11 16-#5 x 14′-5	2-#3	4	#6 x 32′-7 #7 x 24′-7	2-#6 x 7′-6	3.95	10
.898	5-#4 x 9′-6 5-#4 x 8′-9	4	#5 x 34′-8 #4 x 16′-2	2-#4 x 15′-11 9-#4 x 14′-5	—	4	#5 x 32′-9 #4 x 24′-4	1-#5 x 7′-6	1.84	11
.898	5-#5 x 9′-6 5-#5 x 8′-9	4	#5 x 34′-8 #5 x 16′-2	4-#4 x 15′-11 13-#4 x 14′-5	—	4	#5 x 32′-9 #5 x 24′-5	1-#5 x 7′-6	2.14	12
.898	5-#5 x 9′-6 6-#5 x 8′-9	4	#6 x 34′-8 #5 x 16′-2	4-#5 x 15′-11 10-#5 x 14′-5	—	4	#5 x 32′-9 #6 x 24′-6	1-#5 x 7′-6	2.54	13
.898	5-#6 x 9′-6 5-#6 x 8′-9	4	#6 x 34′-8 #6 x 16′-6	4-#5 x 15′-11 12-#5 x 14′-5	2-#3	4	#5 x 32′-9 #6 x 24′-6	2-#5 x 7′-6	3.10	14
.898	5-#6 x 9′-6 6-#6 x 8′-9	4	#7 x 34′-8 #6 x 16′-6	4-#6 x 15′-11 10-#6 x 14′-5	2-#3	4	#6 x 32′-9 #7 x 24′-7	1-#6 x 7′-6	3.80	15
.981	5-#4 x 9′-6 5-#4 x 8′-9	4	#5 x 34′-9 #4 x 16′-2	1-#4x 15′-11 9-#4 x 14′-5	—	4	#5 x 32′-10 #4 x 24′-4	1-#5 x 7′-6	1.82	16
.981	4-#5 x 9′-6 4-#5 x 8′-9	4	#5 x 34′-9 #5 x 16′-2	3-#4 x 15′-11 12-#4 x 14′-5	—	4	#5 x 32′-10 #4 x 24′-4	1-#5 x 7′-6	2.01	17
.981	5-#5 x 9′-6 5-#5 x 8′-9	4	#6 x 34′-9 #5 x 16′-2	4-#5 x 15′-11 8-#5 x 14′-5	—	4	#5 x 32′-10 #5 x 24′-5	1-#5 x 7′-6	2.37	18
.981	4-#6 x 9′-6 4-#6 x 8′-9	4	#6 x 34′-9 #6 x 16′-6	3-#5 x 15′-11 11-#5 x 14′-5	—	4	#5 x 32′-10 #6 x 24′-6	2-#5 x 7′-6	2.74	19
.981	5-#6 x 9′-6 5-#6 x 8′-9	4	#7 x 34′-9 #6 x 16′-6	4-#6 x 15′-11 9-#6 x 14′-5	2-#3	4	#6 x 32′-10 #6 x 24′-6	1-#6 x 7′-6	3.61	20
1.153	3-#5 x 9′-6 3-#5 x 8′-9	4	#6 x 35′-1 #5 x 16′-2	— 5-#5 x 14′-5	—	4	#6 x 33′-2 #5 x 24′-5	1-#6 x 7′-6	2.50	21
1.153	4-#5 x 9′-6 4-#5 x 8′-9	4	#6 x 35′-1 #5 x 16′-2	— 6-#5 x 14′-5	—	4	#6 x 33′-2 #5 x 24′-5	1-#6 x 7′-6	2.55	22
1.153	5-#5 x 9′-6 5-#5 x 8′-9	4	#6 x 35′-1 #5 x 16′-2	1-#5 x 15′-11 7-#5 x 14′-5	—	4	#6 x 33′-2 #5 x 24′-5	1-#6 x 7′-6	2.63	23
1.153	5-#5 x 9′-6 5-#5 x 8′-9	4	#6 x 35′-1 #5 x 16′-2	2-#5 x 15′-11 9-#5 x 14′-5	—	4	#6 x 33′-2 #5 x 24′-5	1-#6 x 7′-6	2.76	24
1.153	5-#6 x 9′-6 5-#6 x 8′-9	4	#6 x 35′-1 #6 x 16′-6	4-#5 x 15′-11 13-#5 x 14′-5	2-#3	4	#6 x 33′-2 #5 x 24′-5	1-#6 x 7′-6	3.31	25
.597	6-#5 x 10′-5 6-#5 x 9′-8	4	#6 x 38′-3 #5 x 19′-2	5-#5 x 17′-10 10-#5 x 16′-3	—	5	#5 x 36′-1 #5 x 27′-5	1-#5 x 8′-3	2.31	26
.597	5-#6 x 10′-5 5-#6 x 9′-8	4	#7 x 38′-3 #6 x 19′-6	4-#6 x 17′-10 9-#6 x 16′-3	2-#3	5	#5 x 36′-1 #6 x 27′-6	2-#5 x 8′-3	3.16	27

*,**,† For notes, see page 9-9.

WAFFLE FLAT SLABS—SQUARE PANELS—30-IN.-WIDE DOMES

For general instructions and notes on the use of this table, see pages 9-3 to 9-9 incl.

	Span Drop-D Form Depth plus Top Slab	Live Load (psf)	t_1 (in.)	Min. Col. Dia. 12'-0 Story Height (in.)	Min. Col. Cap. C (Shear) (in.)	Interior Square Panel: Each Column Strip: No. Jst.	Each Column Strip: Bars: Trussed Straight	Each Column Strip: Bars: Top **	Each Column Strip: Bars: Stirrups per Jst.*	Each Middle Strip: No. Jst.	Each Middle Strip: Bars: Trussed Straight	Wt.† of Steel (psf)
1	L = 27'-0	50	15	16	12	4	#5 x 45'-10 #5 x 19'-2	3-#5 x 17'-10 9-#5 x 16'-3	—	5	#4 x 41'-6 #4 x 27'-8	1.95
2	D = 9'-6	100	15	19	15	4	#6 x 45'-10 #5 x 19'-2	3-#5 x 17'-10 12-#5 x 16'-3	2-#3	5	#5 x 41'-6 #4 x 27'-8	2.65
3	12 + 3	150	15	22	22	4	#6 x 45'-10 #6 x 19'-6	4-#6 x 17'-10 10-#6 x 16'-3	2-#3	5	#5 x 41'-6 #5 x 27'-10	3.15
4		200	15	24	29	4	#7 x 45'-10 #6 x 19'-6	3-#6 x 17'-10 12-#6 x 16'-3	2-#3	5	#5 x 41'-6 #6 x 28'-0	3.66
5	L = 27'-0	50	17	16	12	4	#5 x 45'-11 #5 x 19'-2	3-#5 x 17'-10 8-#5 x 16'-3	—	5	#5 x 41'-7 #4 x 27'-8	2.12
6	D = 9'-6	100	17	19	12	4	#6 x 45'-11 #5 x 19'-2	3-#5 x 17'-10 10-#5 x 16'-3	—	5	#5 x 41'-7 #4 x 27'-8	2.44
7	14 + 3	150	17	22	17	4	#6 x 45'-11 #6 x 19'-6	3-#6 x 17'-10 10-#6 x 16'-3	2-#3	5	#5 x 41'-7 #5 x 27'-10	3.09
8		200	17	24	23	4	#7 x 45'-11 #6 x 19'-6	3-#6 x 17'-10 10-#6 x 16'-3	2-#3	5	#5 x 41'-7 #5 x 27'-10	3.36
9		300	17	27	35	4	#7 x 45'-11 #7 x 19'-10	3-#7 x 17'-10 11-#7 x 16'-3	2-#3	5	#6 x 41'-7 #5 x 27'-10	4.16
10	L = 27'-0	50	19	16	12	4	#5 x 46'-1 #4 x 19'-2	3-#4 x 17'-10 12-#4 x 16'-3	—	5	#5 x 41'-9 #4 x 27'-8	1.97
11	D = 9'-6	100	19	19	12	4	#6 x 46'-1 #4 x 19'-2	3-#4 x 17'-10 15-#4 x 16'-3	—	5	#5 x 41'-9 #4 x 27'-8	2.30
12	16 + 3	150	19	22	13	4	#6 x 46'-1 #6 x 19'-6	3-#6 x 17'-10 9-#6 x 16'-3	2-#3	5	#5 x 41'-9 #4 x 27'-8	2.89
13		200	19	24	18	4	#7 x 46'-1 #5 x 19'-2	3-#5 x 17'-10 14-#5 x 16'-3	2-#3	5	#5 x 41'-9 #5 x 27'-10	3.19
14		300	19	27	29	4	#7 x 46'-1 #7 x 19'-10	3-#7 x 17'-10 9-#7 x 16'-3	2-#3	5	#6 x 41'-9 #5 x 27'-10	3.99
15	L = 27'-0	50	23	16	12	4	#5 x 46'-4 #5 x 19'-2	2-#5 x 17'-10 7-#5 x 16'-3	—	5	#5 x 42'-0 #5 x 27'-10	2.18
16	D = 9'-6	100	23	19	12	4	#5 x 46'-4 #5 x 19'-2	3-#5 x 17'-10 10-#5 x 16'-3	—	5	#5 x 42'-0 #5 x 27'-10	2.37
17	20 + 3	150	23	22	12	4	#6 x 46'-4 #5 x 19'-2	3-#5 x 17'-10 11-#5 x 16'-3	—	5	#5 x 42'-0 #5 x 27'-10	2.65
18		200	23	24	12	4	#6 x 46'-4 #6 x 19'-6	3-#6 x 17'-10 10-#6 x 16'-3	2-#3	5	#5 x 42'-0 #5 x 27'-10	3.13
19		300	23	27	19	4	#7 x 46'-4 #6 x 19'-6	3#-6 x 17'-10 11-#6 x 16'-3	2-#3	5	#6 x 42'-0 #4 x 27'-8	3.60
20	L = 27'-0	50	12½	16	15	4	#6 x 45'-7 #5 x 19'-2	3-#5 x 17'-10 10-#5 x 16'-3	2-#3	5	#5 x 41'-4 #4 x 27'-8	2.54
21	D = 9'-6 8 + 4½	100	12½	19	23	4	#6 x 45'-7 #6 x 19'-6	4-#6 x 17'-10 10-#6 x 16'-3	2-#3	5	#5 x 41'-4 #5 x 27'-10	3.13
22	L = 27'-0	50	14½	16	12	4	#6 x 45'-9 #4 x 19'-2	3-#4 x 17'-10 13-#4 x 16'-3	—	5	#4 x 41'-5 #4 x 27'-8	2.01
23	D = 9'-6	100	14½	19	18	4	#6 x 45'-9 #6 x 19'-6	3-#6 x 17'-10 9-#6 x 16'-3	2-#3	5	#5 x 41'-5 #4 x 27'-8	2.86
24	10 + 4½	150	14½	22	25	4	#7 x 45'-9 #6 x 19'-6	3-#6 x 17'-10 10-#6 x 16'-3	2-#3	5	#5 x 41'-5 #5 x 27'-10	3.34
25		200	14½	23	32	4	#7 x 45'-9 #7 x 19'-10	3-#7 x 17'-10 9-#7 x 16'-3	2-#3	5	#6 x 41'-5 #5 x 27'-10	3.96
26	L = 27'-0	50	16½	16	12	4	#5 x 45'-11 #5 x 19'-2	3-#5 x 17'-10 9-#5 x 16'-3	—	5	#4 x 41'-7 #4 x 27'-8	1.95
27	D = 9'-6	100	16½	19	13	4	#6 x 45'-11 #6 x 19'-6	2-#6 x 17'-10 9-#6 x 16'-3	2-#3	5	#5 x 41'-7 #4 x 27'-8	2.80
28	12 + 4½	150	16½	22	20	4	#7 x 45'-11 #5 x 19'-2	3-#5 x 17'-10 12-#5 x 16'-3	2-#3	5	#5 x 41'-7 #5 x 27'-10	3.08
29		200	16½	24	26	4	#7 x 45'-11 #6 x 19'-6	3-#6 x 17'-10 11-#6 x 16'-3	2-#3	5	#5 x 41'-7 #6 x 28'-0	3.60
30		300	16½	27	39	4	#8 x 45'-11 #6 x 19'-6	3-#6 x 17'-10 13-#6 x 16'-3	4-#4	5	#6 x 41'-7 #6 x 28'-0	4.63

*,**,† For notes, see page 9-9.

WAFFLE FLAT SLABS—SQUARE PANELS—30-IN.-WIDE DOMES

For general instructions and notes on the use of this table, see pages 9-3 to 9-9 incl.

Av.‡ Cu. Ft. Conc. (psf)	Strips Perpendicular to an Exterior Wall								Wt.† of Steel (psf)	
	Column Strip					Middle Strip				
	Top Bars at Ext. Col.**	No. Jsts.	Bars: Trussed / Straight	Top Bars at First Int. Col.	Stir-rups per Joist*	No. Jsts.	Bars: Trussed / Straight	Top Bars at Ext. Support		
.673	5-#5 x 10′-5 5-#5 x 9′-8	4	#6 x 38′-5 #5 x 19′-2	4-#5 x 17′-10 9-#5 x 16′-3	—	5	#4 x 36′-3 #5 x 27′-5	2-#4 x 8′-3	2.14	1
.673	7-#5 x 10′-5 7-#5 x 9′-8	4	#7 x 38′-5 #5 x 19′-2	5-#5 x 17′-10 11-#5 x 16′-3	2-#3	5	#5 x 36′-3 #6 x 27′-6	1-#5 x 8′-3	2.92	2
.673	4-#7 x 10′-5 4-#7 x 9′-8	4	#7 x 38′-5 #7 x 19′-10	5-#6 x 17′-10 11-#6 x 16′-3	2-#3	5	#6 x 36′-3 #5 x 27′-5	1-#6 x 8′-3	3.44	3
.673	7-#6 x 10′-5 7-#6 x 9′-8	4	#8 x 38′-5 #6 x 19′-6	4-#6 x 17′-10 12-#6 x 16′-3	2-#3	5	#6 x 36′-3 #6 x 27′-6	1-#6 x 8′-3	3.92	4
.751	7-#4 x 10′-5 8-#4 x 9′-8	4	#6 x 38′-6 #4 x 19′-2	3-#5 x 17′-10 9-#5 x 16′-3	—	5	#5 x 36′-4 #4 x 27′-4	1-#5 x 8′-3	2.17	5
.751	5-#6 x 10′-5 5-#6 x 9′-8	4	#6 x 38′-6 #6 x 19′-6	4-#5 x 17′-10 12-#5 x 16′-3	—	5	#5 x 36′-4 #5 x 27′-5	1-#5 x 8′-3	2.61	6
.751	5-#6 x 10′-5 6-#6 x 9′-8	4	#7 x 38′-6 #6 x 19′-6	4-#6 x 17′-10 10-#6 x 16′-3	2-#3	5	#5 x 36′-4 #6 x 27′-6	2-#5 x 8′-3	3.33	7
.751	5-#7 x 10′-5 5-#7 x 9′-8	4	#7 x 38′-6 #7 x 19′-10	4-#6 x 17′-10 12-#6 x 16′-3	2-#3	5	#6 x 36′-4 #6 x 27′-6	1-#6 x 8′-3	3.70	8
.751	6-#7 x 10′-5 6-#7 x 9′-8	4	#8 x 38′-6 #7 x 19′-10	4-#7 x 17′-10 11-#7 x 16′-3	2-#3	5	#6 x 36′-4 #7 x 27′-7	2-#6 x 8′-3	4.55	9
.831	5-#5 x 10′-5 5-#5 x 9′-8	4	#5 x 38′-8 #5 x 19′-2	4-#4 x 17 -10 15-#4 x 16′-3	—	5	#5 x 36′-6 #4 x 27′-4	1-#5 x 8′-3	2.05	10
.831	4-#6 x 10′-5 4-#6 x 9′-8	4	#6 x 38′-8 #6 x 19′-6	5-#4 x 17′-10 17-#4 x 16′-3	—	5	#5 x 36′-6 #5 x 27′-5	1-#5 x 8′-3	2.48	11
.831	5-#6 x 10′-5 5-#6 x 9′-8	4	#7 x 38′-8 #6 x 19′-6	4-#6 x 17′-10 9-#6 x 16′-3	2-#3	5	#5 x 36′-6 #6 x 27′-6	2-#5 x 8′-3	3.20	12
.831	4-#7 x 10′-5 5-#7 x 9′-8	4	#7 x 38′-8 #7 x 19′-10	4-#5 x 17′-10 17-#5 x 16′-3	2-#3	5	#6 x 36′-6 #5 x 27′-5	1-#6 x 8′-3	3.48	13
.831	5-#7 x 10′-5 5-#7 x 9′-8	4	#8 x 38′-8 #7 x 19′-10	4-#7 x 17′-10 10-#7 x 16′-3	2-#3	5	#6 x 36′-6 #7 x 27′-7	2-#6 x 8′-3	4.40	14
.998	4-#5 x 10′-5 4-#5 x 9′-8	4	#5 x 38′-11 #5 x 19′-2	2-#5 x 17′-10 9-#5 x 16′-3	—	5	#5 x 36′-9 #5 x 27′-5	1-#5 x 8′-3	2.18	15
.998	5-#5 x 10′-5 5-#5 x 9′-8	4	#6 x 38′-11 #5 x 19′-2	4-#5 x 17′-10 10-#5 x 16′-3	—	5	#5 x 36′-9 #5 x 27′-5	1-#5 x 8′-3	2.44	16
.998	5-#6 x 10′-5 5-#6 x 9′-8	4	#6 x 38′-11 #6 x 19′-6	4-#5 x 17′-10 13-#5 x 16′-3	—	5	#5 x 36′-9 #5 x 27′-5	1-#5 x 8′-3	2.73	17
.998	5-#6 x 10′-5 5-#6 x 9′-8	4	#7 x 38′-11 #6 x 19′-6	4-#6 x 17′-10 10-#6 x 16′-3	2-#3	5	#5 x 36′-9 #6 x 27′-6	2-#5 x 8′-3	3.36	18
.998	5-#7 x 10′-5 5-#7 x 9′-8	4	#7 x 38′-11 #7 x 19′-10	4-#6 x 17′-10 14-#6 x 16′-3	2-#3	5	#6 x 36′-9 #6 x 27′-6	1-#6 x 8′-3	3.87	19
.648	4-#6 x 10′-5 5-#6 x 9′-8	4	#6 x 38′-3 #6 x 19′-6	3-#5 x 17′-10 12-#5 x 16′-3	2-#3	5	#5 x 36′-1 #5 x 27′-5	1-#5 x 8′-3	2.67	20
.648	6-#6 x 10′-5 6-#6 x 9′-8	4	#7 x 38′-3 #6 x 19′-6	4-#6 x 17′-10 11-#6 x 16′-3	2-#3	5	#5 x 36′-1 #6 x 27′-6	2-#5 x 8′-3	3.37	21
.722	4-#6 x 10′-5 4-#6 x 9′-8	4	#6 x 38′-4 #6 x 19′-6	4-#4 x 17′-10 16-#4 x 16′-3	—	5	#5 x 36′-2 #5 x 27′-5	1-#5 x 8′-3	2.31	22
.722	5-#6 x 10′-5 5-#6 x 9′-8	4	#7 x 38′-4 #6 x 19′-6	4-#6 x 17′-10 9-#6 x 16′-3	2-#3	5	#5 x 36′-2 #6 x 27′-6	2-#5 x 8′-3	3.17	23
.722	5-#7 x 10′-5 5-#7 x 9′-8	4	#7 x 38′-4 #7 x 19′-10	4-#6 x 17′-10 12-#6 x 16′-3	2-#3	5	#6 x 36′-2 #6 x 27′-6	1-#6 x 8′-3	3.68	24
.722	5-#7 x 10′-5 5-#7 x 9′-8	4	#8 x 38′-4 #7 x 19′-10	4-#7 x 17′-10 9-#7 x 16′-3	2-#3	5	#6 x 36′-2 #7 x 27′-7	1-#6 x 8′-3	4.25	25
.798	5-#5 x 10′-5 5-#5 x 9′-8	4	#6 x 38′-6 #5 x 19′-2	4-#5 x 17′-10 9-#5 x 16′-3	—	5	#4 x 36′-4 #5 x 27′-5	2-#4 x 8′-3	2.14	26
.798	7-#5 x 10′-5 7-#5 x 9′-8	4	#7 x 38′-6 #5 x 19′-2	3-#6 x 17′-10 9-#6 x 16′-3	2-#3	5	#5 x 36′-4 #6 x 27′-6	1-#5 x 8′-3	3.01	27
.798	4-#7 x 10′-5 4-#7 x 9′-8	4	#7 x 38′-6 #7 x 19′-10	4-#5 x 17′-10 15-#5 x 16′-3	2-#3	5	#6 x 36′-4 #5 x 27′-5	1-#6 x 8′-3	3.36	28
.798	6-#6 x 10′-5 7-#6 x 9′-8	4	#8 x 38′-6 #6 x 19′-6	4-#6 x 17′-10 12-#6 x 16′-3	2-#3	5	#6 x 36′-4 #6 x 27′-6	1-#6 x 8′-3	3.87	29
.798	4-#8 x 10′-5 9-#8 x 9′-8	4	#8 x 38′-6 #8 x 20′-2	4-#6 x 17′-10 15-#6 x 16′-3	4-#4	5	#6 x 36′-4 #7 x 27′-7	2-#6 x 8′-3	4.98	30

*,**,† For notes, see page 9-9.

WAFFLE FLAT SLABS—SQUARE PANELS—30-IN.-WIDE DOMES

For general instructions and notes on the use of this table, see pages 9-3 to 9-9 incl.

	Span / Drop- D / Form Depth plus Top Slab	Live Load (psf)	t_1 (in.)	Min. Col. Dia. 12′-0 Story Height (in.)	Min. Col. Cap. C (Shear) (in.)	Interior Square Panel: Each Column Strip: No. Jst.	Each Column Strip: Bars: Trussed Straight	Each Column Strip: Bars: Top **	Each Column Strip: Bars: Stirrups per Jst.*	Each Middle Strip: No. Jst.	Each Middle Strip: Bars: Trussed Straight	Wt.† of Steel (psf)
1	L = 27′-0	50	18½	16	12	4	#5 x 46′-0 #5 x 19′-2	3-#5 x 17′-10 8-#5 x 16′-3	—	5	#5 x 41′-9 #4 x 27′-8	2.12
2	D = 9′-6	100	18½	19	12	4	#6 x 46′-0 #5 x 19′-2	3-#5 x 17′-10 10-#5 x 16′-3	—	5	#5 x 41′-9 #4 x 27′-8	2.45
3	14 + 4½	150	18½	22	15	4	#6 x 46′-0 #6 x 19′-6	3-#6 x 17′-10 10-#6 x 16′-3	2-#3	5	#5 x 41′-9 #5 x 27′-10	3.10
4		200	18½	24	20	4	#7 x 46′-0 #6 x 19′-6	3-#6 x 17′-10 10-#6 x 16′-3	2-#3	5	#5 x 41′-9 #5 x 27′-10	3.37
5		300	18½	27	32	4	#7 x 46′-0 #7 x 19′-10	3-#7 x 17′-10 10-#7 x 16′-3	2-#3	5	#6 x 41′-9 #5 x 27′-10	4.08
6	L = 27′-0	50	20½	16	12	4	#5 x 46′-2 #5 x 19′-2	2-#5 x 17′-10 8-#5 x 16′-3	—	5	#5 x 41′-10 #4 x 27′-8	2.07
7	D = 9′-6	100	20½	19	12	4	#6 x 46′-2 #5 x 19′-2	2-#5 x 17′-10 10-#5 x 16′-3	—	5	#5 x 41′-10 #4 x 27′-8	2.40
8	16 + 4½	150	20½	22	12	4	#6 x 46′-2 #6 x 19′-6	3-#6 x 17′-10 9-#6 x 16′-3	2-#3	5	#5 x 41′-10 #4 x 27′-8	2.90
9		200	20½	24	16	4	#7 x 46′-2 #5 x 19′-2	3-#5 x 17′-10 13-#5 x 16′-3	2-#3	5	#5 x 41′-10 #5 x 27′-10	3.16
10		300	20½	27	26	4	#7 x 46′-2 #7 x 19′-10	3-#7 x 17′-10 9-#7 x 16′-3	2-#3	5	#6 x 41′-10 #5 x 27′-10	4.01
11	L = 27′-0	50	24½	16	12	4	#6 x 46′-5 #5 x 19′-2	— 6-#5 x 16′-3	—	5	#6 x 42′-2 #5 x 27′-10	2.53
12	D = 9′-6	100	24½	19	12	4	#6 x 46′-5 #5 x 19′-2	2-#5 x 17′-10 8-#5 x 16′-3	—	5	#6 x 42′-2 #5 x 27′-10	2.73
13	20 + 4½	150	24½	22	12	4	#6 x 46′-5 #5 x 19′-2	3-#5 x 17′-10 10-#5 x 16′-3	—	5	#6 x 42′-2 #5 x 27′-10	2.87
14		200	24½	24	12	4	#6 x 46′-5 #6 x 19′-6	3-#6 x 17′-10 9-#6 x 16′-3	2-#3	5	#6 x 42′-2 #5 x 27′-10	3.34
15		300	24½	27	16	4	#7 x 46′-5 #6 x 19′-6	3-#6 x 17′-10 11-#6 x 16′-3	2-#3	5	#6 x 42′-2 #5 x 27′-10	3.75
16	L = 30′-0	50	13	17	18	5	#6 x 50′-8 #5 x 19′-2	3-#5 x 19′-10 13-#5 x 18′-0	—	5	#5 x 45′-10 #5 x 30′-10	2.64
17	D = 12′-6 10 + 3	100	13	20	28	5	#6 x 50′-8 #6 x 19′-6	4-#6 x 19′-10 13-#6 x 18′-0	2-#3	5	#6 x 45′-10 #5 x 30′-10	3.44
18	L = 30′-0	50	15	17	14	5	#6 x 50′-9 #4 x 19′-2	4-#4 x 19′-10 18-#4 x 18′-0	—	5	#5 x 46′-0 #4 x 30′-8	2.35
19	D = 12′-6	100	15	20	23	5	#6 x 50′-9 #6 x 19′-6	4-#6 x 19′-10 11-#6 x 18′-0	2-#3	5	#5 x 46′-0 #6 x 31′-0	3.27
20	12 + 3	150	15	23	31	5	#7 x 50′-9 #6 x 19′-6	3-#6 x 19′-10 13-#6 x 18′-0	2-#3	5	#6 x 46′-0 #5 x 30′-10	3.70
21	L = 30′-0	50	17	17	12	5	#5 x 50′-11 #5 x 19′-2	4-#5 x 19′-10 13-#5 x 18′-0	—	5	#5 x 46′-1 #4 x 30′-8	2.30
22	D = 12′-6	100	17	20	18	5	#6 x 50′-11 #6 x 19′-6	3-#6 x 19′-10 11-#6 x 18′-0	—	5	#5 x 46′-1 #5 x 30′-10	2.93
23	14 + 3	150	17	23	25	5	#7 x 50′-11 #5 x 19′-2	4-#5 x 19′-10 17-#5 x 18′-0	2-#3	5	#6 x 46′-1 #5 x 30′-10	3.53
24		200	17	25	33	5	#7 x 50′-11 #6 x 19′-6	4-#6 x 19′-10 14-#6 x 18′-0	2-#3	5	#6 x 46′-1 #6 x 31′-0	4.00
25		300	17	28	48	5	#7 x 50′-11 #7 x 19′-10	5-#7 x 19′-10 13-#7 x 18′-0	2-#3	5	#7 x 46′-1 #6 x 31′-0	4.81
26	L = 30′-0	50	19	17	12	5	#5 x 51′-1 #5 x 19′-2	4-#5 x 19′-10 11-#5 x 18′-0	—	5	#5 x 46′-3 #4 x 30′-8	2.22
27	D = 12′-6	100	19	20	14	5	#6 x 51′-1 #5 x 19′-2	4-#5 x 19′-10 14-#5 x 18′-0	—	5	#5 x 46′-3 #5 x 30′-10	2.74
28	16 + 3	150	19	23	21	5	#6 x 51′-1 #6 x 19′-6	4-#6 x 19′-10 13-#6 x 18′-0	2-#3	5	#6 x 46′-3 #5 x 30′-10	3.49
29		200	19	25	27	5	#7 x 51′-1 #6 x 19′-6	4-#6 x 19′-10 13-#6 x 18′-0	2-#3	5	#6 x 46′-3 #5 x 30′-10	3.80
30		300	19	28	41	5	#7 x 51′-1 #7 x 19′-10	4-#7 x 19′-10 13-#7 x 18′-0	2-#3	5	#7 x 46′-3 #5 x 30′-10	4.58

*,**,† For notes, see page 9-9.

WAFFLE FLAT SLABS—SQUARE PANELS—30-IN.-WIDE DOMES

For general instructions and notes on the use of this table, see pages 9-3 to 9-9 incl.

Av.‡ Cu. Ft. Conc. (psf)	Strips Perpendicular to an Exterior Wall — Column Strip: Top Bars at Ext. Col.**	No. Jsts.	Bars: Trussed / Straight	Top Bars at First Int. Col.	Stirrups per Joist*	Middle Strip: No. Jsts.	Bars: Trussed / Straight	Top Bars at Ext. Support	Wt.† of Steel (psf)	
.876	5-#5 x 10′-5 5-#5 x 9′-8	4	#6 x 38′-7 #5 x 19′-2	3-#5 x 17′-10 9-#5 x 16′-3	—	5	#5 x 36′-6 #4 x 27′-4	1-#5 x 8′-3	2.22	1
.876	5-#6 x 10′-5 5-#6 x 9′-8	4	#6 x 38′-7 #6 x 19′-6	4-#5 x 17′-10 12-#5 x 16′-3	—	5	#5 x 36′-6 #5 x 27′-5	1-#5 x 8′-3	2.62	2
.876	5-#6 x 10′-5 5-#6 x 9′-8	4	#7 x 38′-7 #6 x 19′-6	4-#6 x 17′-10 10-#6 x 16′-3	2-#3	5	#5 x 36′-6 #6 x 27′-6	2-#5 x 8′-3	3.32	3
.876	5-#7 x 10′-5 5-#7 x 9′-8	4	#7 x 38′-7 #7 x 19′-10	4-#6 x 17′-10 12-#6 x 16′-3	2-#3	5	#6 x 36′-6 #6 x 27′-6	1-#6 x 8′-3	3.71	4
.876	5-#7 x 10′-5 6-#7 x 9′-8	4	#8 x 38′-7 #7 x 19′-10	4-#7 x 17′-10 10-#7 x 16′-3	2-#3	5	#6 x 36′-6 #7 x 27′-7	2-#6 x 8′-3	4.46	5
.956	7-#4 x 10′-5 7-#4 x 9′-8	4	#6 x 38′-9 #4 x 19′-2	3-#5 x 17′-10 8-#5 x 16′-3	—	5	#5 x 36′-7 #4 x 27′-4	1-#5 x 8′-3	2.13	6
.956	4-#6 x 10′-5 4-#6 x 9′-8	4	#6 x 38′-9 #6 x 19′-6	3-#5 x 17′-10 11-#5 x 16′-3	—	5	#5 x 36′-7 #5 x 27′-5	1-#5 x 8′-3	2.53	7
.956	5-#6 x 10′-5 5-#6 x 9′-8	4	#7 x 38′-9 #6 x 19′-6	4-#6 x 17′-10 9-#6 x 16′-3	2-#3	5	#5 x 36′-7 #6 x 27′-6	2-#5 x 8′-3	3.21	8
.956	4-#7 x 10′-5 4-#7 x 9′-8	4	#7 x 38′-9 #7 x 19′-10	4-#5 x 17′-10 16-#5 x 16′-3	2-#3	5	#6 x 36′-7 #5 x 27′-5	1-#6 x 8-3	3.43	9
.956	5-#7 x 10′-5 5-#7 x 9′-8	4	#8 x 38′-9 #7 x 19′-10	4-#7 x 17′-10 9-#7 x 16′-3	2-#3	5	#6 x 36′-7 #7 x 27′-7	2-#6 x 8′-3	4.39	10
1.123	4-#5 x 10′-5 5-#5 x 9′-8	4	#6 x 39′-0 #5 x 19′-2	1-#5 x 17′-10 7-#5 x 16′-3	—	5	#6 x 36′-11 #5 x 27′-5	1-#6 x 8′-3	2.58	11
1.123	5-#5 x 10′-5 6-#5 x 9′-8	4	#6 x 39′-0 #5 x 19′-2	2-#5 x 17′-10 10-#5 x 16′-3	—	5	#6 x 36′-11 #5 x 27′-5	1-#6 x 8′-3	2.75	12
1.123	5-#6 x 10′-5 5-#6 x 9′-8	4	#6 x 39′-0 #6 x 19′-6	4-#5 x 17′-10 12-#5 x 16′-3	—	5	#6 x 36′-11 #5 x 27′-5	1-#6 x 8′-3	2.98	13
1.123	5-#6 x 10′-5 5-#6 x 9′-8	4	#7 x 39′-0 #6 x 19′-6	4-#6 x 17′-10 9-#6 x 16′-3	2-#3	5	#6 x 36′-11 #5 x 27--5	1-#6 x 8′-3	3.45	14
1.123	6-#6 x 10′-5 7-#6 x 9′-8	4	#8 x 39′-0 #6 x 19′-6	4-#6 x 17′-10 12-#6 x 16′-3	2-#3	5	#6 x 36′-11 #6 x 27′-6	1-#6 x 8′-3	3.98	15
.624	6-#6 x 11′-5 6-#6 x 10′-6	5	#6 x 42′-3 #6 x 19′-6	5-#5 x 19′-10 15-#5 x 18′-0	—	5	#5 x 39′-10 #6 x 30′-6	2-#5 x 9′-0	2.86	16
.624	7-#6 x 11′-5 7-#6 x 10′-6	5	#7 x 42′-3 #6 x 19′-6	5-#6 x 19′-10 14-#6 x 18′-0	2-#3	5	#6 x 39′-10 #7 x 30′-7	1-#6 x 9′-0	3.72	17
.705	5-#6 x 11′-5 5-#6 x 10′-6	5	#6 x 42′-4 #6 x 19′-6	6-#4 x 19′-10 21-#4 x 18′-0	—	5	#5 x 40′-0 #6 x 30′-6	2-#5 x 9′-0	2.65	18
.705	6-#6 x 11′-5 7-#6 x 10′-6	5	#7 x 42′-4 #6 x 19′-6	5-#6 x 19′-10 12-#6 x 18′-0	2-#3	5	#6 x 40′-0 #6 x 30′-6	1-#6 x 9′-0	3.50	19
.705	6-#7 x 11′-5 6-#7 x 10′-6	5	#7 x 42′-4 #7 x 19′-10	5-#6 x 19′-10 15-#6 x 18′-0	2-#3	5	#6 x 40′-0 #7 x 30′-7	2-#6 x 9′-0	4.05	20
.788	7-#5 x 11′-5 7-#5 x 10′-6	5	#6 x 42′-6 #5 x 19′-2	5-#5 x 19′-10 13-#5 x 18′-0	—	5	#5 x 40′-1 #6 x 30′-6	2-#5 x 9′-0	2.58	21
.788	8-#5 x 11′-5 9-#5 x 10′-6	5	#7 x 42′-6 #5 x 19′-2	4-#6 x 19′-10 11-#6 x 18′-0	—	5	#6 x 40′-1 #6 x 30′-6	1-#6 x 9′-0	3.17	22
.788	5-#7 x 11′-5 5-#7 x 10′-6	5	#7 x 42′-6 #7 x 19′-10	5-#5 x 19′-10 20-#5 x 18′-0	2-#3	5	#6 x 40′-1 #7 x 30′-7	2-#6 x 9′-0	3.88	23
.788	8-#6 x 11′-5 8-#6 x 10′-6	5	#8 x 42′-6 #6 x 19′-6	5-#6 x 19′-10 15-#6 x 18′-0	2-#3	5	#7 x 40′-1 #7 x 30′-7	1-#7 x 9′-0	4.36	24
.788	5-#8 x 11′-5 6-#8 x 10′-6	5	#8 x 42′-6 #8 x 20′-2	6-#7 x 19′-10 14-#7 x 18′-0	2-#3	5	#7 x 40′-1 #8 x 30′-8	2-#7 x 9′-0	5.29	25
.873	6-#5 x 11′-5 7-#5 x 10′-6	5	#6 x 42′-8 #5 x 19′-2	5-#5 x 19′-10 12-#5 x 18′-0	—	5	#5 x 40′-3 #5 x 30′-5	1-#5 x 9′-0	2.39	26
.873	6-#6 x 11′-5 6-#6 x 10′-6	5	#6 x 42′-8 #6 x 19′-6	5-#5 x 19′-10 17-#5 x 18′-0	—	5	#6 x 40′-3 #6 x 30′-6	1-#6 x 9′-0	3.01	27
.873	7-#6 x 11′-5 7-#6 x 10′-6	5	#7 x 42′-8 #6 x 19′-6	5-#6 x 19′-10 13-#6 x 18′-0	2-#3	5	#6 x 40′-3 #7 x 30′-7	1-#6 x 9′-0	3.76	28
.873	6-#7 x 11′-5 6-#7 x 10′-6	5	#7 x 42′-8 #7 x 19′-10	5-#6 x 19′-10 16-#6 x 18′-0	2-#3	5	#6 x 40′-3 #7 x 30′-7	2-#6 x 9′-0	4.13	29
.873	7-#7 x 11′-5 7-#7 x 10′-6	5	#8 x 42′-8 #7 x 19′-10	5-#7 x 19′-10 13-#7 x 18′-0	2-#3	5	#7 x 40′-3 #8 x 30′-8	1-#7 x 9′-0	4.96	30

*,**,† For notes, see page 9-9.

WAFFLE FLAT SLABS—SQUARE PANELS—30-IN.-WIDE DOMES

For general instructions and notes on the use of this table, see pages 9-3 to 9-9 incl.

	Span / Drop-D / Form Depth plus Top Slab	Live Load (psf)	t_1 (in.)	Min. Col. Dia. 12′-0 Story Height (in.)	Min. Col. Cap. C (Shear) (in.)	Interior Square Panel: Each Column Strip: No. Jst.	Each Column Strip: Bars: Trussed Straight	Each Column Strip: Bars: Top **	Each Column Strip: Bars: Stirrups per Jst.*	Each Middle Strip: No. Jst.	Each Middle Strip: Bars: Trussed Straight	Wt.† of Steel (psf)
1	L = 30′-0	50	23	17	12	5	#5 x 51′-4 #5 x 19′-2	3-#5 x 19′-10 11-#5 x 18′-0	—	5	#5 x 46′-6 #5 x 30′-10	2.31
2	D = 12′-6	100	23	20	12	5	#6 x 51′-4 #5 x 19′-2	3-#5 x 19′-10 12-#5 x 18′-0	—	5	#5 x 46′-6 #5 x 30′-10	2.61
3	20 + 3	150	23	23	12	5	#6 x 51′-4 #6 x 19′-6	4-#6 x 19′-10 11-#6 x 18′-0	—	5	#6 x 46′-6 #4 x 30′-8	3.11
4		200	23	25	18	5	#6 x 51′-4 #6 x 19′-6	5-#6 x 19′-10 13-#6 x 18′-0	2-#3	5	#6 x 46′-6 #5 x 30′-10	3.59
5		300	23	29	29	5	#7 x 51′-4 #7 x 19′-10	3-#7 x 19′-10 12-#7 x 18′-0	2-#3	5	#6 x 46′-6 #6 x 31′-0	4.32
6	L = 30′-0	50	14½	17	17	5	#6 x 50′-9 #5 x 19′-2	3-#5 x 19′-10 13-#5 x 18′-0	—	5	#5 x 45′-11 #5 x 30′-10	2.64
7	D = 12′-6	100	14½	20	26	5	#6 x 50′-9 #6 x 19′-6	4-#6 x 19′-10 13-#6 x 18′-0	2-#3	5	#6 x 45′-11 #5 x 30′-10	3.46
8	10 + 4½	150	14½	23	35	5	#7 x 50′-9 #6 x 19′-6	4-#6 x 19′-10 13-#6 x 18′-0	2-#3	5	#6 x 45′-11 #6 x 31′-0	3.92
9	L = 30′-0	50	16½	17	13	5	#6 x 50′-11 #5 x 19′-2	3-#5 x 19′-10 12-#5 x 18′-0	—	5	#5 x 46′-1 #5 x 30′-10	2.60
10	D = 12′-6	100	16½	20	21	5	#6 x 50′-11 #6 x 19′-6	4-#6 x 19′-10 11-#6 x 18′-0	—	5	#5 x 46′-1 #6 x 31′-0	3.15
11	12 + 4½	150	16½	23	28	5	#7 x 50′-11 #6 x 19′-6	3-#6 x 19′-10 13-#6 x 18′-0	2-#3	5	#6 x 46′-1 #5 x 30′-10	3.71
12		200	16½	25	36	5	#7 x 50′-11 #7 x 19′-10	3-#7 x 19′-10 11-#7 x 18′-0	2-#3	5	#6 x 46′-1 #6 x 31′-0	4.19
13	L = 30′-0	50	18½	17	12	5	#6 x 51′-0 #4 x 19′-2	3-#4 x 19′-10 17-#4 x 18′-0	—	5	#5 x 46′-3 #4 x 30′-8	2.30
14	D = 12′-6	100	18½	20	16	5	#6 x 51′-0 #6 x 19′-6	3-#6 x 19′-10 11-#6 x 18′-0	—	5	#5 x 46′-3 #5 x 30′-10	2.93
15	14 + 4½	150	18½	23	23	5	#7 x 51′-0 #5 x 19′-2	4-#5 x 19′-10 16-#5 x 18′-0	2-#3	5	#6 x 46′-3 #5 x 30′-10	3.50
16		200	18½	25	30	5	#7 x 51′-0 #6 x 19′-6	4-#6 x 19′-10 14-#6 x 18′-0	2-#3	5	#6 x 46′-3 #6 x 31′-0	4.02
17		300	18½	28	44	5	#7 x 51′-0 #7 x 19′-10	4-#7 x 19′-10 13-#7 x 18′-0	2-#3	5	#7 x 46′-3 #6 x 31′-0	4.74
18	L = 30′-0	50	20½	17	12	5	#5 x 51′-2 #5 x 19′-2	4-#5 x 19′-10 12-#5 x 18′-0	—	5	#5 x 46′-4 #4 x 30′-8	2.26
19	D = 12′-6	100	20½	20	12	5	#6 x 51′-2 #5 x 19′-2	4-#5 x 19′-10 14-#5 x 18′-0	—	5	#5 x 46′-4 #5 x 30′-10	2.74
20	16 + 4½	150	20½	23	18	5	#6 x 51′-2 #6 x 19′-6	4-#6 x 19′-10 13-#6 x 18′-0	2-#3	5	#6 x 46′-4 #5 x 30′-10	3.50
21		200	20½	25	25	5	#7 x 51′-2 #6 x 19′-6	3-#6 x 19′-10 13-#6 x 18′-0	2-#3	5	#6 x 46′-4 #6 x 31′-0	3.91
22		300	20½	29	37	5	#7 x 51′-2 #7 x 19′-10	4-#7 x 19′-10 12-#7 x 18′-0	2-#3	5	#6 x 46′-4 #7 x 31′-2	4.58
23	L = 30′-0	50	24½	17	12	5	#6 x 51′-5 #5 x 19′-2	1-#5 x 19′-10 9-#5 x 18′-0	—	5	#6 x 46′-8 #5 x 30′-10	2.64
24	D = 12′-6	100	24½	20	12	5	#6 x 51′-5 #5 x 19′-2	3-#5 x 19′-10 12-#5 x 18′-0	—	5	#6 x 46′-8 #5 x 30′-10	2.85
25	20 + 4½	150	24½	23	12	5	#6 x 51′-5 #6 x 19′-6	3-#6 x 19′-10 12-#6 x 18′-0	—	5	#6 x 46′-8 #5 x 30′-10	3.24
26		200	24½	25	16	5	#7 x 51′-5 #5 x 19′-2	4-#5 x 19′-10 16-#5 x 18′-0	2-#3	5	#6 x 46′-8 #5 x 30′-10	3.55
27		300	24½	29	26	5	#7 x 51′-5 #7 x 19′-10	3-#7 x 19′-10 11-#7 x 18′-0	2-#3	5	#6 x 46′-8 #6 x 31′-0	4.25
28	L = 33′-0	50	15	18	19	5	#6 x 55′-9 #6 x 22′-6	4-#6 x 21′-10 12-#6 x 19′-10	—	6	#5 x 50′-6 #5 x 33′-10	2.95
29	D = 12′-6 12 + 3	100	15	21	30	5	#7 x 55′-9 #6 x 22′-6	4-#6 x 21′-10 15-#6 x 19′-10	2-#3	6	#6 x 50′-6 #5 x 33′-10	3.74

*,**,† For notes, see page 9-9.

WAFFLE FLAT SLABS—SQUARE PANELS—30-IN.-WIDE DOMES

For general instructions and notes on the use of this table, see pages 9-31 to 9-9 incl.

Av.‡ Cu. Ft. Conc. (psf)	Strips Perpendicular to an Exterior Wall									Wt.† of Steel (psf)	
	Column Strip					Middle Strip					
	Top Bars at Ext. Col.**	No. Jsts.	Bars: Trussed Straight	Top Bars at First Int. Col.	Stir-rups per Joist*	No. Jsts.	Bars: Trussed Straight	Top Bars at Ext. Support			
1.048	9-#4 x 11′-5 9-#4 x 10′-6	5	#6 x 42′-11 #4 x 19′-2	4-#5 x 19′-10 11-#5 x 18′-0	—	5	#5 x 40′-6 #5 x 30′-5	1-#5 x 9′-0		2.35	1
1.048	5-#6 x 11′-5 6-#6 x 10′-6	5	#6 x 42′-11 #6 x 19′-6	4-#5 x 19′-10 15-#5 x 18′-0	—	5	#5 x 40′-6 #6 x 30′-6	2-#5 x 9′-0		2.82	2
1.048	6-#6 x 11′-5 7-#6 x 10′-6	5	#7 x 42′-11 #6 x 19′-6	5-#6 x 19′-10 11-#6 x 18′-0	—	5	#6 x 40′-6 #6 x 30′-6	1-#6 x 9′-0		3.36	3
1.048	5-#7 x 11′-5 5-#7 x 10′-6	5	#7 x 42′-11 #7 x 19′-10	6-#6 x 19′-10 14-#6 x 18′-0	2-#3	5	#6 x 40′-6 #7 x 30′-7	2-#6 x 9′-0		3.98	4
1.048	6-#7 x 11′-5 6-#7 x 10′-6	5	#8 x 42′-11 #7 x 19′-10	5-#7 x 19′-10 11-#7 x 18′-0	2-#3	5	#7 x 40′-6 #7 x 30′-7	1-#7 x 9′-0		4.65	5
.749	6-#6 x 11′-5 6-#6 x 10′-6	5	#6 x 42′-4 #6 x 19′-6	5-#5 x 19′-10 15-#5 x 18′-0	—	5	#5 x 39′-11 #6 x 30′-6	2-#5 x 9′-0		2.86	6
.749	7-#6 x 11′-5 7-#6 x 10′-6	5	#7 x 42′-4 #6 x 19′-6	5-#6 x 19′-10 13-#6 x 18′-0	2-#3	5	#6 x 39′-11 #7 x 30′-7	1-#6 x 9′-0		3.72	7
.749	8-#6 x 11′-5 8-#6 x 10′-6	5	#8 x 42′-4 #6 x 19′-6	5-#6 x 19′-10 15-#6 x 18′-0	2-#3	5	#7 x 39′-11 #7 x 30′-7	1-#7 x 9′-0		4.31	8
.830	5-#6 x 11′-5 5-#6 x 10′-6	5	#6 x 42′-6 #6 x 19′-6	4-#5 x 19′-10 14-#5 x 18′-0	—	5	#5 x 40′-1 #6 x 30′-6	2-#5 x 9′-0		2.78	9
.830	6-#6 x 11′-5 7-#6 x 10′-6	5	#7 x 42′-6 #6 x 19′-6	5-#6 x 19′-10 11-#6 x 18′-0	—	5	#6 x 40′-1 #6 x 30′-6	1-#6 x 9′-0		3.37	10
.830	6-#7 x 11′-5 6-#7 x 10′-6	5	#7 x 42′-6 #7 x 19′-10	4-#6 x 19′-10 16-#6 x 18′-0	2-#3	5	#6 x 40′-1 #7 x 30′-7	2-#6 x 9′-0		4.06	11
.830	6-#7 x 11′-5 6-#7 x 10′-6	5	#8 x 42′-6 #7 x 19′-10	4-#7 x 19′-10 12-#7 x 18′-0	2-#3	5	#7 x 40′-1 #7 x 30′-7	1-#7 x 9′-0		4.55	12
.913	5-#6 x 11′-5 5-#6 x 10′-6	5	#6 x 42′-7 #6 x 19′-6	5-#4 x 19′-10 20-#4 x 18′-0	—	5	#5 x 40′-3 #6 x 30′-6	2-#5 x 9′-0		2.61	13
.913	6-#6 x 11′-5 6-#6 x 10′-6	5	#7 x 42′-7 #6 x 19′-6	4-#6 x 19′-10 11-#6 x 18′-0	—	5	#6 x 40′-3 #6 x 30′-6	1-#6 x 9′-0		3.23	14
.913	5-#7 x 11′-5 5-#7 x 10′-6	5	#7 x 42′-7 #7 x 19′-10	5-#5 x 19′-10 20-#5 x 18′-0	2-#3	5	#6 x 40′-3 #7 x 30′-7	2-#6 x 9′-0		3.87	15
.913	8-#6 x 11′-5 8-#6 x 10′-6	5	#8 x 42′-7 #6 x 19′-6	5-#6 x 19′-10 15-#6 x 18′-0	2-#3	5	#7 x 40′-3 #7 x 30′-7	1-#7 x 9′-0		4.38	16
.913	5-#8 x 11′-5 6-#8 x 10′-6	5	#8 x 42′-7 #8 x 20′-2	5-#7 x 19′-10 14-#7 x 18′-0	2-#3	5	#7 x 40′-3 #8 x 30′-8	2-#7 x 9′-0		5.24	17
.998	7-#5 x 11′-5 7-#5 x 10′-6	5	#6 x 42′-9 #5 x 19′-2	5-#5 x 19′-10 12-#5 x 18′-0	—	5	#5 x 40′-4 #5 x 30′-5	1-#5 x 9′-0		2.42	18
.998	8-#5 x 11′-5 8-#5 x 10′-6	5	#7 x 42′-9 #5 x 19′-2	5-#5 x 19′-10 15-#5 x 18′-0	—	5	#6 x 40′-4 #6 x 30′-6	1-#6 x 9′-0		3.05	19
.998	7-#6 x 11′-5 7-#6 x 10′-6	5	#7 x 42′-9 #6 x 19′-6	5-#6 x 19′-10 13-#6 x 18′-0	2-#3	5	#6 x 40′-4 #7 x 30′-7	1-#6 x 9′-0		3.77	20
.998	6-#7 x 11′-5 6-#7 x 10′-6	5	#7 x 42′-9 #7 x 19′-10	5-#6 x 19′-10 15-#6 x 18′-0	2-#3	5	#6 x 40′-4 #7 x 30′-7	2-#6 x 9′-0		4.18	21
.998	7-#7 x 11′-5 7-#7 x 10′-6	5	#8 x 42′-9 #7 x 19′-10	5-#7 x 19′-10 13-#7 x 18′-0	2-#3	5	#7 x 40′-4 #8 x 30′-8	1-#7 x 9′-0		4.97	22
1.173	6-#5 x 11′-5 6-#5 x 10′-6	5	#6 x 43′-0 #5 x 19′-2	2-#5 x 19′-10 11-#5 x 18′-0	—	5	#6 x 40′-8 #5 x 30′-5	1-#6 x 9′-0		2.67	23
1.173	5-#6 x 11′-5 6-#6 x 10′-6	5	#6 x 43′-0 #6 x 19′-6	4-#5 x 19′-10 15-#5 x 18′-0	—	5	#6 x 40′-8 #5 x 30′-5	1-#6 x 9′-0		2.94	24
1.173	6-#6 x 11′-5 6-#6 x 10′-6	5	#7 x 43′-0 #6 x 19′-6	5-#6 x 19′-10 11-#6 x 18′-0	—	5	#6 x 40′-8 #6 x 30′-6	1-#6 x 9′-0		3.41	25
1.173	5-#7 x 11′-5 5-#7 x 10′-6	5	#7 x 43′-0 #7 x 19′-10	5-#5 x 19′-10 20-#5 x 18′-0	2-#3	5	#6 x 40′-8 #7 x 30′-7	2-#6 x 9′-0		3.92	26
1.173	6-#7 x 11′-5 6-#7 x 10′-6	5	#8 x 43′-0 #7 x 19′-10	4-#7 x 19′-10 12-#7 x 18′-0	2-#3	5	#7 x 40′-8 #7 x 30′-7	1-#7 x 9′-0		4.62	27
.687	7-#6 x 12′-5 7-#6 x 11′-5	5	#7 x 46′-4 #6 x 22′-6	5-#6 x 21′-10 12-#6 x 19′-10	—	6	#5 x 43′-9 #6 x 33′-6	2-#5 x 9′-9		3.17	28
.687	6-#7 x 12′-5 6-#7 x 11′-5	5	#8 x 46′-4 #7 x 22′-10	6-#6 x 21′-10 15-#6 x 19′-10	2-#3	6	#6 x 43′-9 #7 x 33′-7	1-#6 x 9′-9		4.09	29

*,**,† For notes, see page 9-9.

WAFFLE FLAT SLABS—SQUARE PANELS—30-IN.-WIDE DOMES

For general instructions and notes on the use of this table, see pages 9-3 to 9-9 incl.

	Span Drop-D Form Depth plus Top Slab	Live Load (psf)	t_1 (in.)	Min. Col. Dia. 12′-0 Story Height (in.)	Min. Col. Cap. C (Shear) (in.)	Interior Square Panel: Each Column Strip: No. Jst.	Each Column Strip: Bars: Trussed Straight	Each Column Strip: Bars: Top **	Each Column Strip: Stirrups per Jst.*	Each Middle Strip: No. Jst.	Each Middle Strip: Bars: Trussed Straight	Wt.† of Steel (psf)
1	L = 33′-0	50	17	18	15	5	#6 x 55′-11 #6 x 22′-6	3-#6 x 21′-10 12-#6 x 19′-10	—	6	#5 x 50′-7 #4 x 33′-8	2.75
2	D = 12′-6	100	17	22	24	5	#7 x 55′-11 #6 x 22′-6	4-#6 x 21′-10 13-#6 x 19′-10	2-#3	6	#6 x 50′-7 #4 x 33′-8	3.50
3	14 + 3	150	17	24	33	5	#7 x 55′-11 #7 x 22′-10	4-#7 x 21′-10 13-#7 x 19′-10	2-#3	6	#6 x 50′-7 #5 x 33′-10	4.11
4		200	17	26	43	5	#8 x 55′-11 #7 x 22′-10	4-#7 x 21′-10 13-#7 x 19′-10	2-#3	6	#6 x 50′-7 #6 x 34′-0	4.60
5	L = 33′-0	50	19	18	12	5	#6 x 56′-0 #5 x 22′-2	4-#5 x 21′-10 15-#5 x 19′-10	—	6	#5 x 50′-9 #4 x 33′-8	2.55
6	D = 12′-6	100	19	22	20	5	#7 x 56′-0 #6 x 22′-6	3-#6 x 21′-10 13-#6 x 19′-10	2-#3	6	#5 x 50′-9 #5 x 33′-10	3.34
7	16 + 3	150	19	24	28	5	#7 x 56′-0 #7 x 22′-10	4-#7 x 21′-10 11-#7 x 19′-10	2-#3	6	#6 x 50′-9 #5 x 33′-10	3.97
8		200	19	27	36	5	#8 x 56′-0 #6 x 22′-6	4-#6 x 21′-10 17-#6 x 19′-10	2-#3	6	#6 x 50′-9 #6 x 34′-0	4.37
9		300	19	30	52	5	#8 x 56′-0 #8 x 23′-2	4-#8 x 21′-10 12-#8 x 19′-10	4-#4	6	#7 x 50′-9 #6 x 34′-0	5.65
10	L = 33′-0	50	23	18	12	5	#6 x 56′-4 #5 x 22′-2	4-#5 x 21′-10 13-#5 x 19′-10	—	6	#5 x 51′-0 #5 x 33′-10	2.63
11	D = 12′-6	100	23	22	12	5	#6 x 56′-4 #6 x 22′-6	4-#6 x 21′-10 14-#6 x 19′-10	—	6	#5 x 51′-0 #5 x 33′-10	3.07
12	20 + 3	150	23	25	19	5	#7 x 56′-4 #6 x 22′-6	4-#6 x 21′-10 14-#6 x 19′-10	2-#3	6	#6 x 51′-0 #4 x 33′-8	3.60
13		200	23	27	25	5	#7 x 56′-4 #7 x 22′-10	4-#7 x 21′-10 12-#7 x 19′-10	2-#3	6	#6 x 51′-0 #5 x 33′-10	4.07
14		300	23	30	39	5	#8 x 56′-4 #7 x 22′-10	4-#7 x 21′-10 14-#7 x 19′-10	2-#3	6	#6 x 51′-0 #6 x 34′-0	4.72
15	L = 33′-0	50	14½	17	22	5	#7 x 55′-9 #5 x 22′-2	4-#5 x 21′-10 16-#5 x 19′-10	2-#3	6	#5 x 50′-5 #5 x 33′-10	3.10
16	D = 12′-6 10 + 4½	100	14½	21	33	5	#7 x 55′-9 #7 x 22′-10	4-#7 x 21′-10 12-#7 x 19′-10	2-#3	6	#6 x 50′-5 #5 x 33′-10	4.01
17	L = 33′-0	50	16½	18	18	5	#6 x 55′-10 #6 x 22′-6	4-#6 x 21′-10 12-#6 x 19′-10	—	6	#5 x 50′-7 #5 x 33′-10	2.95
18	D = 12′-6	100	16½	21	27	5	#7 x 55′-10 #7 x 22′-10	3-#7 x 21′-10 11-#7 x 19′-10	2-#3	6	#6 x 50′-7 #5 x 33′-10	3.87
19	12 + 4½	150	16½	24	37	5	#8 x 55′-10 #6 x 22′-6	4-#6 x 21′-10 16-#6 x 19′-10	2-#3	6	#6 x 50′-7 #6 x 34′-0	4.30
20	L = 33′-0	50	18½	18	14	5	#6 x 56′-0 #6 x 22′-6	4-#6 x 21′-10 11-#6 x 19′-10	—	6	#5 x 50′-9 #5 x 33′-10	2.90
21	D = 12′-6	100	18½	22	22	5	#7 x 56′-0 #6 x 22′-6	4-#6 x 21′-10 13-#6 x 19′-10	2-#3	6	#6 x 50′-9 #5 x 33′-10	3.66
22	14 + 4½	150	18½	24	31	5	#7 x 56′-0 #7 x 22′-10	4-#7 x 21′-10 12-#7 x 19′-10	2-#3	6	#6 x 50′-9 #5 x 33′-10	4.04
23		200	18½	27	39	5	#8 x 56′-0 #7 x 22′-10	3-#7 x 21′-10 13-#7 x 19′-10	2-#3	6	#6 x 50′-9 #6 x 34′-0	4.53
24		300	18½	30	56	5	#8 x 56′-0 #8 x 23′-2	4-#8 x 21′-10 13-#8 x 19′-10	4-#4	6	#7 x 50′-9 #6 x 34′-0	5.74
25	L = 33′-0	50	20½	18	12	5	#6 x 56′-2 #6 x 22′-6	3-#6 x 21′-10 11-#6 x 19′-10	—	6	#5 x 50′-10 #4 x 33′-8	2.70
26	D = 12′-6	100	20½	22	18	5	#7 x 56′-2 #6 x 22′-6	3-#6 x 21′-10 13-#6 x 19′-10	2-#3	6	#5 x 50′-10 #5 x 33′-10	3.35
27	16 + 4½	150	20½	25	26	5	#7 x 56′-2 #7 x 22′-10	4-#7 x 21′-10 11-#7 x 19′-10	2-#3	6	#6 x 50′-10 #5 x 33′-10	3.98
28		200	20½	27	33	5	#8 x 56′-2 #7 x 22′-10	3-#7 x 21′-10 12-#7 x 19′-10	2-#3	6	#6 x 50′-10 #6 x 34′-0	4.47
29		300	20½	30	48	5	#8 x 56′-2 #8 x 23′-2	4-#8 x 21′-10 11-#8 x 19′-10	4-#3	6	#7 x 50′-10 #6 x 34′-0	5.39

*,**,† For notes, see page 9-9.

WAFFLE FLAT SLABS—SQUARE PANELS—30-IN.-WIDE DOMES

For general instructions and notes on the use of this table, see pages 9-3 to 9-9 incl.

Av.‡ Cu. Ft. Conc. (psf)	Strips Perpendicular to an Exterior Wall								Wt.† of Steel (psf)	
	Column Strip					Middle Strip				
	Top Bars at Ext. Col.**	No. Jsts.	Bars: Trussed Straight	Top Bars at First Int. Col.	Stir-rups per Joist*	No. Jsts.	Bars: Trussed Straight	Top Bars at Ext. Support		
.767	6-#6 x 12 -5 6-#6 x 11′-5	5	#7 x 46′-6 #6 x 22′-6	5-#6 x 21′-10 11-#6 x 19′-10	—	6	#5 x 43′-10 #6 x 33′-6	2-#5 x 9′-9	3.03	1
.767	6-#7 x 12′-5 6-#7 x 11′-5	5	#7 x 46′-6 #7 x 22′-10	5-#6 x 21′-10 16-#6 x 19′-10	2-#3	6	#6 x 43′-10 #6 x 33′-6	1-#6 x 9′-9	3.74	2
.767	7-#7 x 12′-5 7-#7 x 11′-5	5	#8 x 46′-6 #7 x 22′-10	5-#7 x 21′-10 13-#7 x 19′-10	2-#3	6	#6 x 43′-10 #7 x 33′-7	2-#6 x 9′-9	4.45	3
.767	6-#8 x 12′-5 6-#8 x 11′-5	5	#8 x 46′-6 #8 x 23′-2	5-#7 x 21′-10 16-#7 x 19′-10	2-#3	6	#7 x 43′-10 #7 x 33′-7	1-#7 x 9′-9	4.94	4
.849	8-#5 x 12′-5 9-#5 x 11′-5	5	#7 x 46′-8 #5 x 22′-2	6-#5 x 21′-10 15-#5 x 19′-10	—	6	#5 x 44′-0 #6 x 33′-6	2-#5 x 9′-9	2.86	5
.849	6-#7 x 12′-5 6-#7 x 11′-5	5	#7 x 46′-8 #7 x 22′-10	4-#6 x 21′-10 15-#6 x 19′-10	2-#3	6	#6 x 44′-0 #6 x 33′-6	1-#6 x 9′-9	3.64	6
.849	6-#7 x 12′-5 7-#7 x 11′-5	5	#8 x 46′-8 #7 x 22′-10	5-#7 x 21′-10 12-#7 x 19′-10	2-#3	6	#6 x 44′-0 #7 x 33′-7	2-#6 x 9′-9	4.35	7
.849	6-#8 x 12′-5 6-#8 x 11′-5	5	#8 x 46′-8 #8 x 23′-2	6-#6 x 21′-10 19-#6 x 19′-10	2-#3	6	#7 x 44′-0 #7 x 33′-7	1-#7 x 9′-9	4.78	8
.849	7-#8 x 12′-5 7-#8 x 11′-5	5	#9 x 46′-8 #8 x 23′-2	5-#8 x 21′-10 13-#8 x 19′-10	4-#4	6	#7 x 44′-0 #8 x 33′-8	2-#7 x 9′-9	6.11	9
1.020	6-#6 x 12′-5 6-#6 x 11′-5	5	#6 x 46′-11 #6 x 22′-6	5-#5 x 21′-10 16-#5 x 19′-10	—	6	#5 x 44′-3 #5 x 33′-5	1-#5 x 9′-9	2.70	10
1.020	7-#6 x 12′-5 7-#6 x 11′-5	5	#7 x 46′-11 #6 x 22′-6	6-#6 x 21′-10 13-#6 x 19′-10	—	6	#6 x 44′-3 #5 x 33′-5	1-#6 x 9′-9	3.27	11
1.020	6-#7 x 12′-5 6-#7 x 11′-5	5	#7 x 46′-11 #7 x 22′-10	5-#6 x 21′-10 17-#6 x 19′-10	2-#3	6	#6 x 44′-3 #6 x 33′-6	1-#6 x 9′-9	3.82	12
1.020	7-#7 x 12′-5 7-#7 x 11′-5	5	#8 x 46′-11 #7 x 22′-10	5-#7 x 21′-10 13-#7 x 19′-10	2-#3	6	#6 x 44′-3 #7 x 33′-7	2-#6 x 9′-9	4.46	13
1.020	8-#7 x 12′-5 8-#7 x 11′-5	5	#9 x 46′-11 #7 x 22′-10	5-#7 x 21′-10 15-#7 x 19′-10	2-#3	6	#7 x 44′-3 #7 x 33′-7	1-#7 x 9′-9	5.10	14
.734	5-#7 x 12′-5 5-#7 x 11′-5	5	#7 x 46′-4 #7 x 22′-10	5-#5 x 21′-10 20-#5 x 19′-10	2-#3	6	#6 x 43′-8 #6 x 33′-6	1-#6 x 9′-9	3.43	15
.734	6-#7 x 12′-5 7-#7 x 11′-5	5	#8 x 46′-4 #7 x 22′-10	5-#7 x 21′-10 12-#7 x 19′-10	2-#3	6	#6 x 43′-8 #7 x 33′-7	2-#6 x 9′-9	4.35	16
.812	7-#6 x 12′-5 7-#6 x 11′-5	5	#7 x 46′-6 #6 x 22′-6	5-#6 x 21′-10 13-#6 x 19′-10	—	6	#6 x 43′-10 #5 x 33′-5	1-#6 x 9′-9	3.18	17
.812	6-#7 x 12′-5 6-#7 x 11′-5	5	#8 x 46′-6 #7 x 22′-10	4-#7 x 21′-10 11-#7 x 19′-10	2-#3	6	#6 x 43′-10 #7 x 33′-7	1-#6 x 9′-9	4.15	18
.812	5-#8 x 12′-5 6-#8 x 11′-5	5	#8 x 46′-6 #8 x 23′-2	5-#6 x 21′-10 19-#6 x 19′-10	2-#3	6	#7 x 43′-10 #7 x 33′-7	1-#7 x 9′-9	4.69	19
.892	6-#6 x 12′-5 7-#6 x 11′-5	5	#7 x 46′-7 #6 x 22′-6	5-#6 x 21′-10 12-#6 x 19′-10	—	6	#5 x 44′-0 #6 x 33′-6	2-#5 x 9′-9	3.14	20
.892	8-#6 x 12′-5 8-#6 x 11′-5	5	#8 x 46′-7 #6 x 22′-6	5-#6 x 21′-10 14-#6 x 19′-10	2-#3	6	#6 x 44′-0 #6 x 33′-6	1-#6 x 9′-9	3.86	21
.892	7-#7 x 12′-5 7-#7 x 11′-5	5	#8 x 46′-7 #7 x 22′-10	5-#7 x 21′-10 13-#7 x 19′-10	2-#3	6	#6 x 44′-0 #7 x 33′-7	2-#6 x 9′-9	4.42	22
.892	6-#8 x 12′-5 6-#8 x 11′-5	5	#8 x 46′-7 #8 x 23′-2	5-#7 x 21′-10 15-#7 x 19′-10	2-#3	6	#7 x 44′-0 #7 x 33′-7	1-#7 x 9′-9	4.89	23
.892	5-#9 x 12′-5 6-#9 x 11′-5	5	#9 x 46′-7 #9 x 23′-7	5-#8 x 21′-10 13-#8 x 19′-10	4-#4	6	#7 x 44′-0 #8 x 33′-8	2-#7 x 9′-9	6.23	24
.974	6-#6 x 12′-5 6-#6 x 11′-5	5	#7 x 46′-9 #6 x 22′-6	4-#6 x 21′-10 12-#6 x 19′-10	—	6	#5 x 44′-1 #6 x 33′-6	2-#5 x 9′-9	3.01	25
.974	6-#7 x 12′-5 6-#7 x 11′-5	5	#7 x 46′-9 #7 x 22′-10	5-#6 x 21′-10 15-#6 x 19′-10	2-#3	6	#6 x 44′-1 #6 x 33′-6	1-#6 x 9′-9	3.66	26
.974	6-#7 x 12′-5 7-#7 x 11′-5	5	#8 x 46′-9 #7 x 22′-10	5-#7 x 21′-10 12-#7 x 19′-10	2-#3	6	#6 x 44′-1 #7 x 33′-7	2-#6 x 9′-9	4.36	27
.974	6-#8 x 12′-5 6-#8 x 11′-5	5	#8 x 46′-9 #8 x 23′-2	4-#7 x 21′-10 14-#7 x 19′-10	2-#3	6	#7 x 44′-1 #7 x 33′-7	1-#7 x 9′-9	4.83	28
.974	6-#8 x 12′-5 7-#8 x 11′-5	5	#9 x 46′-9 #8 x 23′-2	5-#8 x 21′-10 12-#8 x 19′-10	4-#3	6	#7 x 44′-1 #8 x 33′-8	2-#7 x 9′-9	5.85	29

*, **, † For notes, see page 9-9.

WAFFLE SLABS—SQUARE PANELS—30-IN.-WIDE DOMES

For general instructions and notes on the use of this table, see pages 9-3 to 9-9 incl.

	Span Drop-D Form Depth plus Top Slab	Live Load (psf)	t_1 (in.)	Min. Col. Dia. 12′-0 Story Height (in.)	Min. Col. Cap. C (Shear) (in.)	Interior Square Panel Each Column Strip No. Jst.	Each Column Strip Bars Trussed Straight	Each Column Strip Bars Top **	Each Column Strip Stirrups per Jst.*	Each Middle Strip No. Jst.	Each Middle Strip Bars Trussed Straight	Wt.† of Steel (psf)
1	L = 33′-0	50	24½	18	12	5	#6 x 56′-5 #5 x 22′-2	4-#5 x 21′-10 14-#5 x 19′-10	—	6	#6 x 51′-2 #5 x 33′-10	2.93
2	D = 12′-6	100	24½	22	12	5	#7 x 56′-5 #5 x 22′-2	4-#5 x 21′-10 16-#5 x 19′-10	—	6	#6 x 51′-2 #5 x 33′-10	3.28
3	20 + 4½	150	24½	25	17	5	#7 x 56′-5 #6 x 22′-6	4-#6 x 21′-10 14-#6 x 19′-10	2-#3	6	#6 x 51′-2 #5 x 33′-10	3.75
4		200	24½	27	23	5	#7 x 56′-5 #7 x 22′-10	4-#7 x 21′-10 12-#7 x 19′-10	2-#3	6	#6 x 51′-2 #5 x 33′-10	4.08
5		300	24½	31	36	5	#8 x 56′-5 #7 x 22′-10	4-#7 x 21′-10 14-#7 x 19′-10	2-#3	6	#6 x 51′-2 #6 x 34′-0	4.73
6	L = 36′-0	50	17	19	20	7	#6 x 60′-10 #5 x 25′-2	5-#5 x 23′-10 19-#5 x 21′-8	2-#3	5	#6 x 55′-1 #6 x 37′-0	3.32
7	D = 12′-6	100	17	23	31	7	#6 x 60′-10 #6 x 25′-6	6-#6 x 23′-10 18-#6 x 21′-8	2-#3	5	#7 x 55′-1 #6 x 37′-0	4.06
8	14 + 3	150	17	26	42	7	#7 x 60′-10 #7 x 26′-0	7-#7 x 23′-10 13-#7 x 21′-8	4-#3	5	#7 x 55′-1 #7 x 37′-0	5.08
9	L = 36′-0	50	19	19	17	7	#6 x 61′-0 #5 x 25′-2	4-#5 x 23′-10 18-#5 x 21′-8	—	5	#6 x 55′-3 #5 x 36′-10	2.99
10	D = 12′-6	100	19	23	26	7	#6 x 61′-0 #6 x 25′-6	5-#6 x 23′-10 17-#6 x 21′-8	2-#3	5	#7 x 55′-3 #5 x 36′-10	3.84
11	16 + 3	150	19	26	36	7	#7 x 61′-0 #6 x 25′-6	5-#6 x 23′-10 18-#6 x 21′-8	2-#3	5	#7 x 55′-3 #7 x 37′-2	4.53
12	L = 36′-0	50	23	19	12	7	#6 x 61′-3 #4 x 25′-2	5-#4 x 23′-10 26-#4 x 21′-8	—	5	#6 x 55′-6 #5 x 36′-10	2.82
13	D = 12′-6	100	23	23	18	7	#6 x 61′-3 #6 x 25′-6	5-#6 x 23′-10 15-#6 x 21′-8	2-#3	5	#6 x 55′-6 #6 x 37′-0	3.66
14	20 + 3	150	23	26	26	7	#7 x 61′-3 #5 x 25′-2	5-#5 x 23′-10 24-#5 x 21′-8	2-#3	5	#7 x 55′-6 #6 x 37′-0	4.13
15		200	23	28	34	7	#7 x 61′-3 #6 x 25′-6	5-#6 x 23′-10 20-#6 x 21′-8	2-#3	5	#7 x 55′-6 #7 x 37′-2	4.66
16		300	23	32	49	7	#7 x 61′-3 #7 x 25′-10	6-#7 x 23′-10 19-#7 x 21′-8	4-#4	5	#8 x 55′-6 #7 x 37′-2	5.96
17	L = 36′-0	50	18½	19	19	7	#6 x 61′-0 #5 x 25′-2	5-#5 x 23′-10 20-#5 x 21′-8	2-#3	5	#6 x 55′-3 #6 x 37′-0	3.36
18	D = 12′-6	100	18½	23	29	7	#7 x 61′-0 #5 x 25′-2	5-#5 x 23′-10 22-#5 x 21′-8	2-#3	5	#7 x 55′-3 #6 x 37′-0	4.02
19	14 + 4½	150	18½	26	38	7	#7 x 61′-0 #7 x 26′-0	7-#7 x 23′-10 13-#7 x 21′-8	4-#3	5	#7 x 55′-3 #7 x 37′-0	5.08
20	L = 36′-0	50	20½	19	16	7	#6 x 61′-1 #5 x 25′-2	5-#5 x 23′-10 18-#5 x 21′-8	—	5	#6 x 55′-4 #6 x 37′-0	3.16
21	D = 12′-6	100	20½	23	25	7	#6 x 61′-1 #6 x 25′-6	5-#6 x 23′-10 18-#6 x 21′-8	2-#3	5	#7 x 55′-4 #6 x 37′-0	4.03
22	16 + 4½	150	20½	26	34	7	#7 x 61′-1 #6 x 25′-6	5-#6 x 23′-10 18-#6 x 21′-8	2-#3	5	#7 x 55′-4 #7 x 37′-2	4.54
23		200	20½	28	41	7	#7 x 61′-1 #7 x 26′-0	7-#7 x 23′-10 14-#7 x 21′-8	4-#3	5	#8 x 55′-4 #7 x 37′-0	5.19
24	L = 36′-0	50	24½	19	12	7	#6 x 61′-5 #5 x 25′-2	4-#5 x 23′-10 17-#5 x 21′-8	—	5	#6 x 55′-8 #5 x 36′-10	2.97
25	D = 12′-6	100	24½	23	17	7	#6 x 61′-5 #6 x 25′-6	5-#6 x 23′-10 15-#6 x 21′-8	2-#3	5	#6 x 55′-8 #6 x 37′-0	3.68
26	20 + 4½	150	24½	26	24	7	#7 x 61′-5 #6 x 25′-6	4-#6 x 23′-10 17-#6 x 21′-8	2-#3	5	#7 x 55′-8 #6 x 37′-0	4.32
27		200	24½	28	31	7	#7 x 61′-5 #6 x 25′-6	5-#6 x 23′-10 20-#6 x 21′-8	2-#3	5	#7 x 55′-8 #7 x 37′-2	4.68
28		300	24½	32	46	7	#7 x 61′-5 #7 x 25′-10	6-#7 x 23′-10 18-#7 x 21′-8	4-#4	5	#8 x 55′-8 #7 x 37′-2	5.92

*, **, † For notes, see page 9-9.

WAFFLE SLABS—SQUARE PANELS—30-IN.-WIDE DOMES

For general instructions and notes on the use of this table, see pages 9-3 to 9-9 incl.

Av.‡ Cu. Ft. Conc. (psf)	Strips Perpendicular to an Exterior Wall								Wt.† of Steel (psf)	
	Column Strip					Middle Strip				
	Top Bars at Ex. Col.**	No. Jsts.	Bars Trussed Straight	Top Bars at First Int. Col.	Stir-rups per Joist*	No. Jsts.	Bars Trussed Straight	Top Bars at Ext. Support		
1.145	6-#6 x 12′-5 6-#6 x 11′-5	5	#6 x 47′-0 #6 x 22′-6	5-#5 x 21′-10 17-#5 x 19′-10	—	6	#6 x 44′-5 #5 x 33′-5	1-#6 x 9′-9	2.99	1
1.145	5-#7 x 12′-5 5-#7 x 11′-5	5	#7 x 47′-0 #7 x 22′-10	5-#5 x 21′-10 20-#5 x 19′-10	—	6	#6 x 44′-5 #6 x 33′-6	1-#6 x 9′-9	3.49	2
1.145	6-#7 x 12′-5 6-#7 x 11′-5	5	#8 x 47′-0 #7 x 22′-10	5-#6 x 21′-10 15-#6 x 19′-10	2-#3	6	#6 x 44′-5 #7 x 33′-7	2-#6 x 9′-9	4.19	3
1.145	7-#7 x 12′-5 7-#7 x 11′-5	5	#8 x 47′-0 #7 x 22′-10	5-#7 x 21′-10 13-#7 x 19′-10	2-#3	6	#6 x 44′-5 #7 x 33′-7	2-#6 x 9′-9	4.47	4
1.145	6-#8 x 12′-5 6-#8 x 11′-5	5	#9 x 47′-0 #8 x 23′-2	5-#7 x 21′-10 15-#7 x 19′-10	2-#3	6	#7 x 44′-5 #7 x 33′-7	1-#7 x 9′-9	5.17	5
.751	8-#6 x 13′-5 8-#6 x 12′-4	7	#6 x 50′-6 #6 x 25′-6	7-#5 x 23′-10 22-#5 x 21′-8	2-#3	5	#7 x 47′-7 #7 x 36′-7	1-#7 x 10′-6	3.59	6
.751	10-#6 x 13′-5 10-#6 x 12′-4	7	#7 x 50′-6 #6 x 25′-6	8-#6 x 23′-10 18-#6 x 21′-8	2-#3	5	#7 x 47′-7 #8 x 36′-8	2-#7 x 10′-6	4.42	7
.751	10-#7 x 13′-5 10-#7 x 12′-4	7	#8 x 50′-6 #7 x 25′-6	8-#7 x 23′-10 14-#7 x 21′-8	4-#3	5	#8 x 48′-0 #8 x 36′-8	2-#7 x 10′-6	5.69	8
.831	7-#6 x 13′-5 8-#6 x 12′-4	7	#6 x 50′-8 #6 x 25′-6	6-#5 x 23′-10 21-#5 x 21′-8	—	5	#6 x 47′-9 #7 x 36′-7	2-#6 x 10′-6	3.28	9
.831	9-#6 x 13′-5 9-#6 x 12′-4	7	#7 x 50′-8 #6 x 25′-6	7-#6 x 23′-10 18-#6 x 21′-8	2-#3	5	#7 x 47′-9 #8 x 36′-8	2-#7 x 10′-6	4.27	10
.831	8-#7 x 13′-5 8-#7 x 12′-4	7	#7 x 50′-8 #7 x 25′-10	7-#6 x 23′-10 22-#6 x 21′-8	2-#3	5	#8 x 47′-9 #8 x 36′-8	1-#8 x 10′-6	4.87	11
.998	7-#6 x 13′-5 7-#6 x 12′-4	7	#6 x 50′-11 #6 x 25′-6	8-#4 x 23′-10 30-#4 x 21′-8	—	5	#6 x 48′-0 #7 x 36′-7	2-#6 x 10′-6	3.15	12
.998	9-#6 x 13′-5 9-#6 x 12′-4	7	#7 x 50′-11 #6 x 25′-6	6-#6 x 23′-10 16-#6 x 21′-8	2-#3	5	#7 x 48′-0 #7 x 36′-7	1-#7 x 10′-6	3.99	13
.998	7-#7 x 13′-5 8-#7 x 12′-4	7	#7 x 50′-11 #7 x 25′-10	7-#5 x 23′-10 29-#5 x 21′-8	2-#3	5	#7 x 48′-0 #8 x 36′-8	2-#7 x 10′-6	4.55	14
.998	8-#7 x 13′-5 9-#7 x 12′-4	7	#7 x 50′-11 #7 x 25′-10	7-#6 x 23′-10 24-#6 x 21′-8	2-#3	5	#8 x 48′-0 #8 x 36′-8	1-#8 x 10′-6	5.00	15
.998	7-#8 x 13′-5 8-#8 x 12′-4	7	#8 x 50′-11 #8 x 26′-2	8-#7 x 23′-10 19-#7 x 21′-8	4-#4	5	#8 x 48′-0 #9 x 36′-10	2-#8 x 10′-6	6.45	16
.876	11-#5 x 13′-5 11-#5 x 12′-4	7	#7 x 50′-7 #5 x 25′-2	7-#5 x 23′-10 20-#5 x 21′-8	2-#3	5	#7 x 47′-9 #7 x 36′-7	1-#7 x 10′-6	3.67	17
.876	7-#7 x 13′-5 7-#7 x 12′-4	7	#7 x 50′-7 #7 x 25′-10	7-#5 x 23′-10 27-#5 x 21′-8	2-#3	5	#7 x 47′-9 #8 x 36′-8	2-#7 x 10′-6	4.44	18
.876	10-#7 x 13′-5 10-#7 x 12′-4	7	#8 x 50′-11 #7 x 25′-10	8-#7 x 23′-10 14-#7 x 21′-8	4-#3	5	#8 x 48′-0 #8 x 36′-8	2-#7 x 10′-6	5.69	19
.956	8-#6 x 13′-5 8-#6 x 12′-4	7	#6 x 50′-9 #6 x 25′-6	6-#5 x 23′-10 23-#5 x 21′-8	—	5	#7 x 47′-10 #7 x 36′-7	1-#7 x 10′-6	3.46	20
.956	9-#6 x 13′-5 9-#6 x 12′-4	7	#7 x 50′-9 #6 x 25′-6	7-#6 x 23′-10 18-#6 x 21′-8	2-#3	5	#7 x 47′-10 #8 x 36′-8	2-#7 x 10′-6	4.38	21
.956	8-#7 x 13′-5 8-#7 x 12′-4	7	#7 x 50′-9 #7 x 25′-10	7-#6 x 23′-10 22-#6 x 21′-8	2-#3	5	#8 x 47′-10 #8 x 36′-8	1-#8 x 10′-6	4.88	22
.956	11-#7 x 13′-5 11-#7 x 12′-4	7	#8 x 50′-11 #7 x 25′-10	8-#7 x 23′-10 16-#7 x 21′-8	4-#3	5	#9 x 48′-0 #8 x 36′-8	2-#7 x 10′-6	5.83	23
1.123	7-#6 x 13′-5 7-#6 x 12′-4	7	#6 x 51′-0 #6 x 25′-6	5-#5 x 23′-10 21-#5 x 21′-8	—	5	#6 x 48′-2 #7 x 36′-7	2-#6 x 10′-6	3.25	24
1.123	9-#6 x 13′-5 9-#6 x 12′-4	7	#7 x 51′-0 #6 x 25′-6	6-#6 x 23′-10 16-#6 x 21′-8	2-#3	5	#7 x 48′-2 #7 x 36′-7	1-#7 x 10′-6	4.01	25
1.123	7-#7 x 13′-5 8-#7 x 12′-4	7	#7 x 51′-0 #7 x 25′-10	5-#6 x 23′-10 20-#6 x 21′-8	2-#3	5	#7 x 48′-2 #8 x 36′-8	2-#7 x 10′-6	4.65	26
1.123	11-#6 x 13′-5 11-#6 x 12′-4	7	#8 x 51′-0 #6 x 25′-6	7-#6 x 23′-10 21-#6 x 21′-8	2-#3	5	#8 x 48′-2 #8 x 36′-8	1-#8 x 10′-6	5.05	27
1.123	7-#8 x 13′-5 8-#8 x 12′-4	7	#8 x 51′-0 #8 x 26′-2	7-#7 x 23′-10 20-#7 x 21′-8	4-#4	5	#8 x 48′-2 #9 x 36′-10	2-#8 x 10′-6	6.45	28

*, **, †, ‡ For notes, see page 9-9.

WAFFLE SLABS—SQUARE PANELS—30-IN.-WIDE DOMES

For general instructions and notes on the use of this table, see pages 9-3 to 9-9 incl.

	Span Drop-D Form Depth plus Top Slab	Live Load (psf)	t_1 (in.)	Min. Col. Dia. 12′-0 Story Height (in.)	Min. Col. Cap. C (Shear) (in.)	Interior Square Panel: Each Column Strip: No. Jst.	Each Column Strip: Bars: Trussed Straight	Each Column Strip: Bars: Top **	Each Column Strip: Stirrups per Jst.*	Each Middle Strip: No. Jst.	Each Middle Strip: Bars: Trussed Straight	Wt.† of Steel (psf)
1	L = 39′-0	50	17	19	28	6	#7 x 65′-10 #6 x 25′-6	5-#6 x 25′-9 18-#6 x 23′-5	—	7	#6 x 59′-7 #5 x 39′-10	3.66
2	D = 15′-6	100	17	24	40	6	#8 x 65′-10 #7 x 25′-10	4-#7 x 25′-9 16-#7 x 23′-5	2-#3	7	#6 x 59′-7 #6 x 40′-0	4.55
3	14 + 3	150	17	27	52	6	#8 x 65′-10 #8 x 26′-0	6-#8 x 25′-9 14-#8 x 23′-5	4-#3	7	#7 x 59′-7 #7 x 40′-6	5.69
4	L = 39′-0	50	19	20	24	6	#7 x 66′-0 #6 x 25′-6	5-#6 x 25′-9 17-#6 x 23′-5	—	7	#6 x 59′-9 #5 x 39′-10	3.62
5	D = 15′-6	100	19	24	35	6	#8 x 66′-0 #6 x 25′-6	5-#6 x 25′-9 20-#6 x 23′-5	2-#3	7	#6 x 59′-9 #6 x 40′-0	4.35
6	16 + 3	150	19	27	46	6	#8 x 66′-0 #8 x 26′-2	4-#8 x 25′-9 14-#8 x 23′-5	2-#3	7	#7 x 59′-9 #6 x 40′-0	5.23
7	L = 39′-0	50	23	20	17	6	#7 x 66′-3 #6 x 25′-6	4-#6 x 25′-9 16-#6 x 23′-5	—	7	#6 x 60′-0 #4 x 39′-8	3.39
8	D = 15′-6	100	23	24	26	6	#7 x 66′-3 #7 x 25′-10	5-#7 x 25′-9 15-#7 x 23′-5	2-#3	7	#6 x 60′-0 #6 x 40′-0	4.27
9	20 + 3	150	23	27	35	6	#8 x 66′-3 #8 x 26′-2	5-#7 x 25′-9 14-#8 x 23′-5	2-#3	7	#7 x 60′-0 #6 x 40′-0	4.79
10		200	23	30	44	6	#8 x 66′-3 #8 x 26 -2	5-#8 x 25′-9 14-#8 x 23′-5	2-#3	7	#7 x 60′-0 #6 x 40′-0	5.35
11		300	23	33	63	6	#9 x 66′-3 #8 x 26′-2	5-#8 x 25′-9 16-#8 x 23′-5	4-#3	7	#7 x 60′-0 #7 x 40′-2	6.21
12	L = 39′-0	50	18½	19	27	6	#7 x 65′-11 #7 x 25′-10	4-#7 x 25′-9 13-#7 x 23′-5	—	7	#6 x 59′-9 #5 x 39′-10	3.78
13	D = 15′-6	100	18½	24	38	6	#8 x 65′-11 #7 x 25′-10	4-#7 x 25′-9 16-#7 x 23′-5	2-#3	7	#6 x 59′-9 #7 x 40′-2	4.77
14	14 + 4½	150	18½	27	50	6	#8 x 65′-11 #8 x 26′-2	5-#8 x 25′-9 14-#8 x 23′-5	2-#3	7	#7 x 59′-9 #6 x 40′-0	5.32
15	L = 39′-0	50	20½	20	23	6	#7 x 66′-1 #7 x 25′-10	4-#7 x 25′-9 13-#7 x 23′-5	—	7	#6 x 59′-10 #5 x 39′-10	3.79
16	D = 15′-6	100	20½	24	33	6	#8 x 66′-1 #7 x 25′-10	4-#7 x 25′-9 15-#7 x 23′-5	2-#3	7	#6 x 59′-10 #6 x 40′-0	4.51
17	16 + 4½	150	20½	27	44	6	#8 x 66′-1 #8 x 26′-2	4-#8 x 25′-9 14-#8 x 23′-5	2-#3	7	#7 x 59′-10 #6 x 40′-0	5.24
18		200	20½	29	54	6	#9 x 66′-1 #7 x 25′-10	5-#7 x 25′-9 19-#7 x 23′-5	4-#3	7	#7 x 59′-10 #7 x 40′-2	5.82
19	L = 39′-0	50	24½	20	16	6	#7 x 66′-4 #6 x 25′-6	4-#6 x 25′-9 17-#6 x 23′-5	—	7	#6 x 60′-2 #5 x 39′-10	3.58
20	D = 15′-6	100	24½	24	25	6	#7 x 66′-4 #7 x 25′-10	5-#7 x 25′-9 15-#7 x 23′-5	2-#3	7	#6 x 60′-2 #6 x 40′-0	4.28
21	20 + 4½	150	24½	27	33	6	#8 x 66′-4 #7 x 25′-10	5-#7 x 25′-9 16-#7 x 23′-5	2-#3	7	#7 x 60′-2 #5 x 39′-10	4.80
22		200	24½	30	42	6	#8 x 66′-4 #8 x 26′-2	5-#8 x 25′-9 14-#8 x 23′-5	2-#3	7	#7 x 60′-2 #6 x 40′-0	5.36
23		300	24½	34	59	6	#9 x 66′-4 #8 x 26′-2	5-#8 x 25′-9 16-#8 x 23′-5	4-#3	7	#7 x 60′-2 #7 x 40′-2	6.23
24	L = 42′-0 D = 15′-6 14 + 3	50	17	21	30	8	#7 x 71′-3 #7 x 28′-10	8-#7 x 27′-9 13-#7 x 25′-3	4-#3	6	#7 x 64′-6 #7 x 43′-2	4.81
25	L = 42′-0 D = 15′-6 14 + 4½	75	18½	21	41	8	#7 x 71′-3 #7 x 28′-10	8-#7 x 27′-9 16-#7 x 25′-3	4-#3	6	#7 x 64′-6 #7 x 43′-2	4.97
26	L = 42′-0	50	23	21	22	8	#6 x 71′-3 #6 x 28′-6	7-#6 x 27′-9 21-#6 x 25′-3	—	6	#7 x 64′-6 #5 x 42′-10	3.80
27	D = 15′-6	100	23	25	33	8	#7 x 71′-3 #6 x 28′-6	7-#6 x 27′-9 23-#6 x 25′-3	2-#3	6	#7 x 64′-6 #7 x 43′-2	4.66
28	20 + 3	150	23	28	43	8	#7 x 71′-3 #7 x 28′-10	7-#7 x 27′-9 21-#7 x 25′-3	2-#3	6	#8 x 64′-6 #6 x 43′-0	5.28
29		200	23	30	52	8	#8 x 71′-3″ #8 x 29′-3″	8-#8 x 27′-9 14-#8 x 25′-3	4-#3	6	#8 x 64′-6 #8 x 43′-8	6.12

*,**,† For notes, see page 9-9.

WAFFLE SLABS—SQUARE PANELS—30-IN.-WIDE DOMES

For general instructions and notes on the use of this table, see pages 9-3 to 9-9 incl.

Av.‡ Cu. Ft. Conc. (psf)	Strips Perpendicular to an Exterior Wall								Wt.† of Steel (psf)	
	Column Strip					Middle Strip				
	Top Bars at Ext. Col.**	No. Jsts.	Bars Trussed Straight	Top Bars at First Int. Col.	Stir-rups per Joist*	No. Jsts.	Bars Trussed Straight	Top Bars at Ext. Support		
.779	7-#7 x 14′-5 8-#7 x 13′-3	6	#8 x 54′-6 #7 x 25′-10	7-#6 x 25′-9 19-#6 x 23′-5	—	7	#6 x 51′-4 #7 x 39′-7	2-#6 x 11′-3	4.08	1
.779	7-#8 x 14′-5 7-#8 x 13′-3	6	#8 x 54′-6 #8 x 26′-2	6-#7 x 25′-9 19-#7 x 23′-5	2-#3	7	#7 x 51′-4 #7 x 39′-7	1-#7 x 11′-3	4.88	2
.779	10-#8 x 14′-5 10-#8 x 13′-3	6	#9 x 54′-7 #9 x 26′-7	7-#7 x 25′-9 15-#7 x 23′-5	4-#3	7	#8 x 51′-9 #8 x 39′-8	2-#7 x 11′-3	6.36	3
.862	10-#6 x 14′-5 10-#6 x 13′-3	6	#8 x 54′-7 #6 x 25′-6	6-#6 x 25′-9 18-#6 x 23′-5	—	7	#6 x 51′-6 #7 x 39′-7	2-#6 x 11′-3	3.98	4
.862	7-#8 x 14′-5 7-#8 x 13′-3	6	#8 x 54′-7 #8 x 26′-2	7-#6 x 25′-9 23-#6 x 23′-5	2-#3	7	#7 x 51′-6 #7 x 39′-7	1-#7 x 11′-3	4.73	5
.862	8-#8 x 14′-5 8-#8 x 13′-3	6	#9 x 54′-7 #8 x 26′-2	6-#8 x 25′-9 14-#8 x 23′-5	2-#3	7	#7 x 51′-6 #8 x 39′-8	2-#7 x 11′-3	5.67	6
1.036	7-#7 x 14′-5 7-#7 x 13′-3	6	#7 x 54′-11 #7 x 25′-10	6-#6 x 25′-9 19-#6 x 23′-5	—	7	#6 x 51′-9 #6 x 39′-6	1-#6 x 11′-3	3.61	7
1.036	8-#7 x 14′-5 8-#7 x 13′-3	6	#8 x 54′-11 #7 x 25′-10	6-#7 x 25′-9 16-#7 x 23′-5	2-#3	7	#6 x 51′-9 #7 x 39′-7	2-#6 x 11′-3	4.52	8
1.036	7-#8 x 14′-5 8-#8 x 13′-3	6	#8 x 54′-11 #8 x 26′-2	6-#7 x 25′-9 20-#7 x 23′-5	2-#3	7	#7 x 51′-9 #7 x 39′-7	1-#7 x 11′-3	5.05	9
1.036	8-#8 x 14′-5 8-#8 x 13′-3	6	#9 x 54′-11 #8 x 26′-2	6-#8 x 25′-9 16-#8 x 23′-5	2-#3	7	#7 x 51′-9 #8 x 39′-8	2-#7 x 11′-3	5.78	10
1.036	9-#8 x 14′-5 9-#8 x 13′-3	6	#10 x 54′-11 #8 x 26′-2	6-#8 x 25′-9 18-#8 x 23′-5	4-#3	7	#8 x 51′-9 #8 x 39′-8	1-#8 x 11′-3	6.63	11
.904	7-#7 x 14′-5 8-#7 x 13′-3	6	# 8 x 54′-7 # 7 x 25′-10	5-#7 x 25′-9 14-#7 x 23′-5	—	7	#6 x 51′-6 #7 x 39′-7	2-#6 x 11′-3	4.14	12
.904	7-#8 x 14′-5 7-#8 x 13′-3	6	# 8 x 54′-7 # 8 x 26′-2	6-#7 x 25′-9 19-#7 x 23′-5	2-#3	7	#7 x 51′-6 #7 x 39′-7	1-#7 x 11′-3	4.99	13
.904	6-#9 x 14′-5 6-#9 x 13′-3	6	# 9 x 54′-7 # 9 x 26′-7	6-#8 x 25′-9 15-#8 x 23′-5	2-#3	7	#7 x 51′-6 #8 x 39′-8	2-#7 x 11′-3	5.79	14
.987	7-#7 x 14′-5 7-#7 x 13′-3	6	#8 x 54′-9 #7 x 25′-10	5-#7 x 25′-9 13-#7 x 23′-5	—	7	#6 x 51′-7 #7 x 39′-7	2-#6 x 11′-3	4.11	15
.987	7-#8 x 14′-5 7-#8 x 13′-3	6	#8 x 54′-9 #8 x 26′-2	5-#7 x 25′-9 18-#7 x 23′-5	2-#3	7	#7 x 51′-7 #7 x 39′-7	1-#7 x 11′-3	4.84	16
.987	8-#8 x 14′-5 8-#8 x 13′-3	6	#9 x 54′-9 #8 x 26′-2	5-#8 x 25′-9 15-#8 x 23′-5	2-#3	7	#7 x 51′-7 #8 x 39′-8	2-#7 x 11′-3	5.68	17
.987	7-#9 x 14′-5 7-#9 x 13′-3	6	#9 x 54′-9 #9 x 26′-7	7-#7 x 25′-9 22-#7 x 23′-5	4-#3	7	#8 x 51′-7 #8 x 39′-8	1-#8 x 11′-3	6.27	18
1.161	9-#6 x 14′-5 10-#6 x 13′-3	6	#8 x 55′-0 #6 x 25′-6	6-#6 x 25′-9 17-#6 x 23′-5	—	7	#6 x 51′-11 #7 x 39′-7	2-#6 x 11′-3	3.94	19
1.161	6-#8 x 14′-5 6-#8 x 13′-3	6	#8 x 55′-0 #8 x 26′-2	6-#7 x 25′-9 16-#7 x 23′-5	2-#3	7	#7 x 51′-11 #7 x 39′-7	1-#7 x 11′-3	4.67	20
1.161	7-#8 x 14′-5 7-#8 x 13′-3	6	#9 x 55′-0 #8 x 26′-2	6-#7 x 25′-9 18-#7 x 23′-5	2-#3	7	#7 x 51′-11 #7 x 39′-7	1-#7 x 11′-3	5.17	21
1.161	8-#8 x 14′-5 8-#8 x 13′-3	6	#9 x 55′-0 #8 x 26′-2	6-#8 x 25′-9 15-#8 x 23′-5	2-#3	7	#7 x 51′-11 #8 x 39′-8	2-#7 x 11′-3	5.77	22
1.161	7-#9 x 14′-5 7-#9 x 13′-3	6	#10 x 55′-0 #9 x 26′-7	6-#8 x 25′-9 17-#8 x 23′-5	4-#3	7	#8 x 51′-11 #8 x 39′-8	1-#8 x 11′-3	6.71	23
.783	12-#7 x 14′-5 12-#7 x 13′-3	8	#8 x 59′-0 #7 x 28′-10	8-#7 x 27′-9 16-#7 x 25′-3	4-#3	6	#8 x 55′-6 #8 x 42′-8	2-#8 x 12′-0	5.56	24
.903	13-#7 x 14′-5 13-#7 x 13′-3	8	#8 x 59′-0 #7 x 28′-10	8-#7 x 27′-9 18-#7 x 25′-3	4-#3	6	#8 x 55′-9 #8 x 42′-8	2-#8 x 12′-0	5.61	25
1.015	11-#6 x 15′-5 11-#6 x 14′-2	8	#7 x 58′-11 #6 x 28′-6	9-#6 x 27′-9 21-#6 x 25′-3	—	6	#7 x 55′-6 #8 x 42′-8	2-#7 x 12′-0	4.20	26
1.015	10-#7 x 15′-5 10-#7 x 14′-2	8	#8 x 58′-11 #7 x 28′-10	9-#6 x 27′-9 25-#6 x 25′-3	2-#3	6	#8 x 55′-6 #8 x 42′-8	1-#8 x 12′-0	5.11	27
1.015	8-#8 x 15′-5 9-#8 x 14′-2	8	#8 x 58′-11 #8 x 29′-2	9-#7 x 27′-9 22-#7 x 25′-3	2-#3	6	#8 x 55′-6 #9 x 42′-10	2-#8 x 12′-0	5.86	28
1.015	12-#8 x 15′-5 12-#8 x 14′-2	8	#9 x 59′-3 #8 x 29′-2	8-#8 x 27′-9 16-#8 x 25′-3	4-#3	6	#9 x 55′-9 #9 x 42′-10	2-#8 x 12′-0	7.06	29

*,**,†,‡ For notes see page 9-9.

WAFFLE SLABS—SQUARE PANELS—30-IN.-WIDE DOMES

For explanation of limitations, especially on spans of 45′-0 or more, see page 9-52.

For general instructions and notes on the use of this table, see pages 9-3 to 9-9 incl.

	Span Drop-D Form Depth plus Top Slab	Live Load (psf)	t_1 (in.)	Min. Col. Dia. 12′-0 Story Height (in.)	Min. Col. Cap. C (Shear) (in.)	Interior Square Panel — Each Column Strip: No. Jst.	Each Column Strip — Bars: Trussed Straight	Each Column Strip — Bars: Top **	Stirrups per Jst.*	Each Middle Strip: No. Jst.	Each Middle Strip — Bars: Trussed Straight	Wt.† of Steel (psf)
1	L = 42′-0	50	24½	21	22	8	#7 x 71′-4 #5 x 28′-2	6-#5 x 27′-9 27-#5 x 25′-3	—	6	#7 x 64′-8 #6 x 43′-0	3.93
2	D = 15′-6	100	24½	25	32	8	#7 x 71′-4 #7 x 28′-10	5-#7 x 27′-9 18-#7 x 25′-3	2-#3	6	#7 x 64′-8 #7 x 43′-2	4.87
3	20 + 4½	150	24½	29	41	8	#8 x 71′-4 #6 x 28′-6	6-#6 x 27′-9 25-#6 x 25′-3	2-#3	6	#8 x 64′-8 #7 x 43′-2	5.39
4		200	24½	31	51	8	#8 x 71′-4 #7 x 28′-10	6-#7 x 27′-9 22-#7 x 25′-3	4-#3	6	#8 x 64′-8 #8 x 43′-4	6.18
5	L = 45′-0	50	23	21	28	8	#7 x 76′-3 #6 x 31′-6	7-#6 x 29′-9 24-#6 x 27′-0	2-#3	7	#7 x 69′-0 #6 x 46′-0	4.44
6	D = 15′-6	100	23	26	40	8	#8 x 76′-3 #6 x 31′-6	7-#6 x 29′-9 27-#6 x 27′-0	2-#3	7	#7 x 69′-0 #7 x 46′-2	5.12
7	20 + 3	150	23	30	52	8	#8 x 76′-3 #8 x 32′-2	6-#8 x 29′-9 18-#8 x 27′-0	4-#3	7	#8 x 69′-0 #7 x 46′-2	6.19
8		200	23	32	66	7	#9 x 76′-3 #9 x 29′-7	5-#9 x 29′-9 17-#9 x 27′-0	4-#3	8	#8 x 69′-0 #6 x 46′-0	6.73
9	L = 45′-0	50	20½	21	35	8	#7 x 76′-1 #7 x 31′-10	6-#7 x 29′-9 20-#7 x 27′-0	2-#3	7	#7 x 68′-10 #6 x 46′-0	4.75
10	D = Note 1 16 + 4½	100	20½	26	51	7	#8 x 76′-1 #8 x 29′-2	6-#8 x 29′-9 18-#8 x 27′-0	2-#3	8	#7 x 68′-10 #7 x 46′-2	5.64
11	L = 45′-0	50	24½	22	27	8	#7 x 76′-4 #7 x 31′-10	5-#7 x 29′-9 18-#7 x 27′-0	2-#3	7	#7 x 69′-2 #6 x 46′-0	4.60
12	D = 15′-6	100	24½	26	39	8	#8 x 76′-4 #7 x 31′-10	5-#7 x 29′-9 20-#7 x 27′-0	2-#3	7	#7 x 69′-2 #7 x 46′-2	5.26
13	20 + 4½	150	24½	30	50	8	#8 x 76′-4 #8 x 32′-2	6-#8 x 29′-9 18-#8 x 27′-0	4-#3	7	#8 x 69′-2 #7 x 46′-2	6.21
14	L = 48′-0 D = 18′-6 16 + 4½	50	20½	25	46	9	#8 x 81′-2 #7 x 31′-10	7-#8 x 31′-9 14-#8 x 28′-10	4-#3	7	#8 x 73′-8 #7 x 49′-2	5.59
15	L = 48′-0	50	23	22	36	9	#7 x 81′-2 #7 x 31′-10	7-#7 x 31′-9 22-#7 x 28′-10	2-#3	7	#7 x 73′-6 #7 x 49′-2	4.97
16	D = 18′-6 20 + 3	100	23	27	50	9	#8 x 81′-4 #8 x 32′-2	7-#8 x 31′-9 14-#8 x 28′-10	4-#3	7	#8 x 73′-8 #8 x 49′-2	5.97
17	L = 48′-0	50	24½	22	36	9	#7 x 81′-4 #7 x 31′-10	7-#7 x 31′-9 23-#7 x 28′-10	2-#3	7	#7 x 73′-8 #7 x 49′-2	5.03
18	D = 18′-6 20 + 4½	100	24½	27	49	9	#8 x 81′-4 #7 x 31′-10	7-#7 x 31′-9 25-#7 x 28′-10	2-#3	7	#8 x 73′-8 #7 x 49′-2	5.81
19	L = 51′-0	50	23	23	42	9	#8 x 86′-2 #7 x 34′-10	7-#7 x 33′-8 24-#7 x 30′-8	2-#3	8	#7 x 78′-0 #7 x 52′-2	5.35
20	D = Note 2 20 + 3	100	23	28	60	8	#9 x 86′-2 #8 x 32′-2	7-#8 x 33′-8 23-#8 x 30′-8	2-#3	9	#8 x 78′-0 #6 x 52′-0	6.33
21	L = 51′-0	50	24½	23	42	9	#8 x 86′-3 #7 x 34′-10	7-#7 x 33′-8 25-#7 x 30′-8	2-#3	8	#7 x 78′-2 #8 x 52′-4	5.61
22	D = 18′-6 20 + 4½	100	24½	28	57	9	#9 x 86′-3 #7 x 34′-10	7-#7 x 33′-8 28-#7 x 30′-8	4-#3	8	#8 x 78′-2 #8 x 52′-4	6.60

Note 1 *D* = 15′-6 for 50 psf *LL*; 18′-6 for 100 psf *LL*.
Note 2 *D* = 18′-6 for 50 psf *LL*; 21′-6 for 100 psf *LL*.

*,**,† For notes, see page 9-9.

WAFFLE SLABS—SQUARE PANELS—30-IN.-WIDE DOMES

Av.‡ Cu. Ft. Conc. (psf)	Strips Perpendicular to an Exterior Wall								Wt.† of Steel (psf)	
	Column Strip					Middle Strip				
	Top Bars at Ext. Col.**	No. Jsts.	Bars Trussed Straight	Top Bars at First Int. Col.	Stir-rups per Joist *	No. Jsts.	Bars Trussed Straight	Top Bars at Ext. Support		
1.140	8-#7 x 15'-5 8-#7 x 14'-2	8	#7 x 59'-0 #7 x 28'-10	8-#5 x 27'-9 32-#5 x 25'-3	—	6	#7 x 55'-8 #8 x 42'-8	2-#7 x 12'-0	4.32	1
1.140	10-#7 x 15'-5 10-#7 x 14'-2	8	#8 x 59'-0 #7 x 28'-10	7-#7 x 27'-9 18-#7 x 25'-3	2-#3	6	#8 x 55'-8 #8 x 42'-8	1-#8 x 12'-0	5.22	2
1.140	8-#8 x 15'-5 9-#8 x 14'-2	8	#8 x 59'-0 #8 x 29'-2	8-#6 x 27'-9 31-#6 x 25'-3	2-#3	6	#8 x 55'-8 #9 x 42'-10	2-#8 x 12'-0	5.88	3
1.140	9-#8 x 15'-5 10-#8 x 14'-2	8	#9 x 59'-0 #8 x 29'-2	8-#7 x 27'-9 23-#7 x 25'-3	4-#3	6	#9 x 55'-8 #9 x 42'-10	1-#9 x 12'-0	6.68	4
.998	10-#7 x 16'-5 10-#7 x 15'-0	8	#8 x 62'-11 #7 x 31'-10	9-#6 x 29'-9 25-#6 x 27'-0	2-#3	7	#7 x 59'-3 #8 x 45'-8	2-#7 x 12'-9	4.90	5
.998	9-#8 x 16'-5 9-#8 x 15'-0	8	#8 x 62'-11 #8 x 32'-2	9-#6 x 29'-9 32-#6 x 27'-0	2-#3	7	#8 x 59'-3 #8 x 45'-8	1-#8 x 12'-9	5.51	6
.998	10-#8 x 16'-5 10-#8 x 15'-0	8	#9 x 62'-11 #8 x 32'-2	7-#8 x 29'-9 20-#8 x 27'-0	4-#3	7	#8 x 59'-3 #9 x 45'-10	2-#8 x 12'-9	6.64	7
1.048	9-#9 x 16'-5 9-#9 x 15'-0	7	#10 x 62'-11 #9 x 29'-7	7-#9 x 29'-9 17-#9 x 27'-0	4-#3	8	#8 x 59'-3 #9 x 45'-10	2-#8 x 12'-9	7.29	8
.956	10-#7 x 16'-5 11-#7 x 15'-0	8	#8 x 62'-8 #7 x 31'-10	8-#7 x 29'-9 20-#7 x 27'-0	2-#3	7	#7 x 59'-1 #8 x 45'-8	2-#7 x 12'-9	5.10	9
.998	8-#9 x 16'-5 8-#9 x 15'-0	7	#9 x 62'-8 #9 x 29'-7	8-#8 x 29'-9 20-#8 x 27'-0	2-#3	8	#8 x 59'-1 #8 x 45'-8	1-#8 x 12'-9	6.13	10
1.123	10-#7 x 16'-5 10-#7 x 15'-0	8	#8 x 63'-0 #7 x 31'-10	7-#7 x 29'-9 19-#7 x 27'-0	2-#3	7	#7 x 59'-5 #8 x 45'-8	2-#7 x 12'-9	5.00	11
1.123	9-#8 x 16'-5 9-#8 x 15'-0	8	#8 x 63'-0 #8 x 32'-2	7-#7 x 29'-9 24-#7 x 27'-0	2-#3	7	#8 x 59'-5 #8 x 45'-8	1-#8 x 12'-9	5.60	12
1.123	10-#8 x 16'-5 10-#8 x 15'-0	8	#9 x 63'-0 #8 x 32'-2	7-#8 x 29'-9 20-#8 x 27'-0	4-#3	7	#8 x 59'-5 #9 x 45'-10	2-#8 x 12'-9	6.66	13
.968	13-#8 x 17'-5 13-#8 x 15'-11	9	#8 x 66'-10 #8 x 31'-10	8-#8 x 31'-9 17-#8 x 28'-10	4-#3	7	#9 x 63'-0 #8 x 48'-8	2-#8 x 12'-9	6.36	14
1.028	12-#7 x 17'-5 12-#7 x 15'-11	9	#8 x 66'-10 #7 x 31'-10	9-#7 x 31'-9 23-#7 x 28'-10	2-#3	7	#8 x 63'-0 #8 x 48'-8	1-#8 x 13'-6	5.30	15
1.028	13-#8 x 17'-5 13-#8 x 15'-11	9	#9 x 67'-0 #8 x 32'-2	9-#8 x 31'-9 18-#8 x 28'-10	4-#3	7	#9 x 63'-2 #9 x 48'-10	2-#9 x 13'-6	6.65	16
1.153	9-#8 x 17'-5 9-#8 x 15'-11	9	#8 x 67'-0 #8 x 32'-2	9-#7 x 31'-9 24-#7 x 28'-10	2-#3	7	#8 x 63'-2 #8 x 48'-8	1-#8 x 13'-6	5.43	17
1.153	11-#8 x 17'-5 11-#8 x 15'-11	9	#9 x 67'-0 #8 x 32'-2	9-#7 x 31'-9 27-#7 x 28'-10	2-#3	7	#9 x 63'-2 #9 x 48'-10	1-#9 x 13'-6	6.40	18
1.012	10-#8 x 18'-4 11-#8 x 16'-10	9	#8 x 70'-10 #8 x 35'-2	9-#7 x 33'-8 29-#7 x 30'-8	2-#3	8	#8 x 66'-9 #8 x 51'-8	1-#8 x 14'-3	5.66	19
1.058	10-#9 x 18'-4 10-#9 x 16'-10	8	#10 x 70'-10 #9 x 32'-7	9-#8 x 33'-8 25-#8 x 30'-8	2-#3	9	#8 x 66'-9 #9 x 51'-10	2-#8 x 14'-3	6.99	20
1.137	11-#8 x 18'-4 11-#8 x 16'-10	9	#9 x 71'-0 #8 x 35'-2	9-#7 x 33'-8 27-#7 x 30'-8	2-#3	8	#8 x 66'-11 #9 x 51'-10	2-#8 x 14'-3	6.20	21
1.137	10-#9 x 18'-4 10-#9 x 16'-10	9	#9 x 71'-0 #9 x 35'-7	10-#7 x 33'-8 34-#7 x 30'-8	4-#3	8	#9 x 66'-11 #9 x 51'-10	1-#9 x 14'-3	7.07	22

For explanation of limitations, especially on spans of 45'-0 or more, see page 9-52.

*,**,† ‡ For notes, see page 9-9.

WAFFLE SLABS—SQUARE PANELS—19-IN.-WIDE DOMES

For general instructions and notes on the use of this table, see pages 9-3 to 9-9 incl.

	Span Drop-D Form Depth plus Top Slab	Live Load (psf)	t_1 (in.)	Min. Col. Dia. 12′-0″ Story Height (in.)	Min. Col. Cap. C (Shear) (in.)	Interior Square Panel: Each Column Strip: No. Jst.	Each Column Strip: Bars: Trussed Straight	Each Column Strip: Bars: Top **	Each Column Strip: Bars: Stirrups per Jst.*	Each Middle Strip: No. Jst.	Each Middle Strip: Bars: Trussed Straight	Wt.† of Steel (psf)
1	L = 16′-0	50	8½	12	12	4	#4 x 27′-1 #4 x 11′-3	— 4-#4 x 9′-8	—	4	#4 x 24′-6 #4 x 16′-8	1.86
2	D = 6′-5	100	8½	14	12	4	#4 x 27′-1 #4 x 11′-3	1-#4 x 10′-7 5-#4 x 9′-8	—	4	#4 x 24′-6 #4 x 16′-8	1.97
3	6 + 2½	150	8½	16	14	4	#4 x 27′-1 #4 x 11′-3	2-#4 x 10′-7 6-#4 x 9′-8	—	4	#4 x 24′-6 #4 x 16′-8	2.07
4		200	8½	17	19	4	#4 x 27′-1 #4 x 11′-3	3-#4 x 10′-7 8-#4 x 9′-8	2-#3	4	#4 x 24′-6 #4 x 16′-8	2.37
5	L = 16′-0	50	10½	12	12	4	#4 x 27′-3 #4 x 11′-3	— 3-#4 x 9′-8	—	4	#4 x 24′-8 #4 x 16′-8	1.82
6	D = 6′-5	100	10½	14	12	4	#4 x 27′-3 #4 x 11′-3	— 4-#4 x 9′-8	—	4	#4 x 24′-8 #4 x 16′-8	1.87
7	8 + 2½	150	10½	16	12	4	#4 x 27′-3 #4 x 11′-3	1-#4 x 10′-7 5-#4 x 9′-8	—	4	#4 x 24′-8 #4 x 16′-8	1.97
8		200	10½	17	12	4	#4 x 27′-3 #4 x 11′-3	2-#4 x 10′-7 7-#4 x 9′-8	—	4	#4 x 24′-8 #4 x 16′-8	2.13
9		300	10½	20	20	4	#4 x 27′-3 #4 x 11′-3	3-#4 x 10′-7 10-#4 x 9′-8	2-#3	4	#4 x 24′-8 #4 x 16′-8	2.50
10	L = 16′-0	50	12½	12	12	4	#4 x 27′-4 #4 x 11′-3	— 3-#4 x 9′-8	—	4	#4 x 24′-10 #4 x 16′-8	1.82
11	D = 6′-5	100	12½	14	12	4	#4 x 27′-4 #4 x 11′-3	— 4-#4 x 9′-8	—	4	#4 x 24′-10 #4 x 16′-8	1.87
12	10 + 2½	150	12½	16	12	4	#4 x 27′-4 #4 x 11′-3	— 4-#4 x 9′-8	—	4	#4 x 24′-10 #4 x 16′-8	1.87
13		200	12½	17	12	4	#4 x 27′-4 #4 x 11′-3	1-#4 x 10′-7 6-#4 x 9′-8	—	4	#4 x 24′-10 #4 x 16′-8	2.03
14		300	12½	19	13	4	#4 x 27′-4 #4 x 11′-3	3-#4 x 10′-7 8-#4 x 9′-8	2-#3	4	#4 x 24′-10 #4 x 16′-8	2.42
15	L = 16′-0	50	14½	12	12	4	#4 x 27′-6 #4 x 11′-3	— 3-#4 x 9′-8	—	4	#4 x 24′-11 #4 x 16′-8	1.83
16	D = 6′-5	100	14½	14	12	4	#4 x 27′-6 #4 x 11′-3	— 3-#4 x 9′-8	—	4	#4 x 24′-11 #4 x 16′-8	1.83
17	12 + 2½	150	14½	16	12	4	#4 x 27′-6 #4 x 11′-3	— 4-#4 x 9′-8	—	4	#4 x 24′-11 #4 x 16′-8	1.88
18		200	14½	17	12	4	#4 x 27′-6 #4 x 11′-3	1-#4 x 10′-7 5-#4 x 9′-8	—	4	#4 x 24′-11 #4 x 16′-8	1.98
19		300	14½	19	12	4	#4 x 27′-6 #4 x 11′-3	2-#4 x 10′-7 7-#4 x 9′-8	—	4	#4 x 24′-11 #4 x 16′-8	2.14
20	L = 16′-0	50	10½	12	12	4	#4 x 27′-3 #4 x 11′-3	— 3-#4 x 9′-8	—	4	#4 x 24′-8 #4 x 16′-8	1.82
21	D = 6′-5	100	10½	14	12	4	#4 x 27′-3 #4 x 11′-3	— 4-#4 x 9′-8	—	4	#4 x 24′-8 #4 x 16′-8	1.87
22	6 + 4½	150	10½	16	12	4	#4 x 27′-3 #4 x 11′-3	1-#4 x 10′-7 6-#4 x 9′-8	—	4	#4 x 24′-8 #4 x 16′-8	2.02
23		200	10½	17	13	4	#4 x 27′-3 #4 x 11′-3	2-#4 x 10′-7 7-#4 x 9′-8	2-#3	4	#4 x 24′-8 #4 x 16′-8	2.29
24		300	10½	19	21	4	#4 x 27′-3 #4 x 11′-3	3-#4 x 10′-7 10-#4 x 9′-8	2-#3	4	#4 x 24′-8 #4 x 16′-8	2.50
25	L = 16′-0	50	12½	12	12	4	#4 x 27′-4 #4 x 11′-3	— 3-#4 x 9′-8	—	4	#4 x 24′-10 #4 x 16′-8	1.82
26	D = 6′-5	100	12½	14	12	4	#4 x 27′-4 #4 x 11′-3	— 4-#4 x 9′-8	—	4	#4 x 24′-10 #4 x 16′-8	1.87
27	8 + 4½	150	12½	16	12	4	#4 x 27′-4 #4 x 11′-3	1-#4 x 10′-7 5-#4 x 9′-8	—	4	#4 x 24′-10 #4 x 16′-8	1.98
28		200	12½	17	12	4	#4 x 27′-4 #4 x 11′-3	1-#4 x 10′-7 6-#4 x 9′-8	—	4	#4 x 24′-10 #4 x 16′-8	2.03
29		300	12½	19	14	4	#4 x 27′-4 #4 x 11′-3	3-#4 x 10′-7 8-#4 x 9′-8	2-#3	4	#4 x 24′-10 #4 x 16′-8	2.42

*,**,† For notes, see page 9-9.

WAFFLE SLABS—SQUARE PANELS—19-IN.-WIDE DOMES

Av.‡ Cu. Ft. Conc. (psf)	Strips Perpendicular to an Exterior Wall								Wt.† of Steel (psf)	
	Column Strip					Middle Strip				
	Top Bars at Ext. Col.**	No. Jsts.	Bars Trussed Straight	Top Bars at First Int. Col.	Stir-rups per Joist*	No. Jsts.	Bars Trussed Straight	Top Bars at Ext. Support		
.453	3-#4 x 6′-10 3-#4 x 6′-4	4	#4 x 23′-4 #4 x 11′-3	— 4-#4 x 9′-8	—	4	#4 x 22′-0 #4 x 16′-4	—	1.85	1
.453	4-#4 x 6′-10 4-#4 x 6′-4	4	#4 x 23′-4 #4 x 11′-3	1-#4 x 10′-7 6-#4 x 9′-8	—	4	#4 x 22′-0 #4 x 16′-4	1-#4 x 5′-6	2.03	2
.453	4-#4 x 6′-10 4-#4 x 6′-4	4	#4 x 23′-4 #4 x 11′-3	2-#4 x 10′-7 8-#4 x 9′-8	—	4	#4 x 22′-0 #4 x 16′-4	1-#4 x 5′-6	2.12	3
.453	5-#4 x 6′-10 5-#4 x 6′-4	4	#5 x 23′-4 #4 x 11′-3	4-#4 x 10′-7 8-#4 x 9′-8	2-#3	4	#4 x 22′-0 #4 x 16′-4	1-#4 x 5′-6	2.54	4
.541	2-#4 x 6′-10 2-#4 x 6′-4	4	#4 x 23′-5 #4 x 11′-3	— 3-#4 x 9′-8	—	4	#4 x 22′-2 #4 x 16′-4	0-#4 x 5′-6	1.78	5
.541	3-#4 x 6′-10 3-#4 x 6′-4	4	#4 x 23′-5 #4 x 11′-3	— 5-#4 x 9′-8	—	4	#4 x 22′-2 #4 x 16′-4	0-#4 x 5′-6	1.86	6
.541	4-#4 x 6′-10 4-#4 x 6′-4	4	#4 x 23′-5 #4 x 11′-3	1-#4 x 10′-7 7-#4 x 9′-8	—	4	#4 x 22′-2 #4 x 16′-4	1-#4 x 5′-6	2.05	7
.541	4-#4 x 6′-10 5-#4 x 6′-4	4	#4 x 23′-5 #4 x 11′-3	3-#4 x 10′-7 8-#4 x 9′-8	—	4	#4 x 22′-2 #4 x 16′-4	1-#4 x 5′-6	2.18	8
.541	5-#4 x 6′-10 6-#4 x 6′-4	4	#5 x 23′-5 #4 x 11′-3	4-#4 x 10′-7 9-#4 x 9′-8	2-#3	4	#4 x 22′-2 #5 x 16′-5	1-#4 x 5′-6	2.74	9
.631	2-#4 x 6′-10 2-#4 x 6′-4	4	#4 x 23′-7 #4 x 11′-3	— 3-#4 x 9′-8	—	4	#4 x 22′-4 #4 x 16′-4	1-#4 x 5′-6	1.84	10
.631	3-#4 x 6′-10 3-#4 x 6′-4	4	#4 x 23′-7 #4 x 11′-3	— 4-#4 x 9′-8	—	4	#4 x 22′-4 #4 x 16′-4	1-#4 x 5′-6	1.91	11
.631	3-#4 x 6′-10 3-#4 x 6′-4	4	#4 x 23′-7 #4 x 11′-3	1-#4 x 10′-7 5-#4 x 9′-8	—	4	#4 x 22′-4 #4 x 16′-4	1-#4 x 5′-6	1.94	12
.631	4-#4 x 6′-10 4-#4 x 6′-4	4	#4 x 23′-7 #4 x 11′-3	2-#4 x 10′-7 6-#4 x 9′-8	—	4	#4 x 22′-4 #4 x 16′-4	1-#4 x 5′-6	2.08	13
.631	5-#4 x 6′-10 5-#4 x 6′-4	4	#5 x 23′-7 #4 x 11′-3	4-#4 x 10′-7 8-#4 x 9′-8	2-#3	4	#4 x 22′-4 #4 x 16′-4	1-#4 x 5′-6	2.59	14
.724	2-#4 x 6′-10 2-#4 x 6′-4	4	#4 x 23′-9 #4 x 11′-3	— 3-#4 x 9′-8	—	4	#4 x 22′-5 #4 x 16′-4	1-#4 x 5′-6	1.85	15
.724	3-#4 x 6′-10 3-#4 x 6′-4	4	#4 x 23′-9 #4 x 11′-3	— 4-#4 x 9′-8	—	4	#4 x 22′-5 #4 x 16′-4	1-#4 x 5′-6	1.89	16
.724	3-#4 x 6′-10 3-#4 x 6′-4	4	#4 x 23′-9 #4 x 11′-3	— 4-#4 x 9′-8	—	4	#4 x 22′-5 #4 x 16′-4	1-#4 x 5′-6	1.92	17
.724	3-#4 x 6′-10 4-#4 x 6′-4	4	#4 x 23′-9 #4 x 11′-3	1-#4 x 10′-7 5-#4 x 9′-8	—	4	#4 x 22′-5 #4 x 16′-4	1-#4 x 5′-6	2.02	18
.724	4-#4 x 6′-10 5-#4 x 6′-4	4	#4 x 23′-9 #4 x 11′-3	3-#4 x 10′-7 8-#4 x 9′-8	—	4	#4 x 22′-5 #4 x 16′-4	1-#4 x 5′-6	2.19	19
.620	2-#4 x 6′-10 3-#4 x 6′-4	4	#4 x 23′-5 #4 x 11′-3	— 4-#4 x 9′-8	—	4	#4 x 22′-2 #4 x 16′-4	0-#4 x 5′-6	1.81	20
.620	3-#4 x 6′-10 3-#4 x 6′-4	4	#4 x 23′-5 #4 x 11′-3	1-#4 x 10′-7 5-#4 x 9′-8	—	4	#4 x 22′-2 #4 x 16′-4	1-#4 x 5′-6	1.94	21
.620	4-#4 x 6′-10 4-#4 x 6′-4	4	#4 x 23′-5 #4 x 11′-3	2-#4 x 10′-7 6-#4 x 9′-8	—	4	#4 x 22′-2 #4 x 16′-4	1-#4 x 5′-6	2.07	22
.620	5-#4 x 6′-10 5-#4 x 6′-4	4	#4 x 23′-5 #4 x 11′-3	3-#4 x 10′-7 8-#4 x 9′-8	2-#3	4	#4 x 22′-2 #4 x 16′-4	1-#4 x 5′-6	2.36	23
.620	5-#4 x 6′-10 6-#4 x 6′-4	4	#5 x 23′-5 #4 x 11′-3	4-#4 x 10′-7 10-#4 x 9′-8	2-#3	4	#4 x 22′-2 #4 x 16′-4	1-#4 x 5′-6	2.65	24
.707	2-#4 x 6′-10 2-#4 x 6 -4	4	#4 x 23′-7 #4 x 11′-3	— 3-#4 x 9′-8	—	4	#4 x 22′-4 #4 x 16′-4	1-#4 x 5′-6	1.84	25
.707	3-#4 x 6′-10 3-#4 x 6′-4	4	#4 x 23′-7 #4 x 11′-3	— 4-#4 x 9′-8	—	4	#4 x 22′-4 #4 x 16′-4	1-#4 x 5′-6	1.91	26
.707	3-#4 x 6′-10 3-#4 x 6′-4	4	#4 x 23′-7 #4 x 11′-3	1-#4 x 10′-7 5-#4 x 9′-8	—	4	#4 x 22′-4 #4 x 16′-4	1-#4 x 5′-6	1.99	27
.707	4-#4 x 6′-10 4-#4 x 6′-4	4	#4 x 23′-7 #4 x 11′-3	2-#4 x 10′-7 7-#4 x 9′-8	—	4	#4 x 22′-4 #4 x 16′-4	1-#4 x 5′-6	2.09	28
.707	5-#4 x 6′-10 5-#4 x 6′-4	4	#5 x 23′-7 #4 x 11′-3	4-#4 x 10′-7 8-#4 x 9′-8	2-#3	4	#4 x 22′-4 #4 x 16′-4	1-#4 x 5′-6	2.59	29

*,**,†,‡ For notes, see page 9-9.

WAFFLE SLABS—SQUARE PANELS—19-IN.-WIDE DOMES

For general instructions and notes on the use of this table, see pages 9-3 to 9-9 incl.

	Span Drop-D Form Depth plus Top Slab	Live Load (psf)	t_1 (in.)	Min. Col. Dia. 12'-0" Story Height (in.)	Min. Col. Cap. C (Shear) (in.)	Interior Square Panel: Each Column Strip: No. Jst.	Each Column Strip: Bars: Trussed Straight	Each Column Strip: Bars: Top **	Each Column Strip: Bars: Stirrups per Jst.*	Each Middle Strip: No. Jst.	Each Middle Strip: Bars: Trussed Straight	Wt.† of Steel (psf)
1	L = 16'-0	50	14½	12	12	4	#4 x 27'-6 #4 x 11'-3	— 3-#4 x 9'-8	—	4	#4 x 24'-11 #4 x 16'-8	1.83
2	D = 6'-5	100	14½	14	12	4	#4 x 27'-6 #4 x 11'-3	— 4-#4 x 9'-8	—	4	#4 x 24'-11 #4 x 16'-8	1.88
3	10 + 4½	150	14½	16	12	4	#4 x 27'-6 #4 x 11'-3	— 4-#4 x 9'-8	—	4	#4 x 24'-11 #4 x 16'-8	1.88
4		200	14½	17	12	4	#4 x 27'-6 #4 x 11'-3	1-#4 x 10'-7 5-#4 x 9'-8	—	4	#4 x 24'-11 #4 x 16'-8	1.98
5		300	14½	19	12	4	#4 x 27'-6 #4 x 11'-3	2-#4 x 10'-7 7-#4 x 9'-8	—	4	#4 x 24'-11 #4 x 16'-8	2.14
6	L = 16'-0	50	16½	12	12	4	#4 x 27'-8 #4 x 11'-3	— 3-#4 x 9'-8	—	4	#4 x 25'-1 #4 x 16'-8	1.84
7	D = 6'-5	100	16½	14	12	4	#4 x 27'-8 #4 x 11'-3	— 3-#4 x 9'-8	—	4	#4 x 25'-1 #4 x 16'-8	1.84
8	12 + 4½	150	16½	16	12	4	#4 x 27'-8 #4 x 11'-3	— 4-#4 x 9'-8	—	4	#4 x 25'-1 #4 x 16'-8	1.89
9		200	16½	17	12	4	#4 x 27'-8 #4 x 11'-3	— 4-#4 x 9'-8	—	4	#4 x 25'-1 #4 x 16'-8	1.89
10		300	16½	19	12	4	#4 x 27'-8 #4 x 11'-3	2-#4 x 10'-7 6-#4 x 9'-8	—	4	#4 x 25'-1 #4 x 16'-8	2.10
11	L = 18'-0	50	8½	12	12	4	#4 x 30'-5 #4 x 13'-3	1-#4 x 11'-11 5-#4 x 10'-10	—	5	#4 x 27'-6 #4 x 18'-8	1.94
12	D = 6'-5	100	8½	15	14	4	#4 x 30'-5 #4 x 13'-3	2-#4 x 11'-11 8-#4 x 10'-10	2-#3	5	#4 x 27'-6 #4 x 18'-8	2.24
13	6 + 2½	150	8½	17	20	4	#5 x 30'-5 #4 x 13'-3	2-#4 x 11'-11 8-#4 x 10'-10	2-#3	5	#4 x 27'-6 #4 x 18'-8	2.52
14	L = 18'-0	50	10½	12	12	4	#4 x 30'-7 #4 x 13'-3	— 4-#4 x 10'-10	—	5	#4 x 27'-8 #4 x 18'-8	1.86
15	D = 6'-5	100	10½	15	12	4	#4 x 30'-7 #4 x 13'-3	2-#4 x 11'-11 6-#4 x 10'-10	—	5	#4 x 27'-8 #4 x 18'-8	2.04
16	8 + 2½	150	10½	17	13	4	#4 x 30'-7 #4 x 13'-3	3-#4 x 11'-11 9-#4 x 10'-10	2-#3	5	#4 x 27'-8 #4 x 18'-8	2.35
17		200	10½	19	18	4	#5 x 30'-7 #4 x 13'-3	2-#4 x 11'-11 9-#4 x 10'-10	2-#3	5	#4 x 27'-8 #4 x 18'-8	2.59
18		300	10½	21	27	4	#5 x 30'-7 #5 x 13'-3	2-#5 x 11'-11 8-#5 x 10'-10	2-#3	5	#4 x 27'-8 #4 x 18'-8	2.92
19	L = 18'-0	50	12½	12	12	4	#4 x 30'-8 #4 x 13'-3	— 4-#4 x 10'-10	—	5	#4 x 27'-10 #4 x 18'-8	1.86
20	D = 6'-5	100	12½	15	12	4	#4 x 30'-8 #4 x 13'-3	1-#4 x 11'-11 5-#4 x 10'-10	—	5	#4 x 27'-10 #4 x 18'-8	1.96
21	10 + 2½	150	12½	17	12	4	#4 x 30'-8 #4 x 13'-3	2-#4 x 11'-11 7-#4 x 10'-10	—	5	#4 x 27'-10 #4 x 18'-8	2.09
22		200	12½	18	12	4	#4 x 30'-8 #4 x 13'-3	3-#4 x 11'-11 10-#4 x 10'-10	2-#3	5	#4 x 27'-10 #4 x 18'-8	2.42
23		300	12½	21	20	4	#5 x 30'-8 #4 x 13'-3	3-#4 x 11'-11 10-#4 x 10'-10	2-#3	5	#4 x 27'-10 #4 x 18'-8	2.70
24	L = 18'-0	50	14½	12	12	4	#4 x 30'-10 #4 x 13'-3	— 4-#4 x 10'-10	—	5	#4 x 27'-11 #4 x 18'-8	1.87
25	D = 6'-5	100	14½	15	12	4	#4 x 30'-10 #4 x 13'-3	— 5-#4 x 10'-10	—	5	#4 x 27'-11 #4 x 18'-8	1.91
26	12 + 2½	150	14½	17	12	4	#4 x 30'-10 #4 x 13'-3	1-#4 x 11'-11 6-#4 x 10'-10	—	5	#4 x 27'-11 #4 x 18'-8	2.00
27		200	14½	18	12	4	#4 x 30'-10 #4 x 13'-3	2-#4 x 11'-11 8-#4 x 10'-10	—	5	#4 x 27'-11 #4 x 18'-8	2.14
28		300	14½	21	14	4	#5 x 30'-10 #4 x 13'-3	2-#4 x 11'-11 10-#4 x 10'-10	2-#3	5	#4 x 27'-11 #4 x 18'-8	2.67

*,**,† For notes, see page 9-9.

WAFFLE SLABS—SQUARE PANELS—19-IN.-WIDE DOMES

Av.‡ Cu. Ft. Conc. (psf)	Strips Perpendicular to an Exterior Wall										
	Column Strip					Middle Strip			Wt.† of Steel (psf)	
	Top Bars at Ext. Col.**	No. Jsts.	Bars Trussed Straight	Top Bars at First Int. Col.	Stir-rups per Joist*	No. Jsts.	Bars Trussed Straight	Top Bars at Ext. Support		
.798	2-#4 x 6′-10 2-#4 x 6′-4	4	#4 x 23′-9 #4 x 11′-3	— 3-#4 x 9′-8	—	4	#4 x 22′-5 #4 x 16′-4	1-#4 x 5′-6	1.85	1
.798	3-#4 x 6′-10 3-#4 x 6′-4	4	#4 x 23′-9 #4 x 11′-3	— 4-#4 x 9′-8	—	4	#4 x 22′-5 #4 x 16′-4	1-#4 x 5′-6	1.92	2
.798	3-#4 x 6′-10 3-#4 x 6′-4	4	#4 x 23′-9 #4 x 11′-3	1-#4 x 10′-7 5-#4 x 9′-8	—	4	#4 x 22′-5 #4 x 16′-4	1-#4 x 5′-6	1.95	3
.798	4-#4 x 6′-10 4-#4 x 6′-4	4	#4 x 23′-9 #4 x 11′-3	1-#4 x 10′-7 6-#4 x 9′-8	—	4	#4 x 22′-5 #4 x 16′-4	1-#4 x 5′-6	2.05	4
.798	5-#4 x 6′-10 5-#4 x 6′-4	4	#4 x 23′-9 #4 x 11′-3	3-#4 x 10′-7 9-#4 x 9′-8	—	4	#4 x 22′-5 #4 x 16′-4	1-#4 x 5′-6	2.22	5
.891	2-#4 x 6′-10 2-#4 x 6′-4	4	#4 x 23′-10 #4 x 11′-3	— 3-#4 x 9′-8	—	4	#4 x 22′-7 #4 x 16′-4	1-#4 x 5′-6	1.85	6
.891	2-#4 x 6′-10 3-#4 x 6′-4	4	#4 x 23′-10 #4 x 11′-3	— 4-#4 x 9′-8	—	4	#4 x 22′-7 #4 x 16′-4	1-#4 x 5′-6	1.88	7
.891	3-#4 x 6′-10 3-#4 x 6′-4	4	#4 x 23′-10 #4 x 11′-3	— 4-#4 x 9′-8	—	4	#4 x 22′-7 #4 x 16′-4	1-#4 x 5′-6	1.93	8
.891	3-#4 x 6′-10 3-#4 x 6′-4	4	#4 x 23′-10 #4 x 11′-3	1-#4 x 10′-7 5-#4 x 9′-8	—	4	#4 x 22′-7 #4 x 16′-4	1-#4 x 5′-6	1.95	9
.891	4-#4 x 6′-10 4-#4 x 6′-4	4	#4 x 23′-10 #4 x 11′-3	2-#4 x 10′-7 8-#4 x 9′-8	—	4	#4 x 22′-7 #4 x 16′-4	1-#4 x 5′-6	2.14	10
.444	4-#4 x 7′-6 4-#4 x 6′-11	4	#4 x 26′-0 #4 x 13′-3	1-#4 x 11′-11 6-#4 x 10′-10	—	5	#4 x 24′-6 #4 x 18′-4	0-#4 x 6′-0	1.94	11
.444	5-#4 x 7′-6 5-#4 x 6′-11	4	#4 x 26′-0 #4 x 13′-3	3-#4 x 11′-11 10-#4 x 10′-10	2-#3	5	#4 x 24′-6 #4 x 18′-4	1-#4 x 6′-0	2.30	12
.444	6-#4 x 7′-6 6-#4 x 6′-11	4	#5 x 26′-0 #4 x 13′-3	3-#4 x 11′-11 10-#4 x 10′-10	2-#3	5	#4 x 24′-6 #4 x 18′-4	1-#4 x 6′-0	2.59	13
.529	3-#4 x 7′-6 3-#4 x 6′-11	4	#4 x 26′-1 #4 x 13′-3	1-#4 x 11′-11 5-#4 x 10′-10	—	5	#4 x 24′-8 #4 x 18′-4	0-#4 x 6′-0	1.85	14
.529	4-#4 x 7′-6 4-#4 x 6′-11	4	#4 x 26′-1 #4 x 13′-3	2-#4 x 11′-11 7-#4 x 10′-10	—	5	#4 x 24′-8 #4 x 18′-4	1-#4 x 6′-0	2.07	15
.529	5-#4 x 7′-6 5-#4 x 6′-11	4	#5 x 26′-1 #4 x 13′-3	4-#4 x 11′-11 8-#4 x 10′-10	2-#3	5	#4 x 24′-8 #4 x 18′-4	1-#4 x 6′-0	2.48	16
.529	6-#4 x 7′-6 6-#4 x 6′-11	4	#5 x 26′-1 #4 x 13′-3	3-#4 x 11′-11 10-#4 x 10′-10	2-#3	5	#4 x 24′-8 #4 x 18′-4	1-#4 x 6′-0	2.63	17
.529	5-#5 x 7′-6 5-#5 x 6′-11	4	#5 x 26′-1 #5 x 13′-3	3-#5 x 11′-11 10-#5 x 10′-10	2-#3	5	#4 x 24′-8 #5 x 18′-5	2-#4 x 6′-0	3.17	18
.617	3-#4 x 7′-6 3-#4 x 6′-11	4	#4 x 26′-3 #4 x 13′-3	— 4-#4 x 10′-10	—	5	#4 x 24′-10 #4 x 18′-4	1-#4 x 6′-0	1.90	19
.617	4-#4 x 7′-6 4-#4 x 6′-11	4	#4 x 26′-3 #4 x 13′-3	1-#4 x 11′-11 6-#4 x 10′-10	—	5	#4 x 24′-10 #4 x 18′-4	1-#4 x 6′-0	2.01	20
.617	4-#4 x 7′-6 5-#4 x 6′-11	4	#4 x 26′-3 #4 x 13′-3	3-#4 x 11′-11 8-#4 x 10′-10	—	5	#4 x 24′-10 #4 x 18′-4	1-#4 x 6′-0	2.14	21
.617	5-#4 x 7′-6 6-#4 x 6′-11	4	#5 x 26′-3 #4 x 13′-3	4-#4 x 11′-11 9-#4 x 10′-10	2-#3	5	#4 x 24′-10 #4 x 18′-4	1-#4 x 6′-0	2.55	22
.617	4-#5 x 7′-6 4-#5 x 6′-11	4	#5 x 26′-3 #5 x 13′-3	4-#4 x 11′-11 12-#4 x 10′-10	2-#3	5	#4 x 24′-10 #4 x 18′-4	1-#4 x 6′-0	2.81	23
.708	3-#4 x 7′-6 3-#4 x 6′-11	4	#4 x 26′-5 #4 x 13′-3	— 4-#4 x 10′-10	—	5	#4 x 24′-11 #4 x 18′-4	1-#4 x 6′-0	1.90	24
.708	3-#4 x 7′-6 3-#4 x 6′-11	4	#4 x 26′-5 #4 x 13′-3	1-#4 x 11′-11 5-#4 x 10′-10	—	5	#4 x 24′-11 #4 x 18′-4	1-#4 x 6′-0	1.95	25
.708	4-#4 x 7′-6 4-#4 x 6′-11	4	#4 x 26′-5 #4 x 13′-3	2-#4 x 11′-11 7-#4 x 10′-10	—	5	#4 x 24′-11 #4 x 18′-4	1-#4 x 6′-0	2.06	26
.708	5-#4 x 7′-6 5-#4 x 6′-11	4	#4 x 26′-5 #4 x 13′-3	3-#4 x 11′-11 10-#4 x 10′-10	—	5	#4 x 24′-11 #4 x 18′-4	1-#4 x 6′-0	2.20	27
.708	4-#5 x 7′-6 4-#5 x 6′-11	4	#5 x 26′-5 #5 x 13′-3	3-#4 x 11′-11 12-#4 x 10′-10	2-#3	5	#4 x 24′-11 #4 x 18′-4	1-#4 x 6′-0	2.79	28

*,**,†,‡ For notes, see page 9-9.

WAFFLE SLABS—SQUARE PANELS—19-IN.-WIDE DOMES

For general instructions and notes on the use of this table, see pages 9-3 to 9-9 incl.

	Span Drop-D Form Depth plus Top Slab	Live Load (psf)	t_1 (in.)	Min. Col. Dia. 12′-0″ Story Height (in.)	Min. Col. Cap. C (Shear) (in.)	Interior Square Panel — Each Column Strip — No. Jst.	Each Column Strip — Bars — Trussed Straight	Each Column Strip — Bars — Top **	Each Column Strip — Stirrups per Jst.*	Each Middle Strip — No. Jst.	Each Middle Strip — Bars — Trussed Straight	Wt.† of Steel (psf)
1	L = 18′-0	50	10½	12	12	4	#4 x 30′-7 #4 x 13′-3	— 5-#4 x 10′-10	—	5	#4 x 27′-8 #4 x 18′-8	1.90
2	D = 6′-5	100	10½	15	12	4	#4 x 30′-7 #4 x 13′-3	2-#4 x 11′-11 7-#4 x 10′-10	—	5	#4 x 27′-8 #4 x 18′-8	2.09
3	6 + 4½	150	10½	17	14	4	#4 x 30′-7 #4 x 13′-3	3-#4 x 11′-11 9-#4 x 10′-10	2-#3	5	#4 x 27′-8 #4 x 18′-8	2.35
4		200	10½	18	19	4	#5 x 30′-7 #4 x 13′-3	2-#4 x 11′-11 9-#4 x 10′-10	2-#3	5	#4 x 27′-8 #4 x 18′-8	2.59
5	Note 1–	300	10½	21	29	5	#4 x 30′-7 #4 x 11′-3	5-#4 x 11′-11 14-#4 x 10′-10	2-#3	4	#4 x 27′-8 #4 x 18′-8	2.65
6	L = 18′-0	50	12½	12	12	4	#4 x 30′-8 #4 x 13′-3	— 4-#4 x 10′-10	—	5	#4 x 27′-10 #4 x 18′-8	1.86
7	D = 6′-5	100	12½	15	12	4	#4 x 30′-8 #4 x 13′-3	1-#4 x 11′-11 6-#4 x 10′-10	—	5	#4 x 27′-10 #4 x 18′-8	2.00
8	8 + 4½	150	12½	17	12	4	#4 x 30′-8 #4 x 13′-3	2-#4 x 11′-11 8-#4 x 10′-10	—	5	#4 x 27′-10 #4 x 18′-8	2.14
9		200	12½	18	13	4	#4 x 30′-8 #4 x 13′-3	3-#4 x 11′-11 11-#4 x 10′-10	2-#3	5	#4 x 27′-10 #4 x 18′-8	2.46
10		300	12½	21	20	4	#5 x 30′-8 #4 x 13′-3	3-#4 x 11′-11 11-#4 x 10′-10	2-#3	5	#4 x 27′-10 #4 x 18′-8	2.75
11	L = 18′-0	50	14½	12	12	4	#4 x 30′-10 #4 x 13′-3	— 4-#4 x 10′-10	—	5	#4 x 27′-11 #4 x 18′-8	1.87
12	D = 6′-5	100	14½	15	12	4	#4 x 30′-10 #4 x 13′-3	1-#4 x 11′-11 5-#4 x 10′-10	—	5	#4 x 27′-11 #4 x 18′-8	1.96
13	10 + 4½	150	14½	17	12	4	#4 x 30′-10 #4 x 13′-3	2-#4 x 11′-11 6-#4 x 10′-10	—	5	#4 x 27′-11 #4 x 18′-8	2.05
14		200	14½	18	12	4	#4 x 30′-10 #4 x 13′-3	3-#4 x 11′-11 8-#4 x 10′-10	—	5	#4 x 27′-11 #4 x 18′-8	2.19
15		300	14½	21	15	4	#5 x 30′-10 #4 x 13′-3	2-#4 x 11′-11 10-#4 x 10′-10	2-#3	5	#4 x 27′-11 #4 x 18′-8	2.67
16	L = 18′-0	50	16½	12	12	4	#4 x 30′-11 #4 x 13′-3	— 4-#4 x 10′-10	—	5	#4 x 28′-1 #4 x 18′-8	1.87
17	D = 6′-5	100	16½	15	12	4	#4 x 30′-11 #4 x 13′-3	— 4-#4 x 10′-10	—	5	#4 x 28′-1 #4 x 18′-8	1.87
18	12 + 4½	150	16½	17	12	4	#4 x 30′-11 #4 x 13′-3	1-#4 x 11′-11 6-#4 x 10′-10	—	5	#4 x 28′-1 #4 x 18′-8	2.01
19		200	16½	18	12	4	#4 x 30′-11 #4 x 13′-3	2-#4 x 11′-11 7-#4 x 10′-10	—	5	#4 x 28′-1 #4 x 18′-8	2.10
20		300	16½	21	12	4	#5 x 30′-11 #4 x 13′-3	2-#4 x 11′-11 8-#4 x 10′-10	2-#3	5	#4 x 28′-1 #4 x 18′-8	2.61
21	L = 20′-0	50	8½	13	12	5	#4 x 33′-9 #4 x 13′-3	1-#4 x 13′-3 7-#4 x 12′-0	—	5	#4 x 30′-6 #4 x 20′-8	1.96
22	D = 8′-5 6 + 2½	100	8½	16	19	5	#4 x 33′-9 #4 x 13′-3	3-#4 x 13′-3 11-#4 x 12′-0	—	5	#4 x 30′-6 #4 x 20′-8	2.21
23	L = 20′-0	50	10½	13	12	5	#4 x 33′-10 #4 x 13′-3	1-#4 x 13′-3 6-#4 x 12′-0	—	5	#4 x 30′-8 #4 x 20′-8	1.93
24	D = 8′-5	100	10½	16	13	5	#4 x 33′-10 #4 x 13′-3	2-#4 x 13′-3 10-#4 x 12′-0	—	5	#4 x 30′-8 #4 x 20′-8	2.13
25	8 + 2½	150	10½	18	18	5	#4 x 33′-10 #4 x 13′-3	4-#4 x 13′-3 13-#4 x 12′-0	—	5	#4 x 30′-8 #4 x 20′-8	2.34
26		200	10½	20	24	5	#5 x 33′-10 #4 x 13′-3	3-#4 x 13′-3 12-#4 x 12′-0	2-#3	5	#4 x 30′-8 #4 x 20′-8	2.70
27		300	10½	22	36	5	#5 x 33′-10 #5 x 13′-3	3-#5 x 13′-3 11-#5 x 12′-0	2-#3	5	#5 x 30′-8 #4 x 20′-8	3.40

*,**,† For notes, see page 9-9.

Note 1: *D* = 8′-5″ for 300 psf L.L.

WAFFLE SLABS—SQUARE PANELS—19-IN.-WIDE DOMES

Av.‡ Cu. Ft. Conc. (psf)	Strips Perpendicular to an Exterior Wall								Wt.† of Steel (psf)	
	Column Strip					Middle Strip				
	Top Bars at Ext. Col.**	No. Jsts.	Bars Trussed Straight	Top Bars at First Int. Col.	Stir-rups per Joist*	No. Jsts.	Bars Trussed Straight	Top Bars at Ext. Support		
.611	3-#4 x 7'-6 3-#4 x 6'-11	4	#4 x 26'-1 #4 x 13'-3	1-#4 x 11'-11 5-#4 x 10'-10	—	5	#4 x 24'-8 #4 x 18'-4	—	1.88	1
.611	4-#4 x 7'-6 4-#4 x 6'-11	4	#4 x 26'-1 #4 x 13'-3	2-#4 x 11'-11 9-#4 x 10'-10	—	5	#4 x 24'-8 #4 x 18'-4	1-#4 x 6'-0	2.12	2
.611	5-#4 x 7'-6 5-#4 x 6'-11	4	#5 x 26'-1 #4 x 13'-3	4-#4 x 11'-11 9-#4 x 10'-10	2-#3	5	#4 x 24'-8 #4 x 18'-4	1-#4 x 6'-0	2.49	3
.611	6-#4 x 7'-6 6-#4 x 6'-11	4	#5 x 26'-1 #4 x 13'-3	3-#4 x 11'-11 11-#4 x 10'-10	2-#3	5	#4 x 24'-8 #4 x 18'-4	1-#4 x 6'-0	2.64	4
.637	7-#4 x 7'-6 7-#4 x 6'-11	5	#5 x 26'-1 #4 x 11'-3	6-#4 x 11'-11 13-#4 x 10'-10	2-#3	4	#5 x 24'-8 #5 x 18'-5	1-#5 x 6'-0	3.00	5
.696	3-#4 x 7'-6 3-#4 x 6'-11	4	#4 x 26'-3 #4 x 13'-3	— 5-#4 x 10'-10	—	5	#4 x 24'-10 #4 x 18'-4	1-#4 x 6'-0	1.91	6
.696	4-#4 x 7'-6 4-#4 x 6'-11	4	#4 x 26'-3 #4 x 13'-3	2-#4 x 11'-11 6-#4 x 10'-10	—	5	#4 x 24'-10 #4 x 18'-4	1-#4 x 6'-0	2.04	7
.696	5-#4 x 7'-6 5-#4 x 6'-11	4	#5 x 26'-3 #4 x 13'-3	3-#4 x 11'-11 7-#4 x 10'-10	—	5	#4 x 24'-10 #4 x 18'-4	1-#4 x 6'-0	2.29	8
.696	6-#4 x 7'-6 6-#4 x 6'-11	4	#5 x 26'-3 #4 x 13'-3	4-#4 x 11'-11 10-#4 x 10'-10	2-#3	5	#4 x 24'-10 #4 x 18'-4	1-#4 x 6'-0	2.60	9
.696	5-#5 x 7'-6 5-#5 x 6'-11	4	#5 x 26'-3 #5 x 13'-3	4-#4 x 11'-11 14-#4 x 10'-10	2-#3	5	#4 x 24'-10 #5 x 18'-5	1-#4 x 6'-0	3.00	10
.784	3-#4 x 7'-6 3-#4 x 6'-11	4	#4 x 26'-5 #4 x 13'-3	— 4-#4 x 10'-10	—	5	#4 x 24'-11 #4 x 18'-4	1-#4 x 6'-0	1.90	11
.784	4-#4 x 7'-6 4-#4 x 6'-11	4	#4 x 26'-5 #4 x 13'-3	1-#4 x 11'-11 6-#4 x 10'-10	—	5	#4 x 24'-11 #4 x 18'-4	1-#4 x 6'-0	2.01	12
.784	4-#4 x 7'-6 4-#4 x 6'-11	4	#4 x 26'-5 #4 x 13'-3	2-#4 x 11'-11 8-#4 x 10'-10	—	5	#4 x 24'-11 #4 x 18'-4	1-#4 x 6'-0	2.09	13
.784	5-#4 x 7'-6 5-#4 x 6'-11	4	#5 x 26'-5 #4 x 13'-3	3-#4 x 11'-11 8-#4 x 10'-10	—	5	#4 x 24'-11 #4 x 18'-4	1-#4 x 6'-0	2.33	14
.784	4-#5 x 7'-6 4-#5 x 6'-11	4	#5 x 26'-5 #5 x 13'-3	3-#4 x 11'-11 12-#4 x 10'-10	2-#3	5	#4 x 24'-11 #4 x 18'-4	1-#4 x 6'-0	2.79	15
.874	3-#4 x 7'-6 3-#4 x 6'-11	4	#4 x 26'-6 #4 x 13'-3	— 4-#4 x 10'-10	—	5	#4 x 25'-1 #4 x 18'-4	1-#4 x 6'-0	1.91	16
.874	3-#4 x 7'-6 3-#4 x 6'-11	4	#4 x 26'-6 #4 x 13'-3	1-#4 x 11'-11 5-#4 x 10'-10	—	5	#4 x 25'-1 #4 x 18'-4	1-#4 x 6'-0	1.93	17
.874	4-#4 x 7'-6 4-#4 x 6'-11	4	#4 x 26'-6 #4 x 13'-3	2-#4 x 11'-11 6-#4 x 10'-10	—	5	#4 x 25'-1 #4 x 18'-4	1-#4 x 6'-0	2.05	18
.874	5-#4 x 7'-6 5-#4 x 6'-11	4	#4 x 26'-6 #4 x 13'-3	3-#4 x 11'-11 9-#4 x 10'-10	—	5	#4 x 25'-1 #4 x 18'-4	1-#4 x 6'-0	2.17	19
.874	6-#4 x 7'-6 6-#4 x 6'-11	4	#5 x 26'-6 #4 x 13'-3	2-#4 x 11'-11 11-#4 x 10'-10	2-#3	5	#4 x 25'-1 #4 x 18'-4	1-#4 x 6'-0	2.67	20
.459	5-#4 x 8'-2 5-#4 x 7'-6	5	#4 x 28'-7 #4 x 13'-3	2-#4 x 13'-3 9-#4 x 12'-0	—	5	#4 x 27'-0 #4 x 20'-4	1-#4 x 6'-6	2.02	21
.459	6-#4 x 8'-2 6-#4 x 7'-6	5	#5 x 28'-7 #4 x 13'-3	5-#4 x 13'-3 10-#4 x 12'-0	—	5	#4 x 27'-0 #4 x 20'-4	1-#4 x 6'-6	2.35	22
.548	4-#4 x 8'-2 4-#4 x 7'-6	5	#4 x 28'-9 #4 x 13'-3	1-#4 x 13'-3 7-#4 x 12'-0	—	5	#4 x 27'-2 #4 x 20'-4	1-#4 x 6'-6	1.95	23
.548	6-#4 x 8'-2 6-#4 x 7'-6	5	#4 x 28'-9 #4 x 13'-3	4-#4 x 13'-3 11-#4 x 12'-0	—	5	#4 x 27'-2 #4 x 20'-4	1-#4 x 6'-6	2.18	24
.548	7-#4 x 8'-2 7-#4 x 7'-6	5	#5 x 28'-9 #4 x 13'-3	5-#4 x 13'-3 12-#4 x 12'-0	—	5	#4 x 27'-2 #5 x 20'-5	1-#4 x 6'-6	2.56	25
.548	5-#5 x 8'-2 5-#5 x 7'-6	5	#5 x 28'-9 #5 x 13'-3	4-#4 x 13'-3 15-#4 x 12'-0	2-#3	5	#4 x 27'-2 #5 x 20'-5	2-#4 x 6'-6	2.96	26
.548	6-#5 x 8'-2 6-#5 x 7'-6	5	#6 x 28'-9 #5 x 13'-3	4-#5 x 13'-3 11-#5 x 12'-0	2-#3	5	#5 x 27'-2 #5 x 20'-5	1-#5 x 6'-6	3.66	27

*,**,† For notes, see page 9-9.

WAFFLE SLABS—SQUARE PANELS—19-IN.-WIDE DOMES

For general instructions and notes on the use of this table, see pages 9-3 to 9-9 incl.

	Span Drop-D Form Depth plus Top Slab	Live Load (psf)	t_1 (in.)	Min. Col. Dia. 12′-0″ Story Height (in.)	Min. Col. Cap. C (Shear) (in.)	Interior Square Panel: Each Column Strip: No. Jst.	Each Column Strip: Bars: Trussed Straight	Each Column Strip: Bars: Top **	Each Column Strip: Stirrups per Jst.*	Each Middle Strip: No. Jst.	Each Middle Strip: Bars: Trussed Straight	Wt.† of Steel (psf)
1	L = 20′-0	50	12½	13	12	5	#4 x 34′-0 #4 x 13′-3	— 5-#4 x 12′-0	—	5	#4 x 30′-10 #4 x 20′-8	1.85
2	D = 8′-5	100	12½	16	12	5	#4 x 34′-0 #4 x 13′-3	2-#4 x 13′-3 7-#4 x 12′-0	—	5	#4 x 30′-10 #4 x 20′-8	2.02
3	10 + 2½	150	12½	18	13	5	#4 x 34′-0 #4 x 13′-3	3-#4 x 13′-3 11-#4 x 12′-0	—	5	#4 x 30′-10 #4 x 20′-8	2.22
4		200	12½	20	17	5	#5 x 34′-0 #4 x 13′-3	2-#4 x 13′-3 11-#4 x 12′-0	—	5	#4 x 30′-10 #4 x 20′-8	2.50
5		300	12½	22	27	5	#5 x 34′-0 #4 x 13′-3	4-#4 x 13′-3 14-#4 x 12′-0	2-#3	5	#4 x 30′-10 #4 x 20′-8	2.85
6	L = 20′-0	50	14½	13	12	5	#4 x 34′-2 #4 x 13′-3	— 5-#4 x 12′-0	—	5	#4 x 30′-11 #4 x 20′-8	1.85
7	D = 8′-5	100	14½	16	12	5	#4 x 34′-2 #4 x 13′-3	1-#4 x 13′-3 7-#4 x 12′-0	—	5	#4 x 30′-11 #4 x 20′-8	1.98
8	12 + 2½	150	14½	18	12	5	#4 x 34′-2 #4 x 13′-3	2-#4 x 13′-3 10-#4 x 12′-0	—	5	#4 x 30′-11 #4 x 20′-8	2.14
9		200	14½	20	12	5	#4 x 34′-2 #4 x 13′-3	4-#4 x 13′-3 12-#4 x 12′-0	—	5	#4 x 30′-11 #4 x 20′-8	2.31
10		300	14½	22	20	5	#5 x 34′-2 #4 x 13′-3	3-#4 x 13′-3 13-#4 x 12′-0	2-#3	5	#4 x 30′-11 #4 x 20′-8	2.79
11	L = 20′-0	50	10½	13	12	5	#4 x 33′-10 #4 x 13′-3	1-#4 x 13′-3 6-#4 x 12′-0	—	5	#4 x 30′-8 #4 x 20′-8	1.93
12	D = 8′-5	100	10½	16	14	5	#4 x 33′-10 #4 x 13′-3	3-#4 x 13′-3 10-#4 x 12′-0	—	5	#4 x 30′-8 #4 x 20′-8	2.18
13	6 + 4½	150	10½	18	20	5	#4 x 33′-10 #4 x 13′-3	4-#4 x 13′-3 14-#4 x 12′-0	2-#3	5	#4 x 30′-8 #4 x 20′-8	2.51
14		200	10½	19	25	5	#5 x 33′-10 #4 x 13′-3	3-#4 x 13′-3 13-#4 x 12′-0	2-#3	5	#4 x 30′-8 #4 x 20′-8	2.74
15	L = 20′-0	50	12½	13	12	5	#4 x 34′-0 #4 x 13′-3	— 6-#4 x 12′-0	—	5	#4 x 30′-10 #4 x 20′-8	1.89
16	D = 8′-5	100	12½	16	12	5	#4 x 34′-0 #4 x 13′-3	2-#4 x 13′-3 8-#4 x 12′-0	—	5	#4 x 30′-10 #4 x 20′-8	2.06
17	8 + 4½	150	12½	18	14	5	#4 x 34′-0 #4 x 13′-3	3-#4 x 13′-3 12-#4 x 12′-0	—	5	#4 x 30′-10 #4 x 20′-8	2.26
18		200	12½	20	19	5	#5 x 34′-0 #4 x 13′-3	2-#4 x 13′-3 11-#4 x 12′-0	2-#3	5	#4 x 30′-10 #4 x 20′-8	2.64
19		300	12½	22	28	5	#5 x 34′-0 #4 x 13′-3	4-#4 x 13′-3 15-#4 x 12′-0	2-#3	5	#4 x 30′-10 #5 x 20′-10	3.09
20	L = 20′-0	50	14½	13	12	5	#4 x 34′-2 #4 x 13′-3	— 5-#4 x 12′-0	—	5	#4 x 30′-11 #4 x 20′-8	1.85
21	D = 8′-5	100	14½	16	12	5	#4 x 34′-2 #4 x 13′-3	1-#4 x 13′-3 7-#4 x 12′-0	—	5	#4 x 30′-11 #4 x 20′-8	1.98
22	10 + 4½	150	14½	18	12	5	#4 x 34′-2 #4 x 13′-3	3-#4 x 13′-3 10-#4 x 12′-0	—	5	#4 x 30′-11 #4 x 20′-8	2.19
23		200	14½	20	13	5	#4 x 34′-2 #4 x 13′-3	4-#4 x 13′-3 13-#4 x 12′-0	—	5	#4 x 30′-11 #4 x 20′-8	2.35
24		300	14½	22	21	5	#5 x 34′-2 #4 x 13′-3	3-#4 x 13′-3 14-#4 x 12′-0	2-#3	5	#4 x 30′-11 #4 x 20′-8	2.83
25	L = 20′-0	50	16½	13	12	5	#4 x 34′-3 #4 x 13′-3	— 5-#4 x 12′-0	—	5	#4 x 31′-1 #4 x 20′-8	1.86
26	D = 8′-5	100	16½	16	12	5	#4 x 34′-3 #4 x 13′-3	1-#4 x 13′-3 6-#4 x 12′-0	—	5	#4 x 31′-1 #4 x 20′-8	1.94
27	12 + 4½	150	16½	18	12	5	#4 x 34′-3 #4 x 13′-3	2-#4 x 13′-3 9-#4 x 12′-0	—	5	#4 x 31′-1 #4 x 20′-8	2.11
28		200	16½	20	12	5	#4 x 34′-3 #4 x 13′-3	3-#4 x 13′-3 11-#4 x 12′-0	—	5	#4 x 31′-1 #4 x 20′-8	2.23
29		300	16½	22	16	5	#5 x 34′-3 #4 x 13′-3	3-#4 x 13′-3 12-#4 x 12′-0	2-#3	5	#4 x 31′-1 #4 x 20′-8	2.77

*,**,† For notes, see page 9-9.

WAFFLE SLABS—SQUARE PANELS—19-IN.-WIDE DOMES

Av.‡ Cu. Ft. Conc. (psf)	Strips Perpendicular to an Exterior Wall									
	Column Strip					Middle Strip				
	Top Bars at Ext. Col.**	No. Jsts.	Bars: Trussed / Straight	Top Bars at First Int. Col.	Stir-rups per Joist*	No. Jsts.	Bars: Trussed / Straight	Top Bars at Ext. Support	Wt.† of Steel (psf)	
.640	4-#4 x 8'-2 4-#4 x 7'-6	5	#4 x 28'-11 #4 x 13'-3	1-#4 x 13'-3 6-#4 x 12'-0	—	5	#4 x 27'-4 #4 x 20'-4	1-#4 x 6'-6	1.90	1
.640	5-#4 x 8'-2 5-#4 x 7'-6	5	#4 x 28'-11 #4 x 13'-3	2-#4 x 13'-3 10-#4 x 12'-0	—	5	#4 x 27'-4 #4 x 20'-4	1-#4 x 6'-6	2.07	2
.640	6-#4 x 8'-2 6-#4 x 7'-6	5	#5 x 28'-11 #4 x 13'-3	4-#4 x 13'-3 10-#4 x 12'-0	—	5	#4 x 27'-4 #4 x 20'-4	1-#4 x 6'-6	2.35	3
.640	7-#4 x 8'-2 7-#4 x 7'-6	5	#5 x 28'-11 #4 x 13'-3	3-#4 x 13'-3 13-#4 x 12'-0	—	5	#4 x 27'-4 #5 x 20'-5	2-#4 x 6'-6	2.69	4
.640	6-#5 x 8'-2 6-#5 x 7'-6	5	#5 x 28'-11 #5 x 13'-3	5-#4 x 13'-3 18-#4 x 12'-0	2-#3	5	#5 x 27'-4 #5 x 20'-5	1-#5 x 6'-6	3.23	5
.735	4-#4 x 8'-2 4-#4 x 7'-6	5	#4 x 29'-0 #4 x 13'-3	— 5-#4 x 12'-0	—	5	#4 x 27'-5 #4 x 20'-4	1-#4 x 6'-6	1.89	6
.735	5-#4 x 8'-2 5-#4 x 7'-6	5	#4 x 29'-0 #4 x 13'-3	2-#4 x 13'-3 8-#4 x 12'-0	—	5	#4 x 27'-5 #4 x 20'-4	1-#4 x 6'-6	2.03	7
.735	6-#4 x 8'-2 6-#4 x 7'-6	5	#4 x 29'-0 #4 x 13'-3	3-#4 x 13'-3 11-#4 x 12'-0	—	5	#4 x 27'-5 #4 x 20'-4	1-#4 x 6'-6	2.18	8
.735	7-#4 x 8'-2 7-#4 x 7'-6	5	#5 x 29'-0 #4 x 13'-3	5-#4 x 13'-3 11-#4 x 12'-0	—	5	#4 x 27'-5 #4 x 20'-4	1-#4 x 6'-6	2.45	9
.735	5-#5 x 8'-2 5-#5 x 7'-6	5	#5 x 29'-0 #5 x 13'-3	4-#4 x 13'-3 16-#4 x 12'-0	2-#3	5	#5 x 27'-5 #4 x 20'-4	1-#5 x 6'-6	3.04	10
.625	5-#4 x 8'-2 5-#4 x 7'-6	5	#4 x 28'-9 #4 x 13'-3	2-#4 x 13'-3 7-#4 x 12'-0	—	5	#4 x 27'-2 #4 x 20'-4	1-#4 x 6'-6	1.99	11
.625	6-#4 x 8'-2 6-#4 x 7'-6	5	#4 x 28'-9 #4 x 13'-3	4-#4 x 13'-3 12-#4 x 12'-0	—	5	#4 x 27'-2 #4 x 20'-4	1-#4 x 6'-6	2.21	12
.625	7-#4 x 8'-2 7-#4 x 7'-6	5	#5 x 28'-9 #4 x 13'-3	6-#4 x 13'-3 12-#4 x 12'-0	2-#3	5	#4 x 27'-2 #5 x 20'-5	2-#4 x 6'-6	2.77	13
.625	5-#5 x 8'-2 5-#5 x 7'-6	5	#5 x 28'-9 #5 x 13'-3	4-#4 x 13'-3 16-#4 x 12'-0	2-#3	5	#4 x 27'-2 #5 x 20'-5	2-#4 x 6'-6	2.99	14
.715	4-#4 x 8'-2 4-#4 x 7'-6	5	#4 x 28'-11 #4 x 13'-3	1-#4 x 13'-3 6-#4 x 12'-0	—	5	#4 x 27'-4 #4 x 20'-4	1-#4 x 6'-6	1.93	15
.715	5-#4 x 8'-2 5-#4 x 7'-6	5	#4 x 28'-11 #4 x 13'-3	3-#4 x 13'-3 10-#4 x 12'-0	—	5	#4 x 27'-4 #4 x 20'-4	1-#4 x 6'-6	2.10	16
.715	6-#4 x 8'-2 7-#4 x 7'-6	5	#5 x 28'-11 #4 x 13'-3	5-#4 x 13'-3 10-#4 x 12'-0	—	5	#4 x 27'-4 #4 x 20'-4	1-#4 x 6'-6	2.40	17
.715	7-#4 x 8'-2 7-#4 x 7'-6	5	#5 x 28'-11 #4 x 13'-3	3-#4 x 13'-3 13-#4 x 12'-0	2-#3	5	#4 x 27'-4 #5 x 20'-5	2-#4 x 6'-6	2.83	18
.715	6-#5 x 8'-2 6-#5 x 7'-6	5	#5 x 28'-11 #5 x 13'-3	6-#4 x 13'-3 18-#4 x 12'-0	2-#3	5	#5 x 27'-4 #5 x 20'-5	1-#5 x 6'-6	3.36	19
.807	4-#4 x 8'-2 4-#4 x 7'-6	5	#4 x 29'-0 #4 x 13'-3	1-#4 x 13'-3 6-#4 x 12'-0	—	5	#4 x 27'-5 #4 x 20'-4	1-#4 x 6'-6	1.91	20
.807	5-#4 x 8'-2 5-#4 x 7'-6	5	#4 x 29'-0 #4 x 13'-3	2-#4 x 13'-3 9-#4 x 12'-0	—	5	#4 x 27'-5 #4 x 20'-4	1-#4 x 6'-6	2.04	21
.807	6-#4 x 8'-2 6-#4 x 7'-6	5	#5 x 29'-0 #4 x 13'-3	4-#4 x 13'-3 9-#4 x 12'-0	—	5	#4 x 27'-5 #4 x 20'-4	1-#4 x 6'-6	2.33	22
.807	7-#4 x 8'-2 7-#4 x 7'-6	5	#5 x 29'-0 #4 x 13'-3	5-#4 x 13'-3 12-#4 x 12'-0	—	5	#4 x 27'-5 #5 x 20'-5	1-#4 x 6'-6	2.57	23
.807	5-#5 x 8'-2 6-#5 x 7'-6	5	#5 x 29'-0 #5 x 13'-3	5-#4 x 13'-3 16-#4 x 12'-0	2-#3	5	#5 x 27'-5 #4 x 20'-4	1-#5 x 6'-6	3.09	24
.902	4-#4 x 8'-2 4-#4 x 7'-6	5	#4 x 29'-2 #4 x 13'-3	— 5-#4 x 12'-0	—	5	#4 x 27'-7 #4 x 20'-4	1-#4 x 6'-6	1.89	25
.902	4-#4 x 8'-2 5-#4 x 7'-6	5	#4 x 29'-2 #4 x 13'-3	2-#4 x 13'-3 7-#4 x 12'-0	—	5	#4 x 27'7 #4 x 20'-4	1-#4 x 6'-6	1.99	26
.902	5-#4 x 8'-2 5-#4 x 7'-6	5	#4 x 29'-2 #4 x 13'-3	3-#4 x 13'-3 10-#4 x 12'-0	—	5	#4 x 27'-7 #4 x 20'-4	1-#4 x 6'-6	2.13	27
.902	6-#4 x 8'-2 6-#4 x 7'-6	5	#5 x 29'-2 #4 x 13'-3	4-#4 x 13'-3 11-#4 x 12'-0	—	5	#4 x 27'-7 #4 x 20'-4	1-#4 x 6'-6	2.37	28
.902	5-#5 x 8'-2 5-#5 x 7'-6	5	#5 x 29'-2 #5 x 13'-3	4-#4 x 13'-3 14-#4 x 12'-0	2-#3	5	#4 x 27'-7 #5 x 20'-5	2-#4 x 6'-6	3.02	29

*,**,†,‡ For notes, see page 9-9.

WAFFLE SLABS—SQUARE PANELS—19-IN.-WIDE DOMES

For general instructions and notes on the use of this table, see pages 9-3 to 9-9 incl.

	Span / Drop-D / Form Depth plus Top Slab	Live Load (psf)	t_1 (in.)	Min. Col. Dia. 12′-0″ Story Height (in.)	Min. Col. Cap. C (Shear) (in.)	Interior Square Panel: Each Column Strip: No. Jst.	Each Column Strip: Bars: Trussed Straight	Each Column Strip: Bars: Top **	Each Column Strip: Bars: Stirrups per Jst.*	Each Middle Strip: No. Jst.	Each Middle Strip: Bars: Trussed Straight	Wt.† of Steel (psf)
1	L = 22′-0	50	10½	14	12	5	#4 x 37′-2 #4 x 15′-3	2-#4 x 14′-7 9-#4 x 13′-3	—	6	#4 x 33′-8 #4 x 22′-8	2.07
2	D = Note 1	100	10½	17	17	5	#5 x 37′-2 #4 x 15′-3	2-#4 x 14′-7 11-#4 x 13′-3	—	6	#4 x 33′-8 #4 x 22′-8	2.43
3	8 + 2½	150	10½	19	24	5	#5 x 37′-2 #4 x 15′-3	4-#4 x 14′-7 14-#4 x 13′-3	2-#3	6	#4 x 33′-8 #4 x 22′-8	2.72
4		200	10½	21	31	6	#5 x 37′-2 #4 x 13′-3	4-#4 x 14′-7 17-#4 x 13′-3	2-#3	5	#5 x 33′-8 #4 x 22′-8	3.13
5	L = 22′-0	50	12½	14	12	5	#4 x 37′-4 #4 x 15′-3	2-#4 x 14′-7 7-#4 x 13′-3	—	6	#4 x 33′-10 #4 x 22′-8	2.00
6	D = 8′-5	100	12½	17	12	5	#4 x 37′-4 #4 x 15′-3	4-#4 x 14′-7 12-#4 x 13′-3	—	6	#4 x 33′-10 #4 x 22′-8	2.26
7	10 + 2½	150	12½	19	17	5	#5 x 37′-4 #4 x 15′-3	3-#4 x 14′-7 13-#4 x 13′-3	2-#3	6	#4 x 33′-10 #4 x 22′-8	2.66
8		200	12½	21	23	5	#5 x 37′-4 #5 x 15′-3	3-#5 x 14′-7 10-#5 x 13′-3	2-#3	6	#4 x 33′-10 #4 x 22′-8	2.95
9		300	12½	23	35	5	#6 x 37′-4 #4 x 15′-3	4-#4 x 14′-7 17-#4 x 13′-3	2-#3	6	#4 x 33′-10 #5 x 22′-10	3.42
10	L = 22′-0	50	14½	14	12	5	#4 x 37′-6 #4 x 15′-3	1-#4 x 14′-7 7-#4 x 13′-3	—	6	#4 x 33′-11 #4 x 22′-8	1.96
11	D = 8′-5	100	14½	17	12	5	#4 x 37′-6 #4 x 15′-3	3-#4 x 14′-7 10-#4 x 13′-3	—	6	#4 x 33′-11 #4 x 22′-8	2.15
12	12 + 2½	150	14½	19	12	5	#5 x 37′-6 #4 x 15′-3	2-#4 x 14′-7 12-#4 x 13′-3	—	6	#4 x 33′-11 #4 x 22′-8	2.48
13		200	14½	21	17	5	#5 x 37′-6 #4 x 15′-3	4-#4 x 14′-7 14-#4 x 13′-3	2-#3	6	#4 x 33′-11 #4 x 22′-8	2.76
14		300	14½	24	27	5	#5 x 37′-6 #5 x 15′-3	4-#5 x 14′-7 12-#5 x 13′-3	2-#3	6	#4 x 33′-11 #4 x 22′-8	3.14
15	L = 22′-0	50	10½	14	12	5	#4 x 37′-2 #4 x 15′-3	3-#4 x 14′-7 10-#4 x 13′-3	—	6	#4 x 33′-8 #4 x 22′-8	2.14
16	D = Note 1	100	10½	17	18	5	#5 x 37′-2 #4 x 15′-3	2-#4 x 14′-7 12-#4 x 13′-3	2-#3	6	#4 x 33′-8 #4 x 22′-8	2.57
17	6 + 4½	150	10½	19	25	5	#5 x 37′-2 #4 x 15′-3	4-#4 x 14′-7 16-#4 x 13′-3	2-#3	6	#4 x 33′-8 #4 x 22′-8	2.80
18		200	10½	20	33	6	#5 x 37′-2 #4 x 13′-3	4-#4 x 14′-7 17-#4 x 13′-3	2-#3	5	#5 x 33′-8 #4 x 22′-8	3.13
19	L = 22′-0	50	12½	14	12	5	#4 x 37′-4 #4 x 15′-3	2-#4 x 14′-7 9-#4 x 13′-3	—	6	#4 x 33′-10 #4 x 22′-8	2.07
20	D = 8′-5	100	12½	17	13	5	#5 x 37′-4 #4 x 15′-3	2-#4 x 14′-7 10-#4 x 13′-3	—	6	#4 x 33′-10 #4 x 22′-8	2.40
21	8 + 4½	150	12½	19	19	5	#5 x 37′-4 #4 x 15′-3	3-#4 x 14′-7 14-#4 x 13′-3	2-#3	6	#4 x 33′-10 #4 x 22′-8	2.70
22		200	12½	21	24	5	#5 x 37′-4 #5 x 15′-3	3-#5 x 14′-7 11-#5 x 13′-3	2-#3	6	#4 x 33′-10 #4 x 22′-8	3.00
23		300	12½	23	36	5	#6 x 37′-4 #5 x 15′-3	3-#5 x 14′-7 12-#5 x 13′-3	4-#3	6	#5 x 33′-10 #4 x 22′-8	3.85
24	L = 22′-0	50	14½	14	12	5	#4 x 37′-6 #4 x 15′-3	2-#4 x 14′-7 7-#4 x 13′-3	—	6	#4 x 33′-11 #4 x 22′-8	2.00
25	D = 8′-5	100	14½	17	12	5	#4 x 37′-6 #4 x 15′-3	3-#4 x 14′-7 11-#4 x 13′-3	—	6	#4 x 33′-11 #4 x 22′-8	2.19
26	10 + 4½	150	14½	19	14	5	#5 x 37′-6 #4 x 15′-3	2-#4 x 14′-7 12-#4 x 13′-3	—	6	#4 x 33′-11 #4 x 22′-8	2.48
27		200	14½	21	18	5	#5 x 37′-6 #5 x 15′-3	3-#5 x 14′-7 9-#5 x 13′-3	2-#3	6	#4 x 33′-11 #4 x 22′-8	2.91
28		300	14½	23	28	5	#5 x 37′-6 #5 x 15′-3	4-#5 x 14′-7 13-#5 x 13′-3	2-#3	6	#4 x 33′-11 #5 x 22′-10	3.41

Note 1: *D*-8′-5″ for 50, 100, 150 psf *LL*; 10′-5 for 200 psf *LL*.

*,**,† For notes, see page 9-9.

WAFFLE SLABS—SQUARE PANELS—19-IN.-WIDE DOMES

Av.‡ Cu. Ft. Conc. (psf)	Strips Perpendicular to an Exterior Wall								Wt.† of Steel (psf)	
	Column Strip					Middle Strip				
	Top Bars at Ext. Col.**	No. Jsts.	Bars Trussed Straight	Top Bars at First Int. Col.	Stir-rups per Joist*	No. Jsts.	Bars Trussed Straight	Top Bars at Ext. Support		
.537	6-#4 x 8'-10 6-#4 x 8'-2	5	#4 x 31'-5 #4 x 15'-3	3-#4 x 14'-7 11-#4 x 13'-3	—	6	#4 x 29'-8 #4 x 22'-4	1-#4 x 7'-0	2.12	1
.537	7-#4 x 8'-10 7-#4 x 8'-2	5	#5 x 31'-5 #4 x 15'-3	3-#4 x 14'-7 13-#4 x 13'-3	—	6	#4 x 29'-8 #4 x 22'-4	1-#4 x 7'-0	2.46	2
.537	6-#5 x 8'-10 6-#5 x 8'-2	5	#5 x 31'-5 #5 x 15'-3	5-#4 x 14'-7 18-#4 x 13'-3	2-#3	6	#4 x 29'-8 #5 x 22'-5	2-#4 x 7'-0	3.00	3
.566	7-#5 x 8'-10 7-#5 x 8'-2	6	#5 x 31'-5 #5 x 13'-3	6-#4 x 14'-7 20-#4 x 13'-3	2-#3	5	#5 x 29'-8 #6 x 22'-6	1-#5 x 7'-0	3.45	4
.627	5-#4 x 8'-10 5-#4 x 8'-2	5	#4 x 31'-7 #4 x 15'-3	2-#4 x 14'-7 9-#4 x 13'-3	—	6	#4 x 29'-10 #4 x 22'-4	1-#4 x 7'-0	2.03	5
.627	7-#4 x 8'-10 7-#4 x 8'-2	5	#5 x 31'-7 #4 x 15'-3	5-#4 x 14'-7 11-#4 x 13'-3	—	6	#4 x 29'-10 #4 x 22'-4	1-#4 x 7'-0	2.38	6
.627	5-#5 x 8'-10 5-#5 x 8'-2	5	#5 x 31'-7 #5 x 15'-3	4-#4 x 14'-7 15-#4 x 13'-3	2-#3	6	#4 x 29'-10 #4 x 22'-4	1-#4 x 7'-0	2.75	7
.627	9-#4 x 8'-10 9-#4 x 8'-2	5	#6 x 31'-7 #4 x 15'-3	4-#5 x 14'-7 10-#5 x 13'-3	2-#3	6	#4 x 29'-10 #5 x 22'-5	2-#4 x 7'-0	3.20	8
.627	7-#5 x 8'-10 7-#5 x 8'-2	5	#6 x 31'-7 #5 x 15'-3	5-#4 x 14'-7 22-#4 x 13'-3	2-#3	6	#5 x 29'-10 #5 x 22'-5	1-#5 x 7'-0	3.70	9
.720	5-#4 x 8'-10 5-#4 x 8'-2	5	#4 x 31'-8 #4 x 15'-3	2-#4 x 14'-7 8-#4 x 13'-3	—	6	#4 x 29'-11 #4 x 22'-4	1-#4 x 7'-0	2.01	10
.720	6-#4 x 8'-10 6-#4 x 8'-2	5	#5 x 31'-8 #4 x 15'-3	4-#4 x 14'-7 10-#4 x 13'-3	—	6	#4 x 29'-11 #4 x 22'-4	1-#4 x 7'-0	2.29	11
.720	7-#4 x 8'-10 7-#4 x 8'-2	5	#5 x 31'-8 #4 x 15'-3	3-#4 x 14'-7 14-#4 x 13'-3	—	6	#4 x 29'-11 #4 x 22'-4	1-#4 x 7'-0	2.50	12
.720	6-#5 x 8'-10 6-#5 x 8'-2	5	#5 x 31'-8 #5 x 15'-3	5-#4 x 14'-7 17-#4 x 13'-3	2-#3	6	#4 x 29'-11 #5 x 22'-5	2-#4 x 7'-0	3.03	13
.720	7-#5 x 8'-10 7-#5 x 8'-2	5	#6 x 31'-8 #5 x 15'-3	5-#5 x 14'-7 12-#5 x 13'-3	2-#3	6	#5 x 29'-11 #4 x 22'-4	1-#5 x 7'-0	3.46	14
.617	6-#4 x 8'-10 6-#4 x 8'-2	5	#4 x 31'-5 #4 x 15'-3	4-#4 x 14'-7 12-#4 x 13'-3	—	6	#4 x 29'-8 #4 x 22'-4	1-#4 x 7'-0	2.17	15
.617	8-#4 x 8'-10 8-#4 x 8'-2	5	#5 x 31'-5 #4 x 15'-3	4-#4 x 14'-7 14-#4 x 13'-3	2-#3	6	#4 x 29'-8 #4 x 22'-4	1-#4 x 7'-0	2.63	16
.617	6-#5 x 8'-10 6-#5 x 8'-2	5	#5 x 31'-5 #5 x 15'-3	6-#4 x 14'-7 19-#4 x 13'-3	2-#3	6	#4 x 29'-8 #5 x 22'-5	2-#4 x 7'-0	3.06	17
.639	7-#5 x 8'-10 7-#5 x 8'-2	6	#5 x 31'-5 #5 x 13'-3	6-#4 x 14'-7 20-#4 x 13'-3	2-#3	5	#5 x 29'-8 #5 x 22'-5	1-#5 x 7'-0	3.34	18
.704	5-#4 x 8'-10 5-#4 x 8'-2	5	#4 x 31'-7 #4 x 15'-3	3-#4 x 14'-7 10-#4 x 13'-3	—	6	#4 x 29'-10 #4 x 22'-4	1-#4 x 7'-0	2.09	19
.704	7-#4 x 8'-10 7-#4 x 8'-2	5	#5 x 31'-7 #4 x 15'-3	3-#4 x 14'-7 12-#4 x 13'-3	—	6	#4 x 29'-10 #4 x 22'-4	1-#4 x 7'-0	2.44	20
.704	5-#5 x 8'-10 5-#5 x 8'-2	5	#5 x 31'-7 #5 x 15'-3	4-#4 x 14'-7 16-#4 x 13'-3	2-#3	6	#4 x 29'-10 #5 x 22'-5	1-#4 x 7'-0	2.88	21
.704	6-#5 x 8'-10 6-#5 x 8'-2	5	#6 x 31'-7 #5 x 15'-3	4-#5 x 14'-7 11-#5 x 13'-3	2-#3	6	#4 x 29'-10 #5 x 22'-5	2-#4 x 7'-0	3.31	22
.704	5-#6 x 8'-10 5-#6 x 8'-2	5	#6 x 31'-7 #6 x 15'-7	4-#5 x 14'-7 14-#5 x 13'-3	4-#3	6	#5 x 29'-10 #5 x 22'-5	1-#5 x 7'-0	4.07	23
.794	5-#4 x 8'-10 5-#4 x 8'-2	5	#4 x 31'-8 #4 x 15'-3	2-#4 x 14'-7 9-#4 x 13'-3	—	6	#4 x 29'-11 #4 x 22'-4	1-#4 x 7'-0	2.03	24
.794	6-#4 x 8'-10 6-#4 x 8'-2	5	#5 x 31'-8 #4 x 15'-3	4-#4 x 14'-7 11-#4 x 13'-3	—	6	#4 x 29'-11 #4 x 22'-4	1-#4 x 7'-0	2.31	25
.794	5-#5 x 8'-10 5-#5 x 8'-2	5	#5 x 31'-8 #5 x 15'-3	4-#4 x 14'-7 14-#4 x 13'-3	—	6	#4 x 29'-11 #4 x 22'-4	1-#4 x 7'-0	2.59	26
.794	6-#5 x 8'-10 6-#5 x 8'-2	5	#5 x 31'-8 #5 x 15'-3	4-#5 x 14'-7 11-#5 x 13'-3	2-#3	6	#4 x 29'-11 #5 x 22'-5	2-#4 x 7'-0	3.12	27
.794	7-#5 x 8'-10 7-#5 x 8'-2	5	#6 x 31'-8 #5 x 15'-3	5-#5 x 14'-7 13-#5 x 13'-3	2-#3	6	#5 x 29'-11 #5 x 22'-5	1-#5 x 7'-0	3.72	28

*,**,†,‡ For notes, see page 9-9.

WAFFLE SLABS—SQUARE PANELS—19-IN.-WIDE DOMES

For general instructions and notes on the use of this table, see pages 9-3 to 9-9 incl.

	Span / Drop-D / Form Depth plus Top Slab	Live Load (psf)	t_1 (in.)	Min. Col. Dia. 12′-0″ Story Height (in.)	Min. Col. Cap. C (Shear) (in.)	Interior Square Panel: Each Column Strip: No. Jst.	Each Column Strip: Bars: Trussed Straight	Each Column Strip: Bars: Top **	Each Column Strip: Bars: Stirrups per Jst.*	Each Middle Strip: No. Jst.	Each Middle Strip: Bars: Trussed Straight	Wt.† of Steel (psf)
1	L = 22′-0	50	16½	14	12	5	#4 x 37′-7 #4 x 15′-3	1-#4 x 14′-7 7-#4 x 13′-3	—	6	#4 x 34′-1 #4 x 22′-8	1.97
2	D = 8′-5	100	16½	17	12	5	#4 x 37′-7 #4 x 15′-3	3-#4 x 14′-7 10-#4 x 13′-3	—	6	#4 x 34′-1 #4 x 22′-8	2.16
3	12 + 4½	150	16½	19	12	5	#5 x 37′-7 #4 x 15′-3	2-#4 x 14′-7 10-#4 x 13′-3	—	6	#4 x 34′-1 #4 x 22′-8	2.41
4		200	16½	21	13	5	#5 x 37′-7 #4 x 15′-3	3-#4 x 14′-7 14-#4 x 13′-3	2-#3	6	#4 x 34′-1 #4 x 22′-8	2.74
5		300	16½	24	22	5	#5 x 37′-7 #5 x 15′-3	4-#5 x 14′-7 11-#5 x 13′-3	2-#3	6	#4 x 34′-1 #4 x 22′-8	3.10
6	L = 24′-0	50	10½	15	13	7	#4 x 40′-6 #4 x 17′-3	2-#4 x 15′-11 11-#4 x 14′-5	—	5	#4 x 36′-8 #4 x 24′-8	2.09
7	D = Note 1	100	10½	18	21	7	#4 x 40′-6 #4 x 17′-3	5-#4 x 15′-11 16-#4 x 14′-5	2-#3	5	#4 x 36′-8 #5 x 24′-10	2.65
8	8 + 2½	150	10½	20	30	6	#5 x 40′-6 #5 x 15′-3	4-#5 x 15′-11 12-#5 x 14′-5	2-#3	6	#4 x 36′-8 #5 x 24′-10	3.22
9	L = 24′-0	50	12½	14	12	7	#4 x 40′-8 #4 x 17′-3	1-#4 x 15′-11 10-#4 x 14′-5	—	5	#4 x 36′-10 #4 x 24′-8	2.02
10	D = Note 2	100	12½	18	16	7	#4 x 40′-8 #4 x 17′-3	4-#4 x 15′-11 14-#4 x 14′-5	—	5	#4 x 36′-10 #4 x 24′-8	2.27
11	10 + 2½	150	12½	20	23	7	#5 x 40′-8 #4 x 17′-3	2-#4 x 15′-11 15-#4 x 14′-5	2-#3	5	#5 x 36′-10 #4 x 24′-8	2.98
12		200	12½	22	29	7	#5 x 40′-8 #4 x 17′-3	4-#4 x 15′-11 19-#4 x 14′-5	2-#3	5	#5 x 36′-10 #5 x 24′-10	3.35
13		300	12½	24	44	6	#6 x 40′-8 #5 x 15′-3	3-#5 x 15′-11 15-#5 x 14′-5	2-#3	6	#5 x 36′-10 #5 x 24′-10	4.02
14	L = 24′-0	50	14½	14	12	7	#4 x 40′-9 #4 x 17′-3	1-#4 x 15′-11 8-#4 x 14′-5	—	5	#4 x 36′-11 #4 x 24′-8	1.96
15	D = 8′-5	100	14½	18	12	7	#4 x 40′-9 #4 x 17′-3	3-#4 x 15′-11 13-#4 x 14′-5	—	5	#4 x 36′-11 #4 x 24′-8	2.20
16	12 + 2½	150	14½	20	17	7	#4 x 40′-9 #4 x 17′-3	5-#4 x 15′-11 17-#4 x 14′-5	2-#3	5	#5 x 36′-11 #4 x 24′-8	2.80
17		200	14½	22	23	7	#5 x 40′-9 #4 x 17′-3	3-#4 x 15′-11 16-#4 x 14′-5	2-#3	5	#5 x 36′-11 #4 x 24′-8	3.07
18		300	14½	25	34	7	#5 x 40′-9 #5 x 17′-3	4-#5 x 15′-11 14-#5 x 14′-5	4-#3	5	#5 x 36′-11 #5 x 24′-10	3.85
19	L = 24′-0	50	10½	14	15	7	#4 x 40′-6 #4 x 17′-3	3-#4 x 15′-11 12-#4 x 14′-5	—	5	#4 x 36′-8 #4 x 24′-8	2.16
20	D = Note 1	100	10½	18	23	7	#4 x 40′-6 #4 x 17′-3	5-#4 x 15′-11 18-#4 x 14′-5	2-#3	5	#5 x 36′-8 #4 x 24′-8	2.80
21	6 + 4½	150	10½	20	32	6	#5 x 40′-6 #4 x 15′-3	6-#4 x 15′-11 20-#4 x 14′-5	2-#3	6	#5 x 36′-8 #4 x 24′-8	3.23
22	L = 24′-0	50	12½	14	12	7	#4 x 40′-8 #4 x 17′-3	2-#4 x 15′-11 11-#4 x 14′-5	—	5	#4 x 36′-10 #4 x 24′-8	2.09
23	D = Note 2	100	12½	18	17	7	#4 x 40′-8 #4 x 17′-3	4-#4 x 15′-11 16-#4 x 14′-5	2-#3	5	#4 x 36′-10 #5 x 24′-10	2.64
24	8 + 4½	150	12½	20	24	7	#5 x 40′-8 #4 x 17′-3	3-#4 x 15′-11 16-#4 x 14′-5	2-#3	5	#5 x 36′-10 #4 x 24′-8	3.05
25		200	12½	22	31	7	#5 x 40′-8 #4 x 17′-3	4-#4 x 15′-11 20-#4 x 14′-5	2-#3	5	#5 x 36′-10 #5 x 24′-10	3.38
26		300	12½	24	45	6	#6 x 40′-8 #5 x 15′-3	4-#5 x 15′-11 15-#5 x 14′-5	2-#3	6	#5 x 36′-10 #5 x 24′-10	4.08

Note 1: *D* = 8′-5 for 50 and 100 psf *LL*; 10′-5 for 150 psf *LL*.
Note 2: *D* = 8′-5 for 50, 100, 150 and 200 psf *LL*; 10′-5 for 300 psf *LL*.

*,**,† For notes, see page 9-9.

WAFFLE SLABS—SQUARE PANELS—19-IN.-WIDE DOMES

Av.‡ Cu. Ft. Conc. (psf)	Strips Perpendicular to an Exterior Wall								Wt.† of Steel (psf)	
	Column Strip					Middle Strip				
	Top Bars at Ext. Col.**	No. Jsts.	Bars Trussed Straight	Top Bars at First Int. Col.	Stir-rups per Joist*	No. Jsts.	Bars Trussed Straight	Top Bars at Ext. Support		
.886	5-#4 x 8′-10 5-#4 x 8′-2	5	#4 x 31′-10 #4 x 15′-3	2-#4 x 14′-7 8-#4 x 13′-3	—	6	#4 x 30′-1 #4 x 22′-4	1-#4 x 7′-0	2.01	1
.886	6-#4 x 8′-10 6-#4 x 8′-2	5	#5 x 31′-10 #4 x 15′-3	4-#4 x 14′-7 9-#4 x 13′-3	—	6	#4 x 30′-1 #4 x 22′-4	1-#4 x 7′-0	2.28	2
.886	7-#4 x 8′-10 7-#4 x 8′-2	5	#5 x 31′-10 #4 x 15′-3	3-#4 x 14′-7 12-#4 x 13′-3	—	6	#4 x 30′-1 #4 x 22′-4	1-#4 x 7′-0	2.45	3
.886	5-#5 x 8′-10 5-#5 x 8′-2	5	#5 x 31′-10 #5 x 15′-3	4-#4 x 14′-7 16-#4 x 13′-3	2-#3	6	#4 x 30′-1 #5 x 22′-5	2-#4 x 7′-0	2.97	4
.886	6-#5 x 8′-10 7-#5 x 8′-2	5	#6 x 31′-10 #5 x 15′-3	5-#5 x 14′-7 11-#5 x 13′-3	2-#3	6	#5 x 30′-1 #4 x 22′-4	1-#5 x 7′-0	3.42	5
.529	7-#4 x 9′-6 7-#4 x 8′-9	7	#4 x 34′-1 #4 x 17′-3	3-#4 x 15′-11 13-#4 x 14′-5	—	5	#4 x 32′-2 #5 x 24′-5	2-#4 x 7′-6	2.25	6
.529	9-#4 x 9′-6 9-#4 x 8′-9	7	#5 x 34′-1 #4 x 17′-3	7-#4 x 15′-11 15-#4 x 14′-15	2-#3	5	#5 x 32′-2 #5 x 24′-5	1-#5 x 7′-6	2.93	7
.553	11-#4 x 9′-6 11-#4 x 8′-9	6	#6 x 34′-1 #4 x 15′-3	5-#5 x 15′-11 12-#5 x 14′-5	2-#3	6	#5 x 32′-2 #5 x 24′-5	1-#5 x 7′-6	3.46	8
.617	6-#4 x 9′-6 6-#4 x 8′-9	7	#4 x 34′-3 #4 x 17′-3	2-#4 x 15′-11 12-#4 x 14′-5	—	5	#4 x 32′-4 #4 x 24′-4	1-#4 x 7′-6	2.05	9
.617	8-#4 x 9′-6 8-#4 x 8′-9	7	#5 x 34′-3 #4 x 17′-3	5-#4 x 15′-11 14-#4 x 14′-5	—	5	#5 x 32′-4 #4 x 24′-4	1-#5 x 7′-6	2.55	10
.617	10-#4 x 9′-6 10-#4 x 8′-9	7	#5 x 34′-3 #4 x 17′-3	4-#4 x 15′-11 18-#4 x 14′-5	2-#3	5	#5 x 32′-4 #5 x 24′-5	1-#5 x 7′-6	3.12	11
.617	7-#5 x 9′-6 7-#5 x 8′-9	7	#5 x 34′-3 #5 x 17′-3	6-#4 x 15′-11 22-#4 x 14′-5	2-#3	5	#5 x 32′-4 #6 x 24′-6	2-#5 x 7′-6	3.63	12
.647	6-#6 x 9′-6 6-#6 x 8′-9	6	#6 x 34′-3 #6 x 15′-7	5-#5 x 15′-11 17-#5 x 14′-5	2-#3	6	#5 x 32′-4 #6 x 24′-6	2-#5 x 7′-6	4.33	13
.708	6-#4 x 9′-6 6-#4 x 8′-9	7	#4 x 34′-4 #4 x 17′-3	2-#4 x 15′-11 10-#4 x 14′-5	—	5	#4 x 32′-5 #4 x 24′-4	1-#4 x 7′-6	2.01	14
.708	8-#4 x 9′-6 8-#4 x 8′-9	7	#4 x 34′-4 #4 x 17′-3	4-#4 x 15′-11 16-#4 x 14′-5	—	5	#4 x 32′-5 #5 x 24′-5	2-#4 x 7′-6	2.36	15
.708	9-#4 x 9′-6 9-#4 x 8′-9	7	#5 x 34′-4 #4 x 17′-3	7-#4 x 15′-11 16-#4 x 14′-5	2-#3	5	#5 x 32′-5 #5 x 24′-5	1-#5 x 7′-6	3.03	16
.708	10-#4 x 9′-6 10-#4 x 8′-9	7	#5 x 34′-4 #4 x 17′-3	5-#4 x 15′-11 19-#4 x 14′-5	2-#3	5	#5 x 32′-5 #6 x 24′-6	1-#5 x 7′-6	3.29	17
.708	12-#4 x 9′-6 13-#4 x 8′-9	7	#6 x 34′-4 #4 x 17′-3	5-#5 x 15′-11 15-#5 x 14′-5	4-#3	5	#6 x 32′-5 #6 x 24′-6	1-#6 x 7′-6	4.23	18
.611	7-#4 x 9′-6 8-#4 x 8′-9	7	#4 x 34′-1 #4 x 17′-3	4-#4 x 15′-11 15-#4 x 14′-5	—	5	#4 x 32′-2 #5 x 24′-5	2-#4 x 7′-6	2.32	19
.611	9-#4 x 9′-6 10-#4 x 8′-9	7	#5 x 34′-1 #4 x 17′-3	7-#4 x 15′-11 17-#4 x 14′-5	2-#3	5	#5 x 32′-2 #5 x 24′-5	1-#5 x 7′-6	3.03	20
.629	7-#5 x 9′-6 8-#5 x 8′-9	6	#5 x 34′-1 #5 x 15′-3	8-#4 x 15′-11 24-#4 x 14′-5	2-#3	6	#5 x 32′-2 #5 x 24′-5	1-#5 x 7′-6	3.42	21
.696	7-#4 x 9′-6 7-#4 x 8′-9	7	#4 x 34′-3 #4 x 17′-3	3-#4 x 15′-11 13-#4 x 14′-5	—	5	#4 x 32′-4 #5 x 24′-5	1-#4 x 7′-6	2.21	22
.696	9-#4 x 9′-6 9-#4 x 8′-9	7	#5 x 34′-3 #4 x 17′-3	6-#4 x 15′-11 15-#4 x 14′-5	2-#3	5	#5 x 32′-4 #5 x 24′-5	1-#5 x 7′-6	2.92	23
.696	7-#5 x 9′-6 7-#5 x 8′-9	7	#5 x 34′-3 #5 x 17′-3	4-#4 x 15′-11 19-#4 x 14′-5	2-#3	5	#5 x 32′-4 #6 x 24′-6	1-#5 x 7′-6	3.36	24
.696	8-#5 x 9′-6 8-#5 x 8′-9	7	#5 x 34′-3 #5 x 17′-3	7-#4 x 15′-11 23-#4 x 14′-5	2-#3	5	#5 x 32′-4 #6 x 24′-6	2-#5 x 7′-6	3.69	25
.720	7-#6 x 9′-6 7-#6 x 8′-9	6	#6 x 34′-3 #6 x 15′-7	5-#5 x 15′-11 19-#5 x 14′-5	2-#3	6	#5 x 32′-4 #6 x 24′-6	2-#5 x 7′-6	4.43	26

*,**,†,‡ For notes, see page 9-9.

WAFFLE SLABS—SQUARE PANELS—19-IN.-WIDE DOMES

For general instructions and notes on the use of this table, see pages 9-3 to 9-9 incl.

	Span / Drop-D / Form Depth plus Top Slab	Live Load (psf)	t_1 (in.)	Min. Col. Dia. 12′-0″ Story Height (in.)	Min. Col. Cap. C (Shear) (in.)	Interior Square Panel: Each Column Strip: No. Jst.	Each Column Strip: Bars: Trussed Straight	Each Column Strip: Bars: Top **	Each Column Strip: Stirrups per Jst.*	Each Middle Strip: No. Jst.	Each Middle Strip: Bars: Trussed Straight	Wt.† of Steel (psf)
1	$L = 24'$-0	50	14½	14	12	7	#4 x 40′-9 #4 x 17′-3	1-#4 x 15′-11 9-#4 x 14′-5	—	5	#4 x 36′-11 #4 x 24′-8	1.99
2	$D = 8'$-5	100	14½	18	13	7	#4 x 40′-9 #4 x 17′-3	4-#4 x 15′-11 13-#4 x 14′-5	—	5	#4 x 36′-11 #4 x 24′-8	2.24
3	10 + 4½	150	14½	20	18	7	#5 x 40′-9 #4 x 17′-3	2-#4 x 15′-11 14-#4 x 14′-5	2-#3	5	#5 x 36′-11 #4 x 24′-8	2.96
4		200	14½	22	24	7	#5 x 40′-9 #4 x 17′-3	3-#4 x 15′-11 18-#4 x 14′-5	2-#3	5	#5 x 36′-11 #4 x 24′-8	3.13
5		300	14½	25	36	7	#5 x 40′-9 #5 x 17′-3	4-#5 x 15′-11 15-#5 x 14′-5	4-#3	5	#5 x 36′-11 #5 x 24′-10	3.91
6	$L = 24'$-0	50	16½	15	12	7	#4 x 40′-11 #4 x 17′-3	1-#4 x 15′-11 8-#4 x 14′-5	—	5	#4 x 37′-1 #4 x 24′-8	1.96
7	$D = 8'$-5	100	16½	18	12	7	#4 x 40′-11 #4 x 17′-3	3-#4 x 15′-11 12-#4 x 14′-5	—	5	#4 x 37′-1 #4 x 24′-8	2.17
8	12 + 4½	150	16½	20	14	7	#4 x 40′-11 #4 x 17′-3	5-#4 x 15′-11 16-#4 x 14′-5	2-#3	5	#4 x 37′-1 #5 x 24′-10	2.71
9		200	16½	22	19	7	#5 x 40′-11 #4 x 17′-3	3-#4 x 15′-11 15-#4 x 14′-5	2-#3	5	#5 x 37′-1 #4 x 24′-8	3.05
10		300	16½	25	29	7	#5 x 40′-11 #5 x 17′-3	4-#5 x 15′-11 13-#5 x 14′-5	2-#3	5	#5 x 37′-1 #5 x 24′-10	3.67
11	$L = 26'$-0	50	10½	15	17	6	#5 x 43′-10 #4 x 17′-3	3-#4 x 17′-2 13-#4 x 15′-8	—	7	#4 x 39′-8 #4 x 26′-8	2.44
12	$D = 10'$-5 8 + 2½	100	10½	18	27	6	#5 x 43′-10 #5 x 17′-3	4-#5 x 17′-2 13-#5 x 15′-8	2-#3	7	#4 x 39′-8 #4 x 26′-8	2.98
13	$L = 26'$-0	50	12½	15	13	6	#4 x 44′-0 #4 x 17′-3	5-#4 x 17′-2 15-#4 x 15′-8	—	7	#4 x 39′-10 #4 x 26′-8	2.28
14	$D = 10'$-5 10 + 2½	100	12½	19	21	6	#5 x 44′-0 #4 x 17′-3	4-#4 x 17′-2 18-#4 x 15′-8	—	7	#4 x 39′-10 #4 x 26′-8	2.63
15		150	12½	21	29	6	#5 x 44′-0 #5 x 17′-3	5-#5 x 17′-2 15-#5 x 15′-8	2-#3	7	#4 x 39′-10 #4 x 26′-8	3.15
16		200	12½	23	37	6	#6 x 44′-0 #5 x 17′-3	4-#5 x 17′-2 15-#5 x 15′-8	2-#3	7	#5 x 39′-10 #4 x 26′-8	3.76
17	$L = 26'$-0	50	14½	15	12	6	#4 x 44′-1 #4 x 17′-3	4-#4 x 17′-2 14-#4 x 15′-8	—	7	#4 x 39′-11 #4 x 26′-8	2.22
18	$D = 10'$-5	100	14½	19	16	6	#5 x 44′-1 #4 x 17′-3	4-#4 x 17′-2 16-#4 x 15′-8	—	7	#4 x 39′-11 #4 x 26′-8	2.57
19	12 + 2½	150	14½	21	23	6	#5 x 44′-1 #5 x 17′-3	4-#5 x 17′-2 13-#5 x 15′-8	2-#3	7	#4 x 39′-11 #4 x 26′-8	3.01
20		200	14½	23	29	6	#6 x 44′-1 #4 x 17′-3	4-#4 x 17′-2 22-#4 x 15′-8	2-#3	7	#5 x 39′-11 #4 x 26′-8	3.54
21		300	14½	26	43	6	#6 x 44′-1 #5 x 17′-3	5-#5 x 17′-2 18-#5 x 15′-8	4-#3	7	#5 x 39′-11 #4 x 26′-8	4.09
22	$L = 26'$-0	50	10½	15	19	6	#5 x 43′-10 #4 x 17′-3	3-#4 x 17′-2 16-#4 x 15′-8	—	7	#4 x 39′-8 #4 x 26′-8	2.53
23	D = Note 1 6 + 4½	100	10½	18	30	7	#5 x 43′-10 #4 x 15′-3	5-#4 x 17′-2 20-#4 x 15′-8	—	6	#5 x 39′-8 #4 x 26′-8	3.00
24	$L = 26'$-0	50	12½	15	14	6	#5 x 44′-0 #4 x 17′-3	2-#4 x 17′-2 14-#4 x 15′-8	—	7	#4 x 39′-10 #4 x 26′-8	2.44
25	D = Note 2 8 + 4½	100	12½	19	22	6	#5 x 44′-0 #5 x 17′-3	4-#5 x 17′-2 12-#5 x 15′-8	2-#3	7	#4 x 39′-10 #4 x 26′-8	2.95
26		150	12½	21	30	6	#5 x 44′-0 #5 x 17′-3	5-#5 x 17′-2 16-#5 x 15′-8	2-#3	7	#4 x 39′-10 #5 x 26′-10	3.40
27		200	12½	23	39	7	#5 x 44′-0 #5 x 15′-3	6-#5 x 17′-2 17-#5 x 15′-8	2-#3	6	#5 x 39′-10 #5 x 26′-10	3.77

Note 1: D = 10′-5 for 50 psf *LL*; 12′-5 for 100 psf *LL*.
Note 2: D = 10′-5 for 50, 100, and 150 psf *LL*; 12′-5 for 200 psf *LL*.

*,**,† For notes, see page 9-9.

WAFFLE SLABS—SQUARE PANELS—19-IN.-WIDE DOMES

Av.‡ Cu. Ft. Conc. (psf)	Strips Perpendicular to an Exterior Wall									
	Column Strip					Middle Strip			Wt.† of Steel (psf)	
	Top Bars at Ext. Col.**	No. Jsts.	Bars Trussed Straight	Top Bars at First Int. Col.	Stir-rups per Joist*	No. Jsts.	Bars Trussed Straight	Top Bars at Ext. Support		
.784	6-#4 x 9′-6 6-#4 x 8′-9	7	#4 x 34′-4 #4 x 17′-3	2-#4 x 15′-11 11-#4 x 14′-5	—	5	#4 x 32′-5 #4 x 24′-4	1-#4 x 7′-6	2.03	1
.784	8-#4 x 9′-6 8-#4 x 8′-9	7	#5 x 34′-4 #4 x 17′-3	5-#4 x 15′-11 13-#4 x 14′-5	—	5	#5 x 32′-5 #4 x 24′-4	1-#5 x 7′-6	2.53	2
.784	9-#4 x 9′-6 10-#4 x 8′-9	7	#5 x 34′-4 #4 x 17′-3	3-#4 x 15′-11 17-#4 x 14′-5	2-#3	5	#5 x 32′-5 #5 x 24′-5	1-#5 x 7′-6	3.09	3
.784	7-#5 x 9′-6 7-#5 x 8′-9	7	#5 x 34′-4 #5 x 17′-3	5-#4 x 15′-11 21-#4 x 14′-5	2-#3	5	#5 x 32′-5 #6 x 24′-6	2-#5 x 7′-6	3.51	4
.784	8-#5 x 9′-6 8-#5 x 8′-9	7	#6 x 34′-4 #5 x 17′-3	6-#5 x 15′-11 14-#5 x 14′-5	4-#3	5	#6 x 32′-5 #6 x 24′-6	1-#6 x 7′-6	4.34	5
.874	6-#4 x 9′-6 6-#4 x 8′-9	7	#4 x 34′-6 #4 x 17′-3	2-#4 x 15′-11 10-#4 x 14′-5	—	5	#4 x 32′-7 #4 x 24′-4	1-#4 x 7′-6	2.01	6
.874	7-#4 x 9′-6 8-#4 x 8′-9	7	#4 x 34′-6 #4 x 17′-3	4-#4 x 15′-11 15-#4 x 14′-5	—	5	#4 x 32′-7 #5 x 24′-5	2-#4 x 7′-6	2.33	7
.874	9-#4 x 9′-6 9-#4 x 8′-9	7	#5 x 34′-6 #4 x 17′-3	6-#4 x 15′-11 16-#4 x 14′-5	2-#3	5	#5 x 32′-7 #5 x 24′-5	1-#5 x 7′-6	2.99	8
.874	7-#5 x 9′-6 7-#5 x 8′-9	7	#5 x 34′-6 #5 x 17′-3	4-#4 x 15′-11 19-#4 x 14′-5	2-#3	5	#5 x 32′-7 #6 x 24′-6	1-#5 x 7′-6	3.39	9
.874	8-#5 x 9′-6 8-#5 x 8′-9	7	#5 x 34′-6 #5 x 17′-3	5-#5 x 15′-11 16-#5 x 14′-5	2-#3	5	#6 x 32′-7 #6 x 24′-6	1-#6 x 7′-6	3.97	10
.543	9-#4 x 10′-1 9-#4 x 9′-4	6	#5 x 36′-9 #4 x 17′-3	4-#4 x 17′-2 16-#4 x 15′-8	—	7	#4 x 34′-8 #4 x 25′-4	1-#4 x 8′-0	2.47	11
.543	7-#5 x 10′-1 8-#5 x 9′-4	6	#6 x 36′-9 #5 x 17′-3	5-#5 x 17′-2 13-#5 x 15′-8	2-#3	7	#4 x 34′-8 #5 x 26′-5	2-#4 x 8′-0	3.27	12
.635	8-#4 x 10′-1 8-#4 x 9′-4	6	#5 x 36′-11 #4 x 17′-3	6-#4 x 17′-2 15-#4 x 15′-8	—	7	#4 x 34′-10 #4 x 26′-4	1-#4 x 8′-0	2.38	13
.635	7-#5 x 10′-1 7-#5 x 9′-4	6	#5 x 36′-11 #5 x 17′-3	6-#4 x 17′-2 22-#4 x 15′-8	—	7	#4 x 34′-10 #5 x 26′-5	2-#4 x 8′-0	2.89	14
.635	8-#5 x 10′-1 8-#5 x 9′-4	6	#6 x 36′-11 #5 x 17′-3	6-#5 x 17′-2 15-#5 x 15′-8	2-#3	7	#5 x 34′-10 #5 x 26′-5	1-#5 x 8′-0	3.52	15
.635	6-#6 x 10′-1 7-#6 x 9′-4	6	#6 x 36′-11 #6 x 17′-7	5-#5 x 17′-2 18-#5 x 15′-8	2-#3	7	#5 x 34′-10 #5 x 26′-5	1-#5 x 8′-0	3.97	16
.729	8-#4 x 10′-1 8-#4 x 9′-4	6	#5 x 37′-0 #4 x 17′-3	5-#4 x 17′-2 13-#4 x 15′-8	—	7	#4 x 34′-11 #4 x 26′-4	1-#4 x 8′-0	2.33	17
.729	6-#5 x 10′-1 6-#5 x 9′-4	6	#5 x 37′-0 #5 x 17′-3	5-#4 x 17′-2 19-#4 x 15′-8	—	7	#4 x 34′-11 #5 x 26′-5	2-#4 x 8′-0	2.80	18
.729	7-#5 x 10′-1 8-#5 x 9′-4	6	#6 x 37′-0 #5 x 17′-3	5-#5 x 17′-2 14-#5 x 15′-8	2-#3	7	#5 x 34′-11 #4 x 26′-4	1-#5 x 8′-0	3.32	19
.729	8-#5 x 10′-1 9-#5 x 9′-4	6	#6 x 37′-0 #5 x 17′-3	6-#4 x 17′-2 26-#4 x 15′-8	2-#3	7	#5 x 34′-11 #5 x 26′-5	1-#5 x 8′-0	3.73	20
.729	10-#5 x 10′-1 10-#5 x 9′-4	6	#7 x 37′-0 #5 x 17′-3	7-#5 x 17′-2 18-#5 x 15′-8	4-#3	7	#5 x 34′-11 #6 x 26′-6	2-#5 x 8′-0	4.56	21
.622	6-#5 x 10′-1 6-#5 x 9′-4	6	#5 x 36′-9 #5 x 17′-3	5-#4 x 17′-2 18-#4 x 15′-8	—	7	#4 x 34′-8 #4 x 26′-4	1-#4 x 8′-0	2.60	22
.641	8-#5 x 10′-1 8-#5 x 9′-4	7	#5 x 36′-9 #5 x 15′-3	7-#4 x 17′-2 24-#4 x 15′-8	—	6	#5 x 34′-8 #5 x 26′-5	1-#5 x 8′-0	3.18	23
.710	9-#4 x 10′-1 9-#4 x 9′-4	6	#5 x 36′-11 #4 x 17′-3	4-#4 x 17′-2 16-#4 x 15′-8	—	7	#4 x 34′-10 #4 x 26′-4	1-#4 x 8′-0	2.47	24
.710	11-#4 x 10′-1 11-#4 x 9′-4	6	#6 x 36′-11 #4 x 17′-3	5-#5 x 17′-2 12-#5 x 15′-8	2-#3	7	#4 x 34′-10 #5 x 26′-5	2-#4 x 8′-0	3.18	25
.710	8-#5 x 10′-1 8-#5 x 9′-4	6	#6 x 36′-11 #5 x 17′-3	6-#5 x 17′-2 16-#5 x 15′-8	2-#3	7	#5 x 34′-10 #5 x 26′-5	1-#5 x 8′-0	3.67	26
.735	9-#5 x 10′-1 9-#5 x 9′-4	7	#6 x 36′-11 #5 x 15′-3	7-#5 x 17′-2 18-#5 x 15′-8	2-#3	6	#6 x 34′-10 #6 x 26′-6	1-#6 x 8′-0	4.19	27

*,**,†,‡ For notes, see page 9-9.

WAFFLE SLABS—SQUARE PANELS—19-IN.-WIDE DOMES

For general instructions and notes on the use of this table, see pages 9-3 to 9-9 incl.

	Span Drop-D Form Depth plus Top Slab	Live Load (psf)	t_1 (in.)	Min. Col. Dia. 12'-0" Story Height (in.)	Min. Col. Cap. C (Shear) (in.)	Interior Square Panel: Each Column Strip: No. Jst.	Each Column Strip: Bars: Trussed Straight	Each Column Strip: Bars: Top **	Each Column Strip: Bars: Stirrups per Jst.*	Each Middle Strip: No. Jst.	Each Middle Strip: Bars: Trussed Straight	Wt.† of Steel (psf)
1	L = 26'-0	50	14½	15	12	6	#5 x 44'-1 #4 x 17'-3	2-#4 x 17'-2 12-#4 x 15'-8	—	7	#4 x 39'-11 #4 x 26'-8	2.38
2	D = 10'-5	100	14½	19	17	6	#5 x 44'-1 #4 x 17'-3	4-#4 x 17'-2 17-#4 x 15'-8	—	7	#4 x 39'-11 #4 x 26'-8	2.60
3	10 + 4½	150	14½	21	24	6	#5 x 44'-1 #5 x 17'-3	4-#5 x 17'-2 15-#5 x 15'-8	2-#3	7	#4 x 39'-11 #4 x 26'-8	3.11
4		200	14½	23	31	6	#6 x 44'-1 #5 x 17'-3	3-#5 x 17'-2 14-#5 x 15'-8	2-#3	7	#5 x 39'-11 #4 x 26'-8	3.67
5		300	14½	26	44	6	#6 x 44'-1 #6 x 17'-7	4-#6 x 17'-2 13-#6 x 15'-8	4-#3	7	#5 x 39'-11 #5 x 26'-10	4.52
6	L = 26'-0	50	16½	15	12	6	#4 x 44'-3 #4 x 17'-3	4-#4 x 17'-2 14-#4 x 15'-8	—	7	#4 x 40'-1 #4 x 26'-8	2.22
7	D = 10'-5	100	16½	19	13	6	#5 x 44'-3 #4 x 17'-3	4-#4 x 17'-2 15-#4 x 15'-8	—	7	#4 x 40'-1 #4 x 26'-8	2.55
8	12 + 4½	150	16½	21	19	6	#5 x 44'-3 #5 x 17'-3	4-#5 x 17'-2 13-#5 x 15'-8	—	7	#4 x 40'-1 #4 x 26'-8	2.90
9		200	16½	23	25	6	#6 x 44'-3 #4 x 17'-3	4-#4 x 17'-2 20-#4 x 15'-8	2-#3	7	#5 x 40'-1 #4 x 26'-8	3.50
10		300	16½	26	36	6	#6 x 44'-3 #5 x 17'-3	5-#5 x 17'-2 17-#5 x 15'-8	2-#3	7	#5 x 40'-1 #4 x 26'-8	3.94
11	L = 28'-0	50	12½	16	16	8	#4 x 47'-3 #4 x 19'-3	5-#4 x 18'-6 18-#4 x 16'-10	—	6	#4 x 42'-10 #4 x 28'-8	2.31
12	D = Note 1	100	12½	19	25	8	#5 x 47'-3 #4 x 19'-3	4-#4 x 18'-6 21-#4 x 16'-10	2-#3	6	#5 x 42'-10 #4 x 28'-8	3.09
13	10 + 2½	150	12½	22	35	7	#5 x 47'-3 #5 x 17'-3	6-#5 x 18'-6 19-#5 x 16'-10	2-#3	7	#5 x 42'-10 #4 x 28'-8	3.59
14	L = 28'-0	50	14½	16	12	8	#4 x 47'-5 #4 x 19'-3	4-#4 x 18'-6 17-#4 x 16'-10	—	6	#4 x 42'-11 #4 x 28'-8	2.26
15	D = Note 2	100	14½	19	20	8	#5 x 47'-5 #4 x 19'-3	3-#4 x 18'-6 19-#4 x 16'-10	—	6	#5 x 42'-11 #4 x 28'-8	2.89
16	12 + 2½	150	14½	22	28	8	#5 x 47'-5 #4 x 19'-3	6-#4 x 18'-6 24-#4 x 16'-10	2-#3	6	#5 x 42'-11 #5 x 28'-10	3.43
17		200	14½	24	36	8	#5 x 47'-5 #5 x 19'-3	5-#5 x 18'-6 19-#5 x 16'-10	2-#3	6	#5 x 42'-11 #5 x 28'-10	3.79
18		300	14½	27	52	7	#6 x 47'-5 #6 x 17'-7	5-#6 x 18'-6 15-#6 x 16'-10	2-#3	7	#5 x 42'-11 #5 x 28'-10	4.51
19	L = 28'-0	50	12½	16	18	8	#4 x 47'-3 #4 x 19'-3	6-#4 x 18'-6 20-#4 x 16'-10	—	6	#4 x 42'-10 #5 x 28'-10	2.57
20	D = Note 1	100	12½	19	28	8	#5 x 47'-3 #4 x 19'-3	5-#4 x 18'-6 22-#4 x 16'-10	2-#3	6	#5 x 42'-10 #4 x 28'-8	3.15
21	8 + 4½	150	12½	22	37	7	#6 x 47'-3 #5 x 17'-3	4-#5 x 18'-6 16-#5 x 16'-10	2-#3	7	#5 x 42'-10 #5 x 28'-10	3.94
22	L = 28'-0	50	14½	16	14	8	#4 x 47'-5 #4 x 19'-3	5-#4 x 18'-6 18-#4 x 16'-10	—	6	#4 x 42'-11 #4 x 28'-8	2.32
23	D = Note 2	100	14½	19	22	8	#5 x 47'-5 #4 x 19'-3	4-#4 x 18'-6 19-#4 x 16'-10	2-#3	6	#5 x 42'-11 #4 x 28'-8	3.05
24	10 + 4½	150	14½	22	30	8	#5 x 47'-5 #5 x 19'-3	4-#5 x 18'-6 16-#5 x 16'-10	2-#3	6	#5 x 42'-11 #5 x 28'-10	3.61
25		200	14½	24	37	8	#5 x 47'-5 #5 x 19'-3	6-#5 x 18'-6 19-#5 x 16'-10	2-#3	6	#5 x 42'-11 #6 x 29'-0	4.05
26		300	14½	27	54	7	#6 x 47'-5 #6 x 17'-7	5-#6 x 18'-6 16-#6 x 16'-10	4-#3	7	#5 x 42'-11 #6 x 29'-0	4.93

Note 1: *D* = 10'-5 for 50 and 100 psf *LL*; 12'-5 for 150 psf *LL*.
Note 2: *D* = 10'-5 for 50, 100, 150, and 200 psf *LL*; 12'-5 for 300 psf *LL*.

*,**,† For notes, see page 9-9.

WAFFLE SLABS—SQUARE PANELS—19-IN.-WIDE DOMES

Av.‡ Cu. Ft. Conc. (psf)	Strips Perpendicular to an Exterior Wall: Column Strip — Top Bars at Ext. Col.**	No. Jsts.	Bars Trussed Straight	Top Bars at First Int. Col.	Stirrups per Joist*	Middle Strip — No. Jsts.	Bars Trussed Straight	Top Bars at Ext. Support	Wt.† of Steel (psf)	
.801	8-#4 x 10′-1 8-#4 x 9′-4	6	#5 x 37′-0 #4 x 17′-3	3-#4 x 17′-2 14-#4 x 15′-8	—	7	#4 x 34′-11 #4 x 26′-4	1-#4 x 8′-0	2.40	1
.801	7-#5 x 10′-1 7-#5 x 9′-4	6	#5 x 37′-0 #5 x 17′-3	6-#4 x 17′-2 21-#4 x 15′-8	—	7	#4 x 34′-11 #5 x 26′-5	2-#4 x 8′-0	2.86	2
.801	8-#5 x 10′-1 8-#5 x 9′-4	6	#6 x 37′-0 #5 x 17′-3	6-#5 x 17′-2 14-#5 x 15′-8	2-#3	7	#5 x 34′-11 #5 x 26′-5	1-#5 x 8′-0	3.50	3
.801	6-#6 x 10′-1 6-#6 x 9′-4	6	#6 x 37′-0 #6 x 17′-7	4-#5 x 17′-2 17-#5 x 15′-8	2-#3	7	#5 x 34′-11 #5 x 26′-5	1-#5 x 8′-0	3.89	4
.801	7-#6 x 10′-1 8-#6 x 9′-4	6	#7 x 37′-0 #6 x 17′-7	5-#6 x 17′-2 13-#6 x 15′-8	4-#3	7	#5 x 34′-11 #6 x 26′-6	2-#5 x 8′-0	4.88	5
.895	8-#4 x 10′-1 8-#4 x 9′-4	6	#5 x 37′-2 #4 x 17′-3	5-#4 x 17′-2 13-#4 x 15′-8	—	7	#4 x 35′-1 #4 x 26′-4	1-#4 x 8′-0	2.33	6
.895	6-#5 x 10′-1 6-#5 x 9′-4	6	#5 x 37′-2 #5 x 17′-3	5-#4 x 17′-2 19-#4 x 15′-8	—	7	#4 x 35′-1 #5 x 26′-5	2-#4 x 8′-0	2.79	7
.895	7-#5 x 10′-1 7-#5 x 9′-4	6	#6 x 37′-2 #5 x 17′-3	5-#5 x 17′-2 13-#5 x 15′-8	—	7	#5 x 35′-1 #4 x 26′-4	1-#5 x 8′-0	3.19	8
.895	8-#5 x 10′-1 8-#5 x 9′-4	6	#6 x 37′-2 #5 x 17′-3	6-#4 x 17′-2 23-#4 x 15′-8	2-#3	7	#5 x 35′-1 #5 x 26′-5	1-#5 x 8′-0	3.68	9
.895	10-#5 x 10′-1 10-#5 x 9′-4	6	#7 x 37′-2 #5 x 17′-3	6-#5 x 17′-2 18-#5 x 15′-8	2-#3	7	#5 x 35′-1 #6 x 26′-6	2-#5 x 8′-0	4.43	10
.625	10-#4 x 10′-9 10-#4 x 9′-11	8	#5 x 39′-6 #4 x 19′-3	7-#4 x 18′-6 16-#4 x 16′-10	—	6	#5 x 37′-4 #4 x 28′-4	1-#5 x 8′-6	2.57	11
.625	8-#5 x 10′-9 8-#5 x 9′-11	8	#5 x 39′-6 #5 x 19′-3	6-#4 x 18′-6 25-#4 x 16′-10	2-#3	6	#5 x 37′-4 #6 x 28′-6	1-#5 x 8′-6	3.38	12
.652	10-#5 x 10′-9 10-#5 x 9′-11	7	#6 x 39′-6 #5 x 17′-3	8-#5 x 18′-6 19-#5 x 16′-10	2-#3	7	#5 x 37′-4 #6 x 28′-6	2-#5 x 8′-6	4.01	13
.717	9-#4 x 10′-9 10-#4 x 9′-11	8	#5 x 39′-8 #4 x 19′-3	6-#4 x 18′-6 15-#4 x 16′-10	—	6	#4 x 37′-5 #5 x 28′-5	2-#4 x 8′-6	2.52	14
.717	11-#4 x 10′-9 12-#4 x 9′-11	8	#5 x 39′-8 #4 x 19′-3	5-#4 x 18′-6 22-#4 x 16′-10	—	6	#5 x 37′-5 #5 x 28′-5	1-#5 x 8′-6	3.00	15
.717	9-#5 x 10′-9 9-#5 x 9′-11	8	#5 x 39′-8 #5 x 19′-3	8-#4 x 18′-6 29-#4 x 16′-10	2-#3	6	#5 x 37′-5 #6 x 28′-6	2-#5 x 8′-6	3.70	16
.717	10-#5 x 10′-9 10-#5 x 9′-11	8	#6 x 39′-8 #5 x 19′-3	7-#5 x 18′-6 19-#5 x 16′-10	2-#3	6	#6 x 37′-5 #6 x 28′-6	1-#6 x 8′-6	4.22	17
.749	9-#6 x 10′-9 9-#6 x 9′-11	7	#7 x 39′-8 #6 x 17′-7	6-#6 x 18′-6 16-#6 x 16′-10	2-#3	7	#6 x 37′-5 #6 x 28′-6	1-#6 x 8′-6	4.99	18
.702	10-#4 x 10′-9 11-#4 x 9′-11	8	#5 x 39′-6 #4 x 19′-3	8-#4 x 18′-6 18-#4 x 16′-10	—	6	#5 x 37′-4 #5 x 28′-5	1-#5 x 8′-6	2.81	19
.702	8-#5 x 10′-9 9-#5 x 9′-11	8	#5 x 39′-6 #5 x 19′-3	7-#4 x 18′-6 26-#4 x 16′-10	2-#3	6	#5 x 37′-4 #6 x 28′-6	2-#5 x 8′-6	3.51	20
.724	7-#6 x 10′-9 7-#6 x 9′-11	7	#6 x 39′-6 #6 x 17′-7	5-#5 x 18′-6 20-#5 x 16′-10	2-#3	7	#5 x 37′-4 #6 x 28′-6	2-#5 x 8′-6	4.24	21
.791	10-#4 x 10′-9 10-#4 x 9′-11	8	#5 x 39′-8 #4 x 19′-3	7-#4 x 18′-6 17-#4 x 16′-10	—	6	#5 x 37′-5 #5 x 28′-5	1-#5 x 8′-6	2.67	22
.791	8-#5 x 10′-9 8-#5 x 9′-11	8	#5 x 39′-8 #5 x 19′-3	6-#4 x 18′-6 23-#4 x 16′-10	2-#3	6	#5 x 37′-5 #6 x 28′-6	1-#5 x 8′-6	3.36	23
.791	14-#4 x 10′-9 14-#4 x 9′-11	8	#6 x 39′-8 #4 x 19′-3	6-#5 x 18′-6 16-#5 x 16′-10	2-#3	6	#6 x 37′-5 #6 x 28′-6	1-#6 x 8′-6	3.97	24
.791	10-#5 x 10′-9 11-#5 x 9′-11	8	#6 x 39′-8 #5 x 19′-3	8-#5 x 18′-6 19-#5 x 16′-10	2-#3	6	#6 x 37′-5 #6 x 28′-6	1-#6 x 8′-6	4.37	25
.818	9-#6 x 10′-9 9-#6 x 9′-11	7	#7 x 39′-8 #6 x 17′-7	6-#6 x 18′-6 17-#6 x 16′-10	4-#3	7	#6 x 37′-5 #6 x 28′-6	1-#6 x 8′-6	5.27	26

*,**,†,‡ For notes, see page 9-9.

WAFFLE SLABS—SQUARE PANELS—19-IN.-WIDE DOMES

	Span Drop-D Form Depth plus Top Slab	Live Load (psf)	t_1 (in.)	Min. Col. Dia. 12′-0″ Story Height (in.)	Min. Col. Cap. C (Shear) (in.)	Interior Square Panel — Each Column Strip: No. Jst.	Each Column Strip — Bars: Trussed Straight	Each Column Strip — Bars: Top **	Each Column Strip — Bars: Stirrups per Jst.*	Each Middle Strip: No. Jst.	Each Middle Strip — Bars: Trussed Straight	Wt.† of Steel (psf)
1	L = 28′-0	50	16½	16	12	8	#4 x 47′-7 #4 x 19′-3	5-#4 x 18′-6 16-#4 x 16′-10	—	6	#4 x 43′-1 #4 x 28′-8	2.26
2	D = 10′-5	100	16½	19	17	8	#5 x 47′-7 #4 x 19′-3	3-#4 x 18′-6 18-#4 x 16′-10	—	6	#5 x 43′-1 #4 x 28′-8	2.87
3	12 + 4½	150	16½	22	24	8	#5 x 47′-7 #4 x 19′-3	5-#4 x 18′-6 23-#4 x 16′-10	2-#3	6	#5 x 43′-1 #5 x 28′-10	3.38
4		200	16½	24	31	8	#5 x 47′-7 #5 x 19′-3	5-#5 x 18′-6 18-#5 x 16′-10	2-#3	6	#5 x 43′-1 #5 x 28′-10	3.77
5		300	16½	27	44	8	#6 x 47′-7 #5 x 19′-3	4-#5 x 18′-6 19-#5 x 16′-10	4-#3	6	#6 x 43′-1 #5 x 28′-10	4.65
6	L = 30′-0	50	12½	16	20	8	#5 x 50′-7 #4 x 21′-3	3-#4 x 19′-10 19-#4 x 18′-0	—	7	#4 x 45′-10 #4 x 30′-8	2.58
7	D = Note 1 10 + 2½	100	12½	20	31	7	#6 x 50′-7 #4 x 19′-3	5-#4 x 19′-10 25-#4 x 18′-0	2-#3	8	#5 x 45′-10 #4 x 30′-8	3.50
8	L = 30′-0	50	14½	17	16	8	#5 x 50′-9 #4 x 21′-3	3-#4 x 19′-10 17-#4 x 18′-0	—	7	#4 x 45′-11 #4 x 30′-8	2.53
9	D = Note 2	100	14½	20	25	8	#5 x 50′-9 #4 x 21′-3	6-#4 x 19′-10 25-#4 x 18′-0	2-#3	7	#5 x 45′-11 #4 x 30′-8	3.21
10	12 + 2½	150	14½	23	34	8	#5 x 50′-9 #5 x 21′-3	6-#5 x 19′-10 21-#5 x 18′-0	2-#3	7	#5 x 45′-11 #5 x 30′-10	3.84
11		200	14½	25	43	7	#6 x 50′-9 #6 x 19′-7	5-#6 x 19′-10 15-#6 x 18′-0	2-#3	8	#5 x 45′-11 #5 x 30′-10	4.40
12	L = 30′-0	50	12½	16	22	8	#5 x 50′-7 #4 x 21′-3	4-#4 x 19′-10 21-#4 x 18′-0	2-#3	7	#5 x 45′-10 #4 x 30′-8	3.03
13	D = Note 1 8 + 4½	100	12½	20	34	7	#6 x 50′-7 #5 x 19′-3	4-#5 x 19′-10 17-#5 x 18′-0	2-#3	8	#5 x 45′-10 #4 x 30′-8	3.69
14	L = 30′-0	50	14½	17	18	8	#5 x 50′-9 #4 x 21′-3	3-#4 x 19′-10 19-#4 x 18′-0	—	7	#4 x 45′-11 #4 x 30′-8	2.58
15	D = Note 2	100	14½	20	27	8	#5 x 50′-9 #5 x 21′-3	5-#5 x 19′-10 16-#5 x 18′-0	2-#3	7	#5 x 45′-11 #4 x 30′-8	3.41
16	10 + 4½	150	14½	23	36	8	#6 x 50′-9 #4 x 21′-3	5-#4 x 19′-10 28-#4 x 18′-0	4-#3	7	#5 x 45′-11 #5 x 30′-10	3.97
17		200	14½	25	45	7	#6 x 50′-9 #6 x 19′-7	5-#6 x 19′-10 17-#6 x 18′-0	2-#3	8	#5 x 45′-11 #5 x 30′-10	4.52
18	L = 30′-0	50	16½	17	14	8	#5 x 50′-11 #4 x 21′-3	3-#4 x 19′-10 17-#4 x 18′-0	—	7	#4 x 46′-1 #4 x 30′-8	2.54
19	D = Note 3	100	16½	20	22	8	#5 x 50′-11 #5 x 21′-3	4-#5 x 19′-10 15-#5 x 18′-0	2-#3	7	#5 x 46′-1 #4 x 30′-8	3.34
20	12 + 4½	150	16½	23	29	8	#5 x 50′-11 #5 x 21′-3	6-#5 x 19′-10 20-#5 x 18′-0	2-#3	7	#5 x 46′-1 #5 x 30′-10	3.82
21		200	16½	25	37	8	#6 x 50′-11 #5 x 21′-3	4-#5 x 19′-10 20-#5 x 18′-0	4-#3	7	#5 x 46′-1 #5 x 30′-10	4.27
22		300	16½	28	53	7	#7 x 50′-11 #6 x 19′-7	4-#6 x 19′-10 16-#6 x 18′-0	4-#3	8	#5 x 46′-1 #6 x 31′-0	5.20
23	L = 32′-0	50	12½	17	24	9	#5 x 53′-11 #4 x 21′-3	5-#4 x 21′-2 24-#4 x 19′-3	—	7	#5 x 48′-10 #4 x 32′-8	2.98 3.57
24	D = Note 4 10 + 2½	100	12½	21	37	8	#6 x 53′-11 #5 x 19′-3	5-#5 x 21′-2 20-#5 x 19′-3	—	8	#5 x 48′-10 #5 x 32′-10	3.91
25	L = 32′-0	50	14½	17	20	9	#5 x 54′-1 #4 x 21′-3	4-#4 x 21′-2 22-#4 x 19′-3	—	7	#5 x 48′-11 #4 x 32′-8	2.90
26	D = Note 5	100	14½	21	30	9	#5 x 54′-1 #5 x 21′-3	6-#5 x 21′-2 19-#5 x 19′-3	2-#3	7	#5 x 48′-11 #5 x 32′-10	3.67
27	12 + 2½	150	14½	24	40	9	#6 x 54′-1 #4 x 21′-3	6-#4 x 21′-2 33-#4 x 19′-3	2-#3	7	#6 x 48′-11 #4 x 32′-8	4.09
28		200	14½	26	52	8	#6 x 54′-1 #6 x 19′-7	6-#6 x 21′-2 18-#6 x 19′-3	2-#3	8	#5 x 48′-11 #6 x 33′-0	4.79

Note 1: *D* = 10′-5 for 50 psf *LL*; 12′-5 for 100 psf *LL*.
Note 2: *D* = 10′-5 for 50, 100, and 150 psf *LL*; 12′-5 for 200 psf *LL*.
Note 3: *D* = 10′-5 for 50, 100, 150, and 200 psf *LL*; 12′-5 for 300 psf *LL*.
Note 4: *D* = 12′-5 for 50 psf *LL*; 14′-5 for 100 psf *LL*.
Note 5: *D* = 12′-5 for 50, 100, and 150 psf *LL*; 14′-5 for 200 psf *LL*.
*,**,†,‡,§ For notes, see page 9-9.

WAFFLE SLABS—SQUARE PANELS—19-IN.-WIDE DOMES

Av.‡ Cu. Ft. Conc. (psf)	Strips Perpendicular to an Exterior Wall								Wt.† of Steel (psf)	
	Column Strip					Middle Strip				
	Top Bars at Ext. Col.**	No. Jsts.	Bars: Trussed / Straight	Top Bars at First Int. Col.	Stir-rups per Joist*	No. Jsts.	Bars: Trussed / Straight	Top Bars at Ext. Support		
.884	9-#4 x 10′-9 10-#4 x 9′-11	8	#5 x 39′-10 #4 x 19′-3	6-#4 x 18′-6 15-#4 x 16′-10	—	6	#5 x 37′-7 #4 x 28′-4	1-#5 x 8′-6	2.53	1
.884	7-#5 x 10′-9 8-#5 x 9′-11	8	#5 x 39′-10 #5 x 19′-3	5-#4 x 18′-6 22-#4 x 16′-10	—	6	#5 x 37′-7 #5 x 28′-5	1-#5 x 8′-6	3.07	2
.884	9-#5 x 10′-9 9-#5 x 9′-11	8	#5 x 39′-10 #5 x 19′-3	8-#4 x 18′-6 27-#4 x 16′-10	2-#3	6	#5 x 37′-7 #6 x 28′-6	2-#5 x 8′-6	3.67	3
.884	10-#5 x 10′-9 10-#5 x 9′-11	8	#6 x 39′-10 #5 x 19′-3	7-#5 x 18′-6 17-#5 x 16′-10	2-#3	6	#6 x 37′-7 #6 x 28′-6	1-#6 x 8′-6	4.19	4
.884	8-#6 x 10′-9 8-#6 x 9′-11	8	#6 x 39′-10 #6 x 19′-7	6-#5 x 18′-6 23-#5 x 16′-10	4-#3	6	#6 x 37′-7 #7 x 28′-7	2-#6 x 8′-6	5.12	5
.617	8-#5 x 11′-5 8-#5 x 10′-6	8	#5 x 42′-2 #5 x 21′-3	5-#4 x 19′-10 23-#4 x 18′-0	—	7	#5 x 39′-10 #5 x 30′-5	1-#5 x 9′-0	2.92	6
.640	7-#6 x 11′-5 7-#6 x 10′-6	7	#6 x 42′-2 #6 x 19′-7	7-#4 x 19′-10 30-#4 x 18′-0	2-#3	8	#5 x 39′-10 #5 x 30′-5	1-#5 x 9′-0	3.76	7
.708	11-#4 x 11′-5 11-#4 x 10′-6	8	#5 x 42′-4 #4 x 21′-3	4-#4 x 19′-10 21-#4 x 18′-0	—	7	#5 x 39′-11 #4 x 30′-4	1-#5 x 9′-0	2.69	8
.708	9-#5 x 11′-5 9-#5 x 10′-6	8	#5 x 42′-4 #5 x 21′-3	9-#4 x 19′-10 29-#4 x 18′-0	2-#3	7	#5 x 39′-11 #5 x 30′-5	1-#5 x 9′-0	3.39	9
.708	10-#5 x 11′-5 11-#5 x 10′-6	8	#6 x 42′-4 #5 x 21′-3	8-#5 x 19′-10 20-#5 x 18′-0	2-#3	7	#5 x 39′-11 #6 x 30′-6	2-#5 x 9′-0	4.14	10
.735	9-#6 x 11′-5 9-#6 x 10′-6	7	#7 x 42′-4 #6 x 19′-7	6-#6 x 19′-10 16-#6 x 18′-0	2-#3	8	#5 x 39′-11 #6 x 30′-6	2-#5 x 9′-0	4.76	11
.696	8-#5 x 11′-5 8-#5 x 10′-6	8	#5 x 42′-2 #5 x 21′-3	6-#4 x 19′-10 25-#4 x 18′-0	2-#3	7	#5 x 39′-10 #5 x 30′-5	1-#5 x 9′-0	3.22	12
.715	7-#6 x 11′-5 7-#6 x 10′-6	7	#6 x 42′-2 #6 x 19′-7	6-#5 x 19′-10 20-#5 x 18′-0	2-#3	8	#5 x 39′-10 #6 x 30′-6	1-#5 x 9′-0	4.00	13
.784	8-#5 x 11′-5 8-#5 x 10′-6	8	#5 x 42′-4 #5 x 21′-3	5-#4 x 19′-10 23-#4 x 18′-0	—	7	#5 x 39′-11 #5 x 30′-5	1-#5 x 9′-0	2.93	14
.784	9-#5 x 11′-5 10-#5 x 10′-6	8	#6 x 42′-4 #5 x 21′-3	6-#5 x 19′-10 17-#5 x 18′-0	2-#3	7	#5 x 39′-11 #6 x 30′-6	2-#5 x 9′-0	3.85	15
.784	8-#6 x 11′-5 8-#6 x 10′-6	8	#6 x 42′-4 #6 x 21′-7	8-#4 x 19′-10 33-#4 x 18′-0	4-#3	7	#6 x 39′-11 #6 x 30′-6	1-#6 x 9′-0	4.46	16
.807	9-#6 x 11′-5 9-#6 x 10′-6	7	#7 x 42′-4 #6 x 19′-7	6-#6 x 19′-10 17-#6 x 18′-0	2-#3	8	#6 x 39′-11 #6 x 30′-6	1-#6 x 9′-0	4.95	17
.874	7-#5 x 11′-5 8-#5 x 10′-6	8	#5 x 42′-6 #5 x 21′-3	5-#4 x 19′-10 21-#4 x 18′-0	—	7	#5 x 40′-1 #4 x 30′-4	1-#5 x 9′-0	2.79	18
.874	14-#4 x 11′-5 14-#4 x 10′-6	8	#6 x 42′-6 #4 x 21′-3	6-#5 x 19′-10 15-#5 x 18′-0	2-#3	7	#5 x 40′-1 #6 x 30′-6	1-#5 x 9′-0	3.64	19
.874	10-#5 x 11′-5 11-#5 x 10′-6	8	#6 x 42′-6 #5 x 21′-3	8-#5 x 19′-10 19-#5 x 18′-0	2-#3	7	#5 x 40′-1 #6 x 30′-6	2-#5 x 9′-0	4.13	20
.874	8-#6 x 11′-5 8-#6 x 10′-6	8	#6 x 42′-6 #6 x 21′-7	6-#5 x 19′-10 23-#5 x 18′-0	4-#3	7	#6 x 40′-1 #6 x 30′-6	1-#6 x 9′-0	4.66	21
.902	7-#7 x 11′-5 7-#7 x 10′-6	7	#7 x 42′-6 #7 x 19′-11	5-#6 x 19′-10 20-#6 x 18′-0	4-#3	8	#6 x 40′-1 #6 x 30′-6	1-#6 x 9′-0	5.50	22
.631	9-#5 x 12′-1 9-#5 x 11′-2	9	#5 x 44′-10 #5 x 21′-3	7-#4 x 21′-2 29-#4 x 19′-3	—	7	#5 x 42′-4 #6 x 32′-6	1-#5 x 9′-6	3.25	23
.655	8-#6 x 12′-1 9-#6 x 11′-2	8	#6 x 44′-10 #6 x 19′-7	6-#5 x 21′-2 24-#5 x 19′-3	—	8	#5 x 42′-4 #6 x 32′-6	2-#5 x 9′-6	4.18	24
.724	9-#5 x 12′-1 9-#5 x 11′-2	9	#5 x 45′-0 #5 x 21′-3	6-#4 x 21′-2 26-#4 x 19′-3	—	7	#5 x 42′-5 #5 x 32′-5	1-#5 x 9′-6	3.09	25
.724	11-#5 x 12′-1 11-#5 x 11′-2	9	#6 x 45′-0 #5 x 21′-3	7-#5 x 21′-2 20-#5 x 19′-3	2-#3	7	#5 x 42′-5 #6 x 32′-6	2-#5 x 9′-6	3.99	26
.724	9-#6 x 12′-1 9-#6 x 11′-2	9	#6 x 45′-0 #6 x 21′-7	10-#4 x 21′-2 38-#4 x 19′-3	2-#3	7	#6 x 42′-5 #6 x 32′-6	1-#6 x 9′-6	4.48	27
.753	10-#6 x 12′-1 10-#6 x 11′-2	8	#7 x 45′-0 #6 x 19′-7	7-#6 x 21′-2 20-#6 x 19′-3	2-#3	8	#6 x 42′-5 #6 x 32′-6	1-#6 x 9′-6	5.11	28

*,**,†,‡ For notes, see page 9-9.

WAFFLE SLABS—SQUARE PANELS—19-IN.-WIDE DOMES

For general instructions and notes on the use of this table, see pages 9-3 to 9-9 incl.

	Span (boxed) Drop-D Form Depth plus Top Slab	Live Load (psf)	t_1 (in.)	Min. Col. Dia. 12'-0" Story Height (in.)	Min. Col. Cap. C (Shear) (in.)	Interior Square Panel: Each Column Strip: No. Jst.	Each Column Strip: Bars: Trussed Straight	Each Column Strip: Bars: Top **	Each Column Strip: Bars: Stirrups per Jst.*	Each Middle Strip: No. Jst.	Each Middle Strip: Bars: Trussed Straight	Wt.† of Steel (psf)
1	L = 32'-0	50	12½	17	27	9	#5 x 53'-11 #4 x 21'-3	6-#4 x 21'-2 26-#4 x 19'-3	—	7	#5 x 48'-10 #4 x 32'-8	3.05
2	D = Note 1 8 + 4½	100	12½	21	40	8	#6 x 53'-11 #5 x 19'-3	5-#5 x 21'-2 21-#5 x 19'-3	2-#3	8	#5 x 48'-10 #5 x 32'-10	4.04
3	L = 32'-0	50	14½	17	22	9	#5 x 54'-1 #4 x 21'-3	5-#4 x 21'-2 24-#4 x 19'-3	—	7	#5 x 48'-11 #4 x 32'-8	2.98
4	D = Note 2	100	14½	21	32	9	#5 x 54'-1 #5 x 21'-3	6-#5 x 21'-2 21-#5 x 19'-3	2-#3	7	#5 x 48'-11 #5 x 32'-10	3.75
5	10 + 4½	150	14½	24	43	9	#6 x 54'-1 #5 x 21'-3	5-#5 x 21'-2 21-#5 x 19'-3	2-#3	7	#6 x 48'-11 #5 x 32'-10	4.45
6		200	14½	26	54	8	#6 x 54'-1 #6 x 19'-7	6-#6 x 21'-2 20-#6 x 19'-3	2-#3	8	#6 x 48'-11 #5 x 32'-10	5.01
7	L = 32'-0	50	16½	17	18	9	#5 x 54'-2 #4 x 21'-3	4-#4 x 21'-2 23-#4 x 19'-3	—	7	#5 x 49'-1 #4 x 32'-8	2.93
8	D = Note 2	100	16½	21	27	9	#5 x 54'-2 #5 x 21'-3	5-#5 x 21'-2 19-#5 x 19'-3	2-#3	7	#5 x 49'-1 #5 x 32'-10	3.64
9	12 + 4½	150	16½	24	36	9	#6 x 54'-2 #4 x 21'-3	6-#4 x 21'-2 31-#4 x 19'-3	2-#3	7	#5 x 49'-1 #6 x 33'-0	4.13
10		200	16½	26	45	9	#6 x 54'-2 #5 x 21'-3	6-#5 x 21'-2 23-#5 x 19'-3	4-#3	7	#6 x 49'-1 #5 x 32'-10	4.71
11		300	16½	29	63	8	#7 x 54'-2 #6 x 19'-7	5-#6 x 21'-2 20-#6 x 19'-3	4-#3	8	#6 x 49'-1 #5 x 32'-10	5.53
12	L = 34'-0	50	14½	18	24	9	#5 x 57'-5 #4 x 23'-3	7-#4 x 22'-6 28-#4 x 20'-5	—	8	#5 x 51'-11 #4 x 34'-8	3.09
13	D = 12'-5 12 + 2½	100	14½	22	35	9	#6 x 57'-5 #4 x 23'-3	7-#4 x 22'-6 32-#4 x 20'-5	2-#3	8	#5 x 51'-11 #5 x 34'-10	3.87
14	L = 34'-0	50	14½	18	26	9	#5 x 57'-5 #5 x 23'-3	6-#5 x 22'-6 19-#5 x 20'-5	2-#3	8	#5 x 51'-11 #4 x 34'-8	3.42
15	D = Note 1 10 + 4½	100	14½	22	39	8	#6 x 57'-5 #6 x 21'-7	5-#6 x 22'-6 17-#6 x 20'-5	2-#3	9	#5 x 51'-11 #5 x 34'-10	4.33
16	L = 34'-0	50	16½	18	22	9	#5 x 57'-6 #5 x 23'-3	5-#5 x 22'-6 18-#5 x 20'-5	—	8	#5 x 52'-1 #4 x 34'-8	3.25
17	D = Note 2	100	16½	22	32	9	#6 x 57'-6 #5 x 23'-3	4-#5 x 22'-6 21-#5 x 20'-5	2-#3	8	#5 x 52'-1 #5 x 34'-10	4.02
18	12 + 4½	150	16½	25	42	9	#6 x 57'-6 #5 x 23'-3	7-#5 x 22'-6 25-#5 x 20'-5	4-#3	8	#6 x 52'-1 #5 x 34'-10	4.73
19		200	16½	27	53	8	#7 x 57'-6 #6 x 21'-7	5-#6 x 22'-6 19-#6 x 20'-5	2-#3	9	#6 x 52'-1 #5 x 34'-10	5.26
20	L = 36'-0	50	14½	18	28	9	#5 x 60'-8 #5 x 25'-3	7-#5 x 23'-10 23-#5 x 21'-8	2-#3	9	#5 x 54'-11 #4 x 36'-8	3.54
21	D = Note 3 12 + 2½	100	14½	22	43	9	#6 x 60'-8 #5 x 21'-3	7-#5 x 23'-10 28-#5 x 21'-8	—	9	#5 x 54'-11 #5 x 36'-10	4.15
22	L = 36'-0	50	16½	18	26	9	#6 x 60'-10 #4 x 25'-3	5-#4 x 23'-10 30-#4 x 21'-8	2-#3	9	#5 x 55'-1 #4 x 36'-8	3.53
23	D = Note 4	100	16½	23	37	9	#6 x 60'-10 #6 x 25'-7	5-#6 x 23'-10 18-#6 x 21'-8	2-#3	9	#5 x 55'-1 #5 x 36'-10	4.41
24	12 + 4½	150	16½	25	49	10	#6 x 60'-10 #6 x 23'-7	6-#6 x 23'-10 21-#6 x 21'-8	2-#3	8	#6 x 55'-1 #6 x 37'-0	5.17
25		200	16½	28	62	9	#7 x 60'-10 #6 x 21'-7	6-#6 x 23'-10 22-#6 x 21'-8	2-#3	9	#6 x 55'-1 #6 x 37'-0	5.63
26	L = 38'-0	50	16½	19	31	10	#6 x 64'-2 #5 x 25'-3	5-#5 x 25'-1 23-#5 x 22'-10	—	9	#5 x 58'-1 #5 x 38'-10	3.90
27	D = Note 5	100	16½	23	44	10	#6 x 64'-2 #6 x 25'-7	6-#6 x 25'-1 22-#6 x 22'-10	2-#3	9	#6 x 58'-1 #5 x 38'-10	4.92
28	12 + 4½	150	16½	26	58	10	#7 x 64'-2 #6 x 21'-7	5-#6 x 25'-1 23-#6 x 22'-10	2-#3	9	#6 x 58'-1 #6 x 39'-0	5.53

Note 1: *D* = 12'-5 for 50 psf *LL*; 14'-5 for 100 psf *LL*.
Note 2: *D* = 12'-5 for 50, 100, and 150 psf *LL*; 14'-5 over 150 psf *LL*.
Note 3: *D* = 12'-5 for 50 psf *LL*; 16'-5 for 100 psf *LL*.
Note 4: *D* = 12'-5 for 50 and 100 psf *LL*; 14'-5 for 150, 16'-5 for 200.
Note 5: *D* = 14'-5 for 50 and 100 psf *LL*; 18'-5 for 150 psf *LL*.

*,**,†,‡,§ For notes, see page 9-9.

WAFFLE SLABS—SQUARE PANELS—19-IN.-WIDE DOMES

Av.‡ Cu. Ft. Conc. (psf)	Strips Perpendicular to an Exterior Wall								Wt.† of Steel (psf)	
	Column Strip					Middle Strip				
	Top Bars at Ext. Col.**	No. Jsts.	Bars Trussed Straight	Top Bars at First Int. Col.	Stir-rups per Joist*	No. Jsts.	Bars Trussed Straight	Top Bars at Ext. Support		
.707	10-#5 x 12'-1 10-#5 x 11'-2	9	#5 x 44'-10 #5 x 21'-3	9-#4 x 21'-2 32-#4 x 19'-3	—	7	#5 x 42'-4 #6 x 32'-6	2-#5 x 9'-6	3.42	1
.727	9-#6 x 12'-1 9-#6 x 11'-2	8	#6 x 44'-10 #6 x 19'-7	7-#5 x 21'-2 26-#5 x 19'-3	2-#3	8	#6 x 42'-4 #5 x 32'-5	1-#6 x 9'-6	4.33	2
.798	9-#5 x 12'-1 9-#5 x 11'-2	9	#5 x 45'-0 #5 x 21'-3	7-#4 x 21'-2 29-#4 x 19'-3	—	7	#5 x 42'-5 #6 x 32'-6	1-#5 x 9'-6	3.26	3
.798	11-#5 x 12'-1 12-#5 x 11'-2	9	#6 x 45'-0 #5 x 21'-3	8-#5 x 21'-2 21-#5 x 19'-3	2-#3	7	#6 x 42'-5 #6 x 32'-6	1-#6 x 9'-6	4.16	4
.798	9-#6 x 12'-1 9-#6 x 11'-2	9	#6 x 45'-0 #6 x 21'-7	7-#5 x 21'-2 26-#5 x 19'-3	2-#3	7	#6 x 42'-5 #7 x 32'-7	1-#6 x 9'-6	4.80	5
.822	10-#6 x 12'-1 11-#6 x 11'-2	8	#7 x 45'-0 #6 x 19'-7	8-#6 x 21'-2 20-#6 x 19'-3	2-#3	8	#6 x 42'-5 #7 x 32'-7	1-#6 x 9'-6	5.40	6
.891	9-#5 x 12'-1 9-#5 x 11'-2	9	#5 x 45'-2 #5 x 21'-3	7-#4 x 21'-2 26-#4 x 19'-3	—	7	#5 x 42'-7 #5 x 32'-5	1-#5 x 9'-6	3.11	7
.891	11-#5 x 12'-1 11-#5 x 11'-2	9	#6 x 45'-2 #5 x 21'-3	7-#5 x 21'-2 19-#5 x 19'-3	2-#3	7	#5 x 42'-7 #6 x 32'-6	2-#5 x 9'-6	3.98	8
.891	9-#6 x 12'-1 9-#6 x 11'-2	9	#6 x 45'-2 #6 x 21'-7	9-#4 x 21'-2 37-#4 x 19'-3	2-#3	7	#6 x 42'-7 #6 x 32'-6	1-#6 x 9'-6	4.49	9
.891	10-#6 x 12'-1 10-#6 x 11'-2	9	#6 x 45'-2 #6 x 21'-7	8-#5 x 21'-2 29-#5 x 19'-3	4-#3	7	#6 x 42'-7 #7 x 32'-7	2-#6 x 9'-6	5.17	10
.920	9-#7 x 12'-1 9-#7 x 11'-2	8	#7 x 45'-2 #7 x 19'-11	7-#6 x 21'-2 24-#6 x 19'-3	4-#3	8	#6 x 42'-7 #7 x 32'-7	2-#6 x 9'-6	6.02	11
.715	10-#5 x 12'-9 11-#5 x 11'-9	9	#5 x 47'-8 #5 x 23'-3	10-#4 x 22'-6 34-#4 x 20'-5	—	8	#5 x 44'-11 #5 x 34'-5	1-#5 x 10'-0	3.27	12
.715	9-#6 x 12'-9 9-#6 x 11'-9	9	#6 x 47'-8 #6 x 23'-7	10-#4 x 22'-6 39-#4 x 20'-5	2-#3	8	#6 x 44'-11 #6 x 34'-6	1-#6 x 10'-0	4.34	13
.790	11-#5 x 12'-9 11-#5 x 11'-9	9	#6 x 47'-8 #5 x 23'-3	7-#5 x 22'-6 20-#5 x 20'-5	2-#3	8	#5 x 44'-11 #6 x 34'-6	2-#5 x 10'-0	3.84	14
.812	9-#6 x 12'-9 10-#6 x 11'-9	8	#7 x 47'-8 #6 x 21'-7	6-#6 x 22'-6 18-#6 x 20'-5	2-#3	9	#5 x 44'-11 #6 x 34'-6	2-#5 x 10'-0	4.67	15
.882	10-#5 x 12'-9 11-#5 x 11'-9	9	#6 x 47'-10 #5 x 23'-3	7-#5 x 22'-6 18-#5 x 20'-5	—	8	#5 x 45'-1 #6 x 34'-6	1-#5 x 10'-0	3.61	16
.882	9-#6 x 12'-9 9-#6 x 11'-9	9	#6 x 47'-10 #6 x 23'-7	6-#5 x 22'-6 25-#5 x 20'-5	2-#3	8	#6 x 45'-1 #6 x 34'-6	1-#6 x 10'-0	4.42	17
.882	14-#5 x 12'-9 15-#5 x 11'-9	9	#7 x 47'-10 #5 x 23'-3	9-#5 x 22'-6 26-#5 x 20'-5	4-#3	8	#6 x 45'-1 #7 x 34'-7	1-#6 x 10'-0	5.15	18
.907	8-#7 x 12'-9 9-#7 x 11'-9	8	#7 x 47'-10 #7 x 21'-11	6-#6 x 22'-6 24-#6 x 20'-5	2-#3	9	#6 x 45'-1 #7 x 34'-7	1-#6 x 10'-0	5.63	19
.708	12-#5 x 13'-5 12-#5 x 12'-4	9	#6 x 50'-4 #5 x 25'-3	9-#5 x 23'-10 23-#5 x 21'-8	2-#3	9	#5 x 47'-5 #6 x 36'-6	1-#5 x 10'-6	3.87	20
.756	15-#5 x 13'-5 15-#5 x 12'-4	9	#7 x 50'-4 #5 x 21'-3	10-#5 x 23'-10 28-#5 x 21'-8	—	9	#6 x 47'-5 #6 x 36'-6	1-#6 x 10'-6	4.58	21
.874	12-#5 x 13'-5 12-#5 x 12'-4	9	#6 x 50'-5 #5 x 25'-3	8-#4 x 23'-10 36-#4 x 21'-8	2-#3	9	#5 x 47'-7 #6 x 36'-6	2-#5 x 10'-6	3.91	22
.874	14-#5 x 13'-5 15-#5 x 12'-4	9	#7 x 50'-5 #5 x 25'-3	7-#6 x 23'-10 18-#6 x 21'-8	2-#3	9	#6 x 47'-7 #6 x 36'-6	1-#6 x 10'-6	4.77	23
.897	12-#6 x 13'-5 12-#6 x 12'-4	10	#7 x 50'-5 #6 x 23'-7	8-#6 x 23'-10 22-#6 x 21'-8	2-#3	8	#7 x 47'-7 #7 x 36'-7	1-#7 x 10'-6	5.66	24
.923	10-#7 x 13'-5 10-#7 x 12'-4	9	#7 x 50'-5 #7 x 21'-11	8-#6 x 23'-10 28-#6 x 21'-8	2-#3	9	#6 x 47'-7 #7 x 36'-7	2-#6 x 10'-6	5.99	25
.888	10-#6 x 14'-1 10-#6 x 12'-11	10	#6 x 53'-1 #6 x 25'-7	7-#5 x 25'-1 28-#5 x 22'-10	—	9	#6 x 50'-1 #6 x 38'-6	1-#6 x 11'-0	4.29	26
.888	12-#6 x 14'-1 12-#6 x 12'-11	10	#7 x 53'-1 #6 x 25'-7	8-#6 x 25'-1 22-#6 x 22'-10	2-#3	9	#6 x 50'-1 #7 x 38'-7	1-#6 x 11'-0	5.30	27
.938	10-#7 x 14'-1 10-#7 x 12'-11	10	#7 x 53'-1 #7 x 21'-11	7-#6 x 25'-1 28-#6 x 22'-10	2-#3	9	#7 x 50'-1 #7 x 38'-7	1-#7 x 11'-0	5.95	28

*,**,†,‡ For notes, see page 9-9.

WAFFLE FLAT SLABS—SQUARE PANELS

limitations

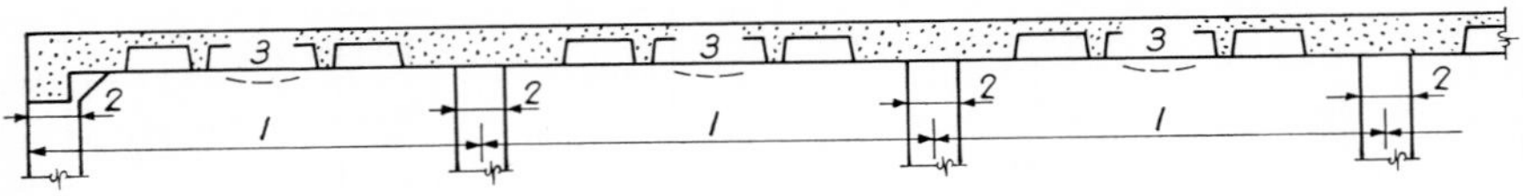

On longer spans in particular the designer must check that:—

1—There are at least three continuous spans of approximately equal length (or empirical formulas do not apply).

2—Frame action with the columns is accounted for.

3—The computed deflections are acceptable, and minimized as discussed for concrete joist construction on page 7-4.

SAFE LOAD TABLES

Beams

Section 10

REINFORCED CONCRETE BEAMS

SINGLE SPAN SIMPLY SUPPORTED

The first set of tables beginning on pages 10-8 and 10-9 gives the total safe uniform load per lineal foot (live and dead) * on rectangular and tee beams for single spans simply supported at each end, computed in conformity with the American Concrete Institute's "Building Code Requirements for Reinforced Concrete (ACI 318-63)"; for span lengths varying from 6 to 40 feet in two-foot multiples; for one set of stresses, viz. $f_s = 24{,}000$ psi and $f_c = 1688$ psi; for depths from 12 to 30 inches, in two-inch multiples, as well as 36 and 42 in.; for several stem widths (b') in each depth; with many choices of bar combination for each stem width. In all cases, the flange thickness is the distance down to the neutral axis of a rectangular beam whose breadth is equal to the flange width tabulated and which is reinforced with the scheduled bars. The depth of flange equals the depth to the neutral axis as fixed by the chosen stresses. In using these tables the tributary slab may be thinner than the depth in the table. Approximate results satisfactory for many purposes will be obtained by widening the flange (b) so that the total area outside of the beam stem is the same as that given by the flange scheduled in the tables. This is slightly on the safe side and the tee may be computed accurately, if desired, always keeping within the limitations of ACI 906.

The necessary stirrups are given in the tables. For each safe load given, there is also scheduled a mark for a stirrup combination. The make-up of these combinations starts on page 10-42. Each variation of load, span or beam size requires a different stirrup arrangement. The example on page 10-5 shows how the arrangement can be checked. For designing stirrups, see pages 4-23 and ff. For stirrup design, f_v is here taken as 20,000 psi.

Bond has been computed on the basis of deformed bars meeting ASTM. Plain bars will not afford sufficient bond to develop the values in the tables.

The safe carrying capacity in these beam tables was obtained by taking the least of the values determined by shear, bond or flexure.

One of the main advantages of reinforced concrete construction is the wide range of sizes open to the designer. Concrete beams may be wide and shallow, narrow and deep, or of more economical proportions with d equal to about two to three times b'. With deep beams, relatively little reinforcement is needed (though p must $\geqq \frac{200}{f_y} b'd$, ACI 911); while with shallow beams, a wide tee

* In the various slab tables throughout this book, the weight of the slab has been deducted so that the values given in the tables are the safe superimposed loads. In the case of beams, there is no advantage in deducting the minor weight of the beam stem, as it is the weight of the tributary slab that is the main element of dead load. So in these tables the capacity given is the total safe load, dead plus live.

REINFORCED CONCRETE BEAMS
SINGLE SPAN SIMPLY SUPPORTED

and considerably heavier reinforcement are required. Sometimes compressive steel is used when space is not available for a wide tee. It is impracticable to tabulate all possible beam sizes and steel combinations, so the following example may prove useful for those who wish to design beyond the scope of the tables or to see how they were prepared:—

Example—For the table on pages 10-10 and 10-11, determine the safe carrying capacity on a span of 20 feet of a 12 x 20 in. beam stem reinforced with 2-#10 bars in the bottom and 1-#11 bar trussed, placed in one layer; check the flange value of 6 x 18 in., and also the stirrup combination.

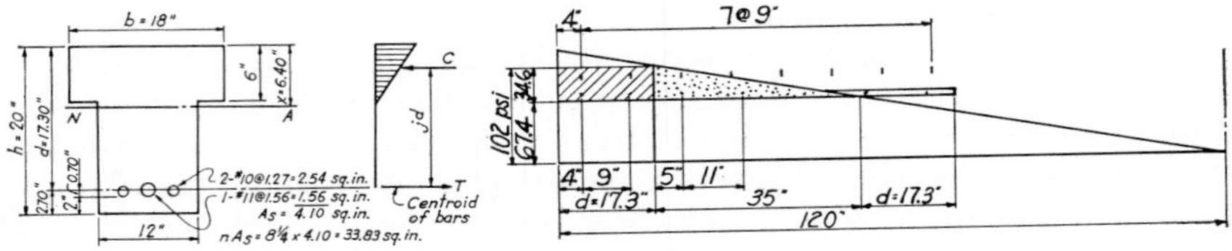

Solution—Safe load tables reverse the process of design by selecting a section and determining its safe capacity. Take this as a tee beam and assume that the neutral axis is at the bottom of the flange. The centroid of the transformed section can be located thus:—

$$\frac{18x^2}{2} - 33.8(17.30 - x) = 0$$
$$9x^2 + 33.8x = 584.74$$
$$x^2 + 3.76x + (1.88)^2 = 64.97 + 3.53 = 68.50$$
$$x = -1.88 \pm 8.28 = 6.40 \text{ in. } (0.37d)$$

Hence, if the tee were 6.40 in. deep, it would extend all the way down to the neutral axis, making this in effect a rectangular beam. The difference between 6.0 and 6.40 with the low stress near the neutral axis is too slight to make any appreciable difference in the computation.

Flexure—The arm of the internal couple $= jd = 17.30 - \dfrac{6.40}{3} = 15.17$ in.

$$M_s = A_s f_s jd = 4.10 \times 24{,}000 \times 15.17 = 1{,}493{,}000 \text{ lb in.}$$
$$M_c = bkd\frac{f_c}{2}jd = 18 \times 6.40 \times \frac{1688}{2} \times 15.17 = 1{,}475{,}000 \text{ lb in.}$$

This approximate equality of moments indicates essentially "balanced reinforcement." *

$$w = \frac{M}{l'^2\frac{12}{8}} = \frac{1{,}475{,}000\,^*}{\frac{12}{8} \times 20 \times 20} = 2461 \text{ plf (in table)}$$

Bond—On 2-#10 bottom bars:—

$$u = \frac{4.8\sqrt{f'_c}}{D} = \frac{4.8\sqrt{3750}}{1.27} = 231 \text{ psi}$$

---

* If the beam is a freestanding tee beam, then M_c is the value to use. If the beam is monolithic with a floor slab, the width of tee, b, is arbitrary and a slightly greater width might be taken, permitting the increase to $M_s = 1{,}493{,}000$ lb-in.

REINFORCED CONCRETE BEAMS
SINGLE SPAN SIMPLY SUPPORTED

$$V = \Sigma ojdu = 2 \times 3.99 \times 15.17 \times 231 = 27{,}930 \text{ lb} = \frac{wl'}{2}$$

$$w = \frac{27{,}930}{10} = 2793 \text{ plf, or more than allowed by flexure}$$

Shear—For spacing stirrups, it is not practicable to work backwards, so take the capacity from flexure, 2461 plf, and design the web reinforcement to take care of this. Shear at distance $d = 17.30$ in. $= 1.44$ ft from the face of the support is:—

$$V = w\left(\frac{l'}{2} - d\right) = 2461(10 - 1.44) = 21{,}100 \text{ lb.}$$

$$v = \frac{V}{b'd} = \frac{21{,}100}{12 \times 17.30} = 102 > v_c = 1.1\sqrt{f'_c} = 67.4 \text{ psi}$$

so stirrups are required. $< 5\sqrt{f'_c} = 306$ psi (ACI 318, Sect. 1205)

From the shear diagram on page 10-4:—

(1) Stippled volume has height $102 - 67.4 = 34.6$ psi, and a base of

$$a = \frac{34.6}{2461/(12 \times 12 \times 17.30)} = 35 \text{ in.}$$

$$A_v = \frac{12 \times 34.6 \times 35}{2 \times 20{,}000} = 0.36 \text{ sq in. 2-\#3 U-shaped stirrups} = 0.44 \text{ sq in.}$$

Spacing $= 5''$, $11''$ (19)

$$\text{Max. spacing:} \begin{cases} s = \dfrac{0.22}{0.0015 \times 12} = 12 \text{ in.} \\ \dfrac{d}{2} = \dfrac{17.30}{2} = 8.65 \text{ in. (use 9 in.)} \end{cases}$$

(2) Hatched volume requires: $A_v = \dfrac{34.6 \times 17.30 \times 12}{20{,}000} = 0.36$ sq in.

2-#3 @ 9″ = 0.44 sq in.*

(3) For distance d beyond a, the minimum is 2-#3 @ 9″

The combination of these is shown on the diagram, as 8-#3 stirrups, 4″, 7 @ 9″.

Deflection—Beam depth of 20 in. is well over minimum of $L/20 = 12$ in. (ACI 909b), so deflection should not be excessive, $p_w f_y = 1200 > 500$, so the moment of inertia of the transformed section must be used in deflection computations.

$$I = \frac{bx^3}{3} + nA_s(d - x)^2$$

$$= \frac{18\,(6.40)^3}{3} + 33.8\,(10.90)^2 = 5570 \text{ in.}^4$$

$$E = w^{1.5}\,33\sqrt{f'_c}$$

$$= (145)^{1.5} \times 33\sqrt{3750}$$

$$= 3{,}530{,}000 \text{ psi}$$

Assuming $DL = \frac{1}{2}\,LL$

$$\text{Immediate } LL \text{ deflection} = \frac{5 \times \frac{2}{3} \times 2461 \times (20)^4 \times (12)^3}{384 \times 3{,}530{,}000 \times 5570} = 0.31 \text{ in.}$$

$$\text{Max. allowable deflection} = \frac{L}{360} = \frac{20 \times 12}{360} = 0.67 \text{ in.}$$

---

* #3 is the minimum size deformed bar. It is recommended as the minimum size stirrup for general use. Even where #2 (an obsolete designation for plain ¼″ ϕ) with special anchorage would satisfy design requirements, overall economy will usually be achieved by use of #3 stirrups.

REINFORCED CONCRETE BEAMS
SINGLE SPAN SIMPLY SUPPORTED

Applies to the tables on pages 10-8 to 10-17 incl.

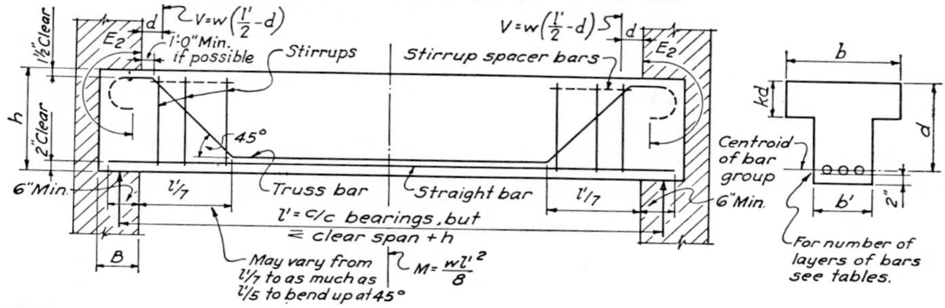

STRESSES:—

$f_s = 24{,}000$ psi

$f'_c = 3750$ psi

$f_c = 1688$ psi

$v_c = 1.1\sqrt{f'_c} = 67.4$ psi

$v = 5\sqrt{f'_c} = 306$ psi

$u = \dfrac{4.8\sqrt{f'_c}}{D} = \dfrac{294}{D}$ psi for bottom bars

$= \dfrac{3.4\sqrt{f'_c}}{D} = \dfrac{208}{D}$ psi for top bars with over 12" of concrete under them

CODES:—

"Building Code Requirements for Reinforced Concrete (ACI 318-63)," also "Manual of Standard Practice for Detailing Reinforced Concrete Structures (ACI 315)."

E_1 = 6 in. minimum for bottom bars

E_2 = 6 in. for #3 bars, 10 in. for #4 bars; $21D^2$ for #5 and larger ($29D^2$ for #5 and larger when $d > 12$ in.) (obtained by straight embedment if possible, hooked if necessary).

B = ordinarily 8" minimum but sufficient in any case to keep the bearing pressure on the wall within the allowable for the material of which the wall is made (see page 5-6).

For stirrup combinations, see pages 10-42 to 10-58, incl.

Bending truss bar at l'/7 from the support must leave sufficient straight bottom bar as required for anchorage bond, viz., 20.5 D^2 for bar sizes #5 through #11.

REINFORCED CONCRETE BEAMS—SINGLE SPAN

For limitations and explanation of use of this table, see pages 10-3 to 10-7.

	Stem		Flange		Bar Combinations					TOTAL SAFE CARRYING CAPACITY* (plf)—UNIFORMLY DISTRIBUTED							
										Span l′ in Feet							
					Straight		Trussed			6		8		10		12	
	h (in.)	b′ (in.)	t (in.)	b (in.)	No.	Size	No.	Size	No. Layers	Stirrup Mark	Safe Load	Stirrup Mark	Safe Load	Stirrup Mark	Safe Load	Stirrup Mark	Safe Load
1		6	—	6	2	#4	—	—	1	—	1569	—	882	—	565	—	392
2		8	—	8	2	#4	1	#5	1	A001	2741	—	1542	—	986	—	685
3			3.5	9	2	#5	1	#6	1	A002	4008	A003	2254	A004	1442	—	1002
4		10	3.5	12	2	#6	2	#5	1	A005	5214	A006	3162	A007	2023	A008	1405
5	12		3.5	17	2	#7	2	#6	1	A009	5185	A010	3889	A011	2803	A012	1946
6			3.5	21	2	#8	1	#9	1	A016	5080	A017	3840	A018	3072	A019	2371
7			3.4	25	2	#9	1	#9	1	A024	5030	A025	3820	A026	3062	A027	2552
8			3.1	33	2	#9	2	#8	2	A032	4499	A033	3408	A034	2753	A035	2305
9			3.2	37	3	#8	3	#7	2	A040	6823	A041	5164	A042	4169	A043	3433
10			3.2	41	3	#9	2	#8	2	A048	6859	A049	5186	A050	4183	A051	3514
11		8	—	8	2	#4	—	—	1	—	1927	—	1084	—	693	—	481
12			—	8	2	#4	1	#5	1	A056	3334	—	1875	—	1200	—	833
13			—	8	2	#5	1	#6	1	A057	4855	A058	2731	A059	1748	—	1213
14		10	—	10	2	#6	2	#5	1	A060	6297	A061	3832	A062	2453	A063	1703
15			4.2	14	2	#7	2	#6	1	A064	6265	A065	4699	A066	3387	A067	2352
16	14	12	4.2	17	3	#6	2	#7	1	A071	9404	A072	6416	A073	4106	A074	2851
17			4.2	20	2	#9	1	#9	1	A078	6142	A079	4631	A080	3705	A081	3087
18			4.2	24	2	#9	2	#8	1	A087	6110	A088	4645	A089	3716	A090	3096
19			4.2	27	2	#9	2	#9	1	A096	6068	A097	4607	A098	3708	A099	3090
20			3.9	33	3	#9	2	#8	2	A105	8485	A106	6426	A107	5191	A108	4346
21			3.9	37	3	#9	2	#9	2	A114	8341	A115	6314	A116	5098	A117	4287
22			3.8	46	3	#9	2	#11	2	A123	8051	A124	6083	A125	4903	A126	4116
23		8	—	8	2	#5	—	—	1	—	3442	—	1936	—	1239	—	860
24			—	8	2	#5	1	#6	1	A132	5734	A133	3225	A134	2064	—	1433
25		10	—	10	2	#6	2	#5	1	A135	7439	A136	4532	A137	2900	A138	2014
26			5.0	12	2	#7	2	#6	1	A139	7349	A140	5511	A141	3972	A142	2758
27	16	12	5.0	14	3	#6	2	#7	1	A146	11005	A147	7375	A148	4720	A149	3277
28			5.0	17	2	#9	1	#9	1	A153	7255	A154	5441	A155	4353	A156	3627
29			4.9	21	2	#9	2	#8	1	A162	7229	A163	5463	A164	4371	A165	3642
30			4.9	24	2	#10	1	#11	1	A173	7113	A174	5409	A175	4327	A176	3606
31			4.7	28	3	#9	2	#8	2	A184	10113	A185	7677	A186	6190	A187	5159
32			4.6	31	3	#9	2	#9	2	A195	9976	A196	7562	A197	6113	A198	5103
33			4.5	39	3	#9	2	#11	2	A206	9668	A207	7313	A208	5901	A209	4959
34			4.5	44	3	#10	2	#11	2	A217	9667	A218	7305	A219	5888	A220	4943

* Deduct dead load from these values.

Where dash occurs in stirrup column no stirrups are required.

REINFORCED CONCRETE BEAMS—SINGLE SPAN

For stirrup combinations, see pages 10-42 to 10-58, incl.

TOTAL SAFE CARRYING CAPACITY * (plf)—
UNIFORMLY DISTRIBUTED

Span l' in Feet

14		16		18		20		22		24		26		
Stir-rup Mark	Safe Load	Stir-rup Mark	Safe Load	Stir-rup Mark	Safe Load	Stir-rup Mark	Safe Load	Stir-rup Mark	Safe Load	Stir-rup Mark	Safe Load	Stir-rup Mark	Safe Load	
—	288	—	220	—	174	—	141							1
—	503	—	385	—	304	—	246							2
—	736	—	563	—	445	—	360							3
—	1032	—	790	—	624	—	505							4
A013	1430	A014	1095	A015	865	—	700							5
A020	1742	A021	1334	A022	1054	A023	853							6
A028	2030	A029	1554	A030	1228	A031	994							7
A036	1976	A037	1675	A038	1324	A039	1072							8
A044	2569	A045	1967	A046	1554	A047	1259							9
A052	2864	A053	2193	A054	1732	A055	1403							10
—	354	—	271	—	214	—	173	—	143					11
—	612	—	468	—	370	—	300	—	248					12
—	891	—	682	—	539	—	437	—	361					13
—	1251	--	958	—	757	—	613	—	506					14
A068	1728	A069	1323	A070	1045	—	846	—	699					15
A075	2095	A076	1604	A077	1267	—	1026	—	848					16
A082	2426	A083	1857	A084	1468	A085	1189	A086	982					17
A091	2654	A092	2234	A093	1765	A094	1430	A095	1181					18
A100	2648	A101	2317	A102	1973	A103	1598	A104	1321					19
A109	3505	A110	2683	A111	2120	A112	1717	A113	1419					20
A118	3680	A119	2905	A120	2295	A121	1859	A122	1536					21
A127	3554	A128	3124	A129	2715	A130	2199	A131	1818					22
—	632	—	484	—	382	—	309	—	256	—	215	—	183	23
—	1053	—	806	—	637	—	516	—	426	—	358	—	305	24
—	1479	—	1133	—	895	—	725	—	599	—	503	—	429	25
A143	2026	A144	1551	A145	1226	—	993	—	820	—	689	—	587	26
A150	2408	A151	1843	A152	1456	—	1180	—	975	—	819	—	698	27
A157	2848	A158	2180	A159	1723	A160	1395	A161	1153	—	969	—	825	28
A166	3122	A167	2647	A168	2091	A169	1694	A170	1400	A171	1176	A172	1002	29
A177	3090	A178	2704	A179	2371	A180	1921	A181	1587	A182	1334	A183	1136	30
A188	4177	A189	3198	A190	2527	A191	2046	A192	1691	A193	1421	A194	1211	31
A199	4374	A200	3453	A201	2729	A202	2210	A203	1826	A204	1535	A205	1307	32
A210	4268	A211	3735	A212	3259	A213	2640	A214	2182	A215	1833	A216	1562	33
A221	4269	A222	3744	A223	3328	A224	2995	A225	2477	A226	2081	A227	1773	34

$d = h - (2'' +$ distance from bottom of bars to their centroid).

REINFORCED CONCRETE BEAMS—SINGLE SPAN

For limitations and explanation of use of this table, see pages 10-3 to 10-7.

	Stem		Flange		Bar Combinations					TOTAL SAFE CARRYING CAPACITY* (plf)— UNIFORMLY DISTRIBUTED; Span l' in feet							
					Straight		Trussed			14		16		18		20	
	h (in.)	b′ (in.)	t (in.)	b (in.)	No.	Size	No.	Size	No. Layers	Stirrup Mark	Safe Load	Stirrup Mark	Safe Load	Stirrup Mark	Safe Load	Stirrup Mark	Safe Load
1		8	—	8	2	#5	–	—	1	—	728	—	557	—	440	—	357
2			—	8	2	#5	1	#6	1	—	1215	—	930	—	735	—	595
3		10	—	10	2	#6	2	#5	1	—	1708	—	1308	—	1033	—	837
4			—	10	2	#7	2	#6	1	A228	2267	A229	1736	A230	1371	—	1111
5	18	12	—	12	2	#7	2	#6	1	A231	2342	—	1793	—	1416	—	1147
6			5.6	13	3	#6	2	#7	1	A232	2822	A233	2160	A234	1707	—	1382
7			5.7	15	2	#9	1	#9	1	A235	3302	A236	2528	A237	1997	A238	1618
8			5.7	18	2	#9	2	#8	1	A240	3582	A241	3037	A242	2400	A243	1944
9			5.6	21	2	#10	1	#11	1	A248	3555	A249	3111	A250	2728	A251	2210
10			5.3	27	3	#9	2	#9	2	A257	5072	A258	4004	A259	3164	A260	2563
11			5.2	33	3	#9	2	#11	2	A266	4959	A267	4339	A268	3763	A269	3048
12		8	—	8	2	#5	—	—	1	—	825	—	631	—	499	—	404
13			—	8	2	#5	1	#6	1	—	1378	—	1055	—	833	—	675
14		10	—	10	2	#6	2	#5	1	—	1937	—	1483	—	1172	—	949
15			—	10	2	#7	2	#6	1	A284	2634	A285	2016	A286	1593	—	1290
16	20	12	—	12	3	#6	2	#7	1	A287	3190	A288	2443	A289	1930	—	1563
17			6.4	13	2	#9	1	#9	1	A290	3677	A291	2815	A292	2224	A293	1802
18			6.4	16	2	#9	2	#8	1	A295	4047	A296	3431	A297	2711	A298	2196
19			6.4	18	2	#10	1	#11	1	A302	4012	A303	3510	A304	3038	A305	2461
20			6.1	23	3	#9	2	#9	2	A311	5757	A312	4492	A313	3549	A314	2875
21			6.0	29	3	#9	2	#11	2	A321	5655	A322	4948	A323	4296	A324	3480
22			6.0	33	3	#10	2	#11	2	A331	5668	A332	4959	A333	4408	A334	3966
23			5.9	41	3	#11	3	#10	2	A341	5648	A342	4942	A343	4393	A344	3953
24		8	—	8	2	#5	1	#6	1	—	1541	—	1180	—	932	—	755
25			—	8	2	#6	2	#5	2	A361	2062	—	1579	—	1247	—	1010
26		10	—	10	2	#7	2	#6	1	A362	2950	A363	2258	—	1784	—	1445
27		12	—	12	3	#6	2	#7	1	A364	3573	A365	2735	A366	2161	—	1751
28			—	12	2	#9	1	#9	1	A367	4178	A368	3199	A369	2527	A370	2047
29	22		7.2	14	2	#9	2	#8	1	A372	4504	A373	3769	A374	2978	A375	2412
30			7.2	16	2	#10	1	#11	1	A379	4473	A380	3913	A381	3369	A382	2729
31		14	7.1	20	3	#9	2	#9	1	A388	6754	A389	5331	A390	4212	A391	3412
32			6.7	26	3	#9	2	#11	2	A398	6352	A399	5558	A400	4845	A401	3925
33			6.7	29	3	#10	2	#11	2	A409	6358	A410	5563	A411	4945	A412	4413
34			6.8	34	4	#10	3	#9	2	A420	8596	A421	7521	A422	6500	A423	5265
35			6.8	38	4	#10	4	#9	2	A431	8519	A432	7454	A433	6626	A434	5827

* Deduct dead load from these values.

Where dash occurs in stirrup column, no stirrups are required.

REINFORCED CONCRETE BEAMS—SINGLE SPAN

For stirrup combinations, see pages 10-42 to 10-58, incl.

TOTAL SAFE CARRYING CAPACITY * (plf)—
UNIFORMLY DISTRIBUTED

Span l' in Feet

22		24		26		28		30		32		34		
Stir-rup Mark	Safe Load	Stir-rup Mark	Safe Load	Stir-rup Mark	Safe Load	Stir-rup Mark	Safe Load	Stir-rup Mark	Safe Load	Stir-rup Mark	Safe Load	Stir-rup Mark	Safe Load	
—	295	—	247	—	211	—	182	—	158					1
—	492	—	413	—	352	—	303	—	264					2
—	691	—	581	—	495	—	427	—	372					3
—	918	—	771	—	657	—	566	—	493					4
—	948	—	796	—	679	—	585	—	510					5
—	1142	—	960	—	818	—	705	—	614					6
A239	1337	—	1123	—	957	—	825	—	719					7
A244	1606	A245	1350	A246	1150	A247	991	—	864					8
A252	1826	A253	1534	A254	1307	A255	1127	A256	982					9
A261	2118	A262	1779	A263	1516	A264	1307	A265	1139					10
A270	2519	A271	2117	A272	1804	A273	1555	A274	1355					11
—	334	—	280	—	239	—	206	—	179	—	157			12
—	558	—	468	—	399	—	344	—	300	—	263			13
—	784	—	659	—	561	—	484	—	422	—	370			14
—	1066	—	896	—	763	—	658	—	573	—	504			15
—	1292	—	1085	—	925	—	797	—	694	—	610			16
A294	1489	—	1251	—	1066	—	919	—	800	—	703			17
A299	1815	A300	1525	A301	1299	—	1120	—	976	—	857			18
A306	2034	A307	1709	A308	1456	A309	1255	A310	1093	—	961			19
A315	2376	A316	1996	A317	1701	A318	1467	A319	1277	A320	1123			20
A325	2876	A326	2416	A327	2059	A328	1775	A329	1546	A330	1359			21
A335	3278	A336	2754	A337	2347	A338	2023	A339	1763	A340	1549			22
A345	3594	A346	3294	A347	2867	A348	2472	A349	2153	A350	1893			23
—	624	—	524	—	446	—	385	—	335	—	295	—	261	24
—	835	—	701	—	598	—	515	—	449	—	394	—	349	25
—	1194	—	1003	—	855	—	737	—	642	—	564	—	500	26
—	1447	—	1215	—	1036	—	893	—	778	—	683	—	605	27
A371	1692	—	1421	—	1211	—	1044	—	909	—	799	—	708	28
A376	1993	A377	1675	A378	1427	—	1230	—	1072	—	942	—	834	29
A383	2255	A384	1895	A385	1615	A386	1392	A387	1213	—	1066	—	944	30
A392	2820	A393	2369	A394	2019	A395	1740	A396	1516	A397	1332	—	1180	31
A402	3243	A403	2725	A404	2322	A405	2002	A406	1744	A407	1533	A408	1358	32
A413	3647	A414	3064	A415	2611	A416	2251	A417	1961	A418	1723	A419	1527	33
A424	4351	A425	3656	A426	3115	A427	2686	A428	2340	A429	2056	A430	1821	34
A435	4815	A436	4046	A437	3448	A438	2973	A439	2589	A440	2276	A441	2016	35

$d = h - (2'' +$ distance from bottom of bars to their centroid).

REINFORCED CONCRETE BEAMS—SINGLE SPAN

For limitations and explanation of use of this table, see pages 10-3 to 10-7.

	Stem		Flange		Bar Combinations					TOTAL SAFE CARRYING CAPACITY* (plf)—UNIFORMLY DISTRIBUTED; Span l' in Feet							
					Straight		Trussed			20		22		24		26	
	h (in.)	b′ (in.)	t (in.)	b (in.)	No.	Size	No.	Size	No. Layers	Stirrup Mark	Safe Load	Stirrup Mark	Safe Load	Stirrup Mark	Safe Load	Stirrup Mark	Safe Load
1		10	—	10	2	#5	1	#6	1	—	843	—	696	—	585	—	498
2			—	10	2	#6	2	#5	1	—	1175	—	971	—	816	—	695
3			—	10	2	#7	2	#6	1	—	1600	—	1323	—	1111	—	947
4		12	—	12	3	#6	2	#7	1	—	1939	—	1602	—	1346	—	1147
5			—	12	2	#9	1	#9	1	A453	2270	—	1876	—	1576	—	1343
6			7.8	13	2	#9	2	#8	1	A454	2699	A455	2230	A456	1874	A457	1597
7			7.8	15	2	#10	1	#11	1	A458	3073	A459	2540	A460	2134	A461	1818
8	24		7.6	17	3	#9	2	#8	2	A464	3309	A465	2734	A466	2298	A467	1958
9		14	7.8	17	3	#9	2	#8	1	A472	3456	A473	2856	A474	2400	A475	2045
10			7.9	18	3	#9	2	#9	1	A478	3744	A479	3094	A480	2600	A481	2215
11			7.5	23	3	#9	2	#11	2	A485	4300	A486	3554	A487	2986	A488	2544
12			7.4	27	3	#10	2	#11	2	A496	4945	A497	4089	A498	3436	A499	2928
13			7.5	31	4	#10	3	#9	2	A507	5835	A508	4823	A509	4052	A510	3453
14			7.4	35	4	#10	4	#9	2	A518	6508	A519	5379	A520	4519	A521	3851
15		16	7.4	35	4	#10	4	#9	2	A529	6508	A530	5379	A531	4519	A532	3851
16			7.5	39	4	#11	4	#9	2	A540	6619	A541	6017	A542	5095	A543	4341
17			7.4	43	4	#11	4	#10	2	A551	6562	A552	5966	A553	5469	A554	4727
18		10	—	10	2	#5	1	#6	1	—	924	—	763	—	641	—	546
19			—	10	2	#6	2	#5	1	—	1289	—	1065	—	895	—	762
20			—	10	2	#7	2	#6	1	—	1756	—	1451	—	1219	—	1039
21		12	—	12	3	#6	2	#7	1	—	2127	—	1758	—	1477	—	1259
22			—	12	2	#9	1	#9	1	A562	2493	—	2060	—	1731	—	1475
23			—	12	2	#9	2	#8	1	A563	2952	A564	2439	A565	2050	A566	1746
24			8.5	14	2	#10	1	#11	1	A567	3365	A568	2781	A569	2337	A570	1991
25			8.2	16	3	#9	2	#8	2	A573	3659	A574	3024	A575	2541	A576	2165
26	26	14	8.6	15	3	#9	2	#8	1	A581	3742	A582	3093	A583	2599	A584	2214
27			8.5	17	3	#9	2	#9	1	A586	4121	A587	3405	A588	2861	A589	2438
28			8.2	21	3	#9	2	#11	2	A593	4734	A594	3912	A595	3287	A596	2801
29			8.2	24	3	#10	2	#11	2	A604	5407	A605	4468	A606	3754	A607	3199
30			8.2	28	4	#10	3	#9	2	A615	6400	A616	5289	A617	4445	A618	3787
31			8.1	32	4	#10	4	#9	2	A626	7148	A627	5907	A628	4964	A629	4229
32		16	8.1	32	4	#10	4	#9	2	A637	7148	A638	5907	A639	4964	A640	4229
33			8.2	36	4	#11	4	#9	2	A648	7273	A649	6612	A650	5600	A651	4772
34			8.1	40	4	#11	4	#10	2	A659	7219	A660	6563	A661	6016	A662	5236

* Deduct dead load from these values.

Where dash occurs in stirrup column, no stirrups are required.

REINFORCED CONCRETE BEAMS—SINGLE SPAN

For stirrup combinations, see pages 10-42 to 10-58, incl.

TOTAL SAFE CARRYING CAPACITY * (plf)—
UNIFORMLY DISTRIBUTED

Span l' in Feet

28		30		32		34		36		38		40		
Stir-rup Mark	Safe Load	Stir-rup Mark	Safe Load	Stir-rup Mark	Safe Load	Stir-rup Mark	Safe Load	Stir-rup Mark	Safe Load	Stir-rup Mark	Safe Load	Stir-rup Mark	Safe Load	
—	430	—	374	—	329	—	291	—	260	—	233	—	210	1
—	599	—	522	—	459	—	406	—	362	—	325	—	293	2
—	816	—	711	—	625	—	553	—	494	—	443	—	400	3
—	989	—	861	—	757	—	670	—	598	—	537	—	484	4
—	1158	—	1009	—	886	—	785	—	700	—	628	—	567	5
—	1377	—	1199	—	1054	—	934	—	833	—	747	—	674	6
A462	1568	A463	1366	—	1200	—	1063	—	948	—	851	—	768	7
A468	1688	A469	1470	A470	1292	A471	1145	—	1021	—	916	—	827	8
A476	1763	A477	1536	—	1350	—	1195	—	1066	—	957	—	864	9
A482	1910	A483	1664	A484	1462	—	1295	—	1155	—	1037	—	936	10
A489	2194	A490	1911	A491	1679	A492	1488	A493	1327	A494	1191	A495	1075	11
A500	2524	A501	2199	A502	1933	A503	1712	A504	1527	A505	1370	A506	1237	12
A511	2977	A512	2593	A513	2279	A514	2019	A515	1801	A516	1616	A517	1458	13
A522	3320	A523	2892	A524	2542	A525	2252	A526	2008	A527	1802	A528	1627	14
A533	3320	A534	2892	A535	2542	A536	2252	A537	2008	A538	1802	A539	1627	15
A544	3743	A545	3260	A546	2866	A547	2538	A548	2264	A549	2032	A550	1834	16
A555	4075	A556	3550	A557	3120	A558	2764	A559	2465	A560	2212	A561	1997	17
—	471	—	410	—	360	—	319	—	285	—	255	—	231	18
—	657	—	572	—	503	—	446	—	397	—	357	—	322	19
—	896	—	780	—	686	—	607	—	542	—	486	—	439	20
—	1085	—	945	—	831	—	736	—	656	—	589	—	531	21
—	1272	—	1108	—	974	—	862	—	769	—	690	—	623	22
—	1506	—	1312	—	1153	—	1021	—	911	—	817	—	738	23
A571	1716	A572	1495	—	1314	—	1164	—	1038	—	932	—	841	24
A577	1867	A578	1626	A579	1429	A580	1266	—	1129	—	1013	—	914	25
A585	1909	—	1663	—	1462	—	1295	—	1155	—	1036	—	935	26
A590	2102	A591	1831	A592	1609	—	1426	—	1271	—	1141	—	1030	27
A597	2415	A598	2104	A599	1849	A600	1638	A601	1461	A602	1311	A603	1183	28
A608	2758	A609	2403	A610	2112	A611	1870	A612	1668	A613	1497	A614	1351	29
A619	3265	A620	2844	A621	2500	A622	2214	A623	1975	A624	1773	A625	1600	30
A630	3647	A631	3177	A632	2792	A633	2473	A634	2206	A635	1980	A636	1787	31
A641	3647	A642	3177	A643	2792	A644	2473	A645	2206	A646	1980	A647	1787	32
A652	4114	A653	3584	A654	3150	A655	2790	A656	2489	A657	2234	A658	2016	33
A663	4515	A664	3933	A665	3456	A666	3062	A667	2731	A668	2451	A669	2212	34

$d = h - (2'' +$ distance from bottom of bars to their centroid).

REINFORCED CONCRETE BEAMS—SINGLE SPAN

For limitations and explanation of use of this table, see pages 10-3 to 10-7.

	Stem		Flange		Bar Combinations					TOTAL SAFE CARRYING CAPACITY * (plf)— UNIFORMLY DISTRIBUTED, Span l' in Feet							
					Straight		Trussed		No. Layers	20		22		24		26	
	h (in.)	b′ (in.)	t (in.)	b (in.)	No.	Size	No.	Size		Stirrup Mark	Safe Load	Stirrup Mark	Safe Load	Stirrup Mark	Safe Load	Stirrup Mark	Safe Load
1		12	—	12	2	#6	1	#5	1	—	1130	—	934	—	784	—	668
2			—	12	2	#6	2	#5	1	—	1413	—	1167	—	981	—	836
3			—	12	2	#7	2	#6	1	—	1928	—	1593	—	1339	—	1141
4			—	12	3	#6	2	#7	1	—	2317	—	1914	—	1609	—	1371
5			—	12	2	#9	1	#9	1	A670	2717	—	2246	—	1887	—	1608
6			—	12	2	#9	2	#8	1	A671	3217	A672	2659	A673	2234	A674	1904
7			9.2	13	2	#10	1	#11	1	A675	3655	A676	3020	A677	2538	A678	2162
8	28	14	—	14	3	#9	2	#8	1	A681	4095	A682	3384	A683	2844	A684	2423
9			9.4	15	3	#9	2	#9	1	A686	4410	A687	3645	A688	3062	A689	2609
10			8.8	20	3	#9	2	#11	2	A692	5224	A693	4317	A694	3628	A695	3091
11			8.9	22	3	#10	2	#11	2	A703	5887	A704	4865	A705	4088	A706	3483
12			8.9	26	4	#10	3	#9	2	A714	6972	A715	5762	A716	4842	A717	4125
13		16	8.9	29	4	#10	4	#9	2	A725	7781	A726	6430	A727	5403	A728	4604
14			8.9	33	4	#11	4	#9	2	A736	7922	A737	7202	A738	6100	A739	5197
15			8.9	36	4	#11	4	#10	2	A747	7860	A748	7146	A749	6550	A750	5671
16			8.8	40	4	#11	4	#11	2	A758	7811	A759	7100	A760	6509	A761	6008
17		18	8.9	45	5	#11	5	#10	2	A769	9825	A770	8932	A771	8188	A772	7088
18			8.8	50	5	#11	5	#11	2	A780	9763	A781	8876	A782	8136	A783	7510
19		12	—	12	2	#6	1	#5	1	—	1221	—	1009	—	848	—	722
20			—	12	2	#6	2	#5	1	—	1527	—	1262	—	1060	—	903
21			—	12	2	#7	2	#6	1	—	2086	—	1724	—	1448	—	1234
22			—	12	3	#6	2	#7	1	—	2506	—	2071	—	1740	—	1483
23			—	12	2	#9	1	#9	1	A791	2942	—	2431	—	2043	—	1740
24			—	12	2	#9	2	#8	1	A792	3484	A793	2879	A794	2419	—	2061
25			—	12	2	#10	1	#11	1	A795	3942	A796	3258	A797	2738	A798	2333
26		14	—	14	3	#9	2	#8	1	A801	4435	A802	3665	A803	3079	A804	2624
27			—	14	3	#9	2	#9	1	A806	4778	A807	3949	A808	3318	A809	2827
28	30		9.6	18	3	#9	2	#11	2	A812	5625	A813	4649	A814	3906	A815	3328
29			9.7	20	3	#10	2	#11	2	A823	6302	A824	5208	A825	4376	A826	3729
30			9.7	24	4	#10	3	#9	2	A834	7540	A835	6231	A836	5236	A837	4461
31		16	9.6	27	4	#10	4	#9	2	A845	8422	A846	6960	A847	5848	A848	4983
32			9.7	30	4	#11	4	#9	2	A856	8563	A857	7785	A858	6572	A859	5600
33			9.5	34	4	#11	4	#10	2	A867	8519	A868	7744	A869	7099	A870	6179
34			9.6	37	4	#11	4	#11	2	A878	8460	A879	7691	A880	7050	A881	6507
35		18	9.6	42	5	#11	5	#10	2	A889	10642	A890	9674	A891	8868	A892	7718
36			9.5	47	5	#11	5	#11	2	A900	10584	A901	9622	A902	8820	A903	8142

* Deduct dead load from these values.

Where dash occurs in stirrup column, no stirrups are required.

REINFORCED CONCRETE BEAMS—SINGLE SPAN

For stirrup combinations, see pages 10-42 to 10-58, incl.

TOTAL SAFE CARRYING CAPACITY* (plf)—
UNIFORMLY DISTRIBUTED

Span l' in Feet

28		30		32		34		36		38		40		
Stir-rup Mark	Safe Load	Stir-rup Mark	Safe Load	Stir-rup Mark	Safe Load	Stir-rup Mark	Safe Load	Stir-rup Mark	Safe Load	Stir-rup Mark	Safe Load	Stir-rup Mark	Safe Load	
—	576	—	502	—	441	—	391	—	348	—	313	—	282	1
—	720	—	628	—	551	—	488	—	436	—	391	—	353	2
—	983	—	857	—	753	—	667	—	595	—	534	—	482	3
—	1182	—	1029	—	905	—	801	—	715	—	641	—	579	4
—	1386	—	1207	—	1061	—	940	—	838	—	752	—	679	5
—	1641	—	1430	—	1256	—	1113	—	993	—	891	—	804	6
A679	1864	A680	1624	—	1427	—	1264	—	1128	—	1012	—	913	7
A685	2089	—	1820	—	1599	—	1417	—	1264	—	1134	—	1023	8
A690	2250	A691	1960	—	1722	—	1526	—	1361	—	1221	—	1102	9
A696	2665	A697	2322	A698	2040	A699	1807	A700	1612	A701	1447	A702	1306	10
A707	3003	A708	2616	A709	2299	A710	2037	A711	1817	A712	1630	A713	1471	11
A718	3557	A719	3098	A720	2723	A721	2412	A722	2152	A723	1931	A724	1743	12
A729	3970	A730	3458	A731	3039	A732	2692	A733	2401	A734	2155	A735	1945	13
A740	4481	A741	3904	A742	3431	A743	3039	A744	2711	A745	2433	A746	2196	14
A751	4889	A752	4259	A753	3743	A754	3316	A755	2958	A756	2654	A757	2396	15
A762	5361	A763	4670	A764	4104	A765	3636	A766	3243	A767	2910	A768	2627	16
A773	6112	A774	5324	A775	4679	A776	4145	A777	3697	A778	3318	A779	2995	17
A784	6701	A785	5837	A786	5131	A787	4545	A788	4054	A789	3638	A790	3283	18
—	623	—	542	—	477	—	422	—	376	—	338	—	305	19
—	779	—	678	—	596	—	528	—	471	—	423	—	381	20
—	1064	—	927	—	814	—	721	—	643	—	577	—	521	21
—	1278	—	1114	—	979	—	867	—	773	—	694	—	626	22
—	1501	—	1307	—	1149	—	1018	—	908	—	815	—	735	23
—	1777	—	1548	—	1360	—	1205	—	1075	—	965	—	871	24
A799	2011	A800	1752	—	1540	—	1364	—	1216	—	1092	—	985	25
A805	2262	—	1971	—	1732	—	1534	—	1368	—	1228	—	1108	26
A810	2438	A811	2123	—	1866	—	1653	—	1474	—	1323	—	1194	27
A816	2870	A817	2500	A818	2197	A819	1946	A820	1736	A821	1558	A822	1406	28
A827	3215	A828	2801	A829	2462	A830	2180	A831	1945	A832	1745	A833	1575	29
A838	3846	A839	3351	A840	2945	A841	2609	A842	2327	A843	2088	A844	1885	30
A849	4297	A850	3743	A851	3290	A852	2914	A853	2599	A854	2333	A855	2105	31
A860	4829	A861	4206	A862	3697	A863	3275	A864	2921	A865	2621	A866	2366	32
A871	5327	A872	4641	A873	4079	A874	3613	A875	3223	A876	2892	A877	2610	33
A882	5813	A883	5064	A884	4450	A885	3942	A886	3516	A887	3156	A888	2848	34
A893	6655	A894	5797	A895	5095	A896	4513	A897	4026	A898	3613	A899	3261	35
A904	7297	A905	6357	A906	5587	A907	4949	A908	4414	A909	3962	A910	3575	36

$d = h - (2'' +$ distance from bottom of bars to their centroid).

REINFORCED CONCRETE BEAMS—SINGLE SPAN

For limitations and explanation of use of this table, see pages 10-3 to 10-7.

	Stem		Flange		Bar Combinations					TOTAL SAFE CARRYING CAPACITY* (plf)— UNIFORMLY DISTRIBUTED — Span l' in Feet							
					Straight		Trussed			24		26		28		30	
	h (in.)	b′ (in.)	t (in.)	b (in.)	No.	Size	No.	Size	No. Layers	Stirrup Mark	Safe Load	Stirrup Mark	Safe Load	Stirrup Mark	Safe Load	Stirrup Mark	Safe Load
1		12	—	12	2	#8	2	#8	1	—	2646	—	2254	—	1944	—	1693
2			—	12	2	#9	2	#9	1	D001	3305	D002	2816	D003	2428	—	2115
3		16	—	16	3	#8	3	#9	1	D004	4440	D005	3783	D006	3262	—	2841
4			—	16	3	#9	2	#11	1	D007	5010	D008	4269	D009	3681	D010	3206
5			—	16	3	#10	2	#11	1	D012	5594	D013	4767	D014	4110	D015	3580
6			11.8	19	4	#9	3	#10	2	D020	6169	D021	5256	D022	4532	D023	3948
7	36†	20	12.0	21	5	#9	5	#8	2	D031	7011	D032	5973	D033	5150	D034	4487
8			11.9	24	5	#9	4	#10	2	D039	7893	D040	6725	D041	5799	D042	5051
9			11.8	27	5	#10	3	#11	2	D050	8718	D051	7428	D052	6405	D053	5579
10			11.8	30	5	#10	4	#11	2	D061	9801	D062	8351	D063	7201	D064	6273
11			11.9	33	6	#10	4	#11	2	D072	10844	D073	9239	D074	7967	D075	6940
12		24	11.8	41	6	#11	6	#10	2	D083	13074	D084	11379	D085	9812	D086	8547
13			11.8	45	6	#11	6	#11	2	D094	13005	D095	12005	D096	10706	D097	9326
14			11.7	53	7	#11	7	#11	2	D105	15180	D106	14013	D107	12560	D108	10941
15		12	—	12	2	#8	2	#8	1	—	3143	—	2678	—	2309	—	2011
16			—	12	2	#9	2	#9	1	D116	3929	D117	3348	—	2887	—	2515
17		16	—	16	3	#8	3	#9	1	D118	5278	D119	4497	—	3877	—	3377
18			—	16	3	#9	2	#11	1	D120	5961	D121	5079	D122	4379	D123	3815
19			—	16	3	#10	2	#11	1	D125	6703	D126	5711	D127	4924	D128	4289
20			—	16	4	#9	3	#10	2	D132	7312	D133	6230	D134	5372	D135	4679
21	42†	20	—	20	5	#9	5	#8	2	D142	8455	D143	7204	D144	6212	D145	5411
22			—	20	5	#9	4	#10	2	D150	9283	D151	7909	D152	6820	D153	5941
23			14.1	22	5	#10	3	#11	2	D161	10213	D162	8702	D163	7503	D164	6536
24			13.9	26	5	#10	4	#11	2	D172	11741	D173	10004	D174	8626	D175	7514
25			14.0	28	6	#10	4	#11	2	D183	12909	D184	10999	D185	9484	D186	8262
26		24	13.9	35	6	#11	6	#10	2	D194	15518	D195	13506	D196	11645	D197	10144
27			14.0	38	6	#11	6	#11	2	D205	15439	D206	14251	D207	12727	D208	11087
28			13.9	45	7	#11	7	#11	2	D216	18026	D217	16640	D218	14914	D219	12992

* Deduct dead load from these values.

Where dash occurs in stirrup column, no stirrups are required.

† Beams as deep as 36 and 42 in. may require more complete analysis of loading conditions, deflections, etc.

REINFORCED CONCRETE BEAMS—SINGLE SPAN

For stirrup combinations, see pages 10-42 to 10-58, incl.

TOTAL SAFE CARRYING CAPACITY * (plf)—
UNIFORMLY DISTRIBUTED

Span l' in Feet

32		34		36		38		40		42		44		
Stir-rup Mark	Safe Load	Stir-rup Mark	Safe Load	Stir-rup Mark	Safe Load	Stir-rup Mark	Safe Load	Stir-rup Mark	Safe Load	Stir-rup Mark	Safe Load	Stir-rup Mark	Safe Load	
—	1488	—	1318	—	1176	—	1055	—	952	—	864	—	787	1
—	1859	—	1647	—	1469	—	1318	—	1189	—	1079	—	983	2
—	2497	—	2212	—	1973	—	1771	—	1598	—	1449	—	1321	3
D011	2818	—	2496	—	2227	—	1998	—	1803	—	1636	—	1490	4
D016	3147	D017	2787	D018	2486	D019	2231	—	2014	—	1826	—	1664	5
D024	3470	D025	3073	D026	2741	D027	2460	D028	2220	D029	2014	D030	1835	6
D035	3943	D036	3493	D037	3116	D038	2796	—	2523	—	2289	—	2085	7
D043	4439	D044	3932	D045	3508	D046	3148	D047	2841	D048	2577	D049	2348	8
D054	4903	D055	4343	D056	3874	D057	3477	D058	3138	D059	2846	D060	2593	9
D065	5513	D066	4883	D067	4356	D068	3909	D069	3528	D070	3200	D071	2916	10
D076	6099	D077	5403	D078	4819	D079	4325	D080	3903	D081	3540	D082	3226	11
D087	7512	D088	6654	D089	5935	D090	5327	D091	4808	D092	4361	D093	3973	12
D098	8196	D099	7260	D100	6476	D101	5812	D102	5246	D103	4758	D104	4335	13
D109	9616	D110	8518	D111	7598	D112	6819	D113	6154	D114	5582	D115	5086	14
—	1767	—	1566	—	1396	—	1253	—	1131	—	1026	—	935	15
—	2210	—	1958	—	1746	—	1567	—	1414	—	1283	—	1169	16
—	2968	—	2629	—	2345	—	2105	—	1900	—	1723	—	1570	17
D124	3353	—	2970	—	2649	—	2378	—	2146	—	1946	—	1773	18
D129	3770	D130	3339	D131	2979	—	2673	—	2413	—	2188	—	1994	19
D136	4113	D137	3643	D138	3249	D139	2916	D140	2632	D141	2387	—	2175	20
D146	4756	D147	4213	D148	3758	D149	3372	—	3044	—	2761	—	2515	21
D154	5221	D155	4625	D156	4125	D157	3702	D158	3341	D159	3031	D160	2761	22
D165	5745	D166	5089	D167	4539	D168	4074	D169	3676	D170	3334	D171	3038	23
D176	6604	D177	5850	D178	5218	D179	4683	D180	4226	D181	3833	D182	3493	24
D187	7261	D188	6432	D189	5737	D190	5149	D191	4647	D192	4215	D193	3840	25
D198	8916	D199	7898	D200	7045	D201	6322	D202	5706	D203	5175	D204	4716	26
D209	9744	D210	8631	D211	7699	D212	6910	D213	6236	D214	5656	D215	5154	27
D220	11419	D221	10115	D222	9022	D223	8097	D224	7308	D225	6628	D226	6039	28

$d = h - (2'' + \text{distance from bottom of bars to their centroid})$.

REINFORCED CONCRETE BEAMS

CONTINUOUS END SPAN

The tables on pages 10-22 to 10-29 give the total safe uniform load per lineal foot (live and dead) * on reinforced concrete beams for the end span only of continuous runs of beams, computed in conformity with the American Concrete Institute's "Building Code Requirements for Reinforced Concrete (ACI 318-63)"; for span lengths varying from 6 to 40 feet in two-foot multiples; for one set of stresses, viz. $f_s = 24{,}000$ psi and $f_c = 1688$ psi; for depths from 12 to 30 inches in two-inch multiples, 36 and 42 in.; for several widths in each depth; with many bar combinations.

There is no advantage in listing more heavily reinforced continuous beams, because negative bending quite sharply limits their maximum capacity. This may be seen in a general fashion by considering a continuous rectangular beam of about the width and depth covered by these tables. Consider the negative moment at the first interior support when the length of the interior span equals 1.2 times that of the end span, and the bending moment equals 1/10 of w times the square of the average span length (ACI 904(c)). Taking as a practical limit a steel ratio of perhaps 2 or 2½ per cent, the value of $R = \dfrac{M}{bd^2}$ is around 500, and the (stem) width will then be $b' = \dfrac{M}{Rd^2} = \dfrac{w\,(1.1\,L)^2}{10 \times 500d^2} = \dfrac{wL^2}{4130d^2}$.

Turning to the positive moment in the end span, taking a bending moment of $wL^2/11$ (outer end freely supported without restraint), and computing the (flange) width (which is the same as the width of the tee beam in the previous tables, with superfluous concrete below the neutral axis removed), and taking $R = M/bd^2 = 271$ for balanced reinforcement, the flange width $b = \dfrac{M}{Rd^2} = \dfrac{wL^2}{11 \times 271d^2} = \dfrac{wL^2}{2981d^2}$. So for equal resistance to positive and negative moment $b = \dfrac{4130}{2981}\,b' = 1.39b'$. Thus the maximum useable flange width in this special case is 1.39 times the stem width and the maximum practical reinforcement is 1.39 times that required for balanced reinforcement of the stem. Beyond that limit, there is no advantage in increasing reinforcement or flange width.

The limitations and arrangement of the following table parallel so closely those of the single span that pages 10-3 to 10-6 should be studied carefully before reading further. This applies especially to stirrup arrangements and

---

* In the various slab tables throughout this book, the weight of the slab has been deducted so that the values given in the tables are the safe superimposed loads. In the case of beams, there is no advantage in deducting the minor weight of the beam stem, as it is the weight of the tributary slab that is the main element of dead load. So in these tables the capacity given is the total safe load, dead plus live.

REINFORCED CONCRETE BEAMS
CONTINUOUS END SPAN

bond, and to the fact that bars must meet ASTM A305, and that carrying capacity is taken as the least of the limits set by shear, bond, positive or negative flexure.

The 1963 ACI Building Code recommends a value for positive moment in end spans of $wl'^2/11$ where the outer end is freely supported (and that is used here) or of $wl'^2/14$ where the outer end is monolithic with a reinforced concrete frame (which will usually increase the capacity over what is given here).

The following example may prove useful for those who wish to design beyond the scope of the tables or to see how they were prepared:—

Example—For the table on pages 10-24 and 10-25, determine the safe carrying capacity on an end span of 20 feet of a 12 x 24 in. beam stem reinforced with 2-#9 bottom bars, 1-#11 truss bar, all in one layer, with 1-#10 added top bar over the support at the continuous end, assuming 1-#10 truss bar bent up and carried through from the adjacent span. Check the stirrup combination.

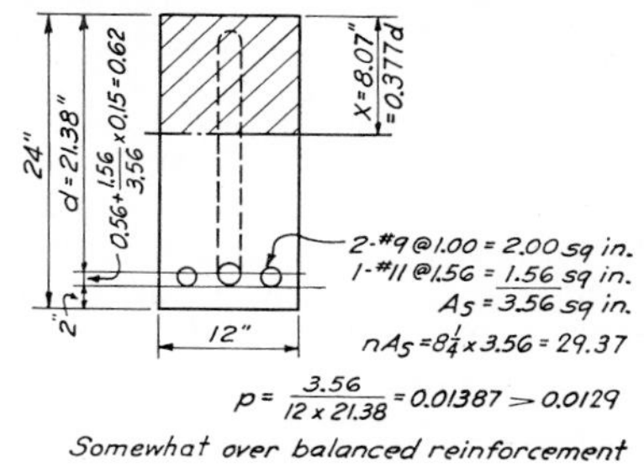

Solution—From the figure, determine first the distance "x" down to the neutral axis by equating statical moments of the transformed areas about the neutral axis:—

$$\frac{12x^2}{2} = 29.37(21.38 - x)$$

$$6x^2 + 29.37x = 627.9$$

$$x^2 + 4.90x + (2.45)^2 = 104.65 + 6.00 = 110.65$$

$$x = -2.45 \pm 10.52 = 8.07 \text{ in.} \quad (0.377d)$$

Positive Flexure—The arm of the internal couple, jd, $= 21.38 - \dfrac{8.07}{3} = 18.7$ in.

$$M_s = A_s f_s jd = 3.56 \times 24{,}000 \times 18.7 = 1{,}618{,}000 \text{ lb-in.}$$

$$M_c = bkd\frac{f_c}{2}jd = 12 \times 8.07 \times \frac{1688}{2} \times 18.7 = 1{,}528{,}000 \text{ lb-in.}$$

} somewhat over-reinforced.

Since the amount of tension steel is definitely established, the stem width, b', is set (and is given in the following tables); if the beam is in monolithic construction, a tee is available for positive moment. An asterisk on b' in the tables indicates that a tee is required. Steel is tabulated only to a value where the maximum b (page 10-18) is $1.50b'$, i.e. a maximum overhang of $b'/4$ each side. If the beam were free-standing, an analysis of the top flange for lateral support would be indicated. Hence use $M_s =$ 1,618,000 lb-in. and compute the safe load as determined by positive moment:—

$$w = \frac{M}{l'^2\frac{12}{11}} = \frac{1{,}618{,}000}{20 \times 20 \times \frac{12}{11}} = 3700 \text{ plf}$$

Bond on Bottom Bars—The bond on the bottom bars is to be computed in that part of the positive bending zone which has the highest external shear, i.e., either the free end or the point of inflection of the continuous end. Since the ACI Building Code sets the shear at the free end at $wl'/2$, it is unlikely that the shear at the point of inflection will normally be that large:—

$$u = \frac{4.8\sqrt{f'_c}}{D} = \frac{4.8\sqrt{3750}}{1.128} = 260 \text{ psi}$$

$$V = \Sigma ojdu = 2 \times 3.544 \times 18.7 \times 260 = 34{,}660 \text{ lb} = wl'/2$$

$$w = \frac{34{,}660}{10} = 3466 \text{ plf, or slightly less than allowed by flexure.}$$

Shear—To allow for the fact that continuity in an end span increases the shear at the continuous end, ACI 904(c) requires an increase of 15 per cent over $wl'/2$. For spacing stirrups, it is not practicable to work backwards. Take the capacity of the beam at

REINFORCED CONCRETE BEAMS—CONTINUOUS END SPAN

3466 plf as computed for bond and design the web reinforcement to take care of this:—

Allowable shear, $v_c = 1.1\sqrt{f'_c} = 1.1\sqrt{3750} = 67.4$ psi
At distance $d = 21.38'' = 1.78$ ft from the interior support, $V = w(1.15\frac{l}{2} - d) = 3466(11.5 - 1.78) = 33{,}700$ lb

$$v = \frac{V}{bd} = \frac{33{,}700}{12 \times 21.38} = 132 \text{ psi} > 67.4 \text{ psi} < 3\sqrt{f'_c} = 184 \text{ psi}$$

Deducting $v_c = 67.4$ from 132 leaves 64.6 psi to be carried by stirrups at $f_v = 20{,}000$ psi. Although there is a bent bar which might displace a few stirrups, the sloping portion frequently is not well located for that purpose (being bent for positive and negative moment); also, such refinement is mainly used in large girders where making detailed layouts justifies the effort.

From the sketch, the three portions of the span that need web reinforcement require:—

1) from support for distance d, $A'_v = \dfrac{64.6 \times 12 \times 21.38}{20{,}000} = 0.83$ sq in.
   4-#3 stirrups @ 6″ = 0.88 sq in.
2) for distance a as shown on the figure, $A''_v = 1.12$ sq in.
   5-#3 stirrups @ 3, 6, 7, 9, 10, (22½″) = 1.10 sq in.
3) for distance d beyond a, $A'''_v = 0.0015 \times 12 \times 21.37 = 0.384$ sq in.
   2-#3 stirrups = 0.44 sq in.

Maximum spacing $= d/2 = 10$ in.
$A'_v + A''_v + A'''_v = 12$-#3 stirrups @ 3, 6, 6, 6, 6, 7, 9, 10, 10, 10, 10, 10.
The same arrangement will be used on the free end for simplicity in detailing and to prevent reversal in the field.

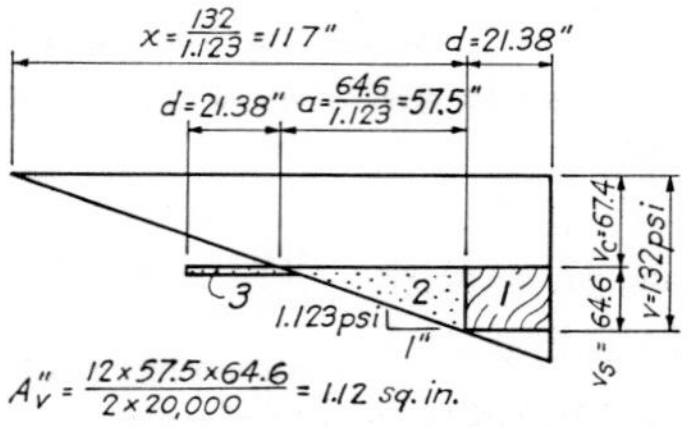

Negative Flexure—By ACI 904(c) the negative moment factor is to be taken as $\frac{1}{10}$; the adjacent span is limited to a range between $\gtrless 0.833\ l'$ to $\lessgtr 1.20\ l'$. With varying span lengths, different amounts of steel will be bent up. This computation is based upon the assumption that the adjacent span = 1.00 l' and that the trussed bar in it is 1-#10.

Then:—

$$-M = wl'^2/10$$

Since the added top bar increases A_s over that used in "positive flexure" above, the beam is over-reinforced and compression steel will be needed, obtained by lapping the bottom bars $\dfrac{f_sD}{4u} = \dfrac{24{,}000 \times 1.128}{4 \times 398} = 17$ in., increased to $24D = 28$ in. past each other to afford 2-#9 for compression. As shown below, compute x by taking moments about the bottom of the beam and using $(2n - 1)$ times A'_s (ACI 1102(c)).

$$x = \frac{\frac{12x^2}{2} + 31 \times 2.56 + 33.83 \times 21.84}{12x + 31 + 33.83}$$

$$6x^2 + 64.83x = 820.4$$
$$x^2 + 10.8x + (5.40)^2 = 136.7 + 29.4 = 166.1$$
$$x = 12.9\text{-}5.4 = 7.50 \text{ in.}$$

$$C_c = 12 \times 7.50 \times \frac{1688}{2} = 75{,}900 \text{ lb}$$

$$C_s = 31 \times 1688 \times \frac{4.94}{7.50} = \frac{34{,}500}{110{,}400} \text{ lb}$$

$$z = 2.56 + \frac{75{,}900}{110{,}400}\left(\frac{7.50}{3} - 2.56\right) = 2.52 \text{ in.}$$

$$jd = 19.32 \text{ in.}$$

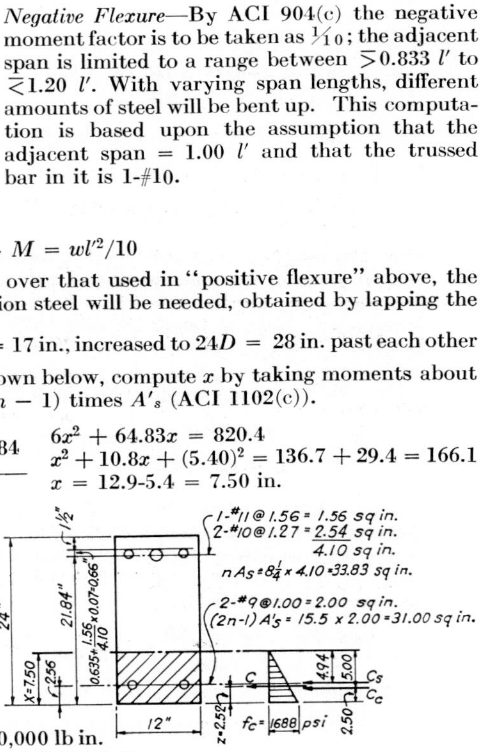

$$M_c = Cjd = 110{,}400 \times 19.32 = 2{,}130{,}000 \text{ lb in.}$$
$$M_s = Tjd = 4.10 \times 24{,}000 \times 19.32 = 1{,}900{,}000 \text{ lb in.}$$

$$w = \frac{M}{l'^2\ 1\frac{2}{10}} = \frac{1{,}900{,}000}{20 \times 20 \times 1.2} = 3960 > 3466 \text{ lb (by bond)}$$

REINFORCED CONCRETE BEAMS—CONTINUOUS END SPAN

Check Deflection—$pf_y = 0.01387 \times 60{,}000 = 832 > 500$ (ACI 909(c)). Use I_c of cracked section, average of positive and negative.

$$I_{pos} = \frac{1}{3} \times 12 \times \overline{8.07}^3 + 29.37\ (21.38 - 8.07)^2 = 7290 \text{ in.}^4$$

$$I_{neg} = \frac{1}{3} \times 12 \times \overline{7.50}^3 + 33.83\ (21.84 - 7.50)^2 + 31\ (7.50 - 2.56)^2 = 9420 \text{ in.}^4$$

$$\frac{I_{pos} + I_{neg}}{2} = \frac{7290 + 9420}{2} = 8360 \text{ in.}^4$$

$$E = 145^{1.5}\ 33\sqrt{3750} = 3{,}540{,}000 \text{ psi}$$

$$\text{Immediate } \triangle = \frac{wl'^4}{185EI} = \frac{3{,}466\ (20)^4 \times 1728}{185 \times 3{,}540{,}000 \times 8360} = 0.18 \text{ in.}$$

$$\left.\begin{array}{l}\text{If } LL = 2DL, \text{ immediate L.L. deflection} = \frac{2}{3}\,0.18 = 0.12 \text{ in.}\\ \frac{A'_s}{A_s} = 0, \text{ add creep deflection } 2.0 \times \frac{1}{3}\,0.18 = 0.12 \text{ in.}\end{array}\right\} 0.24 = \frac{L}{1000}$$

These computations indicate the great range of choices open to the designer, the impracticability of a complete set of beam tables, and the fact that continuity not only affects the moments and shears in this span but the amount of steel brought through from the adjacent span. These tables can serve for making estimates of sizes, but any major structure should be finally checked by computation.

FOR THE TABLES ON PAGES 10-22 TO 10-29 INCL.

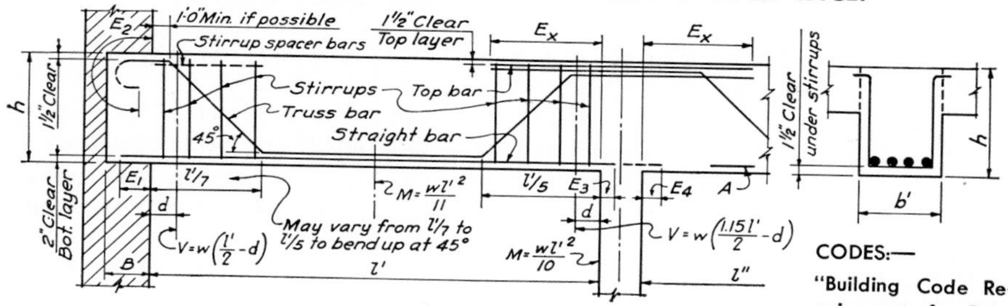

CODES:—

"Building Code Requirements for Reinforced Concrete (ACI 318-63)," also "Manual of Standard Practice for Detailing Reinforced Concrete Structures (ACI 315)."

STRESSES:—

$f_s = 24{,}000$ psi

$f'_c = 3750$ psi

$f_c = 1688$ psi

$v_c = 1.1\sqrt{3750} = 67.4$ psi

$v = 3\sqrt{f'_c} = 184$ psi;
$= 5\sqrt{f'_c} = 306$ psi

$u = \dfrac{4.8\sqrt{3750}}{D}$ psi for bottom bars

$= \dfrac{3.4\sqrt{3750}}{D}$ psi for top bars with over 12" of concrete under them (see page 3-13)

E_1 = 6 in. minimum for bottom bars.

E_2 = 6 in. for #3 bars; 10 in. for #4 bars; 21 D^2 for #5 and larger, (29 D^2 for #5 and larger, when $d >$ 12 in.) (obtained by straight embedment if possible, hooked if necessary).

E_3 = bottom bar to extend 6 in. into the support except when values in the load tables are printed in boldface type.

E_4 = when the values in the load tables are printed in boldface type, bottom bars must lap bars of adjoining span by "development length" so that they may serve for compressive reinforcement, as shown in example in the text.

E_x = $0.3l'$ or l'', whichever is greater. Extend top bars past innermost position of point of inflection $l/16$, or the effective depth, d, whichever is greater.

B = ordinarily 8 in. minimum and sufficient in any case to keep the bearing pressure on the wall within the allowable for the material of which the wall is made. (See page 5-6.)

A = bars in adjoining span, not shown.

For stirrup combinations, see pages 10-42 ff.

CONTINUOUS REINFORCED CONCRETE BEAMS—END SPAN

For limitations and explanation of use of this table, see pages 10-18 to 10-21.

	Stem		Bar Combinations							TOTAL SAFE CARRYING CAPACITY * (plf)— UNIFORMLY DISTRIBUTED, Span l' in Feet							
			Straight		Trussed		No. Layers	Top		8		10		12		14	
	h (in.)	b′ (in.)	No.	Size	No.	Size		No.	Size	Stirrup Mark	Safe Load	Stirrup Mark	Safe Load	Stirrup Mark	Safe Load	Stirrup Mark	Safe Load
1	12	6	2	#4	1	#5	2	1	#5	A911	1943	A912	1243	A913	863	A914	634
2		8	2†	#5	1	#6	1	1	#6	A916	**3091**	A917	**1978**	A918	**1373**	A919	**1009**
3		10	2	#5	2	#5	1	1	#6	A923	3626	A924	2321	A925	1611	A926	1184
4			2†	#5	2	#6	1	1	#4	A929	3911	A930	**2796**	A931	**1942**	A932	**1426**
5	14	8	2	#5	1	#6	1	1	#6	A937	3755	A938	2403	A939	1669	A940	1226
6			1	#7	1	#8	1	1	#4	A943	2336	A944	1869	A945	1557	A946	1335
7		10	2	#5	2	#6	1	1	#4	A953	4722	A954	3376	A955	2344	A956	1722
8		12	2†	#6	2	#7	1	1	#5	A961	4698	A962	3758	A963	**3132**	A964	**2375**
9			3†	#6	3	#6	2	1	#8	A971	**6537**	A972	**5229**	A973	**3807**	A974	**2797**
10	16	8	2	#5	1	#6	1	1	#6	A981	4435	A982	2838	A983	1971	A984	1448
11			2	#5	1	#8	2	1	#4	A987	5136	A988	**3451**	A989	**2396**	A990	**1761**
12		10	2	#5	2	#6	1	1	#4	A997	5578	A998	3988	A999	2769	B000	2034
13			2†	#6	2	#7	1	1	#5	B005	5508	B006	4407	B007	**3672**	B008	**2785**
14		12	3†	#6	3	#6	2	1	#8	B016	7753	B017	**6202**	B018	**4515**	B019	**3317**
15	18	8	2	#5	1	#6	1	1	#6	B027	5117	B028	3275	B029	2274	B030	1671
16		10	2	#5	2	#6	1	1	#4	B033	6440	B034	4604	B035	3197	B036	2349
17			2	#6	2	#7	1	1	#5	B041	6319	B042	5055	B043	4213	B044	**3195**
18		12	3†	#6	3	#6	2	1	#8	B052	8969	B053	**7175**	B054	**5223**	B055	**3838**
19			3†	#6	2	#8	1	1	#6	B063	9460	B064	7568	B065	**6052**	B066	**4446**
20			3†	#7	2	#8	2	1	#9	B074	8913	B075	7131	B076	**5942**	B077	**4882**

* Deduct dead load from these values.

† Longitudinal reinforcement exceeds $p = 0.0129$ and tee will be required for positive moment (see page 10-18).

Where dash occurs in stirrup column, no stirrups are required.

Extend bottom bars to E_4 (page 10-21) for values in boldface type.

CONTINUOUS REINFORCED CONCRETE BEAMS—END SPAN

For stirrup combinations, see pages 10-42 to 10-58, incl.

TOTAL SAFE CARRYING CAPACITY * (plf)—
UNIFORMLY DISTRIBUTED

Span l' in Feet

16		18		20		22		24		26		28		
Stir-rup Mark	Safe Load	Stir-rup Mark	Safe Load	Stir-rup Mark	Safe Load	Stir-rup Mark	Safe Load	Stir-rup Mark	Safe Load	Stir-rup Mark	Safe Load	Stir-rup Mark	Safe Load	
A915	485	—	383	—	310	—	256							1
A920	772	A921	610	A922	494	—	408							2
A927	906	A928	716	—	580	—	479							3
A933	1092	A934	863	A935	699	A936	577							4
A941	938	A942	741	—	600	—	496	—	417	—	355			5
A947	1168	A948	955	A949	773	A950	639	A951	537	A952	457			6
A957	1318	A958	1042	A959	844	A960	697	—	586	—	499			7
A965	1818	A966	1437	A967	1164	A968	962	A969	808	A970	688			8
A975	2141	A976	1692	A977	1370	A978	1132	A979	951	A980	811			9
A985	1108	A986	876	—	709	—	586	—	492	—	419	—	362	10
A991	1348	A992	1065	A993	862	A994	713	A995	599	A996	510	—	440	11
B001	1557	B002	1230	B003	997	B004	824	—	692	—	590	—	508	12
B009	2132	B010	1685	B011	1365	B012	1128	B013	947	B014	807	B015	696	13
B020	2540	B021	2006	B022	1625	B023	1343	B024	1128	B025	961	B026	829	14
B031	1279	B032	1010	—	818	—	676	—	568	—	484	—	417	15
B037	1798	B038	1421	B039	1151	B040	951	—	799	—	681	—	587	16
B045	2446	B046	1933	B047	1565	B048	1294	B049	1087	B050	926	B051	798	17
B056	2938	B057	2321	B058	1880	B059	1554	B060	1305	B061	1112	B062	959	18
B067	3404	B068	2689	B069	2178	B070	1800	B071	1513	B072	1289	B073	1111	19
B078	3738	B079	2953	B080	2392	B081	1977	B082	1661	B083	1415	B084	1220	20

$d = h - (2'' +$ distance from bottom of bars to their centroid).

CONTINUOUS REINFORCED CONCRETE BEAMS—END SPAN

For limitations and explanation of use of this table, see pages 10-18 to 10-21.

	Stem		Bar Combinations							TOTAL SAFE CARRYING CAPACITY* (plf)—UNIFORMLY DISTRIBUTED; Span l' in Feet							
			Straight		Trussed		No. Layers	Top		16		18		20		22	
	h (in.)	b′ (in.)	No.	Size	No.	Size		No.	Size	Stirrup Mark	Safe Load	Stirrup Mark	Safe Load	Stirrup Mark	Safe Load	Stirrup Mark	Safe Load
1		8	2	#5	1	#6	1	1	#6	B085	1450	B086	1146	—	928	—	767
2		10	2	#5	2	#6	1	1	#4	B087	2040	B088	1611	B089	1305	—	1079
3			2	#6	2	#7	1	1	#5	B090	2773	B091	2191	B092	1774	B093	1466
4	20	12	2	#7	3	#6	1	1	#7	B098	3359	B099	2654	B100	2149	B101	1776
5			2†	#7	2	#8	1	1	#5	B106	3553	B107	**2905**	B108	**2353**	B109	**1944**
6			2†	#8	2	#8	1	1	#8	B116	3548	B117	**3153**	B118	**2670**	B119	**2207**
7			2†	#8	2	#9	1	1	#6	B127	3540	B128	**3147**	B129	**2832**	B130	**2495**
8		8	2	#5	1	#6	1	1	#6	B138	1622	B139	1282	—	1038	—	858
9		10	2	#5	2	#6	1	1	#4	B140	2282	B141	1803	B142	1460	—	1207
10			2	#6	2	#7	1	1	#5	B143	3105	B144	2453	B145	1987	B146	1642
11		12	2	#7	3	#6	1	1	#7	B151	3761	B152	2972	B153	2407	B154	1989
12	22		2	#8	2	#8	1	1	#8	B159	3953	B160	**3514**	B161	**2975**	B162	**2459**
13			2†	#8	2	#9	1	1	#6	B170	3946	B171	3507	B172	**3156**	B173	**2781**
14		14	3†	#7	2	#9	1	1	#7	B181	**5590**	B182	**4417**	B183	**3577**	B184	**2956**
15			2†	#9	2	#10	1	1	#7	B192	3932	B193	3495	B194	3145	B195	2859
16			3†	#8	2	#10	1	1	#9	B203	**5908**	B204	**5252**	B205	**4607**	B206	**3807**
17		10	2	#5	1	#6	1	1	#6	—	1811	—	1431	—	1159	—	958
18			2	#5	2	#6	1	1	#4	B214	2525	B215	1995	B216	1616	—	1335
19			2	#6	2	#7	1	1	#5	B217	3439	B218	2717	B219	2201	B220	1819
20	24	12	2	#7	3	#6	1	1	#7	B225	4166	B226	3291	B227	2666	B228	2203
21			2	#8	2	#8	1	1	#8	B233	4370	B234	3884	B235	3289	B236	2718
22			2†	#8	2	#9	1	1	#6	B244	4351	B245	3868	B246	**3481**	B247	**3067**
23			2†	#9	1	#11	1	1	#10	B255	4333	B256	3851	B257	**3466**	B258	**3037**
24		14	3†	#7	2	#9	1	1	#7	B266	**6170**	B267	**4875**	B268	**3948**	B269	**3263**
25			3†	#7	2	#10	1	1	#5	B277	**6521**	B278	**5549**	B279	**4495**	B280	**3715**
26			3†	#8	2	#10	1	1	#9	B288	6517	B289	**5793**	B290	**5081**	B291	**4199**

* Deduct dead load from these values.

† Longitudinal reinforcement exceeds $p = 0.0129$ and tee will be required for positive moment (see page 10-18).

Where dash occurs in stirrup column, no stirrups are required.

Extend bottom bars to E_4 (page 10-21) for values in boldface type.

CONTINUOUS REINFORCED CONCRETE BEAMS—END SPAN

For stirrup combinations, see pages 10-42 to 10-58, incl.

TOTAL SAFE CARRYING CAPACITY* (plf)—
UNIFORMLY DISTRIBUTED

Span l' in Feet

24		26		28		30		32		34		36		
Stirrup Mark	Safe Load	Stirrup Mark	Safe Load	Stirrup Mark	Safe Load	Stirrup Mark	Safe Load	Stirrup Mark	Safe Load	Stirrup Mark	Safe Load	Stirrup Mark	Safe Load	
—	644	—	549	—	473	—	412	—	362	—	321	—	286	1
—	906	—	772	—	666	—	580	—	510	—	451	—	402	2
B094	1232	B095	1050	B096	905	B097	788	—	693	—	614	—	547	3
B102	1492	B103	1272	B104	1096	B105	955	—	839	—	743	—	663	4
B110	1634	B111	1392	B112	1200	B113	1045	B114	919	B115	814	—	726	5
B120	1854	B121	1580	B122	1362	B123	1186	B124	1043	B125	924	B126	824	6
B131	2096	B132	1786	B133	1540	B134	1342	B135	1179	B136	1044	B137	931	7
—	721	—	614	—	529	—	461	—	405	—	359	—	320	8
—	1014	—	864	—	745	—	649	—	570	—	505	—	450	9
B147	1380	B148	1176	B149	1014	B150	883	—	776	—	687	—	613	10
B155	1671	B156	1424	B157	1228	B158	1070	—	940	—	833	—	743	11
B163	2066	B164	1760	B165	1518	B166	1322	B167	1162	B168	1029	B169	918	12
B174	2337	B175	1991	B176	1716	B177	1495	B178	1314	B179	1164	B180	1038	13
B185	2484	B186	2117	B187	1825	B188	1590	B189	1397	B190	1238	B191	1104	14
B196	2621	B197	2419	B198	2169	B199	1890	B200	1661	B201	1471	B202	1312	15
B207	3199	B208	2726	B209	2350	B210	2047	B211	1799	B212	1594	B213	1422	16
—	805	—	685	—	591	—	515	—	452	—	401	—	357	17
—	1122	—	956	—	824	—	718	—	631	—	559	—	498	18
B221	1528	B222	1302	B223	1123	B224	978	—	859	—	761	—	679	19
B229	1851	B230	1577	B231	1360	B232	1185	—	1041	—	922	—	822	20
B237	2284	B238	1946	B239	1678	B240	1462	B241	1285	B242	1138	B243	1015	21
B248	2577	B249	2195	B250	1893	B251	1649	B252	1449	B253	1284	B254	1145	22
B259	2552	B260	2174	B261	1874	B262	1633	B263	1435	B264	1271	B265	1134	23
B270	2742	B271	2336	B272	2014	B273	1755	B274	1542	B275	1366	B276	1218	24
B281	3121	B282	2659	B283	2293	B284	1997	B285	1755	B286	1555	B287	1387	25
B292	3528	B293	3006	B294	2592	B295	2258	B296	1985	B297	1758	B298	1568	26

$d = h - (2'' +$ distance from bottom of bars to their centroid).

CONTINUOUS REINFORCED CONCRETE BEAMS—END SPAN

For limitations and explanation of use of this table, see pages 10-18 to 10-21.

	Stem		Bar Combinations							TOTAL SAFE CARRYING CAPACITY* (plf)—UNIFORMLY DISTRIBUTED: Span l' in Feet							
			Straight		Trussed		No. Layers	Top		20		22		24		26	
	h (in.)	b′ (in.)	No.	Size	No.	Size		No.	Size	Stirrup Mark	Safe Load	Stirrup Mark	Safe Load	Stirrup Mark	Safe Load	Stirrup Mark	Safe Load
1		10	2	#5	1	#6	1	1	#6	—	1270	—	1050	—	882	—	751
2			2	#5	2	#6	1	1	#4	B299	1772	—	1464	—	1230	—	1048
3			2	#6	2	#7	1	1	#5	B300	2415	B301	1996	B302	1677	B303	1429
4	26	12	2	#7	3	#6	1	1	#7	B306	2925	B307	2418	B308	2031	B309	1731
5			2	#8	2	#8	1	1	#8	B312	3612	B313	2985	B314	2508	B315	2137
6			2	#8	2	#9	1	1	#6	B322	3808	B323	**3354**	B324	**2818**	B325	**2401**
7			2†	#9	2	#9	1	1	#9	B333	3800	B334	**3455**	B335	**3144**	B336	**2678**
8		14	3†	#7	2	#10	1	1	#5	B344	**4914**	B345	**4061**	B346	**3412**	B347	**2907**
9			3†	#8	2	#10	1	1	#9	B355	**5555**	B356	**4591**	B357	**3858**	B358	**3287**
10		12	2	#5	2	#6	1	1	#4	—	1942	—	1605	—	1349	—	1149
11			2	#6	2	#7	1	1	#5	B366	2651	B367	2191	B368	1841	—	1569
12			2	#7	3	#6	1	1	#7	B369	3186	B370	2633	B371	2212	B372	1885
13			2	#8	2	#8	1	1	#8	B375	3936	B376	3253	B377	2733	B378	2329
14			2	#8	2	#9	1	1	#6	B385	4150	B386	3656	B387	3072	B388	2618
15	28		2†	#9	2	#9	1	1	#9	B396	4125	B397	3750	B398	**3412**	B399	**2907**
16		14	3	#7	2	#10	1	1	#5	B407	5349	B408	4420	B409	3714	B410	3165
17			3†	#8	2	#10	1	1	#9	B418	**6030**	B419	**4983**	B420	**4187**	B421	**3568**
18			4†	#8	3	#9	2	1	#11	B429	**7287**	B430	**6022**	B431	**5060**	B432	**4311**
19		16	4†	#8	4	#9	2	1	#8	B440	**7897**	B441	**6957**	B442	**5846**	B443	**4981**
20		18	5†	#8	4	#9	2	2	#9	B451	**9391**	B452	**7761**	B453	**6522**	B454	**5557**
21		12	2	#5	2	#6	1	1	#4	—	2100	—	1735	—	1458	—	1242
22			2	#6	2	#7	1	1	#5	B462	2868	B463	2370	—	1991	—	1697
23			2	#7	3	#6	1	1	#7	B464	3446	B465	2848	B466	2393	B467	2039
24			2	#8	2	#8	1	1	#8	B470	4260	B471	3521	B472	2959	B473	2521
25			2	#8	2	#9	1	1	#6	B480	4494	B481	3959	B482	3326	B483	2834
26			2	#9	2	#9	1	1	#9	B491	4463	B492	4057	B493	3691	B494	3145
27	30	14	3	#7	2	#10	1	1	#5	B502	5792	B503	4787	B504	4022	B505	3427
28			3	#8	2	#10	1	1	#9	B513	**6506**	B514	**5377**	B515	**4518**	B516	**3349**
29			4†	#8	3	#9	2	1	#11	B524	**7382**	B525	**6514**	B526	**5473**	B527	**4664**
30		16	4†	#8	4	#9	2	1	#8	B535	**8546**	B536	**7529**	B537	**6326**	B538	**5390**
31		18	5†	#8	4	#9	2	2	#9	B546	**10159**	B547	**8396**	B548	**7055**	B549	**6011**

* Deduct dead load from these values.

† Longitudinal reinforcement exceeds $p = 0.0129$ and tee will be required for positive moment (see page 10-18).

Where dash occurs in stirrup column, no stirrups are required.

Extend bottom bars to E_4 (page 10-21) for values in boldface type.

CONTINUOUS REINFORCED CONCRETE BEAMS—END SPAN

For stirrup combinations, see pages 10-42 to 10-58, incl.

TOTAL SAFE CARRYING CAPACITY* (plf)—
UNIFORMLY DISTRIBUTED

Span l' in Feet

28		30		32		34		36		38		40		
Stir-rup Mark	Safe Load	Stir-rup Mark	Safe Load	Stir-rup Mark	Safe Load	Stir-rup Mark	Safe Load	Stir-rup Mark	Safe Load	Stir-rup Mark	Safe Load	Stir-rup Mark	Safe Load	
—	648	—	564	—	496	—	439	—	392	—	351	—	317	1
—	904	—	787	—	692	—	613	—	547	—	491	—	443	2
B304	1232	B305	1073	—	943	—	835	—	745	—	669	—	603	3
B310	1492	B311	1300	—	1142	—	1012	—	903	—	810	—	731	4
B316	1843	B317	1605	B318	1411	B319	1250	B320	1114	B321	1000	—	903	5
B326	**2071**	B327	**1804**	B328	**1585**	B329	**1404**	B330	**1252**	B331	**1124**	B332	**1014**	6
B337	**2309**	B338	**2012**	B339	**1768**	B340	**1566**	B341	**1397**	B342	**1254**	B343	**1131**	7
B348	**2507**	B349	**2184**	B350	**1919**	B351	**1700**	B352	**1516**	B353	**1361**	B354	**1228**	8
B359	2834	B360	2469	B361	**2170**	B362	**1922**	B363	**1714**	B364	**1539**	B365	**1388**	9
—	991	—	863	—	758	—	672	—	599	—	538	—	485	10
—	1352	—	1178	—	1035	—	917	—	818	—	734	—	662	11
B373	1625	B374	1416	—	1244	—	1102	—	983	—	882	—	796	12
B379	2008	B380	1749	B381	1537	B382	1362	B383	1214	B384	1090	—	984	13
B389	2257	B390	1966	B391	1728	B392	1530	B393	1365	B394	1225	B395	1106	14
B400	**2507**	B401	**2183**	B402	**1919**	B403	**1700**	B404	**1516**	B405	**1361**	B406	**1228**	15
B411	2729	B412	2377	B413	2089	B414	1850	B415	1650	B416	1481	B417	1337	16
B422	**3076**	B423	**2680**	B424	**2355**	B425	**2086**	B426	**1861**	B427	**1670**	B428	**1507**	17
B433	**3717**	B434	**3238**	B435	**2846**	B436	**2521**	B437	**2249**	B438	**2018**	B439	**1821**	18
B444	**4295**	B445	**3741**	B446	**3288**	B447	**2913**	B448	**2598**	B449	**2332**	B450	**2104**	19
B455	**4791**	B456	**4174**	B457	**3668**	B458	**3249**	B459	**2898**	B460	**2601**	B461	**2347**	20
—	1071	—	933	—	820	—	726	—	648	—	581	—	525	21
—	1463	—	1274	—	1120	—	992	—	885	—	794	—	717	22
B468	1758	B469	1531	—	1346	—	1192	—	1063	—	954	—	861	23
B474	2173	B475	1893	B476	1664	B477	1474	B478	1315	B479	1180	—	1065	24
B484	2444	B485	2129	B486	1871	B487	1657	B488	1478	B489	1327	B490	1197	25
B495	2712	B496	2362	B497	2076	B498	1839	B499	1640	B500	1472	B501	1329	26
B506	2955	B507	2574	B508	2262	B509	2004	B510	1787	B511	1604	B512	1448	27
B517	**3319**	B518	**2891**	B519	**2541**	B520	**2251**	B521	**2008**	B522	**1802**	B523	**1626**	28
B528	**4021**	B529	**3503**	B530	**3078**	B531	**2727**	B532	**2432**	B533	**2183**	B534	**1970**	29
B539	**4648**	B540	**4049**	B541	**3558**	B542	**3152**	B543	**2811**	B544	**2523**	B545	**2277**	30
B550	**5183**	B551	**4515**	B552	**3968**	B553	**3515**	B554	**3135**	B555	**2814**	B556	**2539**	31

$d = h - (2'' +$ distance from bottom of bars to their centroid).

CONTINUOUS REINFORCED CONCRETE BEAMS—END SPAN

For limitations and explanation of use of this table, see pages 10-18 to 10-21.

	Stem		Bar Combinations							TOTAL SAFE CARRYING CAPACITY* (plf)—UNIFORMLY DISTRIBUTED; Span l' in Feet							
			Straight		Trussed		No. Layers	Top		24		26		28		30	
	h (in.)	b′ (in.)	No.	Size	No.	Size		No.	Size	Stirrup Mark	Safe Load	Stirrup Mark	Safe Load	Stirrup Mark	Safe Load	Stirrup Mark	Safe Load
1		12	2	#8	2	#8	1	1	#8	D227	3638	D228	3100	D229	2673	D230	2328
2			2	#8	2	#10	1	—	—	D234	4569	D235	3980	D236	3432	D237	2989
3		16	3	#8	3	#9	1	1	#7	D245	6105	D246	5201	D247	4485	D248	3907
4			3	#9	2	#11	1	1	#10	D256	6805	D257	5870	D258	5061	D259	4409
5	36‡		4†	#8	4	#9	2	1	#8	D267	**7767**	D268	**6618**	D269	**5706**	D270	**4971**
6		20	4†	#8	5	#9	2	1	#3	D278	**8721**	D279	**7523**	D280	**6486**	D281	**5650**
7			4†	#9	4	#10	2	1	#9	D289	8705	D290	**8035**	D291	**7205**	D292	**6276**
8			5†	#8	5	#10	2	—	—	D300	**10875**	D301	**9473**	D302	**8168**	D303	**7115**
9		24	5†	#9	4	#11	2	1	#10	D311	**10872**	D312	**10035**	D313	**8911**	D314	**7762**
10			5†	#10	4	#11	2	2	#10	D322	10881	D323	**10044**	D324	**9326**	D325	**8703**
11		12	2	#8	2	#8	1	1	#8	D333	4321	D334	3682	D335	3175	D336	2765
12			2	#8	2	#10	1	—	—	D340	5433	D341	4733	D342	4081	D343	3555
13		16	3	#8	3	#9	1	1	#7	D351	7257	D352	6183	D353	5331	D354	4644
14			3	#9	2	#11	1	1	#10	D362	8096	D363	6984	D364	6022	D365	5246
15	42‡		4	#8	4	#9	2	1	#8	D373	9255	D374	7886	D375	6800	D376	5923
16		20	4	#8	5	#9	2	1	#3	D384	10437	D385	9003	D386	7763	D387	6762
17			4	#9	4	#10	2	1	#9	D395	10370	D396	9573	D397	8583	D398	7477
18			5†	#8	5	#10	2	—	—	D406	**12902**	D407	**11239**	D408	**9690**	D409	**8441**
19		24	5	#9	4	#11	2	1	#10	D417	12931	D418	11936	D419	**10599**	D420	**9233**
20			5†	#10	4	#11	2	2	#10	D428	12908	D429	11915	D430	**11064**	D431	**10323**

* Deduct dead load from these values.

† Longitudinal reinforcement exceeds $p = 0.0129$ and tee will be required for positive moment (see page 10-18).

‡ Beams as deep as 36 and 42 in. may require more complete analysis of loading conditions, end restraints, deflections, etc.

Where dash occurs in stirrup column, no stirrups are required.

Extend bottom bars to E_4 (page 10-21) for values in boldface type.

CONTINUOUS REINFORCED CONCRETE BEAMS—END SPAN

For stirrup combinations, see pages 10-42 to 10-58, incl.

TOTAL SAFE CARRYING CAPACITY* (plf)—
UNIFORMLY DISTRIBUTED

Span l' in Feet

32		34		36		38		40		42		44		
Stirrup Mark	Safe Load	Stirrup Mark	Safe Load	Stirrup Mark	Safe Load	Stirrup Mark	Safe Load	Stirrup Mark	Safe Load	Stirrup Mark	Safe Load	Stirrup Mark	Safe Load	
D231	2046	D232	1812	D233	1617	—	1451	—	1309	—	1188	—	1082	1
D238	2627	D239	2327	D240	2076	D241	1863	D242	1681	D243	1525	D244	1389	2
D249	3434	D250	3041	D251	2713	D252	2435	D253	2197	D254	1993	D255	1816	3
D260	3875	D261	3433	D262	3062	D263	2748	D264	2480	D265	2249	D266	2049	4
D271	4369	D272	3870	D273	3452	D274	3098	D275	2796	D276	2536	D277	2311	5
D282	4966	D283	4399	D284	3924	D285	3521	D286	3178	D287	2883	D288	2626	6
D293	5516	D294	4886	D295	4358	D296	3912	D297	3530	D298	3202	D299	2917	7
D304	6253	D305	5539	D306	4941	D307	4434	D308	4002	D309	3630	D310	3307	8
D315	6822	D316	6043	D317	5390	D318	4838	D319	4366	D320	3960	D321	3608	9
D326	7649	D327	6775	D328	6043	D329	5424	D330	4895	D331	4440	D332	4045	10
D337	2430	D338	2153	D339	1920	—	1723	—	1555	—	1411	—	1285	11
D344	3124	D345	2767	D346	2468	D347	2215	D348	1999	D349	1813	D350	1652	12
D355	4082	D356	3616	D357	3225	D358	2894	D359	2612	D360	2369	D361	2159	13
D366	4610	D367	4084	D368	3643	D369	3269	D370	2950	D371	2676	D372	2438	14
D377	5206	D378	4611	D379	4113	D380	3692	D381	3332	D382	3022	D383	2753	15
D388	5943	D389	5265	D390	4696	D391	4214	D392	3803	D393	3450	D394	3143	16
D399	6572	D400	5821	D401	5192	D402	4660	D403	4206	D404	3815	D405	3476	17
D410	7419	D411	6572	D412	5862	D413	5261	D414	4748	D415	4307	D416	3924	18
D421	8115	D422	7188	D423	6412	D424	5755	D425	5193	D426	4711	D427	4292	19
D432	9074	D433	8038	D434	7169	D435	6434	D436	5807	D437	5267	D438	4799	20

$d = h - (2'' +$ distance from bottom of bars to their centroid).

REINFORCED CONCRETE BEAMS

CONTINUOUS INTERIOR SPANS

The tables on pages 10-34 to 10-39 incl. give the total safe uniform load per lineal foot (live and dead) * on reinforced concrete beams for the interior spans only of continuous runs of beams, computed in conformity with the American Concrete Institute's "Building Code Requirements for Reinforced Concrete (ACI 318-63)"; for span lengths varying from 10 to 44 feet in two-foot multiples; for one set of stresses, viz. $f_s = 24{,}000$ psi and $f_c = 1688$ psi; for depths from 12 to 30 inches in two-inch multiples, 36 and 42 inches; for varying widths (b', page 10-33) in each depth; with bar combinations to produce balanced reinforcement ($p = 0.0129$) for a rectangular beam of the size given.

There is no great advantage in listing much more heavily reinforced continuous beams, because negative bending quite sharply limits their maximum capacity. Following the argument developed for this same situation for the continuous end of an end span, it can be shown that the limit is nearer $\left(\frac{11 \times 500}{16 \times 271 \times (1.1)^2}\right) = 1.05$ than 1.39 (see page 10-18).

The limitations and arrangement of the following table parallel so closely those of the single span that pages 10-3 to 10-5 should be studied carefully before reading further. This applies especially to stirrup arrangements and bond, and to the fact that bars must meet ASTM A305, and that carrying capacity is taken as the least of the limits set by shear, bond, positive or negative flexure.

The following example may prove useful for those who wish to design beyond the scope of the tables or to see how they were prepared:—

Example—For the table on page 10-38, determine the safe carrying capacity on an interior span (of a continuous run) of 22 feet of a 14 × 26 in. beam stem reinforced with 3-#6 bottom bars, 2-#9 truss bars, all in one layer, and 1-#9 top bar over each support, assuming 2-#9 truss bars bent up and extended through from adjacent span. Check the stirrup combination B978.

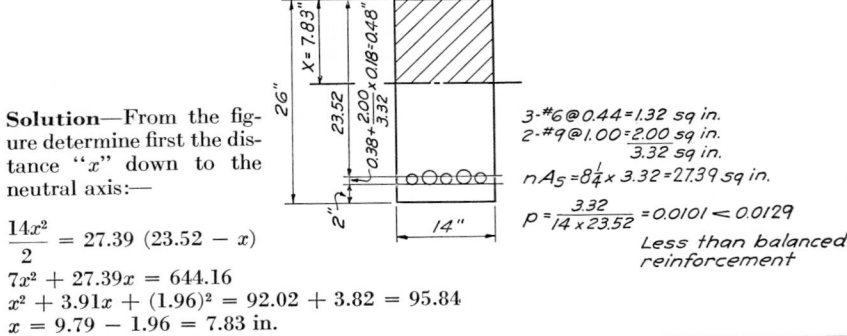

Solution—From the figure determine first the distance "x" down to the neutral axis:—

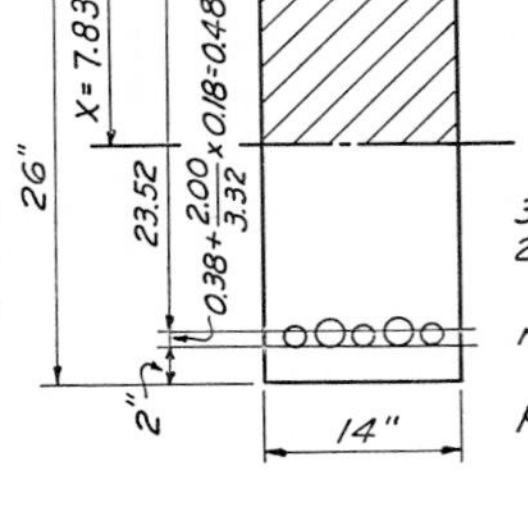

3-#6 @ 0.44 = 1.32 sq in.
2-#9 @ 1.00 = 2.00 sq in.
3.32 sq in.

$nA_s = 8\frac{1}{4} \times 3.32 = 27.39$ sq in.

$p = \frac{3.32}{14 \times 23.52} = 0.0101 < 0.0129$

Less than balanced reinforcement

$$\frac{14x^2}{2} = 27.39\,(23.52 - x)$$

$$7x^2 + 27.39x = 644.16$$

$$x^2 + 3.91x + (1.96)^2 = 92.02 + 3.82 = 95.84$$

$$x = 9.79 - 1.96 = 7.83 \text{ in.}$$

* In the various slab tables throughout this book, the weight of the slab has been deducted so that the values given in the tables are the safe superimposed loads. In the case of beams, there is no advantage in deducting the minor weight of the beam stem, as it is the weight of the tributary slab that is the main element of dead load. So in these tables the capacity given is the total safe load, dead plus live.

REINFORCED CONCRETE BEAMS
CONTINUOUS INTERIOR SPANS

Positive Flexure—The arm of the internal couple, $jd = 23.52 - \dfrac{7.83}{3} = 20.91$ in.

$$M_s = A_s f_s\, jd = 3.32 \times 24{,}000 \times 20.91 = 1{,}666{,}000 \text{ lb-in.}$$
$$M_c = bkd\frac{f_c}{2}jd = 14 \times 7.83 \times \frac{1688}{2} \times 20.91 = 1{,}935{,}000 \text{ lb-in.}$$

} a somewhat under-reinforced beam.

$$w = \frac{M}{l'^2\frac{12}{16}} = \frac{1{,}666{,}000}{22 \times 22 \times \frac{12}{16}} = 4590 \text{ plf (4589 in table)}$$

Bond on Bottom Bars—The bond on the bottom bars is to be computed in that part of the positive bending zone which has the highest external shear, i.e., the point of inflection. Since the maximum positive moment is $wl'^2/16$, the point of inflection is 0.147 l' from the support (chart, page 4-21), at which point the shear is approximately 70 per cent of $wl'/2$.

$$u = \frac{4.8\sqrt{3750}}{3/4} = 392 \text{ psi}$$
$$V = \Sigma o jdu = 3 \times 2.356 \times 20.91 \times 392 = 58{,}700 \text{ lb}$$
$$w = \frac{58{,}700}{0.70 \times 11} = 7630 \text{ plf} > 4590 \text{ plf, (allowed by flexure)}$$

Shear—At distance $d = 23.52'' = 1.96$ ft from the face of the support

$$V = 4590\,(11 - 1.96) = 41{,}490 \text{ lb.}$$
$$v = \frac{V}{bd} = \frac{41{,}490}{14 \times 23.52} = 126 \text{ psi}$$
$$v_c = 1.1\sqrt{3750} = 67.4 \text{ psi} \qquad v - v_c = 58.6 \text{ psi on stirrups @ } f_v = 20{,}000 \text{ psi}$$

Neglecting bent bars, as on page 10-20, and from the sketch, the three portions of the span that need web reinforcement require:—*

1—From support for distance d, $A'_v = \dfrac{58.6 \times 14 \times 23.52}{20{,}000} = 0.97$ sq in.
  2″ + 5-#3 stirrups @ 5″ = 1.10 sq in.

2—For distance a, as shown in the figure, A''_v = 1.04 sq in.
  5-#3 stirrups @ 3½, 5, 6, 8, 9 (19″) = 1.10 sq in. (1½″ in rectangle. + 3½″ in triangle = 5″ c/c stirrups).
  2-#3 stirrups @ 10″, 10″ (to fill out triangle).

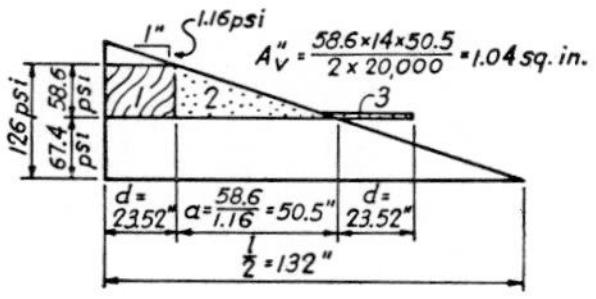

3—For distance d beyond a, $A'''_v = 0.0015 \times 14 \times 23.52 = 0.50$ sq in.
  3-#3 stirrups @ 10, 10, 10, = 0.66 sq in.

To explain a little further, the first stirrup is 2 in. from the support, then four spaces at 5 in. ends about 1½ in. inside distance d. Five more stirrups end about 19 in. inside the triangular prism, requiring 2 @ 10 in. The distance d then requires over two so say three stirrups at 10 in.

Negative Flexure—By Code, the negative moment is to be taken as $wl^2_{av}/11$, and the adjacent span is limited to a range between $\ngtr 0.833\ l'$ and $\nless 1.20\ l'$. With varying span lengths, different amounts of steel will be bent up. This computation is based upon the assumption that the adjacent span = 1.00 l' and the truss bars in it are also 2-#9. Then:—

$$-M = -wl'^2/11$$

* Assuming live load over one-half the span, the maximum live shear should not be taken as zero at midspan but as $wl'/8$ (one-quarter of the end shear); against this the bent-up bars provide some web reinforcement.

REINFORCED CONCRETE BEAMS
CONTINUOUS INTERIOR SPANS

Since the added top bar increases A_s over the area used in "positive flexure," and since p is quite a bit over 0.0129, the beam is overreinforced and compressive steel is needed, obtained by lapping the bottom bars 24 diameters past each other, thus affording 3-#6 for compression. From the figure below, compute x by taking moments about the bottom of the beam and using $2n$ times A'_s as per ACI 71102(c).

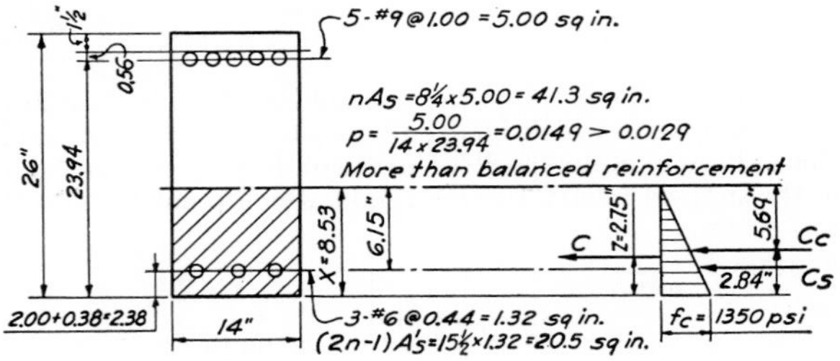

$$x = \frac{\frac{14x^2}{2} + (20.5 \times 2.38) + (41.3 \times 23.94)}{14x + 20.5 + 41.3}$$

$$7x^2 + 61.8x = 48.8 + 990 = 1038.8$$
$$x^2 + 8.83x + (4.41)^2 = 148.4 + 19.6 = 168.0$$
$$x = -4.41 \pm 12.94 = 8.53 \text{ in.}$$

$$C_c = \frac{8.53 \times 1688 \times 14}{2} = 101{,}000 \text{ lb}$$

$$C_s = 20.5 \times \frac{6.15}{8.53} \times 1688 = \underline{25{,}900 \text{ lb}}$$

$$C = C_c + C_s = 126{,}900 \text{ lb}$$

$$z = 2.38 + \frac{101.0}{126.9} \times \left(\frac{8.53}{3} - 2.38\right) = 2.72 \text{ in.}; \quad jd = 23.94 - 2.72 = 21.22 \text{ in.}$$

$$M_c = 126{,}900 \times 21.22 = 2{,}700{,}000 \text{ lb-in.}$$
$$M_s = 5.00 \times 24{,}000 \times 21.22 = 2{,}540{,}000 \text{ lb-in.}$$

$$w = \frac{2{,}540{,}000 \times 11}{22 \times 22 \times 12} = 4820 \text{ plf} > 4589 \text{ plf, so positive moment}$$

governs (when $l'' \lesseqgtr l'$).

Bond on Negative Bars—The maximum end shear:—

$$V = 4589 \times 11 = 50{,}500 \text{ lb}$$

This is taken by 5-#9. Then $u = \frac{V}{\Sigma o j d} = \frac{50{,}500}{5 \times 3.544 \times 21.22} =$

$$137 \text{ psi} < \left(\frac{3.4\sqrt{3750}}{1.128} = 184 \text{ psi}\right)$$

Comment—The bending and extension of truss bars, possible staggering of bends, length of top bar, extension or lap of bottom bars, and so on can be computed, but the foregoing is sufficient to illustrate the make-up of the tables.

Under the extreme case of $l'' = 1.20\, l'$, it would be necessary to check negative flexure to make sure both that the extra top bar combined with the truss bars from the two spans provides sufficient tension steel (adding extra top steel if needed) and that the bottom bars provide sufficient compression steel (extending the bars through the support if necessary to increase the area available and carrying them out to a point where the concrete alone provides adequate compression resistance).

CONTINUOUS REINFORCED CONCRETE BEAMS—INTERIOR SPANS

Applies to the Tables on pages 10-34 to 10-40.

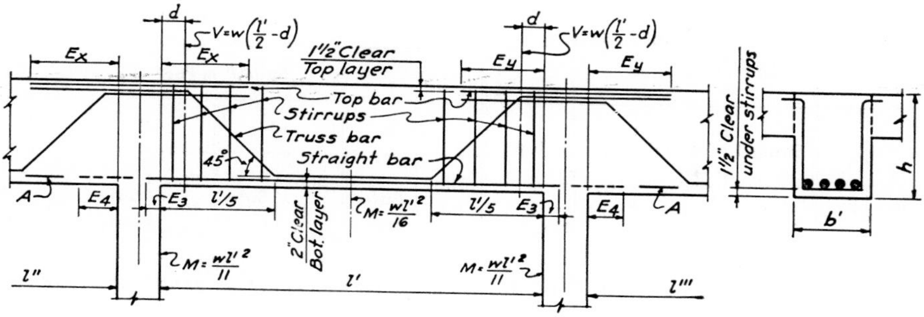

STRESSES:—

$f_s = 24{,}000$ psi

$f'_c = 3750$ psi

$f_c = 1688$ psi

$v_c = 1.1\sqrt{f'_c} = 67.4$ psi

$v = \begin{cases} 3\sqrt{f'_c} = 183 \text{ psi} \\ 5\sqrt{f'_c} = 306 \text{ psi} \end{cases}$

$u = \dfrac{4.8\sqrt{f'_c}}{D}$ psi for bottom bars

$= \dfrac{3.4\sqrt{f'_c}}{D}$ psi for top bars with over 12″ of concrete under them. (See page 3-13).

CODES:—

"Building Code Requirements for Reinforced Concrete (ACI 318-63)," also "Manual of Standard Practice for Detailing Reinforced Concrete Structures (ACI 315)."

E_3 = bottom bar to extend 6 in. into the support except when values in the load tables are printed in boldface type.

E_4 = When the values in the load tables are printed in boldface type, bottom bars must lap bars of adjoining span 29 D^2 so that they may serve for compressive reinforcement, as shown in the example in the text. Closed ties are required in compressive areas.*

$E_x = E_y = 0.3l'$ or $0.3l''$ whichever is greater

Extend top bars past the innermost position of the point of inflection $l/16$, or the effective depth, d, whichever is greater.

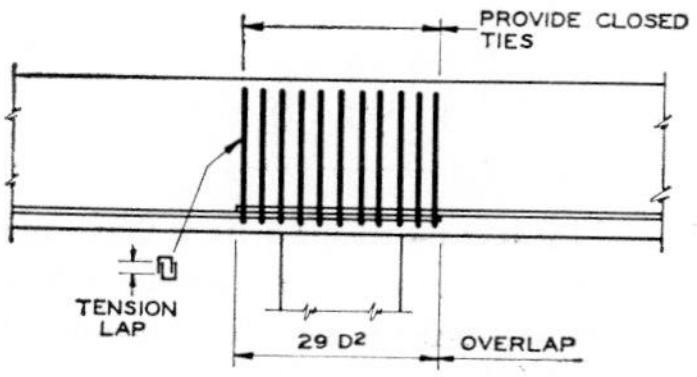

WHERE POSSIBLE, USE TWO-PIECE CLOSED TIES FOR EASIER ASSEMBLY IN FORMS.

A = Bars in adjoining span, not shown.

For stirrup combinations, see pages 10-42 to 10-58.

* E_4—Closed ties required

CONTINUOUS REINFORCED CONCRETE BEAMS—INTERIOR SPANS

For limitations and use of this table, see pages 10-30 to 10-33.

	Stem		Bar Combinations							TOTAL SAFE CARRYING CAPACITY* (plf)— UNIFORMLY DISTRIBUTED							
										Span l' in Feet							
			Straight		Trussed		No. Layers	Top		8		10		12		14	
	h (in.)	b′ (in.)	No.	Size	No.	Size		No.	Size	Stirrup Mark	Safe Load	Stirrup Mark	Safe Load	Stirrup Mark	Safe Load	Stirrup Mark	Safe Load
1	12	6	1	#5	1	#4	1	1	#6	B557	2217	B558	1419	B559	985	B560	724
2		8	2	#4	1	#5	1	1	#6	B562	3084	B563	1973	B564	1370	B565	1007
3		10	2	#4	1	#6	1	1	#6	B567	3643	B568	2331	B569	1619	B570	1189
4			2	#4	2	#5	1	1	#5	B572	**4395**	B573	**2813**	B574	**1953**	B575	**1435**
5	14	8	2	#4	1	#5	1	1	#6	B578	3751	B579	2400	B580	1667	B581	1224
6			1	#6	1	#7	1	1	#6	B583	3380	B584	2704	B585	**2253**	B586	**1740**
7		10	2	#4	2	#5	1	1	#5	B592	5349	B593	3423	B594	2377	B595	1746
8		12	2	#5	2	#6	1	1	#6	B598	6810	B599	**4957**	B600	**3442**	B601	**2529**
9			2	#6	3	#5	1	1	#8	B607	6751	B608	**5400**	B609	**4117**	B610	**3024**
10	16	8	2	#4	1	#5	1	1	#6	B618	4421	B619	2829	B620	1965	B621	1443
11			2	#4	1	#7	1	1	#5	B623	6091	B624	3898	B625	2707	B626	1989
12		10	2	#4	2	#5	1	1	#5	B632	6308	B633	4037	B634	2803	B635	2060
13			2	#5	2	#6	1	1	#6	B638	7969	B639	**5801**	B640	**4028**	B641	**2959**
14		12	2	#6	3	#5	1	1	#8	B649	7972	B650	**6378**	B651	**4862**	B652	**3572**
15			2	#6	2	#7	1	1	#8	B660	7873	B661	6298	B662	**5248**	B663	**4053**
16	18	8	2	#4	1	#5	1	1	#6	B671	5095	B672	3260	B673	2264	B674	1663
17		10	2	#4	2	#5	1	1	#5	B676	7272	B677	4654	B678	3232	B679	2374
18			2	#5	2	#6	1	1	#6	B682	9200	B683	**6697**	B684	**4650**	B685	**3416**
19		12	2	#6	3	#5	1	1	#8	B693	9203	B694	7362	B695	**5612**	B696	**4123**
20			2	#6	2	#7	1	1	#8	B704	9097	B705	7278	B706	**6065**	B707	**4684**
21			3	#5	2	#7	1	1	#8	B715	**13653**	B716	**9408**	B717	**6533**	B718	**4800**

* Deduct dead load from these values.

Where dash occurs in stirrup column, no stirrups are required.

Extend bottom bars to E_4 (page 10-33) for values in boldface type.

CONTINUOUS REINFORCED CONCRETE BEAMS—INTERIOR SPANS

For stirrup combinations, see pages 10-42 to 10-58, incl.

TOTAL SAFE CARRYING CAPACITY* (plf)—
UNIFORMLY DISTRIBUTED

Span l' in Feet

16		18		20		22		24		26		28		
Stir-rup Mark	Safe Load	Stir-rup Mark	Safe Load	Stir-rup Mark	Safe Load	Stir-rup Mark	Safe Load	Stir-rup Mark	Safe Load	Stir-rup Mark	Safe Load	Stir-rup Mark	Safe Load	
B561	554	—	438	—	354	—	293	—	246					1
B566	771	—	609	—	493	—	407	—	342					2
B571	910	—	719	—	582	—	481	—	404					3
B576	1098	B577	868	—	703	—	581	—	488					4
B582	937	—	741	—	600	—	496	—	416	—	355	—	306	5
B587	1332	B588	1052	B589	852	B590	704	B591	592	—	504	—	435	6
B596	1337	B597	1056	—	855	—	707	—	594	—	506	—	436	7
B602	1936	B603	1530	B604	1239	B605	1024	B606	860	—	733	—	632	8
B611	2315	B612	1829	B613	1482	B614	1224	B615	1029	B616	877	B617	756	9
B622	1105	—	873	—	707	—	584	—	491	—	418	—	360	10
B627	1522	B628	1203	B629	974	B630	805	B631	676	—	576	—	497	11
B636	1577	B637	1246	—	1009	—	834	—	700	—	597	—	515	12
B642	2266	B643	1790	B644	1450	B645	1198	B646	1007	B647	858	B648	739	13
B653	2735	B654	2161	B655	1750	B656	1446	B657	1215	B658	1035	B659	893	14
B664	3103	B665	2452	B666	1986	B667	1641	B668	1379	B669	1175	B670	1013	15
B675	1273	—	1006	—	815	—	673	—	566	—	482	—	415	16
B680	1818	B681	1436	—	1163	—	961	—	808	—	688	—	593	17
B686	2616	B687	2067	B688	1674	B689	1383	B690	1162	B691	990	B692	854	18
B697	3157	B698	2494	B699	2020	B700	1669	B701	1403	B702	1195	B703	1030	19
B708	3586	B709	2833	B710	2295	B711	1896	B712	1593	B713	1358	B714	1171	20
B719	3675	B720	2903	B721	2352	B722	1943	B723	1633	B724	1391	B725	1200	21

$d = h - (2'' +$ distance from bottom of bars to their centroid).

CONTINUOUS REINFORCED CONCRETE BEAMS—INTERIOR SPANS

For limitations and use of this table, see pages 10-30 to 10-33.

	Stem		Bar Combinations							TOTAL SAFE CARRYING CAPACITY* (plf)— UNIFORMLY DISTRIBUTED							
										Span l' in Feet							
			Straight		Trussed		No. Layers	Top		16		18		20		22	
	h (in.)	b′ (in.)	No.	Size	No.	Size		No.	Size	Stirrup Mark	Safe Load	Stirrup Mark	Safe Load	Stirrup Mark	Safe Load	Stirrup Mark	Safe Load
1		8	2	#4	1	#5	1	1	#6	—	1442	—	1139	—	923	—	763
2		10	2	#4	2	#5	1	1	#5	B726	2059	B727	1627	—	1318	—	1089
3			2	#5	2	#6	1	1	#6	B728	2967	B729	2344	B730	1899	B731	1569
4	20	12	2	#6	3	#5	1	1	#8	B735	3581	B736	2829	B737	2291	B738	1894
5			2	#6	2	#7	1	1	#8	B742	**4071**	B743	**3216**	B744	**2605**	B745	**2153**
6			3	#5	2	#7	1	1	#8	B751	**4171**	B752	**3295**	B753	**2669**	B754	**2206**
7			2	#6	2	#8	1	1	#6	B761	**4761**	B762	**3762**	B763	**3047**	B764	**2518**
8		8	2	#4	1	#5	1	1	#6	—	1611	—	1273	—	1031	—	852
9		10	2	#4	2	#5	1	1	#5	B772	2302	B773	1819	—	1473	—	1217
10			2	#5	2	#6	1	1	#6	B774	3320	B775	2623	B776	2124	B777	1756
11		12	2	#6	3	#5	1	1	#8	B781	4006	B782	3165	B783	2564	B784	2119
12	22		2	#6	2	#7	1	1	#8	B788	4557	B789	3601	B790	2917	B791	2410
13			3	#5	2	#7	1	1	#8	B797	4669	B798	3689	B799	2988	B800	2469
14			2	#6	2	#8	1	1	#6	B807	**5333**	B808	**4214**	B809	**3413**	B810	**2821**
15			2	#7	2	#8	1	1	#9	B818	**5679**	B819	**4728**	B820	**3829**	B821	**3165**
16		14	2	#7	2	#9	1	1	#8	B829	5670	B830	**5040**	B831	**4401**	B832	**3637**
17			3	#6	2	#9	1	1	#9	B840	**7131**	B841	**5634**	B842	**4564**	B843	**3772**
18		10	2	#4	1	#5	1	1	#6	—	1795	—	1418	—	1149	—	949
19			2	#4	2	#5	1	1	#5	B851	2545	—	2011	—	1628	—	1346
20			2	#5	2	#6	1	1	#6	B852	3673	B853	2902	B854	2351	B855	1943
21		12	2	#6	3	#5	1	1	#8	B859	4433	B860	3502	B861	2837	B862	2344
22	24		3	#5	2	#7	1	1	#8	B866	5168	B867	4084	B868	3308	B869	2733
23			2	#6	2	#8	1	1	#6	B875	**5908**	B876	**4668**	B877	**3781**	B878	**3124**
24			2	#8	1	#9	1	2	#9	B886	**6160**	B887	**4867**	B888	**3942**	B889	**3258**
25		14	2	#7	2	#8	1	1	#9	B897	6341	B898	5278	B899	4275	B900	3533
26			2	#7	2	#9	1	1	#8	B908	6283	B909	**5585**	B910	**4877**	B911	**4030**
27			3	#6	2	#9	1	1	#9	B919	**7902**	B920	**6244**	B921	**5057**	B922	**4179**

* Deduct dead load from these values.
Where dash occurs in stirrup column, no stirrups are required.
Extend bottom bars to E_4 (page 10-33) for values in boldface type.

CONTINUOUS REINFORCED CONCRETE BEAMS—INTERIOR SPANS

For stirrup combinations, see pages 10-42 to 10-58, incl.

TOTAL SAFE CARRYING CAPACITY* (plf)— UNIFORMLY DISTRIBUTED														
Span l' in Feet														
24		26		28		30		32		34		36		
Stir-rup Mark	Safe Load	Stir-rup Mark	Safe Load	Stir-rup Mark	Safe Load	Stir-rup Mark	Safe Load	Stir-rup Mark	Safe Load	Stir-rup Mark	Safe Load	Stir-rup Mark	Safe Load	
—	641	—	546	—	471	—	410	—	360	—	319	—	284	1
—	915	—	780	—	672	—	585	—	514	—	456	—	406	2
B732	1318	*B733*	1123	*B734*	968	—	844	—	741	—	657	—	586	3
B739	1591	*B740*	1356	*B741*	1169	—	1018	—	895	—	793	—	707	4
B746	**1809**	*B747*	**1541**	*B748*	**1329**	*B749*	**1158**	*B750*	**1017**	—	**901**	—	**804**	5
B755	**1853**	*B756*	**1579**	*B757*	**1362**	*B758*	**1186**	*B759*	**1042**	*B760*	**923**	—	**823**	6
B765	**2116**	*B766*	**1803**	*B767*	**1554**	*B768*	**1354**	*B769*	**1190**	*B770*	**1054**	*B771*	**940**	7
—	716	—	610	—	526	—	458	—	402	—	356	—	318	8
—	1023	—	871	—	751	—	654	—	575	—	509	—	454	9
B778	1475	*B779*	1257	*B780*	1084	—	944	—	830	—	735	—	655	10
B785	1780	*B786*	1517	*B787*	1308	—	1139	—	1001	—	887	—	791	11
B792	2025	*B793*	1726	*B794*	1488	*B795*	1296	*B796*	1139	—	1009	—	900	12
B801	2075	*B802*	1768	*B803*	1524	*B804*	1328	*B805*	1167	*B806*	1034	—	922	13
B811	**2370**	*B812*	**2019**	*B813*	**1741**	*B814*	**1517**	*B815*	**1333**	*B816*	**1181**	*B817*	**1053**	14
B822	**2659**	*B823*	**2266**	*B824*	**1953**	*B825*	**1702**	*B826*	**1495**	*B827*	**1325**	*B828*	**1182**	15
B833	**3056**	*B834*	**2604**	*B835*	**2245**	*B836*	**1956**	*B837*	**1719**	*B838*	**1522**	*B839*	**1358**	16
B844	**3169**	*B845*	**2700**	*B846*	**2328**	*B847*	**2028**	*B848*	**1782**	*B849*	**1579**	*B850*	**1408**	17
—	797	—	679	—	586	—	510	—	448	—	397	—	354	18
—	1131	—	963	—	831	—	723	—	636	—	563	—	502	19
B856	1632	*B857*	1391	*B858*	1199	—	1045	—	918	—	813	—	725	20
B863	1970	*B864*	1678	*B865*	1447	—	1261	—	1108	—	981	—	875	21
B870	2297	*B871*	1957	*B872*	1687	*B873*	1470	*B874*	1292	—	1144	—	1021	22
B879	**2625**	*B880*	**2237**	*B881*	**1929**	*B882*	**1680**	*B883*	**1477**	*B884*	**1308**	*B885*	**1167**	23
B890	**2738**	*B891*	**2333**	*B892*	**2011**	*B893*	**1752**	*B894*	**1540**	*B895*	**1364**	*B896*	**1216**	24
B901	2969	*B902*	2530	*B903*	2181	*B904*	1900	*B905*	1670	*B906*	1479	*B907*	1319	25
B912	**3387**	*B913*	**2886**	*B914*	**2488**	*B915*	**2167**	*B916*	**1905**	*B917*	**1687**	*B918*	**1505**	26
B923	**3512**	*B924*	**2992**	*B925*	**2580**	*B926*	**2247**	*B927*	**1975**	*B928*	**1750**	*B929*	**1561**	27

$d = h - (2'' +$ distance from bottom of bars to their centroid).

CONTINUOUS REINFORCED CONCRETE BEAMS—INTERIOR SPANS

For limitations and use of this table, see pages 10-30 to 10-33.

	Stem		Bar Combinations							TOTAL SAFE CARRYING CAPACITY* (plf)—UNIFORMLY DISTRIBUTED							
										Span l' in Feet							
			Straight		Trussed		No. Layers	Top		20		22		24		26	
	h (in.)	b′ (in.)	No.	Size	No.	Size		No.	Size	Stirrup Mark	Safe Load	Stirrup Mark	Safe Load	Stirrup Mark	Safe Load	Stirrup Mark	Safe Load
1		10	2	#4	1	#5	1	1	#6	—	1258	—	1039	—	873	—	744
2			2	#4	2	#5	1	1	#5	—	1784	—	1475	—	1239	—	1056
3			2	#5	2	#6	1	1	#6	B930	2578	B931	2130	B932	1790	B933	1525
4		12	2	#6	3	#5	1	1	#8	B934	3111	B935	2571	B936	2160	B937	1840
5	26		3	#5	2	#7	1	1	#8	B938	3628	B939	2999	B940	2520	B941	2147
6			2	#6	2	#8	1	1	#6	B945	4149	B946	3429	B947	2881	B948	2455
7			2	#7	2	#8	1	1	#9	B955	**4658**	B956	**3849**	B957	**3234**	B958	**2756**
8		14	2	#7	2	#9	1	1	#8	B966	**5355**	B967	**4425**	B968	**3718**	B969	**3168**
9			3	#6	2	#9	1	1	#9	B977	**5552**	B978	**4589**	B979	**3856**	B980	**3285**
10		12	2	#4	2	#5	1	1	#5	—	1953	—	1614	—	1356	—	1155
11			2	#5	2	#6	1	1	#6	B988	2826	—	2335	—	1962	—	1672
12			2	#6	3	#5	1	1	#8	B989	3385	B990	2798	B991	2351	B992	2003
13			3	#5	2	#7	1	1	#8	B993	3950	B994	3264	B995	2743	B996	2337
14			2	#6	2	#8	1	1	#6	C000	4519	C001	3735	C002	3138	C003	2674
15			2	#7	2	#8	1	1	#9	C010	5074	C011	4193	C012	3523	C013	3002
16	28		2	#7	2	#9	1	1	#8	C021	**5790**	C022	**4785**	C023	**4021**	C024	**3426**
17		14	3	#6	2	#9	1	1	#9	C032	**6049**	C033	**4999**	C034	**4200**	C035	**3579**
18			4	#6	3	#8	2	1	#10	C043	**7147**	C044	**5907**	C045	**4963**	C046	**4229**
19		16	4	#6	4	#8	2	1	#9	C054	**8449**	C055	**6983**	C056	**5867**	C057	**4999**
20		18	5	#6	4	#8	2	1	#11	C065	**9260**	C066	**7653**	C067	**6430**	C068	**5479**
21		12	2	#4	2	#5	1	1	#5	—	2110	—	1743	—	1465	—	1248
22			2	#5	2	#6	1	1	#6	C076	3055	—	2524	—	2121	—	1807
23			2	#6	3	#5	1	1	#8	C077	3660	C078	3025	C079	2542	C080	2166
24			3	#5	2	#7	1	1	#8	C081	4272	C082	3531	C083	2967	C084	2528
25			2	#6	2	#8	1	1	#6	C088	4890	C089	4041	C090	3395	C091	2893
26			2	#7	2	#8	1	1	#9	C098	5491	C099	4538	C100	3813	C101	3249
27	30		2	#7	2	#9	1	1	#8	C109	**6268**	C110	**5180**	C111	**4353**	C112	**3709**
28		14	3	#6	2	#9	1	1	#9	C120	6547	C121	5410	C122	4546	C123	3874
29			4	#6	3	#8	2	1	#10	C131	**7761**	C132	**6414**	C133	**5390**	C134	**4592**
30		16	4	#6	4	#8	2	1	#9	C142	**9179**	C143	**7586**	C144	**6374**	C145	**5431**
31		18	5	#6	4	#8	2	1	#11	C153	**10056**	C154	**8311**	C155	**6984**	C156	**5950**

* Deduct dead load from these values.
Where dash occurs in stirrup column, no stirrups are required.
Extend bottom bars to E_4 (page 10-33) for values in boldface type.

CONTINUOUS REINFORCED CONCRETE BEAMS—INTERIOR SPANS

For stirrup combinations, see pages 10-42 to 10-58, incl.

TOTAL SAFE CARRYING CAPACITY* (plf)—
UNIFORMLY DISTRIBUTED

Span l' in Feet														
28		30		32		34		36		38		40		
Stirrup Mark	Safe Load	Stirrup Mark	Safe Load	Stirrup Mark	Safe Load	Stirrup Mark	Safe Load	Stirrup Mark	Safe Load	Stirrup Mark	Safe Load	Stirrup Mark	Safe Load	
—	642	—	559	—	491	—	435	—	388	—	348	—	314	1
—	910	—	793	—	697	—	617	—	550	—	494	—	446	2
—	1315	—	1145	—	1007	—	892	—	795	—	714	—	644	3
—	1587	—	1382	—	1215	—	1076	—	960	—	861	—	777	4
B942	1851	B943	1612	B944	1417	—	1255	—	1120	—	1005	—	907	5
B949	2117	B950	1844	B951	1621	B952	1435	B953	1280	B954	1149	—	1037	6
B959	**2376**	B960	**2070**	B961	**1819**	B962	**1611**	B963	**1437**	B964	**1290**	B965	**1164**	7
B970	**2732**	B971	**2380**	B972	**2091**	B973	**1853**	B974	**1652**	B975	**1483**	B976	**1338**	8
B981	**2833**	B982	**2467**	B983	**2169**	B984	**1921**	B985	**1713**	B986	**1538**	B987	**1388**	9
—	996	—	868	—	762	—	675	—	602	—	541	—	488	10
—	1441	—	1256	—	1103	—	977	—	872	—	782	—	706	11
—	1727	—	1504	—	1322	—	1171	—	1044	—	937	—	846	12
B997	2015	B998	1755	B999	1543	—	1366	—	1219	—	1094	—	987	13
C004	2305	C005	2008	C006	1765	C007	1563	C008	1394	C009	1251	—	1129	14
C014	2589	C015	2255	C016	1982	C017	1755	C018	1566	C019	1405	C020	1268	15
C025	**2954**	C026	**2573**	C027	**2261**	C028	**2003**	C029	**1787**	C030	**1603**	C031	**1447**	16
C036	**3086**	C037	**2688**	C038	**2363**	C039	**2093**	C040	**1867**	C041	**1675**	C042	**1512**	17
C047	**3646**	C048	**3176**	C049	**2792**	C050	**2473**	C051	**2206**	C052	**1980**	C053	**1786**	18
C058	**4311**	C059	**3755**	C060	**3300**	C061	**2923**	C062	**2607**	C063	**2340**	C064	**2112**	19
C069	**4724**	C070	**4115**	C071	**3617**	C072	**3204**	C073	**2858**	C074	**2565**	C075	**2315**	20
—	1076	—	937	—	824	—	730	—	651	—	584	—	527	21
—	1558	—	1357	—	1193	—	1057	—	942	—	846	—	763	22
—	1867	—	1627	—	1429	—	1266	—	1129	—	1014	—	915	23
C085	2179	C086	1898	C087	1669	—	1478	—	1318	—	1183	—	1068	24
C092	2495	C093	2173	C094	1910	C095	1692	C096	1509	C097	1354	—	1222	25
C102	2801	C103	2440	C104	2145	C105	1900	C106	1694	C107	1521	C108	1372	26
C113	**3198**	C114	**2785**	C115	**2448**	C116	**2168**	C117	**1934**	C118	**1736**	C119	**1567**	27
C124	3340	C125	2909	C126	2557	C127	2265	C128	2020	C129	1813	C130	1636	28
C135	**3960**	C136	**3449**	C137	**3032**	C138	**2685**	C139	**2395**	C140	**2150**	C141	**1940**	29
C146	**4683**	C147	**4079**	C148	**3585**	C149	**3176**	C150	**2833**	C151	**2542**	C152	**2294**	30
C157	**5131**	C158	**4469**	C159	**3928**	C160	**3479**	C161	**3104**	C162	**2785**	C163	**2514**	31

$d = h - (2'' +$ distance from bottom of bars to their centroid).

CONTINUOUS REINFORCED CONCRETE BEAMS—INTERIOR SPANS

For limitations and use of this table, see pages 10-30 to 10-33.

	Stem h (in.)	Stem b′ (in.)	Straight No.	Straight Size	Trussed No.	Trussed Size	No. Layers	Top No.	Top Size	Span 24: Stirrup Mark	Span 24: Safe Load	Span 26: Stirrup Mark	Span 26: Safe Load	Span 28: Stirrup Mark	Span 28: Safe Load	Span 30: Stirrup Mark	Span 30: Safe Load
1	36†	12	2	#7	2	#7	1	1	#10	D439	4075	D440	3472	D441	2994	D442	2608
2			2	#7	2	#9	1	1	#8	D446	5353	D447	4561	D448	3933	D449	3426
3		16	2	#7	3	#8	1	1	#7	D457	6027	D458	5135	D459	4428	D460	3857
4			3	#7	2	#10	1	1	#10	D466	7246	D467	6174	D468	5324	D469	4637
5			3	#7	4	#8	2	1	#9	D477	**7941**	D478	**6766**	D479	**5834**	D480	**5082**
6		20	3	#7	5	#8	2	1	#7	D488	9210	D489	7848	D490	6767	D491	5894
7			4	#7	4	#9	1	1	#11	D499	**10614**	D500	**9044**	D501	**7798**	D502	**6793**
8			4	#7	5	#9	2	1	#8	D510	**11697**	D511	**9966**	D512	**8593**	D513	**7486**
9		24	5	#7	4	#10	2	2	#9	D521	**12854**	D522	**10953**	D523	**9444**	D524	**8227**
10			5	#8	4	#10	2	2	#11	D532	**14302**	D533	**12186**	D534	**10508**	D535	**9153**
11	42†	12	2	#7	2	#7	1	1	#10	D543	4836	D544	4120	D545	3553	D546	3095
12			2	#7	2	#9	1	1	#8	D549	6359	D550	5418	D551	4672	D552	4070
13		16	2	#7	3	#8	1	1	#7	D560	7155	D561	6096	D562	5256	D563	4579
14			3	#7	2	#10	1	1	#10	D569	8610	D570	7336	D571	6325	D572	5510
15			3	#7	4	#8	2	1	#9	D580	9491	D581	8087	D582	6973	D583	6074
16		20	3	#7	5	#8	2	1	#7	D591	11012	D592	9383	D593	8090	D594	7047
17			4	#7	4	#9	1	1	#11	D602	12615	D603	10749	D604	9268	D605	8073
18			4	#7	5	#9	2	1	#8	D613	**13996**	D614	**11926**	D615	**10283**	D616	**8957**
19		24	5	#7	4	#10	2	2	#9	D624	15373	D625	13099	D626	11294	D627	9839
20			5	#8	4	#10	2	2	#11	D635	**17107**	D636	**14576**	D637	**12568**	D638	**10948**

Column groups: Stem (h, b′); Bar Combinations (Straight, Trussed, No. Layers, Top); TOTAL SAFE CARRYING CAPACITY* (plf)—UNIFORMLY DISTRIBUTED, Span l' in Feet (24, 26, 28, 30).

* Deduct dead load from these values.

† Beams as deep as 36 and 42 in. may require more complete analysis of loading conditions, end restraints, deflections, etc.

Where dash occurs in stirrup column, no stirrups are required.

Extend bottom bars to E_4 (page 10-33) for values in boldface type.

CONTINUOUS REINFORCED CONCRETE BEAMS—INTERIOR SPANS

For stirrup combinations, see pages 10-42 to 10-58, incl.

TOTAL SAFE CARRYING CAPACITY* (plf)— UNIFORMLY DISTRIBUTED

Span l' in Feet														
32		34		36		38		40		42		44		
Stirrup Mark	Safe Load	Stirrup Mark	Safe Load	Stirrup Mark	Safe Load	Stirrup Mark	Safe Load	Stirrup Mark	Safe Load	Stirrup Mark	Safe Load	Stirrup Mark	Safe Load	
D443	2292	D444	2030	D445	1811	—	1625	—	1467	—	1330	—	1212	1
D450	3011	D451	2667	D452	2379	D453	2135	D454	1927	D455	1748	D456	1592	2
D461	3390	D462	3003	D463	2678	D464	2404	D465	2169	—	1968	—	1793	3
D470	4076	D471	3610	D472	3220	D473	2890	D474	2608	D475	2366	D476	2156	4
D481	4466	D482	3956	D483	3529	D484	3167	D485	2858	D486	2593	D487	2362	5
D492	5181	D493	4589	D494	4093	D495	3674	D496	3315	D497	3007	D498	2740	6
D503	5970	D504	5288	D505	4717	D506	4234	D507	3821	D508	3466	D509	3158	7
D514	6579	D515	5828	D516	5198	D517	4665	D518	4211	D519	3819	D520	3480	8
D525	7230	D526	6405	D527	5713	D528	5127	D529	4627	D530	4197	D531	3824	9
D536	8045	D537	7126	D538	6356	D539	5705	D540	5148	D541	4670	D542	4255	10
D547	2720	D548	2409	—	2149	—	1929	—	1741	—	1579	—	1438	11
D553	3577	D554	3168	D555	2826	D556	2536	D557	2289	D558	2076	D559	1892	12
D564	4024	D565	3565	D566	3180	D567	2854	D568	2575	—	2336	—	2128	13
D573	4843	D574	4290	D575	3826	D576	3434	D577	3099	D578	2811	D579	2561	14
D584	5339	D585	4729	D586	4218	D587	3786	D588	3417	D589	3099	D590	2823	15
D595	6194	D596	5487	D597	4894	D598	4392	D599	3964	D600	3595	D601	3276	16
D606	7096	D607	6285	D608	5606	D609	5032	D610	4541	D611	4119	D612	3753	17
D617	7873	D618	6974	D619	6220	D620	5583	D621	5038	D622	4570	D623	4164	18
D628	8647	D629	7660	D630	6832	D631	6132	D632	5534	D633	5019	D634	4573	19
D639	9622	D640	8524	D641	7603	D642	6823	D643	6158	D644	5586	D645	5089	20

$d = h - (2'' +$ distance from bottom of bars to their centroid).

STIRRUP COMBINATIONS

The method of computing stirrups is illustrated in the examples on pages 10-4, 10-19, and 10-30 and explained in detail on pages 4-23 ff.

For the beams scheduled on pages 10-8 to 10-41, each beam that requires stirrups has been given a consecutive reference of a letter and three numbers printed in italics. This table gives, for each reference number (also printed in italics), the corresponding number, size and spacing of stirrups.

Since these combinations were electronically computed in direct sequence by reference numbers, the items are not related to each other in number, size or spacing. Simply look up the reference number in direct sequence and find the desired stirrups.

Spacings are given from face of support towards center of span, and are for each end of the beam.

STIRRUPS FOR BEAMS IN PRECEDING TABLES

Mark	Number and size	Spacing on each end	Mark	Number and size	Spacing on each end	Mark	Number and size	Spacing on each end
A001	6-#3	2 4 4 4 4 4	*A061*	8-#3	2 5 5 5 5 5 5 5	*A121*	16-#3	2 15 @ 5
A002	8-#3	2 4 4 4 4 4 4 4	*A062*	7-#3	2 5 5 5 5 5 5	*A122*	16-#3	2 15 @ 5
A003	8-#3	2 4 4 4 4 4 4 4	*A063*	6-#3	2 5 5 5 5 5	*A123*	7-#3	2 5 5 5 5 5 5
A004	7-#3	2 4 4 4 4 4 4	*A064*	7-#3	2 5 5 5 5 5 5	*A124*	10-#3	2 4 4 4 5 5 5 5 5 5
A005	9-#3	2 4 4 4 4 4 4 4 4	*A065*	9-#3	2 5 5 5 5 5 5 5 5	*A125*	13-#3	1 3 3 3 3 4 4 6 @ 5
A006	9-#3	2 4 4 4 4 4 4 4 4	*A066*	9-#3	2 5 5 5 5 5 5 5 5	*A126*	15-#3	1 3 3 3 3 3 4 4 7 @ 5
A007	8-#3	2 4 4 4 4 4 4 4	*A067*	9-#3	2 5 5 5 5 5 5 5 5	*A127*	17-#3	1 3 3 3 3 3 3 4 4 8 @ 5
A008	7-#3	2 4 4 4 4 4 4	*A068*	9-#3	2 5 5 5 5 5 5 5 5	*A128*	19-#3	1 3 3 3 3 3 3 3 4 10 @ 5
A009	9-#3	2 4 4 4 4 4 4 4 4	*A069*	8-#3	2 5 5 5 5 5 5 5	*A129*	21-#3	1 3 3 3 3 3 3 3 4 4 11 @ 5
A010	10-#3	2 4 4 4 4 4 4 4 4 4	*A070*	7-#3	2 5 5 5 5 5 5	*A130*	20-#3	1 3 3 3 3 4 4 4 12 @ 5
A011	11-#3	2 4 4 4 4 4 4 4 4 4 4	*A071*	8-#3	2 5 5 5 5 5 5 5	*A131*	19-#3	2 4 4 4 4 14 @ 5
A012	11-#3	2 4 4 4 4 4 4 4 4 4 4	*A072*	9-#3	2 5 5 5 5 5 5 5 5	*A132*	6-#3	3 6 6 6 6 6
A013	10-#3	2 4 4 4 4 4 4 4 4 4	*A073*	9-#3	2 5 5 5 5 5 5 5 5	*A133*	6-#3	3 6 6 6 6 6
A014	9-#3	2 4 4 4 4 4 4 4 4	*A074*	10-#3	2 5 5 5 5 5 5 5 5 5	*A134*	6-#3	3 6 6 6 6 6
A015	7-#3	2 4 4 4 4 4 4	*A075*	9-#3	2 5 5 5 5 5 5 5 5	*A135*	6-#3	3 6 6 6 6 6
A016	9-#3	2 4 4 4 4 4 4 4 4	*A076*	8-#3	2 5 5 5 5 5 5 5	*A136*	7-#3	3 6 6 6 6 6 6
A017	10-#3	2 4 4 4 4 4 4 4 4 4	*A077*	7-#3	2 5 5 5 5 5 5	*A137*	6-#3	3 6 6 6 6 6
A018	12-#3	2 4 4 4 4 4 4 4 4 4 4 4	*A078*	6-#3	2 5 5 5 5 5	*A138*	6-#3	3 6 6 6 6 6
A019	13-#3	2 12 @ 4	*A079*	8-#3	2 5 5 5 5 5 5 5	*A139*	6-#3	3 6 6 6 6 6
A020	14-#3	1 3 3 3 3 3 8 @ 4	*A080*	9-#3	2 5 5 5 5 5 5 5 5	*A140*	7-#3	3 6 6 6 6 6 6
A021	13-#3	2 12 @ 4	*A081*	10-#3	2 5 5 5 5 5 5 5 5 5	*A141*	8-#3	3 6 6 6 6 6 6 6
A022	12-#3	2 4 4 4 4 4 4 4 4 4 4 4	*A082*	11-#3	2 5 5 5 5 5 5 5 5 5 5	*A142*	8-#3	3 6 6 6 6 6 6 6
A023	10-#3	2 4 4 4 4 4 4 4 4 4	*A083*	10-#3	2 5 5 5 5 5 5 5 5 5	*A143*	8-#3	3 6 6 6 6 6 6 6
A024	9-#3	2 4 4 4 4 4 4 4 4	*A084*	9-#3	2 5 5 5 5 5 5 5 5	*A144*	7-#3	3 6 6 6 6 6 6
A025	10-#3	2 4 4 4 4 4 4 4 4 4	*A085*	8-#3	2 5 5 5 5 5 5 5	*A145*	6-#3	3 6 6 6 6 6
A026	12-#3	2 4 4 4 4 4 4 4 4 4 4 4	*A086*	7-#3	2 5 5 5 5 5 5	*A146*	7-#3	3 6 6 6 6 6 6
A027	13-#3	2 12 @ 4	*A087*	6-#3	2 5 5 5 5 5	*A147*	8-#3	2 5 5 5 6 6 6 6
A028	14-#3	2 13 @ 4	*A088*	8-#3	2 5 5 5 5 5 5 5	*A148*	8-#3	3 6 6 6 6 6 6 6
A029	16-#2	1 3 3 3 3 3 3 9 @ 4	*A089*	9-#3	2 5 5 5 5 5 5 5 5	*A149*	8-#3	3 6 6 6 6 6 6 6
A030	14-#3	2 13 @ 4	*A090*	10-#3	2 5 5 5 5 5 5 5 5 5	*A150*	9-#3	2 5 5 5 5 5 5 5 5
A031	14-#3	2 13 @ 4	*A091*	11-#3	2 5 5 5 5 5 5 5 5 5 5	*A151*	7-#3	3 6 6 6 6 6 6
A032	8-#3	2 4 4 4 4 4 4 4	*A092*	12-#3	2 5 5 5 5 5 5 5 5 5 5 5	*A152*	6-#3	3 6 6 6 6 6
A033	10-#3	2 4 4 4 4 4 4 4 4 4	*A093*	13-#3	2 4 4 4 4 8 @ 5	*A153*	6-#3	3 6 6 6 6 6
A034	11-#3	2 4 4 4 4 4 4 4 4 4 4	*A094*	11-#3	2 5 5 5 5 5 5 5 5 5 5	*A154*	7-#3	3 6 6 6 6 6 6
A035	13-#3	2 12 @ 4	*A095*	10-#3	2 5 5 5 5 5 5 5 5 5	*A155*	8-#3	3 6 6 6 6 6 6 6
A036	15-#3	2 14 @ 4	*A096*	6-#3	2 5 5 5 5 5	*A156*	9-#3	3 6 6 6 6 6 6 6 6
A037	16-#3	2 15 @ 4	*A097*	8-#3	2 5 5 5 5 5 5 5	*A157*	9-#3	3 6 6 6 6 6 6 6 6
A038	17-#3	2 16 @ 4	*A098*	9-#3	2 5 5 5 5 5 5 5 5	*A158*	9-#3	3 6 6 6 6 6 6 6 6
A039	17-#3	2 16 @ 4	*A099*	10-#3	2 5 5 5 5 5 5 5 5 5	*A159*	8-#3	3 6 6 6 6 6 6 6
A040	10-#3	1 3 3 3 3 4 4 4 4 4	*A100*	11-#3	2 5 5 5 5 5 5 5 5 5 5	*A160*	7-#3	3 6 6 6 6 6 6
A041	*		*A101*	13-#3	2 12 @ 5	*A161*	6-#3	3 6 6 6 6 6
A042	*		*A102*	13-#3	2 12 @ 5	*A162*	6-#3	3 6 6 6 6 6
A043	*		*A103*	14-#3	2 4 4 4 4 4 8 @ 5	*A163*	7-#3	3 6 6 6 6 6 6
A044	*		*A104*	12-#3	2 5 5 5 5 5 5 5 5 5 5 5	*A164*	8-#3	3 6 6 6 6 6 6 6
A045	18-#3	2 17 @ 4	*A105*	7-#3	2 5 5 5 5 5 5	*A165*	9-#3	3 6 6 6 6 6 6 6 6
A046	18-#3	2 17 @ 4	*A106*	10-#3	2 4 4 4 5 5 5 5 5 5	*A166*	10-#3	3 6 6 6 6 6 6 6 6 6
A047	19-#3	2 18 @ 4	*A107*	13-#3	1 3 3 3 3 4 4 6 @ 5	*A167*	11-#3	3 6 6 6 6 6 6 6 6 6 6
A048	10-#3	1 3 3 3 3 4 4 4 4 4	*A108*	15-#3	1 3 3 3 3 3 4 4 7 @ 5	*A168*	10-#3	3 6 6 6 6 6 6 6 6 6
A049	*		*A109*	16-#3	1 3 3 3 3 3 4 4 8 @ 5	*A169*	10-#3	3 6 6 6 6 6 6 6 6 6
A050	*		*A110*	15-#3	2 4 4 4 4 10 @ 5	*A170*	9-#3	3 6 6 6 6 6 6 6 6
A051	*		*A111*	15-#3	2 14 @ 5	*A171*	8-#3	3 6 6 6 6 6 6 6
A052	*		*A112*	15-#3	2 14 @ 5	*A172*	7-#3	3 6 6 6 6 6
A053	20-#3	1 3 3 3 3 15 @ 4	*A113*	14-#3	2 13 @ 5	*A173*	6-#3	3 6 6 6 6 6
A054	20-#3	2 19 @ 4	*A114*	7-#3	2 5 5 5 5 5 5	*A174*	7-#3	3 6 6 6 6 6 6
A055	20-#3	2 19 @ 4	*A115*	10-#3	2 4 4 4 5 5 5 5 5 5	*A175*	8-#3	3 6 6 6 6 6 6 6
A056	6-#2	2 5 5 5 5 5	*A116*	13-#3	1 3 3 3 3 4 4 6 @ 5	*A176*	9-#3	3 6 6 6 6 6 6 6 6
A057	7-#3	2 5 5 5 5 5 5	*A117*	15-#3	1 3 3 3 3 3 4 4 7 @ 5	*A177*	10-#3	3 6 6 6 6 6 6 6 6 6
A058	7-#3	2 5 5 5 5 5 5	*A118*	17-#3	1 3 3 3 3 3 3 4 4 8 @ 5	*A178*	11-#3	3 6 6 6 6 6 6 6 6 6 6
A059	6-#3	2 5 5 5 5 5	*A119*	17-#3	1 3 3 3 3 4 4 4 9 @ 5	*A179*	12-#3	3 6 6 6 6 6 6 6 6 6 6 6
A060	7-#3	2 5 5 5 5 5 5	*A120*	16-#3	2 4 4 4 4 11 @ 5	*A180*	11-#3	3 6 6 6 6 6 6 6 6 6 6

* See page 10-58.

STIRRUP COMBINATIONS—CONTINUED

Mark	Number and size	Spacing on each end
A181	11-#3	3 6 6 6 6 6 6 6 6 6 6
A182	11-#3	3 6 6 6 6 6 6 6 6 6 6
A183	10-#3	3 6 6 6 6 6 6 6 6 6
A184	7-#3	3 6 6 6 6 6 6
A185	9-#3	2 4 4 4 5 6 6 6 6
A186	13-#3	1 3 3 3 3 3 4 5 5 @ 6
A187	14-#3	1 3 3 3 3 3 4 4 5 5 @ 6
A188	15-#3	1 3 3 3 3 3 4 4 5 6 @ 6
A189	14-#3	2 4 4 4 4 5 8 @ 6
A190	13-#3	2 5 5 5 9 @ 6
A191	13-#3	3 12 @ 6
A192	12-#3	3 6 6 6 6 6 6 6 6 6 6 6
A193	12-#3	3 6 6 6 6 6 6 6 6 6 6 6
A194	12-#3	3 6 6 6 6 6 6 6 6 6 6 6
A195	7-#3	2 5 5 5 6 6 6
A196	9-#3	2 4 4 4 5 6 6 6 6
A197	13-#3	1 3 3 3 3 3 4 5 5 @ 6
A198	14-#3	1 3 3 3 3 3 4 4 5 5 @ 6
A199	16-#3	1 3 3 3 3 3 3 4 4 5 6 @ 6
A200	15-#3	2 4 4 4 4 4 5 5 7 @ 6
A201	15-#3	2 4 4 4 4 5 9 @ 6
A202	14-#3	2 5 5 5 10 @ 6
A203	13-#3	3 12 @ 6
A204	13-#3	3 12 @ 6
A205	13-#3	3 12 @ 6
A206	7-#3	2 5 5 5 6 6 6
A207	9-#3	2 4 4 4 5 6 6 6 6
A208	13-#3	1 3 3 3 3 3 4 5 5 @ 6
A209	14-#3	1 3 3 3 3 3 4 4 5 5 @ 6
A210	16-#3	1 3 3 3 3 3 3 4 4 5 6 @ 6
A211	18-#3	1 3 3 3 3 3 3 3 4 4 5 7 @ 6
A212	19-#3	1 3 3 3 3 3 3 3 4 4 4 8 @ 6
A213	19-#3	1 3 3 3 3 3 4 4 4 5 5 8 @ 6
A214	17-#3	2 4 4 4 4 5 5 10 @ 6
A215	17-#3	2 5 5 5 5 12 @ 6
A216	16-#3	3 15 @ 6
A217	7-#3	2 5 5 5 6 6 6
A218	9-#3	2 4 4 4 5 6 6 6 6
A219	11-#3	2 4 4 4 4 5 6 6 6 6 6
A220	14-#3	1 3 3 3 3 3 4 4 5 5 @ 6
A221	16-#3	1 3 3 3 3 3 3 4 4 5 6 @ 6
A222	18-#3	1 3 3 3 3 3 3 3 4 4 8 @ 6
A223	20-#3	1 8 @ 3 4 4 5 5 7 @ 6
A224	22-#3	1 9 @ 3 4 4 4 5 8 @ 6
A225	21-#3	1 6 @ 3 4 4 4 5 5 9 @ 6
A226	19-#3	2 4 4 4 4 4 4 5 5 10 @ 6
A227	19-#3	2 4 4 4 4 5 5 12 @ 6
A228	7-#3	3 7 7 7 7 7 7
A229	6-#3	3 7 7 7 7 7
A230	5-#3	3 7 7 7 7
A231	6-#3	3 7 7 7 7 7
A232	7-#3	3 7 7 7 7 7 7
A233	7-#3	3 7 7 7 7 7 7
A234	6-#3	3 7 7 7 7 7
A235	8-#3	3 7 7 7 7 7 7 7
A236	8-#3	3 7 7 7 7 7 7 7
A237	7-#3	3 7 7 7 7 7 7
A238	7-#3	3 7 7 7 7 7 7
A239	6-#3	3 7 7 7 7 7
A240	9-#3	3 7 7 7 7 7 7 7 7
A241	9-#3	3 7 7 7 7 7 7 7 7
A242	9-#3	3 7 7 7 7 7 7 7 7
A243	9-#3	3 7 7 7 7 7 7 7 7
A244	8-#3	3 7 7 7 7 7 7 7
A245	7-#3	3 7 7 7 7 7 7
A246	6-#3	3 7 7 7 7 7
A247	5-#3	3 7 7 7 7
A248	9-#3	3 7 7 7 7 7 7 7 7
A249	10-#3	3 7 7 7 7 7 7 7 7 7
A250	10-#3	3 7 7 7 7 7 7 7 7 7
A251	10-#3	3 7 7 7 7 7 7 7 7 7
A252	10-#3	3 7 7 7 7 7 7 7 7 7
A253	9-#3	3 7 7 7 7 7 7 7 7
A254	9-#3	3 7 7 7 7 7 7 7 7
A255	8-#3	3 7 7 7 7 7 7 7
A256	7-#3	3 7 7 7 7 7 7
A257	16-#3	1 6 @ 3 4 4 5 6 5 @ 7
A258	14-#3	2 4 4 4 4 4 5 5 6 5 @ 7
A259	14-#3	2 4 4 4 4 5 6 7 @ 7
A260	13-#3	2 5 5 5 6 8 @ 7
A261	12-#3	3 11 @ 7
A262	12-#3	3 7 7 7 7 7 7 7 7 7 7 7
A263	12-#3	3 7 7 7 7 7 7 7 7 7 7 7
A264	11-#3	3 7 7 7 7 7 7 7 7 7 7
A265	11-#3	3 7 7 7 7 7 7 7 7 7 7
A266	16-#3	1 6 @ 3 4 4 5 6 5 @ 7
A267	17-#3	1 7 @ 3 4 4 5 6 5 @ 7
A268	19-#3	1 7 @ 3 4 4 4 5 6 6 @ 7
A269	17-#3	2 6 @ 4 5 5 6 7 @ 7
A270	16-#3	2 4 4 4 4 5 5 6 8 @ 7
A271	15-#3	2 5 5 5 5 6 9 @ 7
A272	14-#3	3 6 6 6 10 @ 7
A273	14-#3	3 13 @ 7
A274	14-#3	3 13 @ 7
A275	16-#3	1 6 @ 3 4 4 5 6 5 @ 7
A276	17-#3	1 7 @ 3 4 4 5 6 5 @ 7
A277	19-#3	1 8 @ 3 4 4 5 5 6 5 @ 7
A278	21-#3	1 9 @ 3 4 4 4 5 6 6 @ 7
A279	20-#3	1 6 @ 3 4 4 4 5 5 6 7 @ 7
A280	18-#3	2 6 @ 4 5 5 6 8 @ 7
A281	18-#3	2 4 4 4 4 5 5 6 6 9 @ 7
A282	17-#3	2 5 5 5 5 6 6 10 @ 7
A283	16-#3	3 6 6 6 12 @ 7
A284	6-#3	4 8 8 8 8 8
A285	6-#3	4 8 8 8 8 8
A286	5-#3	4 8 8 8 8
A287	7-#3	4 8 8 8 8 8 8
A288	6-#3	4 8 8 8 8 8
A289	5-#3	4 8 8 8 8
A290	7-#3	4 8 8 8 8 8 8
A291	7-#3	4 8 8 8 8 8 8
A292	7-#3	4 8 8 8 8 8 8
A293	6-#3	4 8 8 8 8 8
A294	5-#3	4 8 8 8 8
A295	8-#3	4 8 8 8 8 8 8 8
A296	9-#3	4 8 8 8 8 8 8 8 8
A297	8-#3	4 8 8 8 8 8 8 8
A298	8-#3	4 8 8 8 8 8 8 8
A299	8-#3	4 8 8 8 8 8 8 8
A300	7-#3	4 8 8 8 8 8 8
A301	6-#3	4 8 8 8 8 8
A302	8-#3	4 8 8 8 8 8 8 8
A303	9-#3	4 8 8 8 8 8 8 8 8
A304	9-#3	4 8 8 8 8 8 8 8 8
A305	9-#3	4 8 8 8 8 8 8 8 8
A306	9-#3	4 8 8 8 8 8 8 8 8
A307	8-#3	4 8 8 8 8 8 8 8
A308	8-#3	4 8 8 8 8 8 8 8
A309	7-#3	4 8 8 8 8 8 8
A310	6-#3	4 8 8 8 8 8
A311	15-#3	1 6 @ 3 4 4 5 7 4 @ 8
A312	14-#3	2 4 4 4 4 4 5 6 7 5 @ 8
A313	13-#3	2 5 5 5 5 6 7 6 @ 8
A314	12-#3	3 6 6 6 7 8 8 8 8 8 8
A315	11-#3	3 7 7 7 8 8 8 8 8 8
A316	10-#3	4 8 8 8 8 8 8 8 8 8
A317	10-#3	4 8 8 8 8 8 8 8 8 8
A318	10-#3	4 8 8 8 8 8 8 8 8 8
A319	9-#3	4 8 8 8 8 8 8 8 8
A320	9-#3	4 8 8 8 8 8 8 8 8
A321	15-#3	1 6 @ 3 4 4 5 7 4 @ 8
A322	17-#3	1 7 @ 3 4 4 5 6 7 4 @ 8
A323	18-#3	1 3 3 3 3 3 3 3 3 4 4 4 5 6 7 4 @ 8
A324	16-#3	2 6 @ 4 5 5 6 7 5 @ 8
A325	16-#3	2 4 4 4 4 4 5 6 7 7 @ 8
A326	14-#3	2 5 5 5 5 6 7 7 @ 8
A327	13-#3	3 6 6 6 7 8 @ 8
A328	13-#3	3 7 7 7 9 @ 8
A329	12-#3	4 8 8 8 8 8 8 8 8 8 8 8
A330	12-#3	4 8 8 8 8 8 8 8 8 8 8 8
A331	15-#3	1 6 @ 3 4 4 5 7 8 8 8 8
A332	17-#3	1 7 @ 3 4 4 5 6 7 4 @ 8
A333	19-#3	1 8 @ 3 4 4 5 5 7 5 @ 8
A334	21-#3	1 9 @ 3 4 4 4 5 6 7 5 @ 8
A335	20-#3	1 6 @ 3 4 4 4 5 5 6 7 6 @ 8
A336	18-#3	2 6 @ 4 5 5 6 7 7 @ 8
A337	16-#3	2 5 @ 5 6 6 7 7 @ 8
A338	16-#3	2 5 5 5 5 6 6 7 8 @ 8
A339	15-#3	3 6 6 6 7 7 9 @ 8
A340	14-#3	3 7 7 7 10 @ 8
A341	15-#3	1 6 @ 3 4 4 5 7 4 @ 8
A342	17-#3	1 7 @ 3 4 4 5 6 7 4 @ 8
A343	19-#3	1 8 @ 3 4 4 5 5 7 5 @ 8
A344	21-#3	1 9 @ 3 4 4 4 5 6 7 5 @ 8
A345	22-#3	1 9 @ 3 4 4 4 5 5 6 7 5 @ 8
A346	24-#3	1 10 @ 3 4 4 4 4 5 5 7 6 @ 8
A347	24-#3	1 9 @ 3 4 4 4 4 5 5 6 7 6 @ 8
A348	23-#3	1 6 @ 3 4 4 4 4 5 5 5 6 7 7 @ 8
A349	21-#3	2 7 @ 4 5 5 6 6 7 8 @ 8
A350	21-#3	2 5 @ 4 5 5 5 6 6 7 9 @ 8
A351	15-#3	1 6 @ 3 4 4 5 7 4 @ 8
A352	17-#3	1 7 @ 3 4 4 5 6 7 4 @ 8
A353	19-#3	1 8 @ 3 4 4 5 5 7 5 @ 8
A354	21-#3	1 9 @ 3 4 4 4 5 6 7 5 @ 8
A355	22-#3	1 9 @ 3 4 4 4 5 5 6 7 5 @ 8
A356	24-#3	1 10 @ 3 4 4 4 4 5 5 7 6 @ 8
A357	26-#3	1 11 @ 3 4 4 4 4 5 5 6 7 6 @ 8
A358	26-#3	1 10 @ 3 4 4 4 4 5 5 6 6 7 6 @ 8
A359	26-#3	1 8 @ 3 4 4 4 4 5 5 5 6 7 8 @ 8
A360	23-#3	2 8 @ 4 5 5 5 6 6 7 8 @ 8
A361	5-#3	4 9 9 9 9
A362	6-#3	4 9 9 9 9 9
A363	6-#3	4 9 9 9 9 9
A364	6-#3	4 9 9 9 9 9
A365	6-#3	4 9 9 9 9 9
A366	5-#3	4 9 9 9 9
A357	7-#3	4 9 9 9 9 9 9
A368	7-#3	4 9 9 9 9 9 9
A369	6-#3	4 9 9 9 9 9
A370	6-#3	4 9 9 9 9 9
A371	5-#3	4 9 9 9 9
A372	7-#3	4 9 9 9 9 9 9
A373	8-#3	4 9 9 9 9 9 9 9
A374	8-#3	4 9 9 9 9 9 9 9
A375	7-#3	4 9 9 9 9 9 9
A376	7-#3	4 9 9 9 9 9 9
A377	6-#3	4 9 9 9 9 9
A378	5-#3	4 9 9 9 9
A379	7-#3	4 9 9 9 9 9 9
A380	8-#3	4 9 9 9 9 9 9 9
A381	9-#3	4 9 9 9 9 9 9 9 9
A382	8-#3	4 9 9 9 9 9 9 9
A383	8-#3	4 9 9 9 9 9 9 9

STIRRUP COMBINATIONS—CONTINUED

Mark	Number and size	Spacing on each end
A384	8-#3	4 9 9 9 9 9 9 9
A385	7-#3	4 9 9 9 9 9 9
A386	6-#3	4 9 9 9 9 9
A387	6-#3	4 9 9 9 9 9
A388	12-#3	2 4 4 4 4 4 5 7 8 9 9 9
A389	11-#3	2 5 5 5 5 6 8 9 9 9 9
A390	10-#3	3 6 6 6 7 8 9 9 9 9
A391	9-#3	4 8 8 8 9 9 9 9 9
A392	9-#3	4 9 9 9 9 9 9 9 9
A393	8-#3	4 9 9 9 9 9 9 9
A394	8-#3	4 9 9 9 9 9 9 9
A395	7-#3	4 9 9 9 9 9 9
A396	7-#3	4 9 9 9 9 9 9
A397	6-#3	4 9 9 9 9 9
A398	12-#3	2 4 4 4 4 4 5 7 8 9 9 9
A399	14-#3	2 4 4 4 4 4 4 5 7 8 4 @ 9
A400	15-#3	2 4 4 4 4 4 4 5 6 8 5 @ 9
A401	13-#3	2 5 5 5 5 5 6 8 5 @ 9
A402	13-#3	2 5 5 5 5 6 8 6 @ 9
A403	11-#3	3 7 7 7 8 9 9 9 9 9 9
A404	10-#3	4 8 8 8 9 9 9 9 9 9
A405	10-#3	4 9 9 9 9 9 9 9 9 9
A406	9-#3	4 9 9 9 9 9 9 9 9
A407	9-#3	4 9 9 9 9 9 9 9 9
A408	8-#3	4 9 9 9 9 9 9 9
A409	12-#3	2 5 @ 4 5 7 8 9 9 9
A410	14-#3	2 6 @ 4 5 7 8 4 @ 9
A411	15-#3	2 7 @ 4 5 7 8 4 @ 9
A412	16-#3	2 7 @ 4 5 5 7 8 4 @ 9
A413	15-#3	2 5 @ 4 5 5 6 8 5 @ 9
A414	14-#3	2 5 5 5 5 5 6 7 8 5 @ 9
A415	13-#3	3 6 6 6 6 7 8 6 @ 9
A416	12-#3	3 7 7 7 8 7 @ 9
A417	11-#3	4 8 8 8 9 9 9 9 9 9 9
A418	11-#3	4 9 9 9 9 9 9 9 9 9 9
A419	10-#3	4 9 9 9 9 9 9 9 9 9
A420	12-#4	2 5 5 5 5 5 7 8 9 9 9 9
A421	15-#4	2 5 @ 4 5 5 7 8 5 @ 9
A422	15-#4	2 5 @ 4 5 5 6 8 5 @ 9
A423	22-#3	1 11 @ 3 4 4 4 5 7 8 4 @ 9
A424	21-#3	1 9 @ 3 4 4 4 5 5 7 8 4 @ 9
A425	20-#3	1 7 @ 3 4 4 4 5 5 6 8 5 @ 9
A426	18-#3	2 6 @ 4 5 5 6 6 8 6 @ 9
A427	16-#3	2 6 @ 5 6 7 8 6 @ 9
A428	16-#3	2 5 5 5 5 6 6 7 8 7 @ 9
A429	14-#3	3 6 6 6 6 7 8 7 @ 9
A430	13-#3	3 7 7 7 8 8 @ 9
A431	12-#4	2 5 5 5 5 5 7 8 9 9 9 9
A432	14-#4	2 5 @ 4 5 5 7 8 4 @ 9
A433	16-#4	2 6 @ 4 5 5 6 8 5 @ 9
A434	17-#4	2 6 @ 4 5 5 6 7 8 5 @ 9
A435	16-#4	2 6 @ 5 6 7 8 6 @ 9
A436	24-#3	1 11 @ 3 4 4 4 5 5 7 8 5 @ 9
A437	23-#3	1 8 @ 3 4 4 4 4 5 5 6 8 6 @ 9
A438	20-#3	2 8 @ 4 5 5 6 6 8 6 @ 9
A439	19-#3	2 6 @ 4 5 5 5 6 7 8 6 @ 9
A440	18-#3	2 6 @ 5 6 6 7 8 7 @ 9
A441	17-#3	2 4 @ 5 6 6 7 8 8 @ 9
A442	12-#4	2 5 5 5 5 5 7 8 9 9 9 9
A443	14-#4	2 4 4 4 4 4 5 5 7 8 4 @ 9
A444	16-#4	2 6 @ 4 5 5 6 8 5 @ 9
A445	18-#4	2 7 @ 4 5 5 6 8 6 @ 9
A446	19-#4	2 7 @ 4 5 5 6 7 8 6 @ 9
A447	19-#4	2 5 @ 4 5 5 5 6 7 8 7 @ 9
A448	17-#4	2 5 @ 5 6 6 7 8 7 @ 9
A449	26-#3	1 11 @ 3 4 4 4 4 5 5 6 8 6 @ 9
A450	25-#3	1 9 @ 3 4 4 4 4 5 5 6 6 8 6 @ 9
A451	22-#3	2 9 @ 4 5 5 6 6 7 8 6 @ 9
A452	22-#3	2 7 @ 4 5 5 5 6 6 7 8 7 @ 9
A453	5-#3	5 10 10 10 10
A454	7-#3	5 10 10 10 10 10 10
A455	7-#3	5 10 10 10 10 10 10
A456	6-#3	5 10 10 10 10 10
A457	5-#3	5 10 10 10 10
A458	8-#3	5 10 10 10 10 10 10 10
A459	8-#3	5 10 10 10 10 10 10 10
A460	7-#3	5 10 10 10 10 10 10
A461	7-#3	5 10 10 10 10 10 10
A462	6-#3	5 10 10 10 10 10
A463	5-#3	5 10 10 10 10
A464	9-#3	4 8 8 9 10 10 10 10 10
A465	8-#3	5 10 10 10 10 10 10 10
A466	8-#3	5 10 10 10 10 10 10 10
A467	8-#3	5 10 10 10 10 10 10 10
A468	7-#3	5 10 10 10 10 10 10
A469	7-#3	5 10 10 10 10 10 10
A470	6-#3	5 10 10 10 10 10
A471	5-#3	5 10 10 10 10
A472	8-#3	5 10 10 10 10 10 10 10
A473	7-#3	5 10 10 10 10 10 10
A474	7-#3	5 10 10 10 10 10 10
A475	6-#3	5 10 10 10 10 10
A476	6-#3	5 10 10 10 10 10
A477	5-#3	5 10 10 10 10
A478	9-#3	4 8 8 9 10 10 10 10 10
A479	8-#3	5 10 10 10 10 10 10 10
A480	8-#3	5 10 10 10 10 10 10 10
A481	7-#3	5 10 10 10 10 10 10
A482	7-#3	5 10 10 10 10 10 10
A483	6-#3	5 10 10 10 10 10
A484	5-#3	5 10 10 10 10
A485	13-#3	2 5 5 5 5 5 6 8 9 4 @ 10
A486	11-#3	3 6 6 6 6 8 9 10 10 10 10
A487	11-#3	3 7 7 7 9 10 10 10 10 10 10
A488	10-#3	4 9 9 9 10 10 10 10 10 10
A489	9-#3	5 10 10 10 10 10 10 10 10
A490	9-#3	5 10 10 10 10 10 10 10 10
A491	8-#3	5 10 10 10 10 10 10 10
A492	8-#3	5 10 10 10 10 10 10 10
A493	7-#3	5 10 10 10 10 10 10
A494	6-#3	5 10 10 10 10 10
A495	5-#3	5 10 10 10 10
A496	16-#3	2 7 @ 4 5 5 7 9 4 @ 10
A497	16-#3	2 6 @ 4 5 5 6 8 5 @ 10
A498	14-#3	2 5 5 5 5 5 6 7 9 5 @ 10
A499	13-#3	3 6 6 6 6 7 9 6 @ 10
A500	12-#3	3 7 7 7 8 9 10 10 10 10 10 10
A501	11-#3	4 8 8 9 10 10 10 10 10 10 10
A502	10-#3	5 10 10 10 10 10 10 10 10 10
A503	10-#3	5 10 10 10 10 10 10 10 10 10
A504	9-#3	5 10 10 10 10 10 10 10 10
A505	9-#3	5 10 10 10 10 10 10 10 10
A506	8-#3	5 10 10 10 10 10 10 10
A507	22-#3	1 11 @ 3 4 4 4 5 7 9 4 @ 10
A508	21-#3	1 9 @ 3 4 4 4 5 5 7 9 4 @ 10
A509	18-#3	2 8 @ 4 5 5 6 8 9 4 @ 10
A510	18-#3	2 6 @ 4 5 5 6 6 8 9 5 @ 10
A511	16-#3	2 6 @ 5 6 7 9 6 @ 10
A512	15-#3	2 5 5 5 5 5 6 7 9 6 @ 10
A513	14-#3	3 6 6 6 6 7 9 7 @ 10
A514	13-#3	3 7 7 7 8 9 7 @ 10
A515	12-#3	4 9 9 9 10 10 10 10 10 10 10 10
A516	11-#3	5 10 10 10 10 10 10 10 10 10 10
A517	11-#3	5 10 10 10 10 10 10 10 10 10 10
A518	17-#4	2 6 @ 4 5 5 6 7 9 5 @ 10
A519	16-#4	2 5 5 5 5 5 5 6 7 9 6 @ 10
A520	23-#3	1 11 @ 3 4 4 4 5 5 6 8 4 @ 10
A521	23-#3	1 9 @ 3 4 4 4 5 5 6 7 9 5 @ 10
A522	20-#3	2 8 @ 4 5 5 6 6 8 9 5 @ 10
A523	19-#3	2 6 @ 4 5 5 5 6 7 9 6 @ 10
A524	17-#3	2 6 @ 5 6 6 7 9 6 @ 10
A525	17-#3	2 5 5 5 5 5 6 7 7 9 7 @ 10
A526	15-#3	3 6 6 6 6 7 8 9 7 @ 10
A527	14-#3	3 7 7 7 7 8 9 7 @ 10
A528	13-#3	4 8 8 8 9 8 @ 10
A529	15-#4	2 6 @ 5 6 7 9 5 @ 10
A530	22-#3	1 11 @ 3 4 4 4 5 7 8 4 @ 9
A531	22-#3	1 9 @ 3 4 4 4 5 5 7 8 5 @ 9
A532	19-#3	2 8 @ 4 5 5 6 8 6 @ 9
A533	18-#3	2 6 @ 4 5 5 6 7 8 6 @ 9
A534	16-#3	2 5 5 5 5 5 6 6 7 8 6 @ 9
A535	15-#3	3 6 6 6 6 6 7 8 7 @ 9
A536	14-#3	3 7 7 7 7 8 8 @ 9
A537	13-#3	4 8 8 8 9 @ 9
A538	12-#3	4 9 9 9 9 9 9 9 9 9 9 9
A539	11-#3	4 9 9 9 9 9 9 9 9 9 9
A540	16-#4	2 6 @ 4 5 6 7 9 5 @ 10
A541	17-#4	2 6 @ 4 5 5 6 7 9 5 @ 10
A542	16-#4	2 6 @ 5 6 7 9 6 @ 10
A543	24-#3	1 11 @ 3 4 4 4 5 5 6 8 5 @ 9
A544	23-#3	1 9 @ 3 4 4 4 5 5 6 7 8 5 @ 9
A545	20-#3	2 8 @ 4 5 5 6 6 8 6 @ 9
A546	19-#3	2 6 @ 4 5 5 5 6 7 8 6 @ 9
A547	18-#3	2 6 @ 5 6 6 7 8 7 @ 9
A548	16-#3	3 6 6 6 6 6 7 8 8 @ 9
A549	16-#3	3 6 6 6 6 7 8 9 @ 9
A550	14-#3	3 7 7 7 8 9 @ 9
A551	16-#4	2 6 @ 4 5 6 7 9 5 @ 10
A552	17-#4	2 6 @ 4 5 5 6 7 9 5 @ 10
A553	18-#4	2 6 @ 4 5 5 5 6 7 9 5 @ 10
A554	17-#4	2 6 @ 5 6 6 7 9 6 @ 10
A555	26-#3	1 13 @ 3 4 4 4 5 5 6 8 5 @ 9
A556	25-#3	1 10 @ 3 4 4 4 4 5 5 6 7 8 5 @ 9
A557	24-#3	1 7 @ 3 4 4 4 4 4 5 5 6 6 8 6 @ 9
A558	22-#3	2 8 @ 4 5 5 5 6 7 8 7 @ 9
A559	21-#3	2 6 @ 4 5 5 5 6 6 7 8 7 @ 9
A560	19-#3	2 6 @ 5 6 6 7 8 8 @ 9
A561	17-#3	3 6 6 6 6 6 7 7 8 8 @ 9
A562	5-#3	5 11 11 11 11
A563	7-#3	5 11 11 11 11 11 11
A564	6-#3	5 11 11 11 11 11
A565	6-#3	5 11 11 11 11 11
A566	5-#3	5 11 11 11 11

STIRRUP COMBINATIONS—CONTINUED

Mark	Number and size	Spacing on each end
A567	7-#3	5 11 11 11 11 11 11
A568	7-#3	5 11 11 11 11 11 11
A569	7-#3	5 11 11 11 11 11 11
A570	7-#3	5 11 11 11 11 11 11
A571	6-#3	5 11 11 11 11 11
A572	5-#3	5 11 11 11 11
A573	9-#3	4 8 8 9 10 11 11 11 11
A574	8-#3	5 10 10 10 11 11 11 11
A575	8-#3	5 11 11 11 11 11 11 11
A576	8-#3	5 11 11 11 11 11 11 11
A577	7-#3	5 11 11 11 11 11 11
A578	7-#3	5 11 11 11 11 11 11
A579	6-#3	5 11 11 11 11 11
A580	5-#3	5 11 11 11 11
A581	8-#3	5 10 10 10 10 10 10 10
A582	7-#3	5 10 10 10 10 10 10
A583	7-#3	5 10 10 10 10 10 10
A584	6-#3	5 10 10 10 10 10
A585	6-#3	5 10 10 10 10 10
A586	9-#3	4 9 9 9 10 10 10 10 10
A587	8-#3	5 10 10 10 10 10 10 10
A588	8-#3	5 10 10 10 10 10 10 10
A589	8-#3	5 10 10 10 10 10 10 10
A590	7-#3	5 10 10 10 10 10 10
A591	6-#3	5 10 10 10 10 10
A592	6-#3	5 10 10 10 10 10
A593	13-#3	2 5 5 5 5 5 6 8 9 4 @ 10
A594	12-#3	3 6 6 6 6 8 9 10 10 10 10 10
A595	11-#3	3 7 7 7 8 10 10 10 10 10 10
A596	10-#3	4 9 9 9 10 10 10 10 10 10
A597	9-#3	5 10 10 10 10 10 10 10 10
A598	9-#3	5 10 10 10 10 10 10 10 10
A599	8-#3	5 10 10 10 10 10 10 10
A600	8-#3	5 10 10 10 10 10 10 10
A601	7-#3	5 10 10 10 10 10 10
A602	6-#3	5 10 10 10 10 10
A603	5-#3	5 10 10 10 10
A604	16-#3	2 7 @ 4 5 5 7 9 4 @ 10
A605	16-#3	2 6 @ 4 5 5 7 9 5 @ 10
A606	14-#3	2 5 5 5 5 5 6 7 9 5 @ 10
A607	13-#3	3 6 6 6 6 7 9 10 5 @ 10
A608	12-#3	3 7 7 7 8 9 10 10 10 10 10 10
A609	11-#3	4 9 9 9 10 10 10 10 10 10 10
A610	10-#3	5 10 10 10 10 10 10 10 10 10
A611	10-#3	5 10 10 10 10 10 10 10 10 10
A612	9-#3	5 10 10 10 10 10 10 10 10
A613	9-#3	5 10 10 10 10 10 10 10 10
A614	8-#3	5 10 10 10 10 10 10 10
A615	22-#3	1 11 @ 3 4 4 4 5 7 9 4 @ 10
A616	21-#3	1 9 @ 3 4 4 4 5 5 7 9 4 @ 10
A617	18-#3	2 8 @ 4 5 5 6 8 9 4 @ 10
A618	18-#3	2 6 @ 4 5 5 6 6 8 9 5 @ 10
A619	16-#3	2 5 5 5 5 5 5 6 7 9 6 @ 10
A620	14-#3	3 6 6 6 6 6 7 9 6 @ 10
A621	13-#3	3 7 7 7 7 8 9 6 @ 10
A622	13-#3	4 8 8 8 9 8 @ 10
A623	12-#3	4 9 9 9 8 @ 10
A624	11-#3	5 10 10 10 10 10 10 10 10 10 10
A625	11-#3	5 10 10 10 10 10 10 10 10 10 10
A626	17-#4	2 6 @ 4 5 5 6 7 9 5 @ 11
A627	24-#3	1 13 @ 3 4 4 4 5 6 8 4 @ 10
A628	24-#3	1 11 @ 3 4 4 4 5 5 6 8 5 @ 10
A629	23-#3	1 9 @ 3 4 4 4 5 5 6 7 9 5 @ 10
A630	20-#3	2 8 @ 4 5 5 6 6 8 9 5 @ 10
A631	19-#3	2 6 @ 4 5 5 5 6 7 8 9 5 @ 10
A632	17-#3	2 6 @ 5 6 6 7 9 6 @ 10
A633	16-#3	3 6 6 6 6 6 7 7 9 7 @ 10
A634	15-#3	3 6 6 6 6 7 8 9 7 @ 10
A635	14-#3	3 7 7 7 7 8 9 7 @ 10
A636	13-#3	4 8 8 8 9 8 @ 10
A637	14-#4	2 5 5 5 5 5 5 6 7 9 4 @ 11
A638	22-#3	1 11 @ 3 4 4 4 5 7 8 4 @ 9
A639	22-#3	1 9 @ 3 4 4 4 5 5 7 8 5 @ 9
A640	19-#3	2 8 @ 4 5 5 6 8 6 @ 9
A641	18-#3	2 6 @ 4 5 5 6 7 8 6 @ 9
A642	16-#3	2 5 5 5 5 5 6 6 7 8 6 @ 9
A643	15-#3	3 6 6 6 6 6 7 8 7 @ 9
A644	14-#3	3 7 7 7 7 8 8 @ 9
A645	13-#3	4 8 8 8 9 @ 9
A646	12-#3	4 9 9 9 9 9 9 9 9 9 9 9
A647	12-#3	4 9 9 9 9 9 9 9 9 9 9 9
A648	15-#4	2 5 5 5 5 5 5 6 7 9 5 @ 11
A649	17-#4	2 6 @ 4 5 5 6 7 9 10 4 @ 11
A650	25-#3	1 13 @ 3 4 4 4 5 6 8 5 @ 9
A651	24-#3	1 11 @ 3 4 4 4 5 5 6 8 5 @ 9
A652	23-#3	1 9 @ 3 4 4 4 5 5 6 7 8 5 @ 9
A653	21-#3	2 8 @ 4 5 5 6 6 8 7 @ 9
A654	20-#3	2 6 @ 4 5 5 5 6 7 8 7 @ 9
A655	18-#3	2 6 @ 5 6 6 7 8 7 @ 9
A656	16-#3	3 6 6 6 6 6 7 8 8 @ 9
A657	16-#3	3 6 6 6 6 7 8 9 @ 9
A658	15-#3	3 7 7 7 8 10 @ 9
A659	14-#4	2 5 5 5 5 5 5 6 7 9 4 @ 11
A660	17-#4	2 6 @ 4 5 5 6 7 9 10 4 @ 11
A661	18-#4	2 6 @ 4 5 5 5 6 7 9 10 4 @ 11
A662	17-#4	2 7 @ 5 6 7 8 10 5 @ 11
A663	27-#3	1 13 @ 3 4 4 4 5 5 6 8 6 @ 9
A664	26-#3	1 11 @ 3 4 4 4 4 5 5 6 8 6 @ 9
A665	25-#3	1 8 @ 3 4 4 4 4 5 5 5 6 7 8 6 @ 9
A666	22-#3	2 8 @ 4 5 5 5 6 7 8 7 @ 9
A667	21-#3	2 6 @ 4 5 5 5 6 6 7 8 7 @ 9
A668	19-#3	2 6 @ 5 6 6 7 8 8 @ 9
A669	18-#3	3 6 6 6 6 6 6 7 8 9 @ 9
A670	5-#3	6 12 12 12 12
A671	6-#3	6 12 12 12 12 12
A672	6-#3	6 12 12 12 12 12
A673	5-#3	6 12 12 12 12
A674	5-#3	6 12 12 12 12
A675	7-#3	6 12 12 12 12 12 12
A676	7-#3	6 12 12 12 12 12 12
A677	6-#3	6 12 12 12 12 12
A678	7-#3	6 12 12 12 12 12 12
A679	6-#3	6 12 12 12 12 12
A680	5-#3	6 12 12 12 12
A681	8-#3	5 10 10 10 10 10 10 10
A682	8-#3	5 10 10 10 10 10 10 10
A683	7-#3	5 10 10 10 10 10 10
A684	7-#3	5 10 10 10 10 10 10
A685	6-#3	5 10 10 10 10 10
A686	9-#3	5 10 10 10 10 10 10 10 10
A687	8-#3	5 10 10 10 10 10 10 10
A688	8-#3	5 10 10 10 10 10 10 10
A689	8-#3	5 10 10 10 10 10 10 10
A690	7-#3	5 10 10 10 10 10 10
A691	6-#3	5 10 10 10 10 10
A692	13-#3	2 5 5 5 5 5 6 8 9 4 @ 10
A693	12-#3	3 6 6 6 6 7 9 10 10 10 10 10
A694	11-#3	4 8 8 8 9 10 10 10 10 10 10
A695	10-#3	4 9 9 9 10 10 10 10 10 10
A696	9-#3	5 10 10 10 10 10 10 10 10
A697	9-#3	5 10 10 10 10 10 10 10 10
A698	9-#3	5 10 10 10 10 10 10 10 10
A699	8-#3	5 10 10 10 10 10 10 10
A700	7-#3	5 10 10 10 10 10 10
A701	7-#3	5 10 10 10 10 10 10
A702	6-#3	5 10 10 10 10 10
A703	16-#3	2 7 @ 4 5 5 7 9 4 @ 10
A704	15-#3	2 6 @ 5 6 7 9 5 @ 10
A705	14-#3	2 5 5 5 5 5 6 7 9 5 @ 10
A706	13-#3	3 6 6 6 6 7 9 6 @ 10
A707	11-#3	4 8 8 8 9 10 10 10 10 10 10
A708	11-#3	4 9 9 9 10 10 10 10 10 10 10
A709	10-#3	5 10 10 10 10 10 10 10 10 10
A710	10-#3	5 10 10 10 10 10 10 10 10 10
A711	9-#3	5 10 10 10 10 10 10 10 10
A712	9-#3	5 10 10 10 10 10 10 10 10
A713	8-#3	5 10 10 10 10 10 10 10
A714	22-#3	1 11 @ 3 4 4 4 5 7 9 4 @ 10
A715	21-#3	1 9 @ 3 4 4 4 5 5 7 9 4 @ 10
A716	19-#3	2 8 @ 4 5 5 6 8 9 5 @ 10
A717	18-#3	2 7 @ 4 5 5 6 8 9 5 @ 10
A718	16-#3	2 5 5 5 5 5 5 6 7 9 6 @ 10
A719	15-#3	3 6 6 6 6 6 7 9 7 @ 10
A720	14-#3	3 7 7 7 7 8 9 7 @ 10
A721	13-#3	4 8 8 8 9 8 @ 10
A722	12-#3	4 9 9 9 10 10 10 10 10 10 10 10
A723	11-#3	5 10 10 10 10 10 10 10 10 10 10
A724	11-#3	5 10 10 10 10 10 10 10 10 10 10
A725	23-#3	1 13 @ 3 4 4 5 7 8 4 @ 9
A726	23-#3	1 11 @ 3 4 4 4 5 7 8 5 @ 9
A727	12-#4	3 7 7 7 7 8 10 12 12 12 12 12
A728	19-#3	2 8 @ 4 5 5 6 8 6 @ 9
A729	17-#3	2 7 @ 5 6 7 8 6 @ 9

STIRRUP COMBINATIONS—CONTINUED

Mark	Number and size	Spacing on each end
A730	17-#3	2 5 5 5 5 5 6 6 7 8 7 @ 9
A731	15-#3	3 6 6 6 6 6 7 8 7 @ 9
A732	14-#3	3 7 7 7 7 8 8 @ 9
A733	13-#3	4 8 8 8 8 8 @ 9
A734	12-#3	4 9 9 9 9 9 9 9 9 9 9 9
A735	12-#3	4 9 9 9 9 9 9 9 9 9 9 9
A736	14-#4	2 6 @ 5 6 7 9 11 3 @ 12
A737	16-#4	2 7 @ 5 6 7 9 11 4 @ 12
A738	25-#3	1 13 @ 3 4 4 4 5 6 8 5 @ 9
A739	14-#4	3 5 @ 6 7 8 10 5 @ 12
A740	13-#4	3 7 7 7 7 7 9 11 5 @ 12
A741	21-#3	2 8 @ 4 5 5 6 6 8 7 @ 9
A742	20-#3	2 7 @ 4 5 5 6 7 8 7 @ 9
A743	18-#3	2 6 @ 5 6 6 7 8 7 @ 9
A744	16-#3	3 6 6 6 6 6 7 8 8 @ 9
A745	16-#3	3 7 7 7 7 7 8 9 @ 9
A746	14-#3	4 8 8 8 8 9 @ 9
A747	14-#4	2 6 @ 5 6 7 9 11 3 @ 12
A748	16-#4	2 7 @ 5 6 7 9 11 4 @ 12
A749	18-#4	2 7 @ 4 5 5 6 7 9 11 4 @ 12
A750	17-#4	2 6 @ 5 6 6 7 9 11 5 @ 12
A751	27-#3	1 13 @ 3 4 4 4 5 5 6 8 6 @ 9
A752	26-#3	1 10 @ 3 4 4 4 4 5 5 6 7 8 6 @ 9
A753	23-#3	2 10 @ 4 5 5 6 6 8 7 @ 9
A754	22-#3	2 8 @ 4 5 5 5 6 7 8 7 @ 9
A755	20-#3	2 8 @ 5 6 7 8 8 @ 9
A756	1 -#3	2 6 @ 5 6 6 7 8 8 @ 9
A757	18-#3	3 5 @ 6 7 7 8 9 @ 9
A758	14-#4	2 6 @ 5 6 7 9 11 3 @ 12
A759	16-#4	2 7 @ 5 6 7 9 11 4 @ 12
A760	18-#4	2 7 @ 4 5 5 6 7 9 11 4 @ 12
A761	19-#4	2 7 @ 5 5 5 6 6 7 9 11 4 @ 12
A762	18-#4	2 8 @ 5 6 7 8 10 11 4 @ 12
A763	30-#3	1 15 @ 3 4 4 4 4 5 5 6 8 6 @ 9
A764	29-#3	1 13 @ 3 4 4 4 4 5 5 6 7 8 6 @ 9
A765	28-#3	1 10 @ 3 4 4 4 4 4 5 5 6 6 8 7 @ 9
A766	25-#3	2 10 @ 4 5 5 5 6 6 8 8 @ 9
A767	24-#3	2 8 @ 4 5 5 5 6 6 7 8 8 @ 9
A768	23-#3	2 7 @ 4 5 5 5 6 6 7 8 8 @ 9
A769	20-#4	1 9 @ 3 4 4 4 5 6 8 10 3 @ 12
A770	22-#4	1 9 @ 3 4 4 4 5 5 6 8 10 4 @ 12
A771	24-#4	1 10 @ 3 4 4 4 4 5 5 6 8 10 4 @ 12
A772	21-#4	2 10 @ 4 5 5 6 6 8 10 4 @ 12
A773	21-#4	2 8 @ 4 5 5 5 6 6 8 10 11 4 @ 12
A774	20-#4	2 7 @ 4 5 5 5 6 7 8 10 11 4 @ 12
A775	19-#4	2 7 @ 5 6 6 7 8 10 11 5 @ 12
A776	18-#4	2 5 @ 5 6 6 7 7 8 10 11 5 @ 12
A777	30-#3	1 11 @ 3 4 4 4 4 4 5 5 6 6 7 8 @ 8
A778	16-#4	3 7 7 7 7 7 8 9 11 7 @ 12
A779	25-#3	2 9 @ 4 5 5 5 6 6 7 9 @ 8
A780	20-#4	1 9 @ 3 4 4 4 5 6 8 10 3 @ 12
A781	22-#4	1 9 @ 3 4 4 4 5 5 6 8 10 4 @ 12
A782	24-#4	1 10 @ 3 4 4 4 4 5 5 6 8 10 4 @ 12
A783	25-#4	1 11 @ 3 4 4 4 4 5 5 6 7 9 11 3 @ 12
A784	26-#4	1 10 @ 3 4 4 4 4 5 5 5 6 7 9 11 4 @ 12
A785	23-#4	2 10 @ 4 5 5 5 6 7 8 10 5 @ 12
A786	22-#4	2 8 @ 4 5 5 5 6 6 7 8 10 5 @ 12
A787	22-#4	2 7 @ 4 5 5 5 6 6 7 8 10 11 5 @ 12
A788	20-#4	2 7 @ 5 6 6 7 7 8 10 11 5 @ 12
A789	19-#4	2 5 @ 5 6 6 6 7 8 9 11 6 @ 12
A790	18-#4	3 5 @ 6 7 7 8 9 11 7 @ 12
A791	5-#3	6 12 12 12 12
A792	6-#3	6 12 12 12 12 12
A793	6-#3	6 12 12 12 12 12
A794	6-#3	6 12 12 12 12 12
A795	7-#3	6 12 12 12 12 12 12
A796	7-#3	6 12 12 12 12 12 12
A797	7-#3	6 12 12 12 12 12 12
A798	6-#3	6 12 12 12 12 12
A799	6-#3	6 12 12 12 12 12
A800	5-#3	6 12 12 12 12
A801	8-#3	5 10 10 10 10 10 10 10
A802	8-#3	5 10 10 10 10 10 10 10
A803	8-#3	5 10 10 10 10 10 10 10
A804	7-#3	5 10 10 10 10 10 10
A805	6-#3	5 10 10 10 10 10
A806	9-#3	5 10 10 10 10 10 10 10 10
A807	9-#3	5 10 10 10 10 10 10 10 10
A808	8-#3	5 10 10 10 10 10 10 10
A809	8-#3	5 10 10 10 10 10 10 10
A810	7-#3	5 10 10 10 10 10 10
A811	7-#3	5 10 10 10 10 10 10
A812	12-#3	3 6 6 6 6 6 8 9 10 10 10 10
A813	12-#3	3 7 7 7 7 9 10 10 10 10 10 10
A814	11-#3	4 8 8 8 9 10 10 10 10 10 10
A815	10-#3	5 10 10 10 10 10 10 10 10 10
A816	10-#3	5 10 10 10 10 10 10 10 10 10
A817	9-#3	5 10 10 10 10 10 10 10 10
A818	9-#3	5 10 10 10 10 10 10 10 10
A819	8-#3	5 10 10 10 10 10 10 10
A820	8-#3	5 10 10 10 10 10 10 10
A821	7-#3	5 10 10 10 10 10 10
A822	6-#3	5 10 10 10 10 10
A823	17-#3	2 7 @ 4 5 5 7 9 5 @ 10
A824	15-#3	2 6 @ 5 6 8 9 5 @ 10
A825	13-#3	3 5 @ 6 8 9 5 @ 10
A826	12-#3	3 7 7 7 7 9 6 @ 10
A827	12-#3	4 8 8 8 9 7 @ 10
A828	11-#3	5 10 10 10 10 10 10 10 10 10 10
A829	10-#3	5 10 10 10 10 10 10 10 10 10
A830	10-#3	5 10 10 10 10 10 10 10 10 10
A831	9-#3	5 10 10 10 10 10 10 10 10
A832	9-#3	5 10 10 10 10 10 10 10 10
A833	8-#3	5 10 10 10 10 10 10 10
A834	22-#3	1 11 @ 3 4 4 4 5 7 9 4 @ 10
A835	12-#4	3 7 7 7 7 8 10 12 13 13 13 13
A836	19-#3	2 8 @ 4 5 5 6 8 9 5 @ 10
A837	17-#3	2 7 @ 5 6 7 9 6 @ 10
A838	16-#3	2 5 5 5 5 5 5 6 7 9 6 @ 10
A839	15-#3	3 6 6 6 6 6 7 9 7 @ 10
A840	14-#3	3 7 7 7 7 8 9 7 @ 10
A841	13-#3	4 8 8 8 9 8 @ 10
A842	12-#3	4 9 9 9 9 10 10 10 10 10 10 10
A843	12-#3	5 10 10 10 10 10 10 10 10 10 10 10
A844	11-#3	5 10 10 10 10 10 10 10 10 10 10
A845	23-#3	1 13 @ 3 4 4 5 7 8 4 @ 9
A846	23-#3	1 11 @ 3 4 4 4 5 7 8 5 @ 9
A847	20-#3	2 9 @ 4 5 5 6 8 6 @ 9
A848	19-#3	2 8 @ 4 5 5 6 8 6 @ 9
A849	17-#3	2 7 @ 5 6 7 8 6 @ 9
A850	17-#3	2 6 @ 5 6 7 8 7 @ 9
A851	15-#3	3 6 6 6 7 8 9 6 @ 9
A852	14-#3	3 7 7 7 7 8 8 @ 9
A853	13-#3	4 12 @ 9
A854	13-#3	4 12 @ 9
A855	12-#3	4 9 9 9 9 9 9 9 9 9 9 9
A856	23-#3	1 13 @ 3 4 4 5 7 8 4 @ 9
A857	16-#4	2 7 @ 5 6 7 9 12 4 @ 13
A858	25-#3	1 13 @ 3 4 4 4 5 6 8 5 @ 9
A859	14-#4	3 6 6 6 6 6 7 8 10 12 4 @ 13
A860	22-#3	2 10 @ 4 5 5 6 8 7 @ 9
A861	21-#3	2 8 @ 4 5 5 6 6 8 7 @ 9
A862	19-#3	2 7 @ 5 6 6 7 8 7 @ 9
A863	18-#3	2 6 @ 5 6 6 7 8 7 @ 9
A864	17-#3	3 6 6 6 6 6 7 8 9 @ 9
A865	15-#3	3 7 7 7 7 8 9 @ 9
A866	15-#3	4 8 8 8 8 10 @ 9
A867	23-#3	1 13 @ 3 4 4 5 7 8 4 @ 9
A868	15-#4	2 7 @ 5 6 7 9 12 3 @ 13
A869	17-#4	2 7 @ 5 6 6 8 10 12 4 @ 13
A870	17-#4	2 7 @ 5 6 7 8 10 12 4 @ 13
A871	15-#4	3 6 @ 6 7 8 10 12 4 @ 13
A872	15-#4	3 5 @ 6 7 8 10 12 5 @ 13
A873	23-#3	2 10 @ 4 5 5 6 6 8 7 @ 9
A874	22-#3	2 8 @ 4 5 5 5 6 7 8 7 @ 9
A875	21-#3	2 8 @ 5 6 6 7 8 8 @ 9
A876	20-#3	2 6 @ 5 6 6 7 8 9 @ 9
A877	18-#3	3 6 6 6 6 6 6 7 8 9 @ 9
A878	23-#3	1 13 @ 3 4 4 5 7 8 4 @ 9
A879	15-#4	2 7 @ 5 6 7 9 12 3 @ 13
A880	17-#4	2 7 @ 5 6 6 8 10 12 4 @ 13
A881	19-#4	2 7 @ 4 5 5 6 6 7 9 11 4 @ 13
A882	18-#4	2 8 @ 5 6 7 8 10 12 4 @ 13

STIRRUP COMBINATIONS—CONTINUED

Mark	Number and size	Spacing on each end
A883	30-#3	1 15 @ 3 4 4 4 4 5 5 6 8 6 @ 9
A884	16-#4	3 6 @ 6 7 8 9 11 5 @ 13
A885	28-#3	1 10 @ 3 4 4 4 4 4 5 5 6 6 8 7 @ 9
A886	25-#3	2 10 @ 4 5 5 5 6 6 8 8 @ 9
A887	24-#3	2 8 @ 4 5 5 5 6 6 7 8 8 @ 9
A888	22-#3	2 8 @ 5 6 6 7 8 9 @ 9
A889	18-#4	2 9 @ 4 5 5 7 9 1 2 3 @ 13
A890	22-#4	1 9 @ 3 4 4 4 5 5 6 8 11 4 @ 13
A891	24-#4	1 10 @ 3 4 4 4 4 5 5 6 8 11 4 @ 13
A892	21-#4	2 10 @ 4 5 5 6 6 8 11 4 @ 13
A893	21-#4	2 9 @ 4 5 5 6 6 7 9 12 4 @ 13
A894	20-#4	2 7 @ 4 5 5 5 6 6 7 9 11 4 @ 13
A895	19-#4	2 7 @ 5 6 6 7 8 10 12 5 @ 13
A896	18-#4	2 6 @ 5 6 6 7 8 10 12 5 @ 13
A897	30-#3	1 12 @ 3 4 4 4 4 5 5 5 6 7 8 @ 8
A898	16-#4	3 7 7 7 7 7 8 9 11 12 6 @ 13
A899	26-#3	2 9 @ 4 5 5 5 6 6 7 10 @ 8
A900	18-#4	2 9 @ 4 5 5 7 9 12 3 @ 13
A901	22-#4	1 9 @ 3 4 4 4 5 5 6 8 11 4 @ 13
A902	24-#4	1 10 @ 3 4 4 4 4 5 5 6 8 11 4 @ 13
A903	25-#4	1 11 @ 3 4 4 4 4 5 5 6 7 9 12 3 @ 13
A904	26-#4	1 10 @ 3 4 4 4 4 5 5 5 6 7 9 11 4 @ 13
A905	23-#4	2 10 @ 4 5 5 5 6 6 8 10 12 4 @ 13
A906	22-#4	2 8 @ 4 5 5 5 6 6 7 8 10 12 4 @ 13
A907	21-#4	2 9 @ 5 6 6 7 8 10 12 5 @ 13
A908	20-#4	2 7 @ 5 6 6 7 7 8 10 12 5 @ 13
A909	20-#4	2 6 @ 5 6 6 7 7 8 10 12 6 @ 13
A910	18-#4	3 6 @ 6 7 8 8 10 12 6 @ 13
A911	11-#3	1 3 3 3 3 4 4 4 4 4 4
A912	10-#3	2 4 4 4 4 4 4 4 4 4
A913	10-#3	2 4 4 4 4 4 4 4 4 4
A914	9-#3	2 4 4 4 4 4 4 4 4
A915	7-#3	2 4 4 4 4 4 4
A916	11-#3	2 4 4 4 4 4 4 4 4 4 4
A917	11-#3	2 4 4 4 4 4 4 4 4 4 4
A918	11-#3	2 4 4 4 4 4 4 4 4 4 4
A919	11-#3	2 4 4 4 4 4 4 4 4 4 4
A920	10-#3	2 4 4 4 4 4 4 4 4 4
A921	8-#3	2 4 4 4 4 4 4 4
A922	5-#3	2 4 4 4 4
A923	11-#3	2 4 4 4 4 4 4 4 4 4 4
A924	12-#3	1 4 4 4 4 4 4 4 4 4 4 4
A925	11-#3	2 4 4 4 4 4 4 4 4 4 4
A926	10-#3	2 4 4 4 4 4 4 4 4 4
A927	8-#3	2 4 4 4 4 4 4 4
A928	6-#3	2 4 4 4 4 4
A929	11-#3	2 4 4 4 4 4 4 4 4 4 4
A930	12-#3	2 4 4 4 4 4 4 4 4 4 4 4
A931	14-#3	1 3 3 3 3 3 3 7 @ 4
A932	12-#3	2 4 4 4 4 4 4 4 4 4 4 4
A933	12-#3	2 4 4 4 4 4 4 4 4 4 4 4
A934	11-#3	2 4 4 4 4 4 4 4 4 4 4
A935	9-#3	2 4 4 4 4 4 4 4 4
A936	7-#3	2 4 4 4 4 4 4
A937	9-#3	2 5 5 5 5 5 5 5 5
A938	10-#3	2 4 4 4 5 5 5 5 5 5
A939	10-#3	2 5 5 5 5 5 5 5 5 5
A940	9-#3	2 5 5 5 5 5 5 5 5
A941	8-#3	2 5 5 5 5 5 5 5
A942	7-#3	2 5 5 5 5 5 5
A943	7-#3	2 5 5 5 5 5 5
A944	8-#3	2 5 5 5 5 5 5 5
A945	9-#3	2 5 5 5 5 5 5 5 5
A946	10-#3	2 5 5 5 5 5 5 5 5 5
A947	11-#3	2 5 5 5 5 5 5 5 5 5 5
A948	11-#3	2 5 5 5 5 5 5 5 5 5 5
A949	10-#3	2 5 5 5 5 5 5 5 5 5
A950	9-#3	2 5 5 5 5 5 5 5 5
A951	8-#3	2 5 5 5 5 5 5 5
A952	6-#3	2 5 5 5 5 5
A953	9-#3	2 5 5 5 5 5 5 5 5
A954	10-#3	2 5 5 5 5 5 5 5 5 5
A955	11-#3	2 5 5 5 5 5 5 5 5 5 5
A956	11-#2	2 5 5 5 5 5 5 5 5 5 5
A957	10-#3	2 5 5 5 5 5 5 5 5 5
A958	9-#3	2 5 5 5 5 5 5 5 5
A959	8-#3	2 5 5 5 5 5 5 5
A960	6-#3	2 5 5 5 5 5
A961	9-#3	2 5 5 5 5 5 5 5 5
A962	10-#3	2 5 5 5 5 5 5 5 5 5
A963	11-#3	2 5 5 5 5 5 5 5 5 5 5
A964	12-#3	2 5 5 5 5 5 5 5 5 5 5 5
A965	12-#3	2 5 5 5 5 5 5 5 5 5 5 5
A966	11-#3	2 5 5 5 5 5 5 5 5 5 5
A967	10-#3	2 5 5 5 5 5 5 5 5 5
A968	9-#3	2 5 5 5 5 5 5 5 5
A969	8-#3	2 5 5 5 5 5 5 5
A970	6-#3	2 5 5 5 5 5
A971	12-#3	1 3 3 3 3 3 4 5 5 5 5 5
A972	*	
A973	16-#3	1 3 3 3 3 3 4 4 5 5 5 5 5 5 5 5
A974	14-#3	2 4 4 4 4 5 5 5 5 5 5 5 5 5
A975	14-#3	2 5 5 5 5 5 5 5 5 5 5 5 5 5
A976	14-#3	2 5 5 5 5 5 5 5 5 5 5 5 5 5
A977	14-#3	2 5 5 5 5 5 5 5 5 5 5 5 5 5
A978	15-#3	2 4 4 4 4 5 5 5 5 5 5 5 5 5 5
A979	13-#3	2 5 5 5 5 5 5 5 5 5 5 5 5
A980	12-#3	2 5 5 5 5 5 5 5 5 5 5 5
A981	8-#3	3 6 6 6 6 6 6 6
A982	9-#3	2 5 5 5 6 6 6 6 6
A983	9-#3	3 6 6 6 6 6 6 6 6
A984	8-#3	3 6 6 6 6 6 6 6
A985	7-#3	3 6 6 6 6 6 6
A986	6-#3	3 6 6 6 6 6
A987	9-#3	2 5 5 5 6 6 6 6 6
A988	9-#3	3 6 6 6 6 6 6 6 6
A989	10-#3	3 6 6 6 6 6 6 6 6 6
A990	10-#3	3 6 6 6 6 6 6 6 6 6
A991	10-#3	3 6 6 6 6 6 6 6 6 6
A992	10-#3	3 6 6 6 6 6 6 6 6 6
A993	9-#3	3 6 6 6 6 6 6 6 6
A994	8-#3	3 6 6 6 6 6 6 6
A995	7-#3	3 6 6 6 6 6 6
A996	5-#3	3 6 6 6 6
A997	8-#3	3 6 6 6 6 6 6 6
A998	9-#3	3 6 6 6 6 6 6 6 6
A999	9-#3	3 6 6 6 6 6 6 6 6
B000	9-#3	3 6 6 6 6 6 6 6 6
B001	9-#3	3 6 6 6 6 6 6 6 6
B002	8-#3	3 6 6 6 6 6 6 6
B003	7-#3	3 6 6 6 6 6 6
B004	5-#3	3 6 6 6 6
B005	8-#3	3 6 6 6 6 6 6 6
B006	10-#3	2 5 5 5 6 6 6 6 6 6
B007	12-#3	2 5 5 5 5 6 6 6 6 6 6 6
B008	11-#3	3 6 6 6 6 6 6 6 6 6 6
B009	12-#3	3 6 6 6 6 6 6 6 6 6 6 6
B010	12-#3	3 6 6 6 6 6 6 6 6 6 6 6
B011	12-#3	2 5 5 5 6 6 6 6 6 6 6 6
B012	11-#3	3 6 6 6 6 6 6 6 6 6 6
B013	10-#3	3 6 6 6 6 6 6 6 6 6
B014	9-#3	3 6 6 6 6 6 6 6 6
B015	8-#3	3 6 6 6 6 6 6 6
B016	12-#3	1 3 3 3 3 3 4 5 6 6 6 6
B017	14-#3	1 3 3 3 3 3 3 3 4 5 4 @ 6
B018	15-#3	1 3 3 3 3 3 4 4 5 6 @ 6
B019	13-#3	2 4 4 4 4 5 7 @ 6
B020	13-#3	2 5 5 5 9 @ 6
B021	12-#3	3 6 6 6 6 6 6 6 6 6 6 6
B022	12-#3	3 6 6 6 6 6 6 6 6 6 6 6
B023	12-#3	3 6 6 6 6 6 6 6 6 6 6 6
B024	11-#3	3 6 6 6 6 6 6 6 6 6 6
B025	10-#3	3 6 6 6 6 6 6 6 6 6
B026	9-#3	3 6 6 6 6 6 6 6 6
B027	7-#3	3 7 7 7 7 7 7
B028	9-#3	2 5 5 5 6 7 7 7 7
B029	8-#3	3 7 7 7 7 7 7 7
B030	7-#3	3 7 7 7 7 7 7
B031	7-#3	3 7 7 7 7 7 7
B032	6-#3	3 7 7 7 7 7
B033	7-#3	3 7 7 7 7 7 7
B034	8-#3	3 7 7 7 7 7 7 7
B035	8-#3	3 7 7 7 7 7 7 7
B036	8-#3	3 7 7 7 7 7 7 7
B037	9-#3	3 6 6 6 6 6 6 6 6
B038	7-#3	3 7 7 7 7 7 7
B039	6-#3	3 7 7 7 7 7
B040	5-#3	3 7 7 7 7
B041	7-#3	3 7 7 7 7 7 7
B042	9-#3	3 6 6 6 7 7 7 7 7
B043	11-#3	2 5 5 5 6 7 7 7 7 7 7
B044	11-#3	3 6 6 6 7 7 7 7 7 7 7
B045	10-#3	3 7 7 7 7 7 7 7 7 7
B046	10-#3	3 7 7 7 7 7 7 7 7 7
B047	10-#3	3 7 7 7 7 7 7 7 7 7
B048	11-#3	3 6 6 6 6 6 6 6 6 6 6
B049	9-#3	3 7 7 7 7 7 7 7 7
B050	8-#3	3 7 7 7 7 7 7 7
B051	7-#3	3 7 7 7 7 7 7
B052	12-#3	1 3 3 3 3 3 4 6 7 7 7 7
B053	14-#3	1 3 3 3 3 3 3 4 5 6 4 @ 7
B054	14-#3	1 3 3 3 3 3 3 4 5 6 4 @ 7
B055	13-#3	2 4 4 4 4 5 6 6 @ 7
B056	12-#3	2 5 5 5 6 7 7 7 7 7 7 7
B057	11-#3	3 7 7 7 7 7 7 7 7 7 7
B058	11-#3	3 7 7 7 7 7 7 7 7 7 7
B059	10-#3	3 7 7 7 7 7 7 7 7 7
B060	10-#3	3 7 7 7 7 7 7 7 7 7
B061	9-#3	3 7 7 7 7 7 7 7 7
B062	8-#3	3 7 7 7 7 7 7 7
B063	10-#3	2 4 4 4 4 5 6 7 7 7
B064	14-#3	1 3 3 3 3 3 3 4 5 6 4 @ 7
B065	16-#3	1 7 @ 3 4 4 6 5 @ 7
B066	14-#3	2 4 4 4 4 4 4 5 6 5 @ 7
B067	13-#3	2 5 5 5 5 5 6 6 @ 7
B068	12-#3	3 6 6 6 6 7 7 7 7 7 7 7
B069	12-#3	3 7 7 7 7 7 7 7 7 7 7 7
B070	12-#3	3 7 7 7 7 7 7 7 7 7 7 7

* See page 10-58.

STIRRUP COMBINATIONS—CONTINUED

Mark	Number and size	Spacing on each end
B071	11-#3	3 7 7 7 7 7 7 7 7 7 7
B072	11-#3	3 7 7 7 7 7 7 7 7 7 7
B073	10-#3	3 7 7 7 7 7 7 7 7 7
B074	12-#3	1 3 3 3 3 3 4 6 7 7 7 7
B075	14-#3	1 3 3 3 3 3 3 4 5 6 4 @ 7
B076	16-#3	1 8 @ 3 4 5 6 4 @ 7
B077	18-#3	1 8 @ 3 4 4 5 6 5 @ 7
B078	18-#3	1 6 @ 3 4 4 4 5 6 6 @ 7
B079	16-#3	2 5 @ 4 5 5 6 7 @ 7
B080	15-#3	2 4 @ 5 6 6 8 @ 7
B081	14-#3	3 6 6 10 @ 7
B082	13-#3	3 12 @ 7
B083	13-#3	3 12 @ 7
B084	13-#3	3 12 @ 7
B085	6-#2	4 8 8 8 8 8
B086	5-#2	4 8 8 8 8
B087	7-#3	4 8 8 8 8 8 8
B088	7-#3	4 8 8 8 8 8 8
B089	6-#3	4 8 8 8 8 8
B090	9-#3	4 8 8 8 8 8 8 8 8
B091	9-#3	4 8 8 8 8 8 8 8 8
B092	9-#3	4 8 8 8 8 8 8 8 8
B093	9-#3	4 8 8 8 8 8 8 8 8
B094	8-#3	4 8 8 8 8 8 8 8
B095	8-#3	4 8 8 8 8 8 8 8
B096	7-#3	4 8 8 8 8 8 8
B097	6-#3	4 8 8 8 8 8
B098	10-#3	3 7 7 7 8 8 8 8 8 8
B099	10-#3	4 8 8 8 8 8 8 8 8 8
B100	9-#3	4 8 8 8 8 8 8 8 8
B101	9-#3	4 8 8 8 8 8 8 8 8
B102	9-#3	4 8 8 8 8 8 8 8 8
B103	8-#3	4 8 8 8 8 8 8 8
B104	7-#3	4 8 8 8 8 8 8
B105	6-#3	4 8 8 8 8 8
B106	11-#3	3 6 6 6 7 8 8 8 8 8 8
B107	11-#3	3 6 6 6 7 8 8 8 8 8 8
B108	10-#3	4 8 8 8 8 8 8 8 8 8
B109	10-#3	4 8 8 8 8 8 8 8 8 8
B110	10-#3	4 8 8 8 8 8 8 8 8 8
B111	9-#3	4 8 8 8 8 8 8 8 8
B112	9-#3	4 8 8 8 8 8 8 8 8
B113	8-#3	4 8 8 8 8 8 8 8
B114	7-#3	4 8 8 8 8 8 8
B115	6-#3	4 8 8 8 8 8
B116	11-#3	3 6 6 6 7 8 8 8 8 8 8
B117	13-#3	2 5 5 5 5 6 7 8 8 8 8 8 8
B118	12-#3	3 6 6 6 7 8 8 8 8 8 8 8
B119	12-#3	3 7 7 7 8 8 8 8 8 8 8 8
B120	11-#3	4 8 8 8 8 8 8 8 8 8 8
B121	11-#3	4 8 8 8 8 8 8 8 8 8 8
B122	11-#3	4 8 8 8 8 8 8 8 8 8 8
B123	10-#3	4 8 8 8 8 8 8 8 8 8
B124	9-#3	4 8 8 8 8 8 8 8 8
B125	8-#3	4 8 8 8 8 8 8 8
B126	7-#3	4 8 8 8 8 8 8
B127	11-#3	3 6 6 6 7 8 8 8 8 8 8
B128	13-#3	2 5 5 5 5 6 7 6 @ 8
B129	14-#3	2 5 5 5 5 6 7 7 @ 8
B130	14-#3	2 5 5 5 5 6 7 7 @ 8
B131	13-#3	3 6 6 6 7 8 @ 8
B132	12-#3	4 8 8 8 8 8 8 8 8 8 8 8
B133	12-#3	4 8 8 8 8 8 8 8 8 8 8 8
B134	12-#3	4 8 8 8 8 8 8 8 8 8 8 8
B135	12-#3	4 8 8 8 8 8 8 8 8 8 8 8
B136	11-#3	4 8 8 8 8 8 8 8 8 8 8
B137	10-#3	4 8 8 8 8 8 8 8 8 8
B138	6-#3	4 9 9 9 9 9
B139	5-#3	4 9 9 9 9
B140	7-#3	4 9 9 9 9 9 9
B141	6-#3	4 9 9 9 9 9
B142	6-#3	4 9 9 9 9 9

Mark	Number and size	Spacing on each end
B143	9-#3	4 9 9 9 9 9 9 9 9
B144	9-#3	4 9 9 9 9 9 9 9 9
B145	9-#3	4 9 9 9 9 9 9 9 9
B146	8-#3	4 9 9 9 9 9 9 9
B147	8-#3	4 9 9 9 9 9 9 9
B148	7-#3	4 9 9 9 9 9 9
B149	6-#3	4 9 9 9 9 9
B150	5-#3	4 9 9 9 9
B151	10-#3	3 7 7 7 8 9 9 9 9 9
B152	9-#3	4 9 9 9 9 9 9 9 9
B153	9-#3	4 9 9 9 9 9 9 9 9
B154	8-#3	4 9 9 9 9 9 9 9
B155	8-#3	4 9 9 9 9 9 9 9
B156	7-#3	4 9 9 9 9 9 9
B157	7-#3	4 9 9 9 9 9 9
B158	6-#3	4 9 9 9 9 9
B159	11-#3	3 6 6 6 7 8 9 9 9 9 9
B160	12-#3	3 6 6 6 6 8 9 9 9 9 9 9
B161	12-#3	3 6 6 6 7 8 9 9 9 9 9 9
B162	11-#3	3 7 7 7 8 9 9 9 9 9 9
B163	10-#3	4 9 9 9 9 9 9 9 9 9
B164	10-#3	4 9 9 9 9 9 9 9 9 9
B165	10-#3	4 9 9 9 9 9 9 9 9 9
B166	9-#3	4 9 9 9 9 9 9 9 9
B167	9-#3	4 9 9 9 9 9 9 9 9
B168	8-#3	4 9 9 9 9 9 9 9
B169	7-#3	4 9 9 9 9 9 9
B170	11-#3	3 6 6 6 7 8 9 9 9 9 9
B171	12-#3	3 6 6 6 6 8 9 9 9 9 9 9
B172	13-#3	2 5 5 5 5 6 7 8 9 9 9 9 9
B173	13-#3	3 6 6 6 6 7 8 9 9 9 9 9 9
B174	12-#3	3 7 7 7 7 8 9 9 9 9 9 9
B175	12-#3	4 8 8 8 9 9 9 9 9 9 9 9
B176	11-#3	4 9 9 9 9 9 9 9 9 9 9
B177	11-#3	4 9 9 9 9 9 9 9 9 9 9
B178	11-#3	4 9 9 9 9 9 9 9 9 9 9
B179	10-#3	4 9 9 9 9 9 9 9 9 9
B180	9-#3	4 9 9 9 9 9 9 9 9
B181	17-#3	1 7 @ 3 4 4 5 6 8 4 @ 9
B182	15-#3	2 4 4 4 4 4 4 5 6 8 5 @ 9
B183	13-#3	2 5 5 5 5 5 6 8 5 @ 9
B184	12-#3	3 6 6 6 6 8 9 9 9 9 9 9
B185	11-#3	3 7 7 7 8 9 9 9 9 9 9
B186	10-#3	4 9 9 9 9 9 9 9 9 9
B187	10-#3	4 9 9 9 9 9 9 9 9 9
B188	10-#3	4 9 9 9 9 9 9 9 9 9
B189	9-#3	4 9 9 9 9 9 9 9 9
B190	8-#3	4 9 9 9 9 9 9 9
B191	8-#3	4 9 9 9 9 9 9 9
B192	9-#3	4 8 8 8 9 9 9 9 9
B193	10-#3	3 7 7 7 8 9 9 9 9 9
B194	11-#3	3 7 7 7 8 9 9 9 9 9 9
B195	12-#3	3 6 6 6 7 8 9 9 9 9 9 9
B196	13-#3	3 6 6 6 6 8 7 @ 9
B197	14-#3	3 6 6 6 6 7 8 7 @ 9
B198	14-#3	3 6 6 6 6 7 8 7 @ 9
B199	13-#3	3 7 7 7 8 8 @ 9
B200	12-#3	4 9 9 9 9 9 9 9 9 9 9 9
B201	11-#3	4 9 9 9 9 9 9 9 9 9 9
B202	11-#3	4 9 9 9 9 9 9 9 9 9 9
B203	18-#3	1 9 @ 3 4 4 5 7 8 3 @ 9
B204	20-#3	1 10 @ 3 4 4 5 6 8 4 @ 9
B205	22-#3	1 10 @ 3 4 4 4 5 6 8 5 @ 9
B206	21-#3	1 8 @ 3 4 4 4 5 5 6 8 5 @ 9
B207	18-#3	2 7 @ 4 5 5 6 7 8 5 @ 9
B208	18-#3	2 5 @ 4 5 5 6 6 8 7 @ 9
B209	16-#3	2 5 5 5 5 5 6 7 8 7 @ 9
B210	15-#3	3 6 6 6 6 7 8 8 @ 9
B211	14-#3	3 7 7 7 8 9 @ 9
B212	13-#3	4 8 8 8 9 @ 9

Mark	Number and size	Spacing on each end
B213	12-#3	4 9 9 9 9 9 9 9 9 9 9 9
B214	6-#3	5 10 10 10 10 10
B215	6-#3	5 10 10 10 10 10
B216	5-#3	5 10 10 10 10
B217	8-#3	4 9 9 9 10 10 10 10
B218	8-#3	5 10 10 10 10 10 10 10
B219	8-#3	5 10 10 10 10 10 10 10
B220	8-#3	5 10 10 10 10 10 10 10
B221	7-#3	5 10 10 10 10 10 10
B222	7-#3	5 10 10 10 10 10 10
B223	6-#3	5 10 10 10 10 10
B224	5-#3	5 10 10 10 10
B225	10-#3	3 7 7 7 8 10 10 10 10 10
B226	9-#3	4 9 9 9 10 10 10 10 10
B227	8-#3	5 10 10 10 10 10 10 10
B228	8-#3	5 10 10 10 10 10 10 10
B229	7-#3	5 10 10 10 10 10 10
B230	7-#3	5 10 10 10 10 10 10
B231	6-#3	5 10 10 10 10 10
B232	5-#3	5 10 10 10 10
B233	10-#3	3 6 6 6 7 9 10 10 10 10
B234	11-#3	3 6 6 6 6 8 9 10 10 10 10
B235	11-#3	3 6 6 6 7 9 10 10 10 10 10
B236	10-#3	4 8 8 8 9 10 10 10 10 10
B237	9-#3	5 10 10 10 10 10 10 10 10
B238	9-#3	5 10 10 10 10 10 10 10 10
B239	9-#3	5 10 10 10 10 10 10 10 10
B240	8-#3	5 10 10 10 10 10 10 10
B241	8-#3	5 10 10 10 10 10 10 10
B242	7-#3	5 10 10 10 10 10 10
B243	7-#3	5 10 10 10 10 10 10
B244	10-#3	3 6 6 6 7 9 10 10 10 10
B245	11-#3	3 6 6 6 6 8 9 10 10 10 10
B246	12-#3	3 6 6 6 6 7 9 10 10 10 10 10
B247	13-#3	3 6 6 6 6 7 9 6 @ 10
B248	12-#3	3 7 7 7 8 9 10 10 10 10 10 10
B249	11-#3	4 8 8 8 9 10 10 10 10 10 10
B250	10-#3	5 10 10 10 10 10 10 10 10 10
B251	10-#3	5 10 10 10 10 10 10 10 10 10
B252	10-#3	5 10 10 10 10 10 10 10 10 10
B253	9-#3	5 10 10 10 10 10 10 10 10
B254	9-#3	5 10 10 10 10 10 10 10 10
B255	10-#3	3 6 6 6 7 9 10 10 10 10
B256	11-#3	3 6 6 6 6 8 9 10 10 10 10
B257	12-#3	3 6 6 6 6 7 9 10 10 10 10 10
B258	13-#3	3 6 6 6 6 7 9 6 @ 10
B259	12-#3	3 7 7 7 8 9 10 10 10 10 10 10
B260	11-#3	4 8 8 9 10 10 10 10 10 10 10
B261	10-#3	5 10 10 10 10 10 10 10 10 10
B262	10-#3	5 10 10 10 10 10 10 10 10 10
B263	10-#3	5 10 10 10 10 10 10 10 10 10
B264	9-#3	5 10 10 10 10 10 10 10 10
B265	9-#3	5 10 10 10 10 10 10 10 10

STIRRUP COMBINATIONS—CONTINUED

Mark	Number and size	Spacing on each end
B266	17-#3	1 8 @ 3 4 4 5 7 9 3 @ 10
B267	15-#3	2 6 @ 4 5 6 8 9 4 @ 10
B268	13-#3	2 5 5 5 5 5 6 8 9 3 @ 10
B269	12-#3	3 6 6 6 6 8 9 10 10 10 10 10
B270	11-#3	3 7 7 7 8 10 10 10 10 10 10
B271	10-#3	4 9 9 9 10 10 10 10 10 10
B272	9-#3	5 10 10 10 10 10 10 10 10
B273	9-#3	5 10 10 10 10 10 10 10 10
B274	8-#3	5 10 10 10 10 10 10 10
B275	8-#3	5 10 10 10 10 10 10 10
B276	7-#3	5 10 10 10 10 10 10
B277	18-#3	1 9 @ 3 4 4 5 7 9 3 @ 10
B278	19-#3	1 9 @ 3 4 4 5 6 8 4 @ 10
B279	17-#3	2 7 @ 4 5 5 6 8 5 @ 10
B280	16-#3	2 6 @ 4 5 5 6 8 9 4 @ 10
B281	14-#3	2 5 5 5 5 5 6 7 9 5 @ 10
B282	13-#3	3 6 6 6 6 7 9 6 @ 10
B283	12-#3	3 7 7 7 8 9 10 10 10 10 10 10
B284	11-#3	4 9 9 9 10 10 10 10 10 10 10
B285	10-#3	5 10 10 10 10 10 10 10 10 10
B286	10-#3	5 10 10 10 10 10 10 10 10 10
B287	9-#3	5 10 10 10 10 10 10 10 10
B288	18-#3	1 3 3 3 3 3 3 3 3 3 4 4 5 7 9 3 @ 10
B289	20-#3	1 3 3 3 3 3 3 3 3 3 3 4 4 5 6 8 4 @ 10
B290	21-#3	1 3 3 3 3 3 3 3 3 3 3 4 4 4 5 6 8 4 @ 10
B291	21-#3	1 3 3 3 3 3 3 3 3 4 4 4 5 5 6 8 5 @ 10
B292	18-#3	2 7 @ 4 5 5 6 7 9 5 @ 10
B293	16-#3	2 6 @ 5 6 6 8 9 5 @ 10
B294	16-#3	2 5 @ 5 6 7 8 9 6 @ 10
B295	14-#3	3 4 @ 6 7 8 9 6 @ 10
B296	13-#3	3 7 7 7 8 9 7 @ 10
B297	12-#3	4 8 8 9 8 @ 10
B298	11-#3	5 10 10 10 10 10 10 10 10 10 10
B299	5-#3	5 11 11 11 11
B300	8-#3	5 11 11 11 11 11 11 11
B301	7-#3	5 11 11 11 11 11 11
B302	7-#3	5 11 11 11 11 11 11
B303	6-#3	5 11 11 11 11 11
B304	6-#3	5 11 11 11 11 11
B305	5-#3	5 11 11 11 11
B306	8-#3	5 11 11 11 11 11 11 11
B307	7-#3	5 11 11 11 11 11 11
B308	7-#3	5 11 11 11 11 11 11
B309	7-#3	5 11 11 11 11 11 11
B310	6-#3	5 11 11 11 11 11
B311	5-#3	5 11 11 11 11
B312	11-#3	3 7 7 7 7 9 11 11 11 11 11
B313	10-#3	4 8 8 8 10 11 11 11 11 11
B314	9-#3	5 10 10 10 11 11 11 11 11
B315	9-#3	5 11 11 11 11 11 11 11 11
B316	8-#3	5 11 11 11 11 11 11 11
B317	8-#3	5 11 11 11 11 11 11 11
B318	8-#3	5 11 11 11 11 11 11 11
B319	7-#3	5 11 11 11 11 11 11
B320	6-#3	5 11 11 11 11 11
B321	5-#3	5 11 11 11 11
B322	12-#3	3 6 6 6 6 7 9 10 11 11 11 11
B323	12-#3	3 6 6 6 6 7 9 10 11 11 11 11
B324	12-#3	3 7 7 7 8 10 11 11 11 11 11 11
B325	11-#3	4 8 8 8 10 11 11 11 11 11 11
B326	10-#3	5 10 10 10 11 11 11 11 11 11
B327	9-#3	5 11 11 11 11 11 11 11 11
B328	9-#3	5 11 11 11 11 11 11 11 11
B329	9-#3	5 11 11 11 11 11 11 11 11
B330	8-#3	5 11 11 11 11 11 11 11
B331	8-#3	5 11 11 11 11 11 11 11
B332	7-#3	5 11 11 11 11 11 11
B333	12-#3	3 6 6 6 6 7 9 10 11 11 11 11
B334	13-#3	3 6 6 6 6 6 7 9 5 @ 11
B335	15-#3	2 5 5 5 5 5 6 7 9 10 5 @ 11
B336	13-#3	3 6 6 6 6 7 8 10 5 @ 11
B337	12-#3	3 7 7 7 8 9 10 11 11 11 11 11
B338	11-#3	4 9 9 9 10 11 11 11 11 11 11
B339	11-#3	5 10 10 10 11 11 11 11 11 11 11
B340	10-#3	5 11 11 11 11 11 11 11 11 11
B341	10-#3	5 11 11 11 11 11 11 11 11 11
B342	9-#3	5 11 11 11 11 11 11 11 11
B343	9-#3	5 11 11 11 11 11 11 11 11
B344	17-#3	2 7 @ 4 5 5 6 8 5 @ 10
B345	15-#3	2 5 5 5 5 5 5 6 7 9 5 @ 10
B346	15-#3	2 5 5 5 5 5 6 7 9 6 @ 10
B347	13-#3	3 6 6 6 6 7 9 6 @ 10
B348	12-#3	4 8 8 8 9 10 10 10 10 10 10 10
B349	11-#3	4 9 9 9 10 10 10 10 10 10 10
B350	10-#3	5 10 10 10 10 10 10 10 10 10
B351	10-#3	5 10 10 10 10 10 10 10 10 10
B352	10-#3	5 10 10 10 10 10 10 10 10 10
B353	9-#3	5 10 10 10 10 10 10 10 10
B354	8-#3	5 10 10 10 10 10 10 10
B355	21-#3	1 10 @ 3 4 4 4 5 6 8 4 @ 10
B356	19-#3	2 9 @ 4 5 5 7 9 5 @ 10
B357	18-#3	2 7 @ 4 5 5 6 7 9 5 @ 10
B358	16-#3	2 6 @ 5 6 6 8 9 5 @ 10
B359	15-#3	3 6 6 6 6 6 7 8 9 6 @ 10
B360	14-#3	3 6 6 6 6 7 8 9 6 @ 10
B361	13-#3	3 7 7 7 8 9 7 @ 10
B362	12-#3	4 9 9 9 10 10 10 10 10 10 10 10
B363	11-#3	5 10 10 10 10 10 10 10 10 10 10
B364	11-#3	5 10 10 10 10 10 10 10 10 10 10
B365	11-#3	5 10 10 10 10 10 10 10 10 10 10
B366	6-#3	6 12 12 12 12 12
B367	5-#3	6 12 12 12 12
B368	5-#3	6 12 12 12 12
B369	7-#3	6 12 12 12 12 12 12
B370	7-#3	6 12 12 12 12 12 12
B371	7-#3	6 12 12 12 12 12 12
B372	6-#3	6 12 12 12 12 12
B373	6-#3	6 12 12 12 12 12
B374	5-#3	6 12 12 12 12
B375	11-#3	3 7 7 7 7 9 11 12 12 12 12
B376	10-#3	4 8 8 8 10 12 12 12 12 12
B377	9-#3	5 10 10 11 12 12 12 12 12
B378	8-#3	6 12 12 12 12 12 12 12
B379	8-#3	6 12 12 12 12 12 12 12
B380	8-#3	6 12 12 12 12 12 12 12
B381	7-#3	6 12 12 12 12 12 12
B382	7-#3	6 12 12 12 12 12 12
B383	6-#3	6 12 12 12 12 12
B384	5-#3	6 12 12 12 12
B385	12-#3	3 6 6 6 6 7 9 11 12 12 12 12
B386	12-#3	3 6 6 6 6 7 8 10 12 12 12 12
B387	11-#3	3 7 7 7 7 9 11 12 12 12 12
B388	10-#3	4 9 9 9 11 12 12 12 12 12
B389	10-#3	5 10 10 11 12 12 12 12 12 12
B390	9-#3	6 12 12 12 12 12 12 12 12
B391	9-#3	6 12 12 12 12 12 12 12 12
B392	8-#3	6 12 12 12 12 12 12 12
B393	8-#3	6 12 12 12 12 12 12 12
B394	7-#3	6 12 12 12 12 12 12
B395	7-#3	6 12 12 12 12 12 12
B396	12-#3	3 6 6 6 6 7 9 11 12 12 12 12
B397	13-#3	3 6 6 6 6 6 7 9 11 4 @ 12
B398	13-#3	3 6 6 6 6 6 7 9 11 4 @ 12
B399	12-#3	3 7 7 7 7 8 10 11 12 12 12 12
B400	11-#3	4 8 8 8 9 11 12 12 12 12 12
B401	11-#3	4 9 9 9 11 12 12 12 12 12 12
B402	10-#3	5 11 11 11 12 12 12 12 12 12
B403	9-#3	6 12 12 12 12 12 12 12 12
B404	9-#3	6 12 12 12 12 12 12 12 12
B405	9-#3	6 12 12 12 12 12 12 12 12
B406	8-#3	6 12 12 12 12 12 12 12
B407	17-#3	2 7 @ 4 5 5 6 8 9 4 @ 10
B408	15-#3	2 5 5 5 5 5 5 6 7 9 5 @ 10
B409	14-#3	3 6 6 6 6 6 7 9 6 @ 10
B410	13-#3	3 7 7 7 7 8 9 6 @ 10
B411	12-#3	4 8 8 8 9 10 10 10 10 10 10 10
B412	11-#3	4 9 9 9 10 10 10 10 10 10 10
B413	11-#3	5 10 10 10 10 10 10 10 10 10 10
B414	10-#3	5 10 10 10 10 10 10 10 10 10
B415	10-#3	5 10 10 10 10 10 10 10 10 10
B416	9-#3	5 10 10 10 10 10 10 10 10
B417	9-#3	5 10 10 10 10 10 10 10 10

STIRRUP COMBINATIONS—CONTINUED

Mark	Number and size	Spacing on each end
B418	22-#3	1 10 @ 3 4 4 4 5 6 8 9 / 4 @ 10
B419	19-#3	2 9 @ 4 5 5 6 8 5 @ 10
B420	18-#3	2 7 @ 4 5 5 6 7 9 5 @ 10
B421	17-#3	2 5 5 5 5 5 5 6 6 7 9 / 6 @ 10
B422	15-#3	3 6 6 6 6 6 7 8 9 6 @ 10
B423	14-#3	3 7 7 7 7 7 9 7 @ 10
B424	13-#3	4 8 8 8 9 8 @ 10
B425	12-#3	4 9 9 9 10 10 10 10 10 10 / 10 10
B426	12-#3	5 10 10 10 10 10 10 10 10 / 10 10 10 10
B427	11-#3	5 10 10 10 10 10 10 10 10 / 10 10 10
B428	11-#3	5 10 10 10 10 10 10 10 10 / 10 10 10
B429	19-#4	2 8 @ 4 5 5 6 7 9 11 / 4 @ 12
B430	17-#4	2 7 @ 5 6 6 7 9 11 / 4 @ 12
B431	27-#3	1 14 @ 3 4 4 4 5 5 6 8 9 / 4 @ 10
B432	15-#4	3 6 6 6 6 6 7 7 9 11 / 5 @ 12
B433	26-#3	1 9 @ 3 4 4 4 4 5 5 5 6 7 / 9 6 @ 10
B434	23-#3	2 9 @ 4 5 5 5 6 7 8 9 / 6 @ 10
B435	22-#3	2 7 @ 4 5 5 5 6 6 7 9 / 7 @ 10
B436	20-#3	2 7 @ 5 6 6 7 8 9 7 @ 10
B437	19-#3	2 5 @ 5 6 6 7 7 8 9 7 @ 10
B438	17-#3	3 6 6 6 6 6 7 8 9 8 @ 10
B439	16-#3	3 7 7 7 7 8 9 9 @ 10
B440	19-#4	2 9 @ 4 5 5 6 8 10 4 @ 12
B441	20-#4	2 9 @ 4 5 5 6 7 9 11 / 4 @ 12
B442	20-#4	2 7 @ 4 5 5 5 6 7 8 10 / 5 @ 12
B443	18-#4	2 7 @ 5 6 6 7 9 11 5 @ 12
B444	29-#3	1 13 @ 3 4 4 4 4 5 5 6 7 8 / 6 @ 9
B445	28-#3	1 11 @ 3 4 4 4 4 5 5 6 6 8 / 7 @ 9
B446	24-#3	2 10 @ 4 5 5 5 6 6 8 / 7 @ 9
B447	23-#3	2 8 @ 4 5 5 5 6 6 7 8 / 7 @ 9
B448	23-#3	2 7 @ 4 5 5 6 6 7 7 8 / 8 @ 9
B449	21-#3	2 6 @ 5 6 6 7 7 8 9 @ 9
B450	19-#3	3 6 6 6 6 6 6 7 8 10 @ 9
B451	23-#4	1 11 @ 3 4 4 4 5 5 6 8 11 / 3 @ 12
B452	23-#4	1 9 @ 3 4 4 4 4 5 5 6 8 10 / 4 @ 12
B453	20-#4	2 9 @ 4 5 5 6 7 8 10 / 4 @ 12
B454	20-#4	2 7 @ 4 5 5 5 6 7 8 10 / 5 @ 12
B455	18-#4	2 7 @ 5 6 6 7 9 11 5 @ 12
B456	16-#4	3 6 @ 6 7 8 9 11 5 @ 12
B457	16-#4	3 5 @ 6 7 8 9 11 6 @ 12
B458	25-#3	2 10 @ 4 5 5 5 6 7 9 @ 8
B459	24-#3	2 8 @ 4 5 5 5 6 6 7 9 @ 8
B460	22-#3	2 8 @ 5 6 6 7 10 @ 8
B461	21-#3	2 6 @ 5 6 6 7 11 @ 8
B462	6-#3	6 12 12 12 12 12 12
B463	6-#3	6 12 12 12 12 12 12
B464	7-#3	6 12 12 12 12 12 12 12
B465	7-#3	6 12 12 12 12 12 12 12

Mark	Number and size	Spacing on each end
B466	7-#3	6 12 12 12 12 12 12 12
B467	6-#3	6 12 12 12 12 12 12
B468	6-#3	6 12 12 12 12 12 12
B469	5-#3	6 12 12 12 12
B470	11-#3	3 7 7 7 7 9 11 12 12 12 12 12
B471	10-#3	4 9 9 9 10 12 12 12 12 12 12
B472	9-#3	5 11 11 11 12 12 12 12 / 12
B473	8-#3	6 12 12 12 12 12 12 12 12
B474	8-#3	6 12 12 12 12 12 12 12 12
B475	8-#3	6 12 12 12 12 12 12 12 12
B476	7-#3	6 12 12 12 12 12 12 12
B477	7-#3	6 12 12 12 12 12 12 12
B478	6-#3	6 12 12 12 12 12 12
B479	5-#3	6 12 12 12 12
B480	12-#3	3 6 6 6 6 7 9 11 12 12 12 / 12
B481	13-#3	3 6 6 6 6 6 8 10 5 @ 12
B482	11-#3	4 8 8 8 8 10 12 12 12 12 / 12
B483	10-#3	4 9 9 9 10 12 12 12 12 12 12
B484	10-#3	5 11 11 11 11 12 12 12 12 / 12 12
B485	9-#3	6 12 12 12 12 12 12 12 / 12
B486	9-#3	6 12 12 12 12 12 12 12 12 12
B487	8-#3	6 12 12 12 12 12 12 12 12
B488	8-#3	6 12 12 12 12 12 12 12 12
B489	7-#3	6 12 12 12 12 12 12 12
B490	7-#3	6 12 12 12 12 12 12 12
B491	12-#3	3 6 6 6 6 7 9 11 12 12 12 / 12
B492	13-#3	3 6 6 6 6 6 7 9 11 4 @ 12
B493	14-#3	3 6 6 6 6 6 7 8 10 5 @ 12
B494	13-#3	3 7 7 7 7 8 10 11 5 @ 12
B495	12-#3	4 8 8 8 9 11 12 12 12 12 / 12 12
B496	11-#3	4 9 9 9 10 12 12 12 12 12 / 12
B497	10-#3	5 11 11 11 11 12 12 12 12 / 12 12
B498	10-#3	6 12 12 12 12 12 12 12 12 / 12 12
B499	9-#3	6 12 12 12 12 12 12 12 12 / 12
B500	9-#3	6 12 12 12 12 12 12 12 12 / 12
B501	8-#3	6 12 12 12 12 12 12 12 12
B502	17-#3	2 7 @ 4 5 5 6 8 9 4 @ 10
B503	15-#3	2 5 5 5 5 5 5 6 7 9 5 @ 10
B504	14-#3	3 6 6 6 6 6 7 9 6 @ 10
B505	13-#3	3 7 7 7 7 8 9 6 @ 10
B506	12-#3	4 8 8 8 9 10 10 10 10 10 / 10 10
B507	11-#3	5 10 10 10 10 10 10 10 10 / 10 10 10 10
B508	11-#3	5 10 10 10 10 10 10 10 10 / 10 10 10
B509	10-#3	5 10 10 10 10 10 10 10 10 / 10 10
B510	10-#3	5 10 10 10 10 10 10 10 10 / 10 10
B511	9-#3	5 10 10 10 10 10 10 10 10 / 10
B512	9-#3	5 10 10 10 10 10 10 10 10 / 10
B513	22-#3	1 10 @ 3 4 4 4 5 6 8 9 / 4 @ 10
B514	19-#3	2 9 @ 4 5 5 6 8 5 @ 10
B515	19-#3	2 7 @ 4 5 5 6 7 9 6 @ 10
B516	17-#3	2 6 @ 5 6 6 7 9 6 @ 10
B517	15-#3	3 6 6 6 6 6 7 8 9 6 @ 10

Mark	Number and size	Spacing on each end
B518	14-#3	3 7 7 7 7 7 9 7 @ 10
B519	13-#3	4 8 8 8 9 8 @ 10
B520	13-#3	4 9 9 9 9 8 @ 10
B521	12-#3	5 10 10 10 10 10 10 10 10 / 10 10 10 10
B522	11-#3	5 10 10 10 10 10 10 10 10 / 10 10 10
B523	11-#3	5 10 10 10 10 10 10 10 10 / 10 10 10
B524	18-#4	2 8 @ 4 5 5 6 7 9 12 / 3 @ 13
B525	17-#4	2 7 @ 5 6 6 7 9 12 / 4 @ 13
B526	27-#3	1 14 @ 3 4 4 4 5 5 6 8 / 5 @ 10
B527	15-#4	3 5 @ 6 7 7 9 11 12 / 4 @ 13
B528	26-#3	1 9 @ 3 4 4 4 4 5 5 5 6 7 / 9 6 @ 10
B529	23-#3	2 9 @ 4 5 5 5 6 7 8 9 / 6 @ 10
B530	22-#3	2 7 @ 4 5 5 5 6 6 7 9 / 7 @ 10
B531	20-#3	2 7 @ 5 6 6 7 8 9 7 @ 10
B532	18-#3	3 6 @ 6 7 7 8 9 7 @ 10
B533	18-#3	3 5 @ 6 7 8 9 9 @ 10
B534	16-#3	3 4 @ 7 8 9 9 @ 10
B535	18-#4	2 8 @ 4 5 5 6 7 9 12 / 3 @ 13
B536	20-#4	2 9 @ 4 5 5 6 7 9 11 / 4 @ 13
B537	19-#4	2 7 @ 4 5 5 5 6 7 9 11 / 4 @ 13
B538	29-#3	1 15 @ 3 4 4 4 4 5 6 7 8 / 5 @ 9
B539	16-#4	3 6 @ 6 7 8 9 11 5 @ 13
B540	28-#3	1 11 @ 3 4 4 4 4 5 5 6 6 8 / 7 @ 9
B541	24-#3	2 10 @ 4 5 5 5 6 6 8 / 7 @ 9
B542	24-#3	2 8 @ 4 5 5 5 6 6 7 8 / 8 @ 9
B543	21-#3	2 8 @ 5 6 6 7 8 8 @ 9
B544	21-#3	2 6 @ 5 6 6 7 7 8 9 @ 9
B545	19-#3	3 6 @ 6 7 8 10 @ 9
B546	23-#4	1 11 @ 3 4 4 4 5 5 6 8 11 / 3 @ 13
B547	20-#4	2 10 @ 4 5 5 6 7 9 12 / 3 @ 13
B548	20-#4	2 8 @ 4 5 5 5 6 7 9 11 / 4 @ 13
B549	19-#4	2 7 @ 4 5 5 6 6 7 8 11 / 4 @ 13
B550	30-#3	1 15 @ 3 4 4 4 4 5 5 7 / 7 @ 8
B551	16-#4	3 6 @ 6 7 8 9 11 5 @ 13
B552	16-#4	3 5 @ 6 7 8 9 11 12 / 5 @ 13
B553	25-#3	2 10 @ 4 5 5 5 6 7 / 9 @ 8
B554	24-#3	2 8 @ 4 5 5 5 6 6 7 / 9 @ 8
B555	22-#3	2 8 @ 5 6 6 7 10 @ 8
B556	21-#3	2 5 5 5 5 5 5 6 6 7 11 @ 8
B557	10-#3	2 4 4 4 4 4 4 4 4 4
B558	10-#3	2 4 4 4 4 4 4 4 4 4
B559	9-#3	2 4 4 4 4 4 4 4 4
B560	8-#3	2 4 4 4 4 4 4 4
B561	6-#3	2 4 4 4 4 4
B562	11-#3	1 4 4 4 4 4 4 4 4 4 4
B563	10-#3	2 4 4 4 4 4 4 4 4 4
B564	9-#3	2 4 4 4 4 4 4 4 4

STIRRUP COMBINATIONS—CONTINUED

Mark	Number and size	Spacing on each end	Mark	Number and size	Spacing on each end	Mark	Number and size	Spacing on each end
B565	8-#3	2 4 4 4 4 4 4 4	B637	6-#3	3 6 6 6 6 6	B709	11-#3	3 7 7 7 7 7 7 7 7 7 7
B566	7-#3	2 4 4 4 4 4 4	B638	10-#3	2 4 4 4 4 5 6 6 6 6	B710	11-#3	3 7 7 7 7 7 7 7 7 7 7
B567	11-#3	1 4 4 4 4 4 4 4 4 4 4	B639	11-#3	2 4 4 4 4 5 6 6 6 6 6	B711	10-#3	3 7 7 7 7 7 7 7 7 7
B568	10-#3	2 4 4 4 4 4 4 4 4 4	B640	11-#3	2 5 5 5 6 6 6 6 6 6 6	B712	10-#3	3 7 7 7 7 7 7 7 7 7
B569	9-#3	2 4 4 4 4 4 4 4 4	B641	11-#3	3 6 6 6 6 6 6 6 6 6 6	B713	9-#3	3 7 7 7 7 7 7 7 7
B570	7-#3	2 4 4 4 4 4 4	B642	11-#3	3 6 6 6 6 6 6 6 6 6 6	B714	8-#3	3 7 7 7 7 7 7 7
B571	5-#3	2 4 4 4 4	B643	11-#3	3 6 6 6 6 6 6 6 6 6 6	B715	12-#4	1 3 3 3 3 3 3 5 7 7 7 7
B572	10-#3	2 4 4 4 4 4 4 4 4 4	B644	10-#3	3 6 6 6 6 6 6 6 6 6	B716	15-#3	1 7 @ 3 4 5 6 4 @ 7
B573	11-#3	2 4 4 4 4 4 4 4 4 4 4	B645	9-#3	3 6 6 6 6 6 6 6 6	B717	15-#3	1 3 3 3 3 3 3 4 4 6 5 @ 7
B574	11-#3	2 4 4 4 4 4 4 4 4 4 4	B646	9-#3	3 6 6 6 6 6 6 6 6	B718	13-#3	2 4 4 4 4 5 6 6 @ 7
B575	10-#3	2 4 4 4 4 4 4 4 4 4	B647	7-#3	3 6 6 6 6 6 6	B719	12-#3	2 5 5 5 6 7 7 7 7 7 7 7
B576	9-#3	2 4 4 4 4 4 4 4 4	B648	6-#3	3 6 6 6 6 6	B720	11-#3	3 7 7 7 7 7 7 7 7 7 7
B577	7-#3	2 4 4 4 4 4 4	B649	9-#3	2 5 5 5 6 6 6 6 6	B721	11-#3	3 7 7 7 7 7 7 7 7 7 7
B578	9-#3	2 4 4 4 5 5 5 5 5	B650	11-#3	2 4 4 4 4 5 6 6 6 6 6	B722	11-#3	3 7 7 7 7 7 7 7 7 7 7
B579	9-#3	2 5 5 5 5 5 5 5 5	B651	12-#3	2 4 4 4 4 5 6 6 6 6 6 6	B723	10-#3	3 7 7 7 7 7 7 7 7 7
B580	8-#3	2 5 5 5 5 5 5 5	B652	11-#3	3 6 6 6 6 6 6 6 6 6 6	B724	10-#3	3 7 7 7 7 7 7 7 7 7
B581	7-#3	2 5 5 5 5 5 5	B653	11-#3	3 6 6 6 6 6 6 6 6 6 6	B725	9-#3	3 7 7 7 7 7 7 7 7
B582	6-#3	2 5 5 5 5 5	B654	11-#3	3 6 6 6 6 6 6 6 6 6 6	B726	6-#3	4 8 8 8 8 8
B583	8-#3	2 5 5 5 5 5 5 5	B655	10-#3	3 6 6 6 6 6 6 6 6 6	B727	5-#3	4 8 8 8 8
B584	10-#3	2 4 4 4 5 5 5 5 5 5	B656	11-#3	2 5 5 5 5 5 5 5 5 5 5	B728	9-#3	4 8 8 8 8 8 8 8 8
B585	12-#3	2 4 4 4 4 5 5 5 5 5 5 5	B657	10-#3	2 5 5 5 5 5 5 5 5 5	B729	9-#3	4 8 8 8 8 8 8 8 8
B586	11-#3	2 5 5 5 5 5 5 5 5 5 5	B658	7-#3	3 6 6 6 6 6 6	B730	8-#3	4 8 8 8 8 8 8 8
B587	11-#3	2 5 5 5 5 5 5 5 5 5 5	B659	6-#3	3 6 6 6 6 6	B731	8-#3	4 8 8 8 8 8 8 8
B588	10-#3	2 5 5 5 5 5 5 5 5 5	B660	9-#3	2 5 5 5 6 6 6 6 6	B732	7-#3	4 8 8 8 8 8 8
B589	9-#3	2 5 5 5 5 5 5 5 5	B661	11-#3	2 4 4 4 4 5 6 6 6 6 6	B733	6-#3	4 8 8 8 8 8
B590	8-#3	2 5 5 5 5 5 5 5	B662	13-#3	2 4 4 4 4 4 5 6 @ 6	B734	5-#3	4 8 8 8 8
B591	6-#3	2 5 5 5 5 5	B663	13-#3	2 4 4 4 4 5 7 @ 6	B735	9-#3	4 8 8 8 8 8 8 8 8
B592	9-#3	2 5 5 5 5 5 5 5 5	B664	12-#3	2 5 5 5 6 6 6 6 6 6 6 6	B736	9-#3	4 8 8 8 8 8 8 8 8
B593	9-#3	2 5 5 5 5 5 5 5 5	B665	12-#3	3 6 6 6 6 6 6 6 6 6 6 6	B737	8-#3	4 8 8 8 8 8 8 8
B594	9-#3	2 5 5 5 5 5 5 5 5	B666	12-#3	3 6 6 6 6 6 6 6 6 6 6 6	B738	8-#3	4 8 8 8 8 8 8 8
B595	9-#3	2 5 5 5 5 5 5 5 5	B667	11-#3	3 6 6 6 6 6 6 6 6 6 6	B739	7-#3	4 8 8 8 8 8 8
B596	8-#3	2 5 5 5 5 5 5 5	B668	11-#3	3 6 6 6 6 6 6 6 6 6 6	B740	6-#3	4 8 8 8 8 8
B597	7-#3	2 5 5 5 5 5 5	B669	10-#3	3 6 6 6 6 6 6 6 6 6	B741	5-#3	4 8 8 8 8
B598	10-#3	2 4 4 4 5 5 5 5 5 5	B670	9-#3	3 6 6 6 6 6 6 6 6	B742	11-#3	3 6 6 6 7 8 8 8 8 8 8
B599	11-#3	2 4 4 4 5 5 5 5 5 5 5	B671	7-#3	3 6 6 6 7 7 7	B743	10-#3	3 7 7 7 8 8 8 8 8 8
B600	11-#3	2 5 5 5 5 5 5 5 5 5 5	B672	7-#3	3 7 7 7 7 7 7	B744	10-#3	4 8 8 8 8 8 8 8 8 8
B601	11-#3	2 5 5 5 5 5 5 5 5 5 5	B673	7-#3	3 7 7 7 7 7 7	B745	9-#3	4 8 8 8 8 8 8 8 8
B602	10-#3	2 5 5 5 5 5 5 5 5 5	B674	6-#3	3 7 7 7 7 7	B746	9-#3	4 8 8 8 8 8 8 8 8
B603	10-#3	2 5 5 5 5 5 5 5 5 5	B675	5-#3	3 7 7 7 7	B747	8-#3	4 8 8 8 8 8 8 8
B604	9-#3	2 5 5 5 5 5 5 5 5	B676	7-#3	3 7 7 7 7 7 7	B748	8-#3	4 8 8 8 8 8 8 8
B605	7-#3	2 5 5 5 5 5 5	B677	7-#3	3 7 7 7 7 7 7	B749	7-#3	4 8 8 8 8 8 8
B606	5-#3	2 5 5 5 5	B678	7-#3	3 7 7 7 7 7 7	B750	6-#3	4 8 8 8 8 8
B607	10-#3	2 4 4 4 5 5 5 5 5 5	B679	7-#3	3 7 7 7 7 7 7	B751	12-#3	2 5 5 5 5 7 8 8 8 8 8 8
B608	12-#3	2 4 4 4 4 5 5 5 5 5 5 5	B680	7-#3	3 6 6 6 6 6 6	B752	10-#3	3 7 7 7 8 8 8 8 8 8
B609	13-#3	2 4 4 4 4 8 @ 5	B681	6-#3	3 6 6 6 6 6	B753	10-#3	4 8 8 8 8 8 8 8 8 8
B610	12-#3	2 5 5 5 5 5 5 5 5 5 5 5	B682	10-#3	2 4 4 4 4 6 7 7 7 7	B754	10-#3	4 8 8 8 8 8 8 8 8 8
B611	12-#3	2 5 5 5 5 5 5 5 5 5 5 5	B683	11-#3	2 4 4 4 4 6 7 7 7 7 7	B755	9-#3	4 8 8 8 8 8 8 8 8
B612	13-#3	2 4 4 4 4 8 @ 5	B684	10-#3	3 6 6 6 7 7 7 7 7 7	B756	9-#3	4 8 8 8 8 8 8 8 8
B613	12-#3	2 5 5 5 5 5 5 5 5 5 5 5	B685	10-#3	3 7 7 7 7 7 7 7 7 7	B757	8-#3	4 8 8 8 8 8 8 8
B614	11-#3	2 5 5 5 5 5 5 5 5 5 5	B686	10-#3	3 7 7 7 7 7 7 7 7 7	B758	7-#3	4 8 8 8 8 8 8
B615	10-#3	2 5 5 5 5 5 5 5 5 5	B687	9-#3	3 7 7 7 7 7 7 7 7	B759	6-#3	4 8 8 8 8 8
B616	8-#3	2 5 5 5 5 5 5 5	B688	9-#3	3 7 7 7 7 7 7 7 7	B760	5-#3	4 8 8 8 8
B617	7-#3	2 5 5 5 5 5 5	B689	10-#3	3 6 6 6 6 6 6 6 6 6	B761	14-#3	2 4 4 4 4 4 5 6 7 5 @ 8
B618	7-#3	3 6 6 6 6 6 6	B690	9-#3	3 6 6 6 6 6 6 6 6	B672	13-#3	2 5 5 5 5 6 7 6 @ 8
B619	8-#3	3 6 6 6 6 6 6 6	B691	7-#3	3 7 7 7 7 7 7	B763	12-#3	3 6 6 6 7 8 8 8 8 8 8 8
B620	7-#3	3 6 6 6 6 6 6	B692	6-#3	3 6 6 6 6 6	B764	11-#3	3 7 7 7 8 8 8 8 8 8 8
B621	7-#3	3 6 6 6 6 6 6	B693	9-#3	2 5 5 5 6 7 7 7 7	B765	11-#3	4 8 8 8 8 8 8 8 8 8 8
B622	5-#3	3 6 6 6 6	B694	11-#3	2 4 4 4 4 6 7 7 7 7 7	B766	10-#3	4 8 8 8 8 8 8 8 8 8
B623	9-#3	2 5 5 5 6 6 6 6 6	B695	11-#3	2 5 5 5 5 6 7 7 7 7 7	B767	10-#3	4 8 8 8 8 8 8 8 8 8
B624	9-#3	3 6 6 6 6 6 6 6 6	B696	10-#3	3 6 6 6 7 7 7 7 7 7	B768	9-#3	4 8 8 8 8 8 8 8 8
B625	9-#3	3 6 6 6 6 6 6 6 6	B697	10-#3	3 7 7 7 7 7 7 7 7 7	B769	9-#3	4 8 8 8 8 8 8 8 8
B626	9-#3	3 6 6 6 6 6 6 6 6	B698	10-#3	3 7 7 7 7 7 7 7 7 7	B770	8-#3	4 8 8 8 8 8 8 8
B627	9-#3	3 6 6 6 6 6 6 6 6	B699	9-#3	3 7 7 7 7 7 7 7 7	B771	7-#3	4 8 8 8 8 8 8
B628	9-#3	3 6 6 6 6 6 6 6 6	B700	9-#3	3 7 7 7 7 7 7 7 7	B772	6-#3	4 9 9 9 9 9
B629	8-#3	3 6 6 6 6 6 6 6	B701	8-#3	3 7 7 7 7 7 7 7	B773	5-#3	4 9 9 9 9
B630	7-#3	3 6 6 6 6 6 6	B702	7-#3	3 7 7 7 7 7 7	B774	8-#3	4 9 9 9 9 9 9 9
B631	5-#3	3 6 6 6 6	B703	6-#3	3 7 7 7 7 7	B775	8-#3	4 9 9 9 9 9 9 9
B632	8-#3	3 6 6 6 6 6 6 6	B704	9-#3	2 5 5 5 6 7 7 7 7	B776	8-#3	4 9 9 9 9 9 9 9
B633	8-#3	3 6 6 6 6 6 6 6	B705	11-#3	2 4 4 4 4 6 7 7 7 7 7	B777	7-#3	4 9 9 9 9 9 9
B634	8-#3	3 6 6 6 6 6 6 6	B706	12-#3	2 4 4 4 4 4 5 6 7 7 7 7	B778	7-#3	4 9 9 9 9 9 9
B635	8-#3	3 6 6 6 6 6 6 6	B707	13-#3	2 4 4 4 4 5 6 6 @ 7	B779	6-#3	4 9 9 9 9 9
B636	7-#3	3 6 6 6 6 6 6	B708	11-#3	3 6 6 6 7 7 7 7 7 7 7	B780	5-#3	4 9 9 9 9

STIRRUP COMBINATIONS—CONTINUED

Mark	Number and size	Spacing on each end
B781	8-#3	4 9 9 9 9 9 9 9
B782	8-#3	4 9 9 9 9 9 9 9
B783	8-#3	4 9 9 9 9 9 9 9
B784	7-#3	4 9 9 9 9 9 9
B785	7-#3	4 9 9 9 9 9 9
B786	6-#3	4 9 9 9 9 9
B787	5-#3	4 9 9 9 9
B788	10-#3	3 6 6 6 7 8 9 9 9 9
B789	9-#3	4 8 8 8 9 9 9 9 9
B790	9-#3	4 9 9 9 9 9 9 9 9
B791	9-#3	4 9 9 9 9 9 9 9 9
B792	8-#3	4 9 9 9 9 9 9 9
B793	8-#3	4 9 9 9 9 9 9 9
B794	7-#3	4 9 9 9 9 9 9
B795	6-#3	4 9 9 9 9 9
B796	6-#3	4 9 9 9 9 9
B797	10-#3	3 6 6 6 7 8 9 9 9 9
B798	10-#3	3 7 7 7 8 9 9 9 9 9
B799	9-#3	4 9 9 9 9 9 9 9 9
B800	9-#3	4 9 9 9 9 9 9 9 9
B801	9-#3	4 9 9 9 9 9 9 9 9
B802	8-#3	4 9 9 9 9 9 9 9
B803	8-#3	4 9 9 9 9 9 9 9
B804	7-#3	4 9 9 9 9 9 9
B805	6-#3	4 9 9 9 9 9
B806	5-#3	4 9 9 9 9
B807	14-#3	2 5 @ 4 5 5 7 8 4 @ 9
B808	13-#3	2 5 5 5 5 5 7 8 5 @ 9
B809	12-#3	3 6 6 6 7 8 9 9 9 9 9 9
B810	10-#3	4 8 8 8 9 9 9 9 9 9
B811	10-#3	4 9 9 9 9 9 9 9 9 9
B812	10-#3	4 9 9 9 9 9 9 9 9 9
B813	9-#3	4 9 9 9 9 9 9 9 9
B814	9-#3	4 9 9 9 9 9 9 9 9
B815	8-#3	4 9 9 9 9 9 9 9
B816	8-#3	4 9 9 9 9 9 9 9
B817	7-#3	4 9 9 9 9 9 9
B818	15-#3	2 6 @ 4 5 5 7 5 @ 9
B819	15-#3	2 6 @ 4 5 5 7 8 4 @ 9
B820	14-#3	2 5 5 5 5 5 6 7 8 5 @ 9
B821	13-#3	3 6 6 6 6 7 8 6 @ 9
B822	12-#3	3 7 7 7 8 9 9 9 9 9 9 9
B823	11-#3	4 8 8 8 9 9 9 9 9 9 9
B824	11-#3	4 9 9 9 9 9 9 9 9 9 9
B825	10-#3	4 9 9 9 9 9 9 9 9 9
B826	10-#3	4 9 9 9 9 9 9 9 9 9
B827	10-#3	4 9 9 9 9 9 9 9 9 9
B828	9-#3	4 9 9 9 9 9 9 9 9
B829	13-#3	2 4 4 4 4 4 5 6 8 4 @ 9
B830	15-#3	2 6 @ 4 5 6 8 5 @ 9
B831	15-#3	2 6 @ 4 5 6 7 8 4 @ 9
B832	14-#3	2 5 5 5 5 5 6 8 6 @ 9
B833	12-#3	3 6 6 6 6 8 6 @ 9
B834	12-#3	3 7 7 7 8 9 9 9 9 9 9 9
B835	10-#3	4 9 9 9 9 9 9 9 9 9
B836	10-#3	4 9 9 9 9 9 9 9 9 9
B837	10-#3	4 9 9 9 9 9 9 9 9 9
B838	9-#3	4 9 9 9 9 9 9 9 9
B839	9-#3	4 9 9 9 9 9 9 9 9
B840	9-#3	1 10 @ 3 4 4 5 7 4 @ 9
B841	18-#3	1 8 @ 3 4 4 5 6 8 4 @ 9
B842	16-#3	2 6 @ 4 5 5 6 8 5 @ 9
B843	14-#3	2 5 5 5 5 5 5 6 8 5 @ 9
B844	14-#3	2 5 5 5 5 6 7 8 6 @ 9
B845	13-#3	3 6 6 6 7 8 7 @ 9
B846	11-#3	4 8 8 8 9 9 9 9 9 9 9
B847	11-#3	4 9 9 9 9 9 9 9 9 9 9
B848	10-#3	4 9 9 9 9 9 9 9 9 9
B849	10-#3	4 9 9 9 9 9 9 9 9 9
B850	9-#3	4 9 9 9 9 9 9 9 9
B851	5-#3	5 10 10 10 10
B852	8-#3	5 10 10 10 10 10 10 10 10
B853	7-#3	5 10 10 10 10 10 10
B854	7-#3	5 10 10 10 10 10 10
B855	7-#3	5 10 10 10 10 10 10
B856	6-#3	5 10 10 10 10 10
B857	6-#3	5 10 10 10 10 10
B858	5-#3	5 10 10 10 10
B859	8-#3	4 9 9 9 10 10 10 10
B860	7-#3	5 10 10 10 10 10 10
B861	7-#3	5 10 10 10 10 10 10
B862	7-#3	5 10 10 10 10 10 10
B863	6-#3	5 10 10 10 10 10
B864	6-#3	5 10 10 10 10 10
B865	5-#3	5 10 10 10 10
B866	10-#3	3 6 6 6 7 9 10 10 10 10
B867	10-#3	3 7 7 7 8 10 10 10 10 10
B868	9-#3	4 9 9 9 10 10 10 10 10
B869	8-#3	5 10 10 10 10 10 10 10
B870	8-#3	5 10 10 10 10 10 10 10
B871	8-#3	5 10 10 10 10 10 10 10
B872	7-#3	5 10 10 10 10 10 10
B873	6-#3	5 10 10 10 10 10
B874	6-#3	5 10 10 10 10 10
B875	14-#3	2 4 4 4 4 4 4 5 7 9 4 @ 10
B876	12-#3	2 5 5 5 5 5 7 9 10 10 10 10
B877	11-#3	3 6 6 6 7 9 10 10 10 10 10
B878	10-#3	4 8 8 9 10 10 10 10 10 10
B879	9-#3	5 10 10 10 10 10 10 10 10
B880	9-#3	5 10 10 10 10 10 10 10 10
B881	9-#3	5 10 10 10 10 10 10 10 10
B882	8-#3	5 10 10 10 10 10 10 10
B883	8-#3	5 10 10 10 10 10 10 10
B884	7-#3	5 10 10 10 10 10 10
B885	6-#3	5 10 10 10 10 10
B886	14-#3	2 4 4 4 4 4 4 5 6 8 4 @ 10
B887	13-#3	2 5 5 5 5 5 6 8 9 4 @ 10
B888	12-#3	3 6 6 6 6 7 9 10 10 10 10 10
B889	11-#3	3 7 7 7 8 9 10 10 10 10 10
B890	10-#3	4 8 8 9 10 10 10 10 10 10
B891	9-#3	5 10 10 10 10 10 10 10 10
B892	9-#3	5 10 10 10 10 10 10 10 10
B893	9-#3	5 10 10 10 10 10 10 10 10
B894	8-#3	5 10 10 10 10 10 10 10
B895	8-#3	5 10 10 10 10 10 10 10
B896	7-#3	5 10 10 10 10 10 10
B897	14-#3	2 4 4 4 4 4 4 5 7 9 4 @ 10
B898	12-#3	2 5 5 5 5 5 6 8 10 10 10 10
B899	11-#3	3 6 6 6 6 8 9 10 10 10 10
B900	10-#3	3 7 7 7 8 10 10 10 10 10
B901	9-#3	4 9 9 9 10 10 10 10 10
B902	9-#3	5 10 10 10 10 10 10 10 10
B903	8-#3	5 10 10 10 10 10 10 10
B904	8-#3	5 10 10 10 10 10 10 10
B905	7-#3	5 10 10 10 10 10 10
B906	7-#3	5 10 10 10 10 10 10
B907	6-#3	5 10 10 10 10 10
B908	12-#3	2 5 5 5 5 5 6 8 10 10 10 10
B909	14-#3	2 6 @ 4 5 6 8 9 3 @ 10
B910	15-#3	2 6 @ 4 5 5 7 9 4 @ 10
B911	14-#3	2 5 5 5 5 5 6 7 9 5 @ 10
B912	12-#3	3 6 6 6 6 7 9 10 10 10 10 10
B913	11-#3	3 7 7 7 8 10 10 10 10 10 10
B914	10-#3	4 9 9 9 10 10 10 10 10 10
B915	9-#3	5 10 10 10 10 10 10 10 10
B916	9-#3	5 10 10 10 10 10 10 10 10
B917	9-#3	5 10 10 10 10 10 10 10 10
B918	8-#3	5 10 10 10 10 10 10 10
B919	19-#3	1 10 @ 3 4 4 5 7 9 3 @ 10
B920	19-#3	1 8 @ 3 4 4 5 5 7 9 4 @ 10
B921	16-#3	2 7 @ 4 5 6 8 9 4 @ 10
B922	14-#3	2 5 5 5 5 5 5 6 8 9 4 @ 10
B923	13-#3	3 6 6 6 6 6 8 9 5 @ 10
B924	12-#3	3 7 7 7 7 9 10 10 10 10 10 10
B925	11-#3	4 8 8 8 9 10 10 10 10 10 10
B926	10-#3	5 10 10 10 10 10 10 10 10 10
B927	10-#3	5 10 10 10 10 10 10 10 10 10
B928	9-#3	5 10 10 10 10 10 10 10 10
B929	9-#3	5 10 10 10 10 10 10 10 10
B930	7-#3	5 11 11 11 11 11 11
B931	7-#3	5 11 11 11 11 11 11
B932	6-#3	5 11 11 11 11 11
B933	5-#3	5 11 11 11 11
B934	7-#3	5 11 11 11 11 11 11
B935	7-#3	5 11 11 11 11 11 11
B936	6-#3	5 11 11 11 11 11
B937	6-#3	5 11 11 11 11 11
B938	8-#3	5 10 10 10 11 11 11 11
B939	8-#3	5 11 11 11 11 11 11 11
B940	8-#3	5 11 11 11 11 11 11 11
B941	7-#3	5 11 11 11 11 11 11
B942	7-#3	5 11 11 11 11 11 11
B943	6-#3	5 11 11 11 11 11
B944	5-#3	5 11 11 11 11
B945	10-#3	3 7 7 7 8 10 11 11 11 11
B946	10-#3	4 8 8 8 10 11 11 11 11 11
B947	9-#3	5 10 10 10 11 11 11 11 11
B948	8-#3	5 11 11 11 11 11 11 11
B949	8-#3	5 11 11 11 11 11 11 11
B950	8-#3	5 11 11 11 11 11 11 11
B951	7-#3	5 11 11 11 11 11 11
B952	7-#3	5 11 11 11 11 11 11
B953	6-#3	5 11 11 11 11 11
B954	5-#3	5 11 11 11 11
B955	13-#3	2 5 5 5 5 5 6 7 9 4 @ 11
B956	12-#3	3 6 6 6 6 7 9 10 11 11 11 11
B957	11-#3	3 7 7 7 8 10 11 11 11 11 11
B958	10-#3	4 9 9 9 10 11 11 11 11 11
B959	10-#3	5 10 10 10 11 11 11 11 11 11
B960	9-#3	5 11 11 11 11 11 11 11 11
B961	9-#3	5 11 11 11 11 11 11 11 11

STIRRUP COMBINATIONS—CONTINUED

Mark	Number and size	Spacing on each end
B962	8-#3	5 11 11 11 11 11 11 11
B963	8-#3	5 11 11 11 11 11 11 11
B964	7-#3	5 11 11 11 11 11 11
B965	7-#3	5 11 11 11 11 11 11
B966	15-#3	2 4 4 4 4 4 4 5 5 7 9 4 @ 10
B967	14-#3	2 5 5 5 5 5 6 7 9 5 @ 10
B968	13-#3	3 6 6 6 6 7 9 6 @ 10
B969	11-#3	4 8 8 8 9 10 10 10 10 10 10
B970	10-#3	4 9 9 9 10 10 10 10 10 10
B971	10-#3	5 10 10 10 10 10 10 10 10 10
B972	9-#3	5 10 10 10 10 10 10 10 10
B973	9-#3	5 10 10 10 10 10 10 10 10
B974	8-#3	5 10 10 10 10 10 10 10
B975	8-#3	5 10 10 10 10 10 10 10
B976	7-#3	5 10 10 10 10 10 10
B977	16-#3	2 7 @ 4 5 6 8 9 4 @ 10
B978	15-#3	2 5 5 5 5 5 5 6 8 9 5 @ 10
B979	13-#3	3 6 6 6 6 6 8 9 5 @ 10
B980	12-#3	3 7 7 7 7 9 10 10 10 10 10 10
B981	11-#3	4 8 8 8 9 10 10 10 10 10 10
B982	10-#3	5 10 10 10 10 10 10 10 10 10
B983	10-#3	5 10 10 10 10 10 10 10 10 10
B984	9-#3	5 10 10 10 10 10 10 10 10
B985	9-#3	5 10 10 10 10 10 10 10 10
B986	8-#3	5 10 10 10 10 10 10 10
B987	8-#3	5 10 10 10 10 10 10 10
B988	5-#3	6 12 12 12 12
B989	7-#3	6 12 12 12 12 12 12
B990	6-#3	6 12 12 12 12 12
B991	6-#3	6 12 12 12 12 12
B992	5-#3	6 12 12 12 12
B993	8-#3	5 10 10 11 12 12 12 12
B994	7-#3	6 12 12 12 12 12 12
B995	7-#3	6 12 12 12 12 12 12
B996	7-#3	6 12 12 12 12 12 12
B997	6-#3	6 12 12 12 12 12
B998	6-#3	6 12 12 12 12 12
B999	5-#3	6 12 12 12 12
C000	10-#3	3 7 7 7 7 10 12 12 12 12
C001	9-#3	4 9 9 9 11 12 12 12 12
C002	9-#3	5 10 10 11 12 12 12 12 12
C003	8-#3	6 12 12 12 12 12 12 12
C004	8-#3	6 12 12 12 12 12 12 12
C005	7-#3	6 12 12 12 12 12 12
C006	7-#3	6 12 12 12 12 12 12
C007	6-#3	6 12 12 12 12 12
C008	6-#3	6 12 12 12 12 12
C009	5-#3	6 12 12 12 12
C010	13-#3	2 5 5 5 5 5 5 7 9 11 3 @ 12
C011	12-#3	3 6 6 6 6 7 9 11 12 12 12 12
C012	11-#3	3 7 7 7 8 10 11 12 12 12 12
C013	10-#3	4 9 9 9 11 12 12 12 12 12
C014	9-#3	5 11 11 11 11 12 12 12 12 12
C015	8-#3	6 12 12 12 12 12 12 12
C016	8-#3	6 12 12 12 12 12 12 12
C017	8-#3	6 12 12 12 12 12 12 12
C018	7-#3	6 12 12 12 12 12 12
C019	7-#3	6 12 12 12 12 12 12
C020	6-#3	6 12 12 12 12 12
C021	17-#3	2 8 @ 4 5 6 8 10 4 @ 12
C022	15-#3	2 7 @ 5 6 8 10 4 @ 12
C023	15-#3	2 6 @ 5 6 7 9 11 4 @ 12
C024	13-#3	3 6 6 6 6 6 8 10 11 4 @ 12
C025	12-#3	3 7 7 7 7 9 11 12 12 12 12 12
C026	11-#3	4 8 8 8 9 11 12 12 12 12 12
C027	10-#3	5 10 10 11 12 12 12 12 12 12
C028	9-#3	6 12 12 12 12 12 12 12 12
C029	9-#3	6 12 12 12 12 12 12 12 12
C030	9-#3	6 12 12 12 12 12 12 12 12
C031	8-#3	6 12 12 12 12 12 12 12
C032	16-#3	2 7 @ 4 5 6 7 9 4 @ 10
C033	15-#3	2 6 @ 5 6 8 9 5 @ 10
C034	13-#3	3 6 6 6 6 6 8 9 5 @ 10
C035	12-#3	3 7 7 7 7 9 10 10 10 10 10 10
C036	11-#3	4 8 8 8 9 10 10 10 10 10 10
C037	10-#3	5 10 10 10 10 10 10 10 10 10
C038	10-#3	5 10 10 10 10 10 10 10 10 10
C039	10-#3	5 10 10 10 10 10 10 10 10 10
C040	9-#3	5 10 10 10 10 10 10 10 10
C041	9-#3	5 10 10 10 10 10 10 10 10
C042	8-#3	5 10 10 10 10 10 10 10
C043	23-#3	1 12 @ 3 4 4 5 5 7 9 4 @ 10
C044	22-#3	1 10 @ 3 4 4 4 5 5 7 9 4 @ 10
C045	19-#3	2 9 @ 4 5 5 6 8 9 4 @ 10
C046	19-#3	2 7 @ 4 5 5 6 6 8 9 5 @ 10
C047	17-#3	2 7 @ 5 6 7 9 6 @ 10
C048	17-#3	2 5 5 5 5 5 5 6 7 9 7 @ 10
C049	15-#3	3 6 6 6 6 6 7 9 7 @ 10
C050	14-#3	3 7 7 7 7 9 8 @ 10
C051	13-#3	4 8 8 8 9 8 @ 10
C052	12-#3	5 10 10 10 10 10 10 10 10 10 10 10 10
C053	11-#3	5 10 10 10 10 10 10 10 10 10 10 10
C054	17-#4	2 7 @ 4 5 5 6 8 10 4 @ 12
C055	15-#4	2 6 @ 5 6 6 8 10 4 @ 12
C056	14-#4	3 6 6 6 6 6 7 8 10 5 @ 12
C057	24-#3	1 9 @ 3 4 4 4 4 5 5 6 8 6 @ 9
C058	21-#3	2 9 @ 4 5 5 6 7 8 6 @ 9
C059	20-#3	2 7 @ 4 5 5 6 6 8 7 @ 9
C060	18-#3	2 6 @ 5 6 6 7 8 7 @ 9
C061	16-#3	3 6 6 6 6 6 7 8 8 @ 9
C062	15-#3	3 7 7 7 7 7 8 8 @ 9
C063	14-#3	4 8 8 8 8 9 @ 9
C064	13-#3	4 12 @ 9
C065	17-#4	2 8 @ 4 5 5 7 9 11 3 @ 12
C066	16-#4	2 7 @ 5 6 7 9 11 4 @ 12
C067	26-#3	1 13 @ 3 4 4 4 5 6 7 6 @ 8
C068	14-#4	3 6 6 6 6 6 7 9 11 5 @ 12
C069	21-#3	2 9 @ 4 5 5 6 7 7 @ 8
C070	21-#3	2 7 @ 4 5 5 5 6 7 8 @ 8
C071	19-#3	2 7 @ 5 6 7 9 @ 8
C072	18-#3	2 5 5 5 5 5 5 6 7 9 @ 8
C073	17-#3	3 6 6 6 6 6 7 10 @ 8
C074	15-#3	3 7 7 7 7 10 @ 8
C075	14-#3	4 13 @ 8
C076	5-#3	6 12 12 12 12
C077	7-#3	6 12 12 12 12 12 12
C078	6-#3	6 12 12 12 12 12
C079	6-#3	6 12 12 12 12 12
C080	5-#3	6 12 12 12 12
C081	8-#3	5 11 11 11 12 12 12 12
C082	7-#3	6 12 12 12 12 12 12
C083	7-#3	6 12 12 12 12 12 12
C084	7-#3	6 12 12 12 12 12 12
C085	7-#3	6 12 12 12 12 12 12
C086	6-#3	6 12 12 12 12 12
C087	5-#3	6 12 12 12 12
C088	11-#3	3 7 7 7 7 9 11 12 12 12 12
C089	9-#3	4 9 9 9 10 12 12 12 12
C090	9-#3	5 11 11 11 12 12 12 12 12
C091	8-#3	6 12 12 12 12 12 12 12
C092	8-#3	6 12 12 12 12 12 12 12
C093	8-#3	6 12 12 12 12 12 12 12
C094	7-#3	6 12 12 12 12 12 12
C095	7-#3	6 12 12 12 12 12 12
C096	6-#3	6 12 12 12 12 12
C097	5-#3	6 12 12 12 12
C098	12-#3	3 6 6 6 6 6 7 9 11 12 12 12
C099	12-#3	3 7 7 7 7 8 10 12 12 12 12 12
C100	11-#3	4 8 8 8 9 11 12 12 12 12 12
C101	10-#3	4 9 9 9 10 12 12 12 12 12
C102	9-#3	5 11 11 11 11 12 12 12 12 12
C103	9-#3	6 12 12 12 12 12 12 12 12
C104	8-#3	6 12 12 12 12 12 12 12
C105	8-#3	6 12 12 12 12 12 12 12
C106	8-#3	6 12 12 12 12 12 12 12
C107	7-#3	6 12 12 12 12 12 12
C108	7-#3	6 12 12 12 12 12 12
C109	17-#3	2 8 @ 4 5 6 7 10 4 @ 12
C110	15-#3	2 7 @ 5 6 8 10 4 @ 12
C111	14-#3	3 6 6 6 6 6 8 10 5 @ 12
C112	14-#3	3 6 6 6 6 6 7 9 11 5 @ 12
C113	12-#3	3 7 7 7 7 9 11 12 12 12
C114	11-#3	4 9 9 9 10 12 12 12 12 12 12
C115	10-#3	5 10 10 11 12 12 12 12 12 12
C116	10-#3	6 12 12 12 12 12 12 12 12 12
C117	9-#3	6 12 12 12 12 12 12 12 12
C118	9-#3	6 12 12 12 12 12 12 12 12
C119	9-#3	6 12 12 12 12 12 12 12 12
C120	17-#3	2 7 @ 4 5 5 7 9 5 @ 10
C121	15-#3	2 5 5 5 5 5 5 6 8 9 5 @ 10
C122	14-#3	3 6 6 6 6 6 8 9 6 @ 10
C123	13-#3	3 7 7 7 7 8 7 @ 10
C124	11-#3	4 9 9 9 9 10 10 10 10 10 10

STIRRUP COMBINATIONS—CONTINUED

Mark	Number and size	Spacing on each end
C125	11-#3	5 10 10 10 10 10 10 10 10 10 10
C126	10-#3	5 10 10 10 10 10 10 10 10 10
C127	10-#3	5 10 10 10 10 10 10 10 10 10
C128	9-#3	5 10 10 10 10 10 10 10 10
C129	9-#3	5 10 10 10 10 10 10 10 10
C130	8-#3	5 10 10 10 10 10 10 10
C131	23-#3	1 12 @ 3 4 4 4 5 7 9 4 @ 10
C132	23-#3	1 10 @ 3 4 4 4 5 5 7 9 5 @ 10
C133	20-#3	2 9 @ 4 5 5 6 8 9 5 @ 10
C134	19-#3	2 7 @ 4 5 5 6 6 8 9 5 @ 10
C135	17-#3	2 7 @ 5 6 7 9 6 @ 10
C136	16-#3	3 6 6 6 6 6 6 7 9 7 @ 10
C137	15-#3	3 6 6 6 7 @ 10
C138	14-#3	3 7 7 7 7 @ 10
C139	13-#3	4 9 9 9 9 8 @ 10
C140	12-#3	5 10 10 10 10 10 10 10 10 10 10 10
C141	12-#3	5 10 10 10 10 10 10 10 10 10 10 10
C142	17-#4	2 7 @ 4 5 5 6 8 11 4 @ 13
C143	25-#3	1 14 @ 3 4 4 5 6 8 5 @ 9
C144	14-#4	3 6 6 6 6 6 6 8 10 12 4 @ 13
C145	13-#4	3 7 7 7 7 7 9 11 12 4 @ 13
C146	21-#3	2 9 @ 4 5 5 6 7 8 6 @ 9
C147	20-#3	2 7 @ 4 5 5 6 6 8 7 @ 9
C148	18-#3	2 6 @ 5 6 6 7 8 7 @ 9
C149	17-#3	3 6 6 6 6 6 6 7 8 8 @ 9
C150	16-#3	3 7 7 7 7 7 8 9 @ 9
C151	14-#3	4 8 8 8 8 9 @ 9
C152	14-#3	4 13 @ 9
C153	17-#4	2 8 @ 4 5 5 7 9 11 3 @ 13
C154	15-#4	2 7 @ 5 6 7 9 12 3 @ 13
C155	26-#3	1 13 @ 3 4 4 4 5 6 7 6 @ 8
C156	14-#4	3 6 6 6 6 6 7 8 10 12 4 @ 13
C157	22-#3	2 9 @ 4 5 5 6 7 8 @ 8
C158	21-#3	2 8 @ 4 5 5 6 7 8 @ 8
C159	19-#3	2 5 5 5 5 5 5 6 7 9 @ 8
C160	17-#3	3 6 6 6 6 6 6 7 9 @ 8
C161	17-#3	3 6 6 6 6 6 7 10 @ 8
C162	9-#4	6 13 13 13 13 13 13 13 13
C163	15-#3	4 14 @ 8
D001	7-#3	6 12 12 12 12 12 12
D002	7-#3	6 12 12 12 12 12 12
D003	6-#3	6 12 12 12 12 12
D004	5-#4	8 16 16 16 16
D005	5-#4	8 16 16 16 16
D006	8-#3	4 9 9 9 9 9 9
D007	6-#4	8 16 16 16 16 16
D008	10-#3	4 9 9 9 9 9 9 9 9
D009	10-#3	4 9 9 9 9 9 9 9 9
D010	5-#4	8 16 16 16 16
D011	5-#4	8 16 16 16 16
D012	12-#3	4 9 9 9 9 9 9 9 9 9 9
D013	12-#3	4 9 9 9 9 9 9 9 9 9 9
D014	11-#3	4 9 9 9 9 9 9 9 9 9
D015	6-#4	8 16 16 16 16 16
D016	10-#3	4 9 9 9 9 9 9 9 9
D017	10-#3	4 9 9 9 9 9 9 9 9
D018	5-#4	8 16 16 16 16
D019	8-#3	4 9 9 9 9 9 9
D020	15-#3	3 6 6 6 6 6 6 8 7 @ 9
D021	14-#3	3 7 7 7 7 7 8 7 @ 9
D022	13-#3	4 8 8 8 8 8 7 @ 9
D023	12-#3	4 9 9 9 9 9 9 9 9 9 9
D024	12-#3	4 9 9 9 9 9 9 9 9 9 9
D025	12-#3	4 9 9 9 9 9 9 9 9 9 9
D026	6-#4	8 16 16 16 16 16
D027	6-#4	8 16 16 16 16 16
D028	10-#3	4 9 9 9 9
D029	5-#4	8 16 16 16 16
D030	8-#3	4 9 9 9 9 9 9
D031	9-#4	6 12 12 12 13 13 13 13 13
D032	8-#4	6 13 13 13 13 13 13 13
D033	8-#4	6 13 13 13 13 13 13 13
D034	14-#3	3 13 @ 7
D035	14-#3	3 13 @ 7
D036	7-#4	6 13 13 13 13 13 13
D037	12-#3	3 7 7 7 7 7 7 7 7 7 7
D038	6-#4	6 13 13 13 13 13
D039	11-#4	4 8 8 8 8 10 12 13 13 13 13
D040	10-#4	5 10 10 10 11 13 13 13 13 13
D041	17-#3	3 6 6 6 6 6 6 10 @ 7
D042	9-#4	6 13 13 13 13 13 13 13 13
D043	9-#4	6 13 13 13 13 13 13 13 13
D044	8-#4	6 13 13 13 13 13 13 13
D045	8-#4	6 13 13 13 13 13 13 13
D046	14-#3	3 13 @ 7
D047	7-#4	6 13 13 13 13 13 13
D048	12-#3	3 7 7 7 7 7 7 7 7 7 7
D049	6-#4	6 13 13 13 13 13
D050	14-#4	3 6 6 6 6 6 7 8 11 5 @ 13
D051	23-#3	2 10 @ 4 5 5 6 9 @ 7
D052	12-#4	4 8 8 8 8 10 12 13 13 13 13 13
D053	11-#4	5 10 10 10 11 13 13 13 13 13 13
D054	10-#4	5 11 11 12 13 13 13 13 13 13
D055	9-#4	6 13 13 13 13 13 13 13 13
D056	9-#4	6 13 13 13 13 13 13 13 13
D057	9-#4	6 13 13 13 13 13 13 13 13
D058	9-#4	6 13 13 13 13 13 13 13 13
D059	8-#4	6 13 13 13 13 13 13 13
D060	14-#3	3 13 @ 7
D061	17-#4	2 8 @ 5 6 7 9 12 4 @ 13
D062	15-#4	3 7 @ 6 7 9 12 4 @ 13
D063	15-#4	3 6 6 6 6 6 6 7 9 11 5 @ 13
D064	14-#4	3 7 7 7 7 7 8 10 12 5 @ 13
D065	13-#4	4 8 8 8 8 9 11 6 @ 13
D066	12-#4	4 9 9 9 10 12 6 @ 13
D067	11-#4	5 11 11 11 12 13 13 13 13 13 13
D068	11-#4	6 12 12 12 13 13 13 13 13 13 13
D069	10-#4	6 13 13 13 13 13 13 13 13 13
D070	10-#4	6 13 13 13 13 13 13 13 13 13
D071	17-#3	3 16 @ 7
D072	20-#4	2 10 @ 4 5 5 6 8 11 4 @ 13
D073	20-#4	2 9 @ 4 5 5 6 7 9 11 4 @ 13
D074	18-#4	2 8 @ 5 6 7 8 10 12 4 @ 13
D075	17-#4	3 7 @ 6 7 8 10 12 5 @ 13
D076	16-#4	3 6 @ 6 7 8 10 12 5 @ 13
D077	26-#3	2 11 @ 4 5 5 6 6 10 @ 7
D078	14-#4	4 8 8 8 8 9 11 12 6 @ 13
D079	23-#3	2 8 @ 5 6 6 12 @ 7
D080	12-#4	5 10 10 10 11 13 13 13 13 13 13 13
D081	11-#4	6 12 12 12 13 13 13 13 13 13 13
D082	11-#4	6 13 13 13 13 13 13 13 13 13 13
D083	25-#4	1 12 @ 3 4 4 4 5 5 6 8 10 4 @ 11
D084	26-#4	1 11 @ 3 4 4 4 4 5 5 6 8 10 5 @ 11
D085	22-#4	2 10 @ 4 5 5 6 6 8 10 5 @ 11
D086	22-#4	2 9 @ 4 5 5 6 6 7 9 6 @ 11
D087	20-#4	2 8 @ 5 6 6 7 9 10 6 @ 11
D088	19-#4	2 7 @ 5 6 6 7 9 10 6 @ 11
D089	18-#4	3 6 @ 6 7 8 9 10 7 @ 11
D090	16-#4	3 7 7 7 7 7 8 9 10 7 @ 11
D091	15-#4	4 8 8 8 8 8 10 8 @ 11
D092	14-#4	4 9 9 9 9 10 8 @ 11
D093	14-#4	5 10 10 10 10 9 @ 11
D094	25-#4	1 12 @ 3 4 4 4 5 5 6 8 10 4 @ 11
D095	28-#4	1 13 @ 3 4 4 4 4 5 5 6 8 10 5 @ 11
D096	28-#4	1 14 @ 3 4 4 4 4 5 5 6 8 10 5 @ 11
D097	24-#4	2 12 @ 4 5 5 6 7 8 10 5 @ 11
D098	24-#4	2 10 @ 4 5 5 5 6 7 8 10 6 @ 11
D099	23-#4	2 9 @ 4 5 5 6 6 7 8 10 6 @ 11
D100	21-#4	2 8 @ 5 6 6 7 8 10 7 @ 11
D101	21-#4	2 7 @ 5 6 6 7 8 9 10 7 @ 11
D102	19-#4	3 6 @ 6 7 7 8 10 8 @ 11
D103	18-#4	3 6 @ 7 8 9 10 8 @ 11
D104	16-#4	4 8 8 8 8 8 9 10 8 @ 11
D105	*	
D106	*	
D107	*	
D108	†	
D109	†	
D110	†	
D111	†	
D112	27-#4	2 11 @ 4 5 5 5 5 6 6 7 9 10 6 @ 11
D113	27-#4	2 10 @ 4 5 5 5 6 6 7 7 9 10 7 @ 11
D114	24-#4	2 10 @ 5 6 6 7 7 9 10 7 @ 11
D115	24-#4	2 8 @ 5 6 6 6 7 8 9 10 8 @ 11
D116	8-#3	6 12 12 12 12 12 12 12 12
D117	7-#3	6 12 12 12 12 12 12 12
D118	10-#3	4 9 9 9 9 9 9 9 9

*† See page 10-58.

STIRRUP COMBINATIONS—CONTINUED

Mark	Number and size	Spacing on each end
D130	6-#4	8 16 16 16 16 16
D131	10-#3	4 9 9 9 9 9 9 9 9 9
D132	8-#4	6 13 13 14 16 16 16 16
D133	14-#3	4 8 8 8 8 8 8 @ 9
D134	13-#3	4 12 @ 9
D135	13-#3	4 12 @ 9
D136	7-#4	8 16 16 16 16 16 16
D137	12-#3	4 9 9 9 9 9 9 9 9 9 9 9
D138	12-#3	4 9 9 9 9 9 9 9 9 9 9 9
D139	11-#3	4 9 9 9 9 9 9 9 9 9 9
D140	6-#4	8 16 16 16 16 16
D141	10-#3	4 9 9 9 9 9 9 9 9 9
D142	9-#4	6 13 13 13 13 13 13 13 13
D143	9-#4	6 13 13 13 13 13 13 13 13
D144	9-#4	6 13 13 13 13 13 13 13 13
D145	8-#4	6 13 13 13 13 13 13 13
D146	8-#4	6 13 13 13 13 13 13 13
D147	14-#3	3 13 @ 7
D148	7-#4	6 13 13 13 13 13 13
D149	12-#3	3 7 7 7 7 7 7 7 7 7 7 7
D150	11-#4	5 10 10 10 11 12 13 13 13 13 13
D151	10-#4	5 11 11 11 12 13 13 13 13 13
D152	9-#4	6 13 13 13 13 13 13 13 13
D153	9-#4	6 13 13 13 13 13 13 13 13
D154	9-#4	6 13 13 13 13 13 13 13 13
D155	9-#4	6 13 13 13 13 13 13 13 13
D156	15-#3	3 14 @ 7
D157	8-#4	6 13 13 13 13 13 13 13
D158	14-#3	3 13 @ 7
D159	7-#4	6 13 13 13 13 13 13
D160	12-#3	3 7 7 7 7 7 7 7 7 7 7 7
D161	12-#4	4 8 8 8 8 8 10 12 13 13 13 13
D162	21-#3	2 9 @ 5 6 10 @ 7
D163	11-#4	5 10 10 10 11 12 13 13 13 13 13
D164	10-#4	6 12 12 12 12 13 13 13 13 13
D165	10-#4	6 13 13 13 13 13 13 13 13 13
D166	10-#4	6 13 13 13 13 13 13 13 13 13
D167	17-#3	3 16 @ 7
D168	9-#4	6 13 13 13 13 13 13 13 13
D169	9-#4	6 13 13 13 13 13 13 13 13
D170	15-#3	3 14 @ 7
D171	8-#4	6 13 13 13 13 13 13 13
D172	17-#4	2 5 5 5 5 5 5 5 6 7 9 12 13 13 13 13
D173	16-#4	3 6 6 6 6 6 6 6 7 9 11 13 13 13 13 13
D174	26-#3	2 12 @ 4 5 5 6 10 @ 7
D175	14-#4	4 8 8 8 8 8 10 12 13 13 13 13 13 13
D176	23-#3	2 10 @ 5 6 11 @ 7
D177	12-#4	5 10 10 10 10 12 13 13 13 13 13 13
D178	21-#3	3 6 6 6 6 6 6 6 13 @ 7
D179	11-#4	6 13 13 13 13 13 13 13 13 13 13
D180	19-#3	3 18 @ 7
D181	10-#4	6 13 13 13 13 13 13 13 13 13
D182	10-#4	6 13 13 13 13 13 13 13 13 13
D183	21-#4	2 10 @ 4 5 5 6 8 11 5 @ 13
D184	19-#4	2 9 @ 5 6 7 9 11 5 @ 13
D185	17-#4	3 8 @ 6 7 9 11 5 @ 13
D186	17-#4	3 7 @ 6 7 8 10 12 5 @ 13
D187	28-#3	2 13 @ 4 5 5 6 11 @ 7
D188	15-#4	4 8 8 8 8 8 9 11 12 6 @ 13
D189	14-#4	4 9 9 9 9 10 12 7 @ 13
D190	13-#4	5 10 10 10 10 12 7 @ 13
D191	12-#4	5 11 11 11 12 13 13 13 13 13 13 13
D192	21-#3	3 20 @ 7
D193	11-#4	6 13 13 13 13 13 13 13 13 13 13
D194	23-#4	2 12 @ 4 5 5 6 8 10 5 @ 11
D195	23-#4	2 12 @ 4 5 5 6 8 10 5 @ 11
D196	23-#4	2 6 @ 4 5 5 6 6 8 10 6 @ 11
D197	21-#4	2 9 @ 5 6 6 7 9 7 @ 11
D198	20-#4	2 8 @ 5 6 6 7 9 10 6 @ 11
D199	18-#4	3 7 @ 6 7 8 10 7 @ 11
D200	17-#4	3 7 7 7 7 7 7 8 9 10 7 @ 11
D201	16-#4	4 8 8 8 8 8 9 10 8 @ 11
D202	16-#4	4 8 8 8 8 8 10 9 @ 11
D203	14-#4	5 10 10 10 10 9 @ 11
D204	14-#4	5 13 @ 11
D205	23-#4	2 12 @ 9 5 5 6 8 10 5 @ 11
D206	28-#4	1 13 @ 3 4 4 4 4 5 5 6 8 10 5 @ 11
D207	29-#4	1 13 @ 3 4 4 4 4 5 5 6 7 9 6 @ 11
D208	25-#4	2 12 @ 4 5 5 6 6 8 10 6 @ 11
D209	24-#4	2 10 @ 4 5 5 5 6 6 8 10 6 @ 11
D210	22-#4	2 10 @ 5 6 7 8 10 7 @ 11
D211	21-#4	2 8 @ 5 6 6 7 8 10 7 @ 11
D212	20-#4	3 7 @ 6 7 7 8 10 8 @ 11
D213	18-#4	3 7 7 7 7 7 7 7 8 10 8 @ 11
D214	18-#4	3 7 7 7 7 7 7 8 9 10 8 @ 11
D215	17-#4	4 8 8 8 8 8 9 10 9 @ 11
D216	30-#4	1 3 3 3 3 3 3 3 3 3 3 3 3 3 3 3 3 3 4 4 4 5 5 7 9 5 @ 11
D217	*	
D218	†	
D219	†	
D220	†	
D221	†	
D222	28-#4	2 13 @ 4 5 5 5 6 6 7 9 10 6 @ 11
D223	28-#4	2 11 @ 4 5 5 5 5 6 6 7 9 10 7 @ 11
D224	27-#4	2 10 @ 4 5 5 5 6 6 7 7 9 10 7 @ 11
D225	25-#4	2 10 @ 5 6 6 7 7 9 10 8 @ 11
D226	24-#4	2 8 @ 5 6 6 6 7 8 9 10 8 @ 11
D227	9-#3	6 12 12 12 12 12 12 12 12
D228	9-#3	6 12 12 12 12 12 12 12 12
D229	9-#3	6 12 12 12 12 12 12 12 12
D230	8-#3	6 12 12 12 12 12 12 12
D231	8-#3	6 12 12 12 12 12 12 12
D232	7-#3	6 12 12 12 12 12 12
D233	7-#3	6 12 12 12 12 12 12
D234	14-#3	3 6 6 6 6 6 6 8 10 5 @ 12
D235	14-#3	3 7 7 7 7 7 8 10 6 @ 12
D236	13-#3	4 8 8 8 8 9 11 6 @ 12
D237	12-#3	4 9 9 9 10 11 12 12 12 12 12 12
D238	11-#3	5 11 11 11 11 12 12 12 12 12 12
D239	10-#3	6 12 12 12 12 12 12 12 12 12
D240	10-#3	6 12 12 12 12 12 12 12 12 12
D241	10-#3	6 12 12 12 12 12 12 12 12 12
D242	10-#3	6 12 12 12 12 12 12 12 12 12
D243	9-#3	6 12 12 12 12 12 12 12 12
D244	9-#3	6 12 12 12 12 12 12 12 12
D245	10-#4	4 9 9 9 9 12 15 16 16 16
D246	10-#4	5 10 10 10 12 15 16 16 16 16
D247	9-#4	6 12 12 13 15 16 16 16 16
D248	8-#4	7 14 14 15 16 16 16 16
D249	14-#3	4 13 @ 9
D250	14-#3	4 13 @ 9
D251	13-#3	4 12 @ 9
D252	7-#4	8 16 16 16 16 16 16
D253	12-#3	4 9 9 9 9 9 9 9 9 9 9 9
D254	12-#3	4 9 9 9 9 9 9 9 9 9 9 9
D255	6-#4	8 16 16 16 16 16
D256	23-#3	2 11 @ 4 5 5 6 8 7 @ 9
D257	12-#4	4 8 8 8 8 8 10 14 16 16 16 16
D258	11-#4	4 9 9 9 9 11 14 16 16 16 16
D259	11-#4	5 10 10 10 11 14 16 16 16 16 16
D260	10-#4	5 11 11 11 13 16 16 16 16 16
D261	9-#4	6 13 13 14 16 16 16 16 16
D262	9-#4	7 15 15 15 16 16 16 16 16
D263	15-#3	4 14 @ 9
D264	8-#4	8 16 16 16 16 16 16 16
D265	14-#3	4 13 @ 9
D266	14-#3	4 13 @ 9
D267	17-#4	2 8 @ 5 6 6 8 10 13 3 @ 16
D268	30-#3	1 15 @ 3 4 4 4 5 5 6 8 7 @ 9
D269	16-#4	3 6 @ 6 7 8 9 11 14 16 16 16 16
D270	25-#3	2 12 @ 4 5 5 6 6 8 7 @ 9
D271	14-#4	4 8 8 8 8 8 9 11 14 5 @ 16
D272	13-#4	4 8 8 8 8 9 11 13 15 4 @ 16
D273	12-#4	4 9 9 9 10 12 14 16 16 16 16 16

* †See Page 10-58.

STIRRUP COMBINATIONS—CONTINUED

Mark	Number and size	Spacing on each end
D274	11-#4	5 11 11 11 13 15 16 16 16 16 16
D275	11-#4	6 12 12 13 15 16 16 16 16 16 16
D276	10-#4	6 13 13 14 16 16 16 16 16 16
D277	17-#3	4 8 8 8 8 8 11 @ 9
D278	18-#4	2 8 @ 5 6 6 8 11 5 @ 13
D279	18-#4	2 7 @ 5 6 6 7 9 11 5 @ 13
D280	16-#4	3 6 @ 6 7 8 10 12 5 @ 13
D281	15-#4	3 7 7 7 7 7 7 8 10 12 5 @ 13
D282	26-#3	2 10 @ 4 5 5 5 6 11 @ 7
D283	14-#4	4 8 8 8 8 9 11 7 @ 13
D284	12-#4	5 10 10 10 11 12 13 13 13 13 13 13
D285	21-#3	3 6 6 6 6 6 6 6 13 @ 7
D286	11-#4	6 12 12 12 13 13 13 13 13 13 13
D287	19-#3	3 18 @ 7
D288	10-#4	6 13 13 13 13 13 13 13 13 13
D289	18-#4	2 8 @ 5 6 6 8 11 5 @ 13
D290	21-#4	2 9 @ 4 5 5 6 7 8 11 5 @ 13
D291	19-#4	2 9 @ 5 6 6 8 10 12 4 @ 13
D292	19-#4	2 7 @ 5 6 6 7 8 10 12 5 @ 13
D293	17-#4	3 7 @ 6 7 8 10 12 5 @ 13
D294	17-#4	3 6 @ 6 7 8 9 11 6 @ 13
D295	28-#3	2 11 @ 4 5 5 5 6 12 @ 7
D296	15-#4	4 8 8 8 8 9 10 12 7 @ 13
D297	14-#4	4 9 9 9 9 11 12 7 @ 13
D298	13-#4	5 10 10 10 11 12 7 @ 13
D299	12-#4	6 12 12 12 13 13 13 13 13 13 13 13
D300	27-#4	1 14 @ 3 4 4 4 5 5 6 7 10 12 3 @ 13
D301	28-#4	1 13 @ 3 4 4 4 4 5 5 6 7 9 12 4 @ 13
D302	24-#4	2 12 @ 4 5 5 6 6 7 9 12 4 @ 13
D303	24-#4	2 10 @ 4 5 5 5 6 6 7 9 11 5 @ 13
D304	24-#4	2 9 @ 4 5 5 5 6 6 7 8 10 12 5 @ 13
D305	21-#4	2 8 @ 5 6 6 6 7 8 10 12 5 @ 13
D306	21-#4	2 7 @ 5 6 6 7 7 8 10 12 6 @ 13
D307	19-#4	3 7 @ 6 7 8 9 10 12 6 @ 13
D308	18-#4	3 6 @ 7 8 8 10 12 7 @ 13
D309	17-#4	3 7 7 7 7 7 8 8 10 12 7 @ 13
D310	16-#4	4 8 8 8 8 8 9 11 12 7 @ 13
D311	25-#4	1 11 @ 3 4 4 4 5 5 6 7 9 5 @ 11
D312	27-#4	1 12 @ 3 4 4 4 4 5 5 6 8 10 5 @ 11
D313	24-#4	2 12 @ 4 5 5 6 6 8 10 5 @ 11
D314	24-#4	2 10 @ 4 5 5 6 6 8 10 6 @ 11
D315	23-#4	2 9 @ 4 5 5 6 6 7 8 10 6 @ 11
D316	21-#4	2 8 @ 5 6 6 7 8 10 7 @ 11
D317	21-#4	2 7 @ 5 6 6 7 8 9 10 7 @ 11

Mark	Number and size	Spacing on each end
D318	19-#4	3 6 @ 6 7 7 8 10 8 @ 11
D319	17-#4	3 7 7 7 7 7 7 8 10 8 @ 11
D320	16-#4	4 8 8 8 8 8 9 10 8 @ 11
D321	15-#4	4 9 9 9 9 10 9 @ 11
D322	25-#4	1 11 @ 3 4 4 4 5 5 6 7 9 5 @ 11
D323	27-#4	1 12 @ 3 4 4 4 4 5 5 6 8 10 5 @ 11
D324	29-#4	1 13 @ 3 4 4 4 4 5 5 6 7 9 10 5 @ 11
D325	†	
D326	30-#4	1 11 @ 3 4 4 4 4 4 5 5 5 6 7 8 10 6 @ 11
D327	26-#4	2 11 @ 4 5 5 5 6 6 7 8 10 6 @ 11
D328	26-#4	2 9 @ 4 5 5 5 5 6 6 7 8 10 7 @ 11
D329	23-#4	2 9 @ 5 6 6 7 7 8 10 7 @ 11
D330	23-#4	2 8 @ 5 6 6 7 7 8 10 8 @ 11
D331	21-#4	3 7 @ 6 7 7 8 9 10 8 @ 11
D332	20-#4	3 6 @ 6 7 7 8 9 10 8 @ 11
D333	10-#3	6 12 12 12 12 12 12 12 12 12
D334	9-#3	6 12 12 12 12 12 12 12 12
D335	9-#3	6 12 12 12 12 12 12 12 12
D336	9-#3	6 12 12 12 12 12 12 12 12
D337	8-#3	6 12 12 12 12 12 12 12
D338	8-#3	6 12 12 12 12 12 12 12
D339	7-#3	6 12 12 12 12 12 12
D340	14-#3	3 7 7 7 7 7 7 9 11 5 @ 12
D341	13-#3	4 8 8 8 8 8 10 11 5 @ 12
D342	13-#3	4 9 9 9 9 10 7 @ 12
D343	12-#3	5 10 10 10 11 7 @ 12
D344	11-#3	6 12 12 12 12 12 12 12 12 12 12
D345	11-#3	6 12 12 12 12 12 12 12 12 12 12
D346	11-#3	6 12 12 12 12 12 12 12 12 12 12
D347	11-#3	6 12 12 12 12 12 12 12 12 12 12
D348	10-#3	6 12 12 12 12 12 12 12 12 12
D349	10-#3	6 12 12 12 12 12 12 12 12 12
D350	9-#3	6 12 12 12 12 12 12 12 12
D351	10-#4	5 10 10 10 11 14 16 16 16 16
D352	10-#4	5 11 11 11 13 15 16 16 16 16
D353	9-#4	6 13 13 13 14 16 16 16 16
D354	15-#3	4 8 8 8 8 8 9 @ 9
D355	8-#4	8 16 16 16 16 16 16 16
D356	14-#3	4 13 @ 9
D357	14-#3	4 13 @ 9
D358	14-#3	4 13 @ 9
D359	7-#4	8 16 16 16 16 16 16
D360	12-#3	4 9 9 9 9 9 9 9 9 9 9 9
D361	12-#3	4 9 9 9 9 9 9 9 9 9 9 9
D362	12-#4	4 8 8 8 8 8 9 13 15 16 16 16
D363	23-#3	2 10 @ 4 5 5 6 7 8 7 @ 9
D364	21-#3	2 9 @ 5 6 7 8 7 @ 9

Mark	Number and size	Spacing on each end
D365	19-#3	3 8 @ 6 7 8 8 @ 9
D366	10-#4	6 12 12 12 14 16 16 16 16 16
D367	10-#4	7 14 14 15 16 16 16 16 16 16
D368	9-#4	8 16 16 16 16 16 16 16 16
D369	9-#4	8 16 16 16 16 16 16 16 16
D370	15-#3	4 14 @ 9
D371	15-#3	4 14 @ 9
D372	14-#3	4 13 @ 9
D373	18-#4	2 8 @ 5 6 6 8 10 13 4 @ 16
D374	16-#4	3 7 @ 6 7 8 10 13 4 @ 16
D375	15-#4	3 7 @ 7 9 11 14 4 @ 16
D376	26-#3	2 12 @ 4 5 5 6 6 8 8 @ 9
D377	14-#4	4 8 8 8 8 8 9 11 14 5 @ 16
D378	23-#3	2 9 @ 5 6 6 7 8 9 @ 9
D379	12-#4	5 10 10 10 10 12 15 16 16 16 16 16
D380	21-#3	3 7 @ 6 7 7 8 10 @ 9
D381	19-#3	3 7 7 7 7 7 7 8 11 @ 9
D382	10-#4	7 14 14 15 16 16 16 16 16 16
D383	17-#3	4 16 @ 9
D384	18-#4	2 8 @ 5 6 6 8 10 12 4 @ 13
D385	17-#4	3 8 @ 6 8 10 12 5 @ 13
D386	17-#4	3 7 @ 6 7 9 11 6 @ 13
D387	15-#4	3 7 7 7 7 7 7 8 10 12 5 @ 13
D388	14-#4	4 8 8 8 8 8 9 11 6 @ 13
D389	24-#3	2 9 @ 5 6 6 12 @ 7
D390	13-#4	5 10 10 10 11 12 7 @ 13
D391	12-#4	6 12 12 12 12 13 13 13 13 13 13 13
D392	11-#4	6 13 13 13 13 13 13 13 13 13 13
D393	11-#4	6 13 13 13 13 13 13 13 13 13 13
D394	11-#4	6 13 13 13 13 13 13 13 13 13 13
D395	18-#4	2 8 @ 5 6 6 8 11 5 @ 13
D396	19-#4	2 9 @ 5 6 6 8 10 12 4 @ 13
D397	20-#4	2 9 @ 5 6 6 8 10 12 5 @ 13
D398	18-#4	3 8 @ 6 7 8 10 12 5 @ 13
D399	18-#4	3 7 @ 6 7 8 10 12 6 @ 13
D400	30-#3	2 13 @ 4 5 5 6 6 12 @ 7
D401	15-#4	4 8 8 8 8 8 9 10 12 6 @ 13
D402	26-#3	2 10 @ 5 6 6 13 @ 7
D403	14-#4	5 10 10 10 10 12 8 @ 13
D404	13-#4	5 11 11 11 12 13 7 @ 13
D405	22-#3	3 21 @ 7
D406	28-#4	1 14 @ 3 4 4 4 5 5 6 7 10 12 4 @ 13
D407	25-#4	2 13 @ 4 5 5 6 7 9 11 5 @ 13
D408	25-#4	2 12 @ 4 5 5 6 6 7 9 12 5 @ 13
D409	24-#4	2 10 @ 4 5 5 5 6 6 7 9 11 5 @ 13
D410	22-#4	2 10 @ 5 6 6 7 8 10 12 5 @ 13
D411	22-#4	2 8 @ 5 6 6 6 7 8 10 12 6 @ 13
D412	20-#4	3 8 @ 6 7 8 9 11 12 6 @ 13

† See page 10-58.

STIRRUP COMBINATIONS—CONTINUED

Mark	Number and size	Spacing on each end
D413	19-#4	3 7 @ 6 7 8 9 10 12 6 @ 13
D414	18-#4	3 6 @ 7 8 9 10 12 7 @ 13
D415	17-#4	4 8 8 8 8 8 8 9 11 12 7 @ 13
D416	16-#4	4 9 9 9 9 9 10 12 8 @ 13
D417	23-#4	2 11 @ 4 5 5 6 7 9 6 @ 11
D418	24-#4	2 12 @ 4 5 5 6 7 9 10 5 @ 11
D419	25-#4	2 12 @ 4 5 5 6 7 9 10 6 @ 11
D420	24-#4	2 10 @ 4 5 5 5 6 6 8 10 6 @ 11
D421	22-#4	2 10 @ 5 6 7 8 10 7 @ 11
D422	21-#4	2 8 @ 5 6 6 7 8 10 7 @ 11
D423	20-#4	3 7 @ 6 7 7 8 10 8 @ 11
D424	18-#4	3 7 7 7 7 7 7 7 8 10 8 @ 11
D425	18-#4	3 7 7 7 7 7 7 8 10 9 @ 11
D426	17-#4	4 8 8 8 8 8 9 10 9 @ 11
D427	28-#3	2 5 5 5 5 5 5 5 5 5 18 @ 6
D428	23-#4	2 11 @ 4 5 5 6 7 9 6 @ 11
D429	24-#4	2 12 @ 4 5 5 6 7 9 6 @ 11
D430	26-#4	2 13 @ 4 5 5 6 6 8 10 6 @ 11
D431	†	
D432	27-#4	2 13 @ 4 5 5 5 6 7 8 10 6 @ 11
D433	27-#4	2 11 @ 4 5 5 5 6 6 7 8 10 7 @ 11
D434	24-#4	2 11 @ 5 6 6 7 8 10 7 @ 11
D435	24-#4	2 9 @ 5 6 6 7 7 8 10 8 @ 11
D436	22-#4	3 8 @ 6 7 7 8 9 10 8 @ 11
D437	21-#4	3 7 @ 6 7 7 8 9 10 8 @ 11
D438	20-#4	3 7 @ 7 8 9 10 9 @ 11
D439	9-#3	6 12 12 12 12 12 12 12 12
D440	8-#3	6 12 12 12 12 12 12 12
D441	8-#3	6 12 12 12 12 12 12 12
D442	8-#3	6 12 12 12 12 12 12 12
D443	7-#3	6 12 12 12 12 12 12
D444	7-#3	6 12 12 12 12 12 12
D445	6-#3	6 12 12 12 12 12
D446	14-#3	3 6 @ 6 7 9 11 4 @ 12
D447	13-#3	3 7 7 7 7 7 9 11 5 @ 12
D448	12-#3	4 8 8 8 8 9 11 12 12 12 12 12
D449	12-#3	4 9 9 9 10 11 12 12 12 12 12 12
D450	11-#3	5 11 11 11 11 12 12 12 12 12 12
D451	10-#3	6 12 12 12 12 12 12 12 12 12
D452	10-#3	6 12 12 12 12 12 12 12 12 12
D453	10-#3	6 12 12 12 12 12 12 12 12 12
D454	9-#3	6 12 12 12 12 12 12 12 12
D455	9-#3	6 12 12 12 12 12 12 12 12
D456	8-#3	6 12 12 12 12 12 12 12
D457	14-#3	3 7 7 7 7 7 8 7 @ 9
D458	12-#3	4 9 9 9 9 9 9 9 9 9 9 9
D459	12-#3	4 9 9 9 9 9 9 9 9 9 9 9
D460	12-#3	4 9 9 9 9 9 9 9 9 9 9 9
D461	11-#3	4 9 9 9 9 9 9 9 9 9 9
D462	6-#4	8 16 16 16 16 16
D463	10-#3	4 9 9 9 9 9 9 9 9 9
D464	10-#3	4 9 9 9 9 9 9 9 9 9
D465	5-#4	8 16 16 16 16
D466	11-#4	4 8 8 8 8 9 13 16 16 16 16
D467	10-#4	4 9 9 9 10 13 16 16 16 16
D468	9-#4	5 11 11 11 13 16 16 16 16
D469	15-#3	3 7 7 7 7 7 8 8 @ 9
D470	14-#3	4 8 8 8 8 8 8 @ 9
D471	14-#3	4 13 @ 9
D472	13-#3	4 12 @ 9
D473	7-#4	8 16 16 16 16 16 16
D474	7-#4	8 16 16 16 16 16 16
D475	12-#3	4 9 9 9 9 9 9 9 9 9 9 9
D476	11-#3	4 9 9 9 9 9 9 9 9 9 9
D477	14-#4	3 6 @ 6 7 9 12 15 3 @ 16
D478	23-#3	2 11 @ 4 5 5 6 8 7 @ 9
D479	12-#4	4 8 8 8 8 9 11 14 16 16 16 16
D480	11-#4	4 9 9 9 9 11 14 16 16 16 16
D481	19-#3	2 7 @ 5 6 6 8 8 @ 9
D482	10-#4	5 11 11 12 14 16 16 16 16 16
D483	9-#4	6 13 13 14 16 16 16 16 16
D484	15-#3	4 8 8 8 8 8 9 @ 9
D485	8-#4	8 16 16 16 16 16 16 16
D486	14-#3	4 13 @ 9
D487	14-#3	4 13 @ 9
D488	14-#4	3 6 @ 6 7 9 11 4 @ 13
D489	14-#4	3 6 @ 6 8 10 12 4 @ 13
D490	13-#4	3 7 7 7 7 7 9 11 5 @ 13
D491	12-#4	4 8 8 8 8 9 12 13 13 13 13 13
D492	11-#4	5 10 10 10 11 13 13 13 13 13 13
D493	19-#3	3 6 6 6 6 6 6 12 @ 7
D494	10-#4	6 13 13 13 13 13 13 13 13 13
D495	17-#3	3 16 @ 7
D496	9-#4	6 13 13 13 13 13 13 13 13
D497	9-#4	6 13 13 13 13 13 13 13 13
D498	9-#4	6 13 13 13 13 13 13 13 13
D499	17-#4	2 9 @ 5 6 8 11 4 @ 13
D500	17-#4	2 7 @ 5 6 6 7 9 12 4 @ 13
D501	16-#4	3 7 @ 6 7 9 11 5 @ 13
D502	15-#4	3 7 7 7 7 7 7 9 11 6 @ 13
D503	14-#4	3 7 7 7 7 7 8 10 12 5 @ 13
D504	13-#4	4 8 8 8 8 9 11 6 @ 13
D505	12-#4	5 10 10 10 11 12 6 @ 13
D506	21-#3	3 6 6 6 6 6 6 6 13 @ 7
D507	19-#3	3 18 @ 7
D508	10-#4	6 13 13 13 13 13 13 13 13 13
D509	10-#4	6 13 13 13 13 13 13 13 13 13
D510	25-#4	1 11 @ 3 4 4 4 4 5 5 6 8 11 4 @ 13
D511	22-#4	2 10 @ 4 5 5 5 6 8 10 12 4 @ 13
D512	21-#4	2 9 @ 4 5 5 6 6 7 9 11 4 @ 13
D513	19-#4	2 8 @ 5 6 6 7 8 10 12 4 @ 13
D514	19-#4	2 7 @ 5 6 6 7 8 10 12 5 @ 13
D515	17-#4	3 6 @ 6 7 7 8 10 12 5 @ 13
D516	16-#4	3 7 7 7 7 7 7 8 10 12 6 @ 13
D517	28-#3	2 11 @ 4 5 5 6 6 12 @ 7
D518	14-#4	4 8 8 8 8 9 10 12 6 @ 13
D519	14-#4	4 9 9 9 9 11 12 7 @ 13
D520	13-#4	5 10 10 10 11 8 @ 13
D521	25-#4	1 12 @ 3 4 4 4 5 5 6 8 10 4 @ 11
D522	22-#4	2 10 @ 4 5 5 6 7 9 10 5 @ 11
D523	21-#4	2 9 @ 4 5 5 6 6 8 10 5 @ 11
D524	19-#4	2 8 @ 5 6 6 7 9 10 5 @ 11
D525	19-#4	2 7 @ 5 6 6 7 9 10 6 @ 11
D526	17-#4	3 6 6 6 6 6 6 7 8 10 7 @ 11
D527	28-#3	2 12 @ 4 5 5 13 @ 6
D528	15-#4	4 8 8 8 8 8 10 8 @ 11
D529	14-#4	4 9 9 9 9 10 8 @ 11
D530	13-#4	5 10 10 10 10 8 @ 11
D531	23-#3	3 22 @ 6
D532	28-#4	1 15 @ 3 4 4 4 5 5 7 9 5 @ 11
D533	28-#4	1 14 @ 3 4 4 4 5 5 6 8 10 5 @ 11
D534	27-#4	1 12 @ 3 4 4 4 4 5 5 6 7 9 5 @ 11
D535	24-#4	2 11 @ 4 5 5 6 6 8 10 6 @ 11
D536	23-#4	2 9 @ 4 5 5 5 6 6 8 10 6 @ 11
D537	21-#4	2 9 @ 5 6 6 7 9 10 6 @ 11
D538	20-#4	2 7 @ 5 6 6 7 7 9 10 6 @ 11
D539	19-#4	3 7 @ 6 7 8 9 10 7 @ 11
D540	17-#4	3 7 7 7 7 7 7 8 9 10 7 @ 11
D541	30-#3	2 11 @ 4 5 5 5 15 @ 11
D542	16-#4	4 8 8 8 8 9 10 9 @ 11
D543	9-#3	6 12 12 12 12 12 12 12 12
D544	9-#3	6 12 12 12 12 12 12 12 12
D545	9-#3	6 12 12 12 12 12 12 12 12
D546	8-#3	6 12 12 12 12 12 12 12
D547	8-#3	6 12 12 12 12 12 12 12
D548	8-#3	6 12 12 12 12 12 12 12
D549	14-#3	3 7 7 7 7 7 7 9 11 5 @ 12
D550	13-#3	4 8 8 8 8 8 10 6 @ 12
D551	12-#3	4 9 9 9 9 10 12 12 12 12 12 12
D552	11-#3	5 11 11 11 11 12 12 12 12 12 12
D553	11-#3	6 12 12 12 12 12 12 12 12 12 12
D554	11-#3	6 12 12 12 12 12 12 12 12 12 12
D555	10-#3	6 12 12 12 12 12 12 12 12 12
D556	10-#3	6 12 12 12 12 12 12 12 12 12

† See page 10-58.

STIRRUP COMBINATIONS—CONTINUED

Mark	Number and size	Spacing on each end
D557	10-#3	6 12 12 12 12 12 12 12 12 12
D558	9-#3	6 12 12 12 12 12 12 12 12
D559	9-#3	6 12 12 12 12 12 12 12 12
D560	14-#3	4 8 8 8 8 8 8 @ 9
D561	7-#4	8 16 16 16 16 16 16
D562	7-#4	8 16 16 16 16 16 16
D563	7-#4	8 16 16 16 16 16 16
D564	12-#3	4 9 9 9 9 9 9 9 9 9 9 9
D565	12-#3	4 9 9 9 9 9 9 9 9 9 9 9
D566	6-#4	8 16 16 16 16 16
D567	10-#3	4 9 9 9 9 9 9 9 9 9
D568	10-#3	4 9 9 9 9 9 9 9 9 9
D569	19-#3	2 9 @ 5 6 8 7 @ 9
D570	17-#3	3 7 @ 6 7 8 7 @ 9
D571	17-#3	3 6 6 6 6 6 6 6 8 8 @ 9
D572	9-#4	7 14 14 15 16 16 16 16 16
D573	8-#4	8 16 16 16 16 16 16 16
D574	14-#3	4 13 @ 9
D575	14-#3	4 13 @ 9
D576	14-#3	4 13 @ 9
D577	13-#3	4 12 @ 9
D578	7-#4	8 16 16 16 16 16 16
D579	12-#3	4 9 9 9 9 9 9 9 9 9 9 9
D580	13-#4	3 7 7 7 7 7 7 9 12 15 3 @ 16
D581	12-#4	4 8 8 8 8 8 10 13 15 16 16 16
D582	12-#4	4 9 9 9 9 10 13 15 16 16 16 16
D583	11-#4	5 10 10 10 10 12 15 16 16 16 16
D584	19-#3	3 7 @ 6 7 8 9 @ 9
D585	10-#4	6 12 12 12 14 16 16 16 16 16
D586	9-#4	7 14 14 15 16 16 16 16 16
D587	9-#4	8 16 16 16 16 16 16 16 16
D588	15-#3	4 14 @ 9
D589	15-#3	4 14 @ 9
D590	8-#4	8 16 16 16 16 16 16 16
D591	15-#4	3 6 6 6 6 6 6 6 8 11 5 @ 13
D592	14-#4	3 7 7 7 7 7 7 9 11 5 @ 13
D593	13-#4	4 8 8 8 8 8 10 12 5 @ 13
D594	12-#4	4 9 9 9 9 10 12 13 13 13 13 13
D595	20-#3	3 6 6 6 6 6 6 6 6 11 @ 7
D596	11-#4	6 12 12 12 12 13 13 13 13 13 13
D597	10-#4	6 13 13 13 13 13 13 13 13 13
D598	10-#4	6 13 13 13 13 13 13 13 13 13
D599	10-#4	6 13 13 13 13 13 13 13 13 13
D600	17-#3	3 16 @ 7
D601	9-#4	6 13 13 13 13 13 13 13 13
D602	18-#4	2 9 @ 5 6 7 10 12 4 @ 13
D603	17-#4	3 8 @ 6 8 10 12 5 @ 13
D604	16-#4	3 7 @ 6 7 9 11 5 @ 13
D605	15-#4	3 7 7 7 7 7 7 8 10 12 5 @ 13
D606	14-#4	4 8 8 8 8 8 10 12 6 @ 13
D607	13-#4	4 9 9 9 9 10 12 6 @ 13
D608	13-#4	5 10 10 10 10 11 12 7 @ 13
D609	12-#4	6 12 12 12 12 12 13 13 13 13 13 13 13
D610	11-#4	6 13 13 13 13 13 13 13 13 13 13
D611	11-#4	6 13 13 13 13 13 13 13 13 13 13
D612	11-#4	6 13 13 13 13 13 13 13 13 13 13
D613	22-#4	2 12 @ 4 5 5 6 8 11 4 @ 13
D614	22-#4	2 11 @ 4 5 5 6 7 9 12 4 @ 13
D615	20-#4	2 10 @ 5 6 7 9 11 5 @ 13
D616	20-#4	2 9 @ 5 6 7 8 10 12 5 @ 13
D617	18-#4	3 8 @ 6 7 8 10 12 5 @ 13
D618	18-#4	3 7 @ 6 7 8 10 12 13 5 @ 13
D619	29-#3	2 13 @ 4 5 5 6 6 11 @ 7
D620	15-#4	4 8 8 8 8 8 9 11 12 6 @ 13
D621	26-#3	2 10 @ 5 6 6 13 @ 7
D622	14-#4	5 10 10 10 10 12 8 @ 13
D623	13-#4	5 11 11 11 12 8 @ 13
D624	23-#4	2 12 @ 4 5 5 7 9 6 @ 11
D625	23-#4	2 11 @ 4 5 5 6 8 10 6 @ 11
D626	20-#4	2 10 @ 5 6 7 9 6 @ 11
D627	20-#4	2 8 @ 5 6 6 7 9 10 6 @ 11
D628	18-#4	3 7 @ 6 7 8 10 7 @ 11
D629	18-#4	3 7 @ 6 7 9 10 7 @ 11
D630	29-#3	2 4 4 4 4 4 4 4 4 4 4 4 4 4 5 5 14 @ 6
D631	15-#4	4 8 8 8 8 8 10 8 @ 11
D632	26-#3	2 9 @ 5 16 @ 6
D633	13-#4	5 12 @ 11
D634	13-#4	5 12 @ 11
D635	29-#4	1 16 @ 3 4 4 4 5 6 8 10 5 @ 11
D636	28-#4	1 14 @ 3 4 4 4 5 5 6 7 9 5 @ 11
D637	25-#4	2 12 @ 4 5 5 5 6 8 10 6 @ 11
D638	25-#4	2 11 @ 4 5 5 5 6 7 9 10 6 @ 11
D639	24-#4	2 10 @ 4 5 5 6 6 7 9 10 6 @ 11
D640	22-#4	2 9 @ 5 6 6 7 8 10 7 @ 11
D641	20-#4	3 8 @ 6 7 8 10 8 @ 11
D642	19-#4	3 7 @ 6 7 8 9 10 7 @ 11
D643	18-#4	3 7 7 7 7 7 7 8 9 10 8 @ 11
D644	17-#4	4 8 8 8 8 8 8 10 9 @ 11
D645	16-#4	4 9 9 9 9 9 10 9 @ 11

* In certain shallow beams, it is not possible to meet the minimum 3 in. spacing imposed by this text simultaneously with the maximum requirements of d/4. The designer must develop a suitable combination.

† In certain long beams, over 30 stirrups will be required. The designer must develop a suitable combination.

Note: #3 is the minimum size deformed bar. It is recommended as the minimum size stirrup for general use. Even where #2 (an obsolete designation for plain ¼″ ϕ) with special anchorage would satisfy design requirements, over-all economy will usually be achieved by use of #3 stirrups.

"Section 806—Lateral reinforcement:

(c) Compression reinforcement in beams or girders shall be anchored by ties or stirrups, which shall be not less than ¼ in. in diameter spaced not farther apart than 16 bar diameters, or 48 tie diameters. At least one tie at each spacing shall extend completely around all longitudinal bars. Such stirrups or ties shall be used throughout the distance where the compression reinforcement is required."

SAFE LOAD TABLES

Columns, Axial and Eccentric Loads

Section 11

COLUMNS OF HIGHER STRENGTH CONCRETES THAN TABULATED

Columns are tabulated for f_y = 60,000 and 75,000 psi, the only grades of steel likely to be used.

Columns are tabulated for f'_c = 3750 and 5000 psi, the concretes likely to be used. Under proper control and supervision, higher strength concretes may be selected at the discretion of the designer. These are not tabulated, but a fairly good value for a first trial can be prorated from these tables by noting that increasing f'_c from 3750 to 5000 psi:

For p = 0.01, increasing f'_c 33⅓% increases *N* an amount varying from 26% for e = 0 down to 0 when e = ∞.

For p = 0.04, increasing f'_c 33⅓% increases *N* an amount varying from 16% for e = 0 down to 0 when e = ∞.

After selecting a column size in this manner, the exact amount of reinforcement can be checked as in the examples on pages 11-7 to 11-9.

AXIALLY AND ECCENTRICALLY LOADED COLUMNS

These tables give the safe carrying capacity in kips for axially (concentrically) loaded reinforced concrete columns and eccentrically loaded ones, of ordinary (normal) height, for concretes of f'_c = 3750 psi and 5000 psi cylinder strengths, with vertical bars of Grade 60 steel (f_y = 60,000 psi, 24,000 psi basis) and Grade 75 (f_y = 75,000 psi, 30,000 psi basis), in square tied columns, spirally reinforced square columns, and spirally reinforced round columns, all in accordance with Working Stress Design by ACI 318-63. Percentages of steel vary from the minimum allowable to the maximum that can be accommodated in a single layer (page 2-19), or the maximum percentage permitted, if that limit is reached.

Loads, N, are expressed in kips. Eccentricities, $e = M/N$, are given in inches. Axial loads, P, are tabulated in the column "$e = 0$" and are printed in boldface type. For the unusual case of an eccentricity greater than tabulated, M_o, the value of the allowable bending moment in pure bending, ($N = 0$), is given in italics to permit extrapolation as explained on page 11-5.

The line of demarcation between where compression governs and tension governs is shown by a zigzag line through the tables as explained on page 11-4.

The tables include #14 and #18 bars, but the designer is advised to check with local suppliers to see about their availability at the job site.

Tables being given for Grade 75 bars, the designer is again advised to check with suppliers as to the extra cost of these bars which are often of a low alloy steel. Note with high strength steel that strain is limited to 0.003. **Also check availability.** See page 2-13 for bundled bars.

The designer of columns under ACI 318-63 may find the task easier if he is familiar with load-moment interaction diagrams.

LOAD-MOMENT INTERACTION DIAGRAMS

A column loaded concentrically as in (a) will carry a greater load than if the load is applied eccentrically as in (b), and the greater the eccentricity, e, the smaller the load, N.

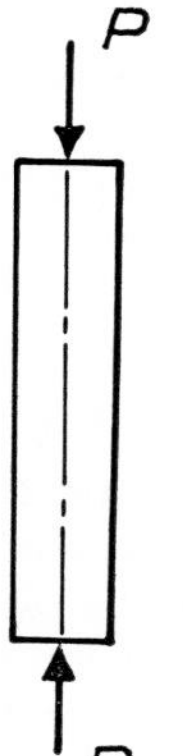

Fig. (a)

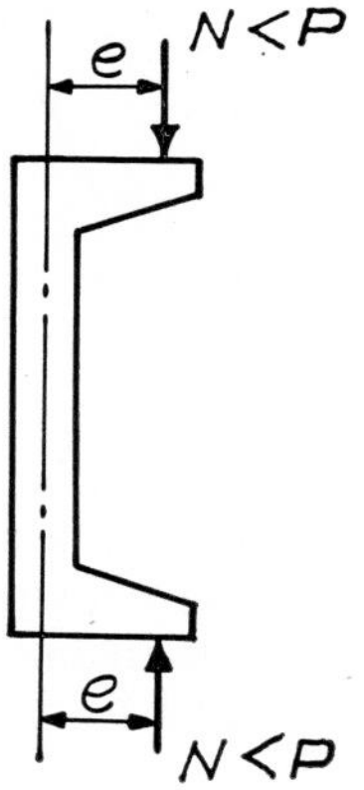

Fig. (b)

Ultimate Capacity. To understand load-moment interaction diagrams in the working stress range, consider first ultimate capacities. The ultimate capacity of an eccentrically loaded column can be plotted, through the complete range of eccentricities, on a load-moment interaction diagram (Fig. c), showing loads, P_u, vertically; moments, $M_u = P_u e$, horizontally; eccentricities, e, being represented by radial lines from the origin. The curve will be of the type shown at (c), whose exact shape will vary somewhat with various types and sizes of columns. Point P_o = the ultimate capacity for pure axial compression (M_u = 0). M_{uo} = the ultimate capacity for

AXIALLY AND ECCENTRICALLY LOADED COLUMNS

pure bending ($P_u = 0$). Increasing eccentricities are indicated by radial lines e_1, e_2, e_3, e_4, etc. Corresponding to each radial line are loads P_{u1}, P_{u2} . . . and moments M_{u1}, M_{u2} . . . . Point b marks the change from a capacity determined by compression to that determined by tension, e_b being the eccentricity of this break-point; P_b, the corresponding load; and $M_b = P_b e_b$, the moment.

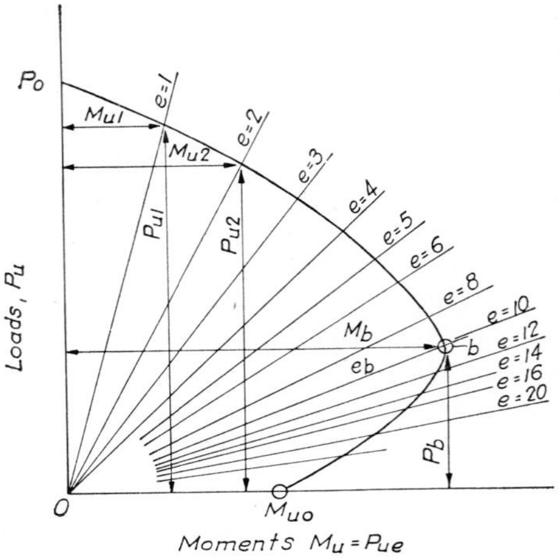

Fig. (c)

Obtaining working stress diagram by safety factors. By applying a safety factor of about 2½ in the three directions marked by arrows 1, 2, 3, on Fig. (d1), that is, by taking about forty percent of the ordinates, the abscissae and the radii, three locii are obtained, numbered curve 1, 2, 3. A rectilinear diagram fitted within these curves and cut off horizontally on the top to allow for possible minor eccentricities gives a reasonable working stress diagram.

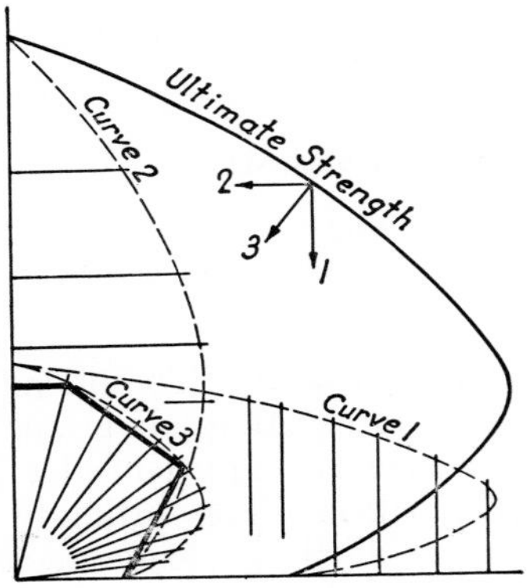

Fig. (d1)

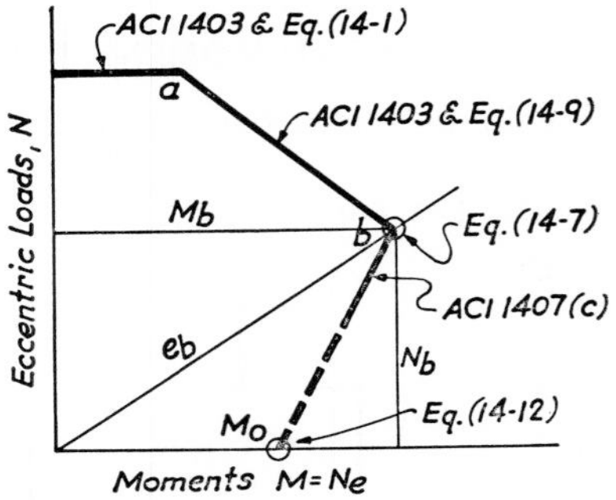

Fig. (d2)

Working stress interaction diagram. The diagram of (d1) is enlarged in (d2), the governing equations of ACI 318-63 are shown and their application indicated. The horizontal line through a allows for unavoidable eccentricities. Along inclined line ab compression controls; b is the break point between compression and tension; while along inclined line bM_o tension governs. From the tables, point a is easily located by intersecting straight lines through the values.

Similar sketching of the slopes of two lines will locate b, whose approximate location is shown by the zigzag line in the tables.

AXIALLY AND ECCENTRICALLY LOADED COLUMNS

The lower part (tension portion) of the diagram, as far as computed in the tables, is in accordance with the suggestion in ACI 318-63 that this may be assumed straight. Because the successive values of e are angular values on the diagram, extrapolation is not a continuation from equally-spaced points. For that reason, the value of M_o is given in the tables as a target. A line from b to M_o will permit extending eccentricities beyond those given in the tables, should the need arise.

Fig. (e) shows the breaking point between where compression controls and tension controls, with its coordinates e_b, N_b, M_b, as well as the value of pure flexure M_o. Connecting M_b and M_o with a straight line and considering point c with coordinates M_c and N_c, by similar triangles, $M_c = M_o + \frac{N_c}{N_b}(M_b - M_o)$. Placing M_c equal to $N_c e_c$, then $N_c = \dfrac{M_o}{e_c + \dfrac{M_o - M_b}{N_b}}$.

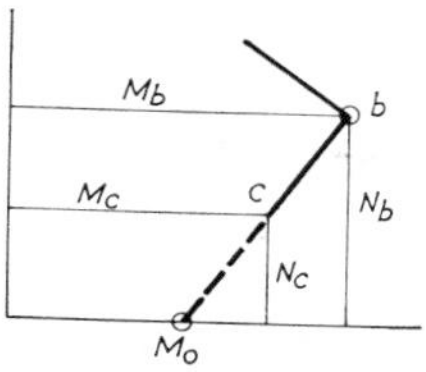

Fig. (e)

SLENDER COLUMNS

The carrying capacity of a long * column is less than the tabulated values for a "short column" of similar size, not only because of possible buckling, but also by any increase in moment due to an increase in moment arm by lateral deflection between the ends of the column.

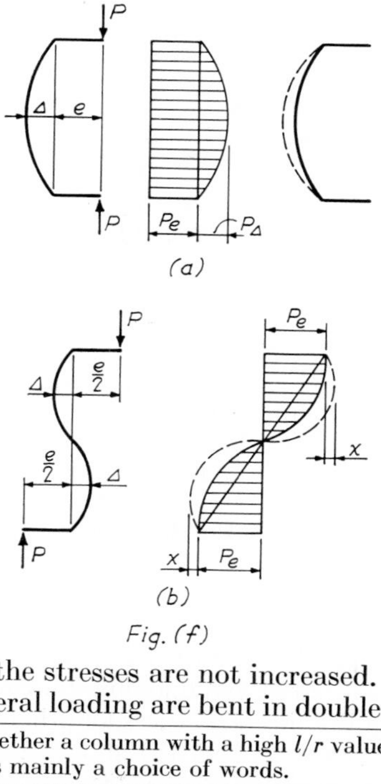

Fig. (f)

Fig. (f)a shows how a column with equal and opposite moments at the ends is bowed in single curvature and how the bowing of the column increases the moment arm at mid-height to $e + \Delta$. It also shows the deflected shape of the column and the increase in bowing. Fig. (f)b shows how a column with equal moment at each end is bowed in double curvature and how the bowing of the column increases the moment arm near the quarter points of the height. It also shows the deflected shape of the column. With double curvature, unless the increase in moment due to the increased arm causes the moment curve to project beyond Pe by some distance x, the stresses are not increased. Restrained columns in frames undergoing lateral loading are bent in double curvature. The bowing and the buck-

* Whether a column with a high l/r value is described as a "long column" or a "slender column" is mainly a choice of words.

AXIALLY AND ECCENTRICALLY LOADED COLUMNS

ling may combine to decrease the capacity. This decrease is the concern of ACI Sections 915 and 916.

The designer must learn to recognize, at least approximately, the conditions of end restraint that determine the mode of buckling, the end stiffnesses that are a measure of bending, and the possibility of the combinations of bowing and buckling causing lateral displacement of one end of the column relative to the other.

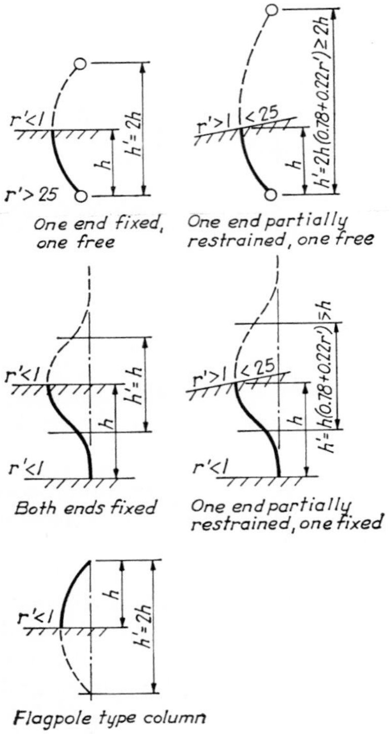

Fig. (g)

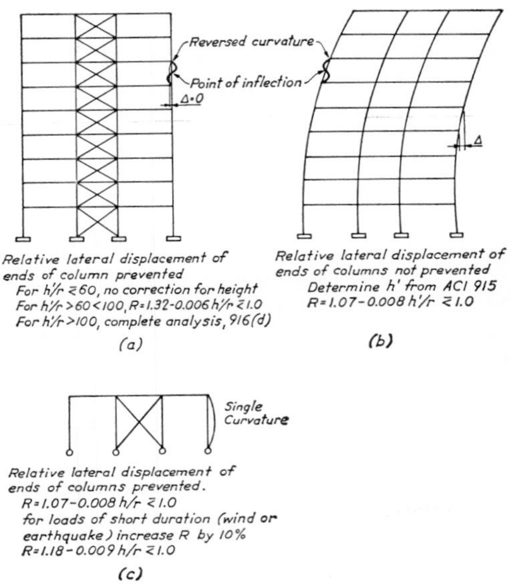

Reversed curvature
Point of inflection
Δ=0
Δ
Relative lateral displacement of ends of column prevented
For h'/r ≤60, no correction for height
For h'/r >60 <100, R=1.32-0.006 h'/r ≤1.0
For h'/r >100, complete analysis, 916(d)
(a)
Relative lateral displacement of ends of columns not prevented
Determine h' from ACI 915
R=1.07-0.008 h'/r ≤1.0
(b)
Single Curvature
Relative lateral displacement of ends of columns prevented.
R=1.07-0.008 h/r ≤1.0
for loads of short duration (wind or earthquake) increase R by 10%
R=1.18-0.009 h/r ≤1.0
(c)

Fig. (h)

ACI Section 915 uses $r' = \dfrac{\Sigma K \text{ (columns)}}{\Sigma K \text{ (floor members)}}$ as a measure of end restraint. Any end of a column with $r' > 25$ is considered hinged. If $r' < 1$, that end is considered fixed. If $r' < 25$ but >1, that end is partially restrained. ACI Section 915 substitutes an effective length, h', for the actual physical length, h, as a device for dealing with slender columns. Fig. (g) shows various combinations of end conditions.

ACI Section 916 separates slender columns first into those governed by compression or those governed by tension, but this is only to permit the assumption of linear variation as outlined in Section 916(b). It then separates columns into those where lateral displacement by buckling-bowing is prevented, as by shear walls, braced bents, adjoining structures, or other methods, and those where lateral movement is possible. Fig. (h) shows some of the various possibilities. ACI Section 916 introduces a divisor, $R \lesssim 1$, obtained from a consideration of the end restraints and bowing represented in Figs. (g) and (h) combined to increase the computed load and moment before entering the safe load tables which are developed for design of "short columns."

SECTION I—SQUARE TIED COLUMNS

This section covers square tied columns only.

The user is referred to the "Manual of Standard Practice for Detailing Reinforced Concrete Structures (ACI 315)" for much helpful information about exact details of columns and the arrangement of reinforcing bars.

For the splicing of column verticals, see Section 2. In lapped splices, column verticals may be offset just below the construction joint at a slope of 1 in. horizontal to 6 in. vertical to come inside of and in contact with the verticals above and ties added to care for the stresses developed. Where the offset would exceed about 4 in., separate dowels should be used.

For a table of volumes of concrete in square columns, see page 5-13.

For a schedule of minimum spacing of column ties, see page 2-19.

The axial capacity of a round tied column can be approximated by taking 82% * of the capacity of a square tied column with side equal to the diameter and with the same number of vertical bars. The axial capacity of a rectangular tied column is fairly close to that of a square column whose side is the mean of the two sides of the rectangle and with the same amount of vertical steel. The minimum side dimension of a main column of reinforced concrete should not be less than 8 in. nor the area less than 96 sq. in.

For axially loaded square tied columns, the vertical bars may be arranged in symmetrical patterns as shown on page 2-14.

For eccentrically loaded square tied columns, one-half of the bars given in the safe load tables is placed in each of the two faces of the column which are perpendicular to the plane of bending (see figure).

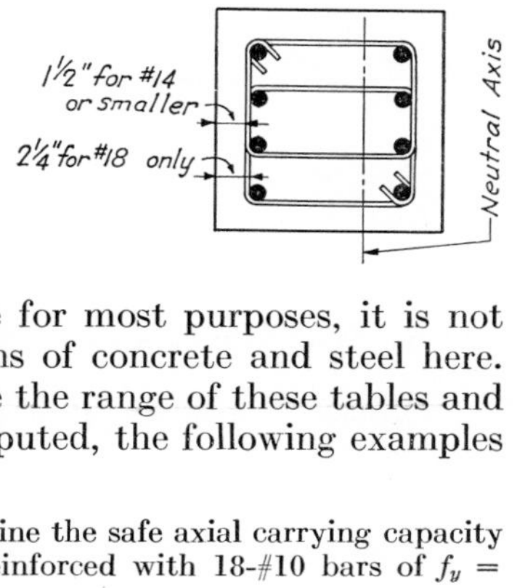

While the scope of these tables is adequate for most purposes, it is not practicable to present all possible combinations of concrete and steel here. For those who want to design a column outside the range of these tables and for those who wish to know how they are computed, the following examples will be instructive:—

Example 1—For the table on page 11-34, determine the safe axial carrying capacity of a column 36″ square, of 3750 psi concrete, reinforced with 18-#10 bars of f_y = 60,000 psi steel.

Solution:—By ACI 1402 and 1403:—

$P = 0.85A_g\ (0.25f'_c + f_sp_g)$ which can be written:

$P = 0.213A_gf'_c + 0.85f_sA_s$ where $f_s = 0.40 \times 60{,}000 = 24{,}000$ psi and $f'_c = 3750$ psi, so:—

$P = 797A_g + 20{,}400\ A_s$.

$P = 36 \times 36 \times 797 = 1033$ kips

$18 \times 1.27 \times 20{,}400 = 466$

1499 kips (as in table)

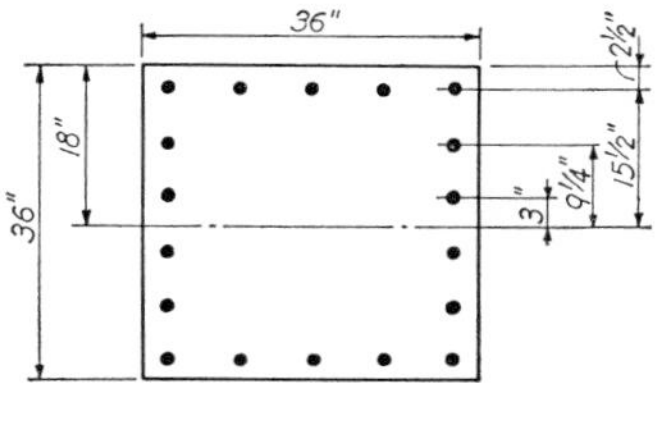

* This varies from 81.2% when $A_s = 0.01$ of the square column to 88.8% when $A_s = 0.04$ of the round column, taking into account all grades of steel and concrete.

SQUARE TIED COLUMNS

Ties-Spacing $\lessapprox$ 16 bar dia. 16 × 1.27 $\lessapprox$ 20 in. $\lessapprox$ 48 tie dia. $\begin{cases} 48 \times 3/8 = 18 \text{ in. for \#3 ties*} \\ 48 \times 1/4 = 12 \text{ in. for \#2 ties} \end{cases}$
$\lessapprox$ Column side $\lessapprox$ 36 in.

Example 2—Solve the same problem if the column is 35 in. square and check by interpolation.

$P = 35 \times 35 \times 797 = 976$ kips
$18 \times 1.27 \times 20{,}400 = \underline{466}$
1442 kips

From table: 36″ square 18-#10 = 1499 kips
34″ square 18-#10 = 1386
2885/2 = 1442 kips

Example 3—If the column in Example 1 were 46′-8″ in unsupported height, what effect would this have on the capacity if the column is fixed at the base, monolithic at the top ($r' < 1$) bent in double curvature, sidesway prevented?

Solution—From Fig. (g), $h' = h = 46.67$ ft. $\quad r = \sqrt{\dfrac{I}{A}}$:—

	Area	*Moment of Inertia*
Concrete 36 × 36	= 1296 in.²	$1296 \dfrac{(36)^2}{12} = 139{,}968$ in.⁴

$$r = \sqrt{\frac{139{,}968}{1296}} = 10.37 \text{ in.}$$

$\dfrac{h'}{r} = \dfrac{46.67 \times 12}{10.37} = 54.$ Since this is less than 60, no change in design because of slenderness is required.

Example 4—For the table on page 11-18, verify the value $N = 382$ kips with an eccentricity of 3 in. for a 20 in. square tied column of 3750 psi concrete, reinforced with 6-#8 vertical bars (3 each face), using $f_y = 60{,}000$ psi.

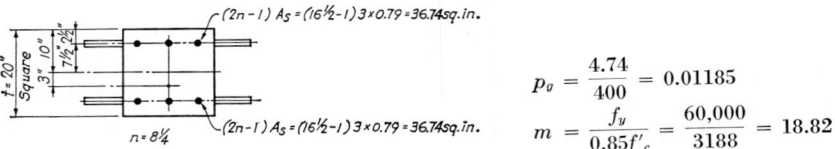

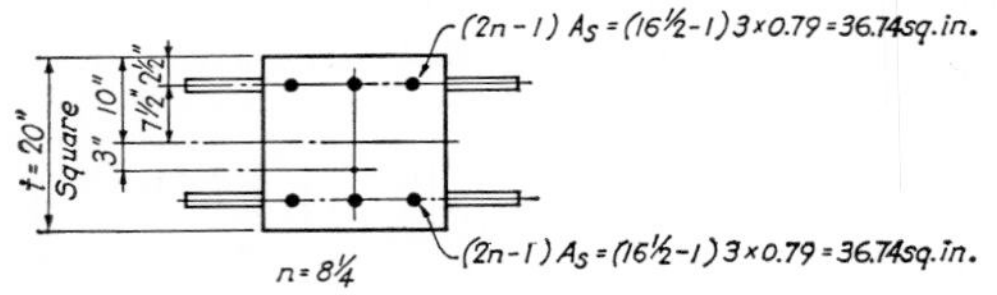

$$p_g = \frac{4.74}{400} = 0.01185$$

$$m = \frac{f_y}{0.85f'_c} = \frac{60{,}000}{3188} = 18.82$$

From Eq. (14-7), $e_b = (0.67p_g m + 0.17)d = (0.67 \times 0.01185 \times 18.82 + 0.17)17.5 =$ 5.60 in., so $e = 3''$ is inside of e_b and the section is governed by compression.

By Eq. (14-9), $\dfrac{f_a}{F_a} + \dfrac{f_{bx}}{F_b} + \dfrac{f_{by}}{F_b} \lessapprox 1$ and for uniaxial bending $\dfrac{f_a}{F_a} + \dfrac{f_b}{F_b} \lessapprox 1.$

By Eq. (14-10), $F_a = 0.34(1 + p_g m)f'_c = 0.34(1 + 0.01186 \times 18.82)3750 = 1559.6$ psi.

Section	*Area Transformed Section*	*Moment of Inertia*	*Section Modulus*
Concrete	20 × 20 = 400 sq in.	$400 \times \dfrac{(20)^2}{12} = 13{,}300$ in.⁴	$S = \dfrac{17{,}433}{10} =$ 1743 in.³
Bars	2 × 36.74 = 73.48	$73.48(7\tfrac{1}{2})^2 = 4{,}133$	
	473.48 sq in.	17,433 in.⁴	

Unit direct stress $= f_a = \dfrac{N}{A_g} = \dfrac{N}{400}$. Unit bending stress $= f_b = \dfrac{Ne}{S} = \dfrac{3N}{1743} = \dfrac{N}{581}$†.

---

* See page 2-21 for table of maximum spacing of column ties based on diameter of vertical bars and of ties. (Spacing to equal the least column dimension will have to be checked in each case.)

† Since the unit direct stress, $\dfrac{N}{400}$, is numerically greater than the unit bending stress, $\dfrac{N}{581}$, the facts that 3 in. eccentricity lies within the kern of the column section and that there is varying compression all across the entire section are checked.

SQUARE TIED COLUMNS

$$\frac{f_a}{F_a} + \frac{f_b}{F_b} \gtrless 1; \frac{N}{400 \times 1.5596} + \frac{N}{581 \times 1.688} = 0.001603N + 0.001020N = 1$$

$$0.002623N = 1; N = 382 \text{ kips (as in the table) *}$$

Example 5—For the same data as in Example 4, increase the eccentricity of the load to 7 in. so that the resultant is definitely outside the kern of the section and check the value of $N = 196$ kips in the table on page 11-18.

Unit direct stress, $f_a = \frac{N}{400}$.

Since the eccentricity of 7 in. exceeds $e_b = 5.60$ in., follow ACI Section 1407(c) for bending on columns controlled by tension and use a linear interpolation between M_b and M_o.

From Example 4:—

$$e_b = 5.60 \text{ in., so } \frac{N_b}{400 \times 1.5596} + \frac{5.60\ N_b}{1{,}743 \times 1.688} \gtrless 1;$$

$$0.001603N_b + 0.001903N_b = 0.003506N_b = 1 \quad N_b = 285.2 \text{ kips}$$

$$M_b = N_b e_b = 285.2 \times 5.60 = 1602 \text{ ki}$$

$$M_o = 0.40A_s f_y\,(d - d') = 0.40 \times 3 \times 0.79 \times 60{,}000 \times 15 = 853.2 \text{ ki}$$

By interpolation:

$$N = \frac{M_o}{e + \frac{M_o - M_b}{N_b}} = \frac{853.2}{7 + \frac{853.2 - 1602}{285.2}} = \frac{853.2}{7 - 2.626} = 195.1 \text{ kips.*}$$

SPECIAL COLUMNS

Where available space determines columns that are restricted in size or unusual in shape, there are many possibilities, a few of which are:—

L-Shaped Tied Columns. Columns in the corners of buildings (or of shafts or courts within a building) are often made L-shaped to eliminate projections into the useable floor space. A quick way to lesign them is to select from the suitable table a square column that carries the required load, then mentally increase the sides by such amount that the area of the added "wings" will equal that removed by the re-entrant corner, then check the capacity.

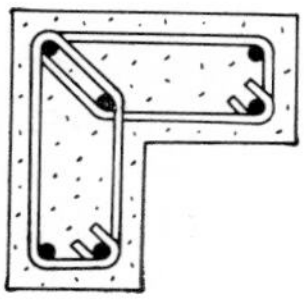

Engaged Columns. For pilasters engaged in reinforced concrete walls, it is possible to include the area of reasonably proportioned "wings" on either side in the gross area, A_g, but such included area should be integrated with the pilaster by means of adequate ties, and no part of the column above should overhang the pilaster.

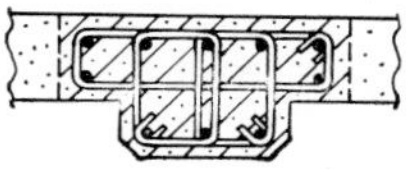

* The tables were computed electronically; the examples, mentally and by slide rule.

SQUARE TIED COLUMNS—Safe Load in Kips for Various Eccentricities in Inches

f'_c = 3750 psi f_s = 24,000 psi basis
(A61 or A432 Bars, f_y = 60,000 psi)

f'_c = 3750 psi
f_y = 60,000 psi

Bars *	p	M/N † = e (in.) 0	1	2	3	4	5	6	7	8	9	10	11	12	14	16	M_o ‡ (kip-in.)
COLUMN SIZE—10″ x 10″																	
4-#5	.0124	**104**	104	81	53	33	24	18	15	13	11	10	9	8	6	5	*87*
4-#6	.0176	**115**	115	86	69	45	33	25	21	18	15	13	12	11	9	8	*121*
4-#7	.0240	**128**	124	93	75	58	43	34	28	23	20	18	16	15	12	10	*162*
4-#8	.0316	**144**	134	100	79	66	51	41	34	29	25	22	20	18	15	13	*199*
4-#9	.0400	**161**	145	107	85	71	60	49	40	35	30	27	24	22	18	16	*245*
4-#10	.0508	**183**	159	117	93	76	65	57	48	41	36	32	29	26	22	19	*303*
4-#11	.0624	**206**	174	127	100	82	70	61	54	47	41	37	33	31	26	23	*362*
6-#5	.0186	**117**	116	88	71	48	35	27	22	19	17	15	13	12	10	8	*131*
6-#6	.0264	**133**	128	97	77	64	47	37	31	26	23	20	18	16	14	12	*182*
6-#7	.0360	**153**	142	107	85	71	60	48	40	34	30	26	24	22	18	16	*243*
6-#8	.0474	**176**	157	116	92	76	65	56	47	41	36	32	29	26	22	19	*298*
COLUMN SIZE—11″ x 11″																	
4-#5	.0102	**121**	121	100	68	40	29	22	18	15	13	12	10	9	8	7	*102*
4-#6	.0145	**132**	132	106	87	56	40	31	25	21	18	16	14	13	11	9	*142*
4-#7	.0198	**145**	145	114	93	72	52	41	33	28	25	22	19	17	15	13	*190*
4-#8	.0261	**160**	159	122	98	83	64	50	41	35	30	27	24	22	18	16	*237*
4-#9	.0331	**178**	172	131	105	88	76	60	50	43	37	33	29	27	22	19	*293*
4-#10	.0420	**200**	188	142	114	96	82	72	60	51	45	40	36	32	27	24	*364*
4-#11	.0516	**223**	204	154	123	103	88	77	68	59	52	46	42	38	32	28	*437*
4-#14S	.0744	**280**	242	180	143	119	101	88	78	70	64	58	53	48	42	36	*600*
6-#5	.0154	**134**	134	108	88	59	43	33	27	23	20	17	16	14	12	10	*153*
6-#6	.0218	**150**	150	118	96	80	58	45	37	32	27	24	22	20	16	14	*213*
6-#7	.0298	**169**	168	129	105	88	74	59	49	41	36	32	29	26	22	19	*286*
6-#8	.0392	**193**	184	140	113	95	82	70	58	50	44	39	35	32	27	23	*355*
6-#9	.0496	**218**	203	154	124	104	89	78	69	59	52	47	42	38	32	28	*440*

Check availability of #14S and #18S bars.

* One-half of the bars are to be placed in each of the two faces of the column that are perpendicular to the plane of bending.

† Below zigzag horizontal line of each group, concrete governs; above, tension governs.

‡ M_o = capacity in pure bending ($N = 0$); for extrapolation, see page 11-5.

SQUARE TIED COLUMNS—Safe Load in Kips for Various Eccentricities in Inches

$f'_c = 3750$ psi $f_s = 24{,}000$ psi basis
(A61 or A432 Bars, $f_y = 60{,}000$ psi)

$f'_c = 3750$ psi
$f_y = 60{,}000$ psi

COLUMN SIZE—12″ x 12″

Bars *	p	M/N † = e (in.) 0	1	2	3	4	5	6	7	8	9	10	12	14	16	18	M_o ‡ (kip-in.)
4-#6	.0122	**150**	150	128	106	68	48	37	30	25	22	19	15	13	11	9	163
4-#7	.0167	**163**	163	137	112	89	63	49	40	33	29	25	20	17	15	13	219
4-#8	.0219	**179**	179	145	119	101	77	60	49	42	36	32	26	21	18	16	274
4-#9	.0278	**196**	196	155	127	108	93	73	60	51	44	39	32	27	23	20	341
4-#10	.0353	**218**	217	168	137	116	100	87	72	62	54	48	39	33	28	25	425
4-#11	.0433	**242**	235	182	148	125	108	95	84	72	63	56	46	39	33	29	512
4-#14S	.0625	**298**	277	212	171	144	124	109	97	88	80	71	59	51	44	39	708
6-#5	.0129	**152**	152	130	107	72	51	39	32	27	23	20	16	14	12	10	175
6-#6	.0183	**168**	168	141	116	97	69	54	44	37	32	28	23	19	16	14	245
6-#7	.0250	**188**	188	153	126	107	90	70	58	49	43	38	30	26	22	19	329
6-#8	.0329	**211**	211	166	136	115	100	85	70	60	52	46	38	32	27	24	412
6-#9	.0417	**237**	233	181	148	125	108	96	84	72	63	56	46	39	33	29	512
6-#10	.0529	**270**	259	200	163	138	119	105	94	85	75	67	55	47	41	36	638
6-#11	.0650	**305**	286	220	179	151	130	114	102	92	84	76	63	54	47	42	768
8-#5	.0172	**165**	165	139	114	93	66	52	42	36	31	27	22	18	16	14	234
8-#6	.0244	**186**	186	153	126	107	89	70	57	49	42	37	30	25	22	19	327
8-#7	.0333	**212**	212	169	139	118	103	89	74	63	55	49	40	34	29	25	439

COLUMN SIZE—13″ x 13″

Bars *	p	M/N † = e (in.) 0	1	2	3	4	5	6	7	8	9	10	12	14	16	18	M_o ‡ (kip-in.)
4-#6	.0104	**170**	170	152	127	82	56	43	35	29	25	22	18	15	12	11	184
4-#7	.0142	**183**	183	161	134	107	74	57	46	39	33	29	24	20	17	15	248
4-#8	.0187	**199**	199	171	142	121	92	71	58	49	42	37	30	25	21	19	312
4-#9	.0237	**216**	216	182	151	129	111	86	70	60	52	45	37	31	26	23	389
4-#10	.0301	**238**	238	196	162	138	120	104	85	73	63	56	45	38	33	29	486
4-#11	.0369	**261**	261	211	174	148	129	114	100	85	74	66	54	45	39	34	587
4-#14S	.0533	**318**	312	244	201	170	148	131	117	106	96	86	71	60	52	46	816
6-#5	.0110	**172**	172	154	128	87	60	46	37	31	27	23	19	16	13	12	198
6-#6	.0156	**188**	188	165	138	117	82	63	51	43	37	33	26	22	19	16	277
6-#7	.0213	**208**	208	179	149	127	106	83	67	57	49	43	35	29	25	22	372
6-#8	.0280	**231**	231	193	160	137	119	101	83	70	61	54	44	37	32	28	469
6-#9	.0355	**257**	257	210	174	148	129	114	99	85	74	65	53	45	39	34	584
6-#10	.0451	**290**	290	231	191	162	141	125	112	101	88	79	65	55	47	42	729
6-#11	.0554	**325**	321	253	208	177	154	136	122	111	101	91	75	64	56	49	880
8-#5	.0147	**185**	185	164	136	112	79	60	49	41	35	31	25	21	18	16	264
8-#6	.0208	**206**	206	178	148	127	105	82	67	56	49	43	35	29	25	22	369
8-#7	.0284	**232**	232	197	163	140	122	105	87	74	64	57	46	39	33	29	496
8-#8	.0374	**263**	263	215	178	152	133	118	105	89	78	69	57	48	41	36	625

Check availability of #14S and #18S bars.

* One-half of the bars are to be placed in each of the two faces of the column that are perpendicular to the plane of bending.

† Below zigzag horizontal line of each group, concrete governs; above, tension governs.

‡ M_o = capacity in pure bending, ($N = 0$); for extrapolation, see page 11-5.

SQUARE TIED COLUMNS—Safe Load in Kips for Various Eccentricities in Inches

$f'_c = 3750$ psi $f_s = 24{,}000$ psi basis
(A61 or A432 Bars, $f_y = 60{,}000$ psi)

COLUMN SIZE—14″ x 14″

Bars*	p	M/N † = e (in.) 0	1	2	3	4	5	6	7	8	9	10	11	12	13	14	15
4-#7	.0122	**205**	205	188	158	128	87	66	53	45	38	33	30	27	24	22	21
4-#8	.0161	**220**	220	198	166	143	108	83	67	56	48	42	38	34	31	28	26
4-#9	.0204	**237**	237	210	176	151	131	101	82	69	59	52	46	42	38	35	32
4-#10	.0259	**259**	259	225	188	162	142	122	99	84	73	64	57	52	47	43	40
4-#11	.0318	**283**	283	241	201	173	151	135	116	99	86	76	68	62	56	52	48
4-#14S	.0459	**339**	339	278	231	198	173	154	138	126	112	100	90	82	75	70	65
6-#6	.0135	**210**	210	192	161	139	96	73	59	49	42	37	33	30	27	25	23
6-#7	.0184	**229**	229	207	173	149	125	96	78	65	56	49	44	40	36	33	31
6-#8	.0242	**252**	252	222	186	160	140	118	96	81	70	62	55	50	45	42	39
6-#9	.0306	**278**	278	240	201	173	151	135	116	98	85	75	68	61	56	51	48
6-#10	.0389	**311**	311	263	219	188	165	147	132	118	103	91	82	74	68	63	58
6-#11	.0478	**347**	347	286	239	205	180	160	144	131	119	106	96	87	80	74	69
6-#14S	.0689	**431**	428	341	284	243	212	188	169	154	141	130	121	112	104	96	90
8-#5	.0127	**206**	206	190	160	135	92	70	56	47	40	35	32	28	26	24	22
8-#6	.0180	**227**	227	206	173	149	124	95	77	65	56	49	44	39	36	33	30
8-#7	.0245	**254**	254	225	189	163	143	122	100	85	73	65	58	52	48	44	41
8-#8	.0322	**285**	285	246	206	177	155	138	122	104	90	80	72	65	59	55	51
8-#9	.0408	**319**	319	270	226	194	170	151	136	124	108	96	87	79	72	67	62

COLUMN SIZE—15″ x 15″

Bars*	p	0	1	2	3	4	5	6	7	8	9	10	11	12	13	14	15
4-#7	.0107	**228**	228	217	183	153	102	76	61	51	43	38	34	30	27	25	23
4-#8	.0140	**243**	243	228	192	166	126	95	76	64	55	48	42	38	35	32	29
4-#9	.0178	**260**	260	241	203	176	153	116	94	78	67	59	53	47	43	39	36
4-#10	.0226	**282**	282	257	216	187	165	141	114	96	83	73	65	59	53	49	45
4-#11	.0277	**306**	306	274	231	199	175	157	134	114	98	87	77	70	64	59	54
4-#14S	.0400	**362**	362	313	263	227	200	178	161	146	130	115	104	94	86	79	74
4-#18S	.0711	**505**	494	392	324	277	241	214	192	174	159	147	136	127	118	110	103
6-#6	.0117	**233**	233	222	187	162	112	84	67	56	48	42	37	33	30	28	26
6-#7	.0160	**252**	252	237	200	173	145	110	89	74	64	56	50	45	41	37	34
6-#8	.0211	**275**	275	253	214	185	163	136	110	92	80	70	62	56	51	47	43
6-#9	.0267	**301**	301	272	230	199	175	156	133	112	97	86	77	69	63	58	54
6-#10	.0339	**334**	334	296	250	216	190	170	154	135	118	104	93	85	77	71	66
6-#11	.0416	**370**	370	321	271	234	206	184	166	152	137	122	110	100	91	84	78
6-#14S	.0600	**454**	454	380	320	276	242	216	195	178	163	151	141	130	120	111	103
8-#5	.0110	**229**	229	219	185	160	107	80	64	53	46	40	35	32	29	26	24
8-#6	.0156	**251**	251	236	200	173	144	109	88	73	63	55	49	44	40	37	34
8-#7	.0213	**277**	277	256	217	188	166	141	114	96	83	73	65	59	54	49	45
8-#8	.0281	**308**	308	278	235	203	179	160	140	119	103	91	81	73	67	62	57
8-#9	.0356	**342**	342	303	256	222	196	175	158	142	124	110	99	89	82	75	70
8-#10	.0452	**386**	386	335	283	245	216	193	174	159	146	132	119	108	99	92	85
8-#11	.0555	**433**	433	369	311	269	237	212	191	175	160	148	137	126	116	107	100

Check availability of #14S and #18S bars.

* One-half of the bars are to be placed in each of the two faces of the column that are perpendicular to the plane of bending.

† Below zigzag horizontal line of each group, concrete governs; above, tension governs.

SQUARE TIED COLUMNS—Safe Load in Kips for Various Eccentricities in Inches

$f'_c = 3750$ psi $f_s = 24{,}000$ psi basis

(A61 or A432 Bars, $f_y = 60{,}000$ psi)

$f'_c = 3750$ psi
$f_y = 60{,}000$ psi

M/N † = e (in.)																	M_o ‡ (kip-in.)
16	17	18	19	20	21	22	23	24	25	26	27	28	29	30	31	32	
COLUMN SIZE—14″ x 14″																	
19	18	17	16	15	14	13	13	12	11	11	11	10	10	9	9	9	*277*
24	23	21	20	19	18	17	16	15	15	14	13	13	12	12	12	11	*350*
30	28	26	25	23	22	21	20	19	18	17	17	16	16	15	14	14	*437*
37	35	33	31	29	28	26	25	24	23	22	21	20	19	19	18	17	*547*
45	42	39	37	35	33	32	30	29	27	26	25	24	23	23	22	21	*661*
60	57	53	50	48	45	43	41	39	38	36	35	34	32	31	30	29	*924*
21	20	19	17	16	16	15	14	13	13	12	12	11	11	10	10	10	*308*
29	27	25	24	22	21	20	19	18	17	17	16	15	15	14	14	13	*415*
36	34	31	30	28	27	25	24	23	22	21	20	19	19	18	17	17	*526*
44	41	39	37	35	33	31	30	28	27	26	25	24	23	22	22	21	*656*
54	51	48	45	43	41	39	37	35	34	32	31	30	29	28	27	26	*821*
64	60	57	54	51	48	46	44	42	40	39	37	36	35	33	32	31	*992*
84	80	75	71	68	65	62	59	57	54	52	50	48	47	45	44	42	*1386*
20	19	18	17	16	15	14	13	13	12	12	11	11	10	10	10	9	*293*
28	26	25	23	22	21	20	19	18	17	16	16	15	15	14	14	13	*411*
38	35	33	31	29	28	27	25	24	23	22	21	20	20	19	18	18	*554*
47	44	41	39	37	35	33	32	30	29	28	27	26	25	24	23	22	*701*
58	54	51	48	45	43	41	39	37	36	34	33	32	31	30	29	28	*875*
COLUMN SIZE—15″ x 15″																	
21	20	19	18	17	16	15	14	13	13	12	12	11	11	10	10	10	*306*
27	25	24	22	21	20	19	18	17	16	16	15	14	14	13	13	12	*388*
34	32	30	28	26	25	24	22	21	20	20	19	18	17	17	16	16	*485*
42	39	37	35	33	31	29	28	27	26	25	24	23	22	21	20	20	*608*
50	47	44	42	39	37	36	34	32	31	30	28	27	26	25	25	24	*736*
69	64	61	57	54	51	49	47	45	43	41	39	38	36	35	34	33	*1032*
96	91	86	81	77	74	70	67	64	62	59	57	55	53	52	50	48	*1579*
24	22	21	20	18	17	17	16	15	14	14	13	13	12	12	11	11	*340*
32	30	28	26	25	23	22	21	20	19	19	18	17	16	16	15	15	*459*
40	38	35	33	31	30	28	27	26	25	24	23	22	21	20	19	19	*583*
50	47	44	41	39	37	35	33	32	31	29	28	27	26	25	24	23	*728*
61	58	54	51	48	46	44	42	40	38	36	35	34	32	31	30	29	*912*
73	68	64	61	58	55	52	50	47	45	44	42	40	39	38	36	35	*1105*
97	91	86	81	77	74	70	67	64	62	59	57	55	53	51	50	48	*1548*
23	21	20	19	17	17	16	15	14	14	13	12	12	11	11	11	10	*323*
32	29	28	26	25	23	22	21	20	19	18	18	17	16	16	15	15	*454*
42	39	37	35	33	31	30	28	27	26	25	24	23	22	21	20	20	*612*
53	50	47	44	41	39	37	36	34	33	31	30	29	28	27	26	25	*777*
65	61	57	54	51	49	46	44	42	40	39	37	36	34	33	32	31	*971*
79	75	70	66	63	60	57	54	52	50	48	46	44	43	41	40	38	*1216*
93	88	83	78	74	71	67	64	62	59	57	55	53	51	49	48	46	*1473*

‡ M_o = capacity in pure bending, ($N = 0$); for extrapolation, see page 11-5.

SQUARE TIED COLUMNS—Safe Load in Kips for Various Eccentricities in Inches

$f'_c = 3750$ psi $f_s = 24{,}000$ psi basis
(A61 or A432 Bars, $f_y = 60{,}000$ psi)

COLUMN SIZE—16″ x 16″

Bars*	p	M/N† = e (in.) 0	1	2	3	4	5	6	7	8	9	10	11	12	13	14	15
4-#8	.0123	**268**	268	260	221	192	146	109	86	72	61	53	47	43	39	35	33
4-#9	.0156	**285**	285	273	232	202	178	133	106	89	76	66	59	53	48	44	41
4-#10	.0198	**307**	307	290	246	214	190	162	130	109	93	82	73	66	60	55	50
4-#11	.0244	**331**	331	308	261	227	201	180	153	129	111	98	87	79	71	66	61
4-#14S	.0352	**387**	387	349	296	257	227	204	185	169	148	131	117	106	97	89	83
4-#18S	.0625	**530**	530	436	365	314	276	246	221	202	185	171	159	148	137	127	119
6-#6	.0103	**257**	257	253	215	187	130	96	76	63	54	47	42	37	34	31	28
6-#7	.0141	**277**	277	269	229	199	168	126	100	84	71	62	55	50	45	41	38
6-#8	.0185	**300**	300	286	243	212	187	155	125	104	90	78	70	63	57	52	48
6-#9	.0234	**326**	326	306	260	226	200	180	151	127	110	96	86	77	71	65	60
6-#10	.0298	**359**	359	331	282	245	217	195	176	154	133	118	105	95	87	80	74
6-#11	.0366	**394**	394	358	304	265	234	210	190	174	156	138	124	112	103	95	88
6-#14S	.0527	**479**	479	420	356	310	274	246	222	203	187	173	162	148	136	126	117
8-#6	.0138	**275**	275	268	228	199	166	124	99	83	71	62	55	49	45	41	38
8-#7	.0188	**301**	301	289	246	215	190	161	130	109	93	82	73	66	60	55	50
8-#8	.0247	**332**	332	312	266	231	205	184	160	134	116	102	91	82	75	69	63
8-#9	.0313	**367**	367	338	288	251	222	200	181	162	140	124	111	100	92	84	78
8-#10	.0397	**411**	411	372	317	276	244	219	199	182	168	149	134	122	112	103	96
8-#11	.0488	**458**	458	407	347	302	267	240	218	199	183	170	156	142	131	121	113
10-#5	.0121	**267**	267	261	222	194	151	112	89	74	63	55	49	44	40	37	34
10-#6	.0172	**293**	293	283	241	210	186	151	121	101	87	76	68	61	55	51	47
10-#7	.0234	**326**	326	309	264	230	204	183	157	132	114	100	89	81	73	67	62
10-#8	.0309	**365**	365	338	288	251	223	200	181	161	140	124	111	100	92	84	78
10-#9	.0391	**408**	408	371	316	276	244	219	199	182	168	149	134	122	111	103	95

COLUMN SIZE—17″ x 17″

Bars*	p	0	1	2	3	4	5	6	7	8	9	10	11	12	13	14	15
4-#8	.0109	**294**	294	294	251	220	169	124	97	80	68	60	53	47	43	39	36
4-#9	.0138	**311**	311	308	263	230	204	151	120	99	85	74	65	59	53	49	45
4-#10	.0176	**333**	333	325	278	243	216	184	147	122	105	91	81	73	66	61	56
4-#11	.0216	**357**	357	344	294	257	228	205	174	145	125	109	97	87	79	73	67
4-#14S	.0311	**413**	413	387	331	289	257	231	210	192	167	147	131	119	108	100	92
4-#18S	.0554	**556**	556	480	407	353	311	279	252	230	212	196	183	170	156	145	135
6-#7	.0125	**303**	303	303	259	227	194	143	113	93	80	69	61	55	50	46	42
6-#8	.0164	**326**	326	321	275	240	214	177	141	117	100	87	78	70	63	58	53
6-#9	.0208	**352**	352	341	293	256	228	205	171	143	123	107	96	86	78	72	66
6-#10	.0264	**385**	385	368	315	276	245	221	201	173	150	131	117	106	96	89	82
6-#11	.0324	**421**	421	396	339	297	264	237	216	198	176	155	139	126	115	105	98
6-#14S	.0467	**505**	505	461	395	345	307	276	251	230	212	197	183	166	153	141	131
8-#6	.0122	**302**	302	302	259	226	192	141	112	92	79	69	61	54	49	45	42
8-#7	.0166	**328**	328	324	278	243	216	183	146	121	104	91	81	73	66	60	56
8-#8	.0219	**359**	359	348	298	261	232	209	180	151	130	114	101	91	83	76	70
8-#9	.0277	**393**	393	375	322	282	251	226	206	182	157	138	124	112	102	94	87
8-#10	.0352	**437**	437	410	352	309	275	247	225	206	189	167	150	136	124	115	106
8-#11	.0432	**484**	484	447	384	336	299	269	245	225	208	193	176	160	146	135	126
10-#5	.0107	**293**	293	293	253	221	174	127	100	83	70	61	54	49	44	40	37
10-#6	.0152	**320**	320	317	272	239	212	171	136	113	97	85	75	67	61	56	52
10-#7	.0208	**352**	352	345	296	260	231	208	177	148	127	111	99	89	81	74	69
10-#8	.0273	**391**	391	375	322	282	251	226	206	182	157	138	123	111	102	93	86
10-#9	.0346	**434**	434	409	351	308	274	247	225	206	189	167	150	136	124	114	106

Check availability of #14S and #18S bars.

* One-half of the bars are to be placed in each of the two faces of the column that are perpendicular to the plane of bending.

† Below zigzag horizontal line of each group, concrete governs; above, tension governs.

SQUARE TIED COLUMNS—Safe Load in Kips for Various Eccentricities in Inches

f'_c = 3750 psi f_s = 24,000 psi basis

(A61 or A432 Bars, f_y = 60,000 psi)

f'_c = 3750 psi
f_y = 60,000 psi

COLUMN SIZE—16″ x 16″

M/N † = e (in.)

16	17	18	19	20	21	22	23	24	25	26	27	28	29	30	31	32	M_o ‡ (kip-in.)
30	28	26	25	23	22	21	20	19	18	17	17	16	15	15	14	14	426
38	35	33	31	29	28	26	25	24	23	22	21	20	19	19	18	17	533
47	44	41	39	36	34	33	31	30	28	27	26	25	24	23	22	22	669
56	53	49	46	44	42	40	38	36	34	33	32	30	29	28	27	26	811
77	72	68	64	61	57	55	52	50	48	46	44	42	41	39	38	37	1140
111	104	99	93	89	84	80	77	74	71	68	65	63	61	59	57	55	1771
26	25	23	22	20	19	18	17	17	16	15	14	14	13	13	12	12	372
35	33	31	29	27	26	25	23	22	21	20	20	19	18	17	17	16	502
45	42	39	37	35	33	31	30	28	27	26	25	24	23	22	21	21	639
56	52	49	46	43	41	39	37	35	34	32	31	30	29	28	27	26	800
69	64	60	57	54	51	48	46	44	42	40	39	37	36	35	34	32	1004
82	77	72	68	64	61	58	55	53	51	49	47	45	43	42	40	39	1217
110	103	97	92	87	83	79	75	72	69	66	64	62	59	57	56	54	1710
35	33	31	29	27	26	24	23	22	21	20	19	19	18	17	17	16	496
47	44	41	39	36	34	33	31	30	28	27	26	25	24	23	22	22	669
59	55	52	49	46	44	41	39	38	36	35	33	32	31	30	29	28	853
73	68	64	60	57	54	51	49	47	45	43	41	40	38	37	36	34	1067
89	83	79	74	70	67	63	61	58	55	53	51	49	47	46	44	43	1338
105	99	93	88	83	79	76	72	69	66	64	61	59	57	55	53	51	1623
31	29	27	26	24	23	22	21	20	19	18	17	17	16	15	15	14	441
44	41	38	36	34	32	30	29	28	26	25	24	23	22	22	21	20	620
58	54	51	48	45	43	41	39	37	35	34	33	31	30	29	28	27	837
73	68	64	60	57	54	51	49	47	45	43	41	40	38	37	36	34	1066
89	83	78	74	70	66	63	60	58	55	53	51	49	47	46	44	43	1334

COLUMN SIZE—17″ x 17″

16	17	18	19	20	21	22	23	24	25	26	27	28	29	30	31	32	M_o ‡ (kip-in.)
33	31	29	27	26	24	23	22	21	20	19	18	18	17	16	16	15	464
42	39	36	34	32	30	29	27	26	25	24	23	22	21	20	20	19	581
52	48	45	43	40	38	36	34	33	31	30	29	28	27	26	25	24	730
62	58	55	51	49	46	44	42	40	38	36	35	33	32	31	30	29	886
86	80	75	71	67	64	61	58	55	53	51	49	47	45	43	42	40	1248
126	118	112	106	100	95	91	87	83	80	76	74	71	68	66	64	62	1963
39	36	34	32	30	29	27	26	25	23	22	21	21	20	19	18	18	545
50	46	43	41	38	36	34	33	31	30	29	27	26	25	24	24	23	696
61	57	54	51	48	45	43	41	39	37	36	34	33	32	31	30	29	872
76	71	67	63	59	56	53	51	49	47	45	43	41	40	38	37	36	1095
91	85	80	75	71	68	64	61	58	56	54	52	50	48	46	45	43	1329
123	115	108	102	97	92	88	84	80	77	74	71	68	66	64	61	59	1872
39	36	34	32	30	28	27	25	24	23	22	21	20	20	19	18	18	538
52	48	45	42	40	38	36	34	33	31	30	29	28	26	26	25	24	727
65	61	57	54	51	48	46	43	41	40	38	36	35	34	33	31	30	929
80	75	71	66	63	60	57	54	52	49	47	45	44	42	41	39	38	1163
99	93	87	82	78	74	70	67	64	61	59	56	54	52	50	49	47	1460
117	110	103	98	92	88	84	80	76	73	70	68	65	63	60	58	57	1773
34	32	30	28	26	25	24	23	22	21	20	19	18	17	17	16	16	478
48	45	42	39	37	35	33	32	30	29	28	27	25	25	24	23	22	673
64	60	56	53	50	47	45	43	41	39	37	36	34	33	32	31	30	909
80	75	70	66	63	59	56	54	51	49	47	45	44	42	40	39	38	1161
99	92	87	82	77	73	70	67	64	61	58	56	54	52	50	48	47	1454

‡ M_o = capacity in pure bending, (N = 0); for extrapolation, see page 11-5.

SQUARE TIED COLUMNS—Safe Load in Kips for Various Eccentricities in Inches

$f'_c = 3750$ psi $f_s = 24{,}000$ psi basis
(A61 or A432 Bars, $f_y = 60{,}000$ psi)

COLUMN SIZE—18″ x 18″

Bars *	p	M/N † = e (in.) 0	1	2	3	4	5	6	7	8	9	10	11	12	13	14	15
4-#9	.0123	339	339	339	296	260	232	171	135	111	94	82	72	65	59	54	49
4-#10	.0157	361	361	361	312	274	244	209	165	136	116	101	90	80	73	67	61
4-#11	.0193	385	385	382	329	289	258	232	195	162	139	121	107	97	88	80	74
4-#14S	.0278	441	441	427	368	323	288	260	237	216	187	164	146	132	120	110	102
4-#18S	.0494	584	584	526	449	392	348	313	284	260	240	223	208	192	176	163	151
6-#7	.0111	331	331	331	292	257	223	161	127	104	88	77	68	61	55	50	46
6-#8	.0146	354	354	354	308	271	242	200	158	130	111	97	86	77	70	64	59
6-#9	.0185	380	380	379	327	288	257	232	192	160	136	119	106	95	86	79	73
6-#10	.0235	413	413	406	351	309	275	249	227	194	167	146	130	117	106	98	90
6-#11	.0289	449	449	435	376	331	295	266	243	223	196	172	154	139	127	116	108
6-#14S	.0417	533	533	503	434	382	341	308	280	258	238	222	204	185	170	157	145
6-#18S	.0741	747	747	651	556	486	431	387	351	322	297	275	257	241	226	214	202
8-#6	.0109	329	329	329	292	256	220	160	125	103	87	76	67	60	54	49	45
8-#7	.0148	356	356	356	311	274	244	207	164	135	115	100	89	80	72	66	61
8-#8	.0195	387	387	386	333	293	261	236	202	168	144	126	112	100	91	84	77
8-#9	.0247	421	421	414	358	315	281	254	232	204	175	154	137	123	112	103	95
8-#10	.0314	465	465	450	389	343	306	277	252	232	211	186	167	151	137	126	117
8-#11	.0385	512	512	489	423	372	332	300	274	252	233	217	196	177	162	150	139
10-#6	.0136	347	347	347	306	269	240	194	153	126	107	93	83	74	67	61	56
10-#7	.0185	380	380	380	330	291	260	235	198	165	141	123	109	98	89	82	75
10-#8	.0244	419	419	413	357	315	281	254	232	203	175	153	136	123	112	103	95
10-#9	.0309	462	462	449	388	342	306	276	252	232	211	186	166	150	137	126	116
10-#10	.0392	517	517	494	428	377	337	305	278	256	237	220	200	182	166	153	142
12-#5	.0115	334	334	334	295	260	232	169	133	109	93	80	71	64	58	53	48
12-#6	.0163	365	365	365	320	281	251	226	179	148	127	110	98	88	80	73	67
12-#7	.0222	405	405	404	349	308	275	249	227	192	165	145	129	116	105	97	89
12-#8	.0293	451	451	441	382	336	301	272	248	228	203	179	160	144	132	121	112

COLUMN SIZE—19″ x 19″

Bars *	p	0	1	2	3	4	5	6	7	8	9	10	11	12	13	14	15
4-#9	.0111	369	369	369	332	292	261	194	150	123	104	90	79	71	64	58	54
4-#10	.0141	391	391	391	348	307	275	236	185	152	129	112	99	88	80	73	67
4-#11	.0173	414	414	414	366	323	289	261	219	180	153	134	118	106	96	88	81
4-#14S	.0249	471	471	468	406	358	321	290	265	241	207	181	161	145	132	121	112
4-#18S	.0443	614	614	572	493	433	386	348	317	291	269	250	234	215	197	182	168
6-#8	.0131	384	384	384	344	304	272	226	176	145	123	106	94	84	76	69	64
6-#9	.0166	410	410	410	364	321	287	260	215	177	151	131	116	104	94	86	79
6-#10	.0211	443	443	443	388	343	307	278	254	216	184	161	143	128	117	107	98
6-#11	.0259	478	478	477	414	366	328	297	271	250	218	191	170	153	139	128	118
6-#14S	.0374	563	563	547	475	420	376	341	311	287	266	247	226	205	188	173	160
6-#18S	.0665	777	777	703	606	532	474	428	390	358	331	308	287	270	254	240	227
8-#7	.0133	385	385	385	347	306	274	233	182	150	127	110	97	87	79	72	66
8-#8	.0175	416	416	416	369	326	292	265	226	187	159	139	123	110	100	91	84
8-#9	.0222	450	450	450	395	349	313	284	259	226	194	169	151	135	123	113	104
8-#10	.0281	494	494	492	428	379	339	308	281	259	235	206	184	166	151	139	128
8-#11	.0346	542	542	532	463	410	367	333	304	280	260	242	216	196	179	164	152
8-#14S	.0499	654	654	625	544	481	432	391	358	330	306	285	267	251	236	219	203

Check availability of #14S and #18S bars

* One-half of the bars are to be placed in each of the two faces of the column that are perpendicular to the plane of bending.

† Below zigzag horizontal line of each group, concrete governs; above, tension governs.

SQUARE TIED COLUMNS—Safe Load in Kips for Various Eccentricities in Inches

$f'_c = 3750$ psi $f_s = 24{,}000$ psi basis

(A61 or A432 Bars, $f_y = 60{,}000$ psi)

$f'_c = 3750$ psi

$f_y = 60{,}000$ psi

COLUMN SIZE—18″ x 18″

M/N † = e (in.)																	
16	17	18	19	20	21	22	23	24	25	26	27	28	30	32	34	36	M_o ‡ (kip-in.)
46	42	40	37	35	33	32	30	29	27	26	25	24	22	21	19	18	*629*
57	53	50	47	44	42	40	38	36	34	33	31	30	28	26	24	23	*791*
69	64	60	56	53	50	48	45	43	41	40	38	37	34	32	30	28	*961*
95	88	83	78	74	70	66	63	60	58	55	53	51	48	44	42	39	*1356*
141	133	125	118	112	106	101	97	92	89	85	82	79	73	69	64	61	*2155*
43	40	37	35	33	31	29	28	27	26	24	23	22	21	19	18	17	*588*
54	51	47	44	42	40	38	36	34	33	31	30	29	27	25	23	22	*753*
67	63	59	55	52	49	47	45	43	41	39	37	36	33	31	29	27	*944*
84	78	73	69	65	62	59	56	53	51	49	47	45	42	39	36	34	*1186*
100	94	88	83	78	74	70	67	64	61	59	56	54	50	47	44	42	*1442*
136	127	120	113	107	102	97	92	88	84	81	78	75	70	65	61	58	*2034*
192	181	172	163	155	148	141	136	130	125	120	116	112	105	98	92	87	*3233*
42	39	37	34	32	31	29	28	26	25	24	23	22	21	19	18	17	*580*
56	53	49	46	44	41	39	37	36	34	32	31	30	28	26	24	23	*784*
72	67	62	59	55	53	50	47	45	43	41	40	38	35	33	31	29	*1004*
88	83	77	73	69	65	62	59	56	54	52	50	48	44	41	39	36	*1259*
109	102	96	90	85	81	77	73	70	67	64	62	59	55	51	48	45	*1582*
129	121	114	107	102	97	92	88	84	80	77	74	71	66	62	58	55	*1922*
52	49	46	43	40	38	36	35	33	31	30	29	28	26	24	22	21	*726*
70	65	61	57	54	51	49	46	44	42	40	39	37	35	32	30	28	*981*
88	82	77	73	69	65	62	59	56	54	51	49	47	44	41	39	36	*1256*
108	101	95	90	85	80	76	73	70	67	64	61	59	55	51	48	45	*1574*
133	124	117	110	104	99	94	90	86	82	79	76	73	68	64	60	56	*1978*
45	42	39	37	35	33	31	29	28	27	26	25	24	22	20	19	18	*619*
62	58	54	51	48	46	43	41	39	38	36	35	33	31	29	27	25	*871*
83	77	73	68	65	61	58	55	53	50	48	46	45	41	39	36	34	*1177*
104	97	91	86	81	77	73	70	67	64	61	59	57	53	49	46	43	*1507*

COLUMN SIZE—19″ x 19″

50	46	43	41	38	36	34	33	31	30	28	27	26	24	22	21	20	*677*
62	58	54	51	48	45	43	41	39	37	36	34	33	30	28	26	25	*852*
75	70	65	61	58	55	52	49	47	45	43	41	40	37	34	32	30	*1036*
104	97	91	85	81	76	73	69	66	63	60	58	56	52	48	45	42	*1464*
157	147	138	131	124	118	112	107	102	98	94	90	87	81	76	71	67	*2347*
59	55	52	48	46	43	41	39	37	35	34	32	31	29	27	25	24	*810*
74	69	64	60	57	54	51	49	46	44	42	41	39	36	34	32	30	*1016*
91	85	80	75	71	67	64	61	58	55	53	51	49	45	42	40	37	*1278*
110	102	96	90	85	81	77	73	70	67	64	61	59	55	51	48	45	*1554*
149	140	131	124	117	111	106	101	96	92	88	85	82	76	71	67	63	*2196*
216	203	192	182	173	165	157	151	144	139	133	128	124	116	109	102	97	*3521*
61	57	53	50	47	45	42	40	38	37	35	34	32	30	28	26	25	*842*
78	73	68	64	60	57	54	52	49	47	45	43	41	38	36	34	32	*1080*
97	90	84	79	75	71	67	64	61	59	56	54	52	48	45	42	39	*1355*
119	111	104	98	93	88	84	80	76	73	70	67	64	60	56	52	49	*1704*
142	133	125	118	111	105	100	96	91	87	84	81	78	72	67	63	59	*2072*
190	178	168	159	151	143	137	130	125	120	115	111	107	99	93	87	82	*2928*

‡ M_o = capacity in pure bending, ($N = 0$); for extrapolation, see page 11-5.

SQUARE TIED COLUMNS—Safe Load in Kips for Various Eccentricities in Inches

$f'_c = 3750$ psi $f_s = 24{,}000$ psi basis

(A61 or A432 Bars, $f_y = 60{,}000$ psi)

Bars*	p	0	1	2	3	4	5	6	7	8	9	10	11	12	13	14	15
		M/N † = e (in.)															
COLUMN SIZE—19″ x 19″ CONT.																	
10-#6	.0122	**377**	377	377	341	301	270	218	170	140	118	103	90	81	73	67	62
10-#7	.0166	**410**	410	410	367	324	291	263	221	182	155	135	120	107	97	89	82
10-#8	.0219	**448**	448	448	395	349	313	283	259	226	193	169	150	135	123	112	104
10-#9	.0277	**491**	491	491	427	378	339	307	281	259	233	205	183	165	150	138	127
10-#10	.0352	**546**	546	538	468	414	372	337	308	284	263	246	221	200	183	168	156
12-#5	.0103	**363**	363	363	330	291	261	190	148	121	102	88	78	70	63	57	53
12-#6	.0146	**395**	395	395	356	314	282	254	200	164	140	121	107	96	87	80	73
12-#7	.0199	**434**	434	434	386	342	307	278	254	213	182	159	141	127	115	106	97
12-#8	.0263	**481**	481	481	420	372	333	302	276	255	225	198	176	159	144	133	122
12-#9	.0332	**532**	532	527	459	406	365	331	303	279	259	238	213	193	176	162	150
COLUMN SIZE—20″ x 20″																	
4-#9	.0100	**400**	400	400	369	327	293	218	167	136	114	99	87	77	70	64	58
4-#10	.0127	**422**	422	422	386	342	307	265	205	168	141	122	108	96	87	79	73
4-#11	.0156	**446**	446	446	404	358	321	291	243	200	169	147	129	116	105	96	88
4-#14S	.0225	**502**	502	502	446	396	355	322	295	268	229	200	177	159	144	132	122
4-#18S	.0400	**645**	645	621	538	475	426	385	352	324	300	279	261	238	218	201	186
6-#8	.0119	**415**	415	415	382	338	304	254	196	160	135	117	103	92	83	76	69
6-#9	.0150	**441**	441	441	402	356	320	290	239	196	166	144	127	114	103	94	86
6-#10	.0191	**474**	474	474	428	379	341	309	283	239	203	177	156	140	127	116	107
6-#11	.0234	**509**	509	509	455	403	363	329	301	278	240	210	186	167	152	139	128
6-#14S	.0338	**594**	594	593	518	460	413	376	344	317	295	275	249	225	206	189	175
6-#18S	.0600	**808**	808	756	656	579	519	470	429	395	366	341	319	300	283	267	254
8-#7	.0120	**416**	416	416	385	341	306	262	203	165	140	121	106	95	86	78	72
8-#8	.0158	**447**	447	447	408	362	325	295	252	206	175	152	134	120	109	99	91
8-#9	.0200	**481**	481	481	435	386	347	315	288	251	214	186	165	148	134	123	113
8-#10	.0254	**526**	526	526	469	416	375	340	312	288	259	227	201	181	165	151	140
8-#11	.0312	**573**	573	573	505	449	404	367	336	310	288	266	238	215	196	180	166
8-#14S	.0450	**685**	685	673	589	524	471	429	393	363	337	314	295	277	260	240	223
10-#6	.0110	**408**	408	408	379	336	301	245	189	154	130	112	99	88	80	73	67
10-#7	.0150	**441**	441	441	405	359	323	293	246	201	171	148	131	117	106	97	89
10-#8	.0198	**479**	479	479	434	385	347	315	288	250	213	185	164	147	134	122	113
10-#9	.0250	**522**	522	522	468	415	374	340	311	287	257	225	200	180	164	150	139
10-#10	.0318	**577**	577	577	510	454	408	371	340	314	292	272	243	219	200	184	170
10-#11	.0390	**636**	636	634	555	494	445	404	371	342	318	297	278	258	236	217	201
12-#6	.0132	**426**	426	426	394	349	314	285	222	181	153	133	117	105	95	86	79
12-#7	.0180	**465**	465	465	425	378	340	309	283	236	200	174	154	138	125	115	106
12-#8	.0237	**512**	512	512	460	409	368	334	307	283	248	217	193	173	157	144	133
12-#9	.0300	**563**	563	563	500	445	401	364	334	308	286	262	234	211	192	177	163
14-#5	.0109	**407**	407	407	378	335	301	244	188	153	129	112	98	88	79	72	66
14-#6	.0154	**444**	444	444	408	363	326	296	253	208	176	153	135	121	109	100	92
14-#7	.0210	**490**	490	490	445	396	357	324	297	268	229	200	177	159	144	132	122
14-#8	.0277	**544**	544	544	486	432	389	354	325	300	278	247	220	198	180	166	153

Check availability of #14S and #18S bars.

* One-half of the bars are to be placed in each of the two faces of the column that are perpendicular to the plane of bending.

† Below zigzag horizontal line of each group, concrete governs; above, tension governs.

SQUARE TIED COLUMNS—Safe Load in Kips for Various Eccentricities in Inches

$f'_c = 3750$ psi $f_s = 24,000$ psi basis
(A61 or A432 Bars, $f_y = 60,000$ psi)

$f'_c = 3750$ psi
$f_y = 60,000$ psi

COLUMN SIZE—19″ x 19″ CONT.

M/N † = e (in.)

16	17	18	19	20	21	22	23	24	25	26	27	28	30	32	34	36	M_o ‡ (kip-in.)
57	53	50	47	44	41	39	37	36	34	33	31	30	28	26	24	23	778
76	71	66	62	59	56	53	50	48	46	44	42	40	37	35	33	31	1053
96	90	84	79	75	71	67	64	61	58	56	54	52	48	45	42	39	1350
118	111	104	98	92	88	83	79	76	72	69	67	64	59	56	52	49	1694
145	136	128	120	114	108	103	98	94	90	86	83	80	74	69	65	61	2130
49	45	42	40	37	35	34	32	30	29	28	27	26	24	22	21	19	664
68	63	59	56	52	50	47	45	43	41	39	37	36	33	31	29	27	934
90	84	79	74	70	66	63	60	57	55	52	50	48	45	42	39	37	1263
114	106	100	94	89	84	80	76	73	69	67	64	61	57	53	50	47	1621
140	130	123	116	109	104	99	94	90	86	82	79	76	71	66	62	58	2033
COLUMN SIZE—20″ x 20″																	
54	50	47	44	41	39	37	35	34	32	31	29	28	26	24	23	21	725
67	63	59	55	52	49	46	44	42	40	38	37	35	33	31	29	27	913
81	76	71	67	63	59	56	54	51	49	47	45	43	40	37	35	33	1111
113	105	99	93	88	83	79	75	71	68	65	63	60	56	52	49	46	1572
173	162	152	144	136	129	123	117	112	107	103	99	95	88	82	77	73	2539
64	60	56	52	49	47	44	42	40	38	37	35	34	31	29	27	25	867
80	74	70	65	62	58	55	52	50	48	46	44	42	39	36	34	32	1088
99	93	87	81	77	73	69	66	63	60	57	55	53	49	46	43	40	1369
119	111	104	98	92	88	83	79	76	72	69	66	64	59	55	52	49	1666
163	152	143	135	127	121	115	109	105	100	96	92	89	82	77	72	68	2358
239	225	212	201	191	182	174	166	159	153	147	141	136	127	119	112	106	3809
67	62	58	54	51	48	46	44	42	40	38	36	35	32	30	28	26	900
85	79	74	69	65	62	59	56	53	51	49	47	45	41	39	36	34	1156
105	98	91	86	81	77	73	69	66	63	61	58	56	52	48	45	42	1451
130	121	113	107	101	95	91	86	82	79	75	72	70	65	60	56	53	1826
155	144	136	128	121	114	109	104	99	95	91	87	84	78	73	68	64	2222
208	195	184	174	164	156	149	142	136	130	125	120	116	108	101	95	89	3144
62	57	54	50	47	45	42	40	38	37	35	34	32	30	28	26	24	831
82	77	72	67	64	60	57	54	52	49	47	45	43	40	38	35	33	1125
104	97	91	86	81	76	73	69	66	63	60	58	56	52	48	45	42	1445
129	120	113	106	100	95	90	86	82	78	75	72	69	64	60	56	53	1814
158	148	139	131	124	117	112	106	102	97	93	89	86	80	75	70	66	2282
188	176	165	156	148	140	133	127	122	116	112	107	103	96	90	84	79	2778
73	68	64	60	57	53	51	48	46	44	42	40	39	36	33	31	29	997
98	91	85	80	76	72	68	65	62	59	56	54	52	48	45	42	40	1350
124	115	108	102	96	91	86	82	78	75	72	69	66	61	57	54	51	1734
152	142	133	125	119	112	107	102	97	93	89	86	82	76	71	67	63	2717
61	57	53	50	47	44	42	40	38	36	35	33	32	30	28	26	24	826
85	79	74	70	66	62	59	56	53	51	49	47	45	42	39	36	34	1164
113	105	99	93	88	83	79	75	72	68	65	63	60	56	52	49	46	1575
142	133	125	117	111	105	100	95	91	87	83	80	77	71	67	62	59	2023

‡ M_o = capacity in pure bending, ($N = 0$); for extrapolation, see page 11-5.

SQUARE TIED COLUMNS—Safe Load in Kips for Various Eccentricities in Inches

f'_c = 3750 psi f_s = 24,000 psi basis

(A61 or A432 Bars, f_y = 60,000 psi)

COLUMN SIZE—21″ x 21″

Bars*	p	M/N † = e (in.) 0	1	2	3	4	5	6	7	8	9	10	11	12	13	14	15
4-#10	.0115	**455**	455	455	426	379	341	298	228	185	155	134	117	105	94	86	79
4-#11	.0141	**478**	478	478	445	396	356	324	270	220	185	160	141	126	114	104	95
4-#14S	.0204	**535**	535	535	489	435	392	356	327	296	251	219	193	173	157	144	132
4-#18S	.0363	**677**	677	670	585	519	466	423	388	358	332	309	290	263	239	220	204
6-#8	.0107	**448**	448	448	422	375	337	285	218	176	148	127	112	100	90	82	75
6-#9	.0136	**473**	473	473	443	394	355	322	265	216	182	157	138	123	111	102	93
6-#10	.0173	**506**	506	506	469	418	376	342	314	263	223	193	171	153	138	126	116
6-#11	.0212	**542**	542	542	497	443	399	363	333	308	264	230	203	182	165	151	139
6-#14S	.0306	**626**	626	626	562	501	452	412	378	349	325	303	273	246	224	206	190
6-#18S	.0544	**841**	841	809	707	628	565	513	470	433	402	375	352	331	312	296	281
8-#7	.0109	**449**	449	449	425	378	340	294	225	182	153	132	116	103	93	85	78
8-#8	.0143	**480**	480	480	449	399	360	327	279	227	192	166	146	131	118	108	99
8-#9	.0181	**514**	514	514	476	424	383	348	320	276	234	203	180	161	146	133	122
8-#10	.0230	**558**	558	558	512	456	411	375	344	318	284	248	220	197	179	164	151
8-#11	.0283	**606**	606	606	549	489	442	403	370	342	318	292	260	234	213	195	180
8-#14S	.0408	**718**	718	718	636	568	513	467	429	397	369	345	324	305	284	262	243
10-#6	.0100	**441**	441	441	418	372	335	275	210	169	142	122	107	96	86	78	72
10-#7	.0136	**473**	473	473	445	397	358	325	272	222	187	162	142	127	115	105	96
10-#8	.0179	**512**	512	512	476	424	382	348	319	275	233	202	179	160	145	132	122
10-#9	.0227	**555**	555	555	510	455	410	374	343	317	283	246	218	196	178	163	150
10-#10	.0288	**610**	610	610	554	494	446	407	374	346	322	298	265	239	218	200	185
10-#11	.0354	**669**	669	669	600	536	484	442	406	376	349	327	307	282	257	236	219
12-#6	.0120	**459**	459	459	434	386	348	316	246	199	168	145	127	114	102	93	86
12-#7	.0163	**498**	498	498	466	416	375	341	313	259	219	190	168	150	136	124	114
12-#8	.0215	**544**	544	544	502	448	404	368	338	313	272	237	210	188	171	156	144
12-#9	.0272	**596**	596	596	544	485	438	400	367	340	316	287	255	230	209	192	177
12-#10	.0346	**662**	662	662	596	533	481	439	404	374	348	325	305	278	254	234	216
14-#5	.0098	**439**	439	439	418	372	335	274	209	168	141	122	107	95	86	78	72
14-#6	.0140	**477**	477	477	449	400	361	328	280	228	193	167	147	131	118	108	99
14-#7	.0190	**522**	522	522	487	434	392	357	328	295	250	218	193	173	156	143	132
14-#8	.0251	**577**	577	577	529	472	427	389	357	330	307	270	240	216	196	180	166

COLUMN SIZE—22″ x 22″

Bars*	p	M/N † = e (in.) 0	1	2	3	4	5	6	7	8	9	10	11	12	13	14	15
4-#10	.0105	**489**	489	489	469	418	377	335	253	203	170	146	127	113	102	93	85
4-#11	.0129	**512**	512	512	488	435	393	358	300	242	203	175	153	137	123	112	103
4-#14S	.0186	**569**	569	569	533	476	430	392	360	326	275	239	210	188	170	155	143
4-#18S	.0331	**712**	712	712	633	564	509	463	425	393	365	341	319	287	262	240	222
6-#9	.0124	**508**	508	508	485	433	391	356	294	237	199	171	150	134	121	110	101
6-#10	.0157	**541**	541	541	513	458	414	377	347	289	244	211	185	165	149	136	125
6-#11	.0193	**576**	576	576	541	484	437	399	367	339	289	250	221	198	179	163	150
6-#14S	.0279	**661**	661	661	609	545	493	450	414	383	357	334	298	268	243	223	206
6-#18S	.0496	**875**	875	864	760	678	611	557	512	473	440	411	386	363	343	326	308

Check availability of #14S and #18S bars.

* One-half of the bars are to be placed in each of the two faces of the column that are perpendicular to the plane of bending.

† Below zigzag horizontal line of each group, concrete governs; above, tension governs.

SQUARE TIED COLUMNS—Safe Load in Kips for Various Eccentricities in Inches

$f'_c = 3750$ psi $f_s = 24{,}000$ psi basis
(A61 or A432 Bars, $f_y = 60{,}000$ psi)

$f'_c = 3750$ psi
$f_y = 60{,}000$ psi

COLUMN SIZE—21″ x 21″

M/N † = e (in.) 16	17	18	19	20	21	22	23	24	25	26	27	28	30	32	34	36	M_o ‡ (kip-in.)
73	68	63	59	56	53	50	48	45	43	41	40	38	35	33	31	29	974
88	82	77	72	68	64	61	58	55	53	50	48	46	43	40	37	35	1186
122	114	107	100	95	90	85	81	77	74	70	68	65	60	56	53	49	1680
189	177	166	157	148	140	134	127	122	116	112	107	103	96	89	84	79	2731
69	64	60	56	53	50	48	45	43	41	39	38	36	33	31	29	27	924
86	80	75	70	66	63	59	56	54	51	49	47	45	42	39	37	34	1160
107	100	94	88	83	78	74	71	67	64	62	59	57	53	49	46	43	1461
129	120	113	106	100	94	90	85	81	78	74	71	69	64	59	56	52	1779
177	165	155	146	138	131	124	118	113	108	104	99	96	89	83	78	73	2520
263	247	233	221	209	199	190	181	174	167	160	154	148	138	129	122	115	4097
72	67	62	58	55	52	49	47	45	43	41	39	37	35	32	30	28	957
91	85	79	75	70	66	63	60	57	55	52	50	48	44	41	39	36	1232
113	106	99	93	87	83	78	75	71	68	65	62	60	56	52	48	46	1547
140	131	122	115	109	103	98	93	89	85	81	78	75	69	65	61	57	1948
168	156	147	138	130	124	117	112	107	102	98	94	90	84	78	73	69	2372
227	212	200	188	178	169	161	154	147	141	135	130	125	116	109	102	96	3360
66	62	58	54	51	48	46	43	41	39	38	36	35	32	30	28	26	884
89	83	77	73	68	65	61	58	55	53	51	49	47	43	40	38	35	1197
113	105	98	92	87	82	78	74	71	68	65	62	60	55	52	48	45	1540
139	130	122	114	108	102	97	92	88	84	81	77	74	69	64	60	57	1934
172	160	150	141	134	127	120	115	109	105	100	96	93	86	80	75	71	2435
204	191	179	169	160	151	144	137	131	126	120	116	111	104	97	91	85	2965
79	74	69	65	61	57	54	52	49	47	45	43	41	38	36	33	31	1061
106	98	92	86	81	77	73	69	66	63	61	58	56	52	48	45	42	1436
134	125	117	110	103	98	93	88	84	81	77	74	71	66	62	58	54	1848
164	153	144	135	128	121	115	110	105	100	96	92	89	82	77	72	68	2321
201	188	177	167	158	150	142	136	130	124	119	114	110	102	95	89	84	2922
66	61	57	54	51	48	45	43	41	39	37	36	34	32	30	28	26	878
92	85	80	75	71	67	63	60	57	55	52	50	48	45	42	39	37	1238
122	114	106	100	94	89	85	81	77	73	70	67	65	60	56	52	49	1675
154	144	134	127	119	113	107	102	98	93	89	86	83	77	71	67	63	2156

COLUMN SIZE—22″ x 22″

M/N † = e (in.) 16	17	18	19	20	22	24	26	28	30	32	34	36	38	40	42	44	M_o ‡ (kip.in.)
79	73	68	64	60	54	49	44	41	38	35	33	31	29	27	26	25	1035
95	88	82	77	73	65	59	54	50	46	43	40	37	35	33	32	30	1260
132	123	115	108	102	91	83	76	70	65	60	56	53	50	47	45	43	1788
206	192	180	170	161	145	131	121	111	103	96	90	85	80	76	72	69	2923
93	86	81	76	71	64	58	53	48	45	42	39	37	35	33	31	29	1232
116	108	101	94	89	80	72	66	61	56	52	49	46	43	41	39	37	1552
139	130	121	114	107	96	87	80	74	68	64	59	56	53	50	47	45	1891
191	178	167	157	149	134	121	111	103	95	89	83	78	74	70	67	63	2682
288	270	254	240	228	206	188	173	161	150	140	132	124	117	111	106	101	4385

‡ M_o = capacity in pure bending, ($N = 0$); for extrapolation, see page 11-5.

SQUARE TIED COLUMNS—Safe Load in Kips for Various Eccentricities in Inches

f'_c = 3750 psi f_s = 24,000 psi basis
(A61 or A432 Bars, f_y = 60,000 psi)

COLUMN SIZE—22″ x 22″ CONT.

Bars*	p	M/N † = e (in.) 0	1	2	3	4	5	6	7	8	9	10	11	12	13	14	15
8-#8	.0131	**514**	514	514	492	439	397	362	309	250	210	181	159	141	127	116	106
8-#9	.0165	**548**	548	548	520	465	420	383	352	304	256	221	195	174	157	144	132
8-#10	.0210	**592**	592	592	556	497	450	411	378	350	311	270	239	214	194	177	163
8-#11	.0258	**640**	640	640	594	532	482	440	405	375	349	319	283	254	231	211	195
8-#14S	.0372	**752**	752	752	684	613	555	507	467	433	403	378	355	335	309	285	264
10-#7	.0124	**508**	508	508	488	436	394	359	301	243	204	176	154	137	124	113	103
10-#8	.0163	**546**	546	546	519	464	420	383	352	302	255	220	194	173	157	143	131
10-#9	.0207	**589**	589	589	555	496	449	410	377	349	309	269	237	213	193	176	162
10-#10	.0262	**644**	644	644	600	537	486	444	409	379	353	325	289	260	236	216	199
10-#11	.0322	**703**	703	703	647	580	526	481	443	410	382	358	336	306	279	256	237
12-#6	.0109	**493**	493	493	476	425	384	350	272	219	183	157	138	123	111	101	92
12-#7	.0149	**532**	532	532	509	456	412	376	346	285	240	207	182	162	147	134	123
12-#8	.0196	**579**	579	579	547	489	443	404	372	344	298	258	228	204	185	169	155
12-#9	.0248	**630**	630	630	589	528	478	437	402	372	347	313	277	249	226	207	191
12-#10	.0315	**696**	696	696	643	577	523	478	440	408	380	356	334	303	276	253	234
14-#6	.0127	**511**	511	511	492	439	397	362	310	250	210	181	159	142	128	116	107
14-#7	.0174	**557**	557	557	531	475	430	393	361	324	274	237	209	187	169	154	142
14-#8	.0229	**611**	611	611	574	514	466	425	392	363	338	294	261	234	212	194	179
14-#9	.0289	**671**	671	671	623	559	507	463	427	395	368	345	315	284	258	237	219

COLUMN SIZE—23″ x 23″

Bars*	p	0	1	2	3	4	5	6	7	8	9	10	11	12	13	14	15
4-#11	.0118	**548**	548	548	533	477	432	394	331	265	221	190	166	148	133	121	111
4-#14S	.0170	**605**	605	605	579	519	470	430	395	358	301	259	228	204	184	167	154
4-#18S	.0302	**747**	747	747	684	611	553	505	464	430	400	374	348	313	284	261	240
6-#9	.0113	**543**	543	543	530	475	430	392	325	260	217	186	162	144	130	118	108
6-#10	.0144	**576**	576	576	558	500	453	414	381	317	266	229	201	179	161	147	135
6-#11	.0177	**612**	612	612	588	527	478	437	402	373	315	272	239	214	193	176	162
6-#14S	.0255	**696**	696	696	657	590	535	489	451	418	390	365	323	290	263	241	222
6-#18S	.0454	**911**	911	911	813	729	660	603	555	514	479	448	421	397	376	356	336
8-#8	.0119	**550**	550	550	537	481	435	398	342	274	228	196	172	152	137	125	114
8-#9	.0151	**584**	584	584	566	507	460	420	387	333	279	240	211	188	170	155	142
8-#10	.0192	**628**	628	628	603	541	491	449	414	383	339	294	259	231	209	191	176
8-#11	.0236	**676**	676	676	642	577	523	479	442	410	382	347	307	275	249	228	210
8-#14S	.0340	**788**	788	788	734	660	600	549	507	470	439	411	387	365	335	308	285
10-#7	.0113	**543**	543	543	533	478	433	395	333	266	222	190	167	148	133	121	111
10-#8	.0149	**582**	582	582	565	507	459	420	387	331	278	239	210	187	169	154	141
10-#9	.0189	**625**	625	625	601	540	489	448	413	383	337	292	257	230	208	190	174
10-#10	.0240	**680**	680	680	647	582	528	483	446	414	386	354	313	281	255	233	215
10-#11	.0295	**739**	739	739	696	626	569	521	481	446	416	390	367	332	302	277	255
10-#14S	.0425	**880**	880	880	811	730	664	609	562	522	487	457	430	406	385	366	342
12-#6	.0100	**529**	529	529	521	466	422	386	300	240	199	170	149	132	119	108	99
12-#7	.0136	**568**	568	568	555	498	451	412	380	312	261	224	197	175	158	144	132
12-#8	.0179	**614**	614	614	593	532	483	442	407	378	324	280	247	221	199	182	167
12-#9	.0227	**666**	666	666	636	572	519	475	438	407	379	340	301	269	244	223	206
12-#10	.0288	**732**	732	732	692	622	565	518	478	444	414	388	364	328	298	273	252
12-#11	.0354	**803**	803	803	750	676	614	563	520	483	451	423	398	376	351	322	298

Check availability of #14S and #18S bars.

* One-half of the bars are to be placed in each of the two faces of the column that are perpendicular to the plane of bending.

† Below zigzag horizontal line of each group, concrete governs; above, tension governs.

SQUARE TIED COLUMNS—Safe Load in Kips for Various Eccentricities in Inches

f'_c = 3750 psi f_s = 24,000 psi basis
(A61 or A432 Bars, f_y = 60,000 psi)

f'_c = 3750 psi
f_y = 60,000 psi

COLUMN SIZE—22″ x 22″ CONT.

M/N † = e (in.)

16	17	18	19	20	22	24	26	28	30	32	34	36	38	40	42	44	M_o ‡ (kip.-in.)
98	91	85	80	75	68	61	56	51	48	44	41	39	37	35	33	31	1308
122	114	106	100	94	84	76	70	64	59	55	52	49	46	43	41	39	1643
151	141	132	124	117	105	95	87	80	74	69	65	61	58	54	52	49	2070
181	169	158	149	140	126	115	105	97	90	84	79	74	70	66	63	60	2521
245	230	216	203	192	174	158	145	134	125	117	109	103	97	92	88	84	3576
96	89	83	78	73	66	59	54	50	46	43	40	38	36	34	32	30	1269
122	113	106	99	93	84	76	69	64	59	55	52	48	46	43	41	39	1635
150	140	131	123	116	104	94	86	80	74	69	64	61	57	54	51	49	2054
185	173	162	152	144	129	117	108	99	92	86	81	76	71	68	64	61	2587
220	206	193	182	172	155	141	129	119	111	104	97	91	86	82	78	74	3152
85	79	74	69	65	58	53	48	44	41	38	36	33	32	30	28	27	1124
114	106	99	93	87	78	71	65	60	55	51	48	45	43	40	38	36	1522
144	134	125	118	111	100	90	83	76	71	66	62	58	55	52	49	47	1962
177	165	155	146	137	124	112	103	95	88	82	77	72	68	65	61	58	2465
217	203	191	180	170	153	139	128	118	109	102	96	90	85	81	77	73	3105
99	92	86	80	76	68	61	56	52	48	44	42	39	37	35	33	31	1312
131	122	114	107	101	91	82	75	69	64	60	56	53	50	47	44	42	1776
166	154	145	136	128	115	105	96	88	82	76	72	67	64	60	57	54	2289
203	190	178	168	158	143	130	119	110	102	95	89	84	79	75	71	68	2876

COLUMN SIZE—23″ x 23″

16	17	18	19	20	22	24	26	28	30	32	34	36	38	40	42	44	M_o ‡ (kip.-in.)
102	95	88	83	78	70	63	58	53	49	46	43	40	38	36	34	32	1335
142	132	123	116	109	98	89	81	74	69	64	60	56	53	50	48	45	1896
223	208	195	183	173	156	142	130	120	111	104	97	91	86	82	78	74	3115
100	93	86	81	76	68	62	56	52	48	44	42	39	37	35	33	31	1304
124	116	108	101	95	85	77	70	65	60	56	52	49	46	44	41	39	1644
150	139	130	122	115	103	93	85	79	73	68	63	60	56	53	50	48	2003
206	192	180	169	159	143	130	119	110	102	95	89	84	79	75	71	68	2844
313	293	276	260	247	223	204	187	173	161	151	142	133	126	120	114	108	4673
106	98	91	86	81	72	65	60	55	51	47	44	41	39	37	35	33	1384
131	122	114	107	101	90	81	74	68	63	59	55	52	49	46	44	42	1739
162	151	141	133	125	112	102	93	86	79	74	69	65	61	58	55	52	2192
195	181	170	160	150	135	123	112	103	96	89	84	79	74	70	67	64	2671
265	247	232	219	207	186	170	156	144	133	125	117	110	104	99	94	89	3792
102	95	89	83	78	70	63	58	53	49	46	43	40	38	36	34	32	1341
130	121	113	106	100	90	81	74	68	63	59	55	52	49	46	44	41	1730
161	150	140	132	124	111	101	92	85	79	73	69	65	61	58	55	52	2174
199	185	174	163	154	138	126	115	106	98	92	86	81	76	72	68	65	2740
237	221	208	195	184	166	151	138	128	119	111	104	98	92	87	83	79	3339
319	299	281	265	251	227	207	190	176	164	153	144	136	128	122	116	110	4740
91	85	79	74	70	62	56	51	47	44	41	38	36	33	32	30	29	1188
122	113	106	99	93	84	76	69	63	59	55	51	48	45	43	41	39	1609
155	144	134	126	119	107	97	88	81	75	70	66	62	58	55	52	50	2076
190	177	166	156	147	132	120	110	101	94	87	82	77	73	69	65	62	2609
234	218	205	193	182	164	149	136	126	117	109	102	96	91	86	82	78	3288
278	260	244	230	217	196	178	164	151	141	131	123	116	110	104	99	94	4007

‡ M_o = capacity in pure bending, (N = 0); for extrapolation, see page 11-5.

SQUARE TIED COLUMNS—Safe Load in Kips for Various Eccentricities in Inches

$f'_c = 3750$ psi $f_s = 24{,}000$ psi basis

(A61 or A432 Bars, $f_y = 60{,}000$ psi)

COLUMN SIZE—23″ x 23″ CONT.

Bars*	p	M/N † = e (in.) 0	1	2	3	4	5	6	7	8	9	10	11	12	13	14	15
14-#6	.0116	**547**	547	547	537	481	436	398	342	274	229	196	172	153	137	125	115
14-#7	.0159	**592**	592	592	576	517	469	430	396	354	298	257	226	202	182	166	152
14-#8	.0209	**647**	647	647	621	558	506	464	428	397	368	319	282	253	229	209	192
14-#9	.0265	**707**	707	707	672	604	549	503	464	431	402	377	342	307	279	255	236

COLUMN SIZE—24″ x 24″

Bars*	p	0	1	2	3	4	5	6	7	8	9	10	11	12	13	14	15
4-#11	.0108	**586**	586	586	581	521	473	432	366	290	241	205	179	159	143	130	119
4-#14S	.0156	**642**	642	642	628	564	512	469	432	392	327	281	247	219	198	180	165
4-#18S	.0278	**785**	785	785	736	660	599	548	505	468	437	409	379	340	308	282	259
6-#9	.0104	**581**	581	581	578	519	470	430	359	284	236	201	175	155	140	127	116
6-#10	.0132	**614**	614	614	606	545	494	453	417	347	289	248	217	193	173	157	144
6-#11	.0163	**649**	649	649	636	572	520	476	439	408	343	295	259	230	208	189	173
6-#14S	.0234	**734**	734	734	707	637	579	531	490	455	425	396	350	313	284	259	238
6-#18S	.0417	**948**	948	948	869	781	709	650	599	556	519	486	458	432	409	388	363
8-#8	.0110	**587**	587	587	584	525	476	436	377	299	248	212	185	164	147	134	123
8-#9	.0139	**622**	622	622	614	552	501	459	423	364	304	260	228	203	182	166	152
8-#10	.0176	**666**	666	666	652	586	533	489	451	419	369	318	280	249	225	205	188
8-#11	.0217	**713**	713	713	692	623	567	520	480	446	416	376	332	297	268	245	225
8-#14S	.0313	**826**	826	826	786	709	646	593	548	509	476	446	420	397	361	331	306
8-#18S	.0556	**1111**	1111	1111	1002	902	820	751	694	644	601	564	530	501	475	451	429
10-#7	.0104	**581**	581	581	580	521	473	433	367	291	241	206	180	159	143	130	119
10-#8	.0137	**620**	620	620	613	551	501	459	423	362	302	259	227	202	181	165	151
10-#9	.0174	**662**	662	662	650	585	532	488	450	418	367	316	278	248	223	203	187
10-#10	.0220	**718**	718	718	697	628	572	524	484	450	420	384	339	303	274	250	230
10-#11	.0271	**777**	777	777	747	674	614	563	521	484	452	424	399	358	325	297	274
10-#14S	.0391	**918**	918	918	865	781	712	654	605	563	526	494	466	440	417	397	369
12-#7	.0125	**605**	605	605	602	542	492	451	416	341	283	243	212	189	170	154	141
12-#8	.0165	**652**	652	652	641	577	525	481	444	413	353	304	267	238	214	195	179
12-#9	.0208	**703**	703	703	686	618	562	516	477	443	414	368	325	290	263	240	220
12-#10	.0265	**769**	769	769	742	670	610	560	518	481	450	422	394	353	321	293	271
12-#11	.0325	**840**	840	840	802	725	661	607	561	522	488	458	432	408	378	347	321
14-#6	.0107	**584**	584	584	584	525	476	436	378	300	249	212	185	164	148	134	123
14-#7	.0146	**630**	630	630	624	562	511	468	432	387	324	278	244	217	195	178	163
14-#8	.0192	**684**	684	684	670	604	549	504	465	432	401	346	305	272	246	224	206
14-#9	.0243	**744**	744	744	722	651	593	544	503	468	437	410	369	331	300	274	253
14-#10	.0309	**821**	821	821	787	711	648	596	551	513	479	450	424	401	365	335	309

COLUMN SIZE—26″ x 26″

Bars*	p	0	1	2	3	4	5	6	7	8	9	10	11	12	13	14	15
4-#14S	.0133	**722**	722	722	722	661	603	554	512	467	386	329	286	253	227	206	189
4-#18	.0237	**865**	865	865	845	763	696	640	592	550	514	483	443	396	357	326	299
6-#10	.0113	**694**	694	694	694	640	583	536	496	414	340	289	251	222	199	180	164
6-#11	.0138	**729**	729	729	729	669	610	561	519	483	404	344	300	266	239	216	198
6-#14S	.0200	**814**	814	814	814	737	673	619	574	534	500	463	406	362	327	297	273
6-#18S	.0355	**1028**	1028	1028	984	891	813	748	693	645	604	567	535	506	480	456	421

Check availability of #14S and #18S bars.

* One-half of the bars are to be placed in each of the two faces of the column that are perpendicular to the plane of bending.

† Below zigzag horizontal line of each group, concrete governs; above, tension governs.

SQUARE TIED COLUMNS—Safe Load in Kips for Various Eccentricities in Inches

f'_c = 3750 psi f_s = 24,000 psi basis

(A61 or A432 Bars, f_y = 60,000 psi)

f'_c = 3750 psi

f_y = 60,000 psi

M/N † = e (in.)																	
16	17	18	19	20	22	24	26	28	30	32	34	36	38	40	42	44	M_o ‡ (kip.in.)
COLUMN SIZE—23″ x 23″ CONT.																	
106	98	92	86	81	72	65	60	55	51	47	44	41	39	37	35	33	*1386*
141	131	122	115	108	97	88	80	74	68	64	59	56	53	50	47	45	*1877*
178	166	155	146	137	123	112	102	94	87	81	76	72	68	64	61	58	*2422*
219	204	191	180	170	153	139	127	117	109	101	95	89	84	80	76	72	*3044*
COLUMN SIZE—24″ x 24″																	
109	101	95	89	83	74	67	61	56	52	48	45	42	40	38	36	34	*1410*
152	142	132	124	117	104	94	86	79	73	68	64	60	57	54	51	48	*2004*
241	224	210	197	186	167	152	139	128	119	111	104	98	92	87	83	79	*3307*
107	99	92	86	81	73	66	60	55	51	47	44	41	39	37	35	33	*1376*
133	124	115	108	102	91	82	75	69	64	59	56	52	49	46	44	42	*1735*
160	149	139	130	123	110	99	91	84	77	72	67	63	60	56	54	51	*2116*
221	206	192	181	170	153	139	127	117	108	101	95	89	84	79	75	72	*3006*
339	317	298	281	266	240	219	201	186	173	161	152	143	135	128	122	116	*4961*
113	105	98	92	86	77	69	63	58	54	50	47	44	41	39	37	35	*1459*
140	130	122	114	107	96	87	79	73	67	63	59	55	52	49	47	44	*1835*
174	162	151	142	134	120	108	99	91	84	79	74	69	65	62	58	56	*2314*
209	194	182	171	161	144	131	120	110	102	95	89	84	79	75	71	67	*2821*
284	265	249	234	221	199	181	166	153	142	133	124	117	111	105	100	95	*4008*
410	392	375	355	337	306	280	258	239	223	209	196	185	175	167	159	151	*6615*
110	102	95	89	83	74	67	61	56	52	48	45	43	40	38	36	34	*1413*
140	130	121	113	107	95	86	79	72	67	62	58	55	52	49	46	44	*1824*
173	161	150	141	133	119	107	98	90	84	78	73	69	65	61	58	55	*2294*
213	199	186	174	165	148	134	122	113	105	97	91	86	81	77	73	69	*2892*
254	237	222	209	197	177	161	147	136	126	118	110	104	98	93	88	84	*3526*
343	321	302	285	269	243	221	203	188	175	163	153	144	137	129	123	117	*5010*
130	121	113	106	99	89	80	73	67	62	58	54	51	48	45	43	41	*1695*
165	154	144	135	127	114	103	94	86	80	74	70	65	62	58	55	53	*2189*
204	190	178	167	157	141	128	117	108	100	93	87	82	77	73	69	66	*2753*
251	234	219	206	194	175	159	145	134	124	116	109	102	96	91	87	83	*3471*
298	278	261	246	232	209	190	175	161	150	140	131	123	116	110	105	100	*4232*
113	105	98	92	86	77	69	63	58	54	50	47	44	41	39	37	35	*1459*
150	140	130	122	115	103	93	85	78	72	67	63	59	56	53	50	48	*1978*
191	177	166	156	147	131	119	109	100	93	86	81	76	72	68	64	61	*2554*
234	218	204	192	181	163	148	135	125	116	108	101	95	90	85	80	77	*3212*
287	268	251	237	223	201	183	168	155	144	134	126	118	112	106	101	96	*4049*
COLUMN SIZE—26″ x 26″																	
174	161	150	141	132	118	107	97	89	83	77	72	67	63	60	57	54	*2220*
277	257	240	226	213	191	173	158	145	135	125	117	110	104	98	93	89	*3691*
151	140	131	122	115	102	92	84	77	72	67	62	58	55	52	49	47	*1918*
182	169	158	148	139	124	112	102	94	87	81	76	71	67	63	60	57	*2340*
252	234	219	205	193	173	157	143	132	122	114	106	100	94	89	84	80	*3330*
391	366	343	323	305	275	250	229	211	196	183	172	162	153	145	137	131	*5537*

‡ M_o = capacity in pure bending, (N = 0); for extrapolation, see page 11-5.

SQUARE TIED COLUMNS—Safe Load in Kips for Various Eccentricities in Inches

$f'_c = 3750$ psi $f_s = 24{,}000$ psi basis

(A61 or A432 Bars, $f_y = 60{,}000$ psi)

COLUMN SIZE—26″ x 26″ CONT.

Bars*	p	M/N † = e (in.) 0	1	2	3	4	5	6	7	8	9	10	11	12	13	14	15
8-#9	.0118	**701**	701	701	701	647	590	543	502	434	357	304	264	233	209	190	173
8-#10	.0150	**745**	745	745	745	684	624	574	532	495	435	371	324	288	258	235	215
8-#11	.0185	**793**	793	793	793	722	660	607	563	524	490	439	385	342	308	281	257
8-#14S	.0266	**905**	905	905	896	812	743	685	635	592	554	521	492	460	417	381	351
8-#18S	.0473	**1191**	1191	1191	1123	1018	931	857	794	740	693	651	614	581	552	525	501
10-#8	.0117	**699**	699	699	699	646	590	542	502	431	355	302	262	232	208	188	172
10-#9	.0148	**742**	742	742	742	682	623	573	530	494	431	369	322	285	256	233	213
10-#10	.0188	**797**	797	797	797	727	665	612	567	528	494	448	393	350	315	287	263
10-#11	.0231	**856**	856	856	855	775	709	653	606	565	529	497	463	414	374	341	314
10-#14S	.0333	**997**	997	997	977	888	813	750	696	649	609	573	541	512	486	459	424
12-#7	.0107	**685**	685	685	685	636	581	534	494	405	333	282	245	217	194	176	161
12-#8	.0140	**732**	732	732	732	674	615	566	524	488	415	354	309	274	246	223	204
12-#9	.0178	**783**	783	783	783	717	655	603	559	520	487	430	376	335	302	274	251
12-#10	.0225	**849**	849	849	849	771	705	650	603	562	526	495	457	408	369	336	309
12-#11	.0277	**920**	920	920	912	828	758	699	649	605	567	533	504	477	436	399	367
14-#7	.0124	**710**	710	710	710	658	600	552	511	461	380	324	282	249	224	203	185
14-#8	.0164	**764**	764	764	764	701	641	590	547	509	471	403	353	314	282	256	235
14-#9	.0207	**824**	824	824	824	751	687	633	587	547	512	481	428	382	345	314	289
14-#10	.0263	**901**	901	901	896	814	745	687	638	595	557	524	495	464	420	384	353
16-#6	.0104	**682**	682	682	682	634	579	532	492	400	328	278	242	213	191	173	158
16-#7	.0142	**734**	734	734	734	679	620	571	529	492	425	363	317	281	252	229	210
16-#8	.0187	**796**	796	796	796	729	666	614	569	530	496	451	395	352	317	289	265
16-#9	.0237	**865**	865	865	865	785	719	663	615	573	537	505	477	427	387	353	325
18-#6	.0117	**700**	700	700	700	650	593	546	505	441	363	309	269	238	213	193	176
18-#7	.0160	**759**	759	759	759	700	640	589	546	509	469	401	351	312	280	255	234
18-#8	.0210	**828**	828	828	828	756	692	638	591	551	516	485	436	389	351	320	294

COLUMN SIZE—28″ x 28″

Bars*	p	M/N † = e (in.) 0	1	2	3	4	5	6	7	8	9	10	11	12	13	14	16
4-#14S	.0115	**808**	808	808	808	766	701	646	600	555	452	381	329	290	259	234	196
4-#18S	.0204	**951**	951	951	951	874	801	739	685	639	599	563	513	456	410	372	315
6-#11	.0119	**815**	815	815	815	774	709	654	607	566	473	399	345	304	272	246	206
6-#14S	.0172	**900**	900	900	900	845	775	716	665	621	582	537	468	415	373	338	285
6-#18S	.0306	**1114**	1114	1114	1107	1008	924	854	793	741	695	654	618	585	556	523	447
8-#9	.0102	**787**	787	787	787	752	688	635	589	515	418	352	303	267	238	215	180
8-#10	.0130	**832**	832	832	832	789	723	668	620	578	509	430	373	329	294	266	224
8-#11	.0159	**879**	879	879	879	830	761	703	653	609	571	509	443	392	352	319	269
8-#14S	.0230	**991**	991	991	991	924	848	784	729	682	640	603	570	528	476	434	368
8-#18S	.0408	**1277**	1277	1277	1251	1140	1047	968	901	842	790	744	703	667	634	604	552

Check availability of #14S and #18S bars.

* One-half of the bars are to be placed in each of the two faces of the column that are perpendicular to the plane of bending.

† Below zigzag horizontal line of each group, concrete governs; above, tension governs.

SQUARE TIED COLUMNS—Safe Load in Kips for Various Eccentricities in Inches

$f'_c = 3750$ psi $f_s = 24{,}000$ psi basis
(A61 or A432 Bars, $f_y = 60{,}000$ psi)

$f'_c = 3750$ psi
$f_y = 60{,}000$ psi

COLUMN SIZE—26″ x 26″ CONT.

M/N † = e (in.)																	M_o ‡
16	17	18	19	20	22	24	26	28	30	32	34	36	38	40	42	44	(kip.in.)
160	148	138	129	121	108	98	89	82	76	70	66	62	58	55	52	49	2027
198	184	171	161	151	135	122	111	102	95	88	82	77	73	69	65	62	2557
238	221	206	193	182	163	147	135	124	115	107	100	94	88	84	79	75	3120
325	303	283	266	251	226	205	187	173	160	149	140	132	124	117	112	106	4440
479	458	434	410	388	351	321	295	273	254	238	223	211	199	189	180	171	7383
159	147	137	128	120	107	97	88	81	75	70	65	61	58	54	52	49	2014
196	182	170	159	150	134	121	110	101	94	87	82	77	72	68	65	62	2534
243	226	211	198	186	167	151	138	127	117	109	102	96	91	86	81	77	3197
290	270	253	237	224	200	182	166	153	142	132	124	116	110	104	98	94	3901
393	367	344	324	306	276	251	230	212	197	184	172	162	153	145	138	131	5550
148	137	127	119	112	100	90	82	75	70	65	61	57	53	51	48	46	1868
188	174	163	152	143	128	116	105	97	90	83	78	73	69	65	62	59	2417
232	216	201	189	178	159	144	131	121	112	104	97	91	86	82	77	74	3041
286	266	249	234	220	197	179	164	151	140	130	122	114	108	102	97	92	3836
340	317	297	279	264	237	215	197	181	168	157	147	138	131	124	117	112	4681
171	158	148	138	130	116	105	95	88	81	75	70	66	62	59	56	53	2179
217	201	188	176	166	148	134	122	112	104	97	91	85	80	76	72	68	2820
267	248	232	218	205	184	166	152	140	130	121	113	106	100	95	90	85	3548
328	305	286	268	253	227	206	189	174	161	150	141	133	125	118	112	107	4476
145	135	125	117	110	98	89	81	74	69	64	60	56	53	50	47	45	1837
193	179	167	157	147	132	119	109	100	92	86	80	75	71	67	64	60	2491
245	227	212	199	188	168	152	139	128	118	110	103	97	91	86	82	78	3223
300	280	262	246	232	208	188	172	159	147	137	128	121	114	108	102	97	4055
163	151	140	131	123	110	99	91	83	77	72	67	63	59	56	53	50	2067
216	200	187	175	165	147	133	121	112	103	96	90	84	80	75	71	68	2802
272	253	236	222	209	187	170	155	143	132	123	115	108	102	97	92	87	3626

COLUMN SIZE—28″ x 28″

M/N † = e (in.)																	M_o ‡
18	20	22	24	26	28	30	32	34	36	38	40	42	44	46	48	50	(kip.in.)
169	148	132	119	108	99	92	85	80	75	70	66	63	60	57	54	52	2436
273	240	215	194	177	163	151	140	131	123	116	110	104	99	94	90	86	4075
177	156	139	125	114	105	97	90	84	79	74	70	66	63	60	57	55	2565
247	217	194	175	160	147	136	126	118	111	105	99	94	89	85	81	78	3654
390	346	310	282	258	238	220	206	193	181	171	162	154	146	140	133	128	6113
155	136	121	109	99	91	84	78	73	68	64	61	57	55	52	50	47	2219
193	169	151	136	124	114	105	98	91	86	81	76	72	69	65	62	60	2801
232	204	182	165	150	138	128	119	111	104	98	93	88	84	80	76	73	3420
320	283	253	229	209	193	179	166	156	146	138	130	124	118	112	107	103	4872
495	442	398	363	333	308	286	267	251	236	223	212	201	192	183	175	168	8151

‡ M_o = capacity in pure bending, ($N = 0$); for extrapolation, see page 11-5.

SQUARE TIED COLUMNS—Safe Load in Kips for Various Eccentricities in Inches

$f'_c = 3750$ psi $\quad f_s = 24{,}000$ psi basis

(A61 or A432 Bars, $f_y = 60{,}000$ psi)

COLUMN SIZE—28″ x 28″ CONT.

Bars*	p	M/N † = e (in) 0	1	2	3	4	5	6	7	8	9	10	11	12	13	14	16
10-#8	.0101	**785**	785	785	785	751	687	634	588	512	416	349	302	265	237	214	179
10-#9	.0128	**828**	828	828	828	788	722	666	619	577	505	427	370	326	292	264	222
10-#10	.0162	**883**	883	883	883	835	766	707	657	614	576	519	452	400	359	326	274
10-#11	.0199	**942**	942	942	942	885	812	751	698	652	612	577	533	474	427	388	328
10-#14S	.0287	**1083**	1083	1083	1083	1002	921	853	794	742	697	657	622	590	561	523	446
10-#18S	.0510	**1440**	1440	1440	1395	1273	1170	1083	1008	942	885	834	789	748	712	678	620
12-#8	.0121	**818**	818	818	818	779	714	659	612	571	485	410	355	313	279	253	212
12-#9	.0153	**869**	869	869	869	823	755	698	648	605	568	498	433	383	343	311	262
12-#10	.0194	**935**	935	935	935	880	808	747	694	649	609	574	526	467	420	382	323
12-#11	.0239	**1006**	1006	1006	1006	940	864	799	744	695	653	615	582	551	497	453	385
12-#14S	.0344	**1175**	1175	1175	1175	1080	994	921	858	803	755	712	674	639	608	580	519
14-#7	.0107	**796**	796	796	796	762	698	644	598	547	444	374	323	285	254	230	192
14-#8	.0141	**850**	850	850	850	808	741	684	635	593	551	467	406	358	321	291	244
14-#9	.0179	**910**	910	910	910	859	789	729	678	633	594	560	493	437	393	357	301
14-#10	.0277	**987**	987	987	987	925	850	786	732	684	642	605	572	531	479	436	370
14-#11	.0279	**1070**	1070	1070	1070	994	915	847	789	738	693	654	618	587	558	516	440
16-#7	.0122	**820**	820	820	820	784	719	664	616	575	497	420	364	321	287	259	218
16-#8	.0161	**882**	882	882	882	836	767	709	659	615	577	522	455	403	361	328	276
16-#9	.0204	**951**	951	951	951	895	822	760	707	661	621	585	550	489	441	401	339
16-#10	.0259	**1039**	1039	1039	1039	969	892	826	769	719	676	637	602	572	535	488	416
18-#6	.0101	**786**	786	786	786	754	691	637	591	523	425	357	308	271	242	218	183
18-#7	.0138	**845**	845	845	845	806	739	683	635	593	547	464	403	356	319	289	243
18-#8	.0181	**914**	914	914	914	864	794	734	682	638	598	564	502	445	400	363	307
18-#9	.0230	**991**	991	991	991	930	855	792	737	689	647	610	577	539	486	443	376

COLUMN SIZE—30″ x 30″

Bars*	p	M/N † = e (in) 0	1	2	3	4	5	6	7	8	9	10	11	12	13	14	16
4-#14S	.0100	**900**	900	900	900	880	808	748	695	650	528	440	377	330	293	264	220
4-#18S	.0178	**1043**	1043	1043	1043	994	913	845	787	735	691	651	590	521	467	422	355
6-#11	.0104	**908**	908	908	908	888	816	755	703	657	551	460	395	346	308	277	231
6-#14S	.0150	**992**	992	992	992	962	885	820	763	714	671	620	536	472	422	382	320
6-#18S	.0267	**1206**	1206	1206	1206	1132	1042	966	900	843	792	747	707	671	639	595	505
8-#10	.0113	**924**	924	924	924	904	831	769	716	670	593	496	427	374	333	300	251
8-#11	.0139	**971**	971	971	971	946	870	806	750	702	660	587	507	446	398	360	301
8-#14S	.0200	**1084**	1084	1084	1084	1043	961	891	831	778	732	691	654	602	540	490	414
8-#18S	.0356	**1369**	1369	1369	1369	1269	1171	1086	1013	949	893	843	798	758	722	689	631
10-#9	.0111	**921**	921	921	921	902	829	768	715	668	588	492	423	371	330	297	248
10-#10	.0141	**976**	976	976	976	951	875	811	755	707	664	598	517	455	406	367	308
10-#11	.0173	**1035**	1035	1035	1035	1002	924	856	798	747	703	663	610	539	483	438	368
10-#14S	.0250	**1176**	1176	1176	1176	1124	1037	963	899	842	793	749	709	674	641	591	502
10-#18S	.0444	**1533**	1533	1533	1533	1407	1299	1206	1126	1056	994	939	889	845	805	768	704

Check availability of #14S and #18S bars.

* One-half of the bars are to be placed in each of the two faces of the column that are perpendicular to the plane of bending.

† Below zigzag horizontal line of each group, concrete governs; above, tension governs.

SQUARE TIED COLUMNS—Safe Load in Kips for Various Eccentricities in Inches

$f'_c = 3750$ psi $f_s = 24{,}000$ psi basis
(A61 or A432 Bars, $f_y = 60{,}000$ psi)

$f'_c = 3750$ psi
$f_y = 60{,}000$ psi

COLUMN SIZE—28″ x 28″ CONT.

M/N † = e (in.)																	
18	20	22	24	26	28	30	32	34	36	38	40	42	44	46	48	50	M_o ‡ (kip.in.)
154	135	120	108	98	90	83	77	72	68	64	60	57	54	52	49	47	2204
191	168	150	135	123	113	104	97	90	85	80	76	72	68	65	62	59	2774
237	209	186	168	153	141	130	121	113	106	100	95	90	85	81	78	74	3502
284	251	224	203	185	170	158	147	137	129	122	115	109	104	99	94	90	4275
389	345	310	281	257	237	220	205	192	181	170	161	153	146	139	133	127	6090
571	530	480	439	404	374	348	326	306	289	273	259	247	235	225	215	207	10189
183	160	143	129	117	108	100	92	86	81	76	72	68	65	62	59	56	2644
226	199	178	160	146	134	124	116	108	101	96	90	86	81	78	74	71	3329
280	247	221	200	182	168	155	144	135	127	120	113	107	102	97	93	89	4202
335	296	265	240	220	202	187	175	163	154	145	137	130	124	118	113	108	5130
455	404	364	331	303	280	260	243	227	214	202	192	182	173	165	158	152	7308
165	145	129	117	106	97	90	83	78	73	69	65	62	59	56	53	51	2381
211	185	165	149	136	125	116	107	100	94	89	84	79	76	72	69	66	3085
261	230	205	186	169	156	144	134	125	118	111	105	99	95	90	86	82	3884
322	284	255	230	211	194	180	167	157	147	139	131	124	118	113	108	103	4903
383	340	305	277	253	233	216	202	189	178	168	159	151	143	137	131	125	5985
188	165	147	132	121	111	102	95	89	83	78	74	70	67	64	61	58	2721
239	210	188	169	155	142	131	122	114	107	101	95	91	86	82	78	75	3526
294	260	232	210	192	177	164	152	142	134	126	119	113	108	103	98	94	4439
362	320	287	261	238	220	204	190	178	167	157	149	141	135	128	123	118	5603
157	138	123	111	101	92	85	79	74	69	65	62	58	55	53	50	48	2257
209	184	164	148	135	124	115	107	100	93	88	83	79	75	71	68	65	3061
266	234	209	189	173	159	147	137	128	120	113	107	101	96	92	88	84	3967
327	289	259	234	214	197	183	170	159	150	141	134	127	121	115	110	105	4994

COLUMN SIZE—30″ x 30″

18	20	22	24	26	28	30	32	34	36	38	40	42	44	46	48	50	M_o ‡ (kip.in.)
189	165	147	132	120	110	101	94	88	82	77	73	69	66	63	60	57	2652
306	269	240	217	197	181	167	156	145	137	129	122	115	109	104	100	95	4459
198	173	154	139	126	115	107	99	92	87	81	77	73	69	66	63	60	2790
276	242	216	194	177	162	150	140	130	122	115	109	103	98	93	89	85	3978
439	388	347	315	287	265	245	228	214	201	189	179	170	162	154	147	141	6689
215	188	167	151	137	126	116	108	101	94	89	84	79	75	72	69	66	3045
259	227	202	182	166	152	141	131	122	115	108	102	97	92	87	83	80	3720
358	315	282	254	232	213	197	184	172	161	152	144	136	129	123	118	113	5304
559	497	447	406	372	343	319	297	279	262	248	235	223	212	203	194	186	8919
213	187	166	149	136	124	115	107	100	93	88	83	79	75	71	68	65	3014
265	232	207	186	170	156	144	134	125	117	110	104	99	94	89	85	82	3806
318	279	249	225	205	188	174	162	151	142	134	127	120	114	109	104	99	4650
436	385	345	312	285	263	243	227	212	199	188	178	169	160	153	146	140	6630
650	598	540	492	452	418	389	363	341	321	304	288	274	261	249	239	229	11149

‡ M_o = capacity in pure bending, ($N = 0$); for extrapolation, see page 11-5.

SQUARE TIED COLUMNS—Safe Load in Kips for Various Eccentricities in Inches

f'_c = 3750 psi f_s = 24,000 psi basis
(A61 or A432 Bars, f_y = 60,000 psi)

COLUMN SIZE—30″ x 30″ CONT.

Bars*	p	M/N † = e (in.) 0	1	2	3	4	5	6	7	8	9	10	11	12	13	14	16
12-#8	.0105	**910**	910	910	910	893	821	760	707	661	565	472	405	355	316	285	237
12-#9	.0133	**961**	961	961	961	939	864	801	746	698	656	574	495	435	388	351	294
12-#10	.0169	**1028**	1028	1028	1028	997	919	852	794	744	699	660	602	531	476	431	362
12-#11	.0208	**1099**	1099	1099	1099	1059	977	906	846	792	745	704	666	627	564	512	432
12-#14S	.0300	**1267**	1267	1267	1267	1204	1113	1034	966	906	853	806	764	726	692	661	585
14-#8	.0123	**942**	942	942	942	923	849	786	732	685	642	538	464	407	363	327	274
14-#9	.0156	**1002**	1002	1002	1002	976	899	833	776	727	683	645	564	497	445	402	338
14-#10	.0198	**1079**	1079	1079	1079	1044	962	893	833	780	734	693	656	604	542	492	415
14-#11	.0243	**1162**	1162	1162	1162	1116	1030	956	893	837	788	744	705	670	638	582	494
16-#7	.0107	**913**	913	913	913	898	826	765	712	666	579	484	416	364	324	292	244
16-#8	.0140	**975**	975	975	975	952	876	812	757	708	666	601	520	457	409	369	309
16-#9	.0178	**1043**	1043	1043	1043	1012	933	866	807	756	711	671	629	556	499	452	380
16-#10	.0226	**1131**	1131	1131	1131	1090	1006	934	872	817	769	726	688	654	606	551	467
16-#11	.0277	**1226**	1226	1226	1226	1172	1083	1006	940	882	830	785	744	707	673	643	553
18-#7	.0120	**937**	937	937	937	920	847	785	731	684	637	535	460	404	360	325	272
18-#8	.0158	**1007**	1007	1007	1007	981	904	838	781	732	688	649	573	506	453	410	344
18-#9	.0200	**1084**	1084	1084	1084	1049	968	898	838	785	739	698	661	613	551	500	422

COLUMN SIZE—32″ x 32″

Bars*	p	0	1	2	3	4	5	6	7	8	9	10	11	12	13	14	16
4-#18S	.0156	**1142**	1142	1142	1142	1121	1034	960	895	839	789	745	675	592	527	476	397
6-#14S	.0132	**1091**	1091	1091	1091	1087	1004	932	870	816	768	713	611	535	476	428	357
6-#18S	.0234	**1305**	1305	1305	1305	1264	1168	1086	1014	952	896	847	803	763	727	671	566
8-#11	.0122	**1070**	1070	1070	1070	1070	988	917	856	803	756	674	577	505	448	403	336
8-#14S	.0176	**1183**	1183	1183	1183	1171	1082	1007	941	883	832	786	745	682	609	550	462
8-#18S	.0313	**1468**	1468	1468	1468	1406	1301	1211	1133	1064	1003	948	899	855	815	779	715
10-#10	.0124	**1075**	1075	1075	1075	1075	993	922	861	807	760	687	589	515	457	412	343
10-#11	.0152	**1134**	1134	1134	1134	1129	1043	970	906	850	801	757	695	611	544	491	411
10-#14S	.0220	**1274**	1274	1274	1274	1254	1161	1081	1011	949	895	847	803	764	728	664	560
10-#18S	.0391	**1632**	1632	1632	1632	1548	1434	1336	1250	1175	1109	1049	996	947	903	864	793
12-#9	.0117	**1060**	1060	1060	1060	1060	982	912	851	798	751	659	564	492	437	393	327
12-#10	.0149	**1126**	1126	1126	1126	1123	1038	965	902	846	797	753	685	601	536	483	404
12-#11	.0183	**1197**	1197	1197	1197	1187	1098	1022	955	897	845	799	758	710	635	574	482
12-#14S	.0264	**1366**	1366	1366	1366	1337	1239	1154	1081	1016	958	907	861	819	781	747	653
14-#8	.0108	**1041**	1041	1041	1041	1041	966	897	837	784	738	618	528	461	408	367	305
14-#9	.0137	**1101**	1101	1101	1101	1101	1017	946	883	828	780	737	642	562	500	451	376
14-#10	.0174	**1178**	1178	1178	1178	1171	1083	1008	942	884	833	788	747	684	611	552	463
14-#11	.0213	**1261**	1261	1261	1261	1245	1153	1074	1004	944	890	842	799	760	721	654	551
14-#14S	.0308	**1458**	1458	1458	1458	1419	1317	1228	1150	1082	1021	967	918	874	834	798	733
16-#8	.0123	**1073**	1073	1073	1073	1073	994	924	862	809	761	690	591	517	460	414	344
16-#9	.0156	**1142**	1142	1142	1142	1139	1053	979	915	859	809	765	716	629	561	507	424
16-#10	.0198	**1230**	1230	1230	1230	1218	1128	1050	982	923	870	823	781	742	683	618	520
16-#11	.0244	**1325**	1325	1325	1325	1303	1208	1125	1053	990	934	884	839	799	762	728	617
18-#7	.0105	**1036**	1036	1036	1036	1036	964	895	835	783	737	614	524	457	405	364	302
18-#8	.0139	**1106**	1106	1106	1106	1106	1023	950	888	833	785	741	653	572	509	459	383
18-#9	.0176	**1183**	1183	1183	1183	1176	1089	1013	947	889	838	793	752	694	620	561	470
18-#10	.0223	**1282**	1282	1282	1282	1266	1173	1092	1022	961	906	858	814	774	738	682	576

Check availability of #14S and #18S bars

* One-half of the bars are to be placed in each of the two faces of the column that are perpendicular to the plane of bending.

† Below zigzag horizontal line of each group, concrete governs; above, tension governs.

SQUARE TIED COLUMNS—Safe Load in Kips for Various Eccentricities in Inches

f'_c = 3750 psi f_s = 24,000 psi basis
(A61 or A432 Bars, f_y = 60,000 psi)

f'_c = 3750 psi
f_y = 60,000 psi

COLUMN SIZE—30″ x 30″ CONT.

M/N † = e (in.)

18	20	22	24	26	28	30	32	34	36	38	40	42	44	46	48	50	M_o ‡ (kip.in.)
204	178	158	143	130	119	110	102	95	89	84	79	75	71	68	65	62	2872
252	221	197	178	162	148	137	127	119	111	105	99	94	89	85	81	78	3617
313	275	245	221	202	185	171	159	149	140	132	124	118	112	107	102	98	4568
374	330	295	267	243	224	207	193	180	169	159	151	143	136	130	124	118	5580
510	452	405	368	337	310	288	268	251	236	223	211	200	191	182	174	167	7956
235	206	183	165	150	138	127	118	110	104	97	92	87	83	79	75	72	3351
291	256	228	206	187	172	159	148	138	129	122	115	109	104	99	94	90	4220
359	316	283	256	233	214	198	184	172	162	153	144	137	130	124	118	113	5329
429	379	339	307	280	258	239	223	208	196	185	175	166	158	150	144	138	6510
209	183	163	146	133	122	113	105	98	91	86	81	77	73	70	66	64	2952
266	234	208	188	171	157	145	135	126	118	111	105	99	94	90	86	82	3829
328	289	258	233	212	195	180	168	157	147	139	131	124	118	113	107	103	4823
404	357	319	289	264	243	225	209	196	184	173	164	156	148	141	135	129	6091
481	426	382	346	317	292	271	252	236	222	209	198	188	179	171	163	156	7440
233	204	182	164	149	137	126	117	109	103	97	91	86	82	78	75	71	3321
296	261	232	210	191	175	162	151	141	132	124	118	111	106	101	96	92	4308
365	322	287	260	237	218	202	188	175	165	155	147	139	132	126	121	115	5426

COLUMN SIZE—32″ x 32″

18	20	22	24	26	28	30	32	34	36	38	40	42	44	46	48	50	M_o ‡ (kip.in.)
341	299	266	240	218	200	185	171	160	150	141	133	126	120	114	109	104	4843
306	268	238	214	195	179	165	153	143	134	126	119	113	107	102	97	93	4302
490	432	386	349	318	292	270	252	235	221	208	197	187	178	169	162	155	7265
288	251	223	201	183	167	154	143	134	125	118	111	105	100	95	91	87	4019
398	349	311	281	255	234	217	201	188	176	166	157	149	141	135	129	123	5736
626	554	497	451	412	380	352	328	307	289	273	258	245	233	222	213	204	9687
294	257	228	205	187	171	158	146	137	128	121	114	108	102	97	93	89	4111
353	309	275	248	226	207	191	178	166	155	146	138	131	124	119	113	108	5024
484	427	381	344	314	289	267	249	232	218	206	194	184	175	167	160	153	7170
734	668	601	547	501	463	430	401	376	354	335	317	301	287	274	262	251	12109
280	245	217	196	178	163	150	139	130	122	115	108	102	97	93	88	85	3905
347	304	271	244	222	203	188	174	163	153	144	136	129	122	116	111	106	4934
416	365	326	294	268	246	227	211	197	185	174	165	156	148	141	135	129	6029
567	501	449	406	371	341	316	295	276	259	244	231	219	209	199	190	182	8604
261	228	202	182	165	151	139	129	121	113	106	100	95	90	86	82	78	3616
323	283	251	226	206	189	174	162	151	141	133	126	119	113	108	103	98	4556
399	350	312	281	256	235	217	202	189	177	167	158	149	142	135	129	124	5756
476	419	375	338	309	284	262	244	228	214	202	191	181	172	164	157	150	7034
646	572	514	466	426	393	364	339	318	299	282	267	253	241	230	220	211	10038
295	258	229	206	188	172	159	147	137	129	121	114	108	103	98	93	89	4133
364	320	285	256	233	214	198	184	172	161	151	143	136	129	123	117	112	5207
449	395	353	318	290	267	247	229	214	201	189	179	170	161	154	147	141	6578
535	472	422	382	349	321	297	277	259	243	229	217	206	196	186	178	171	8039
258	226	200	180	164	150	138	128	120	112	105	99	94	89	85	81	78	3680
329	288	256	231	210	192	178	165	154	144	136	128	121	115	110	105	100	4649
405	356	317	286	261	239	221	205	192	180	170	160	152	144	138	131	126	5858
498	439	392	355	323	297	275	256	239	225	212	200	190	181	172	165	157	7401

‡ M_o = capacity in pure bending, ($N = 0$); for extrapolation, see page 11-5.

SQUARE TIED COLUMNS—Safe Load in Kips for Various Eccentricities in Inches

$f'_c = 3750$ psi $f_s = 24{,}000$ psi basis

(A61 or A432 Bars, $f_y = 60{,}000$ psi)

COLUMN SIZE—34″ x 34″

Bars*	p	M/N † = e (in.) 0	1	2	3	4	5	6	7	8	10	12	14	16	18	20	22
4-#18S	.0138	**1247**	1247	1247	1247	1247	1164	1083	1012	951	847	669	533	442	378	330	293
6-#14S	.0117	**1196**	1196	1196	1196	1196	1131	1053	985	925	817	604	479	396	338	295	262
6-#18S	.0208	**1410**	1410	1410	1410	1404	1302	1213	1136	1068	954	862	753	631	544	477	425
8-#11	.0108	**1175**	1175	1175	1175	1175	1115	1038	970	912	773	569	450	372	318	277	245
8-#14S	.0156	**1288**	1288	1288	1288	1288	1212	1130	1058	995	889	769	615	513	440	385	342
8-#18S	.0277	**1573**	1573	1573	1573	1550	1439	1343	1259	1185	1060	959	875	802	695	613	549
10-#10	.0110	**1180**	1180	1180	1180	1180	1120	1043	975	916	788	580	459	380	324	283	250
10-#11	.0135	**1239**	1239	1239	1239	1239	1171	1092	1022	960	857	688	548	456	390	340	302
10-#14S	.0195	**1380**	1380	1380	1380	1380	1293	1206	1131	1064	952	861	742	622	536	470	419
10-#18S	.0346	**1737**	1737	1737	1737	1696	1576	1473	1382	1301	1166	1056	965	888	823	740	665
12-#9	.0104	**1165**	1165	1165	1165	1165	1108	1031	965	906	755	555	439	363	309	269	238
12-#10	.0132	**1232**	1232	1232	1232	1232	1166	1087	1017	956	854	678	540	448	383	335	297
12-#11	.0162	**1303**	1303	1303	1303	1303	1228	1145	1073	1009	902	800	642	535	459	402	358
12-#14S	.0234	**1471**	1471	1471	1471	1471	1373	1282	1203	1133	1015	919	840	726	627	552	493
14-#9	.0121	**1206**	1206	1206	1206	1206	1145	1066	998	938	837	634	503	417	356	311	276
14-#10	.0154	**1283**	1283	1283	1283	1283	1212	1131	1059	996	890	770	617	514	441	385	343
14-#11	.0189	**1366**	1366	1366	1366	1366	1284	1199	1124	1058	946	856	730	612	526	462	412
14-#14S	.0272	**1563**	1563	1563	1563	1562	1453	1358	1275	1202	1078	977	893	823	715	631	565
16-#8	.0109	**1179**	1179	1179	1179	1179	1121	1044	976	917	791	583	461	382	326	284	252
16-#9	.0138	**1247**	1247	1247	1247	1247	1181	1101	1031	970	866	709	565	470	402	352	312
16-#10	.0176	**1335**	1335	1335	1335	1335	1259	1174	1101	1036	927	838	690	577	496	435	387
16-#11	.0216	**1430**	1430	1430	1430	1430	1340	1252	1175	1106	991	897	815	686	591	520	464
18-#8	.0123	**1211**	1211	1211	1211	1211	1150	1071	1003	943	841	645	512	425	363	317	281
18-#9	.0156	**1288**	1288	1288	1288	1288	1218	1136	1064	1001	895	781	626	522	447	392	348
18-#10	.0198	**1387**	1387	1387	1387	1387	1304	1218	1142	1075	963	871	762	639	550	483	431
18-#11	.0243	**1494**	1494	1494	1494	1494	1396	1305	1225	1154	1035	937	857	757	654	577	515

COLUMN SIZE—36″ x 36″

Bars*	p	0	1	2	3	4	5	6	7	8	10	12	14	16	18	20	22
4-#18S	.0123	**1359**	1359	1359	1359	1359	1302	1214	1137	1070	957	754	594	490	417	363	321
6-#18S	.0185	**1522**	1522	1522	1522	1522	1444	1349	1266	1192	1068	967	840	700	600	525	467
8-#14S	.0139	**1399**	1399	1399	1399	1399	1350	1261	1184	1115	999	864	685	567	484	422	374
8-#18S	.0247	**1685**	1685	1685	1685	1685	1585	1483	1393	1313	1179	1069	978	890	768	676	603
10-#11	.0120	**1350**	1350	1350	1350	1350	1308	1222	1146	1079	966	774	610	504	429	373	330
10-#14S	.0174	**1491**	1491	1491	1491	1491	1433	1340	1259	1186	1064	965	826	688	590	516	458
10-#18S	.0309	**1848**	1848	1848	1848	1848	1726	1616	1520	1434	1289	1170	1072	988	917	816	731

Check availability of #14S and #18S bars.

* One-half of the bars are to be placed in each of the two faces of the column that are perpendicular to the plane of bending.

† Below zigzag horizontal line of each group, concrete governs; above, tension governs.

SQUARE TIED COLUMNS—Safe Load in Kips for Various Eccentricities in Inches

$f'_c = 3750$ psi $f_s = 24{,}000$ psi basis

(A61 or A432 Bars, $f_y = 60{,}000$ psi)

$f'_c = 3750$ psi

$f_y = 60{,}000$ psi

COLUMN SIZE—34″ x 34″

M/N † = e (in.)

24	26	28	30	32	34	36	38	40	42	44	46	48	50	52	54	56	M_o ‡ (kip-in.)
263	239	219	202	188	175	164	154	146	138	131	125	119	114	109	104	100	5227
235	213	195	180	167	155	146	137	129	122	116	111	105	101	97	93	89	4627
384	349	321	296	276	257	241	227	215	204	194	184	176	168	161	155	149	7841
220	200	183	168	156	146	136	128	121	114	109	103	99	94	90	87	83	4319
308	280	256	237	220	205	192	181	171	162	154	146	140	134	128	123	118	6168
497	454	417	386	360	336	316	298	282	267	254	242	232	222	213	204	197	10455
225	204	187	172	160	149	139	131	124	117	111	106	101	96	92	89	85	4416
272	247	226	208	193	180	169	159	150	142	135	129	123	117	112	108	104	5398
378	344	316	292	271	253	238	224	211	200	190	181	173	166	159	153	147	7710
603	552	509	472	440	413	388	366	347	329	313	299	286	274	263	253	243	13069
214	194	178	164	152	141	132	125	117	111	106	100	96	92	88	84	81	4193
267	242	222	205	190	177	166	156	147	140	133	126	120	115	110	106	102	5299
322	293	268	248	230	215	201	190	179	170	161	153	146	140	134	129	124	6478
446	406	374	346	321	301	282	266	251	238	227	216	206	197	189	182	175	9252
248	225	206	190	176	164	154	145	136	129	123	117	111	107	102	98	94	4892
308	280	257	237	220	205	193	181	171	162	154	147	140	134	128	123	118	6183
371	338	310	286	266	249	233	220	207	197	187	178	170	163	156	150	144	7558
511	467	430	398	371	347	326	307	291	276	262	250	239	229	219	211	203	10794
226	205	187	173	160	149	140	132	124	117	112	106	101	97	93	89	85	4436
281	255	234	216	200	187	175	165	155	147	140	133	127	121	116	112	107	5591
349	317	291	269	250	233	219	206	195	184	175	167	159	152	146	140	135	7066
419	382	351	324	302	282	265	249	236	223	212	202	193	185	177	170	164	8638
252	229	210	193	179	167	157	147	139	132	125	119	114	109	104	100	96	4991
313	285	261	241	224	209	196	184	174	165	157	149	142	136	130	125	120	6290
389	354	325	300	279	261	245	230	218	206	196	187	178	171	164	157	151	7949
466	425	391	362	336	315	295	278	263	250	237	226	216	207	198	191	183	9717

COLUMN SIZE—36″ x 36″

24	26	28	30	32	34	36	38	40	42	44	46	48	50	52	54	56	M_o ‡ (kip-in.)
288	261	239	220	204	190	178	167	158	149	142	135	129	123	118	113	109	5611
420	382	350	323	300	280	262	247	233	221	210	200	191	182	175	168	161	8417
336	305	279	257	238	222	208	196	185	175	166	158	151	144	138	132	127	6600
544	496	456	421	392	366	344	324	306	290	276	263	251	240	230	221	213	11223
296	269	246	226	210	196	183	172	162	154	146	139	132	127	121	116	112	5773
412	375	344	317	294	275	258	242	229	217	206	196	187	179	171	165	158	8250
662	605	557	516	480	449	422	398	377	358	340	324	310	297	285	274	263	14029

‡ M_o = capacity in pure bending, ($N = 0$); for extrapolation, see page 11-5.

SQUARE TIED COLUMNS—Safe Load in Kips for Various Eccentricities in Inches

$f'_c = 3750$ psi $f_s = 24{,}000$ psi basis
(A61 or A432 Bars, $f_y = 60{,}000$ psi)

COLUMN SIZE—36″ x 36″ CONT.

Bars*	p	M/N † = e (in.) 0	1	2	3	4	5	6	7	8	10	12	14	16	18	20	22
12-#10	.0118	**1343**	1343	1343	1343	1343	1303	1217	1141	1074	962	762	600	495	421	367	325
12-#11	.0144	**1414**	1414	1414	1414	1414	1366	1277	1199	1129	1012	899	714	592	505	441	391
12-#14S	.0208	**1583**	1583	1583	1583	1583	1515	1419	1333	1258	1130	1025	939	803	691	606	540
12-#18S	.0370	**2011**	2011	2011	2011	2000	1866	1749	1646	1555	1399	1271	1165	1075	998	932	852
14-#9	.0108	**1318**	1318	1318	1318	1318	1281	1196	1121	1056	945	712	560	461	392	340	301
14-#10	.0137	**1395**	1395	1395	1395	1395	1350	1262	1184	1116	1000	866	686	568	484	422	374
14-#11	.0169	**1478**	1478	1478	1478	1478	1424	1332	1251	1180	1058	960	813	676	579	507	450
14-#14S	.0243	**1675**	1675	1675	1675	1675	1597	1497	1408	1329	1195	1086	995	912	788	693	619
16-#9	.0123	**1359**	1359	1359	1359	1359	1318	1232	1155	1088	975	797	629	519	442	385	341
16-#10	.0157	**1447**	1447	1447	1447	1447	1398	1307	1227	1157	1038	941	768	638	546	477	423
16-#11	.0193	**1541**	1541	1541	1541	1541	1482	1387	1303	1230	1104	1002	907	758	651	570	508
16-#14S	.0278	**1767**	1767	1767	1767	1767	1679	1574	1482	1400	1260	1146	1050	969	881	777	695
18-#8	.0110	**1322**	1322	1322	1322	1322	1286	1201	1126	1060	949	725	570	469	399	347	307
18-#9	.0139	**1399**	1399	1399	1399	1399	1356	1267	1190	1121	1005	878	696	576	492	429	380
18-#10	.0176	**1499**	1499	1499	1499	1499	1445	1352	1270	1198	1075	975	847	706	605	530	471
18-#11	.0217	**1605**	1605	1605	1605	1605	1539	1442	1356	1279	1150	1044	956	836	720	633	564
20-#8	.0122	**1355**	1355	1355	1355	1355	1316	1229	1153	1086	973	792	624	516	439	382	338
20-#9	.0154	**1440**	1440	1440	1440	1440	1393	1303	1224	1153	1035	938	761	632	540	472	419
20-#10	.0196	**1550**	1550	1550	1550	1550	1492	1397	1313	1239	1113	1010	923	772	663	582	518

COLUMN SIZE—38″ x 38″

Bars*	p	M/N † = e (in.) 0	2	4	6	8	10	12	14	16	18	20	22	24	26	28	30
4-#18S	.0111	**1477**	1477	1477	1354	1198	1074	848	661	541	458	397	351	314	284	259	239
6-#18S	.0166	**1640**	1640	1640	1493	1324	1189	1080	934	773	660	575	510	458	415	380	351
8-#14S	.0125	**1517**	1517	1517	1402	1243	1116	970	760	625	530	461	407	365	330	302	278
8-#18S	.0222	**1803**	1803	1803	1630	1449	1304	1186	1087	984	845	740	659	594	540	495	457
10-#11	.0108	**1468**	1468	1468	1361	1206	1082	868	677	555	470	407	360	322	291	266	245
10-#14S	.0156	**1609**	1609	1609	1482	1317	1184	1076	917	759	647	564	500	448	407	372	343
10-#18S	.0277	**1966**	1966	1966	1768	1574	1419	1291	1185	1095	1016	895	799	722	659	605	560
12-#10	.0106	**1461**	1461	1461	1355	1201	1078	855	666	545	462	400	353	316	286	261	240
12-#11	.0130	**1532**	1532	1532	1417	1258	1130	1009	792	652	554	481	426	382	346	316	291
12-#14S	.0187	**1701**	1701	1701	1563	1390	1252	1139	1045	885	758	663	588	529	481	441	407
12-#18S	.0332	**2129**	2129	2129	1904	1699	1533	1397	1283	1186	1102	1030	932	845	772	711	659
14-#10	.0123	**1513**	1513	1513	1402	1244	1117	971	761	625	531	461	408	365	331	302	278
14-#11	.0151	**1596**	1596	1596	1474	1309	1178	1070	901	745	635	553	490	440	399	365	336
14-#14S	.0218	**1793**	1793	1793	1643	1464	1320	1201	1103	1006	864	758	674	608	553	507	469
16-#9	.0111	**1477**	1477	1477	1371	1215	1091	894	697	572	485	420	371	332	301	275	253
16-#10	.0141	**1565**	1565	1565	1448	1286	1156	1051	852	703	598	521	461	413	375	343	316
16-#11	.0173	**1659**	1659	1659	1530	1361	1225	1114	1006	835	714	623	553	497	451	413	381
16-#14S	.0249	**1885**	1885	1885	1723	1537	1387	1264	1161	1073	966	849	758	684	623	572	529
18-#9	.0125	**1517**	1517	1517	1407	1249	1122	984	772	635	539	468	414	371	336	307	283
18-#10	.0158	**1617**	1617	1617	1494	1328	1195	1087	939	778	663	578	513	460	418	382	353
18-#11	.0194	**1723**	1723	1723	1586	1412	1273	1158	1063	921	790	691	614	553	502	461	425

Check availability of #14S and #18S bars

* One-half of the bars are to be placed in each of the two faces of the column that are perpendicular to the plane of bending.

† Below zigzag horizontal line of each group, concrete governs; above, tension governs.

SQUARE TIED COLUMNS—Safe Load in Kips for Various Eccentricities in Inches

$f'_c = 3750$ psi $\quad f_s = 24{,}000$ psi basis

(A61 or A432 Bars, $f_y = 60{,}000$ psi)

$f'_c = 3750$ psi

$f_y = 60{,}000$ psi

COLUMN SIZE—36″ x 36″ CONT.

M/N † = e (in.)

24	26	28	30	32	34	36	38	40	42	44	46	48	50	52	54	56	M_o‡ (kip-in.)
291	264	241	222	206	192	180	169	159	151	143	136	130	124	119	114	110	5665
351	319	292	269	250	233	218	205	194	183	174	166	158	151	145	139	134	6927
487	443	407	376	349	326	306	288	272	258	245	233	223	213	204	196	189	9900
773	708	653	606	565	530	498	470	445	423	403	384	367	352	338	325	313	16835
270	245	224	206	191	178	166	156	147	140	132	126	120	115	110	105	101	5228
336	305	279	257	239	223	208	196	185	175	166	158	151	144	138	133	128	6609
405	368	337	311	289	269	253	238	224	213	202	192	183	175	168	161	155	8082
559	509	468	433	403	376	353	333	315	298	284	270	258	247	237	228	219	11550
306	278	254	234	217	202	189	178	168	159	151	144	137	131	125	120	116	5975
380	346	317	292	271	253	237	223	210	199	189	180	172	164	157	151	145	7554
457	416	382	352	327	306	287	270	255	241	229	218	209	200	191	184	177	9237
629	574	528	489	455	426	400	377	356	338	322	307	293	280	269	258	249	13200
275	249	228	210	194	181	170	159	150	142	135	128	122	117	112	108	103	5332
342	310	284	262	243	226	212	199	188	178	169	161	153	147	141	135	130	6722
424	385	353	326	303	283	265	249	235	223	212	202	193	184	176	169	163	8498
508	463	425	393	365	341	320	301	285	270	257	244	233	223	214	206	198	10391
304	275	252	232	215	200	188	176	166	158	150	142	136	130	124	119	115	5925
377	342	313	289	268	250	234	220	208	197	187	178	170	163	156	149	144	7469
466	424	389	360	334	312	293	275	260	247	234	223	213	204	195	188	180	9442

COLUMN SIZE—38″ x 38″

M/N † = e (in.)

32	34	36	38	40	42	44	46	48	50	52	54	56	58	60	62	64	M_o‡ (kip-in.)
221	206	192	181	170	161	153	145	139	133	127	122	117	112	108	105	101	5995
325	303	284	267	252	239	226	216	206	197	188	181	174	167	161	156	150	8993
258	240	225	211	199	188	179	170	162	155	148	142	137	132	127	122	118	7032
425	397	372	350	331	314	298	284	271	259	248	238	229	221	213	206	199	11991
227	211	197	185	175	165	157	149	142	136	130	125	120	115	111	107	104	6147
318	297	278	261	247	233	222	211	201	192	184	177	170	164	158	152	147	8790
521	487	457	431	407	386	367	350	335	320	307	295	284	273	264	255	246	14989
222	207	194	182	172	162	154	146	140	133	128	122	118	113	109	105	102	6031
270	251	235	221	208	197	187	178	170	162	155	149	143	138	133	128	124	7377
377	352	330	311	293	278	264	251	240	229	220	211	203	195	188	182	176	10548
614	575	540	509	482	457	435	415	397	380	364	350	337	325	314	303	293	17987
258	240	225	211	199	188	179	170	162	155	148	142	137	132	127	122	118	7036
312	291	272	256	242	229	217	207	197	188	181	173	166	160	154	149	144	8606
435	407	381	359	339	321	305	291	278	266	255	244	235	226	218	211	204	12306
234	218	204	192	181	171	162	154	147	140	134	129	124	119	115	111	107	6359
293	273	255	240	226	214	203	194	185	176	169	162	156	150	145	140	135	8041
354	330	309	291	274	260	247	235	224	214	205	197	189	182	176	170	164	9836
492	460	432	407	384	364	346	330	315	302	289	278	267	257	248	240	232	14064
262	244	228	215	202	191	182	173	165	158	151	145	139	134	129	124	120	7154
327	305	286	269	253	240	228	217	207	198	189	182	175	168	162	156	151	9047
395	368	345	325	307	291	276	263	251	240	230	221	212	204	197	190	184	11065

‡ M_o = capacity in pure bending, ($N = 0$); for extrapolation, see page 11-5.

SQUARE TIED COLUMNS—Safe Load in Kips for Various Eccentricities in Inches

f'_c = 3750 psi f_s = 24,000 psi basis
(A61 or A432 Bars, f_y = 60,000 psi)

COLUMN SIZE—38″ x 38″ CONT.

Bars*	p	M/N † = e (in.) 0	2	4	6	8	10	12	14	16	18	20	22	24	26	28	30
20-#8	.0109	**1473**	1473	1473	1368	1213	1089	888	692	568	481	417	368	330	298	272	251
20-#9	.0139	**1558**	1558	1558	1444	1282	1153	1048	844	696	592	515	456	409	371	339	312
20-#10	.0176	**1668**	1668	1668	1540	1370	1234	1123	1024	850	727	635	564	507	460	422	389
20-#11	.0216	**1787**	1787	1787	1642	1463	1320	1202	1103	1005	864	757	674	607	553	507	468
22-#8	.0120	**1505**	1505	1505	1397	1240	1114	960	752	618	524	455	402	360	326	298	274
22-#9	.0152	**1599**	1599	1599	1480	1316	1184	1076	913	755	644	561	497	446	405	371	342
22-#10	.0193	**1720**	1720	1720	1586	1412	1273	1158	1063	921	789	691	614	552	502	460	425
22-#11	.0238	**1850**	1850	1850	1698	1514	1367	1246	1144	1058	936	822	733	661	602	553	511

COLUMN SIZE—40″ x 40″

Bars*	p	0	2	4	6	8	10	12	14	16	18	20	22	24	26	28	30
4-#18S	.0100	**1601**	1601	1601	1503	1334	1199	951	733	596	502	433	381	341	308	281	258
6-#18S	.0150	**1764**	1764	1764	1645	1464	1319	1200	1036	851	722	628	555	497	450	411	379
8-#14S	.0113	**1642**	1642	1642	1551	1379	1242	1087	841	686	580	502	442	395	357	326	300
8-#18S	.0200	**1927**	1927	1927	1786	1593	1438	1310	1203	1083	926	808	717	645	585	536	495
10-#14S	.0141	**1734**	1734	1734	1633	1455	1312	1195	1015	833	707	614	542	486	440	402	370
10-#18S	.0250	**2091**	2091	2091	1927	1722	1556	1419	1305	1207	1114	977	871	785	714	656	606
12-#11	.0117	**1656**	1656	1656	1567	1394	1256	1130	876	716	605	524	462	413	374	341	313
12-#14S	.0169	**1825**	1825	1825	1716	1531	1382	1260	1157	973	829	722	639	574	520	476	438
12-#18S	.0300	**2254**	2254	2254	2067	1850	1674	1528	1406	1302	1212	1134	1016	918	838	770	713
14-#10	.0111	**1637**	1637	1637	1550	1380	1243	1087	842	687	580	502	442	395	357	326	300
14-#11	.0137	**1720**	1720	1720	1624	1447	1305	1189	997	818	694	602	532	476	431	394	363
14-#14S	.0197	**1917**	1917	1917	1797	1606	1452	1324	1218	1105	945	825	733	659	598	548	505
16-#9	.0100	**1601**	1601	1601	1518	1350	1216	1001	772	628	529	457	403	359	325	296	272
16-#10	.0127	**1689**	1689	1689	1598	1423	1283	1168	942	772	653	566	500	447	405	370	340
16-#11	.0156	**1784**	1784	1784	1682	1500	1354	1234	1113	917	780	678	600	538	488	446	411
16-#14S	.0225	**2009**	2009	2009	1879	1681	1521	1389	1278	1183	1056	925	823	741	674	618	571
18-#9	.0113	**1642**	1642	1642	1556	1385	1248	1102	854	697	589	509	449	401	363	331	304
18-#10	.0143	**1741**	1741	1741	1645	1467	1323	1205	1039	854	725	630	556	499	452	413	380
18-#11	.0176	**1847**	1847	1847	1739	1553	1403	1280	1176	1012	863	752	667	599	543	497	458
18-#14S	.0253	**2101**	2101	2101	1960	1756	1590	1453	1338	1239	1154	1022	911	822	748	687	635
20-#9	.0125	**1683**	1683	1683	1593	1419	1280	1165	933	764	647	560	495	443	400	366	336
20-#10	.0159	**1793**	1793	1793	1692	1510	1363	1242	1132	934	794	691	612	549	497	455	419
20-#11	.0195	**1911**	1911	1911	1796	1606	1452	1325	1218	1104	944	824	732	658	597	547	505
22-#8	.0109	**1629**	1629	1629	1545	1375	1239	1075	832	678	572	495	436	390	352	321	296
22-#9	.0138	**1723**	1723	1723	1630	1454	1311	1194	1010	829	703	611	539	483	437	400	368
22-#10	.0175	**1844**	1844	1844	1738	1553	1403	1280	1176	1011	862	752	666	598	543	497	458
24-#8	.0119	**1661**	1661	1661	1575	1403	1264	1151	895	732	619	536	473	423	382	349	321
24-#9	.0150	**1764**	1764	1764	1668	1488	1343	1224	1085	893	759	660	584	523	474	433	399
24-#10	.0191	**1896**	1896	1896	1785	1596	1443	1317	1211	1087	929	811	719	647	587	538	496

Check availability of #14S and #18S bars.

* One-half of the bars are to be placed in each of the two faces of the column that are perpendicular to the plane of bending.

† Below zigzag horizontal line of each group, concrete governs; above, tension governs.

SQUARE TIED COLUMNS—Safe Load in Kips for Various Eccentricities in Inches

$f'_c = 3750$ psi $f_s = 24,000$ psi basis
(A61 or A432 Bars, $f_y = 60,000$ psi)

$f'_c = 3750$ psi
$f_y = 60,000$ psi

COLUMN SIZE—38″ x 38″ CONT.

M/N † = e (in.) 32	34	36	38	40	42	44	46	48	50	52	54	56	58	60	62	64	M_o ‡ (kip-in.)
232	216	202	190	179	169	161	153	146	139	133	128	123	118	114	110	106	6304
289	270	253	237	224	212	201	191	183	175	167	160	154	148	143	138	133	7949
361	337	315	297	280	265	252	240	229	219	210	201	194	186	180	173	168	10052
435	406	381	359	339	321	305	291	277	265	254	244	235	226	218	211	204	12295
254	237	222	208	196	186	176	168	160	153	146	140	135	130	125	121	117	6934
317	295	277	260	245	232	220	210	200	191	183	176	169	163	157	151	146	8744
394	368	345	325	307	290	276	263	251	240	230	221	212	204	197	190	184	11057
475	444	416	392	371	351	334	318	304	291	279	268	257	248	239	231	223	13524

COLUMN SIZE—40″ x 40″

32	34	36	38	40	42	44	46	48	50	52	54	56	58	60	62	64	M_o ‡ (kip-in.)
238	222	207	195	183	173	164	156	149	142	136	130	125	121	116	112	108	6379
351	327	306	287	271	257	243	232	221	211	202	194	186	179	173	167	161	9569
277	258	241	227	214	202	192	182	174	166	159	152	146	141	136	131	126	7464
459	428	401	377	356	337	320	305	291	278	267	256	246	237	228	220	213	12759
343	319	299	281	265	250	238	226	216	206	197	189	182	175	169	163	157	9330
563	526	493	464	439	416	395	376	359	344	330	317	304	293	283	273	264	15949
290	270	253	237	224	211	201	191	182	174	166	159	153	147	142	137	132	7826
407	379	355	334	315	298	283	269	257	246	235	226	217	209	201	194	188	11196
663	620	582	549	519	492	468	446	426	408	391	376	362	349	336	325	314	19139
277	258	241	227	214	202	192	182	174	166	159	152	146	141	136	131	126	7463
336	313	293	275	259	245	233	221	211	202	193	185	178	171	165	159	154	9130
469	438	410	386	364	345	328	312	298	285	273	262	252	242	234	225	218	13062
252	234	219	206	194	183	174	165	157	150	144	138	132	127	123	118	114	6743
315	293	274	258	243	230	218	207	198	189	181	173	167	160	154	149	144	8529
381	355	332	312	294	279	265	252	240	229	220	211	203	195	188	181	175	10435
530	495	464	437	413	391	372	354	338	323	310	297	286	275	265	256	248	14928
282	262	245	230	217	205	195	185	176	169	161	155	149	143	138	133	128	7586
352	328	307	288	272	257	244	232	221	212	203	194	187	180	173	167	162	9595
425	396	371	349	329	312	296	282	269	257	246	236	227	219	211	203	196	11739
590	552	517	487	461	437	415	395	378	361	346	333	320	308	297	287	277	16794
311	290	271	255	240	227	215	205	195	187	179	171	165	158	153	147	142	8429
388	362	339	319	301	284	270	257	245	234	224	215	207	199	192	185	179	10661
468	437	410	385	364	344	327	311	297	284	272	261	251	242	233	225	218	13044
273	254	238	223	211	199	189	180	171	163	156	150	144	139	134	129	124	7351
341	317	297	279	263	249	236	225	214	205	196	188	181	174	168	162	156	9272
425	396	371	349	329	311	296	281	269	257	246	236	227	218	210	203	196	11728
297	277	259	243	229	217	205	195	186	178	170	163	157	151	145	140	136	8020
370	345	322	303	286	271	257	244	233	223	213	205	197	189	182	176	170	10115
460	429	402	378	357	338	321	306	292	279	267	257	247	237	229	221	214	12794

‡ M_o = capacity in pure bending, ($N = 0$); for extrapolation, see page 11-5.

SQUARE TIED COLUMNS—Safe Load in Kips for Various Eccentricities in Inches

$f'_c = 5000$ psi $f_s = 24{,}000$ psi basis

(A61 or A432 Bars, $f_y = 60{,}000$ psi)

$f'_c = 5000$ psi
$f_y = 60{,}000$ psi

Bars *	p	M/N † = e (in.)															M_o ‡ (kip-in.)
		0	1	2	3	4	5	6	7	8	9	10	11	12	14	16	
COLUMN SIZE—10″ x 10″																	
4-#5	.0124	**131**	131	104	54	33	24	18	15	13	11	10	9	8	6	5	*87*
4-#6	.0176	**142**	142	110	74	46	33	26	21	18	15	14	12	11	9	8	*121*
4-#7	.0240	**155**	155	117	94	61	44	34	28	24	21	18	16	15	12	11	*162*
4-#8	.0316	**170**	165	124	99	75	54	42	35	29	26	23	20	18	15	13	*199*
4-#9	.0400	**187**	177	132	106	88	66	52	43	36	31	28	25	22	19	16	*245*
4-#10	.0508	**209**	192	143	114	94	79	63	52	44	38	34	30	28	23	20	*303*
4-#11	.0624	**233**	207	153	122	101	86	73	60	52	45	40	36	33	27	24	*362*
6-#5	.0186	**144**	144	112	80	49	36	28	23	19	17	15	13	12	10	8	*131*
6-#6	.0264	**160**	159	121	97	68	49	39	32	27	23	21	18	17	14	12	*182*
6-#7	.0360	**179**	174	132	106	88	64	51	42	36	31	27	24	22	19	16	*243*
6-#8	.0474	**202**	189	142	113	94	78	62	51	43	38	33	30	27	23	20	*298*
COLUMN SIZE—11″ x 11″																	
4-#5	.0102	**153**	153	129	69	41	29	22	18	15	13	12	10	9	8	7	*102*
4-#6	.0145	**164**	164	136	95	57	40	31	25	21	19	16	15	13	11	9	*142*
4-#7	.0198	**177**	177	144	117	75	54	42	34	29	25	22	20	18	15	13	*190*
4-#8	.0261	**193**	193	152	124	93	67	52	42	36	31	27	24	22	18	16	*237*
4-#9	.0331	**210**	210	162	131	110	82	64	52	44	38	34	30	27	23	20	*293*
4-#10	.0420	**232**	227	174	141	118	99	78	64	54	47	42	37	34	28	24	*364*
4-#11	.0516	**255**	244	186	150	126	109	91	75	64	56	49	44	40	34	29	*437*
4-#14S	.0544	**312**	284	214	172	143	123	108	96	83	73	65	59	53	45	39	*600*
6-#5	.0154	**166**	166	138	102	61	43	34	27	23	20	18	16	14	12	10	*153*
6-#6	.0218	**182**	182	148	121	84	60	47	38	32	28	25	22	20	17	14	*213*
6-#7	.0298	**202**	202	160	130	110	79	62	51	43	37	33	29	27	22	19	*286*
6-#8	.0392	**225**	223	172	140	118	97	76	62	53	46	41	36	33	28	24	*355*
6-#9	.0496	**250**	243	186	151	127	110	91	76	64	56	50	45	40	34	29	*440*

Check availability of #14S and #18S bars.

* One-half of the bars are to be placed in each of the two faces of the column that are perpendicular to the plane of bending.

† Below zigzag horizontal line of each group, concrete governs; above, tension governs.

‡ M_o = capacity in pure bending, ($N = 0$), for extrapolation, see page 11-5.

SQUARE TIED COLUMNS—Safe Load in Kips for Various Eccentricities in Inches

f'_c = 5000 psi f_s = 24,000 psi basis
(A61 or A432 Bars, f_y = 60,000 psi)

f'_c = 5000 psi
f_y = 60,000 psi

COLUMN SIZE—12″ x 12″

Bars *	p	M/N † = e (in.) 0	1	2	3	4	5	6	7	8	9	10	12	14	16	18	M_o ‡ (kip-in.)
4-#6	.0122	**188**	188	165	121	69	48	37	30	25	22	19	15	13	11	10	*163*
4-#7	.0167	**201**	201	174	143	92	65	50	40	34	29	26	21	17	15	13	*219*
4-#8	.0219	**217**	217	183	150	114	81	62	50	42	37	32	26	22	19	16	*274*
4-#9	.0278	**234**	234	193	159	135	99	77	62	53	45	40	32	27	23	20	*341*
4-#10	.0353	**256**	256	207	170	144	121	94	77	65	56	49	40	34	29	25	*425*
4-#11	.0433	**280**	280	221	181	153	133	111	91	77	67	59	48	40	35	30	*512*
4-#14S	.0625	**336**	327	253	206	174	151	133	119	102	89	79	64	54	47	41	*708*
6-#5	.0129	**190**	190	167	130	74	52	40	32	27	23	21	16	14	12	10	*175*
6-#6	.0183	**206**	206	178	147	102	72	55	45	38	33	29	23	19	17	14	*245*
6-#7	.0250	**226**	226	191	158	134	95	73	60	51	44	38	31	26	22	20	*329*
6-#8	.0329	**249**	249	204	168	143	117	91	74	63	54	48	39	32	28	24	*412*
6-#9	.0417	**275**	275	221	181	154	134	110	91	77	67	59	48	40	35	30	*512*
6-#10	.0529	**308**	308	241	198	168	145	128	110	93	81	72	59	49	43	37	*638*
6-#11	.0650	**343**	336	262	214	182	157	139	124	109	95	85	69	59	51	45	*768*
8-#5	.0172	**203**	203	176	145	98	69	53	43	36	31	27	22	18	16	14	*234*
8-#6	.0244	**224**	224	190	157	133	94	73	59	50	43	38	31	26	22	19	*327*
8-#7	.0333	**250**	250	208	172	146	123	96	78	66	58	51	41	34	30	26	*439*

COLUMN SIZE—13″ x 13″

Bars *	p	0	1	2	3	4	5	6	7	8	9	10	12	14	16	18	M_o ‡ (kip-in.)
4-#6	.0104	**215**	215	196	154	84	57	44	35	29	25	22	18	15	13	11	*184*
4-#7	.0142	**228**	228	206	171	111	77	58	47	39	34	30	24	20	17	15	*248*
4-#8	.0187	**244**	244	216	179	138	96	73	59	50	43	37	30	25	21	19	*312*
4-#9	.0237	**261**	261	227	189	162	118	90	73	61	53	46	37	31	27	23	*389*
4-#10	.0301	**283**	283	242	201	172	144	111	90	76	66	58	46	39	33	29	*486*
4-#11	.0369	**306**	306	258	214	183	160	131	107	91	78	69	56	47	40	35	*587*
4-#14S	.0533	**363**	363	293	243	207	180	160	143	121	105	93	76	64	55	48	*816*
6-#5	.0110	**217**	217	198	165	90	61	47	38	31	27	24	19	16	13	12	*198*
6-#6	.0156	**233**	233	210	175	123	85	65	52	44	38	33	27	22	19	17	*277*
6-#7	.0213	**253**	253	224	187	160	112	86	70	59	51	44	36	30	26	22	*372*
6-#8	.0280	**276**	276	239	199	170	139	107	87	73	63	56	45	37	32	28	*469*
6-#9	.0355	**301**	301	257	214	183	160	131	107	90	78	69	55	46	40	35	*584*
6-#10	.0451	**335**	335	279	232	198	173	154	130	110	95	84	68	57	49	43	*729*
6-#11	.0554	**370**	370	302	251	214	187	166	149	129	113	100	81	68	59	52	*880*
8-#5	.0147	**230**	230	208	173	118	81	62	50	42	36	32	25	21	18	16	*264*
8-#6	.0208	**251**	251	224	187	160	111	85	69	58	50	44	35	30	25	22	*369*
8-#7	.0284	**277**	277	243	203	174	145	112	91	77	67	59	47	40	34	30	*496*
8-#8	.0374	**308**	308	263	219	187	164	138	113	96	83	73	59	50	43	37	*625*

Check availability of #14S and #18S bars.

* One-half of the bars are to be placed in each of the two faces of the column that are perpendicular to the plane of bending.

† Below zigzag horizontal line of each group, concrete governs; above, tension governs.

‡ M_o = capacity in pure bending, (N = 0), for extrapolation, see page 11-5.

SQUARE TIED COLUMNS—Safe Load in Kips for Various Eccentricities in Inches

f'_c = 5000 psi f_s = 24,000 psi basis
(A61 or A432 Bars, f_y = 60,000 psi)

COLUMN SIZE—14″ x 14″

Bars *	p	M/N † = e (in.) 0	1	2	3	4	5	6	7	8	9	10	11	12	13	14	15
4-#7	.0122	**257**	257	241	202	133	90	68	54	45	39	34	30	27	25	22	21
4-#8	.0161	**272**	272	252	211	166	112	85	68	57	49	43	38	34	31	28	26
4-#9	.0204	**289**	289	264	222	191	138	105	84	71	61	53	47	43	39	36	33
4-#10	.0259	**311**	311	280	235	202	170	129	104	88	75	66	59	53	48	44	41
4-#11	.0318	**335**	335	297	249	214	188	154	125	105	90	79	71	64	58	53	49
4-#14S	.0459	**391**	391	335	281	241	212	188	167	141	123	108	97	87	80	73	68
6-#6	.0135	**262**	262	245	206	147	99	75	60	50	43	38	33	30	27	25	23
6-#7	.0184	**281**	281	261	219	189	131	100	80	67	58	51	45	40	37	34	31
6-#8	.0242	**304**	304	277	232	200	163	124	100	84	72	64	57	51	46	43	39
6-#9	.0306	**330**	330	295	248	214	188	152	123	104	89	79	70	63	58	53	49
6-#10	.0389	**363**	363	319	268	231	203	181	151	127	110	97	87	78	71	66	61
6-#11	.0478	**399**	399	344	289	249	219	195	176	150	130	115	103	93	85	78	73
6-#14S	.0689	**483**	483	402	337	290	254	226	204	186	170	153	138	125	115	106	98
8-#5	.0127	**258**	258	243	204	141	95	72	57	48	41	36	32	29	26	24	22
8-#6	.0180	**280**	280	260	219	189	130	99	79	66	57	50	45	40	36	33	31
8-#7	.0245	**306**	306	280	236	204	170	130	105	88	76	67	59	54	49	45	41
8-#8	.0322	**337**	337	302	254	219	192	161	131	110	95	84	75	67	61	56	52
8-#9	.0408	**371**	371	327	275	237	208	186	159	135	117	103	92	83	76	70	64

COLUMN SIZE—15″ x 15″

Bars *	p	0	1	2	3	4	5	6	7	8	9	10	11	12	13	14	15
4-#7	.0107	**288**	288	279	236	159	104	78	62	51	44	38	34	30	28	25	23
4-#8	.0140	**303**	303	291	246	198	131	98	78	65	55	48	43	39	35	32	29
4-#9	.0178	**320**	320	304	257	223	161	121	97	80	69	60	53	48	44	40	37
4-#10	.0226	**342**	342	321	271	235	198	149	120	100	86	75	67	60	54	50	46
4-#11	.0277	**366**	366	338	286	248	219	178	143	120	103	90	80	72	66	60	56
4-#14S	.0400	**422**	422	379	321	278	245	219	193	162	140	123	110	99	91	83	77
4-#18S	.0711	**565**	565	462	386	331	290	258	232	211	194	177	159	145	132	122	113
6-#6	.0117	**292**	292	284	240	176	116	86	69	57	49	42	38	34	31	28	26
6-#7	.0160	**312**	312	300	254	220	153	114	91	76	65	57	51	45	41	38	35
6-#8	.0211	**335**	335	317	268	233	190	143	115	96	82	72	64	57	52	48	44
6-#9	.0267	**361**	361	337	285	247	218	175	141	118	102	89	79	71	65	60	55
6-#10	.0339	**394**	394	362	307	266	235	210	173	145	125	110	98	88	81	74	68
6-#11	.0416	**430**	430	388	329	286	252	226	204	172	149	131	117	106	96	89	82
6-#14S	.0600	**514**	514	450	381	330	291	261	236	215	198	176	158	143	131	121	112
8-#5	.0110	**289**	289	281	238	168	110	82	65	54	46	40	36	32	29	27	25
8-#6	.0156	**310**	310	299	253	220	151	113	90	75	64	56	50	45	41	37	34
8-#7	.0213	**336**	336	320	272	236	198	149	120	100	86	75	67	60	55	50	46
8-#8	.0281	**367**	367	343	291	253	223	186	150	125	108	95	84	76	69	63	58
8-#9	.0356	**402**	402	369	313	272	241	216	183	154	132	116	104	94	85	78	73
8-#10	.0452	**446**	446	403	342	297	263	235	213	187	162	143	128	116	105	97	90
8-#11	.0555	**493**	493	438	372	323	285	256	232	212	191	169	151	137	125	116	107

Check availability of #14S and #18S bars.

* One-half of the bars are to be placed in each of the two faces of the column that are perpendicular to the plane of bending.

† Below zigzag horizontal line of each group, concrete governs; above, tension governs.

SQUARE TIED COLUMNS—Safe Load in Kips for Various Eccentricities in Inches

f'_c = 5000 psi f_s = 24,000 psi basis
(A61 or A432 Bars, f_y = 60,000 psi)

f'_c = 5000 psi
f_y = 60,000 psi

COLUMN SIZE—14″ x 14″

M/N † = e (in.) 16	17	18	19	20	21	22	23	24	25	26	27	28	29	30	31	32	M_o ‡ (kip-in.)
19	18	17	16	15	14	13	13	12	12	11	11	10	10	9	9	9	277
24	23	21	20	19	18	17	16	15	15	14	13	13	12	12	12	11	350
30	28	27	25	24	22	21	20	19	18	18	17	16	16	15	15	14	437
38	35	33	31	30	28	27	25	24	23	22	21	20	20	19	18	18	547
46	43	40	38	36	34	32	31	29	28	27	26	25	24	23	22	21	661
63	59	55	52	49	47	45	42	41	39	37	36	34	33	32	31	30	924
21	20	19	18	17	16	15	14	13	13	12	12	11	11	10	10	10	308
29	27	25	24	22	21	20	19	18	17	17	16	15	15	14	14	13	415
37	34	32	30	28	27	26	24	23	22	21	20	20	19	18	18	17	526
45	42	40	37	35	34	32	30	29	28	27	25	24	24	23	22	21	656
56	53	49	47	44	42	40	38	36	35	33	32	31	29	28	27	26	821
68	63	59	56	53	50	48	45	43	42	40	38	37	35	34	33	32	992
92	86	81	76	72	69	65	62	60	57	55	53	51	49	47	46	44	1386
20	19	18	17	16	15	14	13	13	12	12	11	11	10	10	10	9	293
29	27	25	24	22	21	20	19	18	17	17	16	15	15	14	14	13	411
38	36	34	32	30	28	27	26	24	23	22	21	21	20	19	18	18	554
48	45	42	40	38	36	34	32	31	30	28	27	26	25	24	23	23	701
60	56	53	50	47	44	42	40	38	37	35	34	33	31	30	29	28	875

COLUMN SIZE—15″ x 15″

16	17	18	19	20	21	22	23	24	25	26	27	28	29	30	31	32	M_o ‡ (kip-in.)
21	20	19	18	17	16	15	14	13	13	12	12	11	11	10	10	10	306
27	25	24	22	21	20	19	18	17	16	16	15	14	14	13	13	12	388
34	32	30	28	26	25	24	23	22	21	20	19	18	17	17	16	16	485
43	40	37	35	33	31	30	28	27	26	25	24	23	22	21	20	20	608
52	48	45	42	40	38	36	34	33	31	30	29	28	27	26	25	24	736
72	67	63	59	56	53	50	48	46	44	42	40	39	37	36	35	34	1032
106	99	93	88	83	79	75	72	69	66	63	61	58	56	54	52	51	1579
24	22	21	20	18	17	17	16	15	14	14	13	13	12	12	11	11	340
32	30	28	27	25	24	22	21	20	19	19	18	17	17	16	15	15	459
41	38	36	34	32	30	29	27	26	25	24	23	22	21	20	20	19	583
51	48	45	42	40	38	36	34	32	31	30	28	27	26	25	25	24	728
63	59	56	52	49	47	45	42	40	39	37	36	34	33	32	31	30	912
76	71	67	63	60	56	54	51	49	47	45	43	41	40	38	37	36	1105
104	98	92	87	82	78	74	71	67	65	62	60	57	55	53	51	50	1548
23	21	20	19	18	17	16	15	14	14	13	12	12	12	11	11	10	323
32	30	28	26	25	23	22	21	20	19	18	18	17	16	16	15	15	454
43	40	38	35	33	32	30	29	27	26	25	24	23	22	21	21	20	612
54	51	48	45	42	40	38	36	35	33	32	30	29	28	27	26	25	777
67	63	59	56	53	50	47	45	43	41	39	38	36	35	34	33	32	971
83	78	73	69	65	62	59	56	54	51	49	47	45	44	42	41	39	1216
100	93	88	83	78	74	71	67	64	62	59	57	55	53	51	49	48	1473

‡ M_o = capacity in pure bending, (N = 0), for extrapolation, see page 11-5.

SQUARE TIED COLUMNS—Safe Load in Kips for Various Eccentricities in Inches

f'_c = 5000 psi f_s = 24,000 psi basis
(A61 or A432 Bars, f_y = 60,000 psi)

COLUMN SIZE—16″ x 16″

Bars *	p	M/N † = e (in.) 0	1	2	3	4	5	6	7	8	9	10	11	12	13	14	15
4-#8	.0123	**336**	336	332	283	236	152	112	88	73	62	54	48	43	39	36	33
4-#9	.0156	**353**	353	346	295	257	187	138	110	91	77	68	60	54	49	45	41
4-#10	.0198	**375**	375	364	310	270	229	171	136	113	96	84	75	67	61	56	51
4-#11	.0244	**399**	399	382	326	284	252	203	162	135	116	101	90	81	73	67	62
4-#14	.0352	**455**	455	426	363	316	280	252	202	185	195	139	124	112	102	93	86
4-#18	.0625	**598**	598	516	436	377	332	297	268	245	225	205	183	166	152	140	129
6-#6	.0103	**325**	325	325	277	210	134	98	78	64	54	47	42	38	34	31	29
6-#7	.0141	**345**	345	342	291	254	177	130	103	86	73	64	56	51	46	42	39
6-#8	.0185	**368**	368	360	307	267	220	164	130	108	92	80	71	64	58	53	49
6-#9	.0234	**394**	394	380	325	283	251	201	160	133	114	100	89	80	72	66	61
6-#10	.0298	**427**	427	407	347	303	269	242	197	164	141	124	110	99	90	83	76
6-#11	.0366	**462**	462	435	371	324	288	258	233	195	168	148	132	119	108	99	92
6-#14	.0527	**547**	547	500	427	372	330	297	269	247	226	199	179	162	148	136	126
8-#6	.0138	**343**	343	341	291	253	175	129	102	85	72	63	56	50	45	41	38
8-#7	.0188	**369**	369	363	310	271	229	170	136	113	96	84	75	67	61	56	51
8-#8	.0247	**400**	400	387	331	289	256	212	170	141	121	106	94	85	77	71	65
8-#9	.0313	**435**	435	415	355	310	275	247	207	174	149	131	116	105	95	87	81
8-#10	.0397	**479**	479	450	385	336	299	269	244	212	183	161	143	129	118	108	100
8-#11	.0488	**526**	526	487	417	364	323	291	264	242	216	191	171	154	141	130	120
10-#5	.0121	**335**	335	334	285	244	157	116	91	76	64	56	50	45	40	37	34
10-#6	.0172	**361**	361	356	305	266	214	159	126	105	89	78	69	62	56	52	48
10-#7	.0234	**394**	394	384	329	287	255	208	166	139	119	104	92	83	75	69	64
10-#8	.0309	**433**	433	414	354	310	275	247	207	173	149	131	116	105	95	87	81
10-#9	.0391	**476**	476	449	384	336	299	269	244	211	182	160	143	129	118	108	100

COLUMN SIZE—17″ x 17″

Bars *	p	0	1	2	3	4	5	6	7	8	9	10	11	12	13	14	15
4-#8	.0109	**371**	371	371	323	282	175	127	100	82	69	60	53	48	43	39	36
4-#9	.0138	**388**	388	388	336	294	216	157	124	102	86	75	66	60	54	49	45
4-#10	.0176	**410**	410	410	352	308	265	194	153	126	108	94	83	74	67	62	57
4-#11	.0216	**434**	434	429	368	323	287	231	183	152	129	113	100	90	81	74	69
4-#14S	.0311	**490**	490	474	407	357	318	286	249	208	178	156	138	124	113	104	96
4-#18S	.0554	**633**	633	572	487	425	376	338	306	280	258	233	208	188	172	158	146
6-#7	.0125	**380**	380	380	332	290	204	148	116	96	81	71	62	56	51	46	43
6-#8	.0164	**403**	403	403	348	305	254	186	146	121	103	90	79	71	64	59	54
6-#9	.0208	**429**	429	427	367	322	286	228	181	149	127	111	98	88	80	73	68
6-#10	.0264	**462**	462	454	391	343	305	275	222	184	158	138	122	110	100	91	84
6-#11	.0324	**498**	498	484	416	365	325	293	263	219	188	165	147	132	120	110	101
6-#14S	.0467	**582**	582	551	475	417	371	335	305	280	254	224	200	180	165	151	140
8-#6	.0122	**378**	378	378	331	290	201	146	115	95	80	70	62	55	50	46	42
8-#7	.0166	**404**	404	404	351	308	263	193	152	126	107	93	83	74	67	61	57
8-#8	.0219	**435**	435	434	373	327	291	241	191	158	135	118	104	94	85	78	72
8-#9	.0277	**470**	470	462	398	349	311	281	234	195	167	146	129	116	106	97	89
8-#10	.0352	**514**	514	499	430	378	337	304	277	238	205	179	160	144	131	120	111
8-#11	.0432	**561**	561	538	464	407	363	328	299	274	243	213	190	172	157	144	133
10-#5	.0107	**370**	370	370	324	284	181	131	103	84	72	62	55	49	45	41	37
10-#6	.0152	**396**	396	396	345	303	246	180	142	117	100	87	77	69	62	57	52
10-#7	.0208	**429**	429	429	371	325	290	236	187	155	132	115	102	92	83	76	70
10-#8	.0273	**468**	468	462	398	349	311	281	233	194	166	145	129	116	105	97	89
10-#9	.0346	**511**	511	498	429	377	337	304	277	237	204	179	159	143	130	120	110

Check availability of #14S and #18S bars.

* One-half of the bars are to be placed in each of the two faces of the column that are perpendicular to the plane of bending.

† Below zigzag horizontal line of each group, concrete governs; above, tension governs.

SQUARE TIED COLUMNS—Safe Load in Kips for Various Eccentricities in Inches

$f'_c = 5000$ psi $f_s = 24{,}000$ psi basis
(A61 or A432 Bars, $f_y = 60{,}000$ psi)

$f'_c = 5000$ psi
$f_y = 60{,}000$ psi

COLUMN SIZE—16″ x 16″

M/N † = e (in.)																	
16	17	18	19	20	21	22	23	24	25	26	27	28	29	30	31	32	M_o ‡ (kip-in.)
30	28	26	25	23	22	21	20	19	18	17	17	16	15	15	14	14	426
38	35	33	31	29	28	26	25	24	23	22	21	20	19	19	18	17	533
48	44	42	39	37	35	33	32	30	29	27	26	25	24	23	23	22	669
58	54	50	47	45	42	40	38	36	35	33	32	31	30	29	28	27	811
80	75	70	66	62	59	56	53	51	49	47	45	43	41	40	39	37	1140
121	113	106	100	95	90	85	81	78	74	71	69	66	64	61	59	57	1771
27	25	23	22	20	19	18	17	17	16	15	15	14	13	13	12	12	372
36	33	31	29	28	26	25	24	22	21	21	20	19	18	18	17	16	502
46	42	40	37	35	33	32	30	29	27	26	25	24	23	22	22	21	639
57	53	50	47	44	42	40	38	36	34	33	32	30	29	28	27	26	800
71	66	62	58	55	52	49	47	45	43	41	40	38	37	35	34	33	1004
85	80	75	70	66	63	60	57	54	52	50	48	46	44	43	41	40	1217
117	109	103	97	92	87	83	79	75	72	69	66	64	62	59	57	55	1710
35	33	31	29	27	26	25	23	22	21	20	19	19	18	17	17	16	496
48	44	42	39	37	35	33	32	30	29	27	26	25	24	23	23	22	669
60	56	53	50	47	44	42	40	38	37	35	34	32	31	30	29	28	853
75	70	66	62	58	55	53	50	48	46	44	42	40	39	37	36	35	1067
93	87	82	77	73	69	65	62	60	57	55	52	50	49	47	45	44	1338
112	104	98	92	87	83	79	75	72	69	66	63	61	59	56	55	53	1623
32	29	27	26	24	23	22	21	20	19	18	17	17	16	15	15	14	441
44	41	39	36	34	32	31	29	28	27	25	24	23	23	22	21	20	620
59	55	52	49	46	44	41	39	38	36	34	33	32	30	29	28	27	837
75	70	66	62	58	55	52	50	48	46	44	42	40	39	37	36	35	1066
93	87	81	77	72	69	65	62	59	57	54	52	50	48	47	45	44	1334

COLUMN SIZE—17″ x 17″

16	17	18	19	20	21	22	23	24	25	26	27	28	29	30	31	32	M_o ‡ (kip-in.)
34	31	29	27	26	24	23	22	21	20	19	18	18	17	16	16	15	464
42	39	37	34	32	31	29	28	26	25	24	23	22	21	21	20	19	581
53	49	46	43	41	38	36	35	33	32	30	29	28	27	26	25	24	730
64	59	56	52	49	47	44	42	40	38	37	35	34	33	31	30	29	886
89	83	78	73	69	65	62	59	56	54	52	49	48	46	44	43	41	1248
136	127	119	112	106	101	96	91	87	83	80	77	74	71	69	66	64	1963
39	37	34	32	30	29	27	26	25	24	23	22	21	20	19	19	18	545
50	47	44	41	39	37	35	33	32	30	29	28	27	26	25	24	23	696
63	58	55	51	48	46	44	41	39	38	36	35	33	32	31	30	29	872
78	73	68	64	61	57	54	52	49	47	45	43	42	40	39	37	36	1095
94	88	82	78	73	69	66	63	60	57	55	53	51	49	47	45	44	1329
130	121	114	107	102	96	92	87	83	80	76	73	71	68	66	63	61	1872
39	36	34	32	30	28	27	26	24	23	22	21	20	20	19	18	18	538
52	49	46	43	40	38	36	35	33	31	30	29	28	27	26	25	24	727
67	62	58	55	52	49	46	44	42	40	38	37	35	34	33	32	31	929
83	77	72	68	64	61	58	55	52	50	48	46	44	43	41	40	38	1163
103	96	90	85	80	76	72	69	66	63	60	58	55	53	51	50	48	1460
124	115	108	102	96	91	87	83	79	76	73	70	67	64	62	60	58	1773
35	32	30	28	27	25	24	23	22	21	20	19	18	17	17	16	16	478
49	45	42	40	37	35	34	32	30	29	28	27	26	25	24	23	22	673
65	61	57	53	50	48	45	43	41	39	38	36	35	33	32	31	30	909
83	77	72	68	64	61	58	55	52	50	48	46	44	43	41	40	38	1161
103	96	90	84	80	76	72	68	65	62	60	57	55	53	51	49	48	1454

‡ M_o = capacity in pure bending, ($N = 0$), for extrapolation, see page 11-5.

SQUARE TIED COLUMNS—Safe Load in Kips for Various Eccentricities in Inches

$f'_c = 5000$ psi $\quad f_s = 24{,}000$ psi basis

(A61 or A432 Bars, $f_y = 60{,}000$ psi)

COLUMN SIZE—18″ x 18″

Bars*	p	M/N † = e (in.) 0	1	2	3	4	5	6	7	8	9	10	11	12	13	14	15
4-#9	.0123	**425**	425	425	379	333	248	178	138	113	96	83	73	66	59	54	50
4-#10	.0157	**447**	447	447	396	348	305	220	172	141	119	104	92	82	74	68	62
4-#11	.0193	**471**	471	471	413	364	325	262	206	169	144	125	110	99	90	82	75
4-#14	.0278	**527**	527	526	455	400	358	323	280	232	198	173	153	137	125	114	105
4-#18	.0494	**670**	670	629	540	474	422	380	346	317	293	262	234	211	192	176	163
6-#7	.0111	**417**	417	417	375	330	234	167	130	106	90	78	69	61	56	51	47
6-#8	.0146	**440**	440	440	392	345	292	210	164	135	114	99	87	78	71	65	59
6-#9	.0185	**466**	466	466	412	362	324	258	202	166	141	123	109	97	88	81	74
6-#10	.0235	**499**	499	499	437	385	344	311	249	206	175	152	135	121	110	100	93
6-#11	.0289	**535**	535	535	463	408	365	330	295	245	209	183	162	146	132	121	112
6-#14	.0417	**619**	619	605	525	463	414	375	342	315	284	249	222	200	182	167	154
6-#18	.0741	**833**	833	760	654	574	511	461	419	385	355	330	309	289	271	250	232
8-#6	.0109	**416**	416	416	374	329	232	165	128	105	89	77	68	61	55	50	46
8-#7	.0148	**442**	442	442	395	348	302	218	170	140	119	103	91	81	74	67	62
8-#8	.0195	**473**	473	473	418	368	329	272	214	176	150	130	115	103	94	85	79
8-#9	.0247	**507**	507	507	444	392	350	317	262	217	185	161	143	128	116	106	98
8-#10	.0314	**551**	551	551	478	421	377	341	312	266	227	199	176	159	144	132	122
8-#11	.0385	**598**	598	591	513	453	405	367	335	309	270	237	211	190	173	158	146
10-#6	.0136	**434**	434	434	389	342	283	203	159	130	110	95	84	75	68	62	57
10-#7	.0185	**466**	466	466	415	366	327	266	209	172	146	127	113	101	91	84	77
10-#8	.0244	**505**	505	505	444	391	350	317	261	216	184	161	142	128	116	106	98
10-#9	.0309	**548**	548	548	477	421	377	341	312	265	226	198	176	158	143	131	121
10-#10	.0392	**603**	603	597	518	458	410	372	340	313	277	243	216	195	177	163	150
12-#5	.0115	**420**	420	420	378	333	246	176	137	112	95	82	72	65	58	53	49
12-#6	.0163	**451**	451	451	404	356	318	240	188	154	131	114	100	90	81	74	68
12-#7	.0222	**491**	491	491	435	384	344	311	246	204	173	151	134	120	109	100	92
12-#8	.0293	**537**	537	537	470	415	371	336	306	254	218	190	169	152	138	126	116

COLUMN SIZE—19″ x 19″

Bars*	p	0	1	2	3	4	5	6	7	8	9	10	11	12	13	14	15
4-#9	.0111	**465**	465	465	425	375	286	201	155	126	106	91	80	72	65	59	54
4-#10	.0141	**487**	487	487	443	391	350	248	192	156	132	114	101	90	81	74	68
4-#11	.0173	**510**	510	510	461	408	365	296	230	188	159	138	121	109	98	90	82
4-#14	.0249	**567**	567	567	504	446	400	362	314	258	219	191	169	151	137	125	115
4-#18	.0443	**709**	709	688	596	525	469	424	387	356	330	292	260	234	213	195	180
6-#8	.0131	**480**	480	480	439	387	335	237	183	149	126	109	96	86	77	71	65
6-#9	.0166	**505**	505	505	459	406	364	291	226	185	156	135	119	107	96	88	81
6-#10	.0211	**539**	539	539	485	429	385	349	278	228	193	168	148	133	120	110	101
6-#11	.0259	**574**	574	574	513	454	407	369	330	272	231	201	178	160	145	132	122
6-#14	.0374	**658**	658	658	577	512	459	417	381	352	315	275	244	220	200	183	169
6-#18	.0665	**873**	873	824	715	631	564	511	466	429	397	370	346	325	302	278	257
8-#7	.0133	**481**	481	481	442	391	347	245	190	155	131	113	99	89	80	73	67
8-#8	.0175	**512**	512	512	466	412	369	307	239	195	165	143	126	113	102	93	86
8-#9	.0222	**546**	546	546	493	436	392	355	292	240	204	177	157	140	127	116	107
8-#10	.0281	**590**	590	590	528	468	420	381	349	295	251	219	194	174	158	144	133
8-#11	.0346	**638**	638	638	564	501	450	408	374	345	299	261	232	208	189	173	160
8-#14	.0499	**750**	750	744	650	577	519	471	432	398	370	345	315	284	259	238	220

Check availability of #14S and #18S bars.

* One-half of the bars are to be placed in each of the two faces of the column that are perpendicular to the plane of bending.

† Below zigzag horizontal line of each group, concrete governs; above, tension governs.

SQUARE TIED COLUMNS—Safe Load in Kips for Various Eccentricities in Inches

f'_c = 5000 psi f_s = 24,000 psi basis
(A61 or A432 Bars, f_y = 60,000 psi)

f'_c = 5000 psi
f_y = 60,000 psi

COLUMN SIZE—18″ x 18″

M/N † = e (in.)

16	17	18	19	20	21	22	23	24	25	26	27	28	30	32	34	36	M_o ‡ (kip-in.)
46	43	40	38	35	33	32	30	29	27	26	25	24	22	21	19	18	*629*
58	54	50	47	44	42	40	38	36	35	33	32	30	28	26	25	23	*791*
70	65	61	57	54	51	48	46	44	42	40	38	37	34	32	30	28	*961*
98	91	85	80	76	72	68	65	62	59	56	54	52	48	45	42	40	*1356*
151	141	133	125	118	112	106	101	97	92	89	85	82	76	71	66	63	*2155*
43	40	37	35	33	31	30	28	27	26	25	24	23	21	19	18	17	*588*
55	51	48	45	42	40	38	36	34	33	31	30	29	27	25	23	22	*753*
69	64	60	56	53	50	48	45	43	41	39	38	36	34	31	29	28	*944*
86	80	75	70	66	63	60	57	54	52	49	47	46	42	39	37	35	*1186*
103	96	90	85	80	76	72	69	65	63	60	57	55	51	48	45	42	*1442*
143	134	125	118	112	106	100	96	91	87	84	80	77	72	67	63	59	*2034*
216	202	190	180	170	162	154	147	141	135	129	124	120	111	104	98	92	*3233*
43	40	37	35	33	31	29	28	27	25	24	23	22	21	19	18	17	*580*
57	53	50	47	44	42	40	38	36	34	33	31	30	28	26	24	23	*784*
73	68	64	60	56	53	51	48	46	44	42	40	39	36	33	31	29	*1004*
91	85	79	74	70	67	63	60	57	55	52	50	48	45	42	39	37	*1259*
113	105	99	93	88	83	79	75	72	68	66	63	61	56	52	49	46	*1582*
136	127	119	112	106	100	95	91	87	83	79	76	73	68	63	59	56	*1922*
53	49	46	43	41	39	37	35	33	32	30	29	28	26	24	22	21	*726*
71	66	62	58	55	52	49	47	45	43	41	39	38	35	33	30	29	*981*
91	84	79	74	70	66	63	60	57	55	52	50	48	45	42	39	37	*1256*
112	105	98	92	87	83	78	75	71	68	65	63	60	56	52	49	46	*1574*
140	130	122	115	109	103	98	93	89	85	81	78	75	70	65	61	57	*1978*
45	42	39	37	35	33	31	30	28	27	26	25	24	22	20	19	18	*619*
63	59	55	52	49	46	44	42	40	38	36	35	33	31	29	27	25	*871*
85	79	74	70	66	62	59	56	54	51	49	47	45	42	39	37	34	*1177*
108	101	94	89	84	79	75	72	68	65	63	60	58	54	50	47	44	*1507*

COLUMN SIZE—19″ x 19″

16	17	18	19	20	21	22	23	24	25	26	27	28	30	32	34	36	M_o ‡ (kip-in.)
50	47	44	41	39	36	34	33	31	30	29	27	26	24	23	21	20	*677*
63	59	55	51	48	46	43	41	39	37	36	34	33	31	28	27	25	*852*
76	71	66	62	59	56	53	50	48	46	44	42	40	37	35	32	30	*1036*
107	99	93	87	82	78	74	70	67	64	61	59	57	52	49	46	43	*1464*
167	156	146	137	130	123	117	111	106	102	97	93	90	83	78	73	69	*2347*
60	56	52	49	46	44	41	39	37	36	34	33	31	29	27	25	24	*810*
75	70	65	61	58	54	52	49	47	45	43	41	39	36	34	32	30	*1016*
94	87	81	77	72	68	65	62	59	56	54	51	49	46	43	40	38	*1278*
113	105	98	93	87	83	78	75	71	68	65	62	60	56	52	49	46	*1554*
157	146	137	129	122	115	109	104	99	95	91	87	84	78	73	68	64	*2196*
240	224	211	199	188	179	170	162	155	148	142	137	132	122	114	107	101	*3521*
62	58	54	51	48	45	43	41	39	37	35	34	33	30	28	26	25	*842*
79	74	69	65	61	58	55	52	50	47	45	44	42	39	36	34	32	*1080*
99	92	86	81	76	72	69	65	62	59	57	55	52	49	45	42	40	*1355*
123	115	108	101	95	90	86	82	78	74	71	68	66	61	57	53	50	*1704*
148	138	130	122	115	109	104	99	94	90	86	83	79	74	69	64	61	*2072*
204	191	179	169	160	151	144	137	131	125	120	115	111	103	96	90	85	*2928*

‡ M_o = capacity in pure bending, (N = 0), for extrapolation, see page 11-5.

SQUARE TIED COLUMNS—Safe Load in Kips for Various Eccentricities in Inches

f'_c = 5000 psi f_s = 24,000 psi basis
(A61 or A432 Bars, f_y = 60,000 psi)

COLUMN SIZE—19" x 19" CONTINUED

Bars*	p	M/N † = e (in.) 0	1	2	3	4	5	6	7	8	9	10	11	12	13	14	15
10-#6	.0122	**473**	473	473	435	385	324	229	177	144	121	105	92	82	74	68	62
10-#7	.0166	**505**	505	505	463	410	367	300	233	191	161	140	123	110	100	91	84
10-#8	.0219	**544**	544	544	492	436	391	355	291	240	203	177	156	140	127	116	106
10-#9	.0277	**587**	587	587	526	467	419	381	348	293	250	218	193	173	157	144	132
10-#10	.0352	**642**	642	642	570	506	455	413	378	349	306	268	238	214	194	178	164
12-#5	.0103	**459**	459	459	424	375	282	198	152	124	104	90	79	71	64	58	53
12-#6	.0146	**491**	491	491	451	399	358	270	209	171	144	125	110	98	89	81	75
12-#7	.0199	**530**	530	530	484	429	385	349	275	225	191	166	147	131	119	108	100
12-#8	.0263	**576**	576	576	519	460	414	375	342	282	240	209	185	166	150	138	127
12-#9	.0332	**628**	628	628	560	497	447	406	372	343	294	257	228	205	186	170	157

COLUMN SIZE—20" x 20"

Bars*	p	0	1	2	3	4	5	6	7	8	9	10	11	12	13	14	15
4-#9	.0100	**506**	506	506	475	420	329	226	172	139	116	100	88	78	71	64	59
4-#10	.0127	**528**	528	528	493	437	392	279	213	173	145	125	110	98	88	81	74
4-#11	.0156	**552**	552	552	512	454	408	333	256	208	175	151	133	119	107	98	90
4-#14	.0225	**608**	608	608	556	494	444	404	349	286	242	209	185	165	149	136	125
4-#18	.0400	**751**	751	749	653	578	519	471	431	397	368	324	287	258	234	214	197
6-#8	.0119	**521**	521	521	488	433	385	266	204	165	138	119	105	93	84	77	70
6-#9	.0150	**547**	547	547	510	452	406	327	251	204	172	148	130	116	105	96	88
6-#10	.0191	**580**	580	580	537	477	429	389	309	252	213	184	162	145	131	119	110
6-#11	.0234	**615**	615	615	565	502	452	411	367	301	255	221	195	174	158	144	132
6-#14	.0338	**700**	700	700	632	562	507	461	423	391	347	302	268	240	218	200	184
6-#18	.0600	**914**	914	890	777	689	619	562	515	475	441	411	385	362	333	307	284
8-#7	.0120	**522**	522	522	491	436	392	276	211	171	143	124	109	97	87	79	73
8-#8	.0158	**553**	553	553	516	458	412	345	265	216	182	157	138	123	111	101	93
8-#9	.0200	**588**	588	588	544	484	435	396	325	265	224	194	171	153	138	126	116
8-#10	.0254	**632**	632	632	580	516	465	423	388	326	276	240	212	190	172	157	145
8-#11	.0312	**679**	679	679	618	551	496	452	415	383	329	287	254	228	206	189	174
8-#14	.0450	**792**	792	792	707	630	569	518	476	440	409	382	346	311	283	260	240
10-#6	.0110	**514**	514	514	485	430	373	257	196	159	133	115	101	90	81	74	68
10-#7	.0150	**547**	547	547	513	456	410	336	259	210	177	153	134	120	108	99	91
10-#8	.0198	**586**	586	586	544	483	435	396	324	264	223	193	170	152	138	126	116
10-#9	.0250	**629**	629	629	579	515	464	422	388	324	275	239	211	189	171	156	144
10-#10	.0318	**684**	684	684	624	556	501	456	419	387	337	294	260	233	212	194	178
10-#11	.0390	**743**	743	743	671	599	540	492	452	418	389	349	310	279	253	232	214
12-#6	.0132	**532**	532	532	501	445	400	303	232	188	158	136	120	107	96	88	81
12-#7	.0180	**571**	571	571	534	475	428	389	305	248	210	181	160	143	129	118	108
12-#8	.0237	**618**	618	618	571	509	458	417	380	311	264	229	202	181	164	150	138
12-#9	.0300	**669**	669	669	614	547	493	449	412	380	323	281	249	223	203	185	171
14-#5	.0109	**513**	513	513	484	430	371	256	195	158	132	114	100	89	80	73	67
14-#6	.0154	**550**	550	550	517	459	413	347	267	217	183	158	139	124	112	102	94
14-#7	.0210	**596**	596	596	556	495	446	406	349	286	242	209	185	165	149	136	125
14-#8	.0277	**650**	650	650	599	534	481	438	402	356	303	263	233	209	189	173	159

Check availability of #14S and #18S bars.

* One-half of the bars are to be placed in each of the two faces of the column that are perpendicular to the plane of bending.
† Below zigzag horizontal line of each group, concrete governs; above, tension governs.

SQUARE TIED COLUMNS—Safe Load in Kips for Various Eccentricities in Inches

$f'_c = 5000$ psi $f_s = 24{,}000$ psi basis
(A61 or A432 Bars, $f_y = 60{,}000$ psi)

COLUMN SIZE—19″ x 19″ CONTINUED

$f'_c = 5000$ psi
$f_y = 60{,}000$ psi

M/N † = e (in.) 16	17	18	19	20	21	22	23	24	25	26	27	28	30	32	34	36	M_o ‡ (kip-in.)
58	54	50	47	44	42	40	38	36	34	33	31	30	28	26	24	23	778
77	72	67	63	60	56	53	51	48	46	44	42	41	38	35	33	31	1053
99	92	86	81	76	72	68	65	62	59	57	54	52	48	45	42	40	1350
123	114	107	101	95	90	85	81	77	74	71	68	65	61	56	53	50	1694
152	142	133	125	118	112	106	101	97	92	88	85	82	76	71	66	62	2130
49	46	43	40	38	36	34	32	31	29	28	27	26	24	22	21	19	664
69	64	60	56	53	50	48	45	43	41	39	38	36	34	31	29	27	934
92	86	81	76	71	67	64	61	58	55	53	51	49	45	42	39	37	1263
118	109	103	96	91	86	82	78	74	71	68	65	62	58	54	51	48	1621
146	136	127	120	113	107	102	97	92	88	85	81	78	72	68	63	59	2033

COLUMN SIZE—20″ x 20″

16	17	18	19	20	21	22	23	24	25	26	27	28	30	32	34	36	M_o ‡ (kip-in.)
54	51	47	44	42	39	37	35	34	32	31	29	28	26	24	23	21	725
68	63	59	56	52	49	47	45	42	41	39	37	36	33	31	29	27	913
83	77	72	68	64	60	57	54	52	49	47	45	43	40	37	35	33	1111
116	108	101	95	89	85	80	76	73	69	66	64	61	57	53	49	46	1572
183	171	160	150	142	134	128	121	116	111	106	102	98	91	85	79	75	2539
65	60	56	53	50	47	45	42	40	38	37	35	34	31	29	27	26	867
81	75	71	66	62	59	56	53	51	48	46	44	42	39	37	34	32	1088
102	94	88	83	78	74	70	67	63	61	58	56	53	49	46	43	40	1369
123	114	107	100	95	89	85	81	77	73	70	67	65	60	56	52	49	1666
171	159	149	140	132	125	119	113	108	103	99	95	91	84	79	74	69	2358
264	247	232	218	206	196	186	177	170	162	156	149	144	134	125	117	110	3809
67	63	58	55	52	49	46	44	42	40	38	37	35	33	30	28	27	900
86	80	75	70	66	63	59	56	54	51	49	47	45	42	39	36	34	1156
107	100	93	88	83	78	74	70	67	64	61	59	57	52	49	46	43	1451
134	125	117	110	103	98	93	88	84	80	77	74	71	66	61	57	54	1826
161	150	141	132	125	118	112	107	102	97	93	89	86	80	74	70	65	2222
223	208	195	184	173	164	156	149	142	136	130	125	120	111	104	98	92	3144
62	58	54	51	48	45	43	41	39	37	35	34	32	30	28	26	25	831
84	78	73	68	64	61	58	55	52	50	48	46	44	41	38	35	33	1125
107	100	93	87	82	78	74	70	67	64	61	59	56	52	49	45	43	1445
133	124	116	109	103	97	92	88	84	80	76	73	70	65	61	57	54	1814
165	154	144	136	128	121	115	109	104	100	96	92	88	82	76	71	67	2282
199	185	174	163	154	146	139	132	126	121	116	111	107	99	92	86	81	2778
75	69	65	61	57	54	51	49	46	44	42	41	39	36	34	31	29	997
100	93	87	82	77	73	69	66	63	60	57	55	53	49	45	42	40	1350
127	119	111	104	98	93	88	84	80	76	73	70	67	62	58	54	51	1734
158	147	138	130	122	116	110	105	100	95	91	88	84	78	73	68	64	2177
62	58	54	50	47	45	43	40	38	37	35	34	32	30	28	26	24	826
87	81	75	71	67	63	60	57	54	52	49	47	45	42	39	37	34	1164
116	108	101	95	89	85	80	76	73	69	67	64	61	57	53	49	47	1575
148	137	129	121	114	108	102	97	93	89	85	82	78	73	68	63	60	2023

‡ M_o = capacity in pure bending, ($N = 0$), for extrapolation, see page 11-5.

SQUARE TIED COLUMNS—Safe Load in Kips for Various Eccentricities in Inches

f'_c = 5000 psi f_s = 24,000 psi basis
(A61 or A432 Bars, f_y = 60,000 psi)

COLUMN SIZE—21″ x 21″

Bars *	p	M/N † = e (in.) 0	1	2	3	4	5	6	7	8	9	10	11	12	13	14	15
4-#10	.0115	**572**	572	572	546	485	437	313	237	190	159	137	120	106	96	87	80
4-#11	.0141	**595**	595	595	565	503	453	374	284	229	192	165	145	129	116	106	97
4-#14S	.0204	**652**	652	652	612	545	491	447	388	315	265	229	201	180	162	148	136
4-#18S	.0363	**794**	794	794	712	634	571	519	476	440	409	356	315	282	256	234	215
6-#8	.0107	**565**	565	565	541	481	433	299	226	181	151	130	114	101	91	83	76
6-#9	.0136	**590**	590	590	563	501	452	367	278	224	188	162	142	126	114	104	95
6-#10	.0173	**624**	624	624	591	527	475	432	343	277	233	201	176	157	142	129	119
6-#11	.0212	**659**	659	659	620	553	499	455	407	331	279	241	212	190	171	156	143
6-#14S	.0306	**743**	743	743	689	616	556	507	466	432	381	331	292	262	237	217	199
6-#18S	.0544	**958**	958	958	841	750	676	616	565	522	486	454	426	401	366	336	310
8-#7	.0109	**566**	566	566	544	484	436	310	234	188	157	135	118	105	94	86	79
8-#8	.0143	**597**	597	597	570	507	457	387	294	237	199	171	150	134	121	110	101
8-#9	.0181	**631**	631	631	599	534	482	439	360	292	246	212	186	166	150	137	125
8-#10	.0230	**675**	675	675	636	568	513	467	430	359	303	262	231	206	186	170	156
8-#11	.0283	**723**	723	723	675	603	545	497	457	423	361	313	277	248	224	205	188
8-#14S	.0408	**835**	835	835	766	686	621	567	522	483	450	421	377	339	308	282	260
10-#6	.0100	**558**	558	558	537	478	429	289	217	174	145	125	109	97	87	79	73
10-#7	.0136	**590**	590	590	566	505	455	377	287	231	194	166	146	130	117	107	98
10-#8	.0179	**629**	629	629	598	533	481	439	359	291	245	211	185	165	149	136	125
10-#9	.0227	**672**	672	672	634	567	512	467	429	357	301	260	229	205	185	169	155
10-#10	.0288	**727**	727	727	680	609	550	502	462	428	369	321	283	254	230	210	193
10-#11	.0354	**786**	786	786	729	653	591	540	497	460	428	382	338	303	275	252	232
12-#6	.0120	**576**	576	576	554	493	445	340	257	207	173	149	130	116	104	95	87
12-#7	.0163	**615**	615	615	588	525	474	432	337	273	229	198	174	155	140	127	117
12-#8	.0215	**661**	661	661	626	559	505	461	421	342	289	250	220	196	177	162	149
12-#9	.0272	**713**	713	713	670	599	542	494	455	418	354	307	271	243	220	201	185
12-#10	.0346	**779**	779	779	725	649	588	537	494	458	426	377	334	299	271	248	229
14-#5	.0098	**557**	557	557	537	478	427	287	216	173	145	124	109	97	87	79	72
14-#6	.0140	**594**	594	594	570	508	458	389	296	238	200	172	151	134	121	110	101
14-#7	.0190	**639**	639	639	610	545	492	449	386	314	264	228	201	179	162	147	135
14-#8	.0251	**694**	694	694	654	585	529	483	444	392	332	287	253	227	205	187	172

COLUMN SIZE—22″ x 22″

Bars *	p	M/N † = e (in.) 0	1	2	3	4	5	6	7	8	9	10	11	12	13	14	15
4-#10	.0105	**617**	617	617	602	537	484	352	262	209	174	149	130	115	104	94	86
4-#11	.0129	**641**	641	641	622	555	501	419	314	251	209	180	157	140	126	114	105
4-#14S	.0186	**697**	697	697	669	598	541	494	429	346	290	249	219	195	175	160	147
4-#18S	.0331	**840**	840	840	774	692	625	570	524	485	451	390	344	308	278	254	234
6-#9	.0124	**636**	636	636	619	553	500	411	308	246	205	176	154	137	123	112	102
6-#10	.0157	**669**	669	669	648	579	524	478	379	305	254	218	191	170	153	139	128
6-#11	.0193	**705**	705	705	678	607	549	502	451	364	305	262	230	205	185	168	155
6-#14S	.0279	**789**	789	789	749	671	608	556	512	475	417	360	318	284	257	234	215
6-#18S	.0496	**1003**	1003	1003	907	812	735	671	618	572	533	498	468	439	399	366	338

Check availability of #14S and #18S bars.

* One-half of the bars are to be placed in each of the two faces of the column that are perpendicular to the plane of bending.

† Below zigzag horizontal line of each group, concrete governs; above, tension governs.

SQUARE TIED COLUMNS—Safe Load in Kips for Various Eccentricities in Inches

$f'_c = 5000$ psi $f_s = 24{,}000$ psi basis

(A61 or A432 Bars, $f_y = 60{,}000$ psi)

$f'_c = 5000$ psi
$f_y = 60{,}000$ psi

COLUMN SIZE—21″ x 21″

M/N † = e (in.)																	M_o ‡ (kip-in.)
16	17	18	19	20	21	22	23	24	25	26	27	28	30	32	34	36	
74	69	64	60	56	53	50	48	46	44	42	40	38	35	33	31	29	974
90	83	78	73	69	65	61	58	56	53	51	49	47	43	40	38	35	1186
126	117	109	102	96	91	86	82	78	75	72	69	66	61	57	53	50	1680
200	186	174	164	154	146	138	132	126	120	115	110	106	98	92	86	81	2731
70	65	61	57	54	51	48	46	43	41	40	38	36	34	31	29	27	924
88	81	76	71	67	63	60	57	54	52	50	48	46	42	39	37	35	1160
110	102	95	89	84	80	75	72	68	65	62	60	57	53	49	46	43	1461
133	123	115	108	102	96	91	87	83	79	76	73	70	65	60	56	53	1779
185	172	161	151	143	135	128	122	116	111	106	102	98	91	85	79	74	2520
288	269	253	238	225	213	203	193	184	176	169	162	156	145	135	127	119	4097
73	67	63	59	56	52	50	47	45	43	41	39	38	35	32	30	28	957
93	86	81	76	71	67	64	61	58	55	53	50	48	45	42	39	37	1232
116	108	101	95	89	84	80	76	72	69	66	63	61	56	52	49	46	1547
145	135	126	118	111	105	100	95	90	86	83	79	76	71	66	62	58	1948
174	162	152	143	135	127	121	115	110	105	100	96	92	86	80	75	70	2372
241	225	211	198	187	177	168	160	153	146	140	135	129	120	112	105	99	3360
67	62	58	55	51	48	46	44	41	40	38	36	35	32	30	28	26	884
90	84	78	74	69	65	62	59	56	53	51	49	47	44	41	38	36	1197
115	107	100	94	89	84	79	75	72	69	66	63	60	56	52	49	46	1540
144	134	125	117	111	105	99	94	90	86	82	79	76	70	65	61	57	1934
179	166	156	146	138	131	124	118	112	107	103	99	95	88	82	77	72	2435
215	200	188	176	166	158	150	142	136	130	124	119	115	106	99	93	87	2965
80	75	70	65	61	58	55	52	50	47	45	44	42	39	36	34	32	1061
108	100	94	88	83	78	74	70	67	64	61	59	56	52	49	45	43	1436
138	128	120	112	106	100	95	90	86	82	79	75	72	67	62	58	55	1848
171	159	149	140	132	125	118	112	107	102	98	94	90	84	78	73	69	2321
212	198	185	174	164	155	148	140	134	128	123	118	113	105	98	92	86	2922
67	62	58	54	51	48	46	43	41	39	38	36	35	32	30	28	26	878
93	87	81	76	72	68	64	61	58	55	53	51	49	45	42	39	37	1238
125	116	109	102	96	91	86	82	78	75	71	68	66	61	57	53	50	1675
159	148	139	130	123	116	110	105	100	95	91	88	84	78	73	68	64	2156

COLUMN SIZE—22″ x 22″

M/N † = e (in.)																	M_o ‡ (kip-in.)
16	17	18	19	20	22	24	26	28	30	32	34	36	38	40	42	44	
80	74	69	64	61	54	49	45	41	38	35	33	31	29	28	26	25	1035
96	90	84	78	74	66	60	54	50	46	43	40	38	36	34	32	30	1260
135	126	117	110	104	93	84	77	71	65	61	57	53	50	48	45	43	1788
216	201	188	177	167	150	136	124	114	106	99	92	87	82	78	74	70	2923
94	88	82	77	72	64	58	53	49	45	42	39	37	35	33	31	30	1232
118	110	102	96	90	81	73	67	61	57	53	49	46	44	41	39	37	1552
143	133	124	116	110	98	89	81	75	69	64	60	56	53	50	48	45	1891
199	185	173	163	153	138	125	114	105	97	91	85	80	75	71	68	64	2682
313	292	274	258	244	219	199	182	168	156	146	137	129	121	115	109	104	4385

‡ M_o = capacity in pure bending, ($N = 0$), for extrapolation, see page 11-5.

SQUARE TIED COLUMNS—Safe Load in Kips for Various Eccentricities in Inches

$f'_c = 5000$ psi $f_s = 24{,}000$ psi basis
(A61 or A432 Bars, $f_y = 60{,}000$ psi)

COLUMN SIZE—22″ x 22″ CONTINUED

Bars *	p	M/N † = e (in.) 0	1	2	3	4	5	6	7	8	9	10	11	12	13	14	15
8-#8	.0131	**643**	643	643	626	559	505	434	325	260	217	186	163	145	130	118	108
8-#9	.0165	**677**	677	677	656	587	531	485	399	321	268	230	202	180	162	147	135
8-#10	.0210	**721**	721	721	694	622	563	514	473	394	331	285	250	223	202	184	169
8-#11	.0258	**768**	768	768	734	658	597	546	503	466	394	341	300	268	242	221	203
8-#14S	.0372	**881**	881	881	828	744	675	618	570	529	493	462	410	368	334	305	281
10-#7	.0124	**636**	636	636	622	556	503	423	317	253	211	181	158	141	126	115	105
10-#8	.0163	**675**	675	675	655	586	530	484	397	319	267	229	201	179	161	147	134
10-#9	.0207	**718**	718	718	692	620	562	513	473	391	329	283	249	222	200	182	167
10-#10	.0262	**773**	773	773	740	664	602	550	507	470	403	349	307	275	248	226	208
10-#11	.0322	**832**	832	832	790	710	644	589	543	504	470	416	367	329	298	272	250
12-#6	.0109	**621**	621	621	609	544	492	381	284	227	189	161	141	125	113	102	94
12-#7	.0149	**661**	661	661	645	577	522	477	373	299	250	215	188	167	151	137	126
12-#8	.0196	**707**	707	707	684	613	555	507	465	376	315	271	238	212	192	174	160
12-#9	.0248	**759**	759	759	729	654	593	542	500	459	387	334	294	263	237	216	199
12-#10	.0315	**825**	825	825	785	706	641	587	541	502	468	410	362	324	293	268	247
14-#6	.0127	**639**	639	639	626	560	506	436	327	261	218	187	163	145	131	119	109
14-#7	.0174	**685**	685	685	667	598	541	495	427	344	288	248	217	193	174	159	146
14-#8	.0229	**739**	739	739	713	639	580	530	488	430	362	312	275	245	221	202	185
14-#9	.0289	**799**	799	799	765	687	624	571	526	488	442	383	338	302	274	250	230

COLUMN SIZE—23″ x 23″

Bars *	p	0	1	2	3	4	5	6	7	8	9	10	11	12	13	14	15
4-#11	.0118	**689**	689	689	681	610	552	470	348	276	228	195	170	151	135	123	112
4-#14S	.0170	**745**	745	745	730	655	593	543	474	379	316	271	237	210	189	172	158
4-#18S	.0302	**888**	888	888	839	752	682	623	574	532	493	426	374	334	302	275	253
6-#9	.0113	**684**	684	684	679	608	550	461	341	270	224	191	166	147	132	120	110
6-#10	.0144	**717**	717	717	708	635	575	526	419	334	277	237	207	184	165	150	137
6-#11	.0177	**753**	753	753	739	663	602	551	498	398	332	285	249	222	199	181	166
6-#14S	.0255	**837**	837	837	812	730	663	607	560	520	454	391	344	307	277	252	232
6-#18S	.0454	**1051**	1051	1051	975	876	796	728	672	623	581	545	512	478	433	397	365
8-#8	.0119	**690**	690	690	685	614	556	486	360	285	236	202	176	156	140	127	116
8-#9	.0151	**725**	725	725	716	642	583	533	440	351	292	250	218	194	174	158	145
8-#10	.0192	**769**	769	769	755	678	616	564	520	431	360	309	271	241	217	197	181
8-#11	.0236	**816**	816	816	796	716	651	596	550	511	430	370	325	290	261	238	218
8-#14S	.0340	**929**	929	929	893	804	732	672	620	576	538	504	445	398	360	329	302
10-#7	.0113	**684**	684	684	681	611	554	474	350	277	230	196	171	151	136	123	113
10-#8	.0149	**723**	723	723	715	642	582	532	438	350	291	249	217	193	174	158	144
10-#9	.0189	**766**	766	766	753	677	615	563	519	428	358	307	269	239	215	196	180
10-#10	.0240	**821**	821	821	802	722	656	601	555	515	439	378	332	296	267	243	224
10-#11	.0295	**880**	880	880	853	769	699	642	593	550	514	451	397	355	321	293	269
10-#14S	.0425	**1021**	1021	1021	974	879	801	736	680	633	591	555	523	485	440	402	371
12-#6	.0100	**669**	669	669	668	599	542	427	314	248	205	175	152	135	121	110	100
12-#7	.0136	**708**	708	708	704	632	573	525	412	328	272	233	203	180	162	147	135
12-#8	.0179	**755**	755	755	745	669	607	556	513	411	343	294	258	229	206	188	172
12-#9	.0227	**806**	806	806	790	711	646	592	547	502	421	362	318	283	255	233	214
12-#10	.0288	**872**	872	872	848	765	696	638	590	548	512	445	392	350	316	288	265
12-#11	.0354	**943**	943	943	910	821	748	687	635	590	551	517	467	418	378	346	318

Check availability of #14S and #18S bars.

* One-half of the bars are to be placed in each of the two faces of the column that are perpendicular to the plane of bending.

† Below zigzag horizontal line of each group, concrete governs; above, tension governs.

SQUARE TIED COLUMNS—Safe Load in Kips for Various Eccentricities in Inches

$f'_c = 5000$ psi $f_s = 24{,}000$ psi basis
(A61 or A432 Bars, $f_y = 60{,}000$ psi)

$f'_c = 5000$ psi
$f_y = 60{,}000$ psi

COLUMN SIZE—22″ x 22″ CONTINUED

M/N † = e (in.)

16	17	18	19	20	22	24	26	28	30	32	34	36	38	40	42	44	M_o ‡ (kip-in.)
100	93	87	81	76	68	62	56	52	48	45	42	39	37	35	33	31	1308
125	116	108	101	96	85	77	71	65	60	56	52	49	46	44	42	39	1643
156	145	135	127	120	107	97	89	81	75	70	66	62	58	55	52	50	2070
188	175	163	153	145	130	117	107	99	92	85	80	75	71	67	64	60	2521
260	243	227	214	202	181	164	150	139	129	120	112	106	100	94	90	85	3576
97	90	84	79	74	66	60	55	50	47	43	40	38	36	34	32	30	1269
124	115	108	101	95	85	77	70	65	60	56	52	49	46	44	41	39	1635
155	144	134	126	119	106	96	88	81	75	70	65	61	58	55	52	49	2054
193	179	167	157	148	133	120	110	101	94	87	82	77	73	69	65	62	2587
232	216	202	190	179	161	146	133	123	114	106	99	93	88	83	79	75	3152
86	80	75	70	66	59	53	49	45	41	38	36	34	32	30	28	27	1124
116	108	101	94	89	79	72	65	60	56	52	49	46	43	41	38	37	1522
148	138	128	121	113	102	92	84	77	72	67	62	59	55	52	50	47	1962
184	171	160	150	141	127	115	105	97	90	83	78	73	69	65	62	59	2465
228	213	199	187	176	158	144	131	121	112	105	98	92	87	82	78	74	3105
100	93	87	81	77	69	62	57	52	48	45	42	39	37	35	33	31	1312
135	125	117	109	103	92	83	76	70	65	60	57	53	50	47	45	43	1776
171	159	149	140	132	118	107	98	90	83	78	73	68	64	61	58	55	2289
213	198	185	174	164	147	133	122	112	104	97	91	85	81	76	72	69	2876

COLUMN SIZE—23″ x 23″

16	17	18	19	20	22	24	26	28	30	32	34	36	38	40	42	44	M_o ‡ (kip-in.)
104	96	90	84	79	70	64	58	53	49	46	43	40	38	36	34	32	1335
145	135	126	118	111	99	90	82	75	70	65	61	57	54	51	48	46	1896
234	217	203	191	180	161	146	133	123	114	106	99	93	88	83	79	75	3115
101	94	88	82	77	69	62	57	52	48	45	42	39	37	35	33	31	1304
127	118	110	103	97	86	78	71	65	61	56	53	49	47	44	42	40	1644
153	142	133	125	117	105	95	87	80	74	69	64	60	57	54	51	48	2003
214	199	186	174	164	147	133	122	112	104	97	90	85	80	76	72	68	2844
339	316	296	278	263	236	214	196	181	168	156	147	138	130	123	117	111	4673
107	99	93	87	82	73	66	60	55	51	47	44	42	39	37	35	33	1384
134	124	116	109	102	91	83	75	69	64	60	56	52	49	47	44	42	1739
167	155	145	136	128	114	104	94	87	80	75	70	66	62	59	56	53	2192
202	188	175	164	155	139	125	115	105	98	91	85	80	75	71	68	64	2671
280	261	244	229	216	194	176	161	148	137	128	120	113	106	101	95	91	3792
104	97	90	84	79	71	64	58	54	49	46	43	40	38	36	34	32	1341
133	124	115	108	102	91	82	75	69	64	59	55	52	49	46	44	42	1730
166	154	144	135	127	114	103	94	86	80	74	69	65	62	58	55	52	2174
207	192	179	168	159	142	129	117	108	100	93	87	82	77	73	69	66	2740
249	231	216	203	191	172	156	142	131	121	113	106	100	94	89	84	80	3339
344	320	300	282	266	239	217	199	183	170	159	149	140	132	125	119	113	4740
92	86	80	75	70	63	57	52	47	44	41	38	36	34	32	30	29	1188
124	115	107	101	95	85	76	70	64	59	55	52	48	46	43	41	39	1609
159	147	138	129	121	109	98	90	82	76	71	66	62	59	56	53	50	2076
197	183	171	161	151	135	123	112	103	95	89	83	78	74	70	66	63	2609
245	228	213	200	189	169	153	140	129	120	111	104	98	92	87	83	79	3288
295	274	257	241	228	204	185	169	156	145	135	126	119	112	106	101	96	4007

‡ M_o = capacity in pure bending, ($N = 0$), for extrapolation, see page 11-5.

SQUARE TIED COLUMNS—Safe Load in Kips for Various Eccentricities in Inches

f'_c = 5000 psi f_s = 24,000 psi basis
(A61 or A432 Bars, f_y = 60,000 psi)

COLUMN SIZE—23″ x 23″ CONTINUED

Bars *	p	0	1	2	3	4	5	6	7	8	9	10	11	12	13	14	15
		M/N † = e (in.)															
14-#6	.0116	**687**	687	687	685	614	557	488	361	286	237	202	176	156	140	127	117
14-#7	.0159	**733**	733	733	727	653	593	543	471	376	313	268	235	209	188	170	156
14-#8	.0209	**787**	787	787	774	696	633	580	535	471	394	339	297	264	238	217	199
14-#9	.0265	**847**	847	847	827	745	678	622	575	534	482	416	366	326	295	269	247

COLUMN SIZE—24″ x 24″

Bars *	p	0	1	2	3	4	5	6	7	8	9	10	11	12	13	14	15
4-#11	.0108	**739**	739	739	739	668	606	528	384	302	248	211	183	162	145	132	120
4-#14S	.0156	**795**	795	795	794	714	649	594	524	415	344	293	256	227	204	185	169
4-#18S	.0278	**938**	938	938	906	815	741	679	626	581	538	463	406	361	326	296	272
6-#9	.0104	**734**	734	734	734	665	604	518	376	295	243	206	179	159	142	129	118
6-#10	.0132	**767**	767	767	767	693	630	577	462	365	301	257	223	198	177	161	147
6-#11	.0163	**802**	802	802	802	722	657	602	549	436	361	308	269	239	214	195	178
6-#14S	.0234	**887**	887	887	877	791	720	661	611	568	494	424	372	331	298	271	248
6-#18S	.0417	**1101**	1101	1101	1046	943	858	788	728	677	632	593	558	518	469	428	394
8-#8	.0110	**740**	740	740	740	672	610	546	397	312	257	218	190	168	150	136	125
8-#9	.0139	**775**	775	775	775	701	637	584	486	384	317	270	236	209	187	170	155
8-#10	.0176	**819**	819	819	819	738	671	616	569	472	392	335	292	259	233	212	194
8-#11	.0217	**866**	866	866	861	777	707	649	600	558	467	401	351	312	281	255	234
8-#14S	.0313	**979**	979	979	960	867	791	727	673	626	586	546	480	429	387	353	324
8-#18S	.0556	**1264**	1264	1264	1185	1070	976	897	829	771	721	677	638	603	572	544	507
10-#7	.0104	**734**	734	734	734	668	607	532	386	303	249	212	184	163	146	132	121
10-#8	.0137	**773**	773	773	773	700	636	583	483	382	316	269	234	208	186	169	155
10-#9	.0174	**815**	815	815	815	736	670	615	368	468	389	332	290	257	231	210	192
10-#10	.0220	**871**	871	871	867	782	712	654	605	562	477	410	359	319	287	261	239
10-#11	.0271	**930**	930	930	919	831	757	696	644	599	560	488	429	382	345	314	288
10-#14S	.0391	**1071**	1071	1071	1042	944	862	793	735	684	640	602	567	522	473	432	398
12-#7	.0125	**758**	758	758	758	690	627	575	454	358	295	251	219	194	174	158	144
12-#8	.0165	**805**	805	805	805	728	663	608	561	449	373	318	278	246	221	201	184
12-#9	.0208	**856**	856	856	855	771	703	645	596	548	457	392	343	305	274	249	229
12-#10	.0265	**922**	922	922	914	826	754	693	641	596	557	481	423	377	340	309	284
12-#11	.0325	**993**	993	993	977	884	807	743	688	640	599	563	504	450	407	371	341
14-#6	.0107	**737**	737	737	737	672	610	548	398	313	257	219	190	168	151	136	125
14-#7	.0146	**783**	783	783	783	712	648	594	519	411	340	290	253	224	201	183	167
14-#8	.0192	**837**	837	837	837	756	689	632	584	514	428	366	320	284	256	232	213
14-#9	.0243	**897**	897	897	893	806	735	676	625	581	523	450	394	351	316	288	264
14-#10	.0309	**974**	974	974	962	870	794	731	677	630	589	551	485	433	391	356	327

COLUMN SIZE—26″ x 26″

Bars *	p	0	1	2	3	4	5	6	7	8	9	10	11	12	13	14	15
4-#14S	.0123	**901**	901	901	901	841	767	705	637	495	404	342	296	261	234	211	193
4-#18S	.0237	**1044**	1044	1044	1044	949	866	797	738	687	636	543	473	419	376	341	312
6-#10S	.0113	**873**	873	873	873	819	747	686	562	435	354	299	258	228	203	184	168
6-#11S	.0138	**909**	909	909	909	849	775	713	660	519	425	359	311	275	246	222	203
6-#14S	.0200	**993**	993	993	993	921	842	776	719	670	581	494	430	381	342	310	283
6-#18S	.0355	**1207**	1207	1207	1194	1083	991	913	847	790	739	695	656	601	542	494	453

Check availability of #14S and #18S bars.

* One-half of the bars are to be placed in each of the two faces of the column that are perpendicular to the plane of bending.

† Below zigzag horizontal line of each group, concrete governs; above, tension governs.

SQUARE TIED COLUMNS—Safe Load in Kips for Various Eccentricities in Inches

$f'_c = 5000$ psi $\quad f_s = 24{,}000$ psi basis

(A61 or A432 Bars, $f_y = 60{,}000$ psi)

$f'_c = 5000$ psi
$f_y = 60{,}000$ psi

COLUMN SIZE—23″ x 23″ CONTINUED																	
M/N † = e (in.)																	M_o ‡ (kip-in.)
16	17	18	19	20	22	24	26	28	30	32	34	36	38	40	42	44	
107	100	93	87	82	73	66	60	55	51	48	44	42	39	37	35	33	*1386*
144	134	125	117	110	98	89	81	75	69	64	60	56	53	50	48	45	*1877*
184	171	159	150	141	126	114	104	96	89	83	77	73	68	65	61	58	*2422*
228	212	198	186	175	157	142	130	120	111	103	97	91	86	81	77	73	*3044*
COLUMN SIZE—24″ x 24″																	
111	103	96	90	84	75	68	62	57	52	49	45	43	40	38	36	34	*1410*
156	144	135	126	119	106	96	87	80	74	69	65	61	57	54	51	49	*2004*
251	233	218	204	193	172	156	142	131	121	113	106	99	94	89	84	80	*3307*
108	100	93	87	82	73	66	60	55	51	48	44	42	39	37	35	33	*1376*
136	126	117	110	103	92	83	76	70	64	60	56	52	49	47	44	42	*1735*
164	152	142	133	125	112	101	92	85	78	73	68	64	60	57	54	51	*2116*
229	213	199	186	176	157	142	130	119	111	103	96	90	85	81	76	73	*3006*
365	340	318	299	282	253	229	210	193	179	167	157	147	139	132	125	119	*4961*
115	106	99	93	87	78	70	64	59	54	50	47	44	42	39	37	35	*1459*
143	133	124	116	109	97	88	80	74	68	63	59	56	52	49	47	45	*1835*
179	166	155	145	136	122	110	101	92	86	80	74	70	66	62	59	56	*2314*
216	201	187	175	165	148	134	122	112	104	97	90	85	80	76	72	68	*2821*
300	279	261	245	231	207	187	171	158	146	136	127	120	113	107	101	96	*4008*
471	440	412	388	367	330	300	275	254	236	220	206	194	183	173	165	157	*6615*
111	103	96	90	84	75	68	62	57	53	49	46	43	40	38	36	34	*1413*
142	132	123	115	108	97	87	80	73	68	63	59	55	52	49	47	44	*1824*
177	165	154	144	135	121	109	100	92	85	79	74	69	65	62	58	56	*2294*
221	205	192	180	169	151	137	125	115	106	99	93	87	82	78	74	70	*2892*
266	248	231	217	204	183	166	151	139	129	120	112	106	100	94	89	85	*3526*
368	343	321	302	284	255	232	212	195	181	169	158	149	140	133	126	120	*5010*
133	123	115	107	101	90	81	74	68	63	59	55	51	48	46	43	41	*1695*
170	157	147	138	129	116	104	95	88	81	75	70	66	62	59	56	53	*2189*
211	196	183	171	161	144	131	119	110	101	94	88	83	78	74	70	67	*2753*
262	244	228	214	201	180	163	149	137	127	118	111	104	98	93	88	84	*3471*
316	294	274	258	243	218	197	180	166	154	143	134	126	119	113	107	102	*4232*
115	106	99	93	87	78	70	64	59	54	50	47	44	42	39	37	35	*1459*
154	143	133	125	117	105	95	86	79	73	68	64	60	56	53	50	48	*1978*
197	182	170	160	150	134	121	111	102	94	88	82	77	73	69	65	62	*2554*
244	227	212	199	187	167	151	138	127	118	110	103	96	91	86	82	78	*3212*
303	282	263	247	233	209	189	173	159	148	137	129	121	114	108	102	97	*4049*
COLUMN SIZE—26″ x 26″																	
177	164	153	143	134	120	108	98	90	83	77	72	68	64	60	57	54	*2220*
288	267	249	233	219	196	177	161	148	137	128	119	112	106	100	95	90	*3691*
154	143	133	124	116	104	94	85	78	72	67	63	59	55	52	49	47	*1918*
187	173	161	150	141	126	114	104	95	88	82	76	72	67	64	60	57	*2340*
261	242	226	211	199	177	160	146	134	124	115	108	101	95	90	85	81	*3330*
419	389	364	341	321	288	261	238	219	203	189	177	166	157	148	141	134	*5537*

‡ M_o = capacity in pure bending, ($N = 0$), for extrapolation, see page 11-5.

SQUARE TIED COLUMNS—Safe Load in Kips for Various Eccentricities in Inches

$f'_c = 5000$ psi $f_s = 24{,}000$ psi basis
(A61 or A432 Bars, $f_y = 60{,}000$ psi)

COLUMN SIZE—26″ x 26″ CONTINUED

Bars *	p	M/N † = e (in.)															
		0	1	2	3	4	5	6	7	8	9	10	11	12	13	14	15
8-#9	.0118	**881**	881	881	881	827	754	694	591	457	373	315	272	240	215	194	177
8-#10	.0150	**925**	925	925	925	865	790	727	674	561	460	390	338	299	267	242	221
8-#11	.0185	**972**	972	972	972	906	828	763	707	659	549	466	406	359	322	292	267
8-#14S	.0266	**1085**	1085	1085	1085	1001	917	846	785	733	687	636	556	494	445	404	370
8-#18S	.0473	**1371**	1371	1371	1339	1217	1115	1029	956	892	836	786	743	703	668	636	585
10-#8	.0117	**879**	879	879	879	826	753	693	588	455	371	313	271	239	213	193	176
10-#9	.0148	**922**	922	922	922	863	789	726	673	557	456	387	335	296	265	240	219
10-#10	.0188	**977**	977	977	977	911	834	768	712	664	560	477	415	367	329	298	273
10-#11	.0231	**1036**	1036	1036	1036	962	881	813	754	703	659	568	496	440	395	359	328
10-#14S	.0333	**1177**	1177	1177	1177	1081	992	916	851	795	745	702	663	602	543	495	454
12-#7	.0107	**865**	865	865	865	815	744	684	552	426	347	292	253	222	199	179	164
12-#8	.0140	**911**	911	911	911	855	781	719	666	534	438	370	321	283	253	229	209
12-#9	.0178	**963**	963	963	963	900	823	758	703	652	536	456	396	351	314	285	260
12-#10	.0225	**1029**	1029	1029	1029	957	877	809	750	700	656	560	489	433	389	353	323
12-#11	.0277	**1100**	1100	1100	1100	1018	934	862	800	747	700	659	583	518	466	424	389
14-#7	.0124	**889**	889	889	889	838	765	704	630	489	399	337	292	257	230	208	190
14-#8	.0164	**943**	943	943	943	884	808	745	690	611	502	426	370	327	293	265	242
14-#9	.0207	**1003**	1003	1003	1003	937	857	791	734	684	613	523	456	404	362	329	301
14-#10	.0263	**1080**	1080	1080	1080	1003	920	849	789	736	690	640	560	498	448	407	373
16-#6	.0104	**861**	861	861	861	813	742	682	545	420	342	288	249	219	196	177	161
16-#7	.0142	**914**	914	914	914	860	786	724	671	549	450	381	330	292	261	236	216
16-#8	.0187	**976**	976	976	976	913	836	770	714	666	564	480	418	370	332	301	275
16-#9	.0237	**1044**	1044	1044	1044	973	892	823	764	713	668	588	513	456	409	372	340
18-#6	.0117	**879**	879	879	879	830	757	697	603	467	380	321	278	245	219	198	180
18-#7	.0160	**938**	938	938	938	883	807	744	690	608	500	424	368	325	291	264	241
18-#8	.0210	**1008**	1008	1008	1008	942	863	796	738	689	625	533	465	412	370	335	307

COLUMN SIZE—28″ x 28″

Bars *	p	M/N † = e (in.)															
		0	1	2	3	4	5	6	7	8	9	10	11	12	13	14	16
4-#14S	.0115	**1016**	1016	1016	1016	979	897	827	767	588	473	396	341	299	266	240	200
4-#18S	.0204	**1159**	1159	1159	1159	1093	1002	925	859	802	746	631	546	481	430	389	327
6-#11	.0119	**1023**	1023	1023	1023	988	905	835	775	616	497	416	358	314	280	252	210
6-#14S	.0172	**1108**	1108	1108	1108	1063	975	901	838	782	679	572	495	436	389	352	295
6-#18S	.0306	**1322**	1322	1322	1322	1234	1133	1048	975	911	856	806	762	691	621	563	476
8-#9	.0102	**996**	996	996	996	964	883	814	719	543	436	364	313	274	244	220	183
8-#10	.0130	**1040**	1040	1040	1040	1004	921	850	789	666	538	451	388	341	304	274	229
8-#11	.0159	**1087**	1087	1087	1087	1047	961	888	825	770	641	540	466	410	366	331	277
8-#14S	.0230	**1200**	1200	1200	1200	1146	1054	975	907	849	797	736	639	565	506	458	386
8-#18S	.0408	**1485**	1485	1485	1485	1373	1264	1171	1090	1020	959	904	855	811	772	726	616

Check availability of #14S and #18S bars.

* One-half of the bars are to be placed in each of the two faces of the column that are perpendicular to the plane of bending.

† Below zigzag horizontal line of each group, concrete governs; above, tension governs.

SQUARE TIED COLUMNS—Safe Load in Kips for Various Eccentricities in Inches
$f'_c = 5000$ psi $\quad f_s = 24{,}000$ psi basis
(A61 or A432 Bars, $f_y = 60{,}000$ psi)

COLUMN SIZE—26″ x 26″ CONTINUED

$f'_c = 5000$ psi
$f_y = 60{,}000$ psi

M/N † = e (in.)																	M_o ‡
16	17	18	19	20	22	24	26	28	30	32	34	36	38	40	42	44	(kip.in.)
163	150	140	131	123	110	99	90	83	76	71	66	62	58	55	52	50	*2027*
203	188	175	164	154	137	124	113	104	96	89	83	78	74	69	66	63	*2557*
246	228	212	198	187	167	150	137	126	116	108	101	95	89	85	80	76	*3120*
342	317	296	277	261	234	211	193	177	164	153	143	134	126	120	113	108	*4440*
542	505	473	444	419	376	341	312	288	267	249	233	219	207	196	186	177	*7383*
162	150	139	130	122	109	98	89	82	76	70	66	62	58	55	52	49	*2014*
202	187	174	163	153	136	123	112	103	95	88	82	77	73	69	65	62	*2534*
251	233	217	203	191	170	154	140	129	119	111	104	97	92	87	82	78	*3197*
303	281	262	246	231	206	187	170	156	145	135	126	118	111	105	100	95	*3901*
420	390	364	342	322	288	261	239	220	203	190	177	167	157	149	141	134	*5550*
150	139	129	121	114	101	91	83	76	70	65	61	57	54	51	48	46	*1868*
193	178	166	155	146	130	117	107	98	91	84	79	74	70	66	62	59	*2417*
240	222	207	194	182	162	147	134	123	114	106	99	93	87	82	78	74	*3041*
298	277	258	242	227	203	184	167	154	142	133	124	116	110	104	98	93	*3836*
359	333	311	292	274	246	222	203	187	173	161	150	141	133	126	119	114	*4681*
174	161	150	141	132	118	106	97	89	82	76	71	67	63	59	56	53	*2179*
223	207	193	180	169	151	136	124	114	105	98	92	86	81	77	73	69	*2820*
277	257	240	224	211	188	170	155	143	132	123	115	108	102	96	91	87	*3548*
344	320	298	280	263	235	213	194	179	165	154	144	135	127	121	114	109	*4476*
148	137	127	119	112	100	90	82	75	69	64	60	56	53	50	47	45	*1837*
198	184	171	160	150	134	121	110	101	93	87	81	76	72	68	64	61	*2491*
253	235	219	205	192	172	155	141	130	120	112	104	98	92	87	83	79	*3223*
314	291	272	255	240	214	194	177	162	150	140	131	123	116	109	104	99	*4055*
166	153	143	134	125	112	101	92	84	78	72	67	63	60	56	53	51	*2067*
222	205	191	179	168	150	136	123	113	105	97	91	85	80	76	72	69	*2802*
283	262	245	229	215	192	174	159	146	135	125	117	110	104	98	93	88	*3626*

COLUMN SIZE—28″ x 28″

M/N † = e (in.)																	M_o ‡
18	20	22	24	26	28	30	32	34	36	38	40	42	44	46	48	50	(kip-in)
172	150	134	120	110	100	93	86	80	75	71	67	63	60	57	55	52	*2436*
281	247	220	199	181	166	154	143	133	125	118	111	105	100	95	91	87	*4075*
181	158	141	127	115	106	98	91	85	79	75	70	67	63	60	58	55	*2565*
254	223	198	179	163	149	138	128	120	112	106	100	95	90	86	82	78	*3654*
411	363	324	293	267	246	227	211	198	186	175	165	157	149	142	136	130	*6113*
157	138	122	110	100	92	85	79	73	69	65	61	58	55	52	50	48	*2219*
197	172	153	138	126	115	106	99	92	86	81	77	73	69	66	63	60	*2801*
238	209	186	168	153	140	129	120	112	105	99	94	89	84	80	77	73	*3420*
333	293	261	236	215	197	183	170	159	149	140	133	126	119	114	109	104	*4872*
535	473	424	384	351	323	299	278	261	245	231	219	207	197	188	180	172	*8151*

‡ M_o = capacity in pure bending, ($N = 0$), for extrapolation, see page 11-5.

SQUARE TIED COLUMNS—Safe Load in Kips for Various Eccentricities in Inches

$f'_c = 5000$ psi $f_s = 24{,}000$ psi basis
(A61 or A432 Bars, $f_y = 60{,}000$ psi)

COLUMN SIZE—28″ x 28″ CONTINUED

Bars *	p	M/N † = e (in.) 0	1	2	3	4	5	6	7	8	9	10	11	12	13	14	16
10-#8	.0101	**994**	994	994	994	963	882	814	716	540	434	362	311	272	242	218	182
10-#9	.0128	**1036**	1036	1036	1036	1002	919	848	788	661	533	447	385	338	301	272	227
10-#10	.0162	**1092**	1092	1092	1092	1052	966	893	830	775	654	551	476	419	374	338	283
10-#11	.0199	**1151**	1151	1151	1151	1105	1016	939	874	817	767	657	569	502	449	407	342
10-#14S	.0287	**1291**	1291	1291	1291	1229	1131	1048	977	914	859	810	767	688	618	561	474
10-#18S	.0510	**1648**	1648	1648	1648	1512	1394	1293	1205	1128	1061	1001	948	900	857	817	748
12-#8	.0121	**1026**	1026	1026	1026	993	911	841	781	634	511	428	368	323	288	260	217
12-#9	.0153	**1077**	1077	1077	1077	1040	955	882	820	766	626	527	455	400	357	322	270
12-#10	.0194	**1143**	1143	1143	1143	1100	1011	935	870	813	764	647	561	495	442	400	336
12-#11	.0239	**1214**	1214	1214	1214	1163	1070	991	923	863	811	765	669	592	530	481	405
12-#14S	.0344	**1383**	1383	1383	1383	1311	1209	1121	1046	980	921	870	823	782	726	660	559
14-#7	.0107	**1004**	1004	1004	1004	975	894	825	766	580	466	390	335	293	261	235	196
14-#8	.0141	**1058**	1058	1058	1058	1024	939	868	806	724	586	492	425	373	333	300	251
14-#9	.0179	**1118**	1118	1118	1118	1078	991	916	852	796	716	604	523	461	412	372	312
14-#10	.0227	**1195**	1195	1195	1195	1147	1056	978	910	851	800	740	643	568	509	461	388
14-#11	.0279	**1278**	1278	1278	1278	1221	1125	1042	971	909	855	807	763	678	609	552	466
16-#7	.0122	**1028**	1028	1028	1028	999	916	846	786	651	525	440	379	332	296	267	223
16-#8	.0161	**1090**	1090	1090	1090	1054	968	895	832	777	659	555	479	422	377	340	285
16-#9	.0204	**1159**	1159	1159	1159	1116	1026	950	884	827	776	679	589	520	465	421	354
16-#10	.0259	**1247**	1247	1247	1247	1195	1100	1020	950	889	836	788	722	640	574	521	439
18-#6	.0101	**994**	994	994	994	967	886	817	734	554	444	371	319	279	248	224	186
18-#7	.0138	**1053**	1053	1053	1053	1022	938	867	806	720	583	490	422	371	331	298	249
18-#8	.0181	**1123**	1123	1123	1123	1084	996	921	857	801	729	616	533	470	420	380	318
18-#9	.0230	**1200**	1200	1200	1200	1153	1062	983	916	857	805	752	653	578	518	469	395

COLUMN SIZE—30″ x 30″

Bars *	p	0	1	2	3	4	5	6	7	8	9	10	11	12	13	14	16
4-#14S	.0100	**1139**	1139	1139	1139	1130	1038	960	893	698	553	457	390	340	301	270	224
4-#18S	.0178	**1282**	1282	1282	1282	1249	1149	1064	991	927	871	728	626	549	489	440	368
6-#11	.0104	**1147**	1147	1147	1147	1138	1047	968	901	731	579	479	409	357	316	284	236
6-#14S	.0150	**1231**	1231	1231	1231	1216	1120	1038	967	905	791	659	565	495	440	396	330
6-#18S	.0267	**1445**	1445	1445	1445	1395	1286	1193	1113	1043	981	926	877	788	705	638	535
8-#10	.0113	**1163**	1163	1163	1163	1155	1063	984	916	789	627	520	444	387	343	309	256
8-#11	.0139	**1210**	1210	1210	1210	1199	1104	1023	953	892	747	622	532	466	414	372	310
8-#14S	.0200	**1323**	1323	1323	1323	1302	1201	1115	1040	974	917	847	730	642	572	517	432
10-#9	.0111	**1160**	1160	1160	1160	1153	1061	982	914	783	622	515	440	384	340	306	254
10-#10	.0141	**1215**	1215	1215	1215	1205	1109	1028	958	897	762	635	544	476	423	380	317
10-#11	.0173	**1274**	1274	1274	1274	1259	1161	1077	1004	941	885	756	650	570	508	458	382
10-#14S	.0250	**1415**	1415	1415	1415	1387	1282	1191	1112	1043	982	928	880	781	699	632	531
10-#18S	.0444	**1772**	1772	1772	1772	1683	1557	1449	1355	1272	1198	1133	1075	1022	974	930	845
12-#8	.0105	**1149**	1149	1149	1149	1144	1052	974	906	752	596	493	421	367	325	292	243
12-#9	.0133	**1201**	1201	1201	1201	1192	1098	1017	948	887	729	607	520	454	403	363	302
12-#10	.0169	**1267**	1267	1267	1267	1254	1156	1072	1000	937	881	745	640	561	500	451	376
12-#11	.0208	**1338**	1338	1338	1338	1319	1218	1131	1055	989	931	879	763	671	599	541	453
12-#14S	.0300	**1507**	1507	1507	1507	1472	1362	1267	1184	1112	1048	991	939	893	821	744	626

Check availability of #14S and #18S bars.

* One-half of the bar are to be placed in each of the two faces of the column that are perpendicular to the plane of bending.

† Below zigzag horizontal line of each group, concrete governs; above, tension governs.

SQUARE TIED COLUMNS—Safe Load in Kips for Various Eccentricities in Inches
f'_c = 5000 psi f_s = 24,000 psi basis
(A61 or A432 Bars, f_y = 60,000 psi)

COLUMN SIZE—28" x 28" CONTINUED

f'_c = 5000 psi
f_y = 60,000 psi

M/N † = e (in.)																	
18	20	22	24	26	28	30	32	34	36	38	40	42	44	46	48	50	M_o ‡ (kip-in.)
156	137	121	109	99	91	84	78	73	68	64	61	57	54	52	50	47	2204
195	171	152	137	124	114	105	98	91	86	81	76	72	69	65	62	60	2774
244	214	190	172	156	143	132	123	115	108	101	96	91	86	82	78	75	3502
294	259	231	208	190	174	161	150	140	131	123	117	111	105	100	96	91	4275
410	361	323	292	266	245	226	211	197	185	174	165	156	149	142	135	130	6090
654	579	520	472	432	398	369	344	322	303	286	271	257	245	233	223	214	10189
186	163	145	131	119	109	101	93	87	82	77	73	69	65	62	59	57	2644
232	204	181	163	149	136	126	117	109	103	97	91	86	82	78	75	71	3329
290	254	227	205	186	171	158	147	137	129	121	115	109	103	98	94	90	4202
349	307	274	248	226	208	192	178	167	157	148	139	132	126	120	114	109	5130
485	428	383	347	316	291	270	251	235	221	208	197	187	177	169	162	155	7308
168	147	131	118	107	98	91	84	79	74	69	65	62	59	56	53	51	2381
216	189	168	152	138	127	117	109	101	95	90	85	80	76	73	69	66	3085
269	236	210	190	173	159	147	136	127	119	112	106	101	96	91	87	83	3884
335	294	263	237	216	199	184	171	160	150	141	133	126	120	115	109	105	4903
403	355	317	287	262	241	223	207	194	182	171	162	154	146	139	133	127	5985
191	168	149	134	122	112	103	96	90	84	79	75	71	67	64	61	58	2721
245	215	192	173	157	144	133	124	116	109	102	97	91	87	83	79	76	3526
305	268	239	216	197	180	167	155	145	136	128	121	115	109	104	99	95	4439
379	334	298	269	246	226	209	194	182	171	161	152	144	137	131	125	119	5603
160	140	124	112	102	93	86	80	75	70	66	62	59	56	53	51	48	2257
214	188	167	151	137	126	116	108	101	94	89	84	80	76	72	69	66	3061
274	241	215	194	176	162	150	139	130	122	115	108	103	98	93	89	85	3967
341	300	267	241	220	202	187	174	163	153	144	136	129	122	117	111	107	4994
COLUMN SIZE—30" x 30"																	
192	167	149	133	121	111	102	95	89	83	78	74	70	66	63	60	57	2652
315	276	246	221	201	184	170	158	148	138	130	123	117	111	105	101	96	4459
201	176	156	140	127	117	108	100	93	87	82	77	73	70	66	63	60	2790
283	248	220	198	180	165	152	141	132	124	116	110	104	99	94	90	86	3978
461	405	361	326	297	273	252	234	219	205	193	183	173	165	157	150	143	6689
219	192	170	153	139	127	117	109	102	95	89	84	80	76	72	69	66	3045
266	232	206	186	169	155	143	132	124	116	109	103	97	93	88	84	80	3720
371	326	290	261	238	218	201	187	175	164	154	146	138	131	125	119	114	5304
217	190	168	151	137	126	116	108	101	94	89	84	79	75	72	68	65	3014
272	238	211	190	173	158	146	135	126	118	111	105	100	95	90	86	82	3806
328	288	256	230	209	192	177	165	154	144	136	128	121	115	110	105	100	4650
457	402	358	323	294	270	250	232	217	204	192	181	172	163	156	149	142	6630
734	648	581	526	480	442	410	382	357	335	316	299	284	270	258	246	236	11149
207	181	161	144	131	120	111	103	96	90	84	80	75	72	68	65	62	2872
259	226	201	181	164	151	139	129	120	113	106	100	95	90	86	82	78	3617
323	283	251	226	206	189	174	162	151	142	133	126	119	113	108	103	99	4568
390	342	304	274	250	229	212	197	184	172	162	153	145	138	131	125	120	5580
541	476	425	384	350	322	298	277	259	243	229	216	205	195	186	178	170	7956

‡ M_o = capacity in pure bending, (N = 0), for extrapolation, see page 11-5.

SQUARE TIED COLUMNS—Safe Load in Kips for Various Eccentricities in Inches

$f'_c = 5000$ psi $f_s = 24{,}000$ psi basis
(A61 or A432 Bars, $f_y = 60{,}000$ psi)

COLUMN SIZE—30″ x 30″ CONTINUED

Bars*	p	M/N † = e (in.) 0	1	2	3	4	5	6	7	8	9	10	11	12	13	14	16
14-#8	.0123	**1181**	1181	1181	1181	1175	1082	1002	933	858	683	567	485	423	376	338	281
14-#9	.0156	**1241**	1241	1241	1241	1231	1135	1052	891	919	833	695	597	523	465	419	349
14-#10	.0198	**1318**	1318	1318	1318	1303	1203	1116	1042	977	919	851	733	645	575	519	434
14-#11	.0243	**1401**	1401	1401	1401	1379	1274	1184	1106	1038	977	924	872	769	688	622	522
16-#7	.0107	**1152**	1152	1152	1152	1149	1057	979	911	772	612	507	432	377	334	300	249
16-#8	.0140	**1214**	1214	1214	1214	1206	1111	1030	960	899	767	639	547	479	425	383	319
16-#9	.0178	**1282**	1282	1282	1282	1270	1172	1087	1014	951	894	781	672	590	525	474	396
16-#10	.0226	**1370**	1370	1370	1370	1352	1249	1160	1084	1016	957	904	824	725	648	586	491
16-#11	.0277	**1465**	1465	1465	1465	1438	1330	1238	1157	1086	1023	967	917	864	774	701	590
18-#7	.0120	**1176**	1176	1176	1176	1173	1080	1001	932	853	678	563	481	420	373	335	279
18-#8	.0158	**1246**	1246	1246	1246	1237	1140	1058	986	924	848	708	608	533	474	427	356
18-#9	.0200	**1323**	1323	1323	1323	1309	1208	1122	1048	982	924	864	754	655	584	527	441

COLUMN SIZE—32″ x 32″

Bars*	p	0	1	2	3	4	5	6	7	8	9	10	11	12	13	14	16
4-#18S	.0156	**1414**	1414	1414	1414	1414	1308	1214	1133	1062	1000	838	714	623	552	495	411
6-#14S	.0132	**1363**	1363	1363	1363	1363	1276	1185	1107	1038	919	757	644	560	495	444	368
6-#18S	.0234	**1577**	1577	1577	1577	1567	1449	1349	1261	1184	1115	1055	1000	893	795	717	598
8-#11	.0122	**1342**	1342	1342	1342	1342	1259	1170	1092	1024	868	714	606	527	465	417	345
8-#14S	.0176	**1455**	1455	1455	1455	1455	1360	1265	1183	1110	1046	972	831	725	644	579	481
8-#18S	.0313	**1740**	1740	1740	1740	1716	1590	1482	1387	1304	1230	1164	1105	1051	1003	924	776
10-#10	.0124	**1347**	1347	1347	1347	1347	1265	1175	1097	1029	886	729	619	538	475	426	353
10-#11	.0152	**1406**	1406	1406	1406	1406	1318	1226	1145	1075	1013	868	740	645	571	513	426
10-#14S	.0220	**1546**	1546	1546	1546	1546	1443	1344	1258	1182	1115	1055	1001	883	786	708	591
10-#18S	.0391	**1904**	1904	1904	1904	1864	1730	1615	1513	1424	1344	1273	1209	1151	1099	1051	945
12-#9	.0117	**1332**	1332	1332	1332	1332	1253	1164	1086	1019	848	697	591	513	454	406	336
12-#10	.0149	**1398**	1398	1398	1398	1398	1313	1221	1141	1071	1009	854	728	634	562	504	419
12-#11	.0183	**1469**	1469	1469	1469	1469	1377	1281	1198	1126	1061	1004	868	758	674	606	504
12-#14S	.0264	**1638**	1638	1638	1638	1638	1525	1423	1333	1254	1183	1121	1064	1013	922	833	698
14-#8	.0108	**1313**	1313	1313	1313	1313	1236	1147	1071	1004	794	651	552	478	422	378	313
14-#9	.0137	**1373**	1373	1373	1373	1373	1291	1200	1121	1052	967	798	679	591	523	469	389
14-#10	.0174	**1450**	1450	1450	1450	1450	1361	1266	1184	1112	1048	975	834	728	646	581	483
14-#11	.0213	**1533**	1533	1533	1533	1533	1435	1337	1251	1176	1109	1050	991	868	773	696	581
14-#14S	.0308	**1730**	1730	1730	1730	1730	1608	1501	1407	1325	1251	1186	1127	1073	1024	954	801
16-#8	.0123	**1345**	1345	1345	1345	1345	1266	1176	1099	1031	891	733	622	541	478	428	355
16-#9	.0156	**1414**	1414	1414	1414	1414	1329	1236	1156	1085	1022	895	764	666	590	530	440
16-#10	.0198	**1502**	1502	1502	1502	1502	1408	1312	1228	1154	1088	1030	936	819	728	656	546
16-#11	.0244	**1597**	1597	1597	1597	1597	1493	1392	1304	1226	1157	1096	1041	975	869	784	656
18-#7	.0105	**1308**	1308	1308	1308	1308	1234	1146	1070	1003	789	646	547	475	419	375	310
18-#8	.0139	**1378**	1378	1378	1378	1378	1296	1205	1126	1057	984	812	691	602	533	478	396
18-#9	.0176	**1455**	1455	1455	1455	1455	1367	1272	1190	1118	1054	990	847	740	657	590	491
18-#10	.0223	**1554**	1554	1554	1554	1554	1456	1357	1271	1195	1127	1067	1013	908	808	729	609

Check availability of #14S and #18S bars.

* One-half of the bars are to be placed in each of the two faces of the column that are perpendicular to the plane of bending.

† Below zigzag horizontal line of each group, concrete governs; above, tension governs.

SQUARE TIED COLUMNS—Safe Load in Kips for Various Eccentricities in Inches

f'_c = 5000 psi f_s = 24,000 psi basis
(A61 or A432 Bars, f_y = 60,000 psi)

COLUMN SIZE—30" x 30" CONTINUED

f'_c = 5000 psi
f_y = 60,000 psi

M/N † = e (in.)

18	20	22	24	26	28	30	32	34	36	38	40	42	44	46	48	50	M_o ‡ (kip-in.)
240	210	187	168	152	140	129	120	112	105	98	93	88	83	79	76	73	3351
300	262	233	210	191	175	161	150	140	131	123	117	110	105	100	95	91	4220
373	327	291	263	239	219	202	188	176	165	155	146	139	132	126	120	115	5329
450	395	352	318	289	266	246	228	213	200	188	178	169	160	153	146	140	6510
213	186	165	148	135	123	114	106	98	92	87	82	78	74	70	67	64	2952
273	239	212	191	174	159	147	136	127	119	112	106	100	95	91	87	83	3829
340	298	265	239	217	199	184	171	159	149	141	133	126	120	114	109	104	4823
423	371	331	298	272	249	230	214	200	188	177	167	158	150	143	137	131	6091
509	447	399	361	329	302	279	260	243	228	214	203	192	183	174	166	159	7440
239	208	185	166	151	139	128	119	111	104	97	92	87	83	79	75	72	3321
306	267	238	214	195	178	165	153	143	134	126	119	113	107	102	97	93	4308
380	333	296	267	243	223	206	191	179	168	158	149	141	134	128	122	117	5426
COLUMN SIZE—32" x 32"																	
351	307	272	244	222	203	187	174	162	152	143	135	128	121	115	110	105	4843
314	274	243	218	198	181	167	155	144	135	127	120	114	108	103	98	94	4302
514	450	400	360	328	301	278	258	241	226	212	201	190	181	172	164	157	7265
294	257	228	204	185	170	156	145	135	127	119	112	106	101	96	92	88	4019
412	360	320	288	261	240	221	205	191	179	169	159	151	143	136	130	124	5736
669	588	524	473	431	395	365	340	317	298	281	265	251	239	228	217	208	9687
301	262	233	209	190	173	160	148	138	129	122	115	109	103	98	94	90	4111
364	318	282	253	230	211	194	180	168	158	148	140	132	126	120	114	109	5024
507	444	395	356	324	297	274	255	238	223	210	198	188	178	170	162	155	7170
818	720	644	582	531	488	451	420	393	369	347	329	312	296	282	270	258	12109
287	250	221	199	180	165	152	141	131	123	116	109	103	98	93	89	85	3905
358	312	277	249	226	207	191	177	165	155	146	137	130	124	118	112	107	4934
432	378	336	302	274	251	232	215	201	188	177	167	158	150	143	137	131	6029
600	527	469	423	385	353	326	303	283	266	250	236	224	213	203	194	185	8604
266	232	206	184	167	153	141	131	122	114	107	101	96	91	87	83	79	3616
332	290	257	231	209	192	177	164	153	143	135	127	120	114	109	104	99	4556
414	362	321	289	262	240	222	206	192	180	169	160	151	144	137	131	125	5756
499	437	388	350	318	291	269	250	233	219	206	194	184	175	167	159	152	7034
691	607	542	489	445	409	378	351	328	308	290	274	260	247	236	225	215	10038
303	264	234	210	191	174	161	149	139	130	122	115	109	104	99	94	90	4133
377	329	292	262	238	218	201	187	174	163	154	145	137	130	124	118	113	5207
469	410	364	328	298	273	252	234	219	205	193	182	173	164	156	149	142	6578
564	494	440	397	361	331	306	284	265	249	234	221	210	199	190	181	173	8039
264	230	204	183	166	152	140	130	121	113	106	100	95	90	86	82	78	3580
338	295	262	235	214	196	180	167	156	146	137	130	123	117	111	106	101	4649
421	368	327	294	267	244	226	209	195	183	172	163	154	146	139	133	127	5858
523	458	407	367	334	306	283	262	245	230	216	204	194	184	175	167	160	7401

‡ M_o = capacity in pure bending, (N = 0), for extrapolation, see page 11-5.

SQUARE TIED COLUMNS—Safe Load in Kips for Various Eccentricities in Inches

$f'_c = 5000$ psi $f_s = 24{,}000$ psi basis
(A61 or A432 Bars, $f_y = 60{,}000$ psi)

COLUMN SIZE—34″ x 34″

Bars *	p	M/N † = e (in.) 0	1	2	3	4	5	6	7	8	10	12	14	16	18	20	22
4-#18S	.0138	**1554**	1554	1554	1554	1554	1477	1375	1286	1208	962	703	554	457	389	338	299
6-#14S	.0117	**1503**	1503	1503	1503	1503	1443	1344	1257	1181	868	631	496	408	347	301	267
6-#18S	.0208	**1717**	1717	1717	1717	1717	1624	1515	1419	1335	1193	1008	802	665	569	497	441
8-#11	.0108	**1482**	1482	1482	1482	1482	1426	1328	1242	1167	819	593	465	383	325	282	250
8-#14S	.0156	**1595**	1595	1595	1595	1595	1530	1426	1336	1257	1112	817	646	534	455	396	351
8-#18S	.0277	**1881**	1881	1881	1881	1881	1769	1653	1551	1460	1308	1184	1034	863	740	648	577
10-#10	.0110	**1487**	1487	1487	1487	1487	1432	1333	1247	1172	835	606	475	391	332	288	255
10-#11	.0135	**1546**	1546	1546	1546	1546	1487	1386	1297	1220	994	726	572	472	402	349	309
10-#14S	.0195	**1687**	1687	1687	1687	1687	1615	1508	1414	1331	1192	994	790	655	560	489	434
10-#18S	.0346	**2044**	2044	2044	2044	2044	1914	1790	1681	1585	1422	1289	1180	1051	905	795	709
12-#9	.0104	**1473**	1473	1473	1473	1473	1419	1321	1236	1161	799	578	453	372	316	275	243
12-#10	.0132	**1539**	1539	1539	1539	1539	1481	1380	1293	1215	979	714	563	464	395	343	304
12-#11	.0162	**1610**	1610	1610	1610	1610	1547	1443	1352	1272	1138	854	676	559	476	415	368
12-#14S	.0234	**1779**	1779	1779	1779	1779	1700	1589	1492	1406	1260	1142	929	773	662	579	515
14-#9	.0121	**1513**	1513	1513	1513	1513	1458	1359	1272	1196	914	665	523	431	366	318	281
14-#10	.0154	**1590**	1590	1590	1590	1590	1530	1427	1338	1258	1116	820	648	535	456	397	352
14-#11	.0189	**1673**	1673	1673	1673	1673	1607	1500	1407	1325	1186	977	776	644	550	480	426
14-#14S	.0272	**1870**	1870	1870	1870	1870	1785	1670	1569	1480	1328	1205	1063	888	762	668	594
16-#8	.0109	**1486**	1486	1486	1486	1486	1433	1334	1249	1173	840	609	478	393	334	290	256
16-#9	.0138	**1554**	1554	1554	1554	1554	1497	1396	1308	1230	1025	750	591	488	415	361	320
16-#10	.0176	**1642**	1642	1642	1642	1642	1579	1474	1382	1301	1165	922	731	605	517	451	400
16-#11	.0216	**1737**	1737	1737	1737	1737	1666	1557	1461	1377	1234	1096	874	727	622	544	483
18-#8	.0123	**1518**	1518	1518	1518	1518	1464	1364	1277	1201	930	677	533	439	373	324	287
18-#9	.0156	**1595**	1595	1595	1595	1595	1536	1433	1343	1264	1130	832	658	544	464	404	358
18-#10	.0198	**1694**	1694	1694	1694	1694	1628	1521	1427	1344	1204	1021	812	674	576	503	447
18-#11	.0243	**1801**	1801	1801	1801	1801	1725	1614	1516	1429	1282	1162	970	808	693	606	539

COLUMN SIZE—36″ x 36″

Bars *	p	0	1	2	3	4	5	6	7	8	10	12	14	16	18	20	22
4-#18S	.0123	**1703**	1703	1703	1703	1703	1659	1548	1451	1365	1103	792	617	506	428	372	328
6-#18S	.0185	**1866**	1866	1866	1866	1866	1810	1692	1588	1496	1342	1134	893	736	627	545	483
8-#14S	.0139	**1744**	1744	1744	1744	1744	1711	1599	1501	1414	1267	918	718	590	500	434	384
8-#18S	.0247	**2029**	2029	2029	2029	2029	1959	1834	1724	1627	1461	1326	1151	955	816	712	632
10-#11	.0120	**1695**	1695	1695	1695	1695	1667	1557	1461	1376	1138	816	636	521	441	383	338
10-#14S	.0174	**1835**	1835	1835	1835	1835	1799	1683	1582	1491	1339	1115	878	724	616	535	474
10-#18S	.0309	**2192**	2192	2192	2192	2192	2107	1976	1859	1756	1580	1436	1317	1163	997	873	776
12-#10	.0118	**1687**	1687	1687	1687	1687	1661	1552	1456	1371	1120	803	625	512	433	376	332
12-#11	.0144	**1758**	1758	1758	1758	1758	1729	1616	1517	1430	1282	959	751	617	523	455	402
12-#14S	.0208	**1927**	1927	1927	1927	1927	1886	1767	1662	1568	1410	1280	1032	854	728	634	562
12-#18S	.0370	**2356**	2356	2356	2356	2356	2255	2116	1994	1884	1698	1546	1418	1310	1173	1029	917

Check availability of #14S and #18S bars.

* One-half of the bars are to be placed in each of the two faces of the column that are perpendicular to the plane of bending.

† Below zigzag horizontal line of each group, concrete governs; above, tension governs.

SQUARE TIED COLUMNS—Safe Load in Kips for Various Eccentricities in Inches

f'_c = 5000 psi f_s = 24,000 psi basis
(A61 or A432 Bars, f_y = 60,000 psi)

f'_c = 5000 psi
f_y = 60,000 psi

M/N † = e (in.)																	
24	26	28	30	32	34	36	38	40	42	44	46	48	50	52	54	56	M_o ‡ (kip-in.)
COLUMN SIZE—34″ x 34″																	
269	243	223	205	190	177	166	156	147	139	132	126	120	115	110	105	101	5227
239	216	198	182	169	157	147	138	130	123	117	111	106	102	97	93	90	4626
396	360	329	304	282	263	246	232	219	207	197	187	179	171	164	157	151	7841
224	203	185	170	158	147	138	129	122	115	109	104	99	95	91	87	84	4319
315	286	261	241	223	208	195	183	173	164	155	148	141	135	129	124	119	6168
519	472	433	400	371	347	325	306	289	274	260	248	237	226	217	208	200	10455
229	207	189	174	161	150	141	132	125	118	112	106	102	97	93	89	86	4416
277	251	230	212	196	183	171	161	152	144	136	130	124	118	113	109	104	5398
390	354	324	299	277	259	242	228	215	204	193	184	176	168	161	154	148	7710
639	582	535	494	459	429	403	379	358	340	323	308	294	281	269	259	249	13069
217	197	180	166	153	143	134	126	118	112	106	101	96	92	88	85	81	4193
273	247	226	208	193	180	168	158	149	141	134	127	122	116	111	107	103	5299
330	300	274	253	234	218	205	192	182	172	163	155	148	142	136	130	125	6478
463	421	386	356	330	308	289	272	257	243	231	220	210	201	192	185	178	9252
252	229	209	192	178	166	156	146	138	130	124	118	112	107	103	99	95	4892
316	287	262	242	224	209	196	184	173	164	156	148	142	135	130	124	119	6183
383	347	318	293	272	254	238	224	211	200	190	181	172	165	158	151	146	7558
535	487	446	412	383	358	335	316	298	282	268	256	244	233	224	215	206	10794
230	208	190	175	162	151	141	133	125	119	112	107	102	97	93	90	86	4436
287	260	238	219	203	189	177	167	157	149	141	134	128	123	117	113	108	5591
359	326	298	275	255	238	223	209	198	187	178	169	161	154	148	142	136	7066
434	394	361	333	309	289	270	254	240	228	216	206	196	188	180	173	166	8638
257	233	213	196	182	169	159	149	141	133	126	120	115	110	105	101	97	4991
321	291	267	246	228	212	199	187	176	167	159	151	144	138	132	126	122	6290
401	364	334	308	286	266	250	235	222	210	199	190	181	173	166	159	153	7949
485	441	404	373	346	323	303	285	269	255	242	231	220	211	202	194	186	9717
COLUMN SIZE—36″ x 36″																	
294	266	243	223	207	192	180	169	159	151	143	136	130	124	119	114	109	5611
433	392	359	331	306	286	267	251	237	224	213	203	193	185	177	170	163	8417
344	311	284	262	242	226	211	198	187	177	168	160	152	146	139	134	128	6600
568	516	472	435	404	377	353	332	313	297	282	268	256	245	235	225	216	11223
302	273	250	230	213	198	185	174	164	155	147	140	134	128	122	117	113	5773
425	385	352	324	301	280	262	247	233	220	209	199	190	181	174	167	160	8250
699	635	583	538	499	466	437	411	389	368	350	333	318	304	291	280	269	14029
297	269	245	226	209	194	182	171	161	152	145	138	131	125	120	115	110	5665
360	326	298	274	254	237	221	208	196	186	176	168	160	153	146	140	135	6927
505	458	419	386	358	334	313	294	278	263	250	238	227	217	208	199	191	9900
827	753	691	638	593	554	520	490	463	439	417	397	379	363	348	334	321	16835

‡ M_o = capacity in pure bending, (N = 0), for extrapolation, see page 11-5.

SQUARE TIED COLUMNS—Safe Load in Kips for Various Eccentricities in Inches

$f'_c = 5000$ psi $f_s = 24{,}000$ psi basis
(A61 or A432 Bars, $f_y = 60{,}000$ psi)

COLUMN SIZE—36″ x 36″ CONTINUED

Bars *	p	M/N † = e (in.) 0	1	2	3	4	5	6	7	8	10	12	14	16	18	20	22
14-#9	.0108	**1662**	1662	1662	1662	1662	1638	1529	1434	1350	1047	747	581	475	402	348	307
14-#10	.0137	**1739**	1739	1739	1739	1739	1712	1600	1502	1415	1269	920	720	591	501	435	384
14-#11	.0169	**1822**	1822	1822	1822	1822	1790	1675	1574	1484	1332	1096	862	710	604	525	465
14-#14S	.0243	**2019**	2019	2019	2019	2019	1973	1850	1741	1644	1480	1345	1180	980	838	731	649
16-#9	.0123	**1703**	1703	1703	1703	1703	1678	1568	1471	1386	1173	842	657	538	456	395	349
16-#10	.0157	**1791**	1791	1791	1791	1791	1762	1648	1548	1460	1310	1034	812	668	567	493	436
16-#11	.0193	**1886**	1886	1886	1886	1886	1851	1733	1630	1538	1382	1229	971	802	683	595	527
16-#14S	.0278	**2111**	2111	2111	2111	2111	2059	1932	1820	1720	1550	1411	1294	1103	945	826	734
18-#8	.0110	**1667**	1667	1667	1667	1667	1643	1535	1440	1355	1065	761	592	484	410	355	313
18-#9	.0139	**1744**	1744	1744	1744	1744	1718	1606	1508	1421	1274	934	731	600	509	442	391
18-#10	.0176	**1843**	1843	1843	1843	1843	1812	1696	1594	1504	1351	1145	902	744	633	551	487
18-#11	.0217	**1949**	1949	1949	1949	1949	1912	1792	1686	1591	1432	1301	1077	892	761	664	588
20-#8	.0122	**1699**	1699	1699	1699	1699	1675	1565	1469	1384	1165	836	652	534	452	392	346
20-#9	.0154	**1784**	1784	1784	1784	1784	1757	1644	1544	1456	1307	1024	804	661	562	488	432
20-#10	.0196	**1895**	1895	1895	1895	1895	1862	1744	1640	1548	1391	1253	990	818	697	607	538

COLUMN SIZE—38″ x 38″

Bars *	p	M/N † = e (in.) 0	2	4	6	8	10	12	14	16	18	20	22	24	26	28	30
4-#18S	.0111	**1860**	1860	1860	1732	1533	1265	889	686	558	470	406	358	319	289	263	242
6-#18S	.0166	**2023**	2023	2023	1880	1669	1500	1272	991	812	688	596	526	471	426	389	358
8-#14S	.0125	**1901**	1901	1901	1784	1582	1422	1030	796	649	548	474	417	373	337	308	283
8-#18S	.0222	**2187**	2187	2187	2026	1803	1624	1478	1277	1052	895	779	689	618	560	512	472
10-#11	.0108	**1852**	1852	1852	1740	1542	1303	915	705	573	483	417	367	328	296	270	248
10-#14S	.0156	**1993**	1993	1993	1870	1662	1496	1250	973	796	674	584	516	461	417	381	351
10-#18S	.0277	**2350**	2350	2350	2172	1937	1748	1592	1462	1281	1094	955	847	761	690	632	583
12-#10	.0106	**1845**	1845	1845	1735	1537	1284	900	693	563	475	410	361	322	291	265	244
12-#11	.0130	**1916**	1916	1916	1801	1599	1437	1075	832	679	573	496	437	391	353	322	296
12-#14S	.0187	**2085**	2085	2085	1956	1741	1569	1428	1143	939	797	692	612	548	496	454	418
12-#18S	.0332	**2513**	2513	2513	2316	2070	1870	1706	1568	1451	1286	1125	1000	900	818	750	692
14-#10	.0123	**1896**	1896	1896	1784	1583	1423	1032	797	650	548	474	418	373	338	308	283
14-#11	.0151	**1979**	1979	1979	1861	1654	1489	1228	955	782	661	573	506	452	409	374	344
14-#14S	.0218	**2176**	2176	2176	2041	1820	1642	1496	1307	1078	917	798	706	633	574	525	484
16-#9	.0111	**1860**	1860	1860	1751	1553	1343	944	728	592	499	431	380	339	306	279	257
16-#10	.0141	**1948**	1948	1948	1834	1629	1465	1159	899	735	621	538	474	424	384	350	322
16-#11	.0173	**2043**	2043	2043	1921	1710	1540	1376	1075	882	748	649	573	513	465	424	391
16-#14S	.0249	**2268**	2268	2268	2125	1898	1714	1563	1437	1212	1034	901	799	717	651	596	549
18-#9	.0125	**1901**	1901	1901	1790	1589	1428	1047	810	660	557	482	425	379	343	313	288
18-#10	.0158	**2000**	2000	2000	1883	1674	1508	1282	999	818	693	600	530	474	429	392	361
18-#11	.0194	**2107**	2107	2107	1981	1765	1591	1449	1192	980	833	724	640	573	519	475	437

Check availability of #14S and #18S bars.

* One-half of the bars are to be placed in each of the two faces of the column that are perpendicular to the plane of bending.

† Below zigzag horizontal line of each group, concrete governs; above, tension governs.

SQUARE TIED COLUMNS—Safe Load in Kips for Various Eccentricities in Inches

f'_c = 5000 psi f_s = 24,000 psi basis
(A61 or A432 Bars, f_y = 60,000 psi)

COLUMN SIZE—36″ x 36″ CONTINUED

f'_c = 5000 psi
f_y = 60,000 psi

M/N † = e (in.)

24	26	28	30	32	34	36	38	40	42	44	46	48	50	52	54	56	M_o ‡ (kip-in.)
275	249	227	209	193	180	168	158	149	141	134	127	121	116	111	106	102	5228
344	312	285	262	243	226	211	199	187	177	168	160	153	146	140	134	129	6609
417	378	345	318	295	275	257	242	228	216	205	195	186	178	170	163	157	8082
583	530	485	447	415	387	363	341	322	305	290	276	263	252	241	232	223	11550
312	283	258	238	220	205	192	180	170	161	152	145	138	132	126	121	116	5975
391	354	324	298	276	257	241	226	213	202	192	182	174	166	159	153	147	7554
473	429	392	362	335	313	293	275	260	246	233	222	212	202	194	186	179	9237
661	601	550	508	472	440	412	388	367	347	330	314	300	287	275	264	254	13200
280	253	231	213	197	183	171	161	152	144	136	130	124	118	113	108	104	5332
350	317	289	266	247	230	215	202	191	180	171	163	155	148	142	136	131	6722
437	396	362	334	309	288	270	254	239	227	215	205	195	187	179	171	165	8498
528	480	439	405	375	350	328	308	291	276	262	249	238	227	218	209	201	10391
310	281	256	236	218	203	190	179	168	159	151	144	137	131	125	120	115	5925
387	350	320	295	273	255	238	224	211	200	190	180	172	164	157	151	145	7469
483	438	401	369	342	319	299	281	265	251	238	227	216	207	198	190	183	9442

COLUMN SIZE—38″ x 38″

M/N † = e (in.)

32	34	36	38	40	42	44	46	48	50	52	54	56	58	60	62	64	M_o ‡ (kip-in.)
224	208	195	183	172	163	154	147	140	134	128	123	118	113	109	105	102	5995
332	309	289	271	256	242	230	218	208	199	191	183	176	169	163	157	152	8993
262	243	228	214	201	190	181	172	164	156	150	144	138	133	128	123	119	7032
437	408	382	359	338	320	304	289	276	264	253	242	233	224	216	208	201	11991
230	214	200	187	177	167	158	150	143	137	131	126	121	116	112	108	104	6147
325	302	283	266	250	237	225	214	204	195	186	179	172	165	159	154	148	8790
541	504	472	444	419	397	377	359	343	328	314	301	289	279	269	259	251	14989
225	210	196	184	173	164	155	148	141	134	129	123	118	114	110	106	102	6031
274	255	239	224	211	200	189	180	172	164	157	150	145	139	134	129	125	7377
387	360	337	317	299	283	268	255	244	233	223	214	205	198	191	184	178	10548
642	600	562	529	499	473	449	428	409	391	374	359	346	333	321	310	299	17987
262	244	228	214	202	191	181	172	164	157	150	144	138	133	128	123	119	7036
318	296	277	260	245	232	220	209	200	191	183	175	168	162	156	150	145	8606
448	418	391	368	347	328	312	297	283	270	259	249	239	230	222	214	207	12306
237	221	206	194	183	173	164	156	148	142	136	130	125	120	116	112	108	6359
298	277	259	244	230	217	206	196	187	178	171	164	157	151	146	141	136	8041
362	337	315	296	279	264	251	239	227	217	208	200	192	185	178	172	166	9836
509	475	445	418	395	374	355	338	322	308	295	283	272	262	252	244	236	4064
266	248	232	217	205	194	184	175	167	159	152	146	140	135	130	125	121	7154
334	311	291	273	258	244	231	220	210	200	192	184	177	170	164	158	153	9047
405	377	353	332	313	296	281	268	255	244	234	224	215	207	200	193	186	11065

‡ M_o = capacity in pure bending, (N = 0), for extrapolation, see page 11-5.

SQUARE TIED COLUMNS—Safe Load in Kips for Various Eccentricities in Inches

f'_c = 5000 psi f_s = 24,000 psi basis
(A61 or A432 Bars, f_y = 60,000 psi)

COLUMN SIZE—38″ x 38″ CONTINUED

Bars *	p	M/N † = e (in.) 0	2	4	6	8	10	12	14	16	18	20	22	24	26	28	30
20-#8	.0109	**1856**	1856	1856	1748	1550	1334	937	722	587	495	428	376	336	304	277	254
20-#9	.0139	**1942**	1942	1942	1829	1625	1462	1148	890	727	615	532	469	420	379	346	318
20-#10	.0176	**2052**	2052	2052	1932	1720	1550	1402	1096	900	763	662	585	524	474	433	399
20-#11	.0216	**2170**	2170	2170	2040	1820	1642	1497	1306	1077	916	797	706	633	574	525	483
22-#8	.0120	**1888**	1888	1888	1779	1579	1419	1019	788	642	541	468	412	368	333	304	279
22-#9	.0152	**1983**	1983	1983	1868	1661	1495	1246	969	793	671	582	513	459	416	379	349
22-#10	.0193	**2104**	2104	2104	1980	1765	1592	1449	1191	980	832	723	639	573	519	475	437
22-#11	.0238	**2234**	2234	2234	2099	1875	1693	1544	1417	1172	998	870	771	692	627	574	529

COLUMN SIZE—40″ x 40″

Bars *	p	0	2	4	6	8	10	12	14	16	18	20	22	24	26	28	30
4-#18S	.0100	**2026**	2026	2026	1928	1712	1453	998	760	614	514	443	389	346	312	284	261
6-#18S	.0150	**2189**	2189	2189	2080	1852	1669	1425	1098	893	752	650	572	511	462	421	387
8-#14S	.0113	**2067**	2067	2067	1980	1762	1587	1153	881	712	598	515	453	404	364	332	305
8-#18S	.0200	**2352**	2352	2352	2230	1991	1798	1639	1413	1157	979	849	749	670	606	554	509
10-#14S	.0141	**2159**	2159	2159	2068	1844	1663	1399	1076	874	736	636	559	499	451	411	378
10-#18S	.0250	**2516**	2516	2516	2379	2128	1925	1758	1617	1408	1196	1040	920	825	747	683	629
12-#11	.0117	**2081**	2081	2081	1997	1778	1603	1203	920	745	626	539	474	423	381	347	319
12-#14S	.0169	**2250**	2250	2250	2156	1925	1739	1585	1263	1030	870	753	664	593	536	489	450
12-#18S	.0300	**2679**	2679	2679	2527	2265	2052	1876	1727	1601	1406	1226	1086	976	885	810	747
14-#10	.0111	**2062**	2062	2062	1980	1763	1588	1155	882	713	599	516	453	404	364	332	305
14-#11	.0137	**2145**	2145	2145	2059	1836	1656	1374	1056	858	722	623	548	489	442	403	370
14-#14S	.0197	**2342**	2342	2342	2243	2006	1814	1656	1443	1182	1001	868	766	685	620	566	521
16-#9	.0100	**2026**	2026	2026	1946	1731	1541	1058	805	650	544	469	411	367	330	301	276
16-#10	.0127	**2114**	2114	2114	2031	1809	1632	1297	994	806	678	585	514	459	414	377	347
16-#11	.0156	**2209**	2209	2209	2120	1893	1709	1539	1188	968	816	706	621	555	502	458	421
16-#14S	.0225	**2434**	2434	2434	2330	2086	1889	1726	1588	1329	1128	980	866	776	703	642	591
18-#9	.0113	**2067**	2067	2067	1986	1768	1593	1173	895	724	608	524	460	410	370	337	310
18-#10	.0143	**2166**	2166	2166	2081	1856	1675	1434	1104	897	756	653	574	513	463	422	383
18-#11	.0176	**2272**	2272	2272	2181	1949	1762	1607	1317	1075	909	787	694	620	561	512	471
18-#14S	.0253	**2526**	2526	2526	2416	2166	1963	1795	1654	1473	1253	1090	965	865	784	717	661
20-#9	.0125	**2108**	2108	2108	2026	1805	1628	1284	984	798	671	578	509	454	409	373	343
20-#10	.0159	**2218**	2218	2218	2131	1903	1719	1567	1211	987	832	720	634	567	512	467	429
20-#11	.0195	**2336**	2336	2336	2242	2006	1814	1656	1442	1181	1000	867	765	684	619	566	520
22-#8	.0109	**2054**	2054	2054	1975	1758	1584	1141	871	704	591	509	447	398	359	327	300
22-#9	.0138	**2148**	2148	2148	2066	1842	1662	1394	1071	870	732	632	556	497	448	409	376
22-#10	.0175	**2269**	2269	2269	2181	1949	1762	1607	1316	1075	908	786	693	620	560	511	470
24-#8	.0119	**2086**	2086	2086	2007	1788	1612	1231	942	762	640	552	485	433	390	356	327
24-#9	.0150	**2189**	2189	2189	2105	1879	1697	1500	1157	941	793	686	604	539	487	444	408
24-#10	.0191	**2321**	2321	2321	2230	1995	1805	1647	1418	1161	982	852	751	672	608	555	511

Check availability of #14S and #18S bars.

* One-half of the bars are to be placed in each of the two faces of the column that are perpendicular to the plane of bending.

† Below zigzag horizontal line of each group, concrete governs; above, tension governs.

SQUARE TIED COLUMNS—Safe Load in Kips for Various Eccentricities in Inches

$f'_c = 5000$ psi $f_s = 24{,}000$ psi basis

(A61 or A432 Bars, $f_y = 60{,}000$ psi)

$f'_c = 5000$ psi
$f_y = 60{,}000$ psi

COLUMN SIZE—38″ x 38″ CONTINUED																	
M/N † = e (in.)																	M_o ‡
32	34	36	38	40	42	44	46	48	50	52	54	56	58	60	62	64	(kip-in.)
235	219	205	192	181	171	162	154	147	140	134	129	124	119	115	111	107	6304
295	274	257	241	227	215	204	194	185	176	169	162	156	150	144	139	134	7949
370	344	322	303	285	270	256	244	232	222	213	204	196	189	182	175	169	10052
448	418	391	367	347	328	311	296	283	270	259	248	239	230	221	214	206	12295
258	240	225	211	199	188	178	169	162	154	148	142	136	131	126	122	117	6934
323	301	281	264	249	236	224	213	203	194	185	178	171	164	158	153	148	8744
405	377	353	332	313	296	281	267	255	244	233	224	215	207	200	193	186	11057
491	457	428	403	380	360	342	325	310	296	284	273	262	252	243	235	227	13524
COLUMN SIZE—40″ x 40″																	
241	224	209	196	185	175	166	157	150	143	137	131	126	121	117	113	109	6379
358	333	311	292	275	260	247	235	224	214	204	196	188	181	174	168	162	9569
282	262	244	229	216	204	194	184	175	167	160	154	147	142	137	132	127	7464
472	439	411	386	364	344	326	311	296	283	271	260	250	240	231	223	216	12759
349	325	304	285	269	254	241	229	218	208	199	191	184	177	170	164	159	9330
583	543	509	478	451	427	405	385	368	351	337	323	310	299	288	278	268	15949
295	274	256	240	226	214	203	193	184	175	168	161	154	149	143	138	133	7826
416	387	362	340	321	303	288	274	261	249	238	229	220	211	204	196	190	11196
693	646	605	569	537	508	483	459	438	419	402	385	370	357	344	332	321	19139
282	262	245	229	216	204	194	184	175	167	160	154	147	142	137	132	127	7463
342	318	297	279	263	249	236	224	214	204	195	187	180	173	167	161	155	9130
482	449	420	395	372	352	334	318	303	289	277	266	255	246	237	228	221	13062
255	237	222	208	196	185	175	167	159	151	145	139	133	128	124	119	115	6743
320	298	278	261	246	233	221	210	200	191	183	175	168	162	156	150	145	8529
389	362	339	318	300	283	269	255	243	233	223	213	205	197	190	183	177	10435
548	510	478	449	423	401	380	362	345	330	316	303	291	280	270	260	252	14928
286	266	248	233	220	208	197	187	178	170	163	156	150	144	139	134	129	7586
359	334	312	293	276	261	248	235	224	214	205	197	189	182	175	169	163	9595
436	406	379	356	336	318	301	286	273	261	250	240	230	221	213	206	199	11739
613	571	534	502	474	449	426	405	387	369	354	340	326	314	303	292	282	16794
317	295	275	258	243	230	218	207	198	189	181	173	166	160	154	149	143	8429
397	370	346	325	306	289	274	261	249	237	227	218	209	201	194	187	181	10661
482	449	420	394	372	352	334	317	303	289	277	265	255	245	236	228	220	13044
278	258	241	226	213	201	191	181	173	165	158	151	145	140	135	130	125	7351
347	323	302	283	267	252	239	228	217	207	198	190	183	176	169	163	158	9272
435	405	379	356	335	317	301	286	273	261	250	239	230	221	213	206	199	11728
302	281	262	246	232	219	208	197	188	180	172	165	158	152	147	141	137	8020
378	351	329	308	291	275	261	248	236	226	216	207	199	191	184	178	172	10115
473	440	412	387	365	345	327	311	297	284	272	261	250	241	232	224	216	12794

‡ M_o = capacity in pure bending, ($N = 0$), for extrapolation, see page 11-5.

SQUARE TIED COLUMNS—Safe Load in Kips for Various Eccentricities in Inches

f'_c = 5000 psi f_s = 30,000 psi basis
(A431 Bars, f_y = 75,000 psi)

COLUMN SIZE—15″ x 15″

Bars *	p	M/N † = e (in.) 0	1	2	3	4	5	6	7	8	9	10	11	12	13	14	15
4-#11	.0277	**398**	398	353	297	256	225	201	167	141	122	108	97	87	80	73	68
4-#14	.0400	**468**	468	400	336	289	253	226	204	184	161	143	129	117	107	99	92
4-#18	.0711	**647**	630	496	409	348	303	268	240	218	199	183	170	158	146	136	127
6-#11	.0416	**477**	477	411	345	297	261	233	210	192	170	151	136	124	114	105	97
6-#14	.0600	**583**	583	482	403	347	304	271	244	222	204	188	174	160	148	137	128
8-#11	.0555	**557**	557	468	393	339	298	266	240	218	200	185	169	155	143	132	124

COLUMN SIZE—16″ x 16″

Bars *	p	0	1	2	3	4	5	6	7	8	9	10	11	12	13	14	15
4-#11	.0244	**431**	431	398	337	293	258	231	191	161	139	122	109	98	89	82	76
4-#14	.0352	**501**	501	448	379	329	290	259	234	211	184	163	146	132	121	111	103
4-#18	.0625	**680**	680	553	462	396	347	309	278	253	232	214	199	184	170	157	147
6-#11	.0366	**510**	510	458	389	337	298	267	241	220	193	171	154	140	128	118	109
6-#14	.0527	**616**	616	534	451	391	345	308	279	255	234	217	199	182	168	156	145
8-#11	.0488	**590**	590	519	440	382	337	302	273	250	230	213	193	176	162	150	139

COLUMN SIZE—17″ x 17″

Bars *	p	0	1	2	3	4	5	6	7	8	9	10	11	12	13	14	15
4-#11	.0216	**466**	466	446	380	332	294	264	216	181	155	136	121	109	99	91	84
4-#14	.0311	**536**	536	498	425	370	328	295	267	239	207	183	164	148	135	124	115
4-#18	.0554	**715**	715	611	516	446	393	351	317	289	266	246	229	210	194	179	167
6-#11	.0324	**545**	545	509	434	379	336	302	274	251	218	192	172	156	143	131	122
6-#14	.0467	**651**	651	587	501	437	387	348	316	289	266	247	225	206	189	175	162
8-#11	.0432	**625**	625	571	488	427	378	340	309	283	261	240	217	197	181	167	156

COLUMN SIZE—18″ x 18″

Bars *	p	M/N † = e (in.) 0	1	2	3	4	5	6	7	8	9	10	11	12	13	14	15
4-#11	.0193	**503**	503	496	426	374	333	300	244	202	173	151	134	121	110	100	92
4-#14	.0278	**573**	573	551	473	415	369	332	302	269	232	204	182	164	150	137	127
4-#18	.0494	**752**	752	671	571	497	440	395	358	328	302	280	261	238	218	202	188
6-#11	.0289	**582**	582	561	483	423	377	340	310	282	243	214	191	173	158	145	134
6-#14	.0417	**688**	688	643	553	485	432	389	354	325	300	279	252	229	210	194	180
6-#18	.0741	**956**	956	823	700	609	539	483	438	400	369	342	318	298	280	264	250
8-#11	.0385	**662**	662	626	539	473	422	380	346	318	294	269	242	220	201	186	172

Check availability of #14 and #18 bars.

* One-half of the bars are to be placed in each of the two faces of the column that are perpendicular to the plane of bending.

† Below zigzag horizontal line of each group, concrete governs; above, tension governs.

SQUARE TIED COLUMNS—Safe Load in Kips for Various Eccentricities in Inches

$f'_c = 5000$ psi $f_s = 30{,}000$ psi basis

(A431 Bars, $f_y = 75{,}000$ psi)

$f'_c = 5000$ psi

$f_y = 75{,}000$ psi

COLUMN SIZE—15″ x 15″

M/N † = e (in.)

16	17	18	19	20	21	22	23	24	25	26	27	28	29	30	31	32	M_o ‡ (kip-in.)
63	59	55	52	49	47	44	42	40	39	37	36	34	33	32	31	30	921
86	80	75	71	67	64	61	58	56	53	51	49	47	46	44	43	41	1290
119	113	106	101	96	92	87	84	80	77	74	71	69	67	64	62	60	1974
91	85	80	76	72	68	65	62	59	57	55	52	50	49	47	45	44	1381
120	113	107	101	96	91	87	83	80	77	74	71	68	66	64	62	60	1935
116	109	103	97	92	88	84	80	77	74	71	68	66	63	61	59	57	1842

COLUMN SIZE—16″ x 16″

16	17	18	19	20	21	22	23	24	25	26	27	28	29	30	31	32	M_o ‡ (kip-in.)
70	66	62	58	55	52	49	47	45	43	41	40	38	37	35	34	33	1014
96	90	85	80	76	72	68	65	62	60	57	55	53	51	49	47	46	1425
138	130	122	116	110	105	100	96	92	88	85	81	79	76	73	71	69	2214
102	95	90	85	80	76	72	69	66	63	61	58	56	54	52	50	49	1521
136	128	120	114	108	103	98	94	90	86	83	80	77	74	72	69	67	2137
130	122	115	109	104	98	94	90	86	82	79	76	73	71	68	66	64	2029

COLUMN SIZE—17″ x 17″

16	17	18	19	20	21	22	23	24	25	26	27	28	29	30	31	32	M_o ‡ (kip-in.)
78	73	68	64	61	57	55	52	50	47	45	44	42	40	39	38	36	1108
107	100	94	89	84	79	76	72	69	66	63	61	58	56	54	52	51	1560
156	147	139	131	124	118	113	108	103	99	95	92	88	85	82	80	77	2454
113	106	100	94	89	84	80	76	73	70	67	64	62	60	58	56	54	1662
152	143	134	127	120	114	109	104	100	96	92	88	85	82	79	77	74	2340
145	136	128	121	115	109	104	99	95	91	87	84	81	78	75	73	71	2216

COLUMN SIZE—18″ x 18″

M/N † = e (in.)

16	17	18	19	20	21	22	23	24	25	26	27	28	30	32	34	36	M_o ‡ (kip-in.)
86	80	75	71	67	63	60	57	54	52	50	48	46	43	40	37	35	1201
118	110	104	98	92	87	83	79	76	72	69	67	64	59	55	52	49	1695
176	165	155	147	139	132	126	120	115	110	106	102	98	91	86	80	76	2694
125	117	109	103	98	92	88	84	80	77	73	71	68	63	59	55	52	1802
168	158	149	140	133	126	120	115	110	105	101	97	93	87	81	76	72	2542
236	223	211	201	191	183	175	167	161	154	149	143	138	130	122	115	108	4042
161	150	142	134	127	120	114	109	104	100	96	92	89	83	77	73	68	2403

‡ M = capacity in pure bending, (N = 0), for extrapolation, see page 11-5.

SQUARE TIED COLUMNS—Safe Load in Kips for Various Eccentricities in Inches

$f'_c = 5000$ psi $f_s = 30{,}000$ psi basis

(A431 Bars, $f_y = 75{,}000$ psi)

COLUMN SIZE—19″ x 19″

Bars *	p	M/N † = e (in.) 0	1	2	3	4	5	6	7	8	9	10	11	12	13	14	15
4-#11	.0173	**542**	542	542	475	418	373	337	273	225	192	167	148	132	120	110	101
4-#14	.0249	**613**	613	606	524	461	412	372	339	300	258	226	201	181	165	151	139
4-#18	.0443	**791**	791	732	629	551	490	441	401	368	340	315	293	266	244	225	209
6-#11	.0259	**622**	622	616	533	470	420	380	347	314	270	237	211	190	173	159	147
6-#14	.0374	**727**	727	701	607	535	478	432	394	362	335	312	280	254	232	214	199
6-#18	.0665	**995**	995	891	764	669	595	536	487	446	412	383	357	335	315	298	282
8-#11	.0346	**701**	701	683	592	522	467	423	386	355	329	299	268	242	222	204	189
8-#14	.0499	**842**	842	797	690	608	544	492	449	413	382	356	333	313	290	269	251

COLUMN SIZE—20″ x 20″

Bars *	p	0	1	2	3	4	5	6	7	8	9	10	11	12	13	14	15
4-#11	.0156	**584**	584	584	526	465	417	377	304	249	211	183	162	145	131	120	110
4-#14	.0225	**654**	654	654	577	510	457	414	379	333	285	249	221	198	180	165	152
4-#18	.0400	**833**	833	796	688	606	541	489	446	410	379	353	326	295	270	249	231
6-#11	.0234	**663**	663	663	587	519	466	422	386	349	299	261	232	209	190	174	160
6-#14	.0338	**769**	769	762	663	587	527	477	437	402	373	345	308	279	255	235	217
6-#18	.0600	**1037**	1037	960	830	730	652	590	538	494	457	425	398	373	352	333	314
8-#11	.0312	**743**	743	743	647	574	515	467	427	394	365	329	294	266	243	223	206
8-#14	.0450	**884**	884	860	749	664	596	540	495	456	423	394	369	347	320	296	275
10-#11	.0390	**822**	822	812	708	628	564	512	469	432	401	374	350	318	291	269	249

COLUMN SIZE—21″ x 21″

Bars *	p	0	1	2	3	4	5	6	7	8	9	10	11	12	13	14	15
4-#11	.0141	**627**	627	627	580	515	463	420	338	275	232	200	176	158	142	130	119
4-#14	.0204	**698**	698	698	633	562	505	459	420	369	313	273	241	216	196	179	165
4-#18	.0363	**876**	876	861	749	663	594	539	493	454	421	392	360	325	297	273	253
6-#11	.0212	**707**	707	707	643	571	514	467	428	385	328	286	253	227	206	189	174
6-#14	.0306	**812**	812	812	722	641	577	525	481	444	412	379	338	305	278	256	236
6-#18	.0544	**1080**	1080	1031	897	794	712	645	590	543	504	469	440	413	390	369	346
8-#11	.0283	**786**	786	786	705	627	565	514	471	435	404	362	322	291	265	243	224
8-#14	.0408	**927**	927	925	810	721	650	591	542	500	465	434	407	382	350	323	300
10-#11	.0354	**866**	866	866	768	683	616	560	514	475	441	412	384	348	318	293	271

COLUMN SIZE—22″ x 22″

Bars *	p	M/N † = e (in.) 0	1	2	3	4	5	6	7	8	9	10	11	12	13	14	15
4-#11	.0129	**673**	673	673	637	567	511	465	375	303	254	218	192	171	154	140	129
4-#14	.0186	**743**	743	743	691	616	555	506	464	406	343	298	263	235	212	194	178
4-#18	.0331	**922**	922	922	813	722	650	591	542	500	464	433	395	357	325	298	276
6-#11	.0193	**752**	752	752	701	625	564	514	472	424	360	312	276	247	223	204	188
6-#14	.0279	**858**	858	858	783	698	631	575	528	488	454	415	369	332	302	277	256
6-#18	.0496	**1126**	1126	1103	965	858	773	703	644	595	552	515	483	455	430	407	379
8-#11	.0258	**832**	832	832	766	683	617	563	517	478	445	395	351	316	287	263	243
8-#14	.0372	**973**	973	973	874	781	705	643	591	547	509	476	447	417	382	351	326
10-#11	.0322	**912**	912	912	830	741	670	611	562	520	484	452	419	379	345	317	294

* One-half of the bars are to be placed in each of the two faces of the column that are perpendicular to the plane of bending. **Check availability of #14 and #18 bars.**

† Below zigzag horizontal line of each group, concrete governs; above, tension governs.

SQUARE TIED COLUMNS—Safe Load in Kips for Various Eccentricities in Inches

f'_c = 5000 psi f_s = 30,000 psi basis
(A431 Bars, f_y = 75,000 psi)

f'_c = 5000 psi
f_y = 75,000 psi

COLUMN SIZE—19″ x 19″

M/N † = e (in.)

16	17	18	19	20	21	22	23	24	25	26	27	28	30	32	34	36	M_o ‡ (kip-in.)
94	87	82	77	73	69	65	62	59	56	54	52	50	46	43	40	38	1295
129	121	113	107	101	95	91	86	82	79	75	72	70	65	60	57	53	1830
195	183	172	162	154	146	139	133	127	122	117	112	108	101	94	88	83	2934
137	128	120	113	106	101	96	91	87	83	80	77	74	68	64	60	56	1943
185	173	163	154	146	138	132	125	120	115	110	106	102	95	89	83	78	2745
265	250	236	224	213	203	194	186	179	172	165	159	153	143	135	127	120	4402
176	165	155	146	138	131	125	119	114	109	105	100	97	90	84	79	74	2590
234	220	208	196	186	177	169	162	155	148	143	137	132	123	115	108	102	3660

COLUMN SIZE—20″ x 20″

16	17	18	19	20	21	22	23	24	25	26	27	28	30	32	34	36	M_o ‡ (kip-in.)
102	95	89	83	79	74	71	67	64	61	58	56	54	50	46	44	41	1389
141	132	123	116	109	104	98	94	89	85	82	78	75	70	65	61	57	1965
215	201	189	179	169	160	153	146	139	133	128	123	118	110	103	96	91	3174
149	139	130	122	115	109	104	99	94	90	86	83	80	74	69	65	61	2083
202	189	178	168	158	150	143	136	130	125	120	115	111	103	96	90	85	2947
294	277	262	248	236	225	214	205	197	189	182	175	169	157	148	139	131	4762
192	180	169	159	150	143	136	129	123	118	113	109	105	97	91	85	80	2778
257	241	227	215	204	193	184	176	168	161	155	149	144	134	125	118	111	3930
232	218	205	193	183	174	166	158	151	145	139	134	129	120	112	105	99	3472

COLUMN SIZE—21″ x 21″

16	17	18	19	20	21	22	23	24	25	26	27	28	30	32	34	36	M_o ‡ (kip-in.)
110	103	96	90	85	80	76	72	69	66	63	60	58	54	50	47	44	1482
153	142	133	125	118	112	106	101	96	92	88	85	81	75	70	66	62	2100
235	220	207	195	184	175	166	158	151	145	139	134	128	119	112	105	99	3414
161	150	141	132	125	118	112	107	102	97	93	89	86	80	74	70	65	2223
220	205	193	182	172	163	155	147	141	135	129	124	119	111	103	97	91	3150
324	305	288	272	258	246	235	224	215	206	198	191	184	172	161	151	143	5122
208	195	183	172	163	154	146	139	133	127	122	117	113	105	98	92	86	2965
280	262	247	233	221	210	200	191	182	175	168	161	155	144	135	127	120	4200
253	236	222	210	198	188	179	171	163	156	150	144	139	129	120	113	106	3706

COLUMN SIZE—22″ x 22″

M/N † = e (in.)

16	17	18	19	20	22	24	26	28	30	32	34	36	38	40	42	44	M_o ‡ (kip-in.)
119	110	103	97	91	82	74	67	62	57	53	50	47	44	42	40	38	1576
165	154	144	135	127	114	103	95	87	81	75	70	66	62	59	56	53	2235
256	239	225	212	200	180	164	150	139	129	120	113	106	100	95	90	86	3654
174	162	151	142	134	120	109	100	92	85	79	74	70	66	62	59	56	2364
238	222	208	196	185	167	151	139	128	119	111	104	98	92	88	83	79	3352
355	333	314	297	282	255	233	215	199	186	174	163	154	146	139	132	126	5482
225	210	197	185	175	157	143	131	121	112	105	98	92	87	83	78	75	3152
304	284	267	252	239	215	196	180	167	155	145	136	128	121	115	109	104	4470
273	255	240	226	214	193	175	161	149	138	129	121	114	108	102	97	92	3940

‡ M_o = capacity in pure bending, (N = 0), for extrapolation, see page 11-5.

SQUARE TIED COLUMNS—Safe Load in Kips for Various Eccentricities in Inches

$f'_c = 5000$ psi $\quad f_s = 30{,}000$ psi basis

(A431 Bars, $f_y = 75{,}000$ psi)

COLUMN SIZE—23″ x 23″

Bars *	p	M/N † = e (in.) 0	1	2	3	4	5	6	7	8	9	10	11	12	13	14	15
4-#11	.0118	**721**	721	721	697	623	563	513	415	332	277	237	208	185	166	151	138
4-#14	.0170	**791**	791	791	753	673	608	555	511	446	375	324	285	254	229	209	192
4-#18	.0302	**970**	970	970	879	784	708	645	593	548	510	476	432	389	353	324	299
6-#11	.0177	**800**	800	800	763	683	617	564	519	466	393	339	299	267	241	220	202
6-#14	.0255	**906**	906	906	847	758	686	627	577	534	497	452	401	360	327	299	276
6-#18	.0454	**1174**	1174	1174	1036	925	836	762	700	648	602	563	529	498	471	445	413
8-#11	.0236	**880**	880	880	829	742	672	614	565	524	488	430	381	342	310	284	261
8-#14	.0340	**1021**	1021	1021	940	843	764	698	643	596	555	520	488	453	414	380	352
10-#11	.0295	**959**	959	959	894	802	727	665	612	567	529	495	456	411	374	343	317
10-#14	.0425	**1135**	1135	1135	1034	927	841	769	709	657	613	574	539	509	482	453	421
12-#11	.0354	**1039**	1039	1039	960	861	781	715	659	611	569	533	501	473	432	398	369

COLUMN SIZE—24″ x 24″

Bars *	p	0	1	2	3	4	5	6	7	8	9	10	11	12	13	14	15
4-#11	.0108	**771**	771	771	760	681	617	564	458	363	301	257	224	199	179	162	148
4-#14	.0156	**841**	841	841	817	733	664	607	559	489	409	351	308	274	247	225	206
4-#18	.0278	**1019**	1019	1019	948	849	768	702	646	598	557	521	470	422	383	350	323
6-#11	.0163	**850**	850	850	827	742	673	616	568	510	428	368	323	288	259	236	217
6-#14	.0234	**956**	956	956	913	820	744	681	628	583	543	492	435	389	353	322	297
6-#18	.0417	**1223**	1223	1223	1109	994	901	823	758	702	654	613	576	543	514	483	448
8-#11	.0217	**930**	930	930	894	804	730	668	616	572	533	467	413	369	334	305	281
8-#14	.0313	**1071**	1071	1071	1009	907	824	755	697	647	603	565	532	491	447	410	379
8-#18	.0556	**1427**	1427	1427	1270	1139	1033	945	870	807	752	704	662	624	591	561	534
10-#11	.0271	**1009**	1009	1009	962	865	786	720	664	617	575	539	494	444	403	369	341
10-#14	.0391	**1185**	1185	1185	1104	994	904	829	765	711	663	622	585	553	524	490	454
12-#11	.0325	**1089**	1089	1089	1029	926	842	772	713	662	618	579	545	512	467	429	397

COLUMN SIZE—26″ x 26″

Bars *	p	0	1	2	3	4	5	6	7	8	9	10	11	12	13	14	15
4-#14	.0133	**947**	947	947	947	861	784	719	665	584	482	411	358	317	284	258	236
4-#18	.0237	**1126**	1126	1126	1093	985	896	822	759	706	659	618	551	492	445	405	373
6-#11	.0138	**956**	956	956	956	871	793	728	673	610	504	430	375	332	298	271	248
6-#14	.0200	**1062**	1062	1062	1054	952	868	798	738	686	642	576	506	451	407	371	340
6-#18	.0355	**1330**	1330	1330	1262	1138	1037	952	880	818	765	718	676	639	606	563	521
8-#11	.0185	**1036**	1036	1036	1035	935	852	783	725	674	630	547	479	427	385	350	321
8-#14	.0266	**1177**	1177	1177	1154	1044	953	876	811	755	706	663	625	570	517	473	436
8-#18	.0473	**1534**	1534	1534	1430	1292	1178	1082	1001	931	870	817	770	728	690	656	625
10-#11	.0231	**1116**	1116	1116	1104	999	912	838	776	723	676	635	575	514	465	424	390
10-#14	.0333	**1291**	1291	1291	1253	1135	1037	954	884	823	771	724	683	646	613	566	523
12-#11	.0277	**1195**	1195	1195	1174	1063	971	893	828	771	721	678	639	594	539	494	455

Check availability of #14 and #18 bars.

* One-half of the bars are to be placed in each of the two faces of the column that are perpendicular to the plane of bending.

† Below zigzag horizontal line of each group, concrete governs; above, tension governs.

SQUARE TIED COLUMNS—Safe Load in Kips for Various Eccentricities in Inches

f'_c = 5000 psi f_s = 30,000 psi basis
(A431 Bars, f_y = 75,000 psi)

f'_c = 5000 psi
f_y = 75,000 psi

M/N † = e (in.) 16	17	18	19	20	22	24	26	28	30	32	34	36	38	40	42	44	M_o ‡ (kip-in.)
COLUMN SIZE—23″ x 23″																	
128	119	111	104	98	87	79	72	66	61	57	53	50	47	45	42	40	1669
178	165	154	145	136	122	111	101	93	86	80	75	71	67	63	60	57	2370
278	259	243	228	216	194	176	162	149	139	129	121	114	108	102	97	92	3894
187	174	162	153	144	129	117	107	98	91	85	79	75	70	67	63	60	2504
256	239	224	210	199	179	162	149	137	127	119	111	105	99	93	89	84	3555
386	362	341	322	305	276	252	232	215	200	187	176	166	157	149	142	135	5842
242	226	212	199	188	169	153	140	129	120	112	105	98	93	88	84	79	3339
328	306	288	271	257	231	211	193	179	166	155	146	137	130	123	117	111	4740
294	275	258	243	229	207	188	172	159	148	138	129	122	115	109	103	99	4174
393	368	347	328	310	281	256	236	218	203	190	179	168	159	151	144	137	5925
343	321	302	285	269	243	221	203	188	175	163	153	144	136	229	123	117	5009
COLUMN SIZE—24″ x 24″																	
137	127	118	111	104	93	84	77	70	65	61	57	53	50	47	45	43	1763
190	177	165	155	146	131	118	108	99	92	86	80	75	71	67	64	60	2505
299	279	261	246	232	208	189	173	160	148	138	130	122	115	109	103	98	4134
200	186	174	163	153	137	124	114	105	97	90	84	79	75	71	67	64	2645
275	256	240	225	213	191	173	158	146	135	126	118	111	105	99	94	90	3757
418	391	368	348	329	297	271	249	231	215	201	188	178	168	159	151	144	6202
260	242	226	213	201	180	163	149	138	128	119	111	105	99	93	89	84	3526
352	329	309	291	275	248	225	207	191	177	165	155	146	138	131	124	118	5010
509	487	460	436	414	376	345	318	295	276	258	243	229	217	206	197	188	8269
316	295	276	260	245	221	201	184	170	157	147	138	129	122	116	110	105	4408
423	396	373	352	333	301	274	252	233	217	203	191	180	170	161	153	146	6262
369	345	324	305	288	260	237	217	201	186	174	163	154	145	138	131	125	5290
COLUMN SIZE—26″ x 26″																	
217	201	188	176	165	148	133	122	112	103	96	90	84	79	75	71	68	2775
345	321	300	281	265	238	215	197	181	168	157	147	138	130	123	117	111	4614
228	212	197	185	174	155	140	128	117	109	101	95	89	84	79	75	71	2925
314	292	273	256	241	216	196	179	165	152	142	133	125	118	111	106	100	4162
484	452	425	400	378	341	310	285	263	244	228	214	201	190	180	171	163	6922
297	276	257	241	227	203	184	168	155	143	133	125	117	111	105	99	94	3901
404	376	352	331	313	281	255	233	215	200	186	174	164	155	147	139	133	5550
597	566	534	504	478	433	396	365	338	315	295	277	261	247	234	223	213	9229
361	336	315	295	278	250	227	207	191	177	165	154	145	137	130	123	117	4876
486	454	426	402	380	342	311	286	264	245	229	215	202	191	181	172	164	6937
422	394	369	347	328	294	267	245	226	210	196	183	172	163	154	146	139	5851

‡ M_o = capacity in pure bending, (N = 0), for extrapolation, see page 11-5.

SQUARE TIED COLUMNS—Safe Load in Kips for Various Eccentricities in Inches

$f'_c = 5000$ psi $\quad f_s = 30{,}000$ psi basis

(A431 Bars, $f_y = 75{,}000$ psi)

COLUMN SIZE—28″ x 28″

Bars *	p	M/N † = e (in.) 0	1	2	3	4	5	6	7	8	9	10	11	12	13	14	16
4-#14	.0115	**1062**	1062	1062	1062	1000	914	842	780	695	566	477	412	363	324	293	245
4-#18	.0204	**1240**	1240	1240	1240	1131	1034	953	883	822	770	724	639	568	511	464	392
6-#11	.0119	**1071**	1071	1071	1071	1010	924	851	789	725	591	499	432	380	340	307	258
6-#14	.0172	**1177**	1177	1177	1177	1096	1003	925	858	800	750	670	584	518	465	422	356
6-#18	.0306	**1444**	1444	1444	1424	1292	1183	1090	1011	943	883	831	784	742	705	648	554
8-#11	.0159	**1151**	1151	1151	1151	1077	986	909	844	787	737	635	553	489	439	398	335
8-#14	.0230	**1291**	1291	1291	1291	1191	1091	1007	935	873	818	770	727	655	592	539	458
8-#18	.0408	**1648**	1648	1648	1599	1453	1331	1228	1140	1063	997	938	885	839	796	758	692
10-#11	.0199	**1230**	1230	1230	1230	1144	1048	967	898	838	785	739	663	590	531	483	409
10-#14	.0287	**1406**	1406	1406	1406	1285	1179	1089	1012	945	887	835	789	747	706	646	552
10-#18	.0510	**1852**	1852	1852	1774	1613	1479	1366	1268	1184	1110	1045	987	935	888	846	772
12-#11	.0239	**1310**	1310	1310	1310	1210	1110	1025	952	889	834	785	741	683	617	563	479
12-#14	.0344	**1521**	1521	1521	1515	1380	1267	1171	1089	1018	955	900	850	806	766	730	640
14-#11	.0279	**1389**	1389	1389	1389	1276	1171	1083	1006	940	882	830	785	744	697	638	545

COLUMN SIZE—30″ x 30″

Bars *	p	0	1	2	3	4	5	6	7	8	9	10	11	12	13	14	16
4-#14	.0100	**1185**	1185	1185	1185	1152	1057	976	907	825	661	551	472	413	367	331	275
4-#18	.0178	**1364**	1364	1364	1364	1289	1183	1093	1016	949	890	838	736	650	582	527	443
6-#11	.0104	**1194**	1194	1194	1194	1162	1066	985	916	855	690	576	494	433	385	346	289
6-#14	.0150	**1300**	1300	1300	1300	1250	1149	1063	988	924	867	774	669	590	527	477	400
6-#18	.0267	**1568**	1568	1568	1568	1456	1338	1238	1152	1077	1011	953	901	854	809	737	627
8-#11	.0139	**1274**	1274	1274	1274	1231	1131	1046	973	909	854	733	633	557	497	449	376
8-#14	.0200	**1415**	1415	1415	1415	1349	1241	1149	1069	1000	940	886	838	748	672	610	515
8-#18	.0356	**1772**	1772	1772	1772	1623	1493	1383	1287	1204	1131	1067	1009	957	910	868	788
10-#11	.0173	**1354**	1354	1354	1354	1300	1195	1106	1030	963	905	853	760	672	602	546	459
10-#14	.0250	**1530**	1530	1530	1530	1447	1332	1234	1150	1076	1012	954	903	857	804	732	622
10-#18	.0444	**1976**	1976	1976	1958	1790	1648	1527	1423	1331	1251	1180	1117	1060	1009	962	880
12-#11	.0208	**1433**	1433	1433	1433	1368	1259	1167	1087	1017	955	901	852	779	700	636	538
12-#14	.0300	**1644**	1644	1644	1644	1544	1423	1320	1231	1153	1084	1023	968	919	875	835	722
14-#11	.0243	**1513**	1513	1513	1513	1437	1323	1227	1143	1070	1006	949	898	853	792	722	613
16-#11	.0277	**1592**	1592	1592	1592	1505	1387	1287	1200	1124	1057	997	944	896	853	802	684

Check availability of #14 and #18 bars.

* One-half of the bars are to be placed in each of the two faces of the column that are perpendicular to the plane of bending.

† Below zigzag horizontal line of each group, concrete governs; above, tension governs.

SQUARE TIED COLUMNS—Safe Load in Kips for Various Eccentricities in Inches

$f'_c = 5000$ psi $f_s = 30,000$ psi basis
(A431 Bars, $f_y = 75,000$ psi)

$f'_c = 5000$ psi
$f_y = 75,000$ psi

COLUMN SIZE—28″ x 28″

M/N † = e (in.)

18	20	22	24	26	28	30	32	34	36	38	40	42	44	46	48	50	M_o ‡ (kip-in.)
211	185	165	149	136	124	115	107	100	94	88	83	79	75	71	68	65	3045
340	300	268	243	221	204	188	175	164	154	145	137	130	124	118	113	108	5094
222	195	174	157	143	131	121	112	105	98	93	88	83	79	75	72	69	3206
303	271	242	219	200	184	170	158	148	139	131	124	117	111	106	101	97	4567
483	429	386	350	321	296	274	256	240	226	213	202	192	182	174	166	159	7642
290	255	228	206	188	172	159	148	139	130	123	116	110	104	100	95	91	4275
398	352	315	286	261	240	223	207	194	182	172	163	155	147	140	134	128	6090
610	545	492	449	412	381	355	332	311	293	277	263	250	238	228	218	209	10189
355	313	280	253	231	213	197	183	172	161	152	144	136	130	124	118	113	5344
482	428	385	349	320	295	274	255	239	225	212	201	191	182	173	166	159	7612
710	649	589	539	497	461	430	402	378	357	338	321	306	291	279	267	256	12737
416	368	330	299	274	252	234	218	204	192	181	171	162	154	147	141	135	6413
561	500	450	410	376	347	323	301	283	266	251	238	226	216	206	197	189	9135
475	422	379	344	315	290	269	251	235	221	209	198	188	179	171	163	156	7482

COLUMN SIZE—30″ x 30″

18	20	22	24	26	28	30	32	34	36	38	40	42	44	46	48	50	M_o ‡ (kip-in.)
236	207	184	165	150	138	127	118	110	103	97	92	87	82	78	75	72	3315
382	336	300	270	246	226	209	195	182	171	161	152	144	137	130	125	119	5574
248	217	193	173	158	145	133	124	116	108	102	96	91	87	82	79	75	3487
344	302	269	243	221	203	188	174	163	153	144	136	129	123	117	111	107	4972
545	482	432	391	358	330	305	285	266	250	236	233	212	202	192	184	176	8362
324	284	253	228	208	191	176	164	153	143	135	127	121	115	109	104	100	4650
446	393	351	317	290	266	246	229	214	201	190	179	170	162	154	147	141	6630
690	614	553	503	461	426	396	369	346	326	308	292	277	264	252	241	231	11149
396	349	311	281	256	235	218	202	189	178	167	158	150	143	136	130	124	5812
541	478	429	388	355	327	303	282	264	248	234	222	210	200	191	182	175	8287
812	733	663	606	557	516	480	449	422	398	376	357	339	324	309	296	284	13937
466	411	368	332	303	279	258	240	225	211	199	188	179	170	162	155	148	6975
630	559	503	456	418	386	358	334	313	294	278	263	250	238	227	217	208	9945
533	471	422	382	349	322	298	278	260	244	230	218	207	197	188	179	172	8137
596	528	474	430	394	363	337	314	294	276	261	247	234	223	213	204	195	9300

‡ M_o = capacity in pure bending, ($N = 0$), for extrapolation, see page 11-5.

SQUARE TIED COLUMNS—Safe Load in Kips for Various Eccentricities in Inches
$f'_c = 5000$ psi $\quad f_s = 30{,}000$ psi basis
(A431 Bars, $f_y = 75{,}000$ psi)

COLUMN SIZE—32″ x 32″

Bars *	p	M/N † = e (in.)															
		0	1	2	3	4	5	6	7	8	9	10	11	12	13	14	16
4-#18	.0156	**1496**	1496	1496	1496	1459	1343	1245	1160	1086	1021	963	842	739	658	594	496
6-#14	.0132	**1432**	1432	1432	1432	1417	1306	1211	1129	1058	995	890	764	669	595	535	446
6-#18	.0234	**1700**	1700	1700	1700	1631	1505	1396	1302	1220	1148	1084	1026	974	918	833	704
8-#11	.0122	**1406**	1406	1406	1406	1397	1287	1194	1113	1042	980	843	722	631	561	504	420
8-#14	.0176	**1546**	1546	1546	1546	1518	1401	1301	1214	1138	1071	1011	958	849	759	686	576
8-#18	.0313	**1904**	1904	1904	1904	1804	1665	1547	1444	1354	1275	1204	1141	1084	1032	985	887
10-#11	.0152	**1485**	1485	1485	1485	1467	1354	1257	1172	1099	1034	976	867	762	679	613	513
10-#14	.0220	**1661**	1661	1661	1661	1619	1496	1390	1298	1217	1146	1083	1027	976	908	824	696
10-#18	.0391	**2108**	2108	2108	2108	1976	1826	1697	1586	1488	1401	1324	1255	1193	1137	1085	996
12-#11	.0183	**1565**	1565	1565	1565	1538	1420	1319	1231	1155	1087	1027	973	883	790	715	601
12-#14	.0264	**1776**	1776	1776	1776	1720	1590	1479	1382	1297	1222	1155	1095	1041	992	948	809
14-#11	.0213	**1644**	1644	1644	1644	1608	1486	1381	1290	1211	1140	1077	1021	970	894	812	685
14-#14	.0308	**1891**	1891	1891	1891	1820	1684	1567	1466	1376	1297	1227	1164	1106	1055	1008	914
16-#11	.0244	**1724**	1724	1724	1724	1679	1552	1444	1349	1266	1193	1128	1069	1016	969	903	765

Check availability of #14 and #18 bars.

* One-half of the bars are to be placed in each of the two faces of the column that are perpendicular to the plane of bending.

† Below zigzag horizontal line of each group, concrete governs; above, tension governs.

SQUARE TIED COLUMNS—Safe Load in Kips for Various Eccentricities in Inches
f'_c = 5000 psi f_s = 30,000 psi basis
(A431 Bars, f_y = 75,000 psi)

COLUMN SIZE—32″ x 32″ | f'_c = 5000 psi, f_y = 75,000 psi

M/N † = e (in.)

18	20	22	24	26	28	30	32	34	36	38	40	42	44	46	48	50	M_o ‡ (kip-in.)
426	374	332	299	272	250	231	214	200	188	177	167	158	150	143	137	131	6054
383	335	298	268	244	223	206	191	179	167	158	149	141	134	127	122	116	5377
609	537	480	434	396	364	337	314	293	276	260	246	233	222	211	202	193	9082
360	314	279	251	228	209	193	179	167	157	147	139	132	125	119	114	109	5024
496	436	388	350	319	293	271	252	235	221	208	196	186	177	168	161	154	7170
774	686	616	559	512	472	438	408	382	359	339	321	305	290	277	265	254	12109
441	386	344	310	282	259	239	222	207	194	183	173	164	156	148	141	135	6280
602	531	475	429	391	360	333	310	290	272	257	243	230	219	209	199	191	8962
920	821	741	675	619	572	532	497	466	439	415	393	374	356	340	326	312	15137
518	455	406	367	334	307	284	264	246	231	218	206	195	185	177	169	161	7536
703	621	557	505	461	425	394	367	343	323	304	288	273	260	248	237	227	10755
593	522	467	422	385	354	327	305	285	267	252	238	226	215	205	196	187	8792
798	708	636	577	528	487	452	422	395	372	351	332	315	300	286	274	262	12548
664	586	525	475	434	400	370	345	322	303	286	270	256	244	233	222	213	10048

‡ M_o = capacity in pure bending, (N = 0), for extrapolation, see page 11-5.

SQUARE TIED COLUMNS—Safe Load in Kips for Various Eccentricities in Inches

$f'_c = 5000$ psi $f_s = 30,000$ psi basis
(A431 Bars, $f_y = 75,000$ psi)

COLUMN SIZE—34″ x 34″

Bars *	p	M/N † = e (in.) 0	1	2	3	4	5	6	7	8	10	12	14	16	18	20	22
4-#18	.0136	**1636**	1636	1636	1636	1636	1515	1408	1315	1233	1097	836	666	553	473	413	366
6-#14	.0117	**1572**	1572	1572	1572	1572	1475	1372	1282	1203	1022	755	598	496	423	369	327
6-#18	.0208	**1840**	1840	1840	1840	1817	1682	1565	1463	1374	1224	1104	936	786	677	595	530
8-#11	.0108	**1546**	1546	1546	1546	1546	1455	1353	1264	1186	968	712	563	466	397	346	307
8-#14	.0156	**1687**	1687	1687	1687	1687	1573	1464	1369	1286	1146	959	767	640	549	480	427
8-#18	.0277	**2044**	2044	2044	2044	1995	1848	1721	1611	1513	1350	1219	1111	992	861	761	681
10-#11	.0135	**1626**	1626	1626	1626	1626	1524	1418	1326	1245	1109	860	685	569	487	425	378
10-#14	.0195	**1801**	1801	1801	1801	1801	1670	1556	1456	1369	1222	1103	923	774	667	586	522
10-#18	.0346	**2248**	2248	2248	2248	2172	2014	1877	1758	1653	1476	1334	1217	1118	1028	913	821
12-#11	.0162	**1705**	1705	1705	1705	1705	1592	1482	1387	1303	1162	997	800	668	573	502	446
12-#14	.0234	**1916**	1916	1916	1916	1906	1767	1648	1543	1451	1297	1172	1067	900	779	686	613
14-#11	.0189	**1785**	1785	1785	1785	1785	1660	1547	1448	1361	1215	1097	908	762	656	576	513
14-#14	.0272	**2031**	2031	2031	2031	2009	1864	1739	1630	1534	1372	1240	1132	1018	885	782	701
16-#11	.0216	**1864**	1864	1864	1864	1863	1728	1611	1509	1419	1268	1146	1011	851	735	647	578
18-#11	.0243	**1944**	1944	1944	1944	1935	1796	1675	1570	1477	1320	1194	1089	937	812	716	640

COLUMN SIZE—36″ x 36″

Bars *	p	0	1	2	3	4	5	6	7	8	10	12	14	16	18	20	22
4-#18	.0123	**1784**	1784	1784	1784	1784	1698	1582	1480	1391	1242	943	743	613	522	454	402
6-#18	.0185	**1988**	1988	1988	1988	1988	1870	1744	1634	1537	1374	1243	1046	872	748	655	582
8-#14	.0139	**1835**	1835	1835	1835	1835	1756	1638	1535	1445	1292	1079	855	708	604	527	467
8-#18	.0247	**2192**	2192	2192	2192	2192	2041	1905	1787	1683	1506	1363	1245	1103	953	839	749
10-#11	.0120	**1774**	1774	1774	1774	1774	1706	1591	1490	1402	1253	968	763	630	536	466	413
10-#14	.0174	**1950**	1950	1950	1950	1950	1856	1733	1626	1530	1370	1240	1029	858	735	643	572
10-#18	.0309	**2396**	2396	2396	2396	2378	2211	2067	1940	1827	1638	1484	1356	1249	1139	1008	904
12-#11	.0144	**1854**	1854	1854	1854	1854	1776	1657	1554	1462	1308	1122	891	739	631	551	488
12-#14	.0208	**2065**	2065	2065	2065	2065	1956	1828	1715	1616	1448	1312	1190	998	859	754	672
12-#18	.0370	**2600**	2600	2600	2600	2559	2382	2227	2092	1972	1769	1604	1467	1352	1253	1164	1048
14-#11	.0169	**1933**	1933	1933	1933	1933	1846	1724	1617	1522	1363	1234	1012	843	722	632	561
14-#14	.0243	**2180**	2180	2180	2180	2180	2055	1922	1805	1701	1526	1383	1265	1129	976	860	768
16-#11	.0193	**2013**	2013	2013	2013	2013	1915	1790	1679	1582	1418	1284	1127	943	810	710	632
16-#14	.0278	**2294**	2294	2294	2294	2294	2155	2016	1894	1786	1604	1455	1331	1227	1088	961	860
18-#11	.0217	**2093**	2093	2093	2093	2093	1985	1856	1742	1642	1472	1334	1220	1038	895	786	701

Check availability of #14 and #18 bars.

* One-half of the bars are to be placed in each of the two faces of the column that are perpendicular to the plane of bending.

† Below zigzag horizontal line of each group, concrete governs; above, tension governs.

SQUARE TIED COLUMNS—Safe Load in Kips for Various Eccentricities in Inches
$f'_c = 5000$ psi $f_s = 30{,}000$ psi basis
(A431 Bars, $f_y = 75{,}000$ psi)

$f'_c = 5000$ psi
$f_y = 75{,}000$ psi

COLUMN SIZE—34″ x 34″																	
M/N † = e (in.)																	M_o ‡ (kip-in.)
24	26	28	30	32	34	36	38	40	42	44	46	48	50	52	54	56	
329	299	274	253	234	219	205	193	182	172	164	156	149	142	136	131	126	6534
294	267	244	225	209	195	182	171	162	153	145	138	132	126	121	116	111	5782
478	436	400	370	344	321	301	284	268	254	242	230	220	210	202	194	186	9802
275	250	229	211	195	182	170	160	151	143	136	129	123	118	113	108	104	5398
384	349	320	296	274	256	240	226	213	202	192	183	175	167	160	154	148	7710
617	564	519	481	448	419	394	371	351	333	317	302	289	277	265	255	245	13069
340	308	283	261	242	226	211	199	188	178	169	161	153	147	141	135	130	6748
471	429	394	364	338	316	297	279	264	250	238	227	216	207	198	191	183	9637
746	683	630	585	546	512	482	455	431	409	389	372	355	341	327	314	303	16337
402	366	335	310	288	268	252	237	224	212	201	192	183	175	168	161	155	8098
554	506	465	430	401	375	352	331	313	297	283	269	257	246	236	227	218	11565
463	421	387	357	332	310	291	274	259	246	233	222	212	203	195	187	180	9447
635	580	534	495	461	431	405	382	362	343	327	312	298	285	274	263	253	13493
522	476	437	404	376	351	330	311	294	279	265	253	241	231	221	213	204	10797
579	529	486	450	419	392	368	347	328	311	296	282	270	258	248	238	229	12147
COLUMN SIZE—36″ x 36″																	
360	327	299	275	255	238	223	209	197	187	177	169	161	154	147	141	136	7014
524	477	437	403	375	350	328	308	291	276	262	250	238	228	218	210	202	10522
420	381	348	321	298	278	260	245	231	219	208	198	189	180	173	166	159	8250
677	617	567	525	488	456	428	404	382	362	344	328	313	300	287	276	266	14029
370	336	307	283	262	245	229	215	203	192	182	174	166	158	152	145	140	7216
515	468	429	396	368	343	322	303	286	271	257	245	234	224	214	206	198	10312
819	749	690	640	596	558	525	495	469	445	423	404	386	370	355	341	328	17537
439	398	365	336	312	291	273	256	242	229	218	207	198	189	181	174	167	8659
606	552	507	468	435	407	381	359	339	322	306	291	278	266	255	245	236	12375
953	874	807	749	699	656	617	583	552	525	500	477	456	437	420	404	389	21044
505	459	421	388	361	337	315	297	280	266	252	240	229	219	210	202	194	10103
694	633	582	539	501	469	440	415	392	372	354	337	322	308	295	284	273	14438
570	519	476	439	408	381	358	337	318	301	286	273	260	249	239	229	221	11546
779	712	655	607	565	529	497	469	443	421	400	382	365	349	335	322	310	16500
633	577	529	489	455	425	399	376	355	337	320	305	291	279	267	257	247	12989

‡ M_o = capacity in pure bending, ($N = 0$), for extrapolation, see page 11-5.

SQUARE TIED COLUMNS—Safe Load in Kips for Various Eccentricities in Inches

f'_c = 5000 psi f_s = 30,000 psi basis
(A431 Bars, f_y = 75,000 psi)

COLUMN SIZE—38″ x 38″

Bars *	p	M/N † = e (in.)															
		0	2	4	6	8	10	12	14	16	18	20	22	24	26	28	30
4-#18	.0111	**1942**	1942	1942	1767	1560	1397	1061	827	677	573	497	439	393	355	324	299
6-#18	.0166	**2146**	2146	2146	1934	1711	1535	1391	1164	964	823	718	636	572	519	475	438
8-#14	.0125	**1993**	1993	1993	1824	1614	1447	1212	950	781	663	576	509	456	413	378	348
8-#18	.0222	**2350**	2350	2350	2101	1862	1672	1517	1388	1221	1050	921	820	739	672	617	570
10-#11	.0108	**1932**	1932	1932	1775	1570	1407	1087	847	694	588	509	450	403	364	333	306
10-#14	.0156	**2107**	2107	2107	1922	1703	1529	1387	1143	946	807	704	624	560	508	465	429
10-#18	.0277	**2554**	2554	2554	2267	2012	1809	1643	1505	1388	1256	1107	990	895	817	752	696
12-#11	.0130	**2011**	2011	2011	1844	1632	1464	1260	989	814	692	602	532	477	432	395	364
12-#14	.0187	**2222**	2222	2222	2019	1791	1609	1461	1322	1101	943	825	733	660	600	550	507
12-#18	.0332	**2758**	2758	2758	2432	2161	1945	1768	1620	1496	1389	1280	1149	1043	954	879	815
14-#11	.0151	**2091**	2091	2091	1912	1694	1521	1380	1124	930	792	691	612	549	498	456	420
14-#14	.0218	**2337**	2337	2337	2116	1879	1690	1536	1407	1247	1073	941	839	756	688	632	584
16-#11	.0173	**2170**	2170	2170	1979	1756	1577	1432	1251	1040	889	777	689	620	563	516	476
16-#14	.0249	**2452**	2452	2452	2212	1967	1770	1610	1476	1362	1195	1052	940	849	774	711	658
18-#11	.0194	**2250**	2250	2250	2047	1817	1634	1484	1360	1145	982	860	765	689	626	574	530
20-#11	.0216	**2329**	2329	2329	2114	1879	1690	1536	1408	1246	1072	941	838	755	688	631	583
22-#11	.0238	**2409**	2409	2409	2182	1940	1747	1588	1456	1343	1159	1019	909	821	748	687	635

Check availability of #14 and #18 bars.

* One-half of the bars are to be placed in each of the two faces of the column that are perpendicular to the plane of bending.

† Below zigzag horizontal line of each group, concrete governs; above, tension governs.

SQUARE TIED COLUMNS—Safe Load in Kips for Various Eccentricities in Inches
$f'_c = 5000$ psi $f_s = 30{,}000$ psi basis
(A431 Bars, $f_y = 75{,}000$ psi)

COLUMN SIZE—38″ x 38″																	$f'_c = 5000$ psi, $f_y = 75{,}000$ psi
M/N † = e (in.)																	M_o ‡ (kip-in.)
32	34	36	38	40	42	44	46	48	50	52	54	56	58	60	62	64	
276	257	241	226	213	202	191	182	174	166	159	152	146	141	136	131	126	*7494*
406	379	355	334	315	298	283	269	257	246	235	226	217	209	202	195	188	*11242*
322	300	281	264	249	235	223	213	203	194	186	178	171	165	159	153	148	*8790*
530	495	464	437	413	391	372	354	338	323	310	298	286	276	266	257	248	*14989*
283	264	247	232	219	207	196	187	178	170	163	156	150	144	139	134	130	*7684*
398	371	347	326	308	292	277	264	251	240	230	221	212	204	197	190	184	*10987*
648	606	569	536	507	481	457	436	417	399	383	368	354	341	329	318	307	*18737*
337	314	294	276	261	247	234	223	212	203	194	186	179	172	166	160	155	*9221*
471	439	412	388	366	347	329	314	299	286	274	263	253	244	235	227	219	*13185*
760	712	670	632	598	568	541	516	493	472	453	436	419	404	390	377	365	*22484*
390	363	340	320	302	286	271	258	246	236	226	217	208	200	193	186	180	*10758*
542	507	475	448	423	401	381	363	346	332	318	305	293	283	273	263	254	*15383*
441	412	386	363	343	325	308	294	280	268	257	246	237	228	220	212	205	*12295*
612	572	537	506	479	454	431	411	393	376	361	346	333	321	310	299	289	*17580*
492	459	431	405	383	363	345	328	313	300	287	276	265	255	246	238	230	*13832*
542	506	475	447	423	400	381	363	346	331	318	305	293	282	272	263	254	*15369*
591	552	518	488	462	438	416	397	379	362	347	334	321	309	298	288	279	*16906*

‡ M_o = capacity in pure bending, ($N = 0$), for extrapolation, see page 11-5.

SQUARE TIED COLUMNS—Safe Load in Kips for Various Eccentricities in Inches

f'_c = 5000 psi f_s = 30,000 psi basis
(A431 Bars, f_y = 75,000 psi)

COLUMN SIZE—40" x 40"

Bars *	p	M/N † = e (in.) 0	2	4	6	8	10	12	14	16	18	20	22	24	26	28	30
4-#18	.0100	**2108**	2108	2108	1965	1741	1563	1191	917	745	628	542	477	426	385	351	322
6-#18	.0150	**2312**	2312	2312	2136	1897	1705	1549	1292	1062	902	784	693	621	562	514	473
8-#14	.0113	**2159**	2159	2159	2022	1795	1614	1359	1052	859	725	627	553	494	447	408	375
8-#18	.0200	**2516**	2516	2516	2307	2052	1847	1680	1541	1346	1151	1006	893	803	730	668	617
10-#14	.0141	**2273**	2273	2273	2122	1886	1698	1543	1267	1041	883	767	677	607	550	502	462
10-#18	.0250	**2720**	2720	2720	2477	2206	1989	1811	1662	1535	1379	1211	1080	974	887	815	753
12-#11	.0117	**2177**	2177	2177	2042	1813	1631	1413	1096	895	757	655	578	516	467	426	392
12-#14	.0169	**2388**	2388	2388	2221	1977	1781	1621	1465	1211	1032	900	797	715	649	594	547
12-#18	.0300	**2924**	2924	2924	2647	2360	2130	1941	1782	1648	1532	1402	1255	1135	1037	954	884
14-#11	.0137	**2256**	2256	2256	2111	1877	1689	1536	1245	1022	867	752	665	595	539	492	453
14-#14	.0197	**2503**	2503	2503	2320	2067	1864	1697	1558	1372	1174	1027	912	820	745	683	630
16-#11	.0156	**2336**	2336	2336	2180	1940	1748	1590	1386	1143	973	846	749	672	609	557	513
16-#14	.0225	**2618**	2618	2618	2419	2158	1947	1774	1629	1507	1309	1148	1022	921	838	769	710
18-#11	.0176	**2416**	2416	2416	2250	2004	1806	1644	1509	1259	1075	937	831	746	677	620	572
18-#14	.0253	**2732**	2732	2732	2518	2248	2030	1851	1701	1573	1438	1265	1129	1019	929	853	789
20-#11	.0195	**2495**	2495	2495	2319	2067	1864	1698	1559	1371	1173	1025	911	819	744	682	629

Check availability of #14 and #18 bars.

* One-half of the bars are to be placed in each of the two faces of the column that are perpendicular to the plane of bending.

† Below zigzag horizontal line of each group, concrete governs; above, tension governs.

SQUARE TIED COLUMNS—Safe Load in Kips for Various Eccentricities in Inches
$f'_c = 5000$ psi $f_s = 30{,}000$ psi basis
(A431 Bars, $f_y = 75{,}000$ psi)

COLUMN SIZE—40″ x 40″

$f'_c = 5000$ psi
$f_y = 75{,}000$ psi

M/N † = e (in.)

32	34	36	38	40	42	44	46	48	50	52	54	56	58	60	62	64	M_o ‡ (kip-in.)
298	277	259	243	229	217	206	195	186	178	170	163	157	151	145	140	135	7974
438	408	382	359	339	321	304	289	276	264	253	242	233	224	216	208	201	11962
347	323	302	283	267	253	240	228	217	207	199	190	183	176	170	164	158	9330
572	534	500	471	444	421	400	381	363	347	333	319	307	296	285	275	266	15949
428	399	373	351	331	313	297	283	269	258	247	237	227	219	211	203	197	11662
700	654	614	578	546	518	492	469	448	429	411	395	380	366	353	341	329	19937
363	338	316	297	280	264	251	239	227	217	208	199	192	184	178	171	166	9783
508	473	443	417	393	372	353	336	321	307	294	282	271	261	251	243	235	13995
823	770	723	682	645	612	582	555	530	508	487	468	450	434	419	405	391	23924
420	391	366	344	324	307	291	277	264	252	242	232	223	214	206	199	192	11413
585	546	511	481	454	430	409	389	371	355	340	327	314	302	292	282	272	16328
475	443	415	390	368	348	331	315	300	287	275	264	253	244	235	227	219	13044
660	616	578	544	514	487	463	441	421	403	386	371	357	343	331	320	309	18660
530	494	463	436	411	389	370	352	336	321	307	295	284	273	263	254	246	14674
734	686	644	606	573	543	517	492	470	450	432	414	399	384	370	358	346	20993
584	545	511	481	454	430	408	389	371	355	340	326	314	302	291	281	272	16305

‡ M_o = capacity in pure bending, ($N = 0$), for extrapolation, see page 11-5.

ECCENTRICALLY LOADED CONCRETE COLUMNS
SECTION II—SPIRALLY REINFORCED SQUARE COLUMNS

This second section covers eccentric loads on spirally reinforced square concrete columns and parallels exactly the previous section, so the explanation on pages 11-3 to 11-9, inclusive, should be read before going on with the following description.

The necessary size and pitch of spiral reinforcement for each size of column is shown at the bottom of each page. Weights and percentages of spirals can also be taken from the tables on pages 11-175 to -179 inclusive. The vertical bars are spaced uniformly around a ring just inside of and in contact with the spiral.

The scope of these tables is sufficient for practically all purposes. Some illustrative examples are shown for those who wish to see how the tables were prepared.

Example 1—For the table on page 11-85, verify the value $N = 269$ kips with an eccentricity of 2 in. for a 16 in. spirally reinforced square column of 3750 psi concrete reinforced with 6-#8 bars, using $f_s = 24{,}000$ psi.

Solution:—Since the point of application of the load is well within the middle third of the 16 x 16 in. section it is likely that compression controls. To check by ACI 1407(a), $e_b = 0.43 p_g m D_s + 0.14t = 0.43 \times 0.0185 \times 18.8 \times 11 + 0.14 \times 16 = 3.88$ in. > 2, so compression does control. Solve using the transformed section, and $2n$:—

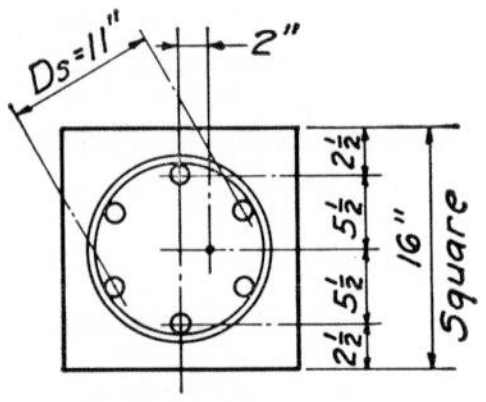

6-#8 Bars = 4.74 sq in. ≈ 73.0 sq in.

Section	Area of Transformed Section	Capacity (Concentric Axial Loading)	Moment of Inertia
Concrete	$16 \times 16 = 256.0$	$256 @ 938 = 240{,}000$ lb	$256 \times \frac{16^2}{12} = 5460$ in.^{4}
Bars	$(16.4-1) \times 6 \times 0.79 = 73.0$	$6 \times 0.79 @ 24{,}000 = 113{,}700$	$\frac{73.0 \times (5.5)^{2*}}{2} = 1102$ in.^{4}
	329.0 sq in.	353,700 lb	6562 in.^{4}

To check $\frac{f_a}{F_a} + \frac{f_b}{F_b} \leqq 1$:—$F_a = 0.34(1 + p_g m)f'_c$ $\qquad F_b = 1688$ psi

$$= 0.34(1 + 0.0185 \times 18.8)3750$$

$$= 1720 \text{ psi}$$

$$\frac{N}{A_g F_a} + \frac{Nec}{IF_b} = \frac{N}{256 \times 1720} + \frac{N \times 2 \times 8}{6562 \times 1688} = 1$$

$$\frac{N}{440{,}000} + \frac{N}{694{,}000} = 1$$

$1.635N = 440{,}000$; $N = \mathbf{269^k}$ as in table.

---

* The transformed steel area is assumed to be a ring with a mean radius r_m of 5.5 in.

$$I = \frac{\pi}{64}(D_1^4 - D_2^4) = \frac{Ar_m^2}{2}$$

ECCENTRICALLY LOADED SPIRALLY REINFORCED SQUARE COLUMNS

Example II—With the same data as in the previous example, show that when the eccentricity is increased to 6 in., the allowable eccentric load, N, is reduced to 93 kips as given in the table on page 11-101.

Solution:—As explained in Ex. I when the eccentricity exceeds e_b (=3.88 in. for these examples) tension controls. The easiest solution is a linear interpolation between M_b and M_o as shown on the figure.

As in the previous example, e_b = 3.88 in.

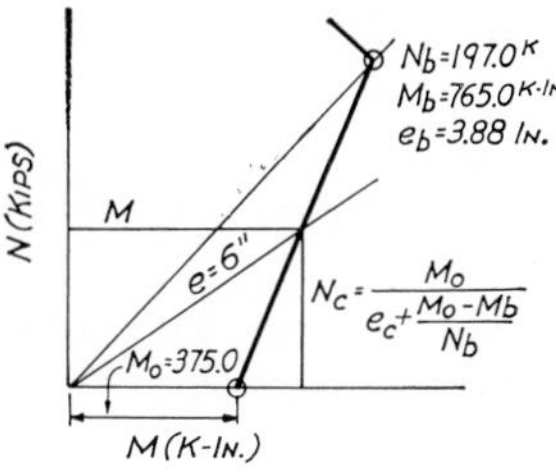

$$\frac{N_b}{256 \times 1720} + \frac{N_b \times 3.88 \times 8}{6562 \times 1688} = 1$$

$$\frac{N_b}{440{,}000} + \frac{N_b}{357{,}000} = 1$$

2.233 N_b = 440,000; N_b = 197,000 lb.
$M_b = N_b e_b$ = 197,000 × 3.88 = 765,000 lb-in.
$M_o = 0.12\, A_{st} F_y D_s$ = 0.12 × 4.74 × 60,000 × 11 = 375,000 lb-in.

Interpolation can be done by the formula developed on page 11-5:—

$$N = \frac{M_o}{e + \dfrac{M_o - M_b}{N_b}} = \frac{375}{6 + \dfrac{375 - 765}{197}} = 93 \text{ kips as in table.}$$

SPECIAL COLUMNS

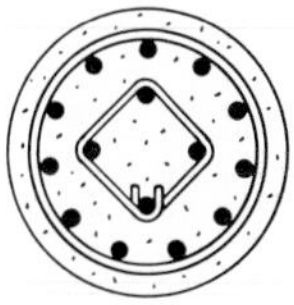

Too Many Vertical Bars for One Ring. Table on p. 2-19 gives the maximum number of vertical bars that can be accommodated in a single ring. When more bars are required, they are placed in an inner ring (page 2-20). The outer spiral should represent the required spiral percentage. The inner ring can be held with closed ties.

Interlocking Spirals. For rectangular spirally-reinforced columns, the spirals are often interlocked as shown and the proportionate share of the spiral percentage is used in each spiral.

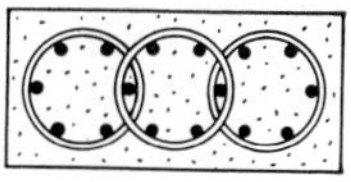

ACI 912 (d) states that the size of spiral columns built integrally with a wall shall be taken as a circle, square, or rectangle at least 1½ in. outside of the spiral on all sides.

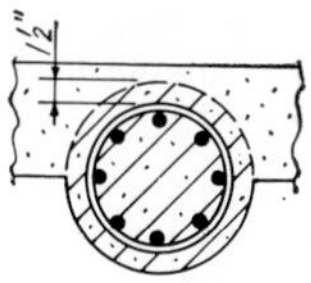

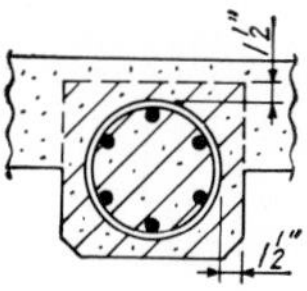

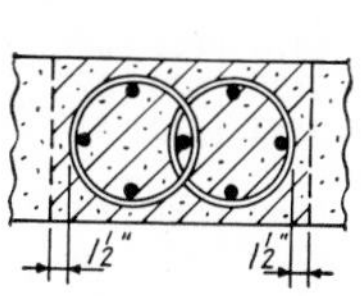

SPIRALLY REINFORCED SQUARE COLUMNS—
Safe Load in Kips for Various Eccentricities in Inches
$f'_c = 3750$ psi (A61 or A432 Bars, $f_y = 60{,}000$ psi) $f_s = 24{,}000$ psi basis

COLUMN SIZE—15″ x 15″ | $f'_c = 3750$ psi | $f_y = 60{,}000$ psi

Bars	p	M/N † = e (in.) 0	1	2	3	4	5	6	7	8	9	10	11	12	13	14	M_o ‡ (kip-in.)
8-#5	.0110	**270**	261	209	175	91	61	45	36	30	26	23	20	18	16	15	*185*
9-#5	.0124	**277**	266	213	178	101	68	51	41	34	29	25	23	20	18	17	*208*
10-#5	.0138	**285**	271	217	181	111	75	56	45	38	32	28	25	22	20	19	*231*
11-#5	.0152	**292**	276	221	184	121	82	62	50	41	35	31	28	25	22	21	*254*
12-#5	.0165	**300**	281	225	187	131	89	67	54	45	39	34	30	27	25	22	*277*
13-#5	.0179	**307**	286	229	190	141	96	72	58	49	42	37	32	29	27	24	*301*
6-#6	.0117	**274**	263	211	176	95	64	48	38	32	27	24	21	19	17	16	*194*
7-#6	.0137	**284**	271	217	180	109	74	55	44	37	32	28	25	22	20	18	*227*
8-#6	.0156	**295**	278	222	185	123	83	63	50	42	36	32	28	25	23	21	*259*
9-#6	.0176	**305**	285	227	189	137	93	70	57	47	41	35	32	28	26	24	*292*
10-#6	.0196	**316**	292	233	193	150	102	78	62	52	45	39	35	31	29	26	*324*
11-#6	.0215	**327**	299	238	198	163	112	85	68	57	49	43	38	35	31	29	*357*
12-#6	.0235	**337**	306	243	202	172	120	92	74	62	53	47	42	38	34	31	*389*
6-#7	.0160	**297**	279	223	185	125	84	64	51	43	36	32	28	25	23	21	*262*
7-#7	.0187	**311**	289	230	191	143	97	73	59	49	42	37	33	30	27	25	*306*
8-#7	.0213	**326**	298	237	197	160	110	83	67	56	48	42	38	34	31	28	*349*
9-#7	.0240	**340**	308	244	203	173	122	93	75	63	54	47	42	38	35	32	*393*
10-#7	.0267	**354**	318	252	208	178	133	102	82	69	60	52	47	42	38	35	*437*
11-#7	.0293	**369**	327	259	214	182	144	111	90	76	65	57	51	46	42	39	*481*
6-#8	.0211	**324**	297	236	196	157	107	81	65	55	47	41	37	33	30	28	*341*
7-#8	.0246	**343**	310	245	203	173	123	94	76	63	55	48	43	38	35	32	*398*
8-#8	.0281	**362**	322	255	211	180	138	106	85	72	62	54	48	44	40	37	*455*
9-#8	.0316	**381**	335	264	218	186	152	117	95	80	69	61	54	49	45	41	*511*
10-#8	.0351	**400**	348	274	226	192	165	128	104	88	76	67	60	54	49	45	*568*
11-#8	.0386	**419**	360	283	233	198	172	138	113	96	83	73	65	59	54	50	*625*
6-#9	.0267	**354**	317	250	207	177	130	100	81	68	58	51	46	41	37	34	*426*
7-#9	.0311	**378**	333	262	216	184	148	114	93	78	67	59	53	48	43	40	*497*
8-#9	.0356	**402**	349	274	226	192	165	128	104	88	76	67	60	54	49	45	*568*
9-#9	.0400	**426**	364	286	235	200	173	141	115	98	85	75	67	60	55	51	*639*
10-#9	.0444	**450**	380	297	244	207	180	153	126	107	93	82	73	66	61	56	*710*
11-#9	.0489	**474**	396	309	253	215	186	165	136	116	101	89	80	72	66	61	*781*
6-#10	.0339	**393**	342	269	221	188	157	121	99	83	72	63	56	51	46	43	*533*
7-#10	.0395	**424**	362	283	233	198	172	138	113	95	82	73	65	59	54	49	*622*
8-#10	.0452	**454**	382	298	245	207	180	153	126	107	93	82	73	66	61	56	*711*
9-#10	.0508	**485**	402	313	256	217	188	166	138	118	103	91	81	74	68	62	*800*
6-#11	.0416	**435**	368	288	236	200	174	142	116	98	85	75	67	61	56	51	*646*
7-#11	.0485	**473**	393	306	250	212	184	160	132	112	97	86	77	70	64	59	*754*
8-#11	.0555	**510**	417	323	264	223	193	170	146	125	109	97	87	79	72	66	*861*
6-#14S	.0600	**534**	430	332	270	228	197	173	151	129	113	100	90	82	75	69	*904*
7-#14S	.0700	**588**	464	356	289	243	210	185	165	145	127	113	102	93	86	79	*1055*

Check availability of #14S and #18S bars.

To provide required amount of spiral reinforcement and minimum clearance between turns (without complying with minimum spacing, D/6), all above columns can have spirals of A432 rod or cold drawn wire ($f_y = 60{,}000$ psi) as follows: ½φ @ 1¾″

Outside diameter of spiral should be 3 in. less than side of column.
† Below zigzag horizontal line of each group, concrete governs; above, tension governs.
‡ M_o = capacity in pure bending, (N = 0); for extrapolation, see page 11-5.

SPIRALLY REINFORCED SQUARE COLUMNS—
Safe Load in Kips for Various Eccentricities in Inches

f'_c = 3750 psi (A61 or A432 Bars, f_y = 60,000 psi) f_s = 24,000 psi basis

COLUMN SIZE—16″ x 16″

f'_c = 3750 psi
f_y = 60,000 psi

Bars	p	M/N † = e (in.) 0	1	2	3	4	5	6	7	8	9	10	11	12	13	14	M_o ‡ (kip-in.)
9-#5	.0109	**306**	301	244	206	119	78	58	46	38	33	28	25	23	20	19	*228*
10-#5	.0121	**314**	307	248	209	131	86	64	51	42	36	32	28	25	23	21	*253*
11-#5	.0133	**321**	312	253	212	143	94	70	56	46	40	35	31	28	25	23	*279*
12-#5	.0145	**329**	317	257	215	155	102	76	61	51	43	38	33	30	27	25	*304*
13-#5	.0157	**336**	322	261	219	166	110	82	66	55	47	41	36	33	30	27	*330*
14-#5	.0170	**344**	328	265	222	177	118	88	71	59	50	44	39	35	32	29	*355*
15-#5	.0182	**351**	333	269	225	188	125	94	75	63	54	47	42	37	34	31	*380*
6-#6	.0103	**303**	299	242	204	112	73	54	43	36	31	27	24	21	19	17	*213*
7-#6	.0120	**313**	306	248	208	129	85	63	50	42	36	31	27	25	22	20	*249*
8-#6	.0138	**324**	314	254	213	146	96	72	57	47	41	35	31	28	26	23	*285*
9-#6	.0155	**335**	321	259	218	162	107	80	64	53	45	40	35	32	29	26	*320*
10-#6	.0172	**345**	328	265	222	177	118	89	71	59	50	44	39	35	32	29	*356*
11-#6	.0189	**356**	336	271	227	192	129	97	77	64	55	48	43	39	35	32	*392*
6-#7	.0141	**326**	315	254	213	147	97	72	58	48	41	36	32	28	26	24	*288*
7-#7	.0164	**340**	325	262	220	169	112	84	67	56	48	42	37	33	30	28	*336*
8-#7	.0188	**355**	335	270	226	189	127	95	76	63	54	47	42	38	34	31	*384*
9-#7	.0211	**369**	345	277	232	199	141	106	85	71	61	53	47	42	39	35	*432*
10-#7	.0234	**384**	355	285	238	205	154	116	94	78	67	59	52	47	43	39	*480*
11-#7	.0258	**398**	365	293	244	210	167	127	102	85	73	64	57	52	47	43	*528*
6-#8	.0185	**353**	334	269	225	185	124	93	74	62	53	46	41	37	34	31	*375*
7-#8	.0216	**372**	347	279	233	200	142	107	86	72	61	54	48	43	39	36	*437*
8-#8	.0247	**391**	360	289	241	207	160	121	97	81	70	61	54	49	44	41	*500*
9-#8	.0278	**410**	373	299	249	213	176	134	108	91	78	68	61	55	50	46	*563*
10-#8	.0309	**429**	386	308	257	220	192	147	119	100	86	75	67	61	55	51	*625*
11-#8	.0339	**448**	399	318	265	227	198	159	129	108	94	82	73	66	60	55	*688*
6-#9	.0234	**384**	354	284	237	203	151	114	92	77	66	57	51	46	42	38	*469*
7-#9	.0273	**408**	371	297	247	212	172	131	105	88	76	67	59	53	49	45	*547*
8-#9	.0313	**432**	387	309	257	220	192	147	119	100	86	75	67	61	55	51	*626*
9-#9	.0352	**456**	404	321	267	228	199	162	131	111	96	84	75	68	62	57	*704*
10-#9	.0391	**480**	420	334	277	237	207	176	144	121	105	92	83	75	68	62	*782*
11-#9	.0430	**504**	436	346	287	245	214	189	155	131	114	101	90	81	74	68	*861*
6-#10	.0298	**422**	380	303	252	216	183	139	112	94	81	71	63	57	52	48	*588*
7-#10	.0347	**453**	401	319	265	227	198	159	129	108	93	82	73	66	60	55	*686*
8-#10	.0397	**483**	422	335	277	237	207	177	144	122	105	93	83	75	68	63	*784*
9-#10	.0446	**514**	442	350	290	247	215	191	158	134	116	103	92	83	76	70	*883*
10-#10	.0496	**544**	463	366	302	258	224	199	172	146	127	112	101	91	83	77	*981*
6-#11	.0366	**464**	408	324	269	229	200	164	133	112	97	85	76	68	62	57	*713*
7-#11	.0427	**502**	433	343	284	242	211	185	151	128	111	98	87	79	72	66	*832*
8-#11	.0488	**539**	458	362	299	254	222	196	168	143	124	109	98	89	81	75	*951*
9-#11	.0548	**576**	484	381	314	267	232	205	183	156	136	121	109	98	90	83	*1070*
6-#14S	.0527	**564**	473	371	306	260	226	200	174	148	129	114	102	93	85	78	*1001*
7-#14S	.0615	**617**	508	398	327	277	240	212	190	167	146	129	116	106	97	89	*1168*

Check availability of #14S and #18S bars.

All above columns require spirals of A432 rod or cold drawn wire (f_y = 60,000 psi):—

½φ @ 2″

Outside diameter of spiral should be 3 in. less than side of column.

† Below zigzag horizontal line of each group, concrete governs; above, tension governs.

‡ M_o = capacity in pure bending, (N = 0); for extrapolation, see page 11-5.

SPIRALLY REINFORCED SQUARE COLUMNS—
Safe Load in Kips for Various Eccentricities in Inches

f'_c = 3750 psi (A61 or A432 Bars, f_y = 60,000 psi) f_s = 24,000 psi basis

COLUMN SIZE—17″ x 17″ — f'_c = 3750 psi, f_y = 60,000 psi

Bars	p	M/N † = e (in.) 0	1	2	3	4	5	6	7	8	9	10	12	14	16	18	M_o ‡ (kip-in.)
7-#6	.0107	**344**	344	282	238	152	97	71	56	47	40	34	27	23	19	17	271
8-#6	.0122	**355**	352	288	243	172	110	81	64	53	45	39	31	26	22	19	310
9-#6	.0137	**365**	359	294	248	191	123	91	72	59	51	44	35	29	25	22	349
10-#6	.0152	**376**	367	300	253	209	136	100	79	66	56	49	39	32	28	24	388
11-#6	.0167	**387**	375	305	258	223	148	110	87	72	62	54	43	35	30	26	426
12-#6	.0183	**397**	382	311	263	227	160	119	94	78	67	58	47	39	33	29	465
14-#6	.0213	**418**	397	323	272	235	183	136	109	91	77	68	54	45	38	34	543
6-#7	.0125	**357**	353	288	244	174	112	82	65	54	46	40	32	26	22	19	314
7-#7	.0145	**371**	363	296	250	199	129	95	75	62	53	46	37	30	26	23	366
8-#7	.0166	**386**	374	305	257	222	145	108	85	71	60	53	42	35	30	26	419
9-#7	.0187	**400**	384	313	263	228	161	120	95	79	68	59	47	39	33	29	471
10-#7	.0208	**414**	394	321	270	233	177	132	105	88	75	65	52	43	37	32	523
11-#7	.0228	**429**	405	329	277	239	192	144	115	96	82	72	57	48	41	36	576
12-#7	.0249	**443**	415	337	283	244	207	155	124	104	89	78	62	52	44	39	628
14-#7	.0291	**472**	435	352	296	255	224	177	143	119	102	90	72	60	51	45	733
6-#8	.0164	**384**	372	303	256	219	142	105	84	69	59	52	41	34	29	25	409
7-#8	.0191	**403**	386	314	264	228	163	122	97	80	69	60	48	40	34	30	477
8-#8	.0219	**422**	399	324	273	236	183	137	109	91	78	68	54	45	39	34	546
9-#8	.0246	**441**	413	335	281	243	203	152	122	102	87	76	61	51	43	38	614
10-#8	.0273	**460**	426	345	290	250	220	167	134	112	96	84	67	56	48	42	682
11-#8	.0301	**479**	440	356	298	257	226	181	146	122	105	92	74	61	53	46	750
12-#8	.0328	**498**	453	366	307	264	232	194	157	132	113	99	80	67	57	50	819
14-#8	.0383	**536**	480	387	324	278	244	217	179	150	130	114	92	77	66	58	955
6-#9	.0208	**414**	394	320	269	232	174	130	103	86	73	64	51	42	36	32	512
7-#9	.0242	**438**	411	333	280	241	198	149	119	99	85	74	59	49	42	37	598
8-#9	.0277	**462**	428	346	290	250	220	167	134	112	96	84	67	56	48	42	683
9-#9	.0311	**486**	445	359	301	259	227	185	149	124	107	94	75	63	54	47	769
10-#9	.0346	**510**	462	372	311	268	235	201	163	137	118	103	83	69	60	52	854
12-#9	.0415	**558**	495	398	333	286	250	223	189	159	138	121	98	82	71	62	1025
6-#10	.0264	**453**	421	340	285	246	211	159	127	106	91	79	64	53	45	40	643
7-#10	.0308	**484**	442	357	299	257	226	181	146	122	105	92	74	61	53	46	750
8-#10	.0352	**514**	464	373	312	268	235	202	163	137	118	104	83	70	60	52	858
9-#10	.0396	**545**	485	389	325	279	245	218	180	151	131	115	93	78	67	59	965
10-#10	.0439	**575**	506	406	339	290	254	226	196	165	143	126	102	86	74	65	1072
11-#10	.0483	**606**	528	422	352	302	264	234	210	178	155	137	111	93	80	71	1179
6-#11	.0324	**495**	449	362	303	260	228	187	151	126	108	95	76	64	55	48	781
7-#11	.0378	**533**	476	382	319	274	240	211	171	144	124	109	88	74	63	55	911
8-#11	.0432	**570**	502	402	335	287	251	224	191	161	139	123	99	83	72	63	1041
9-#11	.0486	**607**	528	422	351	301	263	234	209	177	154	136	110	93	80	70	1171
10-#11	.0540	**645**	554	441	367	314	274	244	219	192	168	148	121	102	88	77	1301
6-#14S	.0467	**594**	517	412	343	293	256	228	199	168	146	129	104	87	75	66	1099
7-#14S	.0545	**648**	554	440	365	312	272	242	217	190	165	146	119	100	86	76	1282
8-#14S	.0623	**702**	591	468	388	331	288	256	230	208	183	163	133	112	97	86	1465

Check availability of #14S and #18S bars.

All above columns require spirals of A432 rod or cold drawn wire (f_y = 60,000 psi):—

½φ @ 2″

Outside diameter of spiral should be 3 in. less than side of column.

† Below zigzag horizontal line of each group, concrete governs; above, tension governs.

‡ M_o = capacity in pure bending, (N = 0); for extrapolation, see page 11-5.

SPIRALLY REINFORCED SQUARE COLUMNS—
Safe Load in Kips for Various Eccentricities in Inches
f'_c = 3750 psi (A61 or A432 Bars, f_y = 60,000 psi) f_s = 24,000 psi basis

COLUMN SIZE—18″ x 18″ | f'_c = 3750 psi | f_y = 60,000 psi

Bars	p	M/N † = e (in.) 0	1	2	3	4	5	6	7	8	9	10	12	14	16	18	M_o ‡ (kip-in.)
8-#6	.0109	**388**	388	324	276	203	126	91	72	59	50	43	34	28	24	21	335
9-#6	.0122	**398**	398	330	281	225	141	102	80	66	56	49	39	32	27	24	377
10-#6	.0136	**409**	408	336	286	246	155	113	89	73	62	54	43	35	30	26	419
12-#6	.0163	**430**	423	349	296	257	182	134	105	87	74	64	51	42	36	31	503
14-#6	.0190	**451**	439	361	306	266	209	154	122	101	86	75	59	49	42	37	587
16-#6	.0217	**472**	455	373	316	275	234	173	138	114	97	85	68	56	48	42	671
6-#7	.0111	**390**	390	325	276	205	128	93	73	60	51	44	35	29	24	21	340
7-#7	.0130	**404**	404	333	283	235	147	107	84	69	59	51	40	33	28	25	396
8-#7	.0148	**418**	415	341	290	252	166	121	96	79	67	58	46	38	33	28	453
9-#7	.0167	**433**	425	350	297	258	185	135	107	88	75	65	52	43	37	32	510
10-#7	.0185	**447**	436	358	304	264	202	149	118	97	83	72	57	48	41	35	567
12-#7	.0222	**476**	457	375	318	276	236	175	139	115	99	86	68	57	49	42	680
14-#7	.0259	**505**	478	391	331	287	253	200	160	133	114	99	79	66	56	49	793
6-#8	.0146	**417**	413	340	289	251	163	119	94	77	66	57	45	37	32	28	443
7-#8	.0171	**436**	427	351	298	259	187	137	108	89	76	66	53	44	37	32	517
8-#8	.0195	**455**	441	362	307	267	210	155	122	101	86	75	60	50	42	37	591
9-#8	.0219	**474**	455	373	316	274	232	172	136	113	97	84	67	56	48	41	665
10-#8	.0244	**493**	469	384	325	282	249	188	150	125	106	93	74	62	53	46	739
12-#8	.0293	**531**	497	406	343	297	262	220	176	147	126	110	88	73	63	55	887
14-#8	.0341	**569**	524	427	361	312	275	245	201	168	144	127	102	85	73	64	1035
6-#9	.0185	**447**	435	357	303	263	199	146	116	96	81	71	56	47	40	35	556
7-#9	.0216	**471**	453	371	314	272	227	168	133	110	94	82	65	54	46	40	648
8-#9	.0247	**495**	470	385	325	282	249	189	150	125	107	93	74	62	53	46	741
9-#9	.0278	**519**	488	398	337	291	257	209	167	139	119	104	83	69	59	52	834
10-#9	.0309	**543**	505	412	348	301	265	228	183	152	131	115	92	76	65	57	926
12-#9	.0370	**591**	540	439	370	320	281	251	213	178	154	135	108	91	78	68	1112
14-#9	.0432	**639**	575	466	392	339	298	266	240	203	175	154	124	104	90	79	1297
6-#10	.0235	**486**	463	379	320	278	242	179	143	118	101	88	70	58	50	43	698
7-#10	.0274	**517**	485	396	335	290	255	205	163	136	116	102	81	68	58	51	814
8-#10	.0314	**547**	507	413	349	301	265	229	183	153	131	115	92	77	66	57	931
9-#10	.0353	**578**	529	430	363	313	276	246	202	170	146	128	103	86	73	64	1047
10-#10	.0392	**608**	551	447	377	325	286	255	221	185	160	140	113	94	81	71	1164
12-#10	.0470	**669**	595	482	405	349	306	273	246	215	186	164	133	111	96	84	1396
6-#11	.0289	**528**	493	402	339	293	258	212	169	141	121	106	84	70	60	53	848
7-#11	.0337	**565**	520	422	356	307	271	240	193	161	139	121	97	81	70	61	989
8-#11	.0385	**603**	547	443	373	322	283	253	215	181	156	137	110	92	79	69	1131
9-#11	.0433	**640**	573	464	390	336	295	263	236	199	172	151	122	102	88	77	1272
10-#11	.0481	**678**	600	485	407	350	308	274	247	217	188	166	134	112	97	85	1414
11-#11	.0530	**715**	627	506	424	365	320	285	257	233	202	179	145	122	106	93	1555
6-#14S	.0417	**627**	562	455	381	329	289	257	225	189	163	143	116	97	83	73	1196
7-#14S	.0486	**681**	601	484	405	349	306	273	246	214	185	164	132	111	96	84	1395
8-#14S	.0556	**735**	639	514	429	369	323	288	259	236	206	182	148	125	108	95	1594
9-#14S	.0625	**789**	677	543	453	389	341	303	273	248	225	200	163	138	119	105	1794

Check availability of #14S and #18S bars.

All above columns require spirals of A432 rod or cold drawn wire (f_y = 60,000 psi):—
½φ @ 2″

Outside diameter of spiral should be 3 in. less than side of column.
† Below zigzag horizontal line of each group, concrete governs; above, tension governs.
‡ M_o = capacity in pure bending, (N = 0); for extrapolation, see page 11-5.

SPIRALLY REINFORCED SQUARE COLUMNS—

Safe Load in Kips for Various Eccentricities in Inches

f'_c = 3750 psi (A61 or A432 Bars, f_y = 60,000 psi) f_s = 24,000 psi basis

COLUMN SIZE—19″ x 19″ — f'_c = 3750 psi, f_y = 60,000 psi

Bars	p	M/N † = e (in.)															M_o‡
		0	1	2	3	4	5	6	7	8	9	10	12	14	16	18	(kip.-in.)
7-#7	.0116	**439**	439	372	318	277	168	120	94	77	65	56	44	37	31	27	*427*
8-#7	.0133	**453**	453	381	326	284	189	136	106	87	74	64	50	42	35	31	*488*
9-#7	.0150	**468**	468	389	333	291	210	152	119	97	83	72	57	47	40	35	*549*
10-#7	.0166	**482**	480	398	340	297	231	167	131	108	91	79	63	52	44	39	*610*
11-#7	.0183	**496**	491	407	347	303	250	182	143	118	100	87	69	57	49	42	*671*
12-#7	.0199	**511**	501	415	354	309	270	197	155	128	109	94	75	62	53	46	*732*
14-#7	.0233	**540**	523	432	369	321	284	225	178	147	125	109	87	72	61	54	*854*
16-#7	.0266	**568**	545	450	383	333	295	252	200	166	142	124	98	82	70	61	*979*
6-#8	.0131	**452**	452	379	324	283	186	133	104	85	72	63	49	41	35	30	*477*
7-#8	.0153	**471**	471	391	334	291	213	154	120	99	84	73	58	48	40	35	*557*
8-#8	.0175	**490**	485	402	343	299	239	174	136	112	95	83	65	54	46	40	*637*
9-#8	.0197	**509**	499	413	353	307	265	193	152	125	106	93	73	61	52	45	*716*
10-#8	.0219	**528**	514	425	362	315	279	212	167	138	117	102	81	67	57	50	*796*
11-#8	.0241	**546**	528	436	371	323	286	230	182	150	128	112	89	74	63	55	*875*
12-#8	.0263	**565**	542	447	381	331	293	247	196	163	139	121	96	80	68	60	*955*
14-#8	.0306	**603**	570	470	399	347	307	275	224	186	160	139	111	93	79	69	*1114*
16-#8	.0350	**641**	598	492	418	363	321	288	250	209	179	157	126	105	90	79	*1274*
6-#9	.0166	**482**	479	397	339	296	227	164	129	106	90	78	62	51	43	38	*599*
7-#9	.0194	**506**	497	411	351	306	259	189	149	122	104	90	72	59	51	44	*699*
8-#9	.0222	**530**	515	425	362	316	280	212	168	138	118	103	81	67	58	50	*799*
9-#9	.0249	**554**	533	440	374	326	288	235	186	154	131	115	91	76	65	56	*898*
10-#9	.0277	**578**	551	454	386	336	297	257	204	169	145	126	101	84	71	62	*998*
11-#9	.0305	**602**	568	468	398	346	306	274	221	184	157	138	110	91	78	68	*1098*
12-#9	.0332	**626**	586	482	409	356	314	282	238	198	170	149	119	99	85	74	*1198*
14-#9	.0388	**674**	622	510	433	376	332	297	269	226	194	170	137	114	98	86	*1398*
6-#10	.0211	**521**	508	419	357	311	276	202	159	131	112	97	77	64	54	47	*753*
7-#10	.0246	**551**	530	437	372	324	287	231	182	151	129	112	89	74	63	55	*878*
8-#10	.0281	**582**	553	455	387	336	298	258	205	170	145	127	101	84	72	63	*1004*
9-#10	.0317	**612**	575	473	402	349	308	276	226	189	161	141	113	94	80	70	*1129*
10-#10	.0352	**643**	598	491	416	361	319	286	247	206	177	155	124	103	89	78	*1255*
11-#10	.0387	**673**	620	509	431	374	330	296	266	223	192	168	135	113	97	85	*1381*
12-#10	.0422	**704**	643	526	446	386	341	305	276	240	207	182	146	122	105	92	*1506*
6-#11	.0259	**563**	538	443	377	328	290	239	189	157	134	116	93	77	66	57	*915*
7-#11	.0302	**600**	566	465	395	343	303	271	216	180	154	134	107	89	76	67	*1068*
8-#11	.0346	**637**	593	487	413	358	316	283	241	201	173	151	121	101	86	76	*1221*
9-#11	.0389	**675**	621	509	431	373	330	295	265	222	191	168	135	112	96	84	*1373*
10-#11	.0432	**712**	648	530	448	389	343	307	277	242	209	183	148	124	106	93	*1526*
11-#11	.0475	**750**	676	552	466	404	356	318	288	261	225	199	160	135	116	102	*1679*
12-#11	.0519	**787**	703	573	484	419	369	330	298	272	241	213	173	145	125	110	*1831*
6-#14S	.0374	**662**	610	499	422	366	323	289	253	211	181	159	127	106	91	80	*1293*
7-#14S	.0436	**716**	649	530	447	387	341	305	276	239	206	181	146	122	105	92	*1509*
8-#14S	.0499	**770**	688	560	472	408	360	321	290	265	230	203	164	138	119	104	*1724*
9-#14S	.0561	**824**	727	591	498	430	378	338	305	278	251	223	181	152	131	116	*1940*
10-#14S	.0623	**878**	767	622	523	451	397	354	319	291	267	241	197	166	144	127	*2155*

Check availability of #14S and #18S bars.

All above columns require spirals of A432 rod or cold drawn wire (f_y = 60,000 psi):—

½φ @ 2″

Outside diameter of spiral should be 3 in. less than side of column.

† Below zigzag horizontal line of each group, concrete governs; above, tension governs.

‡ M_o = capacity in pure bending, (N = 0); for extrapolation, see page 11-5.

SPIRALLY REINFORCED SQUARE COLUMNS—
Safe Load in Kips for Various Eccentricities in Inches
f'_c = 3750 psi (A61 or A432 Bars, f_y = 60,000 psi) f_s = 24,000 psi basis

COLUMN SIZE—20″ x 20″ — f'_c = 3750 psi, f_y = 60,000 psi

Bars	p	M/N † = e (in.) 0	1	2	3	4	5	6	7	8	9	10	12	14	16	18	M_o ‡ (kip-in.)
7-#7	.0105	**475**	475	413	356	312	191	134	104	84	71	61	48	40	34	29	*457*
8-#7	.0120	**490**	490	422	363	319	215	152	118	96	81	70	55	45	38	33	*522*
9-#7	.0135	**504**	504	431	371	325	239	170	132	107	91	78	62	51	43	38	*588*
10-#7	.0150	**519**	519	440	378	331	262	187	145	119	100	87	68	56	48	42	*653*
12-#7	.0180	**547**	547	458	393	344	306	220	172	141	119	103	82	67	57	50	*784*
14-#7	.0210	**576**	570	475	408	357	317	252	197	162	138	119	95	78	67	58	*914*
16-#7	.0240	**605**	592	493	423	370	329	282	222	183	156	135	107	89	76	66	*1045*
18-#7	.0270	**634**	614	511	438	383	340	306	246	203	173	151	120	99	85	74	*1176*
6-#8	.0119	**488**	488	421	362	318	211	149	115	94	79	69	54	44	38	33	*511*
7-#8	.0138	**507**	507	433	372	326	242	172	133	109	92	80	63	52	44	38	*597*
8-#8	.0158	**526**	526	444	382	334	272	194	151	124	104	90	71	59	50	44	*682*
9-#8	.0178	**545**	545	456	391	343	301	216	168	138	117	101	80	66	56	49	*767*
10-#8	.0198	**564**	560	468	401	351	312	237	185	152	129	112	88	73	62	54	*853*
12-#8	.0237	**602**	589	491	420	368	327	277	218	180	153	133	105	87	74	65	*1023*
14-#8	.0277	**640**	618	514	440	384	341	307	249	206	175	153	122	101	86	75	*1194*
16-#8	.0316	**678**	647	537	459	401	356	320	278	231	197	172	137	114	98	85	*1365*
6-#9	.0150	**519**	519	439	377	331	259	184	143	117	99	85	67	55	47	41	*642*
7-#9	.0175	**543**	543	454	389	341	295	212	165	135	114	99	78	64	55	48	*749*
8-#9	.0200	**567**	562	468	402	352	313	238	186	153	129	112	89	73	63	54	*856*
9-#9	.0225	**591**	580	483	414	362	322	263	207	170	144	125	99	82	70	61	*963*
10-#9	.0250	**615**	598	498	426	373	331	288	227	187	159	138	110	91	78	68	*1070*
12-#9	.0300	**663**	635	527	451	393	349	314	265	219	187	163	130	108	92	81	*1284*
14-#9	.0350	**711**	671	556	475	414	367	330	300	250	214	187	150	125	107	93	*1499*
6-#10	.0191	**557**	554	462	396	347	308	226	177	145	123	106	84	69	59	51	*808*
7-#10	.0222	**588**	578	481	412	360	320	259	203	167	141	123	97	81	69	60	*942*
8-#10	.0254	**618**	601	499	427	373	331	289	228	188	160	139	110	91	78	68	*1077*
9-#10	.0286	**649**	624	518	443	386	343	308	252	208	178	155	123	102	87	76	*1212*
10-#10	.0318	**679**	647	536	458	400	354	318	275	228	195	170	136	113	96	84	*1346*
12-#10	.0381	**740**	693	573	489	426	377	339	307	266	228	200	160	133	114	100	*1616*
14-#10	.0445	**801**	739	610	519	452	400	359	326	298	259	227	183	153	132	115	*1885*
6-#11	.0234	**599**	586	487	417	364	323	268	210	173	147	128	101	84	71	62	*983*
7-#11	.0273	**637**	614	510	436	380	337	303	240	199	169	147	117	97	83	72	*1147*
8-#11	.0312	**674**	642	532	454	396	351	316	269	223	190	166	132	110	94	82	*1310*
9-#11	.0351	**711**	670	555	473	412	365	328	296	246	211	184	147	123	105	92	*1474*
10-#11	.0390	**749**	698	577	492	428	379	340	309	268	231	202	162	135	116	101	*1638*
11-#11	.0429	**786**	726	599	510	444	393	353	320	290	249	219	176	147	126	111	*1802*
13-#11	.0507	**861**	783	644	548	476	421	377	342	313	284	251	203	170	147	129	*2130*
6-#14S	.0338	**699**	659	545	464	404	358	322	282	234	200	175	140	116	99	87	*1390*
7-#14S	.0394	**753**	699	577	491	427	378	339	307	266	228	200	160	134	115	100	*1622*
8-#14S	.0450	**807**	739	609	517	450	398	356	323	295	255	224	180	151	129	113	*1854*
9-#14S	.0506	**861**	779	640	544	472	417	374	338	309	279	246	199	167	144	126	*2085*
10-#14S	.0563	**915**	820	672	570	495	437	391	354	323	298	267	217	183	158	139	*2317*
6-#18S	.0600	**951**	835	678	571	493	433	387	349	319	293	262	213	179	155	136	*2285*

Check availability of #14S and #18S bars.

All above columns require spirals of A432 rod or cold drawn wire (f_y = 60,000 psi):—

#14S and smaller—½φ @ 2″

#18S only —½φ @ 1¾″

Outside diameter of spiral should be 3 in. less than side of column.

† Below zigzag horizontal line of each group, concrete governs; above, tension governs.

‡ M_o = capacity in pure bending, (N = 0); for extrapolation, see page 11-5.

SPIRALLY REINFORCED SQUARE COLUMNS—
Safe Load in Kips for Various Eccentricities in Inches

$f'_c = 3750$ psi (A61 or A432 Bars, $f_y = 60{,}000$ psi) $f_s = 24{,}000$ psi basis

COLUMN SIZE—21″ x 21″

$f'_c = 3750$ psi
$f_y = 60{,}000$ psi

Bars	p	M/N † = e (in.) 0	1	2	3	4	5	6	8	10	12	14	16	18	20	22	M_o ‡ (kip-in.)
8-#7	.0109	**528**	528	466	403	355	245	170	105	76	60	49	41	36	32	28	557
9-#7	.0122	**543**	543	475	411	362	272	189	118	85	67	55	47	40	36	32	626
10-#7	.0136	**557**	557	484	418	368	298	208	130	94	74	61	52	45	40	36	696
12-#7	.0163	**586**	586	502	434	382	341	246	154	112	88	73	62	54	48	43	835
14-#7	.0190	**615**	615	521	449	395	352	281	178	130	103	85	72	63	55	50	975
16-#7	.0218	**643**	641	539	465	408	364	315	201	147	116	96	82	71	63	57	1114
18-#7	.0245	**672**	664	557	480	422	376	339	223	164	130	108	92	80	71	63	1253
6-#8	.0107	**527**	527	465	402	354	240	167	103	75	58	48	41	35	31	28	546
7-#8	.0125	**546**	546	477	412	363	275	192	120	87	68	56	47	41	36	32	637
8-#8	.0143	**565**	565	489	422	371	310	217	136	99	77	64	54	47	41	37	728
9-#8	.0161	**584**	584	501	432	380	339	241	151	110	87	71	61	53	47	42	819
10-#8	.0179	**603**	603	513	442	389	347	265	167	122	96	79	67	58	52	46	910
12-#8	.0215	**640**	639	537	462	406	362	310	197	145	114	94	80	70	62	55	1092
14-#8	.0251	**678**	668	560	483	424	378	341	226	167	132	109	93	81	72	64	1274
16-#8	.0287	**716**	698	584	503	441	393	354	254	188	149	124	106	92	82	73	1456
6-#9	.0136	**557**	557	483	417	367	294	205	128	93	73	60	51	44	39	35	685
7-#9	.0159	**581**	581	498	430	378	336	236	148	108	85	70	59	52	46	41	799
8-#9	.0181	**605**	605	514	443	389	347	266	168	122	96	79	68	59	52	47	914
9-#9	.0204	**629**	629	529	456	400	357	294	187	137	108	89	76	66	58	52	1028
10-#9	.0227	**653**	648	544	468	411	367	322	205	151	119	98	84	73	65	58	1142
12-#9	.0272	**701**	685	574	494	433	386	348	241	178	141	117	100	87	77	69	1371
14-#9	.0317	**749**	722	604	519	455	405	365	275	205	163	135	115	101	89	80	1599
16-#9	.0363	**797**	759	634	544	477	424	382	307	230	183	153	131	114	101	91	1828
6-#10	.0173	**596**	596	507	438	385	343	253	159	116	91	75	64	56	49	44	863
8-#10	.0230	**657**	650	545	470	412	367	323	207	152	120	99	84	73	65	58	1150
10-#10	.0288	**718**	697	583	501	440	391	353	251	186	148	122	104	91	81	72	1438
12-#10	.0346	**779**	744	621	533	467	416	374	293	219	174	145	124	108	96	86	1726
14-#10	.0403	**840**	791	659	565	495	440	396	330	249	200	166	143	125	111	100	2013
6-#11	.0212	**638**	635	533	459	403	359	300	190	140	110	91	77	67	60	53	1050
7-#11	.0248	**675**	664	556	478	420	374	337	219	161	127	105	90	78	69	62	1225
8-#11	.0283	**712**	693	579	498	436	388	350	246	182	144	119	102	89	79	71	1400
9-#11	.0318	**750**	721	602	517	453	403	363	272	202	160	133	114	99	88	79	1575
10-#11	.0354	**787**	750	626	537	470	418	376	296	221	176	147	125	110	97	88	1751
12-#11	.0424	**862**	807	672	575	503	447	402	335	258	207	173	148	130	115	104	2101
14-#11	.0495	**937**	865	718	614	536	476	428	356	292	236	198	170	149	133	120	2451
6-#14S	.0306	**737**	710	592	508	445	396	356	259	192	152	126	108	94	83	75	1487
7-#14S	.0357	**791**	751	626	536	469	416	375	294	219	175	145	124	109	97	87	1735
8-#14S	.0408	**845**	792	659	563	492	437	393	327	246	197	164	141	123	109	98	1983
9-#14S	.0459	**899**	833	692	591	516	458	411	342	271	218	182	156	137	122	110	2231
10-#14S	.0510	**953**	874	724	619	540	479	430	357	294	238	199	172	151	134	121	2479
11-#14S	.0561	**1007**	915	757	646	563	499	448	372	317	257	216	186	164	146	132	2727
6-#18S	.0544	**989**	891	732	621	539	477	427	353	290	234	197	169	149	133	120	2458
7-#18S	.0635	**1085**	961	787	667	578	510	457	377	322	265	223	193	170	152	137	2868

Check availability of #14S and #18S bars.

All above columns require spirals of A432 rod or cold drawn wire ($f_y = 60{,}000$ psi):—

#14S and smaller—½φ @ 2″

#18S only —⅝φ @ 2¾″

Outside diameter of spiral should be 3 in. less than side of column.

† Below zigzag horizontal line of each group, concrete governs; above, tension governs.

‡ M_o = capacity in pure bending, ($N = 0$); for extrapolation, see page 11-5.

SPIRALLY REINFORCED SQUARE COLUMNS—
Safe Load in Kips for Various Eccentricities in Inches
f'_c = 3750 psi (A61 or A432 Bars, f_y = 60,000 psi) f_s = 24,000 psi basis

COLUMN SIZE—22″ x 22″

f'_c = 3750 psi
f_y = 60,000 psi

Bars	p	M/N † = e (in.) 0	1	2	3	4	5	6	8	10	12	14	16	18	20	22	M_o‡ (kip-in.)
9-#7	.0112	**583**	583	521	453	400	308	211	129	93	72	59	50	43	38	34	665
10-#7	.0124	**597**	597	531	461	407	338	232	142	102	80	66	56	48	43	38	739
12-#7	.0149	**626**	626	549	477	421	377	273	169	122	96	78	67	58	51	46	887
14-#7	.0174	**655**	655	568	493	435	389	313	195	141	111	91	77	67	59	53	1035
16-#7	.0198	**684**	684	587	509	449	402	351	220	160	126	104	88	77	68	61	1183
18-#7	.0223	**712**	712	606	525	463	414	374	244	179	141	116	99	86	76	68	1331
20-#7	.0248	**741**	739	624	540	477	426	385	268	197	155	128	109	95	84	75	1479
7-#8	.0114	**586**	586	523	454	402	313	214	131	94	73	60	51	44	39	35	676
8-#8	.0131	**605**	605	535	465	411	352	241	148	107	84	69	58	50	44	40	773
9-#8	.0147	**624**	624	548	475	420	376	268	166	120	94	77	65	57	50	45	870
10-#8	.0163	**643**	643	560	486	429	384	295	183	132	104	85	72	63	55	50	966
12-#8	.0196	**681**	681	584	506	447	400	345	216	157	123	102	86	75	66	59	1160
14-#8	.0229	**719**	719	609	527	465	416	376	248	181	143	118	100	87	77	69	1353
16-#8	.0261	**757**	750	633	548	483	432	390	279	205	162	134	114	99	88	79	1547
6-#9	.0124	**597**	597	530	460	406	334	229	140	101	79	65	55	48	42	38	728
7-#9	.0145	**621**	621	545	473	418	374	263	162	117	92	75	64	55	49	44	850
8-#9	.0165	**645**	645	561	486	429	384	296	184	133	104	86	73	63	56	50	971
9-#9	.0186	**669**	669	576	499	441	394	328	205	149	117	96	82	71	63	56	1093
10-#9	.0207	**693**	693	592	513	452	404	358	225	164	129	106	90	78	69	62	1214
12-#9	.0248	**741**	738	623	539	475	424	384	265	194	153	126	107	94	83	74	1457
14-#9	.0289	**789**	775	654	565	497	444	402	302	223	176	146	124	108	96	86	1700
16-#9	.0331	**837**	813	685	591	520	464	419	338	250	199	165	141	123	109	98	1943
6-#10	.0157	**636**	636	554	481	424	380	281	174	126	99	81	69	60	53	47	917
8-#10	.0210	**697**	697	594	514	453	405	361	227	165	130	107	91	79	70	63	1223
10-#10	.0262	**758**	750	633	547	482	430	389	276	203	160	132	113	98	87	78	1529
12-#10	.0315	**819**	798	672	580	510	456	411	322	238	189	156	134	116	103	93	1835
14-#10	.0367	**880**	846	711	613	539	481	434	363	272	217	180	154	135	119	107	2141
6-#11	.0193	**678**	678	581	503	443	396	334	209	152	119	98	83	72	64	57	1118
7-#11	.0226	**715**	715	605	523	461	412	372	240	175	138	114	97	84	74	67	1304
8-#11	.0258	**753**	746	628	543	478	427	386	270	198	156	129	110	96	85	76	1490
9-#11	.0290	**790**	775	652	563	496	443	400	298	220	174	144	123	107	95	85	1677
10-#11	.0322	**828**	804	676	583	513	458	413	326	241	191	159	135	118	105	94	1863
11-#11	.0355	**865**	833	700	604	531	473	427	352	262	208	173	148	129	115	103	2049
13-#11	.0419	**940**	891	748	644	565	504	454	380	301	241	201	172	151	134	120	2422
15-#11	.0483	**1015**	950	795	684	600	534	482	402	338	272	227	195	171	153	137	2795
6-#14S	.0279	**777**	763	642	554	488	435	393	284	209	165	137	116	101	90	81	1585
7-#14S	.0325	**831**	805	676	583	512	457	412	324	239	190	157	134	117	104	93	1849
8-#14S	.0372	**885**	847	710	612	537	479	432	360	269	214	178	152	133	118	106	2113
9-#14S	.0418	**939**	889	744	640	562	500	451	377	296	237	197	169	148	131	118	2377
10-#14S	.0465	**993**	930	778	669	586	522	470	393	322	259	216	186	163	145	130	2641
12-#14S	.0558	**1101**	1014	846	726	635	565	509	424	364	300	252	218	191	171	154	3170
6-#18S	.0496	**1029**	949	787	673	588	521	469	390	319	257	215	184	162	144	130	2631
7-#18S	.0579	**1125**	1021	845	721	628	557	500	415	355	290	244	210	185	165	149	3070

Check availability of #14S and #18S bars.

All above columns require spirals of A432 rod or cold drawn wire (f_y = 60,000 psi):—

#14S and smaller—½φ @ 2″

#18S only —⅝φ @ 2¾″

Outside diameter of spiral should be 3 in. less than side of column.

† Below zigzag horizontal line of each group, concrete governs; above, tension governs.

‡ M_o = capacity in pure bending, (N = 0); for extrapolation, see page 11-5.

SPIRALLY REINFORCED SQUARE COLUMNS—
Safe Load in Kips for Various Eccentricities in Inches
f'_c = 3750 psi (A61 or A432 Bars, f_y = 60,000 psi) f_s = 24,000 psi basis

COLUMN SIZE—23″ x 23″ — f'_c = 3750 psi, f_y = 60,000 psi

Bars	p	M/N † = e (in.) 0	1	2	3	4	5	6	8	10	12	14	16	18	20	22	M_o ‡ (kip-in.)
9-#7	.0102	**625**	625	570	497	441	351	234	140	100	78	64	54	46	41	37	*704*
10-#7	.0113	**639**	639	579	506	449	384	258	155	111	86	70	60	52	45	41	*783*
12-#7	.0136	**668**	668	599	522	463	416	304	184	132	103	84	71	62	54	49	*939*
14-#7	.0159	**697**	697	618	538	477	428	348	212	153	119	98	83	72	63	57	*1096*
16-#7	.0181	**726**	726	637	555	491	441	390	240	173	136	111	94	82	72	65	*1252*
18-#7	.0204	**755**	755	656	571	506	454	411	267	193	151	125	106	92	81	73	*1409*
20-#7	.0227	**783**	783	675	588	520	466	423	293	213	167	138	117	102	90	80	*1566*
7-#8	.0105	**628**	628	572	499	443	356	238	143	102	79	65	55	47	42	37	*716*
8-#8	.0119	**647**	647	584	510	452	400	268	162	116	90	74	62	54	48	43	*819*
9-#8	.0134	**666**	666	597	520	461	414	298	181	130	101	83	70	61	53	48	*921*
10-#8	.0149	**685**	685	609	531	471	423	327	199	143	112	92	78	67	59	53	*1023*
12-#8	.0179	**723**	723	634	553	489	439	383	236	170	133	109	93	80	71	63	*1228*
14-#8	.0209	**761**	761	660	574	508	456	413	271	196	154	127	107	93	82	74	*1433*
16-#8	.0239	**799**	799	685	595	527	472	428	304	222	174	144	122	106	94	84	*1638*
6-#9	.0113	**639**	639	579	505	448	380	254	153	109	85	70	59	51	45	40	*772*
8-#9	.0151	**687**	687	610	532	471	423	329	200	144	112	92	78	68	60	53	*1029*
10-#9	.0189	**735**	735	642	559	495	444	399	246	178	139	114	97	84	74	66	*1286*
12-#9	.0227	**783**	783	674	586	518	465	421	289	210	165	136	115	100	89	79	*1544*
14-#9	.0265	**831**	831	705	613	542	486	440	330	241	190	157	133	116	103	92	*1801*
16-#9	.0302	**879**	869	737	640	565	506	459	370	272	215	178	151	132	117	105	*2058*
6-#10	.0144	**678**	678	604	526	466	419	313	190	136	106	87	74	64	56	50	*972*
8-#10	.0192	**739**	739	644	560	496	445	401	248	179	140	115	98	85	75	67	*1296*
10-#10	.0240	**800**	800	684	595	526	471	427	302	220	173	142	121	105	93	83	*1621*
12-#10	.0288	**861**	854	724	629	555	497	450	352	258	204	168	143	125	111	99	*1945*
14-#10	.0336	**922**	902	764	663	585	524	474	398	295	234	194	166	144	128	115	*2269*
6-#11	.0177	**720**	720	631	549	486	436	372	228	165	129	105	89	78	68	61	*1185*
7-#11	.0206	**758**	758	655	570	504	452	410	262	190	149	122	104	90	80	71	*1382*
8-#11	.0236	**795**	795	680	591	522	468	424	295	215	169	139	118	102	91	81	*1580*
9-#11	.0265	**832**	830	704	612	540	484	438	327	239	188	155	132	115	101	91	*1778*
10-#11	.0295	**870**	860	729	632	558	500	453	357	262	207	171	146	127	112	101	*1975*
11-#11	.0324	**907**	889	753	653	576	516	467	386	285	225	186	159	139	123	110	*2173*
13-#11	.0383	**982**	949	802	695	613	548	495	416	328	261	217	185	162	144	129	*2568*
15-#11	.0442	**1057**	1008	851	736	649	580	524	440	368	295	246	211	184	164	147	*2963*
6-#14S	.0255	**819**	819	694	602	532	476	431	311	227	179	147	125	109	96	86	*1682*
7-#14S	.0298	**873**	861	729	632	558	499	452	355	260	206	170	145	126	111	100	*1962*
8-#14S	.0340	**927**	904	764	662	583	522	472	396	292	232	192	164	143	126	114	*2242*
9-#14S	.0383	**981**	946	799	691	609	544	492	413	323	257	213	182	159	141	127	*2523*
10-#14S	.0425	**1035**	988	834	721	635	567	512	430	352	281	234	200	175	156	140	*2803*
11-#14S	.0468	**1089**	1031	868	750	660	590	533	446	379	304	254	218	191	170	153	*3084*
13-#14S	.0553	**1197**	1115	938	809	711	635	573	480	412	348	292	252	221	197	178	*3644*
6-#18S	.0454	**1071**	1008	844	726	637	568	512	428	350	280	233	200	175	155	140	*2804*
7-#18S	.0529	**1167**	1081	904	776	680	605	545	455	390	317	265	228	200	178	161	*3271*
8-#18S	.0605	**1263**	1155	963	826	723	643	578	482	413	352	296	255	224	200	181	*3739*

Check availability of #14S and #18S bars.

All above columns require spirals of A432 rod or cold drawn wire (f_y = 60,000 psi):—

#14S and smaller—½φ @ 1¾″

#18S only —⅝φ @ 2¾″

Outside diameter of spiral should be 3 in. less than side of column.

† Below zigzag horizontal line of each group, concrete governs; above, tension governs.

‡ M_o = capacity in pure bending, (N = 0); for extrapolation, see page 11-5.

SPIRALLY REINFORCED SQUARE COLUMNS—
Safe Load in Kips for Various Eccentricities in Inches
f'_c = 3750 psi (A61 or A432 Bars, f_y = 60,000 psi) f_s = 24,000 psi basis

COLUMN SIZE—24″ x 24″ — f'_c = 3750 psi, f_y = 60,000 psi

Bars	p	M/N † = e (in.) 0	1	2	3	4	5	6	8	10	12	14	16	18	20	22	M_o ‡ (kip-in.)
10-#7	.0104	**683**	683	631	553	492	438	286	169	120	92	75	64	55	48	43	*826*
12-#7	.0125	**712**	712	650	570	507	456	337	200	142	110	90	76	66	58	52	*991*
14-#7	.0146	**741**	741	670	586	521	469	386	231	165	128	105	89	77	68	60	*1156*
16-#7	.0167	**770**	770	689	603	536	483	432	261	187	146	119	101	87	77	69	*1321*
18-#7	.0188	**799**	799	709	620	551	496	451	290	209	163	133	113	98	86	77	*1487*
20-#7	.0208	**827**	827	728	637	566	509	462	319	230	180	147	125	108	96	86	*1652*
8-#8	.0110	**691**	691	635	557	495	446	298	176	125	97	79	67	58	51	45	*864*
9-#8	.0123	**710**	710	648	568	505	455	331	197	140	108	88	75	65	57	51	*972*
10-#8	.0137	**729**	729	661	579	515	463	364	217	155	120	98	83	72	63	56	*1080*
12-#8	.0165	**767**	767	687	601	534	481	426	257	184	143	117	99	86	76	68	*1296*
14-#8	.0192	**805**	805	712	623	553	498	452	295	212	165	136	115	100	88	79	*1513*
16-#8	.0219	**843**	843	738	645	573	515	468	332	240	187	154	130	113	100	90	*1729*
6-#9	.0104	**683**	683	630	552	491	433	283	167	118	91	74	63	54	48	43	*815*
7-#9	.0122	**707**	707	646	566	503	453	325	193	137	106	87	73	63	56	50	*951*
8-#9	.0139	**731**	731	662	580	516	464	365	218	155	121	99	83	72	64	57	*1087*
10-#9	.0174	**779**	779	695	608	540	486	441	268	192	149	122	103	90	79	71	*1358*
12-#9	.0208	**827**	827	727	635	564	507	461	315	227	177	146	123	107	94	85	*1630*
14-#9	.0243	**875**	875	759	663	588	529	480	360	261	205	168	143	124	110	98	*1902*
16-#9	.0278	**923**	923	792	691	613	551	500	403	294	231	190	162	141	125	112	*2174*
6-#10	.0132	**722**	722	656	574	510	459	348	207	147	114	93	79	68	60	54	*1027*
8-#10	.0176	**783**	783	697	609	541	487	442	270	193	151	123	104	90	80	71	*1370*
10-#10	.0220	**844**	844	738	644	572	514	467	329	237	186	152	129	112	99	89	*1712*
12-#10	.0265	**905**	905	778	679	602	541	491	385	280	220	181	154	134	118	106	*2055*
14-#10	.0309	**966**	961	819	714	633	568	516	435	320	252	208	177	154	137	123	*2397*
6-#11	.0163	**764**	764	683	597	531	477	413	249	178	138	113	96	83	73	65	*1252*
7-#11	.0190	**802**	802	708	619	549	494	449	286	205	160	131	111	96	85	76	*1461*
8-#11	.0217	**839**	839	733	640	568	511	464	322	232	181	149	126	110	97	87	*1670*
9-#11	.0244	**876**	876	758	662	587	527	479	356	258	202	166	141	123	108	97	*1879*
10-#11	.0271	**914**	914	783	683	606	544	494	390	284	223	183	156	136	120	107	*2088*
12-#11	.0325	**989**	978	833	726	643	577	523	441	332	262	217	185	161	142	128	*2505*
14-#11	.0379	**1064**	1038	883	769	680	610	553	466	378	300	249	212	185	164	148	*2923*
16-#11	.0433	**1139**	1098	933	811	718	643	583	491	421	336	280	239	209	186	167	*3340*
6-#14S	.0234	**864**	864	748	652	578	520	472	340	246	192	158	134	116	103	92	*1779*
7-#14S	.0273	**918**	918	784	683	605	543	493	388	282	222	182	155	135	119	107	*2076*
8-#14S	.0313	**972**	962	819	713	632	567	514	433	317	250	206	176	153	135	121	*2372*
9-#14S	.0352	**1026**	1005	855	744	658	590	535	451	350	277	229	196	170	151	136	*2669*
10-#14S	.0391	**1080**	1048	891	774	685	614	556	468	382	304	252	215	188	167	150	*2965*
11-#14S	.0430	**1134**	1091	926	805	711	637	577	486	412	329	274	234	205	182	163	*3262*
13-#14S	.0508	**1242**	1177	998	865	764	684	619	521	449	377	315	271	237	211	190	*3855*
6-#18S	.0417	**1115**	1069	903	781	689	616	557	467	381	303	252	215	188	167	150	*2977*
7-#18S	.0486	**1211**	1144	964	833	733	655	592	496	427	344	287	246	216	192	173	*3473*
8-#18S	.0556	**1307**	1218	1025	884	778	694	627	525	451	383	321	276	242	216	194	*3969*
9-#18S	.0625	**1404**	1293	1086	936	822	733	662	553	476	417	352	304	267	239	216	*4465*

Check availability of #14S and #18S bars.

All above columns require spirals of A432 rod or cold drawn wire (f_y = 60,000 psi):—

#14S and smaller—½φ @ 1¾″

#18S only —⅝φ @ 2¾″

Outside diameter of spiral should be 3 in. less than side of column.

† Below zigzag horizontal line of each group, concrete governs; above, tension governs.

‡ M_o = capacity in pure bending, (N = 0); for extrapolation, see page 11-5.

SPIRALLY REINFORCED SQUARE COLUMNS—
Safe Load in Kips for Various Eccentricities in Inches
$f'_c = 3750$ psi (A61 or A432 Bars, $f_y = 60,000$ psi) $f_s = 24,000$ psi basis

COLUMN SIZE—25″ x 25″

$f'_c = 3750$ psi
$f_y = 60,000$ psi

Bars	p	M/N † = e (in.)															M_o ‡ (kip-in.)
		0	2	4	6	8	10	12	14	16	18	20	22	24	26	28	
11-#7	.0106	**744**	694	545	346	200	141	109	88	74	64	57	50	46	42	38	*956*
13-#7	.0125	**773**	714	560	401	234	165	128	104	88	76	67	60	54	49	45	*1130*
15-#7	.0144	**801**	734	576	454	267	189	147	119	101	87	77	69	62	57	52	*1304*
17-#7	.0163	**830**	754	591	486	300	213	165	135	114	99	87	78	70	64	59	*1477*
19-#7	.0182	**859**	774	606	498	331	236	183	150	127	110	97	87	78	71	66	*1651*
8-#8	.0101	**737**	689	541	331	191	134	104	84	71	61	54	48	43	40	36	*910*
9-#8	.0114	**756**	702	551	368	214	150	116	94	80	69	61	54	49	44	41	*1023*
10-#8	.0126	**775**	715	561	403	236	166	129	105	88	76	67	60	54	49	45	*1137*
12-#8	.0152	**813**	741	581	472	279	198	153	125	105	91	80	72	65	59	54	*1365*
14-#8	.0177	**851**	768	601	494	320	228	177	145	122	106	93	83	75	69	63	*1592*
16-#8	.0202	**889**	794	621	510	361	258	201	164	139	121	106	95	86	78	72	*1820*
7-#9	.0112	**753**	700	549	360	209	147	114	92	78	67	59	53	48	43	40	*1001*
8-#9	.0128	**777**	716	562	406	237	167	129	105	89	77	68	60	54	50	46	*1144*
9-#9	.0144	**801**	733	574	449	264	187	145	118	100	86	76	68	61	56	51	*1287*
10-#9	.0160	**825**	749	587	482	291	207	160	131	110	95	84	75	68	62	57	*1430*
12-#9	.0192	**873**	782	612	502	343	245	190	156	132	114	100	90	81	74	68	*1716*
14-#9	.0224	**921**	815	637	523	392	281	219	180	152	132	117	104	94	86	79	*2003*
16-#9	.0256	**969**	848	662	543	439	317	248	204	173	150	133	119	107	98	90	*2289*
6-#10	.0122	**768**	710	557	386	225	159	123	100	84	73	64	57	52	47	43	*1082*
8-#10	.0163	**829**	752	588	483	293	208	161	132	111	96	85	76	69	62	57	*1443*
10-#10	.0203	**890**	793	620	509	358	256	199	163	138	119	105	94	85	78	72	*1804*
12-#10	.0244	**951**	835	651	534	419	302	236	193	164	142	126	112	102	93	86	*2164*
14-#10	.0284	**1012**	877	683	559	474	345	271	223	189	165	145	130	118	108	99	*2525*
6-#11	.0150	**810**	738	578	459	270	192	148	121	102	88	78	69	63	57	53	*1320*
7-#11	.0175	**848**	763	597	490	311	221	172	140	118	103	90	81	73	67	61	*1540*
8-#11	.0200	**885**	789	616	506	350	250	195	159	135	117	103	92	83	76	70	*1760*
9-#11	.0225	**922**	814	636	521	388	278	217	178	151	131	115	103	93	85	78	*1980*
10-#11	.0250	**960**	840	655	537	424	306	239	196	166	144	128	114	103	94	87	*2200*
11-#11	.0275	**997**	865	674	552	459	333	261	214	182	158	140	125	113	104	95	*2420*
13-#11	.0324	**1072**	916	713	583	493	384	303	250	212	185	164	147	133	122	112	*2860*
15-#11	.0374	**1147**	967	751	614	519	433	343	283	242	211	187	168	152	139	128	*3300*
17-#11	.0424	**1222**	1018	789	645	545	472	381	316	270	236	209	188	171	157	144	*3740*
6-#14S	.0216	**909**	804	627	514	370	265	207	169	143	124	109	98	89	81	74	*1876*
7-#14S	.0252	**963**	841	654	536	422	305	238	195	166	144	127	114	103	94	86	*2189*
8-#14S	.0288	**1017**	877	682	558	472	342	269	221	188	163	144	129	117	107	98	*2502*
9-#14S	.0324	**1071**	913	709	580	490	379	298	246	209	182	161	144	131	120	110	*2814*
10-#14S	.0360	**1125**	950	737	602	508	413	327	270	230	201	178	159	145	132	122	*3127*
12-#14S	.0432	**1233**	1023	791	645	545	472	381	317	271	237	210	189	171	157	145	*3753*
14-#14S	.0504	**1341**	1095	846	689	581	503	432	360	309	271	241	217	197	181	167	*4378*
6-#18S	.0384	**1161**	963	742	603	508	414	328	271	231	202	179	160	145	133	123	*3149*
7-#18S	.0448	**1257**	1026	788	640	539	465	373	310	265	231	205	185	168	154	142	*3674*
8-#18S	.0512	**1353**	1088	834	676	569	491	415	346	297	260	231	208	189	174	160	*4199*
9-#18S	.0576	**1449**	1151	880	713	599	516	454	380	328	288	256	231	210	193	178	*4724*

Check availability of #14S and #18S bars.

All above columns require spirals of A432 rod or cold drawn wire ($f_y = 60,000$ psi):—

#14S and smaller—½φ @ 1¾″

#18S only —⅝φ @ 2¾″

Outside diameter of spiral should be 3 in. less than side of column.

† Below zigzag horizontal line of each group, concrete governs; above, tension governs.

‡ M_o = capacity in pure bending, ($N = 0$); for extrapolation, see page 11-5.

SPIRALLY REINFORCED SQUARE COLUMNS—
Safe Load in Kips for Various Eccentricities in Inches
f'_c = 3750 psi (A61 or A432 Bars, f_y = 60,000 psi) f_s = 24,000 psi basis

COLUMN SIZE—26″ x 26″

f'_c = 3750 psi
f_y = 60,000 psi

Bars	p	M/N † = e (in.) 0	2	4	6	8	10	12	14	16	18	20	22	24	26	28	M_o ‡ (kip-in.)
9-#8	.0105	**804**	758	599	408	232	162	124	101	85	73	64	57	52	47	43	*1075*
10-#8	.0117	**823**	772	610	448	256	179	137	111	94	81	71	63	57	52	48	*1194*
12-#8	.0140	**861**	798	630	520	302	212	164	133	112	97	85	76	69	63	57	*1433*
14-#8	.0164	**899**	825	650	537	348	245	189	154	130	112	99	88	80	73	67	*1672*
16-#8	.0187	**937**	851	671	553	391	277	215	175	148	128	113	101	91	83	76	*1911*
18-#8	.0210	**975**	878	691	570	433	309	240	196	165	143	126	113	102	93	86	*2150*
20-#8	.0234	**1012**	905	712	587	474	339	264	216	183	158	140	125	113	103	95	*2388*
22-#8	.0257	**1050**	931	732	603	513	369	288	236	200	173	153	137	124	113	104	*2627*
7-#9	.0104	**801**	756	598	400	227	158	121	99	83	71	63	56	51	46	42	*1051*
8-#9	.0118	**825**	773	610	450	257	180	138	112	94	81	72	64	58	53	48	*1202*
9-#9	.0133	**849**	790	623	499	287	201	155	126	106	91	80	72	65	59	54	*1352*
10-#9	.0148	**873**	807	636	525	316	222	171	139	117	101	89	80	72	66	60	*1502*
12-#9	.0178	**921**	840	662	546	372	263	203	166	140	121	107	95	86	78	72	*1803*
14-#9	.0207	**969**	874	688	567	425	303	235	192	162	140	124	111	100	91	84	*2103*
16-#9	.0237	**1017**	907	713	588	477	341	266	217	184	159	141	126	114	104	96	*2404*
18-#9	.0266	**1065**	941	739	608	517	378	295	242	205	178	157	141	127	116	107	*2705*
6-#10	.0113	**816**	766	605	429	244	171	131	106	89	77	68	60	55	50	46	*1137*
8-#10	.0150	**877**	809	638	526	318	224	173	140	118	102	90	80	73	66	61	*1516*
10-#10	.0188	**938**	851	670	552	388	275	213	174	147	127	112	100	90	82	76	*1895*
12-#10	.0225	**999**	894	702	579	455	325	252	206	175	151	133	119	108	98	91	*2274*
14-#10	.0263	**1060**	936	735	605	514	372	290	238	202	175	154	138	125	114	105	*2653*
16-#10	.0301	**1121**	978	767	631	536	417	327	269	228	198	175	157	142	130	120	*3032*
6-#11	.0138	**858**	795	627	510	293	206	159	129	109	94	82	74	66	61	56	*1387*
7-#11	.0162	**895**	821	647	533	338	238	184	150	126	109	96	86	77	71	65	*1618*
8-#11	.0185	**933**	847	666	549	380	269	208	170	143	124	109	98	88	80	74	*1850*
9-#11	.0208	**970**	873	686	565	421	300	232	190	160	139	122	109	99	90	83	*2081*
10-#11	.0231	**1008**	899	706	581	461	329	256	210	177	154	135	121	110	100	92	*2312*
12-#11	.0277	**1083**	951	746	613	521	387	302	248	210	182	161	144	131	119	110	*2775*
14-#11	.0323	**1157**	1002	785	645	548	441	346	285	242	211	186	167	151	138	127	*3237*
16-#11	.0369	**1232**	1054	825	677	575	492	388	321	273	238	211	189	171	157	145	*3700*
18-#11	.0415	**1307**	1106	864	709	601	522	429	355	303	265	235	211	191	175	161	*4162*
6-#14S	.0200	**957**	862	678	558	402	286	221	181	153	132	116	104	94	86	79	*1973*
7-#14S	.0233	**1011**	900	706	581	459	328	255	209	177	153	135	121	109	100	92	*2302*
8-#14S	.0266	**1065**	937	734	604	512	369	288	236	200	174	153	137	124	113	104	*2631*
9-#14S	.0300	**1119**	974	762	626	531	408	320	263	223	194	171	153	139	127	117	*2960*
10-#14S	.0333	**1173**	1011	791	649	550	446	351	289	246	214	189	169	153	140	129	*3289*
11-#14S	.0366	**1227**	1048	819	672	569	483	381	314	268	233	206	185	168	154	141	*3618*
13-#14S	.0433	**1335**	1122	875	717	607	527	438	363	310	271	240	216	196	179	166	*4276*
15-#14S	.0499	**1443**	1196	931	762	645	560	491	409	351	307	273	246	223	205	189	*4934*
6-#18S	.0355	**1209**	1025	797	652	551	449	353	291	248	215	190	171	155	142	130	*3322*
7-#18S	.0414	**1305**	1089	845	690	583	505	402	333	284	247	219	197	179	164	151	*3876*
8-#18S	.0473	**1401**	1153	892	728	614	532	448	372	319	278	247	222	202	185	171	*4430*
9-#18S	.0533	**1497**	1217	940	766	646	559	491	410	352	308	274	247	225	206	190	*4984*
10-#18S	.0592	**1593**	1281	988	804	678	586	516	445	383	337	300	271	246	226	209	*5537*

Check availability of #14S and #18S bars.

All above columns require spirals of A432 rod or cold drawn wire (f_y = 60,000 psi):—

#14S and smaller—½φ @ 1¾″

#18S only —⅝φ @ 2¾″

Outside diameter of spiral should be 3 in. less than side of column.

† Below zigzag horizontal line of each group, concrete governs; above, tension governs.

‡ M_o = capacity in pure bending, (N = 0); for extrapolation, see page 11-5.

SPIRALLY REINFORCED SQUARE COLUMNS—
Safe Load in Kips for Various Eccentricities in Inches

$f'_c = 3750$ psi (A61 or A432 Bars, $f_y = 60{,}000$ psi) $f_s = 24{,}000$ psi basis

COLUMN SIZE—27″ x 27″ — $f'_c = 3750$ psi, $f_y = 60{,}000$ psi

Bars	p	M/N † = e (in.) 0	2	4	6	8	10	12	14	16	18	20	22	24	26	28	M_o ‡ (kip-in.)
10-#8	.0108	**873**	830	659	492	274	190	145	117	98	85	74	66	60	54	50	1237
12-#8	.0130	**910**	857	680	564	324	225	173	140	118	101	89	79	72	65	60	1484
14-#8	.0152	**948**	883	701	581	373	260	200	162	136	118	104	92	83	76	70	1731
16-#8	.0173	**986**	910	722	598	420	294	227	184	155	134	118	105	95	87	80	1979
18-#8	.0195	**1024**	937	742	615	465	328	253	206	174	150	132	118	107	97	89	2226
20-#8	.0217	**1062**	964	763	632	509	360	279	227	192	166	146	131	118	108	99	2474
22-#8	.0238	**1100**	991	784	648	551	392	304	248	210	182	160	143	130	118	109	2721
8-#9	.0110	**875**	831	660	495	275	191	146	118	99	85	75	67	60	55	50	1245
9-#9	.0123	**899**	848	673	548	307	213	163	132	111	96	84	75	68	62	57	1401
10-#9	.0137	**923**	865	686	569	338	236	181	146	123	106	93	83	75	68	63	1556
12-#9	.0165	**971**	899	713	590	399	279	215	174	147	127	111	100	90	82	75	1868
14-#9	.0192	**1019**	933	739	611	456	321	248	202	170	147	129	116	104	95	87	2179
16-#9	.0219	**1067**	967	765	633	512	362	281	229	193	167	147	132	119	108	100	2490
18-#9	.0247	**1115**	1000	791	654	557	402	312	255	216	187	165	147	133	122	112	2802
6-#10	.0105	**866**	824	655	472	262	181	138	112	94	81	71	63	57	52	48	1178
8-#10	.0139	**927**	867	688	570	341	238	182	148	124	107	94	84	76	69	63	1571
10-#10	.0174	**988**	910	721	597	417	292	225	183	154	133	117	104	94	86	79	1964
12-#10	.0209	**1049**	953	754	624	488	345	267	217	183	159	140	125	113	103	94	2356
14-#10	.0244	**1110**	996	787	650	554	395	307	251	212	184	162	145	131	119	110	2749
16-#10	.0279	**1171**	1039	820	677	577	444	346	283	240	208	184	164	149	136	125	3142
6-#11	.0128	**908**	853	677	561	315	219	167	136	114	98	86	77	69	63	58	1438
7-#11	.0150	**945**	880	697	577	362	253	194	157	132	114	100	90	81	74	68	1677
8-#11	.0171	**982**	906	717	594	408	286	220	179	151	130	114	102	92	84	77	1917
9-#11	.0193	**1020**	932	737	610	452	318	246	200	169	146	128	114	103	94	87	2157
10-#11	.0214	**1057**	958	758	626	495	350	271	221	186	161	142	127	115	104	96	2396
11-#11	.0235	**1095**	985	778	643	537	381	295	241	204	176	155	139	126	115	105	2636
13-#11	.0278	**1170**	1037	818	675	575	441	343	281	238	206	182	163	147	135	124	3115
15-#11	.0321	**1245**	1089	858	708	603	497	389	320	271	236	208	187	169	154	142	3595
17-#11	.0364	**1319**	1142	898	741	630	548	433	357	304	264	234	210	190	174	160	4074
19-#11	.0407	**1394**	1194	939	773	657	572	475	393	335	292	259	232	211	193	178	4554
6-#14S	.0185	**1007**	922	729	603	432	304	234	190	160	138	122	109	98	90	82	2046
7-#14S	.0216	**1061**	959	758	626	494	349	270	220	186	160	141	126	114	104	96	2387
8-#14S	.0247	**1115**	997	786	649	552	393	305	249	210	182	161	144	130	118	109	2728
9-#14S	.0278	**1169**	1034	815	672	572	435	339	277	235	203	180	161	145	133	122	3070
10-#14S	.0309	**1223**	1072	844	696	592	475	372	305	259	224	198	177	161	147	135	3411
12-#14S	.0370	**1331**	1147	901	742	631	548	434	358	305	265	235	210	191	174	161	4093
14-#14S	.0432	**1439**	1222	958	788	670	582	493	409	349	304	270	242	220	201	186	4775
16-#14S	.0494	**1547**	1297	1016	835	708	615	544	456	391	342	304	273	248	227	210	5457
6-#18S	.0329	**1259**	1089	854	702	596	484	379	311	264	229	203	181	164	150	138	3495
7-#18S	.0384	**1355**	1155	903	741	629	546	432	356	303	264	233	209	190	174	160	4078
8-#18S	.0439	**1451**	1220	952	781	662	574	482	399	341	297	263	237	215	196	181	4660
9-#18S	.0494	**1547**	1285	1001	820	695	602	529	440	376	329	292	263	239	219	202	5243
10-#18S	.0549	**1643**	1350	1051	860	728	631	556	478	411	360	320	288	262	241	222	5825
11-#18S	.0604	**1739**	1415	1100	899	760	659	581	515	443	389	347	313	285	262	242	6408

Check availability of #14S and #18S bars.

All above columns require spirals of A432 rod or cold drawn wire ($f_y = 60{,}000$ psi):—
⅝φ @ 2¾″

Outside diameter of spiral should be 3 in. less than side of column.
† Below zigzag horizontal line of each group, concrete governs; above, tension governs.
‡ M_o = capacity in pure bending, $(N = 0)$; for extrapolation, see page 11-5.

SPIRALLY REINFORCED SQUARE COLUMNS—
Safe Load in Kips for Various Eccentricities in Inches
f'_c = 3750 psi (A61 or A432 Bars, f_y = 60,000 psi) f_s = 24,000 psi basis

COLUMN SIZE—28″ x 28″ — f'_c = 3750 psi, f_y = 60,000 psi

Bars	p	M/N † = e (in.)															M_o ‡ (kip-in.)
		0	2	4	6	8	10	12	14	16	18	20	22	24	26	28	
10-#8	.0101	**924**	891	713	547	296	203	154	124	104	90	79	70	63	57	53	*1294*
12-#8	.0121	**962**	918	734	611	350	241	184	148	124	107	94	84	76	69	63	*1552*
14-#8	.0141	**1000**	946	755	628	403	279	213	172	145	125	109	97	88	80	73	*1811*
16-#8	.0161	**1038**	973	776	646	454	315	242	196	164	142	125	111	100	91	84	*2070*
18-#8	.0181	**1076**	1000	797	663	503	351	270	219	184	159	140	125	112	102	94	*2329*
20-#8	.0202	**1114**	1027	819	680	551	386	297	242	203	176	155	138	125	114	104	*2588*
22-#8	.0222	**1152**	1054	840	698	597	420	324	264	223	192	169	151	137	125	114	*2846*
8-#9	.0102	**926**	892	713	551	298	204	155	125	105	90	79	70	63	58	53	*1303*
9-#9	.0115	**950**	910	727	605	332	228	174	140	118	101	89	79	71	65	60	*1465*
10-#9	.0128	**974**	927	740	616	366	252	192	155	130	112	99	88	79	72	66	*1628*
12-#9	.0153	**1022**	961	767	638	431	299	229	185	156	134	118	105	95	86	79	*1954*
14-#9	.0179	**1070**	996	794	660	494	344	264	214	180	156	137	122	110	100	92	*2280*
16-#9	.0204	**1118**	1030	820	682	554	389	299	243	205	177	156	139	125	114	105	*2606*
18-#9	.0230	**1166**	1064	847	704	602	431	333	271	229	198	174	156	141	128	118	*2931*
8-#10	.0130	**978**	929	742	617	369	255	194	157	132	113	99	89	80	73	67	*1644*
10-#10	.0162	**1039**	973	776	645	451	313	240	194	163	141	124	110	100	91	83	*2055*
12-#10	.0194	**1100**	1016	809	672	529	370	284	231	194	168	148	132	119	108	100	*2466*
14-#10	.0227	**1161**	1060	843	700	598	424	327	267	225	194	171	153	138	126	116	*2877*
16-#10	.0259	**1222**	1103	877	728	622	477	369	301	255	220	194	174	157	143	132	*3288*
18-#10	.0292	**1283**	1147	911	755	645	527	410	335	284	246	217	194	176	160	147	*3700*
6-#11	.0119	**959**	915	731	608	341	234	178	144	121	104	91	81	73	67	61	*1505*
7-#11	.0139	**997**	942	751	625	392	271	207	167	140	121	106	95	85	78	71	*1756*
8-#11	.0159	**1034**	968	772	642	442	307	235	190	160	138	121	108	97	89	81	*2007*
9-#11	.0179	**1071**	995	793	659	490	341	262	212	179	154	136	121	109	99	91	*2258*
10-#11	.0199	**1109**	1022	813	675	537	376	289	235	198	171	150	134	121	110	101	*2509*
12-#11	.0239	**1184**	1075	854	709	606	441	341	278	234	203	179	160	144	131	121	*3011*
14-#11	.0279	**1259**	1128	896	743	634	504	391	320	270	234	207	185	167	152	140	*3512*
16-#11	.0318	**1334**	1181	937	776	663	563	440	361	305	265	234	209	190	173	159	*4014*
18-#11	.0358	**1408**	1234	978	810	691	602	486	400	339	295	261	234	212	193	178	*4516*
20-#11	.0398	**1483**	1288	1019	843	719	627	530	438	373	324	287	257	233	213	197	*5018*
6-#14S	.0172	**1058**	984	784	651	468	326	250	202	170	147	129	115	104	94	87	*2143*
7-#14S	.0201	**1112**	1023	813	675	535	374	288	234	197	170	150	133	121	110	101	*2501*
8-#14S	.0230	**1166**	1061	843	699	597	422	325	265	223	193	170	152	137	125	115	*2858*
9-#14S	.0258	**1220**	1099	872	723	617	467	362	295	249	216	190	170	154	140	129	*3215*
10-#14S	.0287	**1274**	1137	902	747	637	511	397	325	275	238	210	188	170	155	143	*3573*
12-#14S	.0344	**1382**	1213	960	795	678	591	465	382	324	281	249	223	202	184	170	*4287*
14-#14S	.0402	**1490**	1290	1019	842	718	626	528	436	371	323	286	257	233	213	196	*5002*
16-#14S	.0459	**1598**	1366	1078	890	758	660	585	487	416	363	322	289	263	241	222	*5717*
6-#18S	.0306	**1310**	1156	912	754	642	522	406	332	281	244	215	192	174	159	146	*3668*
7-#18S	.0357	**1406**	1222	963	795	676	589	463	381	323	280	248	222	201	184	169	*4279*
8-#18S	.0408	**1502**	1288	1014	836	711	618	517	427	363	316	280	251	228	208	192	*4891*
9-#18S	.0459	**1598**	1355	1064	876	745	648	568	471	402	350	311	279	253	232	214	*5502*
10-#18S	.0510	**1694**	1421	1115	917	779	677	599	512	439	383	341	306	278	255	235	*6113*
11-#18S	.0561	**1790**	1487	1165	958	813	706	624	552	474	415	370	333	303	278	256	*6725*

Check availability of #14S and #18S bars.

All above columns require spirals of A432 rod or cold drawn wire (f_y = 60,000 psi):—

#14S and smaller—⅝φ @ 2¾″

#18S only —⅝φ @ 2½″

Outside diameter of spiral should be 3 in. less than side of column.

† Below zigzag horizontal line of each group, concrete governs; above, tension governs.

‡ M_o = capacity in pure bending, (N = 0); for extrapolation, see page 11-5.

SPIRALLY REINFORCED SQUARE COLUMNS—
Safe Load in Kips for Various Eccentricities in Inches
f'_c = 3750 psi (A61 or A432 Bars, f_y = 60,000 psi) f_s = 24,000 psi basis

COLUMN SIZE—29″ x 29″

f'_c = 3750 psi
f_y = 60,000 psi

Bars	p	M/N † = e (in.) 0	2	4	6	8	10	12	14	16	18	20	22	24	26	28	M_o ‡ (kip-in.)
11-#8	.0103	**996**	968	779	651	350	238	180	145	121	104	91	81	73	66	61	*1485*
13-#8	.0122	**1034**	996	800	669	408	278	211	170	142	122	107	95	86	78	72	*1756*
15-#8	.0141	**1072**	1024	822	687	464	318	242	195	163	141	123	110	99	90	83	*2026*
17-#8	.0160	**1110**	1051	844	705	518	357	272	220	184	159	139	124	112	102	94	*2296*
19-#8	.0178	**1148**	1079	865	722	570	395	302	244	205	177	155	138	125	114	104	*2566*
21-#8	.0197	**1186**	1106	887	740	621	432	331	268	225	194	171	152	137	125	115	*2836*
10-#9	.0119	**1028**	991	796	665	396	270	205	165	138	119	104	92	83	76	70	*1700*
12-#9	.0143	**1076**	1026	823	688	467	320	243	196	164	142	124	111	100	91	83	*2040*
14-#9	.0166	**1124**	1061	851	710	534	369	281	227	191	164	144	129	116	106	97	*2381*
16-#9	.0190	**1172**	1095	878	733	599	416	318	258	217	187	164	146	132	120	110	*2721*
18-#9	.0214	**1220**	1130	905	755	648	462	355	288	242	209	184	164	148	135	124	*3061*
8-#10	.0121	**1032**	993	798	667	399	272	207	166	139	120	105	93	84	77	70	*1717*
10-#10	.0151	**1093**	1037	832	695	488	335	255	206	173	149	130	116	105	95	88	*2147*
12-#10	.0181	**1154**	1082	867	723	572	396	303	245	206	177	156	139	125	114	105	*2576*
14-#10	.0211	**1215**	1126	901	752	644	454	349	283	238	205	180	161	145	132	122	*3005*
16-#10	.0242	**1276**	1170	936	780	668	511	393	320	270	233	205	183	165	151	138	*3435*
18-#10	.0272	**1337**	1214	970	808	692	564	437	356	300	260	229	205	185	169	155	*3864*
6-#11	.0111	**1013**	979	786	657	369	251	190	153	128	110	96	86	77	70	64	*1572*
7-#11	.0130	**1050**	1006	807	674	424	290	220	177	148	128	112	100	90	82	75	*1835*
8-#11	.0148	**1087**	1033	829	692	478	328	250	201	169	145	128	114	102	93	86	*2097*
9-#11	.0167	**1125**	1060	850	709	530	366	279	225	189	163	143	127	115	105	96	*2359*
10-#11	.0185	**1162**	1087	871	726	581	402	308	249	209	180	158	141	127	116	106	*2621*
11-#11	.0204	**1200**	1114	892	744	629	438	336	272	229	197	173	155	140	127	117	*2883*
13-#11	.0241	**1275**	1168	934	778	667	507	391	318	268	231	203	182	164	150	137	*3408*
15-#11	.0278	**1350**	1222	976	813	696	573	443	362	305	264	233	208	188	172	158	*3932*
17-#11	.0315	**1424**	1276	1018	847	725	634	494	404	342	296	261	234	212	193	178	*4456*
19-#11	.0352	**1499**	1330	1061	882	755	660	543	445	378	328	290	259	235	214	197	*4980*
21-#11	.0390	**1574**	1384	1103	916	784	685	589	485	412	359	317	284	258	235	217	*5505*
6-#14S	.0161	**1112**	1049	841	701	507	349	266	215	180	155	136	121	109	99	91	*2241*
7-#14S	.0187	**1166**	1088	871	726	579	401	307	248	209	180	158	141	127	116	106	*2614*
8-#14S	.0214	**1220**	1127	901	751	643	452	347	281	237	204	179	160	145	132	121	*2988*
9-#14S	.0241	**1274**	1166	931	775	664	501	386	314	264	228	201	179	162	148	136	*3361*
10-#14S	.0268	**1328**	1204	961	800	685	548	424	345	291	252	222	198	179	163	150	*3735*
11-#14S	.0294	**1382**	1243	992	825	706	594	460	376	318	275	242	217	196	179	164	*4108*
13-#14S	.0348	**1490**	1321	1052	874	747	653	531	435	369	320	283	253	229	209	193	*4855*
15-#14S	.0401	**1598**	1398	1112	923	789	689	597	492	418	364	322	289	262	239	220	*5602*
17-#14S	.0455	**1706**	1475	1172	972	831	725	643	546	466	406	360	323	293	268	247	*6349*
6-#18S	.0285	**1364**	1224	973	808	690	560	434	354	298	258	228	203	184	168	154	*3841*
7-#18S	.0333	**1460**	1291	1025	850	726	633	495	405	343	297	262	235	212	194	178	*4481*
8-#18S	.0380	**1556**	1359	1077	892	761	664	553	455	386	335	296	266	241	220	202	*5121*
9-#18S	.0428	**1652**	1426	1129	934	797	695	608	502	427	372	329	296	268	245	226	*5761*
10-#18S	.0476	**1748**	1494	1181	976	832	725	643	547	467	408	361	325	295	270	249	*6401*
11-#18S	.0523	**1844**	1561	1233	1018	868	756	669	590	505	442	392	353	321	294	271	*7042*
12-#18S	.0571	**1940**	1628	1285	1061	903	786	696	625	542	475	422	380	346	317	293	*7682*

Check availability of #14S and #18S bars.

All above columns require spirals of A432 rod or cold drawn wire (f_y = 60,000 psi):—

#14S and smaller—⅝φ @ 2¾″

#18S only —⅝φ @ 2½″

Outside diameter of spiral should be 3 in. less than side of column.

† Below zigzag horizontal line of each group, concrete governs; above, tension governs.

‡ M_o = capacity in pure bending, (N = 0); for extrapolation, see page 11-5.

SPIRALLY REINFORCED SQUARE COLUMNS—
Safe Load in Kips for Various Eccentricities in Inches
f'_c = 3750 psi (A61 or A432 Bars, f_y = 60,000 psi) f_s = 24,000 psi basis

COLUMN SIZE—30″ x 30″

f'_c = 3750 psi
f_y = 60,000 psi

Bars	p	M/N † = e (in.) 0	2	4	6	8	10	12	14	16	18	20	22	24	26	28	M_o ‡ (kip-in.)
9-#9	.0100	**1059**	1040	840	705	388	261	196	157	131	113	99	88	79	72	66	*1595*
10-#9	.0111	**1083**	1057	854	717	428	288	217	174	146	125	109	97	88	80	73	*1772*
12-#9	.0133	**1131**	1093	882	740	504	342	258	208	174	149	131	116	105	95	87	*2127*
14-#9	.0156	**1179**	1128	910	763	578	394	299	241	201	173	152	135	122	111	102	*2481*
16-#9	.0178	**1227**	1163	938	786	648	444	338	273	229	197	173	154	139	126	116	*2836*
18-#9	.0200	**1275**	1199	966	809	696	494	377	305	256	220	193	172	155	142	130	*3191*
20-#9	.0222	**1323**	1234	994	832	715	541	415	336	282	243	214	191	172	157	144	*3545*
22-#9	.0244	**1371**	1269	1022	855	735	588	451	366	308	266	234	209	189	172	158	*3900*
24-#9	.0267	**1419**	1304	1049	878	754	632	487	396	334	289	254	227	205	187	172	*4254*
26-#9	.0289	**1467**	1340	1077	901	774	676	522	426	359	311	274	244	221	202	185	*4609*
8-#10	.0113	**1087**	1060	856	718	432	291	219	176	147	126	110	98	88	80	74	*1790*
9-#10	.0127	**1118**	1082	874	732	480	325	245	197	165	141	124	110	99	90	83	*2014*
10-#10	.0141	**1148**	1105	891	747	527	358	271	218	182	157	137	122	110	100	92	*2238*
12-#10	.0169	**1209**	1149	927	776	618	423	322	259	217	187	164	146	132	120	110	*2686*
14-#10	.0198	**1270**	1194	962	805	692	486	371	300	251	216	190	169	153	139	128	*3133*
16-#10	.0226	**1331**	1239	997	834	717	546	418	339	285	246	216	193	174	158	145	*3581*
18-#10	.0254	**1392**	1283	1032	863	742	604	464	377	318	274	241	215	194	177	163	*4029*
20-#10	.0282	**1453**	1328	1067	892	767	660	509	415	350	302	266	238	215	196	180	*4476*
6-#11	.0104	**1068**	1045	844	708	398	268	202	162	135	116	101	90	81	74	68	*1640*
7-#11	.0121	**1105**	1073	866	726	458	310	234	188	157	135	118	105	94	86	79	*1913*
8-#11	.0139	**1143**	1100	888	744	517	351	265	213	178	153	134	119	108	98	90	*2187*
9-#11	.0156	**1180**	1128	909	762	573	391	296	239	200	172	151	134	121	110	101	*2460*
10-#11	.0173	**1218**	1155	931	779	628	430	327	264	221	190	167	148	134	122	112	*2733*
12-#11	.0208	**1293**	1210	974	815	700	506	386	313	262	226	199	177	160	145	134	*3280*
14-#11	.0243	**1367**	1264	1017	850	731	578	444	360	303	261	230	205	185	169	155	*3827*
16-#11	.0277	**1442**	1319	1060	886	761	647	499	406	342	296	261	233	210	192	176	*4374*
18-#11	.0312	**1517**	1374	1103	921	791	693	552	451	381	330	291	260	235	214	197	*4920*
20-#11	.0347	**1592**	1428	1146	957	821	719	603	494	418	363	320	286	259	237	218	*5467*
22-#11	.0381	**1667**	1483	1189	992	851	745	653	536	455	395	349	313	283	259	238	*6014*
6-#14S	.0150	**1167**	1117	900	754	548	373	283	227	190	163	143	128	115	105	96	*2338*
7-#14S	.0175	**1221**	1156	931	779	627	429	326	263	220	190	166	148	134	122	112	*2728*
8-#14S	.0200	**1275**	1195	962	804	691	484	369	298	250	215	189	169	152	138	127	*3117*
9-#14S	.0225	**1329**	1235	993	830	713	536	410	332	279	241	212	189	170	155	142	*3507*
10-#14S	.0250	**1383**	1274	1023	855	734	587	451	366	308	266	234	209	188	172	158	*3897*
12-#14S	.0300	**1491**	1352	1085	906	777	681	528	431	364	315	277	248	224	204	188	*4676*
14-#14S	.0350	**1599**	1431	1146	956	820	718	602	493	417	362	319	286	259	236	217	*5456*
16-#14S	.0400	**1707**	1509	1208	1007	863	755	671	552	469	407	360	323	292	267	246	*6235*
18-#14S	.0450	**1815**	1588	1269	1057	906	792	704	608	518	451	400	359	325	298	274	*7015*
6-#18S	.0267	**1419**	1294	1036	864	740	601	462	376	316	273	240	214	194	177	162	*4013*
7-#18S	.0311	**1515**	1363	1089	907	777	680	528	431	364	315	277	248	224	204	188	*4682*
8-#18S	.0356	**1611**	1431	1142	951	814	712	591	484	410	355	313	280	254	232	213	*5351*
9-#18S	.0400	**1707**	1500	1196	994	851	743	650	535	454	394	348	312	283	258	238	*6020*
10-#18S	.0444	**1803**	1568	1249	1037	887	775	688	583	496	432	383	343	311	285	262	*6689*
11-#18S	.0489	**1899**	1637	1302	1081	924	807	716	629	537	469	416	373	339	310	286	*7358*
12-#18S	.0533	**1995**	1705	1355	1124	960	838	744	668	576	504	448	403	366	335	309	*8027*

Check availability of #14S and #18S bars.

All above columns require spirals of A432 rod or cold drawn wire (f_y = 60,000 psi):—

#14S and smaller—⅝φ @ 2¾″

#18S only —⅝φ @ 2½″

Outside diameter of spiral should be 3 in. less than side of column.

† Below zigzag horizontal line of each group, concrete governs; above, tension governs.

‡ M_o = capacity in pure bending, (N = 0); for extrapolation, see page 11-5.

SPIRALLY REINFORCED SQUARE COLUMNS—
Safe Load in Kips for Various Eccentricities in Inches
f'_c = 3750 psi (A61 or A432 Bars, f_y = 60,000 psi) f_s = 24,000 psi basis

COLUMN SIZE—31″ x 31″ | f'_c = 3750 psi, f_y = 60,000 psi

Bars	p	M/N † = e (in.) 0	3	6	9	12	15	18	21	24	27	30	33	36	39	42	M_o ‡ (kip-in.)
10-#9	.0104	**1140**	1010	770	369	230	167	131	108	92	80	70	63	57	52	48	*1844*
12-#9	.0125	**1188**	1041	794	437	274	200	157	129	110	95	84	76	69	63	58	*2213*
14-#9	.0146	**1236**	1073	817	502	317	231	182	150	128	111	98	88	80	73	67	*2582*
16-#9	.0166	**1284**	1105	841	565	359	263	207	171	146	127	112	101	91	83	77	*2951*
18-#9	.0187	**1332**	1136	864	627	400	293	232	191	163	142	126	113	102	94	86	*3320*
20-#9	.0208	**1380**	1168	888	686	440	324	256	212	181	157	139	125	113	104	96	*3689*
22-#9	.0229	**1428**	1199	912	735	479	354	280	232	198	172	153	137	125	114	105	*4058*
24-#9	.0250	**1476**	1231	935	754	518	383	304	252	215	188	166	149	136	124	114	*4427*
26-#9	.0271	**1524**	1263	959	773	555	412	327	271	232	202	180	161	146	134	124	*4796*
8-#10	.0106	**1144**	1012	771	373	233	169	133	109	93	81	71	64	58	53	49	*1863*
9-#10	.0119	**1175**	1032	786	416	260	189	149	123	104	91	80	72	65	59	55	*2096*
10-#10	.0132	**1205**	1052	801	458	288	210	165	136	115	100	89	80	72	66	61	*2329*
12-#10	.0159	**1266**	1092	831	539	341	250	197	162	138	120	106	95	86	79	73	*2795*
14-#10	.0185	**1327**	1132	861	617	393	289	228	188	160	140	124	111	101	92	85	*3261*
16-#10	.0211	**1388**	1172	891	692	444	327	259	214	182	159	141	126	115	105	97	*3727*
18-#10	.0238	**1449**	1212	920	742	493	364	289	239	204	178	158	142	129	118	108	*4193*
20-#10	.0264	**1510**	1252	950	766	541	401	319	264	226	197	175	157	142	130	120	*4659*
7-#11	.0114	**1163**	1023	780	397	248	180	142	117	99	86	76	68	62	56	52	*1992*
8-#11	.0130	**1200**	1048	798	448	281	205	161	133	113	98	87	78	70	64	59	*2276*
9-#11	.0146	**1237**	1072	816	499	314	230	181	149	127	110	98	87	79	72	67	*2561*
10-#11	.0162	**1275**	1097	834	548	347	254	200	165	140	122	108	97	88	80	74	*2846*
11-#11	.0179	**1312**	1121	853	595	379	278	219	181	154	134	119	107	97	88	81	*3130*
13-#11	.0211	**1387**	1170	889	687	441	325	257	212	181	158	140	125	114	104	96	*3700*
15-#11	.0243	**1462**	1219	925	746	501	370	294	243	208	181	161	144	131	120	110	*4269*
17-#11	.0276	**1537**	1268	962	774	559	415	330	274	234	204	181	163	148	135	125	*4838*
19-#11	.0308	**1612**	1317	998	803	615	458	365	303	260	227	201	181	164	151	139	*5407*
21-#11	.0341	**1687**	1366	1034	832	668	500	400	333	285	249	221	199	181	166	153	*5976*
23-#11	.0373	**1762**	1415	1071	861	720	541	433	361	310	271	241	217	197	181	167	*6546*
6-#14S	.0140	**1224**	1062	808	476	300	219	172	142	121	105	93	83	75	69	63	*2435*
7-#14S	.0164	**1278**	1097	834	547	346	253	200	165	140	122	108	97	88	80	74	*2841*
8-#14S	.0187	**1332**	1133	860	615	392	287	227	187	160	139	123	110	100	92	84	*3247*
9-#14S	.0211	**1386**	1168	886	680	436	321	254	210	179	156	138	124	112	103	95	*3653*
10-#14S	.0234	**1440**	1203	912	735	479	354	280	232	198	172	153	137	125	114	105	*4059*
12-#14S	.0281	**1548**	1273	964	776	562	417	332	275	235	205	182	164	149	136	125	*4871*
14-#14S	.0328	**1656**	1343	1016	817	640	478	382	318	272	238	211	190	172	158	146	*5682*
16-#14S	.0375	**1764**	1413	1068	858	715	537	430	359	308	269	239	215	196	179	166	*6494*
18-#14S	.0421	**1872**	1483	1120	899	751	593	477	399	342	300	267	241	219	201	185	*7306*
6-#18S	.0250	**1476**	1219	921	741	492	364	288	239	204	178	157	141	128	117	108	*4186*
7-#18S	.0291	**1572**	1280	966	776	563	418	332	276	236	206	183	164	149	136	126	*4884*
8-#18S	.0333	**1668**	1341	1011	811	630	470	375	312	267	233	207	186	169	155	143	*5582*
9-#18S	.0375	**1764**	1402	1055	846	693	521	417	347	298	261	232	208	190	174	160	*6280*
10-#18S	.0416	**1860**	1463	1100	881	735	569	457	382	328	287	256	230	209	192	177	*6977*
11-#18S	.0458	**1956**	1524	1144	916	764	616	496	415	357	313	279	252	229	210	194	*7675*
12-#18S	.0499	**2052**	1585	1189	951	793	660	534	448	386	339	302	272	248	228	211	*8373*
13-#18S	.0541	**2148**	1646	1233	986	822	703	570	480	414	364	325	293	267	245	227	*9071*

Check availability of #14S and #18S bars.

All above columns require spirals of A432 rod or cold drawn wire (f_y = 60,000 psi):—

5/8φ @ 2½″

Outside diameter of spiral should be 3 in. less than side of column.

† Below zigzag horizontal line of each group, concrete governs; above, tension governs.

‡ M_o = capacity in pure bending, (N = 0); for extrapolation, see page 11-5.

SPIRALLY REINFORCED SQUARE COLUMNS—
Safe Load in Kips for Various Eccentricities in Inches
f'_c = 3750 psi (A61 or A432 Bars, f_y = 60,000 psi) f_s = 24,000 psi basis

COLUMN SIZE—32″ x 32″

f'_c = 3750 psi
f_y = 60,000 psi

Bars	p	M/N † = e (in.)															M_o ‡ (kip-in.)
		0	3	6	9	12	15	18	21	24	27	30	33	36	39	42	
11-#9	.0107	**1223**	1092	838	432	267	193	151	124	106	92	81	73	66	60	55	*2108*
13-#9	.0127	**1271**	1125	862	503	313	227	178	147	124	108	96	86	77	71	65	*2491*
15-#9	.0146	**1319**	1157	886	572	358	260	205	168	143	124	110	99	89	82	75	*2875*
17-#9	.0166	**1367**	1189	910	639	402	293	231	190	162	141	124	111	101	92	85	*3258*
19-#9	.0186	**1415**	1221	934	704	445	325	256	212	180	157	139	124	113	103	95	*3641*
21-#9	.0205	**1463**	1253	958	766	487	357	282	233	198	173	153	137	124	114	105	*4025*
23-#9	.0225	**1511**	1285	982	795	529	388	307	254	216	188	167	150	136	124	115	*4408*
25-#9	.0244	**1559**	1317	1007	814	569	419	332	275	234	204	181	162	147	135	124	*4791*
9-#10	.0112	**1234**	1099	842	445	276	200	156	129	109	95	84	75	68	62	57	*2179*
10-#10	.0124	**1264**	1119	858	490	305	221	173	142	121	105	93	83	75	69	63	*2421*
12-#10	.0149	**1325**	1160	888	578	362	263	207	170	145	126	111	100	90	82	76	*2905*
14-#10	.0174	**1386**	1200	919	661	417	304	240	197	168	146	129	116	105	96	88	*3389*
16-#10	.0198	**1447**	1241	949	741	471	345	272	224	191	166	147	132	120	109	101	*3874*
18-#10	.0223	**1508**	1282	979	793	523	384	304	251	214	186	165	148	134	123	113	*4358*
20-#10	.0248	**1569**	1322	1010	817	574	423	335	277	237	206	183	164	149	136	126	*4842*
7-#11	.0107	**1222**	1090	836	425	263	190	149	122	104	90	80	71	64	59	54	*2070*
8-#11	.0122	**1259**	1115	854	480	298	216	169	139	118	103	91	81	74	67	62	*2366*
9-#11	.0137	**1296**	1140	873	534	333	242	190	156	133	115	102	91	83	76	70	*2662*
10-#11	.0152	**1334**	1165	892	587	368	268	210	173	147	128	113	101	92	84	77	*2958*
11-#11	.0168	**1371**	1190	910	638	402	293	230	190	161	140	124	111	101	92	85	*3254*
13-#11	.0198	**1446**	1240	947	737	468	342	270	223	190	165	146	131	119	109	100	*3846*
15-#11	.0229	**1521**	1289	985	796	531	391	309	255	218	190	168	151	137	125	115	*4437*
17-#11	.0259	**1596**	1339	1022	826	593	438	347	287	245	214	189	170	154	141	130	*5029*
19-#11	.0289	**1671**	1389	1059	856	653	484	384	319	272	238	211	189	172	157	145	*5621*
21-#11	.0320	**1746**	1438	1096	885	710	528	421	350	299	261	232	208	189	173	160	*6212*
23-#11	.0350	**1821**	1488	1133	915	765	572	457	380	325	284	253	227	206	189	174	*6804*
6-#14S	.0132	**1283**	1130	865	511	318	231	181	149	126	110	97	87	79	72	66	*2532*
7-#14S	.0154	**1337**	1166	892	586	367	267	210	173	147	128	113	101	92	84	77	*2954*
8-#14S	.0176	**1392**	1201	918	659	415	303	239	197	167	146	129	115	105	96	88	*3376*
9-#14S	.0198	**1445**	1237	945	729	462	339	267	220	188	163	144	130	117	107	99	*3799*
10-#14S	.0220	**1499**	1273	971	785	508	373	295	244	207	181	160	144	130	119	110	*4221*
11-#14S	.0242	**1553**	1308	998	807	553	407	322	267	227	198	175	157	143	131	120	*4643*
13-#14S	.0286	**1661**	1380	1051	849	639	473	376	312	266	232	206	185	168	154	142	*5487*
15-#14S	.0330	**1769**	1451	1104	891	721	537	428	356	304	266	236	212	193	176	163	*6331*
17-#14S	.0374	**1877**	1522	1157	933	782	598	478	398	341	299	265	239	217	199	184	*7176*
19-#14S	.0417	**1985**	1593	1210	976	817	657	527	440	378	331	294	265	241	221	204	*8020*
6-#18S	.0234	**1536**	1290	981	792	523	384	304	251	214	186	165	148	134	123	113	*4359*
7-#18S	.0273	**1632**	1352	1027	828	598	442	350	290	248	216	191	172	156	143	132	*5086*
8-#18S	.0313	**1728**	1414	1073	864	670	498	396	328	281	245	217	195	177	162	150	*5812*
9-#18S	.0352	**1824**	1476	1119	900	738	551	440	366	313	274	243	219	199	182	168	*6539*
10-#18S	.0391	**1920**	1538	1164	937	783	603	483	402	345	302	268	241	219	201	186	*7265*
11-#18S	.0430	**2016**	1600	1210	973	813	653	524	438	376	329	293	264	240	220	203	*7992*
12-#18S	.0469	**2112**	1662	1256	1009	843	700	564	472	406	356	317	286	260	239	221	*8719*
13-#18S	.0508	**2208**	1724	1301	1045	873	746	603	506	436	383	341	308	280	257	238	*9445*
14-#18S	.0547	**2304**	1786	1347	1081	903	775	641	539	465	409	365	329	300	275	255	*10172*

Check availability of #14S and #18S bars.

All above columns require spirals of A432 rod or cold drawn wire (f_y = 60,000 psi):—

⅝φ @ 2½″

Outside diameter of spiral should be 3 in. less than side of column.

† Below zigzag horizontal line of each group, concrete governs; above, tension governs.

‡ M_o = capacity in pure bending, (N = 0); for extrapolation, see page 11-5.

SPIRALLY REINFORCED SQUARE COLUMNS—

Safe Load in Kips for Various Eccentricities in Inches

f'_c = 3750 psi (A61 or A432 Bars, f_y = 60,000 psi) f_s = 24,000 psi basis

COLUMN SIZE—33″ x 33″ — f'_c = 3750 psi, f_y = 60,000 psi

Bars	p	M/N † = e (in.) 0	3	6	9	12	15	18	21	24	27	30	33	36	39	42	M_o ‡ (kip-in.)
11-#9	.0101	**1284**	1162	896	462	283	203	159	130	110	96	85	76	68	62	57	*2187*
13-#9	.0119	**1332**	1194	921	539	331	239	187	153	130	113	100	89	81	74	68	*2585*
15-#9	.0138	**1380**	1227	945	613	379	274	215	176	150	130	115	103	93	85	78	*2983*
17-#9	.0156	**1428**	1260	970	684	425	309	242	199	169	147	130	116	105	96	89	*3380*
19-#9	.0174	**1476**	1292	994	753	471	343	269	222	188	164	145	130	118	107	99	*3778*
21-#9	.0193	**1524**	1325	1019	820	516	376	296	244	207	180	160	143	130	119	109	*4176*
23-#9	.0211	**1572**	1357	1044	848	560	409	322	266	226	197	174	156	142	130	119	*4574*
25-#9	.0230	**1620**	1390	1068	867	602	442	349	288	245	213	189	170	154	141	130	*4971*
9-#10	.0105	**1295**	1168	901	477	292	210	164	135	114	99	87	78	71	65	59	*2261*
10-#10	.0117	**1325**	1189	916	525	322	233	182	149	127	110	97	87	79	72	66	*2512*
12-#10	.0140	**1386**	1230	947	619	383	277	217	178	151	131	116	104	94	86	79	*3015*
14-#10	.0163	**1447**	1271	978	708	441	320	251	207	176	153	135	121	110	100	92	*3517*
16-#10	.0187	**1508**	1313	1010	794	498	363	285	235	200	174	154	138	125	114	105	*4020*
18-#10	.0210	**1569**	1354	1041	845	554	405	319	263	224	195	172	155	140	128	118	*4522*
20-#10	.0233	**1630**	1395	1072	870	608	446	352	291	248	216	191	171	155	142	131	*5025*
7-#11	.0100	**1283**	1160	894	455	278	200	156	128	109	94	83	74	67	61	56	*2149*
8-#11	.0115	**1320**	1185	913	514	316	228	178	146	124	107	95	85	77	70	65	*2456*
9-#11	.0129	**1357**	1210	932	572	353	255	199	164	139	121	107	95	86	79	73	*2763*
10-#11	.0143	**1395**	1235	951	629	389	282	221	181	154	134	118	106	96	88	81	*3070*
12-#11	.0172	**1470**	1286	989	737	460	335	263	216	184	160	141	127	115	105	96	*3684*
14-#11	.0201	**1545**	1336	1027	834	529	386	304	251	213	186	164	147	133	122	112	*4299*
16-#11	.0229	**1619**	1387	1065	864	596	437	345	285	242	211	187	168	152	139	128	*4913*
18-#11	.0258	**1694**	1437	1103	895	660	486	384	318	271	236	209	188	170	156	144	*5527*
20-#11	.0287	**1769**	1488	1141	925	723	534	423	351	299	261	231	208	189	173	159	*6141*
22-#11	.0315	**1844**	1538	1179	956	783	581	461	383	327	285	253	228	207	189	174	*6755*
24-#11	.0344	**1919**	1588	1217	986	829	626	499	414	354	310	275	247	224	206	190	*7369*
6-#14S	.0124	**1344**	1200	924	547	337	243	190	156	132	115	101	91	82	75	69	*2629*
7-#14S	.0145	**1398**	1236	951	628	389	282	221	181	154	134	118	106	96	87	80	*3068*
8-#14S	.0165	**1452**	1273	978	706	440	319	251	206	175	152	135	121	109	100	92	*3506*
9-#14S	.0186	**1506**	1309	1005	781	490	357	280	231	196	171	151	135	123	112	103	*3944*
10-#14S	.0207	**1560**	1345	1033	838	539	393	310	255	217	189	167	150	136	124	114	*4383*
12-#14S	.0248	**1668**	1417	1087	881	633	465	367	303	258	225	199	179	162	148	137	*5259*
14-#14S	.0289	**1776**	1490	1141	925	722	533	423	350	299	261	231	208	188	172	159	*6136*
16-#14S	.0331	**1884**	1562	1195	968	806	599	477	396	338	296	262	236	214	196	181	*7013*
18-#14S	.0372	**1992**	1634	1250	1012	850	663	529	440	377	330	293	263	239	219	202	*7889*
20-#14S	.0413	**2100**	1706	1304	1055	886	724	580	484	415	363	323	291	264	242	224	*8766*
6-#18S	.0220	**1596**	1363	1043	845	555	406	320	264	224	195	173	155	140	128	118	*4532*
7-#18S	.0257	**1692**	1426	1090	882	635	467	369	305	260	226	200	180	163	149	137	*5287*
8-#18S	.0294	**1788**	1489	1137	920	711	526	417	345	294	257	228	204	186	170	157	*6043*
9-#18S	.0331	**1884**	1552	1184	957	784	583	463	384	329	287	255	229	208	190	175	*6798*
10-#18S	.0367	**1980**	1615	1231	994	834	637	509	423	362	316	281	253	230	210	194	*7553*
11-#18S	.0404	**2076**	1678	1277	1031	865	690	552	460	395	345	307	276	251	230	212	*8309*
12-#18S	.0441	**2172**	1741	1324	1068	895	741	595	497	427	374	333	299	272	250	231	*9064*
13-#18S	.0478	**2268**	1804	1371	1106	926	790	636	533	458	402	358	322	293	269	249	*9820*
14-#18S	.0514	**2364**	1867	1418	1143	957	823	677	567	489	429	382	345	314	288	266	*10575*

Check availability of #14S and #18S bars.

All above columns require spirals of A432 rod or cold drawn wire (f_y = 60,000 psi):—

⅝φ @ 2½″

Outside diameter of spiral should be 3 in. less than side of column.

† Below zigzag horizontal line of each group, concrete governs; above, tension governs.

‡ M_o = capacity in pure bending, (N = 0); for extrapolation, see page 11-5.

SPIRALLY REINFORCED SQUARE COLUMNS—
Safe Load in Kips for Various Eccentricities in Inches
f'_c = 3750 psi (A61 or A432 Bars, f_y = 60,000 psi) f_s = 24,000 psi basis

COLUMN SIZE—34″ x 34″ — f'_c = 3750 psi, f_y = 60,000 psi

Bars	p	M/N † = e (in.) 0	3	6	9	12	15	18	21	24	27	30	33	36	39	42	M_o ‡ (kip-in.)
12-#9	.0104	**1371**	1250	969	536	325	233	181	148	126	109	96	86	78	71	65	*2472*
14-#9	.0121	**1419**	1283	994	616	375	270	210	173	146	127	112	100	91	83	76	*2885*
16-#9	.0138	**1467**	1316	1019	694	425	306	239	196	166	144	128	114	103	94	87	*3297*
18-#9	.0156	**1515**	1349	1044	770	474	342	268	220	187	162	143	128	116	106	98	*3709*
20-#9	.0173	**1563**	1382	1069	843	522	378	296	244	207	180	159	142	129	118	108	*4121*
22-#9	.0190	**1611**	1415	1094	892	569	413	324	267	227	197	174	156	141	129	119	*4533*
24-#9	.0208	**1659**	1448	1119	912	615	448	352	290	246	214	189	170	154	141	130	*4945*
10-#10	.0110	**1388**	1261	977	562	341	244	191	156	132	115	101	90	82	75	69	*2604*
12-#10	.0132	**1449**	1303	1009	662	404	291	227	186	158	137	121	108	98	90	82	*3125*
14-#10	.0154	**1510**	1345	1041	758	467	337	264	216	184	159	141	126	114	104	96	*3645*
16-#10	.0176	**1571**	1386	1072	850	527	382	299	246	209	181	160	144	130	119	109	*4166*
18-#10	.0198	**1632**	1428	1104	900	586	426	335	275	234	203	180	161	146	133	123	*4687*
20-#10	.0220	**1693**	1470	1136	925	643	469	369	304	259	225	199	179	162	148	136	*5208*
8-#11	.0108	**1383**	1257	974	551	334	239	186	153	129	112	99	88	80	73	67	*2546*
9-#11	.0121	**1420**	1283	993	613	373	268	209	171	145	126	111	99	90	82	76	*2864*
10-#11	.0135	**1458**	1308	1012	673	412	296	231	190	161	140	123	110	100	91	84	*3183*
11-#11	.0148	**1495**	1334	1032	732	450	324	254	208	177	153	135	121	110	100	92	*3501*
13-#11	.0175	**1570**	1385	1071	845	524	379	297	244	208	180	159	143	129	118	109	*4138*
15-#11	.0202	**1645**	1436	1109	904	596	433	340	280	238	207	183	164	149	136	125	*4774*
17-#11	.0229	**1720**	1487	1148	935	665	486	383	315	268	233	207	185	168	154	141	*5411*
19-#11	.0256	**1795**	1538	1187	966	733	537	424	350	298	260	230	206	187	171	158	*6047*
21-#11	.0283	**1869**	1589	1226	997	797	587	464	384	328	285	253	227	206	188	174	*6684*
23-#11	.0310	**1944**	1640	1264	1029	860	636	504	418	357	311	276	248	225	206	190	*7321*
25-#11	.0337	**2019**	1692	1303	1060	893	683	543	451	385	336	298	268	243	223	205	*7957*
6-#14S	.0117	**1407**	1273	985	586	356	256	199	163	138	120	106	95	86	78	72	*2727*
7-#14S	.0136	**1461**	1309	1013	673	411	296	231	190	161	140	123	110	100	91	84	*3181*
8-#14S	.0156	**1515**	1346	1040	756	465	336	263	216	183	159	140	126	114	104	96	*3636*
9-#14S	.0175	**1569**	1383	1068	837	518	375	294	242	205	178	158	141	128	117	107	*4090*
10-#14S	.0195	**1623**	1419	1096	892	570	414	325	267	227	197	175	156	142	129	119	*4545*
11-#14S	.0214	**1677**	1456	1124	915	620	452	355	293	249	216	191	172	155	142	131	*4999*
13-#14S	.0253	**1785**	1529	1179	959	718	526	415	343	292	254	225	202	183	167	154	*5908*
15-#14S	.0292	**1893**	1603	1234	1004	810	597	473	391	334	291	258	231	210	192	177	*6817*
17-#14S	.0331	**2001**	1676	1290	1048	883	666	529	439	375	327	290	261	237	217	200	*7726*
19-#14S	.0370	**2109**	1749	1345	1093	920	732	583	485	415	362	322	289	263	241	222	*8635*
21-#14S	.0409	**2217**	1822	1400	1137	957	795	636	530	454	397	353	318	289	265	244	*9544*
6-#18S	.0208	**1659**	1438	1107	900	588	427	336	276	235	204	180	162	147	134	123	*4705*
7-#18S	.0242	**1755**	1502	1155	938	673	492	387	320	272	237	209	188	170	156	143	*5489*
8-#18S	.0277	**1851**	1566	1203	977	755	554	438	362	308	269	238	214	194	177	163	*6273*
9-#18S	.0311	**1947**	1630	1251	1015	832	615	487	403	344	300	266	239	217	198	183	*7057*
10-#18S	.0346	**2043**	1694	1299	1053	886	673	535	444	379	331	294	264	240	220	202	*7841*
11-#18S	.0381	**2139**	1758	1347	1091	917	729	581	484	414	362	321	289	262	240	222	*8626*
12-#18S	.0415	**2235**	1822	1394	1130	949	783	627	522	448	392	348	313	285	261	241	*9410*
13-#18S	.0450	**2331**	1885	1442	1168	981	836	671	560	481	421	374	337	307	281	260	*10194*
14-#18S	.0484	**2427**	1949	1490	1206	1013	873	713	597	513	450	400	361	328	301	278	*10978*
15-#18S	.0519	**2523**	2013	1538	1244	1045	900	754	633	545	478	426	384	350	321	297	*11762*

Check availability of #14S and #18S bars.

All above columns require spirals of A432 rod or cold drawn wire (f_y = 60,000 psi):—

#14S and smaller—⅝φ @ 2½″

#18S only —⅝φ @ 2¼″

Outside diameter of spiral should be 3 in. less than side of column.

† Below zigzag horizontal line of each group, concrete governs; above, tension governs.

‡ M_o = capacity in pure bending, (N = 0); for extrapolation, see page 11-5.

SPIRALLY REINFORCED SQUARE COLUMNS—
Safe Load in Kips for Various Eccentricities in Inches
f'_c = 3750 psi (A61 or A432 Bars, f_y = 60,000 psi) f_s = 24,000 psi basis

COLUMN SIZE—35″ x 35″

f'_c = 3750 psi
f_y = 60,000 psi

Bars	p	M/N † = e (in.) 0	3	6	9	12	15	18	21	24	27	30	33	36	39	42	M_o ‡ (kip-in.)
13-#9	.0106	**1460**	1341	1045	617	370	264	205	168	142	123	108	97	88	80	73	2772
15-#9	.0122	**1508**	1375	1070	701	423	303	235	193	163	141	125	112	101	92	85	3199
17-#9	.0139	**1556**	1408	1096	783	475	341	266	218	184	160	141	126	114	104	96	3625
19-#9	.0155	**1604**	1441	1121	863	526	378	295	242	205	178	157	141	127	116	107	4052
21-#9	.0171	**1652**	1475	1147	938	576	416	325	267	226	196	173	155	140	128	118	4478
23-#9	.0188	**1700**	1508	1172	959	625	452	354	291	247	214	189	170	154	140	129	4905
25-#9	.0204	**1748**	1541	1198	979	674	488	383	315	267	232	205	184	167	152	140	5331
10-#10	.0104	**1453**	1336	1040	601	360	257	199	163	138	119	105	94	85	78	71	2695
12-#10	.0124	**1514**	1378	1072	708	427	306	238	195	165	143	126	113	102	93	86	3234
14-#10	.0145	**1575**	1420	1105	811	493	354	276	226	192	166	147	131	119	108	100	3773
16-#10	.0166	**1636**	1463	1137	910	557	401	313	257	218	189	167	150	135	124	114	4313
18-#10	.0187	**1697**	1505	1169	956	619	448	350	288	244	212	187	168	152	139	128	4852
20-#10	.0207	**1758**	1547	1202	982	680	493	387	318	270	235	207	186	168	154	142	5391
8-#11	.0102	**1447**	1332	1037	589	352	251	195	160	135	117	103	92	83	76	70	2636
9-#11	.0115	**1485**	1357	1056	656	394	281	219	179	151	131	116	103	94	85	79	2965
10-#11	.0127	**1522**	1383	1076	720	435	311	242	198	168	145	128	115	104	95	87	3295
12-#11	.0153	**1597**	1435	1116	845	515	370	289	237	200	174	154	137	124	114	104	3954
14-#11	.0178	**1672**	1487	1155	944	592	427	334	274	233	202	178	160	145	132	122	4613
16-#11	.0204	**1747**	1539	1195	976	667	483	379	311	264	230	203	182	165	151	139	5272
18-#11	.0229	**1822**	1590	1234	1008	739	538	423	348	296	257	227	204	185	169	156	5931
20-#11	.0255	**1897**	1642	1274	1040	809	591	466	384	327	284	252	226	205	187	172	6590
22-#11	.0280	**1972**	1694	1313	1072	877	643	508	420	357	311	276	247	224	205	189	7250
24-#11	.0306	**2046**	1746	1353	1104	933	694	549	454	387	338	299	269	244	223	206	7909
26-#11	.0331	**2121**	1797	1392	1136	959	744	590	489	417	364	323	290	263	241	222	8568
6-#14S	.0110	**1472**	1347	1048	627	376	269	209	171	144	125	110	99	89	81	75	2824
7-#14S	.0129	**1526**	1385	1076	720	435	311	242	198	168	145	128	115	104	95	87	3295
8-#14S	.0147	**1580**	1422	1105	810	492	353	275	226	191	166	146	131	118	108	100	3765
9-#14S	.0165	**1634**	1459	1133	896	548	395	308	253	214	186	164	147	133	122	112	4236
10-#14S	.0184	**1688**	1496	1161	949	603	435	340	280	237	206	182	163	148	135	124	4707
11-#14S	.0202	**1742**	1533	1190	972	656	475	372	306	260	226	200	179	162	148	136	5177
13-#14S	.0239	**1850**	1607	1246	1017	759	553	435	358	305	265	234	210	190	174	160	6119
15-#14S	.0276	**1958**	1681	1302	1063	858	628	496	409	349	303	269	241	219	200	184	7060
17-#14S	.0312	**2066**	1756	1359	1108	936	701	555	459	392	341	302	272	246	225	208	8002
19-#14S	.0349	**2174**	1830	1415	1154	974	771	612	508	434	379	336	302	274	251	231	8943
21-#14S	.0386	**2282**	1904	1472	1200	1012	838	668	555	475	415	368	331	301	276	254	9885
6-#18S	.0196	**1724**	1515	1173	957	622	450	352	289	245	213	188	169	153	140	128	4877
7-#18S	.0229	**1820**	1580	1222	996	713	518	407	335	284	247	219	196	177	162	149	5690
8-#18S	.0261	**1916**	1645	1271	1036	799	584	460	379	323	281	248	223	202	185	170	6503
9-#18S	.0294	**2012**	1709	1320	1075	882	648	512	423	360	314	278	249	226	207	191	7316
10-#18S	.0327	**2108**	1774	1369	1114	939	709	562	465	397	346	307	276	250	229	211	8129
11-#18S	.0359	**2204**	1839	1418	1153	972	769	611	507	433	378	335	301	274	251	231	8942
12-#18S	.0392	**2300**	1904	1467	1192	1005	827	659	548	469	409	364	327	297	272	251	9755
13-#18S	.0424	**2396**	1969	1515	1232	1037	882	705	587	503	440	391	352	320	293	271	10568
14-#18S	.0457	**2492**	2034	1564	1271	1070	924	750	626	537	471	419	377	343	314	290	11381
15-#18S	.0490	**2588**	2098	1613	1310	1103	952	794	664	571	500	445	401	365	335	309	12194

Check availability of #14S and #18S bars.

All above columns require spirals of A432 rod or cold drawn wire (f_y = 60,000 psi):—

#14S and smaller—⅝φ @ 2½″

#18S only —⅝φ @ 2¼″

Outside diameter of spiral should be 3 in. less than side of column.

† Below zigzag horizontal line of each group, concrete governs; above, tension governs.

‡ M_o = capacity in pure bending, (N = 0); for extrapolation, see page 11-5.

SPIRALLY REINFORCED SQUARE COLUMNS—
Safe Load in Kips for Various Eccentricities in Inches
f'_c = 3750 psi (A61 or A432 Bars, f_y = 60,000 psi) f_s = 24,000 psi basis

COLUMN SIZE—36″ x 36″ — f'_c = 3750 psi, f_y = 60,000 psi

Bars	p	M/N † = e (in.) 0	3	6	9	12	15	18	21	24	27	30	33	36	39	42	M_o ‡ (kip-in.)
13-#9	.0100	**1526**	1418	1110	660	390	277	214	175	148	128	113	101	91	83	76	*2866*
15-#9	.0116	**1574**	1452	1136	750	446	317	246	201	170	147	130	116	105	96	88	*3307*
17-#9	.0131	**1622**	1486	1162	838	501	357	278	227	192	166	147	131	119	108	100	*3748*
19-#9	.0147	**1670**	1519	1188	923	555	397	309	253	214	185	164	146	132	121	111	*4189*
21-#9	.0162	**1718**	1553	1214	996	608	436	340	278	236	204	180	161	146	133	123	*4630*
23-#9	.0177	**1766**	1587	1240	1017	660	475	370	304	257	223	197	176	160	146	134	*5071*
11-#10	.0108	**1550**	1434	1122	701	416	295	229	187	158	137	120	108	97	89	82	*3065*
13-#10	.0127	**1611**	1477	1155	813	486	346	269	220	186	161	142	127	115	105	96	*3623*
15-#10	.0147	**1672**	1520	1187	921	554	396	308	252	213	185	163	146	132	121	111	*4180*
17-#10	.0167	**1733**	1562	1220	1001	621	446	347	285	241	209	184	165	149	136	125	*4738*
19-#10	.0186	**1794**	1605	1253	1028	686	494	386	316	268	233	205	184	166	152	140	*5295*
21-#10	.0206	**1855**	1648	1286	1055	750	541	424	348	295	256	226	203	184	168	154	*5852*
9-#11	.0108	**1551**	1435	1122	701	416	295	229	187	158	137	120	108	97	89	82	*3067*
10-#11	.0120	**1589**	1461	1142	771	459	327	253	207	175	152	134	119	108	99	91	*3407*
11-#11	.0132	**1626**	1487	1162	838	501	358	278	227	192	166	147	131	119	108	100	*3748*
13-#11	.0156	**1701**	1539	1202	968	584	418	326	267	226	196	173	155	140	128	117	*4430*
15-#11	.0181	**1776**	1592	1243	1019	665	478	373	306	259	225	199	178	161	147	135	*5111*
17-#11	.0205	**1851**	1644	1283	1052	743	536	420	344	292	254	224	201	182	166	153	*5793*
19-#11	.0229	**1926**	1696	1323	1084	818	593	465	382	325	282	249	223	202	185	170	*6474*
21-#11	.0253	**2001**	1749	1363	1117	891	649	510	420	357	310	275	246	223	204	188	*7156*
23-#11	.0277	**2076**	1801	1403	1150	962	703	554	457	389	338	299	268	243	223	205	*7837*
25-#11	.0301	**2150**	1853	1444	1182	1001	756	597	493	420	366	324	291	264	241	222	*8519*
27-#11	.0325	**2225**	1906	1484	1215	1028	807	639	529	451	393	348	313	284	260	239	*9201*
6-#14S	.0104	**1538**	1425	1114	671	397	282	218	178	150	130	115	103	93	85	78	*2921*
7-#14S	.0122	**1592**	1462	1142	771	459	327	253	207	175	152	134	119	108	99	91	*3408*
8-#14S	.0139	**1646**	1500	1171	867	519	371	288	236	199	173	152	136	123	112	103	*3895*
9-#14S	.0156	**1701**	1537	1200	959	579	414	323	264	223	194	171	153	138	126	116	*4382*
10-#14S	.0174	**1754**	1575	1229	1007	637	457	356	292	247	215	189	169	153	140	129	*4869*
12-#14S	.0208	**1862**	1650	1286	1054	748	540	423	347	295	256	226	202	183	167	154	*5843*
14-#14S	.0243	**1970**	1725	1344	1101	855	621	488	401	341	296	262	235	213	194	179	*6816*
16-#14S	.0278	**2078**	1800	1401	1147	957	699	551	454	386	336	298	267	242	221	204	*7790*
18-#14S	.0313	**2187**	1875	1459	1194	1010	774	612	506	431	375	333	298	271	248	228	*8764*
20-#14S	.0347	**2294**	1950	1516	1240	1049	847	671	556	475	414	367	330	299	274	252	*9738*
22-#14S	.0382	**2402**	2025	1574	1287	1088	916	729	605	517	452	401	360	327	300	276	*10712*
6-#18S	.0185	**1790**	1594	1241	1016	658	473	369	302	256	222	196	176	159	145	134	*5050*
7-#18S	.0216	**1886**	1660	1291	1056	754	544	426	350	297	258	228	204	185	169	155	*5892*
8-#18S	.0247	**1982**	1726	1341	1096	846	614	482	397	337	293	259	232	210	192	177	*6734*
9-#18S	.0278	**2078**	1791	1391	1137	934	681	536	442	376	327	290	260	235	215	198	*7576*
10-#18S	.0309	**2174**	1857	1441	1177	995	747	590	487	415	361	320	287	260	238	219	*8417*
11-#18S	.0340	**2270**	1923	1491	1217	1028	810	641	531	453	395	350	314	285	261	240	*9259*
12-#18S	.0370	**2366**	1989	1540	1257	1062	871	692	574	490	428	379	341	309	283	261	*10101*
13-#18S	.0401	**2462**	2054	1590	1297	1095	930	741	616	527	460	408	367	334	305	282	*10943*
14-#18S	.0432	**2558**	2120	1640	1337	1129	977	788	656	562	492	437	393	357	327	302	*11785*
15-#18S	.0463	**2654**	2185	1690	1378	1163	1006	835	696	597	523	465	419	381	349	322	*12626*
16-#18S	.0494	**2750**	2251	1740	1418	1196	1035	880	736	632	554	493	444	404	371	342	*13468*

Check availability of #14S and #18S bars.

All above columns require spirals of A432 rod or cold drawn wire (f_y = 60,000 psi):—

#14S and smaller—⅝φ @ 2½″

#18S only —⅝φ @ 2¼″

Outside diameter of spiral should be 3 in. less than side of column.

† Below zigzag horizontal line of each group, concrete governs; above, tension governs.

‡ M_o = capacity in pure bending, (N = 0); for extrapolation, see page 11-5.

SPIRALLY REINFORCED SQUARE COLUMNS—
Safe Load in Kips for Various Eccentricities in Inches
$f'_c = 5000$ psi (A61 or A432 Bars, $f_y = 60{,}000$ psi) $f_s = 24{,}000$ psi basis

COLUMN SIZE—17″ x 17″ — $f'_c = 5000$ psi, $f_y = 60{,}000$ psi

Bars	p	M/N † = e (in.) 0	1	2	3	4	5	6	7	8	9	10	12	14	16	18	M_o ‡ (kip-in.)
7-#6	.0107	**435**	435	363	308	154	97	71	56	46	39	34	27	22	19	16	*266*
8-#6	.0122	**445**	445	369	313	174	110	81	64	52	45	39	31	25	22	19	*304*
9-#6	.0137	**456**	456	375	318	194	124	91	71	59	50	44	35	29	24	21	*342*
10-#6	.0152	**466**	465	381	323	214	137	100	79	65	56	48	38	32	27	24	*380*
11-#6	.0167	**477**	473	387	328	233	149	110	87	72	61	53	42	35	30	26	*418*
12-#6	.0183	**487**	481	394	333	252	162	119	94	78	67	58	46	38	33	28	*456*
14-#6	.0213	**509**	496	406	343	289	187	138	109	91	77	67	54	44	38	33	*532*
6-#7	.0125	**447**	447	370	314	176	112	82	64	53	45	39	31	26	22	19	*307*
7-#7	.0145	**462**	461	378	320	203	129	95	75	62	53	46	36	30	26	22	*359*
8-#7	.0166	**476**	472	386	327	229	147	108	85	70	60	52	41	34	29	25	*410*
9-#7	.0187	**490**	483	395	334	255	164	121	96	79	67	59	47	39	33	29	*461*
10-#7	.0208	**505**	493	403	341	280	181	133	106	87	75	65	52	43	37	32	*513*
11-#7	.0228	**519**	504	411	348	301	197	146	116	96	82	71	57	47	40	35	*564*
12-#7	.0249	**534**	514	420	354	307	214	158	126	104	89	78	62	51	44	38	*615*
14-#7	.0291	**562**	535	436	368	318	245	183	145	121	103	90	72	60	51	45	*718*
6-#8	.0164	**475**	471	385	326	225	144	106	83	69	59	51	40	34	29	25	*401*
7-#8	.0191	**493**	484	396	335	258	166	122	97	80	68	59	47	39	33	29	*467*
8-#8	.0219	**512**	498	407	344	290	188	139	110	91	78	68	54	45	38	33	*534*
9-#8	.0246	**531**	512	418	353	305	209	155	123	102	87	76	60	50	43	37	*601*
10-#8	.0273	**550**	526	428	361	313	230	171	136	113	96	84	67	56	48	42	*668*
11-#8	.0301	**569**	540	439	370	320	250	187	149	123	106	92	74	61	52	46	*735*
12-#8	.0328	**588**	553	450	379	328	290	202	161	134	115	100	80	67	57	50	*802*
14-#8	.0383	**626**	581	472	397	342	301	232	185	155	133	116	93	77	66	58	*935*
6-#9	.0208	**505**	492	402	340	275	177	131	104	86	73	64	51	42	36	31	*502*
7-#9	.0242	**529**	510	416	351	303	204	151	120	99	85	74	59	49	42	36	*585*
8-#9	.0277	**553**	527	429	362	313	230	171	136	113	97	84	67	56	48	42	*669*
9-#9	.0311	**577**	544	443	373	322	256	191	152	126	108	94	75	63	54	47	*753*
10-#9	.0346	**601**	562	456	384	332	280	210	167	139	119	104	83	69	59	52	*836*
12-#9	.0415	**649**	596	483	406	350	308	246	198	165	142	124	99	83	71	62	*1004*
6-#10	.0264	**544**	520	423	357	308	218	162	129	107	91	79	63	53	45	39	*629*
7-#10	.0308	**574**	542	440	371	320	250	186	149	123	106	92	73	61	52	46	*734*
8-#10	.0352	**605**	564	457	385	332	281	210	168	140	120	105	84	70	60	52	*839*
9-#10	.0396	**635**	586	474	399	344	302	233	187	156	134	117	94	78	67	58	*944*
10-#10	.0439	**666**	608	491	412	355	312	256	205	172	147	129	103	86	74	65	*1049*
11-#10	.0483	**696**	629	508	426	367	322	277	223	187	161	141	113	94	81	71	*1154*
6-#11	.0324	**585**	549	446	375	324	259	193	154	128	110	96	76	63	54	47	*764*
7-#11	.0378	**623**	576	466	392	338	296	222	177	148	127	111	89	74	63	55	*891*
8-#11	.0432	**660**	603	487	409	352	309	249	200	167	143	126	101	84	72	63	*1018*
9-#11	.0486	**698**	629	508	425	366	321	275	222	186	160	140	112	94	80	70	*1146*
10-#11	.0540	**735**	656	528	442	380	333	297	243	204	176	154	124	104	89	78	*1273*
6-#14S	.0467	**685**	618	498	417	358	314	261	210	175	151	132	106	88	76	66	*1074*
7-#14S	.0545	**739**	656	527	440	378	331	295	239	201	173	152	122	102	88	77	*1253*
8-#14S	.0623	**793**	694	556	464	398	348	310	268	225	195	171	138	116	99	87	*1432*

Check availability of #14S and #18S bars.

All above columns require spirals of A432 rod or cold drawn wire ($f_y = 60{,}000$ psi):—

⅝φ @ 2¼″

Outside diameter of spiral should be 3 in. less than side of column.

† Below zigzag horizontal line of each group, concrete governs; above, tension governs.

‡ M_o = capacity in pure bending, ($N = 0$); for extrapolation, see page 11-5.

SPIRALLY REINFORCED SQUARE COLUMNS—
Safe Load in Kips for Various Eccentricities in Inches
f'_c = 5000 psi (A61 or A432 Bars, f_y = 60,000 psi) f_s = 24,000 psi basis

COLUMN SIZE—18″ x 18″ — f'_c = 5000 psi, f_y = 60,000 psi

Bars	p	M/N † = e (in.) 0	1	2	3	4	5	6	7	8	9	10	12	14	16	18	M_o ‡ (kip-in.)
8-#6	.0109	**489**	489	417	356	206	126	91	71	58	49	43	34	28	24	21	*329*
9-#6	.0122	**500**	500	423	361	229	141	102	80	66	56	48	38	31	27	23	*370*
10-#6	.0136	**510**	510	430	366	252	156	113	88	73	62	53	42	35	30	26	*411*
12-#6	.0163	**531**	531	442	377	297	185	135	106	87	74	64	51	42	36	31	*494*
14-#6	.0190	**552**	551	455	387	337	214	156	122	101	86	74	59	49	42	36	*576*
16-#6	.0217	**573**	567	468	398	346	242	177	139	115	98	85	67	56	48	41	*658*
6-#7	.0111	**491**	491	418	356	208	128	92	72	59	50	43	34	28	24	21	*333*
7-#7	.0130	**505**	505	426	364	240	148	107	84	69	58	51	40	33	28	24	*389*
8-#7	.0148	**520**	520	435	371	271	168	122	95	78	67	58	46	38	32	28	*444*
9-#7	.0167	**534**	534	444	378	301	188	136	107	88	75	65	51	42	36	31	*500*
10-#7	.0185	**548**	548	452	385	330	207	151	118	97	83	72	57	47	40	35	*556*
12-#7	.0222	**577**	569	469	399	347	244	179	141	116	99	86	68	56	48	42	*667*
14-#7	.0259	**606**	591	487	413	360	281	206	163	134	115	100	79	66	56	49	*778*
6-#8	.0146	**518**	518	434	370	265	165	119	93	77	65	56	45	37	31	27	*435*
7-#8	.0171	**537**	537	445	379	305	190	138	108	89	76	66	52	43	37	32	*507*
8-#8	.0195	**556**	553	456	388	338	215	157	123	101	86	75	59	49	42	36	*580*
9-#8	.0219	**575**	567	467	398	346	239	175	138	114	97	84	67	55	47	41	*652*
10-#8	.0244	**594**	581	479	407	354	263	193	152	126	107	93	74	61	52	46	*725*
12-#8	.0293	**632**	610	501	425	370	309	228	180	149	127	111	88	73	63	55	*870*
14-#8	.0341	**670**	638	524	444	385	341	262	208	172	147	128	102	85	73	63	*1015*
6-#9	.0185	**548**	547	451	384	324	203	148	116	96	81	71	56	46	39	34	*545*
7-#9	.0216	**572**	565	465	396	344	234	171	134	111	94	82	65	54	46	40	*636*
8-#9	.0247	**596**	583	479	407	354	264	193	153	126	107	93	74	61	52	46	*727*
9-#9	.0278	**620**	600	494	419	364	293	215	170	141	120	105	83	69	59	51	*817*
10-#9	.0309	**644**	618	508	431	374	321	237	188	156	133	116	92	76	65	57	*908*
12-#9	.0370	**692**	654	536	454	394	348	279	222	184	157	137	110	91	78	68	*1090*
14-#9	.0432	**740**	689	564	477	414	365	318	254	212	181	159	127	106	90	79	*1272*
6-#10	.0235	**587**	575	473	402	349	250	183	144	119	101	88	70	58	49	43	*684*
7-#10	.0274	**618**	598	491	417	362	287	211	167	138	117	102	81	67	57	50	*798*
8-#10	.0314	**648**	620	509	431	374	322	238	189	156	133	116	92	77	66	57	*912*
9-#10	.0353	**679**	543	527	446	387	342	264	210	174	149	130	103	86	74	64	*1027*
10-#10	.0392	**709**	665	545	461	399	352	290	231	192	164	143	114	95	81	71	*1141*
12-#10	.0470	**770**	710	580	490	424	374	334	271	226	194	170	136	113	97	85	*1369*
6-#11	.0289	**629**	606	497	421	366	297	219	173	143	122	106	84	70	60	52	*831*
7-#11	.0337	**667**	633	519	439	381	336	251	199	165	141	123	98	81	70	61	*970*
8-#11	.0385	**704**	661	540	457	396	349	283	225	187	160	140	111	93	79	69	*1108*
9-#11	.0433	**741**	688	562	475	411	362	313	250	208	178	156	124	104	89	78	*1247*
10-#11	.0481	**779**	716	583	493	426	375	336	274	228	196	172	137	114	98	86	*1386*
11-#11	.0530	**816**	743	605	510	441	389	347	297	248	213	187	150	125	107	94	*1524*
6-#14S	.0417	**728**	677	552	466	403	355	296	236	197	168	147	117	98	84	73	*1171*
7-#14S	.0486	**782**	716	582	491	424	374	334	270	226	193	169	136	113	97	85	*1367*
8-#14S	.0556	**836**	755	613	516	446	392	350	303	253	218	191	153	128	110	96	*1562*
9-#14S	.0625	**891**	794	644	541	467	410	366	330	280	241	212	171	143	123	108	*1757*

Check availability of #14S and #18S bars.

All above columns require spirals of A432 rod or cold drawn wire (f_y = 60,000 psi):—

⅝φ @ 2½″

Outside diameter of spiral should be 3 in. less than side of column.

† Below zigzag horizontal line of each group, concrete governs; above, tension governs.

‡ M_o = capacity in pure bending, (N = 0); for extrapolation, see page 11-5.

SPIRALLY REINFORCED SQUARE COLUMNS—
Safe Load in Kips for Various Eccentricities in Inches
f'_c = 5000 psi (A61 or A432 Bars, f_y = 60,000 psi) f_s = 24,000 psi basis

COLUMN SIZE—19″ x 19″

f'_c = 5000 psi
f_y = 60,000 psi

Bars	p	M/N † = e (in.) 0	1	2	3	4	5	6	7	8	9	10	12	14	16	18	M_o ‡ (kip-in.)
7-#7	.0116	**552**	552	477	410	284	169	120	93	76	64	56	44	36	31	27	*419*
8-#7	.0133	**566**	566	486	417	320	192	137	106	87	73	63	50	41	35	30	*479*
9-#7	.0150	**580**	580	495	425	355	214	153	119	97	82	71	56	46	39	34	*539*
10-#7	.0166	**595**	595	504	432	378	236	169	132	108	91	79	62	51	44	38	*599*
11-#7	.0183	**609**	609	513	439	384	257	185	144	118	100	87	68	57	48	42	*659*
12-#7	.0199	**624**	624	522	447	391	279	201	157	128	109	94	75	62	52	46	*719*
14-#7	.0233	**652**	649	540	462	404	320	231	181	149	126	110	87	72	61	53	*839*
16-#7	.0266	**681**	671	558	477	416	360	261	205	169	143	125	99	82	70	61	*959*
6-#8	.0131	**565**	565	485	416	314	188	134	104	85	72	62	49	40	34	30	*469*
7-#8	.0153	**583**	583	497	426	360	217	155	121	99	83	72	57	47	40	35	*547*
8-#8	.0175	**602**	602	508	435	381	245	176	137	112	95	82	65	54	46	40	*625*
9-#8	.0197	**621**	621	520	445	389	273	197	153	126	107	92	73	60	51	45	*703*
10-#8	.0219	**640**	640	532	455	398	300	217	170	139	118	102	81	67	57	50	*782*
11-#8	.0241	**659**	654	543	465	406	327	237	185	152	129	112	89	73	63	55	*860*
12-#8	.0263	**678**	669	555	474	414	353	256	201	165	141	122	97	80	68	59	*938*
14-#8	.0306	**716**	698	578	494	431	382	294	232	191	163	141	112	93	79	69	*1094*
16-#8	.0350	**754**	726	602	513	448	397	331	262	216	184	160	128	106	90	79	*1251*
6-#9	.0166	**595**	595	503	431	377	232	166	129	106	90	78	61	51	43	37	*588*
7-#9	.0194	**619**	619	518	443	387	267	192	150	123	104	90	71	59	50	44	*686*
8-#9	.0222	**643**	641	533	456	398	301	217	170	140	118	103	81	67	57	50	*784*
9-#9	.0249	**667**	659	547	468	408	335	242	190	156	133	115	91	75	64	56	*882*
10-#9	.0277	**691**	678	562	480	419	367	267	209	172	147	127	101	84	71	62	*980*
11-#9	.0305	**715**	696	577	492	429	381	290	229	189	160	139	111	92	78	68	*1078*
12-#9	.0332	**739**	714	591	504	440	390	314	247	204	174	151	120	100	85	74	*1176*
14-#9	.0388	**787**	750	620	529	461	408	359	284	235	201	175	139	116	99	86	*1373*
6-#10	.0211	**634**	634	526	450	393	286	206	161	132	112	97	77	63	54	47	*739*
7-#10	.0246	**664**	657	545	466	406	328	237	186	153	130	113	89	74	63	55	*862*
8-#10	.0281	**695**	680	563	481	420	368	268	211	173	147	128	101	84	72	62	*986*
9-#10	.0317	**725**	703	582	496	433	384	298	235	193	165	143	114	94	80	70	*1109*
10-#10	.0352	**756**	726	600	512	446	395	327	258	213	182	158	126	104	89	78	*1232*
11-#10	.0387	**786**	749	619	527	459	407	355	281	233	198	173	138	114	98	85	*1355*
12-#10	.0422	**817**	772	637	542	472	418	375	303	251	215	187	149	124	106	93	*1479*
6-#11	.0259	**675**	665	551	470	410	340	246	193	159	135	117	93	77	65	57	*899*
7-#11	.0302	**713**	693	573	489	426	378	283	223	184	156	136	108	89	76	66	*1048*
8-#11	.0346	**750**	721	596	508	442	392	319	252	208	177	154	122	101	87	76	*1198*
9-#11	.0389	**788**	749	618	527	458	406	353	279	231	197	172	137	114	97	85	*1348*
10-#11	.0432	**825**	777	641	545	474	420	376	307	254	217	190	151	126	107	94	*1498*
11-#11	.0475	**863**	806	663	564	490	434	389	333	277	237	207	165	137	118	103	*1648*
12-#11	.0519	**900**	834	686	583	506	448	401	358	298	256	224	179	149	128	112	*1798*
6-#14S	.0374	**775**	738	608	517	450	398	335	265	219	187	163	129	107	92	80	*1269*
7-#14S	.0436	**829**	778	640	544	473	418	375	303	251	215	187	149	124	106	93	*1480*
8-#14S	.0499	**883**	818	672	570	495	438	392	340	283	242	212	169	141	121	105	*1692*
9-#14S	.0561	**937**	858	704	597	518	457	409	371	313	269	235	188	157	135	118	*1903*
10-#14S	.0623	**991**	898	736	623	540	477	427	386	342	294	258	207	173	149	130	*2115*

Check availability of #14S and #18S bars.

All above columns require spirals of A432 rod or cold drawn wire (f_y = 60,000 psi):—
⅝φ @ 2¼″

Outside diameter of spiral should be 3 in. less than side of column.
† Below zigzag horizontal line of each group, concrete governs; above, tension governs.
‡ M_o = capacity in pure bending, (N = 0); for extrapolation, see page 11-5.

SPIRALLY REINFORCED SQUARE COLUMNS—

Safe Load in Kips for Various Eccentricities in Inches

f'_c = 5000 psi (A61 or A432 Bars, f_y = 60,000 psi) f_s = 24,000 psi basis

COLUMN SIZE—20″ x 20″ — f'_c = 5000 psi, f_y = 60,000 psi

Bars	p	M/N † = e (in.) 0	1	2	3	4	5	6	7	8	9	10	12	14	16	18	M_o ‡ (kip-in.)
7-#7	.0105	**600**	600	532	459	337	192	135	103	84	71	61	48	39	33	29	*449*
8-#7	.0120	**615**	615	541	466	380	218	153	118	96	80	69	54	45	38	33	*514*
9-#7	.0135	**629**	629	550	474	417	243	171	132	107	90	78	61	50	43	37	*578*
10-#7	.0150	**644**	644	559	482	423	268	189	146	119	100	86	68	56	47	41	*642*
12-#7	.0180	**672**	672	578	498	437	317	224	174	142	119	103	81	67	57	49	*771*
14-#7	.0210	**701**	701	596	513	450	364	259	201	164	139	120	95	78	66	58	*899*
16-#7	.0240	**730**	730	614	529	464	409	292	227	186	157	136	108	89	76	66	*1028*
18-#7	.0270	**759**	756	633	544	477	425	325	254	208	176	153	121	100	85	74	*1156*
6-#8	.0119	**613**	613	540	465	373	214	150	115	94	79	68	53	44	37	32	*503*
7-#8	.0138	**632**	632	552	475	418	247	174	134	109	92	79	62	51	43	38	*587*
8-#8	.0158	**651**	651	564	486	427	279	197	152	124	104	90	71	58	50	43	*671*
9-#8	.0178	**670**	670	576	496	435	311	220	170	139	117	101	80	66	56	48	*755*
10-#8	.0198	**689**	689	588	506	444	342	243	188	153	130	112	88	73	62	54	*838*
12-#8	.0237	**727**	727	612	526	462	402	287	223	182	154	134	105	87	74	64	*1006*
14-#8	.0277	**765**	760	636	546	479	426	330	257	211	179	155	122	101	86	75	*1174*
16-#8	.0316	**803**	790	660	567	497	442	371	290	239	202	176	139	115	98	85	*1342*
6-#9	.0150	**644**	644	558	481	422	264	186	144	117	98	85	67	55	47	41	*631*
7-#9	.0175	**668**	668	574	494	433	304	215	166	136	114	99	78	64	54	47	*736*
8-#9	.0200	**692**	692	589	507	444	343	244	189	154	130	113	89	73	62	54	*842*
9-#9	.0225	**716**	716	604	519	456	381	271	211	172	146	126	99	82	70	61	*947*
10-#9	.0250	**740**	740	619	532	467	415	299	233	190	161	140	110	91	77	67	*1052*
12-#9	.0300	**788**	777	649	558	488	435	352	275	226	191	166	131	109	92	81	*1263*
14-#9	.0350	**836**	814	679	583	510	454	402	316	260	221	192	152	126	107	94	*1473*
6-#10	.0191	**682**	682	582	501	440	326	231	179	146	123	106	84	69	59	51	*794*
7-#10	.0222	**713**	713	602	517	453	374	266	207	169	143	123	97	80	68	59	*926*
8-#10	.0254	**743**	742	621	533	467	416	300	234	191	162	140	111	91	78	68	*1059*
9-#10	.0286	**774**	766	640	549	481	428	334	261	214	181	157	124	103	87	76	*1191*
10-#10	.0318	**804**	789	659	565	495	440	366	287	236	200	173	137	114	97	84	*1324*
12-#10	.0381	**865**	836	697	597	523	464	418	337	278	236	206	163	135	115	101	*1588*
14-#10	.0445	**926**	883	735	629	550	489	440	385	319	272	237	189	157	134	117	*1853*
6-#11	.0234	**724**	724	608	522	458	388	276	215	176	148	129	101	84	71	62	*966*
7-#11	.0273	**762**	756	631	542	475	422	318	248	203	172	149	118	97	83	72	*1127*
8-#11	.0312	**799**	784	654	561	491	437	358	280	230	195	169	134	111	94	82	*1288*
9-#11	.0351	**836**	813	678	581	508	452	396	311	256	217	189	150	124	106	92	*1449*
10-#11	.0390	**874**	842	701	600	525	466	420	341	281	239	208	165	137	117	102	*1610*
11-#11	.0429	**911**	871	724	620	542	481	433	371	306	261	227	181	150	128	112	*1771*
13-#11	.0507	**986**	928	771	659	575	511	459	417	354	303	264	211	175	150	131	*2093*
6-#14S	.0338	**824**	802	667	572	500	444	376	295	242	206	179	141	117	100	87	*1366*
7-#14S	.0394	**878**	843	701	599	524	465	418	338	279	237	206	164	136	116	101	*1594*
8-#14S	.0450	**932**	884	734	627	547	486	437	379	314	267	233	185	154	132	115	*1821*
9-#14S	.0506	**986**	925	767	655	571	507	455	413	347	297	259	207	172	147	128	*2049*
10-#14S	.0563	**1040**	966	800	682	595	527	473	430	380	325	285	227	189	162	142	*2277*
6-#18S	.0600	**1076**	984	809	687	597	528	473	428	379	325	284	228	190	163	142	*2285*

Check availability of #14S and #18S bars.

All above columns require spirals of A432 rod or cold drawn wire (f_y = 60,000 psi):—

⅝φ @ 2¼″

Outside diameter of spiral should be 3 in. less than side of column.

† Below zigzag horizontal line of each group, concrete governs; above, tension governs.

‡ M_o = capacity in pure bending, (N = 0); for extrapolation, see page 11-5.

SPIRALLY REINFORCED SQUARE COLUMNS—
Safe Load in Kips for Various Eccentricities in Inches
f'_c = 5000 psi (A61 or A432 Bars, f_y = 60,000 psi) f_s = 24,000 psi basis

COLUMN SIZE—21″ x 21″ — f'_c = 5000 psi, f_y = 60,000 psi

Bars	p	M/N † = e (in.)															M_o ‡ (kip-in.)
		0	1	2	3	4	5	6	8	10	12	14	16	18	20	22	
8-#7	.0109	**666**	666	599	519	454	248	171	105	76	59	48	41	36	31	28	*548*
9-#7	.0122	**680**	680	608	527	465	277	191	118	85	66	54	46	40	35	32	*617*
10-#7	.0136	**695**	695	618	535	472	305	211	130	94	74	60	51	44	39	35	*685*
12-#7	.0163	**724**	724	636	551	486	360	250	155	113	88	72	61	53	47	42	*822*
14-#7	.0190	**752**	752	655	567	500	413	289	180	131	103	84	72	62	55	49	*960*
16-#7	.0218	**781**	781	674	583	514	459	326	204	149	117	96	82	71	63	56	*1097*
18-#7	.0245	**810**	810	693	599	528	472	363	228	166	131	108	92	80	70	63	*1234*
6-#8	.0107	**665**	665	597	518	446	243	167	103	74	58	47	40	35	31	27	*537*
7-#8	.0125	**683**	683	610	528	466	281	194	119	86	67	55	47	41	36	32	*627*
8-#8	.0143	**702**	702	622	539	475	318	220	136	98	77	63	54	46	41	37	*716*
9-#8	.0161	**721**	721	635	549	484	354	246	152	110	86	71	60	52	46	41	*806*
10-#8	.0179	**740**	740	647	560	493	389	271	168	122	96	79	67	58	51	46	*895*
12-#8	.0215	**778**	778	672	581	512	456	320	200	146	114	94	80	70	61	55	*1075*
14-#8	.0251	**816**	816	696	602	530	473	368	232	169	133	109	93	81	72	64	*1254*
16-#8	.0287	**854**	854	721	623	548	489	414	262	192	151	125	106	92	82	73	*1433*
6-#9	.0136	**695**	695	617	534	471	301	208	128	93	73	60	50	44	39	35	*674*
7-#9	.0159	**719**	719	632	547	482	346	240	149	108	84	69	59	51	45	40	*787*
8-#9	.0181	**743**	743	648	561	494	390	272	169	123	96	79	67	58	52	46	*899*
9-#9	.0204	**767**	767	663	574	505	433	303	189	138	108	89	75	66	58	52	*1012*
10-#9	.0227	**791**	791	679	587	517	462	334	209	152	120	98	84	73	64	58	*1124*
12-#9	.0272	**839**	839	710	613	540	482	393	248	181	143	118	100	87	77	69	*1349*
14-#9	.0317	**887**	881	741	640	563	502	449	286	209	165	136	116	101	89	80	*1574*
16-#9	.0363	**935**	919	772	666	586	522	472	322	237	187	155	132	115	102	91	*1799*
6-#10	.0173	**734**	734	641	555	489	371	258	160	116	91	75	63	55	49	44	*849*
8-#10	.0230	**795**	795	681	588	518	462	336	210	153	120	99	84	73	65	58	*1132*
10-#10	.0288	**856**	856	720	621	547	488	409	259	189	149	123	105	91	81	72	*1415*
12-#10	.0346	**917**	903	759	655	576	513	463	306	225	178	147	125	109	96	86	*1698*
14-#10	.0403	**977**	951	798	688	604	539	486	351	259	205	170	145	126	112	100	*1981*
6-#11	.0212	**775**	775	668	577	508	441	309	193	140	110	91	77	67	59	53	*1033*
7-#11	.0248	**813**	813	692	597	525	469	355	223	163	128	105	90	78	69	62	*1206*
8-#11	.0283	**850**	850	716	618	543	485	400	253	185	145	120	102	89	79	70	*1378*
9-#11	.0318	**888**	880	740	638	561	500	443	282	206	163	134	114	100	88	79	*1550*
10-#11	.0354	**925**	909	764	658	578	516	465	310	228	180	149	127	110	98	88	*1722*
12-#11	.0424	**1000**	968	811	699	613	547	493	364	269	213	177	151	131	117	105	*2067*
14-#11	.0495	**1075**	1026	859	739	648	577	521	416	309	246	204	174	152	135	121	*2412*
6-#14S	.0306	**875**	868	729	628	552	492	421	267	195	154	127	108	94	83	75	*1463*
7-#14S	.0357	**929**	910	763	657	577	514	464	307	226	178	147	126	109	97	87	*1707*
8-#14S	.0408	**983**	952	798	686	602	536	483	346	255	202	167	143	124	110	99	*1951*
9-#14S	.0459	**1037**	994	832	715	627	558	503	384	284	225	187	160	139	123	111	*2195*
10-#14S	.0510	**1091**	1036	866	744	652	580	522	420	312	248	206	176	154	137	123	*2439*
11-#14S	.0561	**1145**	1078	900	772	676	602	542	452	339	271	225	193	168	149	134	*2683*
6-#18S	.0544	**1127**	1056	877	750	655	582	523	421	313	250	207	177	155	137	123	*2458*
7-#18S	.0635	**1223**	1128	935	799	697	618	555	462	358	286	238	204	179	159	143	*2868*

Check availability of #14S and #18S bars.

All above columns require spirals of A432 rod or cold drawn wire (f_y = 60,000 psi):—

⅝φ @ 2¼″

Outside diameter of spiral should be 3 in. less than side of column.

† Below zigzag horizontal line of each group, concrete governs; above, tension governs.

‡ M_o = capacity in pure bending, (N = 0); for extrapolation, see page 11-5.

SPIRALLY REINFORCED SQUARE COLUMNS—
Safe Load in Kips for Various Eccentricities in Inches
f'_c = 5000 psi (A61 or A432 Bars, f_y = 60,000 psi) f_s = 24,000 psi basis

COLUMN SIZE—22″ x 22″ — f'_c = 5000 psi, f_y = 60,000 psi

Bars	p	M/N † = e (in.)															M_o ‡ (kip-in.)
		0	1	2	3	4	5	6	8	10	12	14	16	18	20	22	
9-#7	.0112	**734**	734	669	583	516	315	213	129	92	72	59	50	43	38	34	*656*
10-#7	.0124	**748**	748	679	591	523	347	235	142	102	80	65	55	48	42	38	*729*
12-#7	.0149	**777**	777	698	607	538	409	279	170	122	95	78	66	57	51	45	*874*
14-#7	.0174	**806**	806	717	624	552	470	321	197	142	111	91	77	67	59	53	*1020*
16-#7	.0198	**835**	835	737	641	567	508	363	223	161	126	104	88	76	67	60	*1166*
18-#7	.0223	**864**	864	756	657	581	521	404	250	181	141	116	99	86	76	68	*1312*
20-#7	.0248	**892**	892	775	674	596	534	443	275	200	157	129	109	95	84	75	*1458*
7-#8	.0114	**737**	737	671	584	517	320	216	131	94	73	60	50	44	39	34	*666*
8-#8	.0131	**756**	756	684	595	527	361	245	149	107	83	68	58	50	44	39	*762*
9-#8	.0147	**775**	775	696	606	536	402	273	167	120	93	77	65	56	50	44	*857*
10-#8	.0163	**794**	794	709	617	546	442	302	184	133	104	85	72	62	55	49	*952*
12-#8	.0196	**832**	832	734	638	564	506	357	219	158	124	102	86	75	66	59	*1143*
14-#8	.0229	**870**	870	760	660	583	523	410	253	183	144	118	100	87	77	69	*1333*
16-#8	.0261	**908**	908	785	682	602	540	461	287	208	163	134	114	99	88	78	*1524*
6-#9	.0124	**748**	748	678	590	522	342	232	140	101	78	64	54	47	42	37	*718*
7-#9	.0145	**772**	772	694	604	534	394	268	163	117	91	75	63	55	48	43	*837*
8-#9	.0165	**796**	796	710	617	546	444	303	185	133	104	85	72	63	55	49	*957*
9-#9	.0186	**820**	820	726	631	558	492	338	207	149	117	96	81	70	62	56	*1077*
10-#9	.0207	**844**	844	742	645	570	511	372	229	165	129	106	90	78	69	62	*1196*
12-#9	.0248	**892**	892	774	672	594	532	437	272	197	154	127	108	93	83	74	*1436*
14-#9	.0289	**940**	940	806	699	618	553	501	313	228	179	147	125	109	96	86	*1675*
16-#9	.0331	**988**	988	838	726	641	574	520	353	258	203	167	142	124	109	98	*1914*
6-#10	.0157	**787**	787	703	612	541	422	287	175	126	98	81	68	59	52	47	*904*
8-#10	.0210	**848**	848	744	646	571	512	374	231	167	130	107	91	79	70	62	*1205*
10-#10	.0262	**909**	909	784	680	601	538	456	284	206	162	133	113	98	87	78	*1506*
12-#10	.0315	**970**	970	824	715	631	565	511	336	244	192	158	135	117	104	93	*1808*
14-#10	.0367	**1031**	1022	865	749	661	591	535	385	282	222	183	156	136	120	108	*2109*
6-#11	.0193	**829**	829	730	634	561	502	345	212	153	119	98	83	72	64	57	*1101*
7-#11	.0226	**867**	867	755	655	579	519	396	245	177	139	114	97	84	74	66	*1284*
8-#11	.0258	**904**	904	780	676	597	535	446	277	201	158	130	110	96	84	76	*1468*
9-#11	.0290	**941**	941	804	697	616	551	494	309	225	176	145	123	107	95	85	*1651*
10-#11	.0322	**979**	979	829	718	634	567	513	340	248	195	161	137	119	105	94	*1835*
11-#11	.0355	**1016**	1009	853	739	652	583	528	370	271	213	176	150	130	115	103	*2018*
13-#11	.0419	**1091**	1069	903	781	689	616	557	429	315	249	206	176	153	135	122	*2385*
15-#11	.0483	**1166**	1128	952	823	725	648	586	485	359	284	235	201	175	155	139	*2752*
6-#14S	.0279	**928**	928	794	688	607	543	471	293	213	167	137	117	101	90	80	*1560*
7-#14S	.0325	**982**	981	829	718	633	566	512	338	246	193	159	136	118	104	93	*1820*
8-#14S	.0372	**1036**	1023	864	748	659	589	532	380	278	219	181	154	134	119	106	*2080*
9-#14S	.0418	**1090**	1066	899	778	685	612	553	422	310	245	202	172	150	133	119	*2341*
10-#14S	.0465	**1144**	1108	934	807	711	635	574	462	341	270	223	190	166	147	132	*2601*
12-#14S	.0558	**1252**	1193	1004	867	763	681	615	515	400	318	264	226	197	175	157	*3121*
6-#18S	.0496	**1180**	1129	947	815	716	638	575	465	343	272	225	192	168	149	133	*2631*
7-#18S	.0579	**1276**	1203	1007	866	760	676	610	509	393	312	259	222	194	172	154	*3070*

Check availability of #14S and #18S bars.

All above columns require spirals of A432 rod or cold drawn wire (f_y = 60,000 psi):—

#14S and smaller—⅝φ @ 2¼″

#18S only —⅝φ @ 2″

Outside diameter of spiral should be 3 in. less than side of column.

† Below zigzag horizontal line of each group, concrete governs; above, tension governs.

‡ M_o = capacity in pure bending, (N = 0); for extrapolation, see page 11-5.

SPIRALLY REINFORCED SQUARE COLUMNS—
Safe Load in Kips for Various Eccentricities in Inches
f'_c = 5000 psi (A61 or A432 Bars, f_y = 60,000 psi) f_s = 24,000 psi basis

COLUMN SIZE—23″ x 23″ | f'_c = 5000 psi | f_y = 60,000 psi

Bars	p	M/N † = e (in.) 0	1	2	3	4	5	6	8	10	12	14	16	18	20	22	24	M_o ‡ (kip-in.)
9-#7	.0102	**790**	790	733	641	570	359	236	140	100	77	63	53	46	41	36	33	694
10-#7	.0113	**805**	805	743	650	577	395	261	155	111	86	70	59	51	45	40	36	772
12-#7	.0136	**834**	834	763	667	592	466	310	185	132	103	84	71	61	54	48	44	926
14-#7	.0159	**862**	862	783	684	607	534	357	215	153	119	98	83	71	63	56	51	1081
16-#7	.0181	**891**	891	802	701	622	560	403	244	175	136	111	94	82	72	64	58	1235
18-#7	.0204	**920**	920	822	718	637	573	449	272	195	152	125	106	92	81	72	65	1389
20-#7	.0227	**949**	949	842	735	652	586	493	300	216	169	138	117	102	90	80	73	1544
7-#8	.0105	**793**	793	735	643	571	364	240	143	101	79	64	54	47	41	37	33	706
8-#8	.0119	**812**	812	748	654	581	411	272	162	116	90	73	62	53	47	42	38	807
9-#8	.0134	**831**	831	761	665	591	458	304	182	130	101	82	69	60	53	47	43	908
10-#8	.0149	**850**	850	774	676	601	503	335	201	144	112	91	77	67	59	53	48	1009
12-#8	.0179	**888**	888	800	699	620	557	396	239	171	133	109	92	80	71	63	57	1211
14-#8	.0209	**926**	926	826	721	640	575	455	277	199	155	127	107	93	82	74	66	1413
16-#8	.0239	**964**	964	852	743	659	592	512	313	225	176	144	122	106	94	84	76	1615
6-#9	.0113	**805**	805	743	649	577	390	258	153	109	85	69	58	50	44	40	36	761
8-#9	.0151	**853**	853	775	677	601	505	337	202	144	112	92	78	67	59	53	48	1015
10-#9	.0189	**901**	901	808	705	626	563	413	250	179	139	114	97	84	74	66	60	1268
12-#9	.0227	**949**	949	840	733	651	584	486	296	213	166	136	115	100	88	79	72	1522
14-#9	.0265	**997**	997	873	761	675	606	550	342	247	193	158	134	116	103	92	83	1776
16-#9	.0302	**1045**	1045	906	790	700	628	570	386	279	219	180	153	133	117	105	95	2030
6-#10	.0144	**844**	844	768	671	596	480	320	192	137	106	87	73	63	56	50	45	959
8-#10	.0192	**905**	905	810	707	627	563	416	252	180	141	115	97	84	74	67	60	1278
10-#10	.0240	**966**	966	851	742	658	591	508	310	223	174	143	121	105	93	83	75	1598
12-#10	.0288	**1027**	1027	892	778	689	619	561	367	265	207	170	145	125	111	99	90	1918
14-#10	.0336	**1087**	1087	933	813	720	646	586	421	306	240	197	168	146	129	115	105	2237
6-#11	.0177	**885**	885	796	695	616	554	384	231	165	129	105	89	77	68	61	55	1168
7-#11	.0206	**923**	923	821	717	635	571	441	267	192	150	122	104	90	79	71	64	1363
8-#11	.0236	**960**	960	847	738	654	588	496	303	218	170	139	118	102	90	81	73	1558
9-#11	.0265	**998**	998	872	760	673	605	549	338	244	190	156	132	115	102	91	82	1752
10-#11	.0295	**1035**	1035	897	781	692	621	564	372	269	210	173	147	127	113	101	91	1947
11-#11	.0324	**1073**	1073	922	803	711	638	579	405	294	230	189	161	140	123	111	100	2142
13-#11	.0383	**1147**	1143	973	846	749	672	609	470	342	269	222	189	164	145	130	118	2531
15-#11	.0442	**1222**	1203	1023	890	787	706	640	532	390	307	254	216	188	167	149	135	2921
6-#14S	.0255	**985**	985	861	750	665	597	524	321	231	181	148	125	109	96	86	78	1657
7-#14S	.0298	**1039**	1039	897	781	692	620	563	369	267	209	172	146	127	112	100	91	1934
8-#14S	.0340	**1093**	1093	933	812	719	644	584	417	302	237	195	166	144	127	114	103	2210
9-#14S	.0383	**1147**	1140	969	843	745	668	606	462	337	265	218	185	161	143	128	116	2486
10-#14S	.0425	**1201**	1184	1005	874	772	692	627	506	370	292	241	205	178	158	142	128	2763
11-#14S	.0468	**1255**	1227	1041	904	799	716	648	546	403	318	263	224	195	173	155	141	3039
13-#14S	.0553	**1363**	1313	1113	966	853	764	691	581	466	370	307	262	228	203	182	165	3592
6-#18S	.0454	**1237**	1205	1019	883	779	696	630	512	375	295	244	208	181	160	143	130	2804
7-#18S	.0529	**1333**	1281	1081	935	824	737	666	559	429	340	281	240	209	185	166	151	3271
8-#18S	.0605	**1429**	1356	1143	988	870	777	702	588	480	382	317	271	237	210	189	171	3739

Check availability of #14S and #18S bars.

All above columns require spirals of A432 rod or cold drawn wire (f_y = 60,000 psi):—

#14S and smaller—⅝φ @ 2¼″

#18S only —⅝φ @ 2″

Outside diameter of spiral should be 3 in. less than side of column.

† Below zigzag horizontal line of each group, concrete governs; above, tension governs.

‡ M_o = capacity in pure bending, (N = 0); for extrapolation, see page 11-5.

SPIRALLY REINFORCED SQUARE COLUMNS—
Safe Load in Kips for Various Eccentricities in Inches
f'_c = 5000 psi (A61 or A432 Bars, f_y = 60,000 psi) f_s = 24,000 psi basis

COLUMN SIZE—24″ x 24″

f'_c = 5000 psi
f_y = 60,000 psi

Bars	p	M/N † = e (in.) 0	1	2	3	4	5	6	8	10	12	14	16	18	20	22	24	M_o ‡ (kip-in.)
10-#7	.0104	**863**	863	811	712	635	451	290	169	119	92	75	63	55	48	43	39	815
12-#7	.0125	**892**	892	831	729	650	531	344	202	143	110	90	76	65	58	51	46	978
14-#7	.0146	**921**	921	851	747	665	600	396	234	166	128	104	88	76	67	60	54	1141
16-#7	.0167	**950**	950	871	764	681	614	448	265	188	146	119	101	87	77	68	62	1304
18-#7	.0188	**979**	979	891	782	696	628	498	296	211	164	134	113	98	86	77	70	1467
20-#7	.0208	**1007**	1007	911	799	712	642	547	327	233	181	148	125	108	96	85	77	1630
8-#8	.0110	**871**	871	816	716	638	470	303	177	125	96	78	66	57	50	45	40	853
9-#8	.0123	**890**	890	829	728	648	522	338	198	140	108	88	74	64	57	50	46	959
10-#8	.0137	**909**	909	842	739	658	573	372	219	155	120	98	82	71	63	56	51	1066
12-#8	.0165	**947**	947	869	762	679	612	440	260	185	143	117	99	85	75	67	61	1279
14-#8	.0192	**985**	985	895	785	699	630	506	301	214	166	136	115	99	88	78	71	1493
16-#8	.0219	**1023**	1023	921	808	719	648	569	341	243	189	155	131	113	100	89	81	1706
6-#9	.0104	**863**	863	810	711	634	445	286	167	118	91	74	62	54	47	42	38	804
7-#9	.0122	**887**	887	827	726	646	512	331	194	137	106	86	73	63	55	49	45	938
8-#9	.0139	**911**	911	844	740	659	576	374	220	156	121	98	83	72	63	56	51	1072
10-#9	.0174	**959**	959	877	769	685	617	459	272	193	150	122	103	89	79	70	64	1340
12-#9	.0208	**1007**	1007	910	798	710	640	540	323	230	179	146	123	107	94	84	76	1608
14-#9	.0243	**1055**	1055	943	827	736	663	603	372	266	207	170	144	124	110	98	89	1877
16-#9	.0278	**1103**	1103	977	855	761	685	623	421	302	235	193	163	142	125	112	101	2145
6-#10	.0132	**902**	902	837	734	654	548	355	209	148	114	93	78	68	60	53	48	1013
8-#10	.0176	**963**	963	879	770	686	618	462	274	195	151	123	104	90	79	71	64	1351
10-#10	.0220	**1024**	1024	921	807	718	647	564	338	241	187	153	130	112	99	88	80	1689
12-#10	.0265	**1085**	1085	963	843	750	675	614	400	286	223	183	155	134	118	106	96	2027
14-#10	.0309	**1146**	1146	1005	880	782	704	640	459	331	258	212	179	156	137	123	111	2365
6-#11	.0163	**944**	944	865	758	675	608	426	252	179	138	113	95	82	73	65	59	1235
7-#11	.0190	**982**	982	891	781	695	626	490	291	207	161	131	111	96	85	76	68	1441
8-#11	.0217	**1019**	1019	916	803	714	643	552	330	235	183	150	126	109	97	86	78	1647
9-#11	.0244	**1056**	1056	942	825	734	661	601	368	263	205	168	142	123	108	97	88	1853
10-#11	.0271	**1094**	1094	968	847	753	678	617	405	291	226	185	157	136	120	107	97	2059
12-#11	.0325	**1169**	1169	1019	892	793	713	648	478	344	269	221	187	162	143	128	116	2471
14-#11	.0379	**1244**	1244	1071	936	832	748	680	547	396	311	255	217	188	166	149	135	2883
16-#11	.0433	**1319**	1312	1122	981	871	783	711	601	447	351	289	246	214	189	170	154	3295
6-#14S	.0234	**1044**	1044	932	815	725	653	583	350	250	194	159	134	116	103	92	83	1755
7-#14S	.0273	**1098**	1098	968	847	753	677	616	403	289	225	184	156	135	119	107	97	2047
8-#14S	.0313	**1152**	1152	1005	879	781	702	638	455	327	256	210	178	154	136	122	110	2340
9-#14S	.0352	**1206**	1206	1042	911	809	727	661	505	365	285	234	199	173	152	137	124	2632
10-#14S	.0391	**1260**	1260	1079	942	836	752	683	553	401	315	259	220	191	169	151	137	2925
11-#14S	.0430	**1314**	1305	1116	974	864	777	705	596	437	343	283	240	209	185	166	150	3217
13-#14S	.0508	**1422**	1393	1189	1037	920	826	750	633	506	399	330	281	245	217	194	176	3802
6-#18S	.0417	**1295**	1284	1094	953	844	757	687	561	407	319	263	223	194	172	154	139	2977
7-#18S	.0486	**1391**	1361	1158	1007	891	799	725	610	466	367	303	258	224	199	178	161	3473
8-#18S	.0556	**1487**	1437	1221	1061	939	841	762	642	523	414	342	292	254	225	202	183	3969
9-#18S	.0625	**1584**	1514	1285	1116	986	883	800	673	577	458	380	325	283	251	226	205	4465

Check availability of #14S and #18S bars.

All above columns require spirals of A432 rod or cold drawn wire (f_y = 60,000 psi):—

#14S and smaller—⅝φ @ 2¼″

#18S only —⅝φ @ 2″

Outside diameter of spiral should be 3 in. less than side of column.

† Below zigzag horizontal line of each group, concrete governs; above, tension governs.

‡ M_o = capacity in pure bending, (N = 0); for extrapolation, see page 11-5.

SPIRALLY REINFORCED SQUARE COLUMNS—
Safe Load in Kips for Various Eccentricities in Inches
f'_c = 5000 psi (A61 or A432 Bars, f_y = 60,000 psi) f_s = 24,000 psi basis

COLUMN SIZE—25″ x 25″

f'_c = 5000 psi
f_y = 60,000 psi

Bars	p	M/N † = e (in.)															M_o ‡ (kip-in.)
		0	2	4	6	8	10	12	14	16	18	20	22	24	26	28	
11-#7	.0106	**939**	892	703	352	201	141	108	88	74	64	56	50	45	41	38	944
13-#7	.0125	**968**	912	719	411	236	166	128	104	87	75	66	59	53	49	45	1116
15-#7	.0144	**997**	933	734	469	271	190	147	119	101	87	76	68	62	56	52	1287
17-#7	.0163	**1026**	953	750	525	305	215	166	135	114	98	86	77	70	64	58	1459
19-#7	.0182	**1054**	974	766	580	338	239	185	150	127	110	97	86	78	71	65	1631
8-#8	.0101	**932**	887	699	336	192	134	103	84	70	61	53	48	43	39	36	898
9-#8	.0114	**951**	900	709	375	215	151	116	94	79	68	60	54	48	44	40	1011
10-#8	.0126	**970**	914	719	414	238	167	128	104	88	76	67	60	54	49	45	1123
12-#8	.0152	**1008**	941	740	488	283	199	153	125	105	91	80	71	64	59	54	1348
14-#8	.0177	**1046**	967	761	561	327	231	178	145	122	106	93	83	75	68	63	1572
16-#8	.0202	**1084**	994	782	631	370	262	203	165	139	121	106	95	86	78	72	1797
7-#9	.0112	**949**	898	707	367	210	147	113	92	77	67	59	52	47	43	40	988
8-#9	.0128	**973**	915	720	416	239	168	129	105	88	76	67	60	54	49	45	1130
9-#9	.0144	**997**	932	733	463	268	188	145	118	99	86	75	67	61	55	51	1271
10-#9	.0160	**1021**	949	746	510	296	208	161	131	110	95	84	75	68	62	57	1412
12-#9	.0192	**1069**	983	773	600	351	248	192	156	132	114	100	90	81	74	68	1695
14-#9	.0224	**1117**	1017	799	658	405	287	222	181	153	132	117	104	94	86	79	1977
16-#9	.0256	**1165**	1051	825	679	457	325	252	206	174	151	133	119	107	98	90	2260
6-#10	.0122	**964**	908	715	395	227	159	122	99	84	72	63	57	51	47	43	1068
8-#10	.0163	**1025**	951	748	514	298	210	162	132	111	96	84	75	68	62	57	1425
10-#10	.0203	**1086**	994	781	626	367	260	201	164	138	120	105	94	85	77	71	1781
12-#10	.0244	**1147**	1037	814	670	434	309	239	195	165	143	126	113	102	93	85	2137
14-#10	.0284	**1207**	1080	847	697	500	356	277	226	192	166	146	131	118	108	99	2493
6-#11	.0150	**1005**	937	737	474	274	193	148	121	102	88	77	69	62	57	52	1303
7-#11	.0175	**1043**	963	757	544	317	223	172	140	118	102	90	80	73	66	61	1520
8-#11	.0200	**1080**	989	777	613	359	254	196	160	135	117	103	92	83	76	69	1737
9-#11	.0225	**1118**	1016	797	656	400	284	220	179	151	131	115	103	93	85	78	1955
10-#11	.0250	**1155**	1042	817	672	441	313	243	198	168	145	128	114	103	94	87	2172
11-#11	.0275	**1193**	1068	837	689	481	343	266	217	184	159	140	125	113	104	95	2389
13-#11	.0324	**1267**	1121	878	721	558	400	311	255	216	187	165	148	134	122	112	2823
15-#11	.0374	**1342**	1173	918	754	632	455	356	292	247	215	189	170	154	140	129	3258
17-#11	.0424	**1417**	1225	958	787	667	509	399	328	278	242	214	191	173	158	146	3692
6-#14S	.0216	**1105**	1005	788	648	381	270	209	170	144	124	109	98	88	81	74	1852
7-#14S	.0252	**1159**	1042	817	672	439	312	242	197	167	144	127	114	103	94	86	2161
8-#14S	.0288	**1213**	1080	846	695	495	353	274	224	190	164	145	130	117	107	98	2469
9-#14S	.0324	**1267**	1118	874	718	550	394	307	251	212	184	162	145	131	120	110	2778
10-#14S	.0360	**1321**	1155	903	741	603	433	338	277	235	204	180	161	146	133	122	3087
12-#14S	.0432	**1429**	1230	960	788	668	510	400	329	279	242	214	192	174	159	146	3704
14-#14S	.0504	**1537**	1305	1018	834	707	583	459	379	322	280	248	222	201	184	170	4322
6-#18S	.0384	**1357**	1171	912	746	612	441	344	282	239	208	183	164	149	136	125	3149
7-#18S	.0448	**1453**	1236	961	785	664	505	396	326	277	240	212	190	172	157	145	3674
8-#18S	.0512	**1549**	1301	1010	825	697	567	446	368	313	272	241	216	196	179	165	4199
9-#18S	.0576	**1645**	1366	1059	864	730	627	495	409	349	304	269	241	219	200	185	4724

Check availability of #14S and #18S bars.

All above columns require spirals of A432 rod or cold drawn wire (f_y = 60,000 psi):—
⅝φ @ 2″

Outside diameter of spiral should be 3 in. less than side of column.
† Below zigzag horizontal line of each group, concrete governs; above, tension governs.
‡ M_o = capacity in pure bending, (N = 0); for extrapolation, see page 11-5.

SPIRALLY REINFORCED SQUARE COLUMNS—
Safe Load in Kips for Various Eccentricities in Inches
f'_c = 5000 psi (A61 or A432 Bars, f_y = 60,000 psi) f_s = 24,000 psi basis

COLUMN SIZE—26″ x 26″ f'_c = 5000 psi, f_y = 60,000 psi

Bars	p	M/N † = e (in.) 0	2	4	6	8	10	12	14	16	18	20	22	24	26	28	M_o ‡ (kip-in.)
9-#8	.0105	**1015**	975	773	417	233	162	124	100	84	73	64	57	51	47	43	1062
10-#8	.0117	**1034**	988	783	459	258	179	137	111	93	81	71	63	57	52	48	1180
12-#8	.0140	**1072**	1016	805	542	307	214	164	133	112	96	85	76	68	62	57	1416
14-#8	.0164	**1110**	1043	826	623	355	248	190	155	130	112	99	88	80	72	67	1652
16-#8	.0187	**1148**	1070	847	700	402	282	217	176	148	128	113	101	91	83	76	1888
18-#8	.0210	**1186**	1097	869	719	448	315	243	197	166	144	126	113	102	93	85	2124
20-#8	.0234	**1224**	1125	890	736	493	348	268	218	184	159	140	125	113	103	95	2360
22-#8	.0257	**1262**	1152	911	754	538	380	294	239	202	175	154	137	124	113	104	2596
7-#9	.0104	**1012**	972	771	408	228	158	121	98	82	71	62	56	50	46	42	1039
8-#9	.0118	**1036**	990	784	462	260	180	138	112	94	81	71	63	57	52	48	1187
9-#9	.0133	**1060**	1007	798	514	290	202	155	126	106	91	80	71	64	59	54	1336
10-#9	.0148	**1084**	1024	811	566	321	224	172	139	117	101	89	79	72	65	60	1484
12-#9	.0178	**1132**	1058	838	666	381	266	205	166	140	121	106	95	86	78	72	1781
14-#9	.0207	**1180**	1093	865	715	439	308	238	193	163	141	124	110	100	91	84	2078
16-#9	.0237	**1228**	1127	892	737	496	350	270	220	185	160	141	126	114	104	95	2375
18-#9	.0266	**1276**	1162	918	759	552	390	302	246	208	180	158	141	128	117	107	2672
6-#10	.0113	**1027**	983	778	439	246	171	131	106	89	77	67	60	54	49	45	1123
8-#10	.0150	**1088**	1026	812	570	324	226	173	141	118	102	90	80	72	66	60	1498
10-#10	.0188	**1149**	1070	846	695	399	279	215	175	147	127	112	100	90	82	75	1872
12-#10	.0225	**1210**	1113	880	728	472	332	256	208	176	152	134	119	108	98	90	2247
14-#10	.0263	**1271**	1157	914	756	542	383	296	242	204	176	155	139	125	114	105	2621
16-#10	.0301	**1332**	1201	948	783	611	434	336	274	232	201	177	158	143	130	120	2996
6-#11	.0138	**1069**	1012	801	527	297	207	159	129	108	93	82	73	66	60	55	1370
7-#11	.0162	**1107**	1039	822	605	344	240	185	150	126	109	96	85	77	70	64	1599
8-#11	.0185	**1144**	1065	843	681	390	273	210	171	144	124	109	97	88	80	74	1827
9-#11	.0208	**1181**	1092	863	714	435	305	235	191	161	139	122	109	99	90	83	2056
10-#11	.0231	**1219**	1119	884	731	479	337	260	212	178	154	136	121	110	100	92	2284
12-#11	.0277	**1294**	1172	925	764	564	399	309	252	213	184	162	145	131	119	110	2741
14-#11	.0323	**1369**	1225	967	798	647	460	357	292	247	214	188	168	152	139	128	3198
16-#11	.0369	**1444**	1279	1008	832	708	519	404	331	280	243	214	192	173	158	146	3655
18-#11	.0415	**1518**	1332	1050	866	737	577	450	369	313	271	240	215	194	177	163	4112
6-#14S	.0200	**1168**	1081	854	706	414	290	223	182	153	132	116	104	94	85	78	1949
7-#14S	.0233	**1222**	1119	884	730	477	336	259	211	178	154	135	121	109	99	91	2274
8-#14S	.0266	**1276**	1158	913	754	538	380	294	240	202	175	154	138	124	113	104	2599
9-#14S	.0300	**1330**	1196	943	778	597	424	328	268	226	196	173	154	139	127	117	2924
10-#14S	.0333	**1384**	1234	972	802	655	467	362	296	250	217	191	171	155	141	130	3249
11-#14S	.0366	**1438**	1272	1002	826	703	509	396	324	274	237	209	187	170	155	142	3574
13-#14S	.0433	**1546**	1349	1061	874	743	590	461	378	321	278	246	220	199	182	167	4224
15-#14S	.0499	**1654**	1425	1120	922	784	668	524	431	366	318	281	252	228	209	192	4873
6-#18S	.0355	**1420**	1251	982	808	667	476	370	302	256	221	195	175	158	144	133	3322
7-#18S	.0414	**1516**	1318	1033	849	720	546	426	349	296	256	226	203	183	167	154	3876
8-#18S	.0473	**1612**	1384	1083	890	755	613	480	394	335	291	257	230	208	190	175	4430
9-#18S	.0533	**1708**	1451	1134	931	789	678	533	439	373	324	287	257	233	213	196	4984
10-#18S	.0592	**1804**	1517	1184	971	823	714	584	482	410	357	316	284	257	235	217	5537

Check availability of #14S and #18S bars.

All above columns require spirals of A432 rod or cold drawn wire (f_y = 60,000 psi):— ⅝φ @ 2″

Outside diameter of spiral should be 3 in. less than side of column.

† Below zigzag horizontal line of each group, concrete governs; above, tension governs.

‡ M_o = capacity in pure bending, (N = 0); for extrapolation, see page 11-5.

SPIRALLY REINFORCED SQUARE COLUMNS—
Safe Load in Kips for Various Eccentricities in Inches
f'_c = 5000 psi (A61 or A432 Bars, f_y = 60,000 psi) f_s = 24,000 psi basis

COLUMN SIZE—27″ x 27″ | f'_c = 5000 psi, f_y = 60,000 psi

Bars	p	M/N † = e (in.) 0	2	4	6	8	10	12	14	16	18	20	22	24	26	28	M_o ‡ (kip-in.)
10-#8	.0108	**1100**	1066	850	510	279	192	146	118	99	85	75	67	60	55	50	1237
12-#8	.0130	**1138**	1094	872	602	332	229	175	141	119	102	90	80	72	66	60	1484
14-#8	.0152	**1176**	1121	894	691	384	266	203	164	138	119	104	93	84	76	70	1731
16-#8	.0173	**1214**	1149	916	761	435	302	231	187	157	136	119	106	96	87	80	1979
18-#8	.0195	**1252**	1177	938	779	485	338	259	210	176	152	134	119	108	98	90	2226
20-#8	.0217	**1290**	1205	959	797	534	373	286	232	195	169	148	132	119	109	100	2474
22-#8	.0238	**1328**	1232	981	815	582	408	313	255	214	185	163	145	131	120	110	2721
8-#9	.0110	**1103**	1067	851	514	281	193	147	119	100	86	75	67	60	55	50	1245
9-#9	.0123	**1127**	1085	865	572	314	217	165	134	112	96	85	75	68	62	57	1401
10-#9	.0137	**1151**	1102	879	629	347	240	183	148	124	107	94	84	76	69	63	1556
12-#9	.0165	**1199**	1137	906	739	412	286	219	177	149	128	113	100	91	82	76	1868
14-#9	.0192	**1247**	1172	934	776	476	331	254	206	173	149	131	117	105	96	88	2179
16-#9	.0219	**1295**	1207	961	798	537	375	288	234	197	170	149	133	120	110	101	2490
18-#9	.0247	**1343**	1242	989	821	598	419	322	262	220	190	167	149	135	123	113	2802
6-#10	.0105	**1094**	1060	845	488	267	183	140	113	94	81	71	64	57	52	48	1178
8-#10	.0139	**1155**	1105	880	634	351	242	185	149	125	108	95	85	76	69	64	1571
10-#10	.0174	**1216**	1149	915	760	432	300	229	186	156	135	118	105	95	87	80	1964
12-#10	.0209	**1277**	1193	950	789	511	356	273	222	186	161	141	126	114	104	95	2356
14-#10	.0244	**1337**	1237	984	817	588	411	316	257	216	187	164	147	132	121	111	2749
16-#10	.0279	**1398**	1282	1019	846	662	465	359	292	246	213	187	167	151	138	127	3142
6-#11	.0128	**1135**	1090	869	585	322	222	170	137	115	99	87	77	70	64	58	1438
7-#11	.0150	**1173**	1117	890	672	373	258	197	159	134	115	101	90	81	74	68	1677
8-#11	.0171	**1210**	1144	911	756	422	293	224	182	152	131	115	103	93	85	78	1917
9-#11	.0193	**1248**	1171	932	774	471	328	251	203	171	148	130	116	104	95	87	2157
10-#11	.0214	**1285**	1199	954	792	519	362	278	225	189	163	144	128	116	105	97	2396
11-#11	.0235	**1323**	1226	975	809	566	396	304	247	208	179	158	141	127	116	106	2636
13-#11	.0278	**1397**	1280	1017	844	657	462	356	290	244	211	186	166	150	137	125	3115
15-#11	.0321	**1472**	1334	1060	879	744	526	407	332	280	242	213	190	172	157	144	3595
17-#11	.0364	**1547**	1388	1102	914	780	589	457	373	315	273	240	215	194	177	163	4074
19-#11	.0407	**1622**	1443	1145	949	810	650	505	413	350	303	267	239	216	197	182	4554
6-#14S	.0185	**1235**	1161	923	766	449	312	239	193	163	140	123	110	99	90	83	2046
7-#14S	.0216	**1289**	1200	953	791	517	361	277	224	189	163	143	128	115	105	97	2387
8-#14S	.0247	**1343**	1238	984	816	583	408	314	255	215	185	163	146	132	120	110	2728
9-#14S	.0278	**1397**	1277	1014	841	648	455	351	286	241	208	183	163	148	135	124	3070
10-#14S	.0309	**1451**	1316	1044	866	711	502	387	316	266	230	203	181	164	149	137	3411
12-#14S	.0370	**1559**	1394	1105	915	781	591	458	374	316	274	241	216	195	178	164	4093
14-#14S	.0432	**1667**	1471	1166	965	823	677	527	432	365	317	280	250	226	207	190	4775
16-#14S	.0494	**1775**	1549	1226	1015	865	754	594	488	414	359	317	284	257	235	216	5457
6-#18S	.0329	**1487**	1334	1055	872	725	512	396	323	272	235	207	185	167	153	140	3495
7-#18S	.0384	**1583**	1402	1107	915	779	588	456	373	315	273	240	215	194	177	163	4078
8-#18S	.0439	**1679**	1469	1159	957	815	661	515	422	357	309	273	244	221	202	186	4660
9-#18S	.0494	**1775**	1537	1211	999	850	731	572	469	398	345	305	273	247	226	208	5243
10-#18S	.0549	**1871**	1605	1263	1042	886	771	627	516	438	381	336	302	273	250	230	5825
11-#18S	.0604	**1967**	1672	1315	1084	922	802	680	561	477	415	367	330	299	273	252	6408

Check availability of #14S and #18S bars.

All above columns require spirals of A432 rod or cold drawn wire (f_y = 60,000 psi):—

⅝φ @ 2″

Outside diameter of spiral should be 3 in. less than side of column.

† Below zigzag horizontal line of each group, concrete governs; above, tension governs.

‡ M_o = capacity in pure bending, (N = 0); for extrapolation, see page 11-5.

SPIRALLY REINFORCED SQUARE COLUMNS—
Safe Load in Kips for Various Eccentricities in Inches
f'_c = 5000 psi (A61 or A432 Bars, f_y = 60,000 psi) f_s = 24,000 psi basis

COLUMN SIZE—28″ x 28″ — f'_c = 5000 psi, f_y = 60,000 psi

Bars	p	M/N † = e (in.)															M_o ‡ (kip-in.)
		0	2	4	6	8	10	12	14	16	18	20	22	24	26	28	
10-#8	.0101	**1169**	1147	920	568	302	206	156	125	105	90	79	70	63	58	53	*1294*
12-#8	.0121	**1207**	1175	942	670	359	245	186	150	126	108	95	84	76	69	63	*1552*
14-#8	.0141	**1245**	1203	965	769	415	285	216	174	146	126	110	98	88	81	74	*1811*
16-#8	.0161	**1283**	1231	987	824	471	323	246	199	167	143	126	112	101	92	84	*2070*
18-#8	.0181	**1321**	1259	1009	842	525	361	276	223	187	161	141	126	113	103	95	*2329*
20-#8	.0202	**1359**	1287	1032	861	578	399	305	247	207	178	157	140	126	115	105	*2588*
22-#8	.0222	**1397**	1316	1054	879	630	436	334	270	227	196	172	153	138	126	116	*2846*
8-#9	.0102	**1171**	1148	921	572	304	207	157	126	106	91	80	71	64	58	53	*1303*
9-#9	.0115	**1195**	1166	935	636	340	232	176	142	119	102	89	80	72	65	60	*1465*
10-#9	.0128	**1219**	1184	949	699	376	257	195	157	132	113	99	88	80	72	66	*1628*
12-#9	.0153	**1267**	1219	977	816	446	306	233	188	157	135	119	106	95	87	80	*1954*
14-#9	.0179	**1315**	1255	1006	839	514	354	270	218	183	158	138	123	111	101	93	*2280*
16-#9	.0204	**1363**	1290	1034	862	581	402	307	248	208	179	158	141	127	115	106	*2606*
18-#9	.0230	**1411**	1326	1062	885	647	448	343	278	233	201	177	158	142	130	119	*2931*
8-#10	.0130	**1223**	1186	951	705	379	259	197	159	133	114	100	89	80	73	67	*1644*
10-#10	.0162	**1284**	1231	986	823	467	321	244	197	165	142	125	111	100	91	84	*2055*
12-#10	.0194	**1345**	1276	1022	852	553	381	291	235	198	170	149	133	120	109	100	*2466*
14-#10	.0227	**1406**	1321	1058	882	636	441	337	273	229	198	174	155	140	127	117	*2877*
16-#10	.0259	**1467**	1366	1093	911	716	499	382	310	261	225	198	176	159	145	133	*3288*
18-#10	.0292	**1528**	1411	1129	941	794	555	427	347	292	252	222	198	179	163	150	*3700*
6-#11	.0119	**1204**	1171	939	652	349	238	181	146	122	105	92	82	74	67	61	*1505*
7-#11	.0139	**1242**	1199	961	748	404	276	210	169	142	122	107	95	86	78	72	*1756*
8-#11	.0159	**1279**	1227	982	819	457	314	239	193	162	139	122	109	98	89	82	*2007*
9-#11	.0179	**1316**	1254	1004	837	510	351	268	216	181	156	137	122	110	100	92	*2258*
10-#11	.0199	**1354**	1282	1026	855	562	388	296	239	201	173	152	135	122	111	102	*2509*
12-#11	.0239	**1429**	1337	1069	891	662	460	352	285	240	207	182	162	146	133	122	*3011*
14-#11	.0279	**1504**	1392	1113	927	759	530	407	330	278	240	211	188	170	155	142	*3512*
16-#11	.0318	**1579**	1447	1156	963	825	598	461	374	315	272	240	214	193	176	162	*4014*
18-#11	.0358	**1653**	1502	1200	999	856	665	513	418	353	305	268	240	217	198	182	*4516*
20-#11	.0398	**1728**	1557	1243	1035	886	729	565	461	389	337	297	265	240	219	201	*5018*
6-#14S	.0172	**1303**	1243	995	829	486	334	255	206	172	148	130	116	105	95	87	*2143*
7-#14S	.0201	**1357**	1283	1026	855	560	387	295	239	200	172	151	135	122	111	102	*2501*
8-#14S	.0230	**1411**	1322	1057	880	632	438	335	271	228	196	173	154	139	126	116	*2858*
9-#14S	.0258	**1465**	1361	1088	906	702	488	374	304	255	220	193	173	156	142	130	*3215*
10-#14S	.0287	**1519**	1401	1119	932	770	538	413	335	282	244	214	191	173	157	145	*3573*
12-#14S	.0344	**1627**	1480	1181	983	841	634	489	398	336	290	255	228	206	188	173	*4287*
14-#14S	.0402	**1735**	1559	1243	1034	885	727	563	459	388	336	296	264	239	218	201	*5002*
16-#14S	.0459	**1843**	1637	1305	1085	928	811	634	519	439	381	336	300	272	248	228	*5717*
6-#18S	.0306	**1555**	1420	1130	939	787	551	423	344	289	250	220	196	177	161	148	*3668*
7-#18S	.0357	**1651**	1489	1184	983	840	632	488	397	335	289	255	228	206	188	172	*4279*
8-#18S	.0408	**1747**	1557	1237	1027	877	711	551	449	379	328	289	259	234	213	196	*4891*
9-#18S	.0459	**1843**	1626	1291	1070	914	787	612	500	423	367	323	289	262	239	220	*5502*
10-#18S	.0510	**1939**	1695	1344	1114	951	830	671	550	466	404	357	320	289	264	243	*6113*
11-#18S	.0561	**2035**	1764	1398	1158	988	862	729	599	508	441	390	349	316	289	266	*6725*

Check availability of #14S and #18S bars.

All above columns require spirals of A432 rod or cold drawn wire (f_y = 60,000 psi):—

⅝φ @ 2″

Outside diameter of spiral should be 3 in. less than side of column.

† Below zigzag horizontal line of each group, concrete governs; above, tension governs.

‡ M_o = capacity in pure bending, (N = 0); for extrapolation, see page 11-5.

SPIRALLY REINFORCED SQUARE COLUMNS—
Safe Load in Kips for Various Eccentricities in Inches
f'_c = 5000 psi (A61 or A432 Bars, f_y = 60,000 psi) f_s = 24,000 psi basis

COLUMN SIZE—29″ x 29″ — f'_c = 5000 psi, f_y = 60,000 psi

Bars	p	M/N † = e (in.) 0	2	4	6	8	10	12	14	16	18	20	22	24	26	28	M_o ‡ (kip-in.)
11-#8	.0103	**1259**	1245	1005	691	358	241	182	146	122	105	92	81	73	67	61	1485
13-#8	.0122	**1297**	1274	1027	802	419	283	214	172	144	123	108	96	86	79	72	1756
15-#8	.0141	**1335**	1302	1050	880	479	325	246	198	165	142	124	111	100	91	83	2026
17-#8	.0160	**1373**	1331	1073	899	538	366	277	223	187	160	141	125	113	103	94	2296
19-#8	.0178	**1411**	1359	1096	918	596	407	309	249	208	179	157	140	126	115	105	2566
21-#8	.0197	**1449**	1388	1119	937	652	447	339	274	229	197	173	154	139	126	116	2836
10-#9	.0119	**1291**	1268	1023	779	406	275	207	167	139	119	105	93	84	76	70	1700
12-#9	.0143	**1339**	1304	1052	881	482	327	248	199	166	143	125	111	100	91	84	2040
14-#9	.0166	**1387**	1340	1080	905	556	379	287	231	193	166	146	130	117	106	98	2381
16-#9	.0190	**1435**	1376	1109	929	628	430	326	263	220	189	166	148	133	121	111	2721
18-#9	.0214	**1483**	1412	1138	953	699	480	365	294	247	212	186	166	150	136	125	3061
8-#10	.0121	**1295**	1271	1025	786	410	277	209	168	140	121	106	94	85	77	71	1717
10-#10	.0151	**1356**	1316	1061	888	505	343	260	209	175	150	132	117	106	96	88	2147
12-#10	.0181	**1417**	1362	1097	919	598	408	310	249	209	180	157	140	126	115	105	2576
14-#10	.0211	**1477**	1407	1133	949	687	471	359	289	242	209	183	163	147	134	123	3005
16-#10	.0242	**1538**	1453	1170	979	774	533	407	329	276	238	209	186	168	153	140	3435
18-#10	.0272	**1599**	1498	1206	1009	859	594	454	368	309	266	234	208	188	171	157	3864
6-#11	.0111	**1275**	1256	1012	727	377	255	192	154	129	111	97	86	78	70	65	1572
7-#11	.0130	**1313**	1284	1035	834	436	295	223	179	150	129	113	100	90	82	75	1835
8-#11	.0148	**1350**	1312	1057	885	494	336	254	204	171	147	129	114	103	94	86	2097
9-#11	.0167	**1388**	1340	1079	903	551	375	285	229	192	165	144	129	116	105	97	2359
10-#11	.0185	**1425**	1368	1101	922	607	415	315	254	212	183	160	143	129	117	107	2621
11-#11	.0204	**1463**	1395	1124	940	662	453	345	278	233	200	176	157	141	129	118	2883
13-#11	.0241	**1537**	1451	1168	977	769	530	404	326	274	236	207	184	166	151	139	3408
15-#11	.0278	**1612**	1507	1212	1014	871	604	462	374	314	271	238	212	191	174	160	3932
17-#11	.0315	**1687**	1563	1257	1051	903	676	518	420	354	305	268	239	216	197	181	4456
19-#11	.0352	**1762**	1619	1301	1088	935	746	574	466	393	339	298	266	240	219	201	4980
21-#11	.0390	**1837**	1674	1346	1125	966	815	629	512	431	373	328	293	265	241	222	5505
6-#14S	.0161	**1375**	1329	1070	895	526	358	271	218	182	157	137	122	110	100	92	2241
7-#14S	.0187	**1429**	1369	1101	921	606	414	314	253	212	182	160	142	128	117	107	2614
8-#14S	.0214	**1483**	1409	1133	948	684	469	357	288	241	207	182	162	146	133	122	2988
9-#14S	.0241	**1537**	1449	1165	974	760	523	399	322	270	233	204	182	164	149	137	3361
10-#14S	.0268	**1591**	1489	1197	1000	833	576	440	356	299	257	226	202	182	166	152	3735
11-#14S	.0294	**1645**	1529	1228	1027	882	628	481	389	327	282	248	221	200	182	167	4108
13-#14S	.0348	**1753**	1609	1292	1079	927	729	561	455	383	331	291	260	235	214	196	4855
15-#14S	.0401	**1861**	1689	1355	1132	972	827	638	520	438	379	334	298	269	246	226	5602
17-#14S	.0455	**1969**	1768	1419	1184	1016	890	714	583	492	426	375	336	303	277	255	6349
6-#18S	.0285	**1627**	1508	1209	1008	853	591	451	365	307	264	232	207	187	170	156	3841
7-#18S	.0333	**1723**	1578	1264	1054	903	678	521	422	355	306	269	240	217	198	182	4481
8-#18S	.0380	**1819**	1648	1318	1099	942	763	588	478	403	348	306	273	247	225	207	5121
9-#18S	.0428	**1915**	1718	1373	1144	980	845	653	532	449	388	342	306	276	252	232	5761
10-#18S	.0476	**2011**	1788	1428	1189	1018	890	717	586	495	429	378	338	305	279	256	6401
11-#18S	.0523	**2107**	1857	1483	1234	1057	924	779	638	540	468	413	369	334	305	281	7042
12-#18S	.0571	**2203**	1927	1538	1279	1095	957	839	688	584	507	447	401	363	331	305	7682

Check availability of #14S and #18S bars.

All above columns require spirals of A432 rod or cold drawn wire (f_y = 60,000 psi):—

⅝φ @ 2″

Outside diameter of spiral should be 3 in. less than side of column.

† Below zigzag horizontal line of each group, concrete governs; above, tension governs.

‡ M_o = capacity in pure bending, (N = 0); for extrapolation, see page 11-5.

SPIRALLY REINFORCED SQUARE COLUMNS—
Safe Load in Kips for Various Eccentricities in Inches

f'_c = 5000 psi (A61 or A432 Bars, f_y = 60,000 psi) f_s = 24,000 psi basis

COLUMN SIZE—30″ x 30″ — f'_c = 5000 psi, f_y = 60,000 psi

Bars	p	M/N † = e (in.) 0	2	4	6	8	10	12	14	16	18	20	22	24	26	28	M_o ‡ (kip-in.)
9-#9	.0100	**1341**	1338	1085	793	397	265	199	159	132	113	99	88	79	72	66	1595
10-#9	.0111	**1364**	1356	1100	871	439	293	220	176	147	126	110	98	88	80	73	1772
12-#9	.0133	**1412**	1393	1129	949	521	349	263	211	176	151	132	117	105	96	88	2127
14-#9	.0156	**1460**	1429	1158	974	600	404	305	245	204	175	153	136	123	112	102	2481
16-#9	.0178	**1508**	1465	1187	998	678	459	346	278	232	200	175	156	140	127	117	2836
18-#9	.0200	**1557**	1502	1217	1023	755	512	387	312	261	224	196	175	157	143	131	3191
20-#9	.0222	**1604**	1538	1246	1047	829	565	428	345	288	248	217	194	174	159	146	3545
22-#9	.0244	**1652**	1575	1275	1072	902	616	468	377	316	272	238	212	191	174	160	3900
24-#9	.0267	**1700**	1611	1305	1096	945	667	508	410	343	296	259	231	208	190	174	4254
26-#9	.0289	**1748**	1647	1334	1121	966	717	547	442	371	319	280	250	225	205	188	4609
8-#10	.0113	**1368**	1359	1101	879	443	296	222	178	148	127	111	99	89	81	74	1790
9-#10	.0127	**1399**	1382	1120	941	495	332	249	200	166	143	125	111	100	91	83	2014
10-#10	.0141	**1429**	1405	1138	957	546	367	276	221	185	158	139	123	111	101	92	2238
12-#10	.0169	**1490**	1451	1175	988	646	436	329	264	220	189	166	147	133	121	111	2686
14-#10	.0198	**1551**	1497	1212	1019	742	503	381	306	256	220	193	172	155	141	129	3133
16-#10	.0226	**1612**	1543	1249	1050	836	570	432	348	291	250	220	195	176	160	147	3581
18-#10	.0254	**1673**	1589	1286	1081	928	635	483	389	326	280	246	219	198	180	165	4029
20-#10	.0282	**1734**	1635	1323	1112	958	699	532	430	360	310	272	243	219	199	183	4476
6-#11	.0104	**1349**	1344	1089	813	408	272	204	163	136	117	102	91	81	74	68	1640
7-#11	.0121	**1387**	1372	1112	932	472	316	237	190	158	136	119	106	95	86	79	1913
8-#11	.0139	**1424**	1400	1134	953	534	359	270	216	180	155	135	120	108	99	90	2187
9-#11	.0156	**1461**	1429	1157	972	596	401	302	242	202	174	152	135	122	111	101	2460
10-#11	.0173	**1499**	1457	1180	991	656	443	334	268	224	193	169	150	135	123	113	2733
12-#11	.0208	**1574**	1513	1225	1029	774	525	398	320	268	230	202	179	162	147	135	3280
14-#11	.0243	**1649**	1570	1270	1067	887	606	460	371	310	267	234	208	188	171	157	3827
16-#11	.0277	**1724**	1626	1316	1105	952	684	521	421	353	303	266	237	214	195	179	4374
18-#11	.0312	**1798**	1683	1361	1142	984	760	581	470	394	340	298	266	240	219	201	4920
20-#11	.0347	**1873**	1739	1406	1180	1017	835	639	518	435	375	330	294	266	242	222	5467
22-#11	.0381	**1948**	1795	1451	1218	1049	908	697	566	476	411	361	322	291	265	244	6014
6-#14S	.0150	**1449**	1417	1147	964	568	382	288	231	193	165	145	129	116	105	96	2338
7-#14S	.0175	**1503**	1458	1180	991	655	442	334	268	224	192	168	150	135	123	112	2728
8-#14S	.0200	**1557**	1498	1212	1018	739	501	379	305	255	219	192	171	154	140	128	3117
9-#14S	.0225	**1611**	1539	1245	1045	821	559	424	341	285	245	215	191	173	157	144	3507
10-#14S	.0250	**1665**	1579	1277	1072	901	616	468	377	316	272	238	212	191	174	160	3897
12-#14S	.0300	**1773**	1660	1342	1126	970	726	554	448	376	324	284	253	228	208	191	4676
14-#14S	.0350	**1881**	1741	1407	1180	1016	833	638	517	434	375	329	294	265	241	222	5456
16-#14S	.0400	**1989**	1822	1471	1234	1062	932	720	584	492	425	374	334	301	275	252	6235
18-#14S	.0450	**2097**	1903	1536	1287	1108	973	799	650	549	474	418	373	337	307	283	7015
6-#18S	.0267	**1700**	1600	1290	1081	924	632	481	388	325	279	245	218	197	179	164	4013
7-#18S	.0311	**1796**	1671	1346	1127	969	727	554	448	376	324	284	253	229	208	191	4682
8-#18S	.0356	**1892**	1741	1402	1173	1009	818	626	507	426	368	323	288	260	237	218	5351
9-#18S	.0400	**1989**	1812	1458	1220	1048	906	696	565	476	411	361	322	291	265	244	6020
10-#18S	.0444	**2084**	1883	1514	1266	1088	954	764	622	524	453	399	356	322	294	270	6689
11-#18S	.0489	**2180**	1954	1570	1312	1127	988	831	678	572	495	436	390	352	322	296	7358
12-#18S	.0533	**2276**	2025	1626	1359	1167	1022	895	732	619	536	473	423	382	349	321	8027

Check availability of #14S and #18S bars.

All above columns require spirals of A432 rod or cold drawn wire (f_y = 60,000 psi):—

#14S and smaller—⅝φ @ 2″

#18S only —¾φ @ 2¾″

Outside diameter of spiral should be 3 in. less than side of column.

† Below zigzag horizontal line of each group, concrete governs; above, tension governs.

‡ M_o = capacity in pure bending, (N = 0); for extrapolation, see page 11-5.

SPIRALLY REINFORCED SQUARE COLUMNS—
Safe Load in Kips for Various Eccentricities in Inches
f'_c = 5000 psi (A61 or A432 Bars, f_y = 60,000 psi) f_s = 24,000 psi basis

COLUMN SIZE—31″ x 31″

f'_c = 5000 psi
f_y = 60,000 psi

Bars	p	M/N † = e (in.) 0	3	6	9	12	15	18	21	24	27	30	33	36	39	42	M_o ‡ (kip-in.)
10-#9	.0104	**1441**	1300	976	377	233	169	132	109	92	80	71	63	57	52	48	*1844*
12-#9	.0125	**1489**	1333	1020	448	278	202	158	130	111	96	85	76	69	63	58	*2213*
14-#9	.0146	**1537**	1366	1045	518	323	235	184	152	129	112	99	89	80	73	67	*2582*
16-#9	.0166	**1585**	1399	1070	587	367	267	210	173	147	128	113	101	92	84	77	*2951*
18-#9	.0187	**1633**	1431	1095	654	411	299	235	194	165	143	127	114	103	94	87	*3320*
20-#9	.0208	**1681**	1464	1120	720	454	331	261	215	183	159	141	126	114	105	96	*3689*
22-#9	.0229	**1729**	1497	1145	785	496	363	286	236	201	175	155	139	126	115	106	*4058*
24-#9	.0250	**1777**	1530	1170	848	538	394	311	257	219	190	168	151	137	125	115	*4427*
26-#9	.0271	**1825**	1563	1196	911	580	425	336	277	236	206	182	163	148	136	125	*4796*
8-#10	.0106	**1445**	1302	985	381	236	171	134	110	93	81	71	64	58	53	49	*1863*
9-#10	.0119	**1475**	1323	1012	426	264	192	150	123	105	91	80	72	65	60	55	*2096*
10-#10	.0132	**1506**	1343	1028	470	293	212	167	137	116	101	89	80	72	66	61	*2329*
12-#10	.0159	**1567**	1385	1060	558	349	253	199	164	139	121	107	96	87	79	73	*2795*
14-#10	.0185	**1627**	1427	1091	643	404	294	231	191	162	141	125	112	101	93	85	*3261*
16-#10	.0211	**1688**	1469	1123	727	458	335	263	217	185	161	142	127	116	106	97	*3727*
18-#10	.0238	**1749**	1510	1155	808	512	374	295	244	207	180	160	143	130	119	109	*4193*
20-#10	.0264	**1810**	1552	1186	888	565	414	327	270	230	200	177	159	144	132	121	*4659*
7-#11	.0114	**1463**	1314	1005	406	251	182	143	117	100	86	76	68	62	57	52	*1992*
8-#11	.0130	**1500**	1339	1025	460	286	208	163	134	114	99	87	78	71	65	60	*2276*
9-#11	.0146	**1538**	1365	1044	514	321	233	183	150	128	111	98	88	80	73	67	*2561*
10-#11	.0162	**1575**	1390	1063	567	355	258	203	167	142	123	109	98	88	81	74	*2846*
11-#11	.0179	**1613**	1416	1083	619	388	283	222	183	156	135	120	107	97	89	82	*3130*
13-#11	.0211	**1687**	1467	1121	722	455	332	261	216	183	160	141	127	115	105	97	*3700*
15-#11	.0243	**1762**	1518	1160	821	520	381	300	248	211	184	162	146	132	121	111	*4269*
17-#11	.0276	**1837**	1569	1199	918	585	429	339	280	238	207	184	165	149	137	126	*4838*
19-#11	.0308	**1912**	1620	1237	1001	648	476	376	311	265	231	205	184	167	153	141	*5407*
21-#11	.0341	**1987**	1671	1276	1032	709	523	414	343	292	255	226	203	184	168	155	*5976*
23-#11	.0373	**2062**	1722	1315	1063	770	569	451	374	319	278	247	221	201	184	170	*6546*
6-#14S	.0140	**1525**	1354	1035	490	305	222	174	143	122	106	93	84	76	69	64	*2435*
7-#14S	.0164	**1579**	1391	1063	566	354	257	202	167	141	123	109	97	88	81	74	*2841*
8-#14S	.0187	**1633**	1428	1091	641	402	293	230	190	161	140	124	111	101	92	85	*3247*
9-#14S	.0211	**1687**	1464	1118	713	450	328	258	213	181	158	139	125	113	104	95	*3653*
10-#14S	.0234	**1741**	1501	1146	785	496	363	286	236	201	175	155	139	126	115	106	*4059*
12-#14S	.0281	**1849**	1574	1201	923	588	431	341	281	240	209	185	166	150	138	127	*4871*
14-#14S	.0328	**1957**	1647	1256	1016	677	499	395	326	278	243	215	193	175	160	148	*5682*
16-#14S	.0375	**2065**	1720	1312	1060	764	565	448	371	316	276	245	220	199	182	168	*6494*
18-#14S	.0421	**2173**	1793	1367	1104	849	629	500	415	354	309	274	246	224	205	189	*7306*
6-#18S	.0250	**1777**	1517	1156	807	511	374	295	243	207	180	159	143	130	118	109	*4186*
7-#18S	.0291	**1873**	1581	1203	924	589	432	342	282	240	209	185	166	151	138	127	*4884*
8-#18S	.0333	**1969**	1645	1251	1009	666	490	388	321	273	238	211	190	172	157	145	*5582*
9-#18S	.0375	**2065**	1708	1298	1047	741	547	433	359	306	267	237	213	193	177	163	*6280*
10-#18S	.0416	**2161**	1772	1346	1085	813	602	478	397	339	295	262	235	214	196	180	*6977*
11-#18S	.0458	**2257**	1836	1393	1123	884	657	522	434	371	324	287	258	234	215	198	*7675*
12-#18S	.0499	**2353**	1899	1441	1161	953	710	566	470	402	352	312	281	255	234	215	*8373*
13-#18S	.0541	**2449**	1963	1488	1199	1003	763	609	507	434	379	337	303	275	252	233	*9071*

Check availability of #14S and #18S bars.

All above columns require spirals of A432 rod or cold drawn wire (f_y = 60,000 psi):—
#14S and smaller—5/8φ @ 2″
#18S only —3/4φ @ 2 3/4″

Outside diameter of spiral should be 3 in. less than side of column.
† Below zigzag horizontal line of each group, concrete governs; above, tension governs.
‡ M_o = capacity in pure bending, (N = 0); for extrapolation, see page 11-5.

SPIRALLY REINFORCED SQUARE COLUMNS—
Safe Load in Kips for Various Eccentricities in Inches
f'_c = 5000 psi (A61 or A432 Bars, f_y = 60,000 psi) f_s = 24,000 psi basis

COLUMN SIZE—34″ x 34″ | f'_c = 5000 psi, f_y = 60,000 psi

Bars	p	M/N † = e (in.) 0	3	6	9	12	15	18	21	24	27	30	33	36	39	42	M_o ‡ (kip-in.)
12-#9	.0104	**1732**	1608	1250	545	327	233	181	148	125	108	96	86	77	71	65	*2451*
14-#9	.0121	**1780**	1642	1276	630	379	271	211	172	146	126	111	100	90	82	76	*2859*
16-#9	.0138	**1828**	1676	1302	713	431	308	240	197	166	144	127	114	103	94	86	*3268*
18-#9	.0156	**1876**	1710	1329	795	482	346	269	221	187	162	143	128	116	106	97	*3677*
20-#9	.0173	**1924**	1744	1355	876	533	383	299	245	207	180	159	142	129	117	108	*4085*
22-#9	.0190	**1972**	1778	1382	954	583	419	327	269	228	197	174	156	141	129	119	*4494*
24-#9	.0208	**2020**	1812	1408	1032	632	456	356	292	248	215	190	170	154	141	129	*4902*
10-#10	.0110	**1749**	1619	1258	572	343	245	191	156	132	114	101	90	81	74	68	*2581*
12-#10	.0132	**1810**	1662	1291	679	409	293	228	187	158	137	121	108	98	89	82	*3097*
14-#10	.0154	**1871**	1705	1325	783	474	340	265	217	184	159	141	126	114	104	96	*3613*
16-#10	.0176	**1932**	1748	1358	884	538	387	302	247	209	182	160	144	130	119	109	*4130*
18-#10	.0198	**1993**	1791	1392	983	601	433	338	277	235	204	180	161	146	133	123	*4646*
20-#10	.0220	**2054**	1834	1425	1080	663	479	374	307	261	226	200	179	162	148	136	*5162*
8-#11	.0108	**1744**	1615	1255	560	336	240	186	152	129	112	98	88	80	73	67	*2524*
9-#11	.0121	**1781**	1641	1275	626	376	269	209	171	145	126	111	99	90	82	75	*2839*
10-#11	.0135	**1819**	1667	1295	691	417	298	232	190	161	139	123	110	99	91	83	*3155*
11-#11	.0148	**1856**	1694	1316	754	456	327	255	209	177	153	135	121	109	100	92	*3470*
13-#11	.0175	**1931**	1747	1357	879	535	384	300	246	208	180	159	143	129	118	108	*4101*
15-#11	.0202	**2006**	1799	1397	1000	612	440	344	282	239	208	183	164	149	136	125	*4732*
17-#11	.0229	**2081**	1852	1438	1117	687	496	388	319	270	235	207	186	168	154	141	*5363*
19-#11	.0256	**2156**	1905	1479	1209	762	551	432	355	301	262	231	207	188	171	158	*5994*
21-#11	.0283	**2231**	1958	1520	1242	835	605	475	391	332	288	255	228	207	189	174	*6625*
23-#11	.0310	**2306**	2011	1561	1275	906	659	518	426	362	315	279	250	226	207	190	*7256*
25-#11	.0337	**2380**	2064	1601	1308	977	712	560	462	393	341	302	271	245	224	207	*7887*
6-#14S	.0117	**1768**	1631	1266	598	359	256	199	163	138	120	105	94	85	78	72	*2702*
7-#14S	.0136	**1822**	1668	1295	690	416	298	232	190	161	139	123	110	99	91	83	*3153*
8-#14S	.0156	**1876**	1706	1325	781	473	339	264	216	183	159	140	125	113	104	95	*3603*
9-#14S	.0175	**1930**	1744	1354	870	529	380	296	243	206	178	157	141	128	116	107	*4054*
10-#14S	.0195	**1984**	1782	1383	956	584	420	328	269	228	198	175	156	142	129	119	*4504*
11-#14S	.0214	**2038**	1820	1412	1041	638	460	360	295	250	217	192	172	156	142	131	*4955*
13-#14S	.0253	**2146**	1896	1470	1201	745	539	422	347	294	256	226	202	183	168	154	*5856*
15-#14S	.0292	**2254**	1971	1529	1248	849	617	484	398	338	294	260	233	211	193	178	*6757*
17-#14S	.0331	**2362**	2047	1587	1296	951	693	545	449	381	332	293	263	238	218	201	*7658*
19-#14S	.0370	**2470**	2123	1645	1343	1050	767	604	499	424	369	327	293	266	243	224	*8558*
21-#14S	.0409	**2578**	2199	1704	1391	1146	841	663	548	467	406	360	323	293	268	247	*9459*
6-#18S	.0208	**2020**	1803	1397	994	608	438	342	281	238	207	182	163	148	135	124	*4705*
7-#18S	.0242	**2116**	1869	1448	1140	702	507	397	326	277	240	212	190	172	157	145	*5489*
8-#18S	.0277	**2212**	1936	1499	1222	794	575	451	371	315	273	242	217	196	179	165	*6273*
9-#18S	.0311	**2308**	2002	1549	1264	883	642	504	415	353	307	271	243	220	201	185	*7057*
10-#18S	.0346	**2404**	2069	1600	1305	971	708	557	459	390	339	300	269	244	223	205	*7841*
11-#18S	.0381	**2500**	2135	1651	1346	1056	772	609	502	427	372	329	295	268	245	226	*8626*
12-#18S	.0415	**2596**	2202	1702	1387	1140	836	660	545	464	404	358	321	291	266	245	*9410*
13-#18S	.0450	**2692**	2268	1753	1428	1205	898	710	587	501	436	386	347	315	288	265	*10194*
14-#18S	.0484	**2788**	2335	1804	1470	1240	959	760	629	537	468	415	372	338	309	285	*10978*
15-#18S	.0519	**2884**	2401	1855	1511	1274	1020	809	670	572	499	443	398	361	331	305	*11762*

Check availability of #14S and #18S bars.

All above columns require spirals of A432 rod or cold drawn wire (f_y = 60,000 psi):—

¾φ @ 2¾″

Outside diameter of spiral should be 3 in. less than side of column.

† Below zigzag horizontal line of each group, concrete governs; above, tension governs.

‡ M_o = capacity in pure bending, (N = 0); for extrapolation, see page 11-5.

SPIRALLY REINFORCED SQUARE COLUMNS—
Safe Load in Kips for Various Eccentricities in Inches

f'_c = 5000 psi (A61 or A432 Bars, f_y = 60,000 psi) f_s = 24,000 psi basis

COLUMN SIZE—35″ x 35″

f'_c = 5000 psi
f_y = 60,000 psi

Bars	p	M/N † = e (in.) 0	3	6	9	12	15	18	21	24	27	30	33	36	39	42	M_o ‡ (kip-in.)
13-#9	.0106	**1843**	1723	1346	629	373	265	205	167	141	122	108	96	87	79	73	*2749*
15-#9	.0122	**1891**	1758	1373	719	428	304	236	193	163	141	124	111	100	92	84	*3172*
17-#9	.0139	**1939**	1792	1400	807	482	344	267	218	184	160	141	126	114	104	95	*3595*
19-#9	.0155	**1987**	1827	1427	894	536	382	297	243	206	178	157	141	127	116	107	*4018*
21-#9	.0171	**2035**	1861	1453	979	589	421	328	268	227	197	173	155	140	128	118	*4441*
23-#9	.0188	**2083**	1895	1480	1062	642	459	358	293	248	215	190	170	154	140	129	*4864*
25-#9	.0204	**2131**	1930	1507	1144	694	497	388	318	269	233	206	184	167	152	140	*5286*
10-#10	.0104	**1836**	1717	1341	613	363	257	200	163	138	119	105	94	85	77	71	*2672*
12-#10	.0124	**1897**	1761	1375	726	432	308	239	195	165	143	126	112	102	93	85	*3207*
14-#10	.0145	**1957**	1805	1409	838	501	357	277	227	192	166	146	131	118	108	99	*3741*
16-#10	.0166	**2018**	1848	1443	946	568	406	316	258	219	189	167	149	135	123	113	*4276*
18-#10	.0187	**2079**	1892	1477	1052	635	455	354	290	245	213	188	168	152	139	128	*4811*
20-#10	.0207	**2140**	1936	1511	1156	701	503	392	321	272	236	208	186	169	154	142	*5345*
8-#11	.0102	**1830**	1713	1338	600	355	252	195	159	135	116	103	92	83	76	69	*2613*
9-#11	.0115	**1868**	1740	1358	670	398	283	219	179	151	131	115	103	93	85	78	*2940*
10-#11	.0127	**1905**	1767	1379	739	440	313	243	199	168	145	128	114	103	94	87	*3267*
12-#11	.0153	**1980**	1820	1421	874	523	374	290	237	201	174	153	137	124	113	104	*3920*
14-#11	.0178	**2055**	1873	1462	1005	606	433	337	276	234	202	179	160	144	132	121	*4574*
16-#11	.0204	**2130**	1927	1504	1133	686	492	384	314	266	231	204	182	165	151	138	*5227*
18-#11	.0229	**2205**	1980	1545	1257	766	550	429	352	298	259	229	205	185	169	156	*5881*
20-#11	.0255	**2280**	2034	1587	1301	843	608	475	390	330	287	253	227	205	188	173	*6534*
22-#11	.0280	**2354**	2087	1628	1335	920	665	520	427	362	315	278	249	225	206	190	*7188*
24-#11	.0306	**2429**	2141	1670	1369	995	721	565	464	394	342	303	271	246	224	207	*7841*
26-#11	.0331	**2504**	2194	1712	1403	1069	776	609	501	426	370	327	293	265	243	223	*8495*
6-#14S	.0110	**1855**	1729	1350	640	379	269	209	171	144	125	110	98	89	81	74	*2800*
7-#14S	.0129	**1909**	1768	1379	739	440	313	243	198	168	145	128	114	103	94	87	*3266*
8-#14S	.0147	**1963**	1806	1409	836	500	356	277	226	191	166	146	131	118	108	99	*3733*
9-#14S	.0165	**2017**	1844	1439	931	559	399	310	254	215	186	164	147	133	121	111	*4200*
10-#14S	.0184	**2071**	1883	1469	1024	617	442	344	281	238	206	182	163	147	135	124	*4666*
11-#14S	.0202	**2125**	1921	1498	1115	675	484	377	309	261	227	200	179	162	148	136	*5133*
13-#14S	.0239	**2233**	1998	1558	1276	788	567	442	363	308	267	236	211	191	174	160	*6066*
15-#14S	.0276	**2341**	2074	1617	1325	898	648	507	416	353	307	271	243	220	201	185	*7000*
17-#14S	.0312	**2449**	2151	1677	1373	1005	728	571	469	398	346	306	274	248	227	209	*7933*
19-#14S	.0349	**2557**	2228	1736	1422	1110	807	634	522	443	385	341	305	277	253	233	*8866*
21-#14S	.0386	**2665**	2304	1795	1471	1212	884	696	573	488	424	375	337	305	279	257	*9800*
6-#18S	.0196	**2107**	1904	1483	1065	643	461	359	294	249	216	190	170	154	141	129	*4877*
7-#18S	.0229	**2203**	1971	1535	1221	742	533	416	341	289	251	221	198	179	164	151	*5690*
8-#18S	.0261	**2299**	2039	1587	1299	839	605	473	388	329	285	252	226	204	187	172	*6503*
9-#18S	.0294	**2395**	2106	1639	1341	934	675	529	434	369	320	283	253	229	210	193	*7316*
10-#18S	.0327	**2491**	2173	1690	1383	1027	745	584	480	408	354	313	281	254	232	214	*8129*
11-#18S	.0359	**2587**	2241	1742	1425	1118	813	638	526	447	388	343	308	279	255	235	*8942*
12-#18S	.0392	**2683**	2308	1794	1468	1206	880	692	571	485	422	374	335	304	278	256	*9755*
13-#18S	.0424	**2779**	2375	1846	1510	1277	945	745	615	523	456	403	362	328	300	276	*10568*
14-#18S	.0457	**2875**	2443	1898	1552	1313	1010	798	659	561	489	433	388	352	322	297	*11381*
15-#18S	.0490	**2971**	2510	1950	1594	1348	1074	849	702	599	522	462	415	376	344	317	*12194*

Check availability of #14S and #18S bars.

All above columns require spirals of A432 rod or cold drawn wire (f_y = 60,000 psi):—

¾φ @ 2½″

Outside diameter of spiral should be 3 in. less than side of column.

† Below zigzag horizontal line of each group, concrete governs; above, tension governs.

‡ M_o = capacity in pure bending, (N = 0); for extrapolation, see page 11-5.

SPIRALLY REINFORCED SQUARE COLUMNS—
Safe Load in Kips for Various Eccentricities in Inches
f'_c = 5000 psi (A61 or A432 Bars, f_y = 60,000 psi) f_s = 24,000 psi basis

COLUMN SIZE—36″ x 36″ | **f'_c = 5000 psi** | **f_y = 60,000 psi**

Bars	p	M/N † = e (in.) 0	3	6	9	12	15	18	21	24	27	30	33	36	39	42	M_o ‡ (kip-in.)
13-#9	.0100	**1931**	1825	1432	673	393	278	215	175	147	127	112	100	91	83	76	*2842*
15-#9	.0116	**1979**	1860	1459	769	451	319	247	201	170	147	129	116	104	95	88	*3280*
17-#9	.0131	**2027**	1895	1487	864	509	360	279	228	192	166	146	131	118	108	99	*3717*
19-#9	.0147	**2075**	1929	1514	956	565	401	311	254	214	185	163	146	132	120	111	*4154*
21-#9	.0162	**2123**	1964	1541	1047	621	442	343	280	236	205	180	161	146	133	122	*4592*
23-#9	.0177	**2171**	1999	1569	1136	677	482	374	306	258	224	197	176	160	146	134	*5029*
11-#10	.0108	**1955**	1841	1445	717	419	296	229	187	158	136	120	107	97	88	81	*3040*
13-#10	.0127	**2016**	1885	1479	837	492	349	270	220	186	161	142	127	114	104	96	*3593*
15-#10	.0147	**2077**	1929	1514	954	564	400	310	253	214	185	163	146	132	120	111	*4146*
17-#10	.0167	**2138**	1974	1548	1069	635	452	350	286	242	209	185	165	149	136	125	*4699*
19-#10	.0186	**2199**	2018	1583	1181	705	502	390	319	270	233	206	184	167	152	140	*5252*
21-#10	.0206	**2260**	2062	1617	1290	774	552	430	351	297	258	227	203	184	168	154	*5804*
9-#11	.0108	**1956**	1842	1445	717	420	297	229	187	158	136	120	107	97	88	81	*3041*
10-#11	.0120	**1994**	1869	1466	791	464	329	254	207	175	151	133	119	108	98	90	*3379*
11-#11	.0132	**2031**	1896	1487	864	509	360	279	228	192	166	146	131	118	108	99	*3717*
13-#11	.0156	**2106**	1950	1529	1006	596	423	328	268	226	196	173	154	140	127	117	*4393*
15-#11	.0181	**2181**	2004	1572	1144	682	486	377	308	260	226	199	178	161	147	135	*5069*
17-#11	.0205	**2256**	2058	1614	1279	766	547	425	348	294	255	225	201	182	166	153	*5745*
19-#11	.0229	**2331**	2112	1656	1362	849	608	473	387	328	284	251	224	203	185	170	*6421*
21-#11	.0253	**2406**	2166	1698	1397	931	668	521	427	361	313	277	247	224	205	188	*7097*
23-#11	.0277	**2481**	2220	1741	1432	1011	727	568	465	394	342	302	271	245	224	206	*7773*
25-#11	.0301	**2555**	2274	1783	1466	1090	786	614	504	427	371	328	293	266	243	223	*8449*
27-#11	.0325	**2630**	2328	1825	1501	1168	843	660	542	460	400	353	316	286	262	241	*9125*
6-#14S	.0104	**1943**	1831	1436	685	400	283	219	178	150	130	114	102	92	84	77	*2897*
7-#14S	.0122	**1997**	1870	1466	791	464	329	254	207	175	151	133	119	108	98	90	*3380*
8-#14S	.0139	**2051**	1909	1496	895	528	374	290	236	199	173	152	136	123	112	103	*3862*
9-#14S	.0156	**2106**	1948	1527	996	590	419	325	265	224	194	171	153	138	126	116	*4345*
10-#14S	.0174	**2159**	1986	1557	1095	651	464	360	294	248	215	190	169	153	140	129	*4828*
12-#14S	.0208	**2267**	2064	1617	1288	772	552	429	351	297	257	227	203	183	167	154	*5794*
14-#14S	.0243	**2375**	2141	1678	1379	890	638	497	407	345	299	264	236	214	195	179	*6760*
16-#14S	.0278	**2483**	2219	1738	1429	1005	723	564	463	392	340	300	269	243	222	205	*7725*
18-#14S	.0313	**2592**	2297	1799	1478	1118	806	631	518	439	381	337	302	273	249	230	*8691*
20-#14S	.0347	**2699**	2374	1859	1528	1227	888	696	572	486	422	373	334	303	276	255	*9657*
22-#14S	.0382	**2807**	2452	1920	1578	1334	969	760	626	532	462	409	366	332	303	279	*10623*
6-#18S	.0185	**2195**	2008	1572	1140	680	484	376	307	259	225	198	177	160	146	134	*5050*
7-#18S	.0216	**2291**	2076	1625	1307	784	560	436	356	302	261	231	206	187	170	157	*5892*
8-#18S	.0247	**2387**	2144	1678	1378	887	636	495	405	343	298	263	235	213	194	179	*6734*
9-#18S	.0278	**2483**	2213	1730	1421	987	710	554	454	385	334	295	264	239	218	201	*7576*
10-#18S	.0309	**2579**	2281	1783	1464	1085	782	612	502	426	369	326	292	265	242	222	*8417*
11-#18S	.0340	**2675**	2349	1836	1507	1181	854	669	550	466	405	358	321	290	265	244	*9259*
12-#18S	.0370	**2771**	2417	1889	1550	1275	925	725	597	507	440	389	349	316	289	266	*10101*
13-#18S	.0401	**2867**	2485	1942	1593	1351	994	781	643	547	475	420	377	341	312	287	*10943*
14-#18S	.0432	**2963**	2553	1995	1637	1388	1062	836	689	586	510	451	405	367	335	309	*11785*
15-#18S	.0463	**3059**	2622	2048	1680	1424	1130	890	735	625	544	482	432	392	358	330	*12626*

Check availability of #14S and #18S bars.

All above columns require spirals of A432 rod or cold drawn wire (f_y = 60,000 psi):—
¾φ @ 2½″

Outside diameter of spiral should be 3 in. less than side of column.
† Below zigzag horizontal line of each group, concrete governs; above, tension governs.
‡ M_o = capacity in pure bending, (N = 0); for extrapolation, see page 11-5.

SPIRALLY REINFORCED SQUARE COLUMNS—

Safe Load in Kips for Various Eccentricities in Inches

$f'_c = 5000$ psi (A431 Bars, $f_y = 75{,}000$ psi) $f_s = 30{,}000$ psi basis

COLUMN SIZE—17″ x 17″

$f'_c = 5000$ psi
$f_y = 75{,}000$ psi

Bars	p	M/N † = e (in.) 0	1	2	3	4	5	6	7	8	9	10	12	14	16	18	M_o ‡ (kip-in.)
6-#11	.0324	**642**	582	467	390	335	293	229	185	155	133	117	94	78	67	59	*955*
7-#11	.0378	**688**	614	491	409	350	307	260	210	177	152	134	108	90	78	68	*1114*
8-#11	.0432	**735**	645	515	428	366	320	284	234	198	171	151	122	102	88	77	*1273*
9-#11	.0486	**782**	677	538	447	382	333	296	256	217	188	166	135	113	98	86	*1432*
10-#11	.0540	**829**	709	562	465	397	347	307	276	235	205	181	148	124	107	95	*1592*
6-#14	.0467	**766**	664	527	437	373	326	289	244	206	179	158	127	107	92	81	*1343*
7-#14	.0545	**833**	709	560	463	395	344	305	273	232	202	179	146	123	106	93	*1567*
8-#14	.0623	**901**	753	594	490	417	363	321	288	256	224	199	162	137	119	105	*1791*

To provide required amount of spiral reinforcement and minimum clearance between turns (without complying with minimum spacing, D/6), all above columns can have spirals of rod or cold drawn wire ($f_y = 60{,}000$ psi) as follows: ⅝φ @ 2″

Check availability of #14 and #18 bars.

Outside diameter of spiral should be 3 in. less than side of column.
† Below zigzag horizontal line of each group, concrete governs; above, tension governs.
‡ M_o = capacity in pure bending, ($N = 0$); for extrapolation, see page 11-5.

SPIRALLY REINFORCED SQUARE COLUMNS—
Safe Load in Kips for Various Eccentricities in Inches
f'_c = 5000 psi (A431 Bars, f_y = 75,000 psi) f_s = 30,000 psi basis

f'_c = 5000 psi
f_y = 75,000 psi

Bars	p	M/N † = e (in.) 0	1	2	3	4	5	6	7	8	9	10	12	14	16	18	M_o ‡ (kip-in.)
COLUMN SIZE—18″ x 18″																	
6-#11	.0289	**685**	639	519	437	378	332	261	208	173	148	130	104	86	74	65	1039
7-#11	.0337	**732**	672	545	458	395	347	295	237	198	170	149	120	100	86	75	1212
8-#11	.0385	**779**	705	570	478	411	361	322	265	222	191	168	135	113	97	85	1386
9-#11	.0433	**826**	738	595	498	428	376	335	290	244	211	186	150	126	108	95	1559
10-#11	.0481	**872**	770	619	518	445	390	347	313	265	230	203	164	138	119	104	1732
11-#11	.0530	**919**	803	644	538	462	404	360	324	285	248	219	178	150	129	114	1905
6-#14	.0417	**809**	724	583	488	419	368	328	276	232	200	176	142	119	102	89	1464
7-#14	.0486	**877**	771	618	516	443	388	345	310	262	227	200	162	136	117	103	1709
8-#14	.0556	**944**	817	653	544	466	408	363	326	290	252	223	181	153	132	116	1953
9-#14	.0625	**1012**	864	689	572	490	428	380	342	311	275	244	200	169	146	129	2197
COLUMN SIZE—19″ x 19″																	
6-#11	.0259	**732**	700	575	488	423	374	294	233	193	164	143	114	95	81	71	1123
7-#11	.0302	**778**	733	601	509	441	390	334	266	221	189	165	132	109	94	82	1311
8-#11	.0346	**825**	767	627	530	459	405	362	297	248	212	186	149	124	106	93	1498
9-#11	.0389	**872**	801	653	551	477	420	376	326	273	235	206	165	138	118	104	1685
10-#11	.0432	**919**	834	679	573	495	436	389	352	297	256	225	181	152	130	114	1872
11-#11	.0475	**966**	868	705	594	513	451	403	364	319	276	244	197	165	142	125	2060
12-#11	.0519	**1012**	901	731	615	530	466	416	376	340	296	261	212	178	154	135	2247
6-#14	.0374	**856**	787	641	541	468	412	369	311	260	223	195	157	131	112	98	1586
7-#14	.0436	**923**	835	678	571	493	434	387	349	294	253	223	179	150	129	113	1850
8-#14	.0499	**991**	883	715	601	518	456	406	367	325	282	248	201	169	145	128	2115
9-#14	.0561	**1058**	931	752	631	543	477	425	384	349	308	272	222	187	161	142	2379
10-#14	.0623	**1126**	978	789	660	568	498	444	400	364	332	295	241	204	176	155	2644
COLUMN SIZE—20″ x 20″																	
6-#11	.0234	**780**	763	633	540	472	418	330	259	213	181	157	125	103	88	77	1208
7-#11	.0273	**827**	797	660	563	491	435	375	296	245	208	181	144	119	102	89	1409
8-#11	.0312	**874**	832	687	585	510	451	405	331	275	234	205	163	135	116	101	1610
9-#11	.0351	**921**	866	714	607	528	468	419	364	303	259	227	181	151	129	113	1812
10-#11	.0390	**968**	901	741	630	547	484	434	393	330	283	248	199	166	142	125	2013
11-#11	.0429	**1014**	935	768	652	566	500	448	406	355	306	269	216	181	155	136	2214
13-#11	.0507	**1108**	1003	822	696	604	533	477	431	394	348	307	249	209	180	158	2617
6-#14	.0338	**905**	853	702	597	519	459	412	347	288	247	215	172	143	122	107	1707
7-#14	.0394	**972**	902	741	629	546	482	432	391	327	281	246	197	164	141	123	1992
8-#14	.0450	**1040**	951	779	660	572	505	452	409	363	313	275	221	185	159	139	2277
9-#14	.0506	**1107**	1000	817	691	599	528	472	427	390	342	302	244	205	177	155	2561
10-#14	.0563	**1175**	1049	856	723	625	551	493	445	406	370	327	266	224	193	170	2846
6-#18	.0600	**1200**	1071	867	728	628	552	492	444	405	368	326	265	224	193	170	2857

Check availability of #14 and #18 bars.

All above columns require spirals of rod or cold drawn wire (f_y = 60,000 psi):—
⅝ φ @ 2¼″

Outside diameter of spiral should be 3 in. less than side of column.
† Below zigzag horizontal line of each group, concrete governs; above, tension governs.
‡ M_o = capacity in pure bending, (N = 0); for extrapolation, see page 11-5.

SPIRALLY REINFORCED SQUARE COLUMNS—
Safe Load in Kips for Various Eccentricities in Inches
f'_c = 5000 psi (A431 Bars, f_y = 75,000 psi) f_s = 30,000 psi basis

COLUMN SIZE—21″ x 21″

f'_c = 5000 psi
f_y = 75,000 psi

Bars	p	M/N † = e (in.)															M_o ‡ (kip-in.)
		0	1	2	3	4	5	6	8	10	12	14	16	18	20	22	
6-#11	.0212	**832**	829	694	596	523	465	370	235	172	136	112	95	83	73	66	*1292*
7-#11	.0248	**878**	864	722	619	543	483	421	270	198	157	130	111	96	85	76	*1507*
8-#11	.0283	**925**	899	750	643	562	500	450	303	224	178	147	125	109	97	87	*1722*
9-#11	.0318	**972**	935	778	666	582	517	465	335	248	198	164	140	122	108	97	*1938*
10-#11	.0354	**1019**	970	806	689	602	534	481	365	272	217	181	154	135	120	108	*2153*
12-#11	.0424	**1112**	1040	861	735	641	569	511	421	317	254	212	182	160	142	128	*2584*
14-#11	.0495	**1206**	1110	917	781	681	603	541	449	358	289	243	209	183	163	147	*3015*
6-#14	.0306	**956**	921	766	655	573	509	458	319	236	187	155	133	116	103	92	*1829*
7-#14	.0357	**1023**	971	806	688	601	533	479	362	270	215	179	153	134	119	107	*2134*
8-#14	.0408	**1091**	1021	845	721	629	557	501	402	302	242	202	173	151	135	121	*2439*
9-#14	.0459	**1158**	1071	885	754	657	582	522	433	332	267	224	192	168	150	135	*2744*
10-#14	.0510	**1226**	1121	925	787	684	606	543	450	361	292	245	211	185	165	149	*3049*
11-#14	.0561	**1293**	1171	964	819	712	630	565	468	388	315	265	229	201	179	162	*3353*
6-#18	.0544	**1271**	1145	938	794	689	608	544	450	361	292	245	212	186	166	149	*3073*
7-#18	.0635	**1391**	1232	1005	849	735	648	579	478	404	329	278	241	212	189	171	*3585*

All above columns require spirals of rod or cold drawn wire (f_y = 60,000 psi):—
⅝ ϕ @ 2¼″

COLUMN SIZE—22″ x 22″

f'_c = 5000 psi
f_y = 75,000 psi

Bars	p	M/N † = e (in.)															M_o ‡ (kip-in.)
		0	1	2	3	4	5	6	8	10	12	14	16	18	20	22	
6-#11	.0193	**885**	885	757	655	576	515	413	258	187	147	121	103	89	79	71	*1376*
7-#11	.0226	**932**	932	786	679	597	533	470	296	216	170	140	119	104	92	82	*1605*
8-#11	.0258	**979**	970	815	703	618	551	498	333	244	193	159	135	118	104	94	*1835*
9-#11	.0290	**1026**	1005	844	727	639	569	514	368	271	214	177	151	132	117	105	*2064*
10-#11	.0322	**1072**	1041	873	751	659	587	530	401	297	236	195	167	146	129	116	*2294*
11-#11	.0355	**1119**	1077	901	775	680	605	546	433	322	257	213	182	159	141	127	*2523*
13-#11	.0419	**1213**	1148	959	823	721	641	578	482	370	296	247	212	185	165	148	*2982*
15-#11	.0483	**1306**	1219	1016	871	762	677	610	508	414	334	279	240	211	188	169	*3441*
6-#14	.0279	**1009**	992	832	716	629	561	506	351	258	204	168	143	125	111	99	*1950*
7-#14	.0325	**1077**	1043	873	751	658	586	528	399	295	234	194	166	144	128	115	*2276*
8-#14	.0372	**1144**	1094	914	785	688	612	551	443	330	263	219	187	164	145	130	*2601*
9-#14	.0418	**1212**	1145	955	819	717	637	574	478	364	291	243	208	182	162	146	*2926*
10-#14	.0465	**1279**	1196	996	853	746	663	596	497	396	318	266	228	200	178	160	*3251*
12-#14	.0558	**1414**	1298	1077	921	804	713	641	533	454	368	309	267	235	209	189	*3901*
6-#18	.0496	**1324**	1221	1011	862	752	666	598	497	398	320	268	230	202	180	162	*3289*
7-#18	.0579	**1444**	1310	1081	920	801	709	636	527	446	361	304	262	231	206	186	*3837*

Check availability of #14 and #18 bars.

All above columns require spirals of rod or cold drawn wire (f_y = 60,000 psi):—
#14 and smaller—⅝ ϕ @ 2¼″
#18 only —⅝ ϕ @ 2″

Outside diameter of spiral should be 3 in. less than side of column.
† Below zigzag horizontal line of each group, concrete governs; above, tension governs.
‡ M_o = capacity in pure bending, (N = 0); for extrapolation, see page 11-5.

SPIRALLY REINFORCED SQUARE COLUMNS—
Safe Load in Kips for Various Eccentricities in Inches
f'_c = 5000 psi (A431 Bars, f_y = 75,000 psi) f_s = 30,000 psi basis

COLUMN SIZE—23″ x 23″ — f'_c = 5000 psi, f_y = 75,000 psi

Bars	p	M/N † = e (in.) 0	1	2	3	4	5	6	8	10	12	14	16	18	20	22	M_o ‡ (kip-in.)
6-#11	.0177	**942**	942	824	716	633	567	460	282	203	159	130	110	96	85	76	*1460*
7-#11	.0206	**988**	988	854	741	655	586	524	324	234	184	151	128	111	98	88	*1704*
8-#11	.0236	**1035**	1035	883	766	676	605	548	364	265	208	171	146	126	112	100	*1947*
9-#11	.0265	**1082**	1079	913	791	698	624	565	403	294	232	191	163	142	125	112	*2191*
10-#11	.0295	**1129**	1116	942	816	719	643	581	440	323	255	211	180	156	138	124	*2434*
11-#11	.0324	**1176**	1152	972	841	741	662	598	476	351	278	230	196	171	151	136	*2677*
13-#11	.0383	**1269**	1224	1031	890	783	699	632	529	403	321	267	228	199	177	159	*3164*
15-#11	.0442	**1363**	1297	1090	940	826	737	665	557	452	362	302	259	227	202	181	*3651*
6-#14	.0255	**1066**	1065	901	780	688	615	556	384	280	220	182	154	134	119	106	*2072*
7-#14	.0298	**1133**	1117	943	815	718	642	580	438	321	253	209	178	155	138	123	*2417*
8-#14	.0340	**1201**	1170	985	851	749	669	604	487	360	285	236	202	176	156	140	*2763*
9-#14	.0383	**1268**	1221	1027	886	779	695	628	525	397	316	263	224	196	174	156	*3108*
10-#14	.0425	**1336**	1273	1069	922	810	722	651	545	432	345	288	247	216	192	172	*3454*
11-#14	.0468	**1403**	1325	1111	957	840	749	675	564	465	374	312	268	235	209	188	*3799*
13-#14	.0553	**1538**	1429	1195	1027	900	802	722	603	517	426	358	309	271	242	218	*4490*
6-#18	.0454	**1381**	1300	1086	932	817	727	655	546	436	349	291	249	218	194	174	*3505*
7-#18	.0529	**1501**	1390	1158	993	868	772	694	578	489	395	331	285	250	222	200	*4089*
8-#18	.0605	**1621**	1481	1230	1052	919	816	734	611	523	437	368	318	280	250	225	*4673*

COLUMN SIZE—24″ x 24″ — f'_c = 5000 psi, f_y = 75,000 psi

Bars	p	M/N † = e (in.) 0	1	2	3	4	5	6	8	10	12	14	16	18	20	22	M_o ‡ (kip-in.)
6-#11	.0663	**1000**	1000	894	780	692	622	512	308	220	171	140	118	102	90	81	*1544*
7-#11	.0190	**1047**	1047	924	806	715	642	583	354	254	198	162	137	119	105	94	*1802*
8-#11	.0217	**1094**	1094	954	832	737	662	600	398	287	224	184	156	135	119	107	*2059*
9-#11	.0244	**1141**	1141	985	857	759	681	618	440	319	250	205	174	151	134	120	*2317*
10-#11	.0271	**1187**	1187	1015	883	782	701	635	481	350	275	226	192	167	148	133	*2574*
12-#11	.0325	**1281**	1267	1075	934	826	740	671	557	409	323	267	228	198	176	158	*3089*
14-#11	.0379	**1375**	1340	1136	986	870	779	705	593	465	369	306	262	228	203	182	*3604*
16-#11	.0433	**1468**	1413	1196	1037	915	818	740	622	517	413	344	295	258	229	206	*4119*
6-#14	.0234	**1125**	1125	972	846	749	672	610	420	304	238	195	166	144	127	114	*2193*
7-#14	.0273	**1192**	1192	1016	883	781	700	635	479	348	273	225	191	166	147	132	*2559*
8-#14	.0313	**1260**	1248	1059	920	813	728	659	534	391	308	254	217	189	167	150	*2925*
9-#14	.0352	**1327**	1301	1102	956	844	756	684	575	431	342	283	241	210	186	167	*3290*
10-#14	.0391	**1395**	1353	1145	993	876	784	709	596	470	374	310	265	231	205	184	*3656*
11-#14	.0430	**1462**	1406	1188	1029	907	811	734	616	507	404	337	288	252	224	201	*4022*
13-#14	.0508	**1597**	1511	1274	1102	970	867	783	657	565	462	387	333	292	260	234	*4753*
6-#18	.0417	**1439**	1381	1163	1005	885	790	713	598	475	379	314	269	235	208	187	*3721*
7-#18	.0486	**1559**	1473	1238	1067	938	837	755	632	535	429	358	307	269	239	215	*4341*
8-#18	.0556	**1679**	1565	1312	1129	991	883	797	666	572	475	399	343	302	269	242	*4961*
9-#18	.0625	**1800**	1657	1386	1191	1045	930	838	700	601	518	437	378	333	297	268	*5582*

Check availability of #14 and #18 bars.

All above columns require spirals of rod or cold drawn wire (f_y = 60,000 psi):—
#14 and smaller—⅝ φ @ 2¼″
#18 only —⅝ φ @ 2″

Outside diameter of spiral should be 3 in. less than side of column.
† Below zigzag horizontal line of each group, concrete governs; above, tension governs.
‡ M_o = capacity in pure bending, (N = 0); for extrapolation, see page 11-5.

SPIRALLY REINFORCED SQUARE COLUMNS—
Safe Load in Kips for Various Eccentricities in Inches
$f'_c = 5000$ psi (A431 Bars, $f_y = 75{,}000$ psi) $f_s = 30{,}000$ psi basis

COLUMN SIZE—25″ x 25″

$f'_c = 5000$ psi
$f_y = 75{,}000$ psi

Bars	p	M/N † = e (in.) 0	2	4	6	8	10	12	14	16	18	20	22	24	26	28	M_o ‡ (kip-in.)
6-#11	.0150	**1062**	966	755	569	335	237	183	150	126	109	96	86	78	71	65	1629
7-#11	.0175	**1108**	997	778	637	385	274	212	173	146	127	112	100	90	82	76	1900
8-#11	.0200	**1155**	1028	801	656	433	309	241	197	166	144	127	114	103	94	86	2172
9-#11	.0225	**1202**	1059	824	674	480	344	268	220	186	161	143	128	115	105	97	2443
10-#11	.0250	**1249**	1090	847	692	524	378	296	243	206	178	158	141	128	117	107	2715
11-#11	.0275	**1296**	1121	870	710	567	411	322	265	225	195	173	155	140	128	118	2986
13-#11	.0324	**1389**	1183	916	747	631	474	373	308	262	228	202	181	164	150	138	3529
15-#11	.0374	**1483**	1245	961	783	661	532	422	349	298	260	230	207	188	172	158	4073
17-#11	.0424	**1576**	1306	1007	819	691	587	468	389	333	291	258	232	211	193	178	4616
6-#14	.0216	**1186**	1047	814	665	458	328	255	209	177	153	135	121	109	100	92	2315
7-#14	.0252	**1253**	1091	846	691	522	376	294	241	205	178	157	140	127	116	107	2701
8-#14	.0288	**1321**	1135	879	717	583	423	332	273	232	201	178	160	144	132	122	3087
9-#14	.0324	**1388**	1180	912	743	627	467	368	303	258	225	199	178	162	148	136	3473
10-#14	.0360	**1456**	1224	944	769	648	509	403	333	284	247	219	197	178	163	150	3859
12-#14	.0432	**1591**	1312	1010	820	691	588	469	390	333	291	259	233	211	193	178	4630
14-#14	.0504	**1726**	1400	1074	872	734	633	529	442	380	333	296	267	243	223	206	5402
6-#18	.0384	**1501**	1243	954	775	652	517	409	339	289	252	223	200	182	166	153	3937
7-#18	.0448	**1621**	1320	1010	818	688	582	464	386	330	289	256	231	209	192	177	4593
8-#18	.0512	**1741**	1396	1066	862	723	623	515	431	370	324	288	260	236	217	200	5249
9-#18	.0576	**1861**	1472	1121	905	759	653	563	473	407	358	319	288	262	241	223	5906

COLUMN SIZE—26″ x 26″

Bars	p	0	2	4	6	8	10	12	14	16	18	20	22	24	26	28	M_o
6-#11	.0138	**1125**	1042	820	632	364	255	196	160	134	116	102	91	82	75	69	1713
7-#11	.0162	**1172**	1074	844	695	418	295	227	185	156	135	119	106	96	87	80	1999
8-#11	.0185	**1219**	1105	867	714	471	333	258	210	177	153	135	121	109	99	91	2284
9-#11	.0208	**1266**	1137	891	733	521	371	288	235	198	172	151	135	122	112	103	2570
10-#11	.0231	**1312**	1168	915	752	570	407	317	259	219	190	167	150	135	124	114	2855
12-#11	.0277	**1406**	1231	962	789	662	477	373	306	260	225	199	178	161	147	136	3426
14-#11	.0323	**1500**	1294	1009	827	701	543	427	352	299	260	230	206	187	171	157	3998
16-#11	.0369	**1593**	1357	1056	865	732	605	478	395	337	294	260	233	212	194	178	4569
18-#11	.0415	**1687**	1420	1103	902	763	661	527	437	374	326	289	260	236	216	199	5140
6-#14	.0200	**1249**	1124	881	724	498	353	274	223	189	163	144	129	116	106	97	2436
7-#14	.0233	**1317**	1169	915	751	568	406	315	258	218	189	167	149	135	123	113	2343
8-#14	.0266	**1384**	1215	948	778	634	456	356	292	247	214	189	169	153	140	129	3249
9-#14	.0300	**1452**	1260	982	805	681	504	395	325	276	239	211	189	172	157	144	3655
10-#14	.0333	**1519**	1305	1016	831	704	550	433	357	303	264	233	209	190	173	160	4061
11-#14	.0366	**1587**	1350	1049	858	726	594	469	388	330	288	255	228	207	190	175	4467
13-#14	.0433	**1722**	1440	1116	912	770	667	538	447	382	334	296	266	242	221	204	5280
15-#14	.0499	**1857**	1529	1183	965	815	705	601	502	431	377	336	302	275	252	233	6092
6-#18	.0355	**1564**	1325	1027	838	708	560	441	363	309	269	238	213	193	177	163	4153
7-#18	.0414	**1684**	1404	1084	884	745	632	501	415	354	309	274	246	223	204	188	4845
8-#18	.0473	**1804**	1482	1142	929	783	676	557	463	397	347	308	277	252	231	213	5537
9-#18	.0533	**1924**	1559	1199	974	820	708	609	509	437	383	341	308	280	257	237	6230
10-#18	.0592	**2044**	1637	1257	1019	858	740	651	552	476	418	373	337	307	282	260	6922

Check availability of #14 and #18 bars.

All above columns require spirals of rod or cold drawn wire (f_y = 60,000 psi):—
⅝ ϕ @ 2″

Outside diameter of spiral should be 3 in. less than side of column.
† Below zigzag horizontal line of each group, concrete governs; above, tension governs.
‡ M_o = capacity in pure bending, ($N = 0$); for extrapolation, see page 11-5.

SPIRALLY REINFORCED SQUARE COLUMNS—
Safe Load in Kips for Various Eccentricities in Inches
f'_c = 5000 psi (A431 Bars, f_y = 75,000 psi) f_s = 30,000 psi basis

COLUMN SIZE—27″ x 27″

f'_c = 5000 psi
f_y = 75,000 psi

Bars	p	M/N † = e (in.) 0	2	4	6	8	10	12	14	16	18	20	22	24	26	28	M_o ‡ (kip-in.)
6-#11	.0128	**1192**	1121	888	703	394	274	210	170	143	123	108	96	87	79	73	*1797*
7-#11	.0150	**1238**	1153	912	755	453	316	243	197	166	143	126	112	101	92	85	*2097*
8-#11	.0171	**1285**	1185	937	774	511	358	275	224	188	163	143	128	115	105	97	*2396*
9-#11	.0193	**1332**	1217	961	794	566	398	307	250	211	182	160	143	129	118	108	*2696*
10-#11	.0214	**1379**	1250	985	814	619	438	339	276	233	201	177	159	143	131	120	*2996*
11-#11	.0235	**1426**	1282	1010	833	670	476	369	302	255	221	194	174	157	143	132	*3295*
13-#11	.0278	**1519**	1346	1058	872	742	550	429	351	297	258	228	204	184	168	155	*3894*
15-#11	.0321	**1613**	1410	1107	911	774	619	485	399	339	294	260	233	211	193	177	*4494*
17-#11	.0364	**1706**	1474	1155	950	807	685	539	445	379	329	292	262	237	217	200	*5093*
19-#11	.0407	**1800**	1538	1204	989	839	729	591	489	417	364	322	290	263	240	222	*5692*
6-#14	.0185	**1316**	1205	951	785	541	380	293	238	201	173	152	136	123	112	103	*2558*
7-#14	.0216	**1383**	1251	985	813	617	436	337	275	232	201	177	158	143	130	120	*2984*
8-#14	.0247	**1451**	1297	1020	841	689	491	381	311	263	228	201	180	162	148	136	*3411*
9-#14	.0278	**1518**	1343	1055	869	738	543	423	346	293	254	224	201	182	166	153	*3837*
10-#14	.0309	**1586**	1389	1089	896	761	593	464	381	323	280	248	222	201	183	169	*4264*
12-#14	.0370	**1721**	1480	1159	952	808	686	541	446	380	331	293	263	238	218	201	*5116*
14-#14	.0432	**1856**	1572	1228	1007	854	741	613	508	434	379	336	302	274	251	231	*5969*
16-#14	.0494	**1991**	1663	1297	1062	900	780	679	566	486	425	378	340	309	283	262	*6822*
6-#18	.0329	**1631**	1410	1102	904	766	604	473	389	330	286	253	227	205	188	173	*4369*
7-#18	.0384	**1751**	1490	1161	951	806	683	538	444	378	329	291	261	237	217	200	*5097*
8-#18	.0439	**1871**	1570	1221	998	845	732	599	497	424	370	328	295	268	245	226	*5825*
9-#18	.0494	**1991**	1649	1280	1046	884	765	656	547	468	410	364	328	298	273	252	*6554*
10-#18	.0549	**2111**	1729	1339	1093	923	799	704	593	510	447	398	359	327	300	277	*7282*
11-#18	.0604	**2231**	1808	1398	1139	962	832	733	637	550	483	431	389	355	326	301	*8010*

Check availability of #14 and #18 bars.

All above columns require spirals of rod or cold drawn wire (f_y = 60,000 psi):—
⅝ φ @ 2″

Outside diameter of spiral should be 3 in. less than side of column.
† Below zigzag horizontal line of each group, concrete governs; above, tension governs.
‡ M_o = capacity in pure bending, (N = 0); for extrapolation, see page 11-5.

SPIRALLY REINFORCED SQUARE COLUMNS—
Safe Load in Kips for Various Eccentricities in Inches
f'_c = 5000 psi (A431 Bars, f_y = 75,000 psi) f_s = 30,000 psi basis

COLUMN SIZE—28″ x 28″

f'_c = 5000 psi
f_y = 75,000 psi

Bars	p	M/N † = e (in.) 0	2	4	6	8	10	12	14	16	18	20	22	24	26	28	M_o ‡ (kip-in.)
6-#11	.0199	**1260**	1203	959	782	427	293	223	180	151	130	114	102	92	84	77	*1881*
7-#11	.0139	**1307**	1236	984	818	491	339	259	209	176	151	133	118	107	97	89	*2195*
8-#11	.0159	**1354**	1268	1009	838	553	384	294	238	200	172	151	135	122	111	102	*2509*
9-#11	.0179	**1401**	1301	1034	858	613	427	328	266	224	193	170	151	137	124	114	*2822*
10-#11	.0199	**1447**	1334	1059	878	671	470	361	293	247	213	188	167	151	138	127	*3136*
12-#11	.0239	**1541**	1399	1109	919	780	551	426	347	293	253	223	199	180	164	151	*3763*
14-#11	.0279	**1635**	1464	1159	959	818	629	489	399	338	293	258	231	209	191	175	*4391*
16-#11	.0318	**1728**	1529	1208	999	851	702	548	450	381	331	292	262	237	216	199	*5018*
18-#11	.0358	**1822**	1594	1258	1039	885	770	605	498	423	368	325	292	264	242	222	*5645*
20-#11	.0398	**1915**	1659	1308	1079	919	800	659	544	464	404	358	321	291	266	245	*6273*
6-#14	.0172	**1384**	1288	1024	849	586	408	312	253	213	183	161	144	130	118	109	*2679*
7-#14	.0201	**1452**	1335	1059	878	669	468	360	293	246	213	187	167	151	137	126	*3126*
8-#14	.0230	**1519**	1382	1095	907	748	527	407	331	279	241	213	190	172	156	144	*3573*
9-#14	.0258	**1587**	1428	1130	935	798	583	452	369	311	270	238	212	192	175	161	*4019*
10-#14	.0287	**1654**	1475	1166	964	822	638	496	406	343	297	262	235	212	194	178	*4466*
12-#14	.0344	**1789**	1568	1237	1021	869	739	579	476	404	351	310	278	252	230	212	*5359*
14-#14	.0402	**1924**	1662	1308	1078	917	798	657	543	462	403	357	320	290	265	245	*6253*
16-#14	.0459	**2059**	1755	1379	1135	965	839	729	605	517	452	401	360	327	300	277	*7146*
6-#18	.0306	**1699**	1498	1179	973	827	651	507	415	351	304	269	240	217	199	183	*4585*
7-#18	.0357	**1819**	1579	1241	1022	868	737	577	475	403	350	309	277	251	230	211	*5349*
8-#18	.0408	**1939**	1661	1302	1070	909	790	643	531	453	394	349	313	284	260	239	*6113*
9-#18	.0459	**2059**	1742	1363	1119	949	824	705	585	500	436	387	348	316	289	267	*6878*
10-#18	.0510	**2179**	1823	1424	1168	990	859	759	636	545	477	424	381	347	318	293	*7642*
11-#18	.0561	**2299**	1903	1484	1216	1030	894	789	684	588	516	459	414	377	346	319	*8406*

Check availability of #14 and #18 bars.

All above columns require spirals of rod or cold drawn wire (f_y = 60,000 psi):—
⅝ φ @ 2″

Outside diameter of spiral should be 3 in. less than side of column.
† Below zigzag horizontal line of each group, concrete governs; above, tension governs.
‡ M_o = capacity in pure bending, (N = 0); for extrapolation, see page 11-5.

SPIRALLY REINFORCED SQUARE COLUMNS—
Safe Load in Kips for Various Eccentricities in Inches
f'_c = 5000 psi (A431 Bars, f_y = 75,000 psi) f_s = 30,000 psi basis

COLUMN SIZE—29″ x 29″

f'_c = 5000 psi
f_y = 75,000 psi

Bars	p	M‡N † = e (in.) 0	2	4	6	8	10	12	14	16	18	20	22	24	26	28	M_o ‡ (kip-in.)
6-#11	.0111	**1332**	1288	1033	863	462	314	238	191	160	137	120	107	97	88	81	*1966*
7-#11	.0130	**1378**	1321	1059	883	531	363	275	222	186	160	140	125	112	102	94	*2293*
8-#11	.0148	**1425**	1355	1084	904	599	411	313	252	211	182	160	142	128	117	107	*2621*
9-#11	.0167	**1472**	1388	1110	925	664	457	349	282	237	204	179	159	144	131	120	*2949*
10-#11	.0185	**1519**	1421	1136	946	726	503	385	311	261	225	198	177	159	145	133	*3276*
11-#11	.0204	**1566**	1454	1161	966	787	548	420	340	286	247	217	194	175	159	146	*3604*
13-#11	.0241	**1659**	1520	1212	1008	863	633	488	397	334	289	254	227	205	187	172	*4260*
15-#11	.0278	**1753**	1586	1263	1049	897	714	553	451	381	330	291	260	235	214	197	*4915*
17-#11	.0315	**1846**	1652	1314	1091	932	791	616	504	427	370	326	292	264	241	222	*5570*
19-#11	.0352	**1940**	1718	1365	1132	967	844	675	555	471	409	361	324	293	268	246	*6226*
21-#11	.0390	**2034**	1784	1416	1173	1002	874	732	604	513	447	395	354	321	294	271	*6881*
6-#14	.0161	**1456**	1375	1099	916	635	437	333	269	225	194	170	152	137	125	114	*2801*
7-#14	.0187	**1523**	1422	1136	945	725	502	384	311	261	225	198	176	159	145	133	*3268*
8-#14	.0214	**1591**	1470	1172	975	811	565	434	352	296	255	224	200	181	165	151	*3735*
9-#14	.0241	**1658**	1517	1209	1005	859	626	482	392	330	285	251	224	202	185	170	*4202*
10-#14	.0268	**1726**	1565	1245	1034	884	684	529	431	364	315	277	248	224	204	188	*4669*
11-#14	.0294	**1793**	1612	1282	1064	909	740	574	469	397	343	303	271	245	223	205	*5135*
13-#14	.0348	**1928**	1707	1354	1122	958	836	661	543	460	399	353	316	286	261	241	*6069*
15-#14	.0401	**2063**	1801	1427	1181	1008	879	742	612	521	453	401	360	326	298	275	*7003*
17-#14	.0455	**2198**	1896	1499	1240	1057	921	816	677	579	505	448	402	365	334	308	*7937*
6-#18	.0285	**1771**	1588	1260	1044	891	700	542	442	373	323	284	254	230	210	193	*4801*
7-#18	.0333	**1891**	1671	1323	1094	933	793	618	506	428	371	328	293	265	242	223	*5601*
8-#18	.0380	**2011**	1754	1385	1145	975	850	689	567	481	418	370	331	300	274	253	*6401*
9-#18	.0428	**2131**	1836	1448	1195	1017	886	756	625	532	464	411	368	334	306	282	*7202*
10-#18	.0476	**2251**	1919	1510	1245	1059	922	816	680	581	507	450	404	367	336	310	*8002*
11-#18	.0523	**2371**	2001	1573	1296	1102	958	847	731	627	549	488	439	399	366	338	*8802*
12-#18	.0571	**2491**	2083	1635	1346	1143	994	879	780	671	589	524	473	430	395	365	*9602*

Check availability of #14 and #18 bars.

All above columns require spirals of rod or cold drawn wire (f_y = 60,000 psi):—
⅝ φ @ 2″

Outside diameter of spiral should be 3 in. less than side of column.
† Below zigzag horizontal line of each group, concrete governs; above, tension governs.
‡ M_o = capacity in pure bending, (N = 0); for extrapolation, see page 11-5.

SPIRALLY REINFORCED SQUARE COLUMNS—
Safe Load in Kips for Various Eccentricities in Inches
$f'_c = 5000$ psi (A431 Bars, $f_y = 75{,}000$ psi) $f_s = 30{,}000$ psi basis

COLUMN SIZE—30″ x 30″

$f'_c = 5000$ psi
$f_y = 75{,}000$ psi

Bars	p	M/N † = e (in.) 0	2	4	6	8	10	12	14	16	18	20	22	24	26	28	M_o ‡ (kip-in.)
6-#11	.0104	**1405**	1377	1110	931	499	335	253	202	169	145	127	113	101	92	85	2050
7-#11	.0121	**1452**	1410	1137	952	574	388	293	235	196	168	148	131	118	107	99	2392
8-#11	.0139	**1499**	1444	1163	973	647	439	332	267	223	192	168	150	135	123	112	2733
9-#11	.0156	**1546**	1477	1189	995	718	489	371	299	250	215	188	168	151	138	126	3075
10-#11	.0173	**1592**	1511	1215	1016	786	538	409	330	276	238	209	186	167	152	140	3417
12-#11	.0208	**1686**	1578	1267	1058	909	632	483	391	328	283	248	221	200	182	167	4100
14-#11	.0243	**1780**	1645	1319	1101	945	722	554	450	378	327	287	256	231	211	194	4784
16-#11	.0277	**1873**	1712	1371	1144	981	807	623	507	428	370	325	291	263	240	220	5467
18-#11	.0312	**1967**	1779	1423	1186	1017	887	688	562	475	411	363	324	293	268	246	6151
20-#11	.0347	**2060**	1846	1475	1228	1052	920	751	615	521	452	399	357	323	295	272	6834
22-#11	.0381	**2154**	1913	1527	1271	1088	951	810	667	566	492	435	390	353	323	297	7518
6-#14	.0150	**1530**	1464	1178	985	687	467	354	285	238	205	179	160	144	131	120	2922
7-#14	.0175	**1597**	1513	1215	1016	784	537	408	329	276	237	208	185	167	152	140	3410
8-#14	.0200	**1665**	1561	1253	1046	877	605	461	373	313	269	237	211	190	173	159	3897
9-#14	.0225	**1732**	1609	1290	1077	924	670	513	415	349	301	265	236	213	194	178	4384
10-#14	.0250	**1800**	1657	1327	1107	949	733	563	457	385	332	292	261	235	215	197	4871
12-#14	.0300	**1935**	1753	1402	1168	1000	851	659	538	454	393	346	309	280	255	235	5844
14-#14	.0350	**2070**	1849	1476	1228	1051	919	749	614	520	451	398	357	323	295	271	6820
16-#14	.0400	**2205**	1945	1550	1289	1102	963	833	686	583	507	449	402	365	333	307	7794
18-#14	.0450	**2340**	2041	1624	1349	1153	1007	894	754	644	561	497	447	405	371	342	8768
6-#18	.0267	**1844**	1682	1343	1117	957	751	578	469	395	341	300	268	242	221	203	5017
7-#17	.0311	**1964**	1766	1407	1169	1001	851	659	538	454	393	346	310	280	255	235	5853
8-#18	.0356	**2084**	1850	1471	1222	1044	912	736	603	511	443	391	350	317	289	266	6689
9-#18	.0400	**2205**	1933	1536	1273	1088	949	808	665	565	491	434	389	353	322	297	7526
10-#18	.0444	**2324**	2017	1600	1325	1131	987	875	724	617	538	476	428	388	355	327	8362
11-#18	.0489	**2444**	2101	1664	1377	1175	1024	908	780	667	582	517	465	422	386	356	9198
12-#18	.0533	**2564**	2185	1728	1429	1218	1062	941	834	715	625	556	500	455	417	385	10034

Check availability of #14 and #18 bars.

All above columns require spirals of rod or cold drawn wire ($f_y = 60{,}000$ psi):—
#14 and smaller—⅝ φ @ 2″
#18 only —¾ φ @ 2¾″

Outside diameter of spiral should be 3 in. less than side of column.
† Below zigzag horizontal line of each group, concrete governs; above, tension governs.
‡ M_o = capacity in pure bending, ($N = 0$); for extrapolation, see page 11-5.

SPIRALLY REINFORCED SQUARE COLUMNS—
Safe Load in Kips for Various Eccentricities in Inches
f'_c = 5000 psi (A431 Bars, f_y = 75,000 psi) f_s = 30,000 psi basis

COLUMN SIZE—31″ x 31″

f'_c = 5000 psi
f_y = 75,000 psi

Bars	p	M/N † = e (in.) 0	3	6	9	12	15	18	21	24	27	30	33	36	39	42	M_o ‡ (kip-in.)
7-#11	.0114	**1528**	1345	1023	497	310	226	177	146	124	108	95	85	77	71	65	2490
8-#11	.0130	**1575**	1375	1045	561	352	257	202	166	141	123	109	97	88	81	74	2846
9-#11	.0146	**1622**	1405	1067	624	394	287	226	186	159	138	122	109	99	91	83	3201
10-#11	.0162	**1669**	1434	1089	685	434	318	250	206	176	153	135	121	110	101	93	3557
11-#11	.0179	**1716**	1464	1111	745	474	347	274	226	193	168	149	133	121	111	102	3913
13-#11	.0211	**1809**	1524	1154	859	551	406	321	266	226	197	175	157	142	130	120	4625
15-#11	.0243	**1903**	1584	1198	963	626	463	367	304	260	226	201	180	164	150	138	5336
17-#11	.0276	**1996**	1643	1242	998	697	518	412	342	292	255	226	203	185	169	156	6048
19-#11	.0308	**2090**	1703	1285	1032	766	571	456	379	324	283	252	226	205	188	174	6759
21-#11	.0341	**2184**	1762	1329	1066	831	623	498	415	356	311	276	249	226	207	191	7471
23-#11	.0373	**2277**	1822	1372	1101	894	673	540	450	386	338	301	271	246	226	209	8182
6-#14	.0140	**1606**	1393	1058	597	375	274	215	178	151	131	116	104	94	86	79	3044
7-#14	.0164	**1673**	1436	1089	684	433	317	250	206	175	153	135	121	110	100	93	3551
8-#14	.0187	**1741**	1478	1120	769	490	359	284	234	200	174	154	138	125	115	106	4059
9-#14	.0211	**1808**	1521	1151	850	545	401	317	262	224	195	173	155	141	129	119	4566
10-#14	.0234	**1876**	1564	1182	927	598	442	350	290	247	216	191	172	156	143	131	5074
12-#14	.0281	**2011**	1649	1245	999	701	521	414	344	294	257	228	205	186	170	157	6088
14-#14	.0328	**2146**	1734	1307	1048	797	596	476	396	339	297	264	237	215	197	182	7103
16-#14	.0375	**2281**	1820	1369	1097	888	668	536	447	384	336	299	269	244	224	207	8118
18-#14	.0421	**2416**	1905	1431	1146	955	737	593	496	427	374	333	300	273	250	231	9133
6-#18	.0250	**1921**	1584	1194	950	615	454	360	298	255	222	197	177	161	147	135	5233
7-#18	.0291	**2041**	1658	1247	1000	702	522	415	345	295	257	228	205	186	171	157	6105
8-#18	.0333	**2161**	1733	1301	1041	785	587	468	390	334	292	259	233	212	194	179	6977
9-#18	.0375	**2281**	1807	1354	1083	863	649	520	433	372	325	289	260	237	217	200	7850
10-#18	.0416	**2401**	1881	1408	1125	936	708	569	476	409	358	319	287	261	240	221	8722
11-#18	.0458	**2521**	1955	1461	1166	970	764	617	517	445	390	348	314	286	262	242	9594
12-#18	.0499	**2641**	2029	1514	1208	1005	818	663	557	480	422	376	340	309	284	263	10466
13-#18	.0541	**2761**	2103	1568	1249	1039	870	707	595	514	453	404	365	333	306	283	11339

Check availability of #14 and #18 bars.

All above columns require spirals of rod or cold drawn wire (f_y = 60,000 psi):—
#14 and smaller—⅝ φ @ 2″
#18 only —¾ φ @ 2¾″

Outside diameter of spiral should be 3 in. less than side of column.
† Below zigzag horizontal line of each group, concrete governs; above, tension governs.
‡ M_o = capacity in pure bending, (N = 0); for extrapolation, see page 11-5.

SPIRALLY REINFORCED SQUARE COLUMNS—
Safe Load in Kips for Various Eccentricities in Inches
$f'_c = 5000$ psi (A431 Bars, $f_y = 75,000$ psi) $f_s = 30,000$ psi basis

COLUMN SIZE—32″ x 32″

$f'_c = 5000$ psi
$f_y = 75,000$ psi

Bars	p	M/N † = e (in.) 0	3	6	9	12	15	18	21	24	27	30	33	36	39	42	M_o ‡ (kip-in.)
7-#11	.0107	**1607**	1434	1098	532	329	238	186	153	130	113	100	89	81	74	68	2588
8-#11	.0122	**1654**	1464	1120	602	373	271	212	174	148	129	114	102	92	84	78	2958
9-#11	.0137	**1701**	1495	1142	669	417	303	238	196	166	144	128	114	104	95	87	3328
10-#11	.0152	**1747**	1525	1165	735	460	335	263	217	184	160	142	127	115	105	97	3698
11-#11	.0168	**1794**	1556	1187	799	502	366	288	238	202	176	155	139	126	115	106	4067
13-#11	.0198	**1888**	1616	1232	921	585	428	338	279	237	207	183	164	149	136	125	4807
15-#11	.0229	**1981**	1677	1277	1030	664	488	386	319	272	237	210	189	171	156	144	5547
17-#11	.0259	**2075**	1737	1321	1066	740	547	433	359	306	267	237	213	193	177	163	6286
19-#11	.0289	**2169**	1798	1366	1101	813	603	480	398	340	297	263	237	215	197	181	7026
21-#11	.0320	**2262**	1858	1410	1136	883	658	525	436	373	326	289	260	236	217	200	7766
23-#11	.0350	**2356**	1919	1455	1172	951	712	569	474	406	355	315	284	258	236	218	8505
6-#14	.0132	**1684**	1483	1133	640	398	289	227	186	158	137	122	109	99	90	83	3165
7-#14	.0154	**1752**	1526	1165	734	460	334	263	216	184	160	141	127	115	105	97	3693
8-#14	.0176	**1819**	1570	1197	825	520	379	299	246	209	182	161	144	131	120	110	4221
9-#14	.0198	**1887**	1613	1229	912	578	423	334	275	235	204	181	162	147	134	124	4748
10-#14	.0220	**1954**	1657	1261	995	635	466	368	304	259	226	200	180	163	149	137	5276
11-#14	.0242	**2022**	1700	1293	1043	691	509	403	333	284	248	219	197	179	163	151	5804
13-#14	.0286	**2157**	1787	1356	1093	797	591	469	389	332	290	257	231	210	192	177	6859
15-#14	.0330	**2292**	1874	1420	1143	897	669	534	444	380	332	295	265	241	220	203	7914
17-#14	.0374	**2427**	1960	1484	1193	990	744	595	496	426	372	331	298	271	248	229	8970
19-#14	.0417	**2562**	2047	1547	1243	1039	815	655	548	470	412	367	330	301	276	255	10025
6-#18	.0234	**2000**	1678	1273	1021	653	480	380	314	267	233	206	185	168	154	142	5449
7-#18	.0273	**2120**	1753	1328	1068	747	552	438	363	309	270	239	215	195	179	165	6357
8-#18	.0313	**2240**	1829	1383	1112	835	621	494	410	351	306	272	244	222	203	187	7265
9-#18	.0352	**2360**	1905	1438	1155	919	687	548	456	391	342	303	273	248	227	210	8174
10-#18	.0391	**2480**	1980	1492	1198	998	750	601	501	430	376	335	301	274	251	232	9082
11-#18	.0430	**2600**	2055	1547	1241	1035	811	652	545	468	410	365	329	299	275	254	9990
12-#18	.0469	**2720**	2131	1602	1283	1071	869	701	587	505	444	395	356	324	298	275	10898
13-#18	.0508	**2840**	2206	1657	1326	1106	924	748	628	542	476	425	383	349	321	296	11807
14-#18	.0547	**2960**	2281	1711	1369	1141	977	794	668	577	508	453	409	373	343	317	12715

Check availability of #14 and #18 bars.

All above columns require spirals of rod or cold drawn wire ($f_y = 60,000$ psi):—
#14 and smaller—⅝ φ @ 2″
#18 only —¾ φ @ 2¾″

Outside diameter of spiral should be 3 in. less than side of column.
† Below zigzag horizontal line of each group, concrete governs; above, tension governs.
‡ M_o = capacity in pure bending, ($N = 0$); for extrapolation, see page 11-5.

SPIRALLY REINFORCED SQUARE COLUMNS—
Safe Load in Kips for Various Eccentricities in Inches
f'_c = 5000 psi (A431 Bars, f_y = 75,000 psi) f_s = 30,000 psi basis

COLUMN SIZE—33″ x 33″

f'_c = 5000 psi
f_y = 75,000 psi

Bars	p	M/N † = e (in.) 0	3	6	9	12	15	18	21	24	27	30	33	36	39	42	M_o ‡ (kip-in.)
7-#11	.0100	**1688**	1526	1174	565	345	248	194	159	135	117	103	92	83	76	70	*2662*
8-#11	.0115	**1735**	1556	1196	639	392	282	221	181	154	133	118	105	95	87	80	*3042*
9-#11	.0129	**1782**	1587	1219	711	438	316	247	203	172	150	132	118	107	98	90	*3423*
10-#11	.0143	**1829**	1617	1242	781	483	349	274	225	191	166	147	131	119	109	100	*3803*
12-#11	.0172	**1922**	1679	1287	915	571	415	326	268	228	198	175	157	142	130	120	*4564*
14-#11	.0201	**2016**	1740	1332	1042	656	479	377	311	264	230	203	182	165	151	139	*5324*
16-#11	.0229	**2110**	1801	1378	1116	738	541	427	353	300	261	231	208	188	172	159	*6085*
18-#11	.0258	**2203**	1862	1423	1151	817	602	476	394	336	292	259	233	211	193	178	*6846*
20-#11	.0287	**2297**	1923	1468	1187	893	660	524	434	370	323	286	257	233	214	197	*7606*
22-#11	.0315	**2390**	1984	1513	1223	966	717	570	473	405	353	313	282	256	234	216	*8367*
24-#11	.0344	**2484**	2045	1559	1259	1036	773	616	512	438	383	340	306	278	254	235	*9128*
6-#14	.0124	**1766**	1575	1210	680	418	301	236	194	164	142	126	113	102	93	86	*3257*
7-#14	.0145	**1833**	1619	1242	780	483	349	274	225	191	166	146	131	119	108	100	*3799*
8-#14	.0165	**1901**	1663	1274	877	546	396	311	256	217	189	167	150	135	124	114	*4342*
9-#14	.0186	**1968**	1707	1307	970	608	442	348	286	243	212	187	168	152	139	128	*4885*
10-#14	.0207	**2036**	1750	1339	1059	668	487	384	316	269	234	207	186	168	154	142	*5428*
12-#14	.0248	**2171**	1838	1404	1136	783	575	455	376	320	279	247	222	201	184	170	*6514*
14-#14	.0289	**2306**	1926	1469	1187	892	660	523	433	370	323	286	257	233	214	197	*7599*
16-#14	.0331	**2441**	2013	1533	1238	995	740	589	490	419	366	324	292	265	243	224	*8685*
18-#14	.0372	**2576**	2101	1598	1289	1080	817	653	544	466	408	362	326	296	271	250	*9771*
20-#14	.0413	**2711**	2188	1662	1340	1122	891	715	597	512	448	399	359	327	300	277	*10856*
6-#18	.0220	**2081**	1774	1355	1095	693	507	399	330	280	244	216	194	176	161	148	*5665*
7-#18	.0257	**2201**	1851	1411	1140	793	583	461	381	325	283	251	225	204	187	172	*6609*
8-#18	.0294	**2321**	1928	1467	1184	887	656	520	431	368	321	284	255	232	212	196	*7553*
9-#18	.0331	**2441**	2005	1524	1229	977	726	578	480	410	358	318	286	259	238	219	*8498*
10-#18	.0367	**2561**	2082	1580	1273	1061	794	634	527	451	395	351	315	287	263	242	*9442*
11-#18	.0404	**2681**	2158	1636	1317	1102	858	688	573	492	431	383	345	313	287	265	*10386*
12-#18	.0441	**2801**	2235	1692	1361	1139	920	740	618	531	466	414	373	340	312	288	*11330*
13-#18	.0478	**2921**	2312	1748	1405	1175	979	790	662	570	500	445	402	366	336	310	*12275*
14-#18	.0514	**3041**	2388	1804	1450	1212	1036	838	704	607	533	476	429	391	359	332	*13219*

Check availability of #14 and #18 bars.

All above columns require spirals of rod or cold drawn wire (f_y = 60,000 psi):—
¾ φ @ 2¾″

Outside diameter of spiral should be 3 in. less than side of column.

† Below zigzag horizontal line of each group, concrete governs; above, tension governs.

‡ M_o = capacity in pure bending, (N = 0); for extrapolation, see page 11-5.

SPIRALLY REINFORCED SQUARE COLUMNS—
Safe Load in Kips for Various Eccentricities in Inches
f'_c = 5000 psi (A431 Bars, f_y = 75,000 psi) f_s = 30,000 psi basis

COLUMN SIZE—34″ x 34″

f'_c = 5000 psi
f_y = 75,000 psi

Bars	p	M/N † = e (in.) 0	3	6	9	12	15	18	21	24	27	30	33	36	39	42	M_o‡ (kip-in.)
8-#11	.0108	**1819**	1652	1277	684	414	297	231	189	160	139	123	110	99	91	83	*3155*
9-#11	.0121	**1866**	1683	1300	761	463	333	259	213	180	156	138	123	112	102	94	*3549*
10-#11	.0135	**1912**	1714	1324	836	511	368	287	235	200	173	153	137	124	113	104	*3943*
11-#11	.0148	**1959**	1745	1347	909	558	402	315	258	219	190	168	150	136	124	114	*4338*
13-#11	.0175	**2053**	1808	1393	1050	650	471	369	303	257	224	198	177	160	146	135	*5126*
15-#11	.0202	**2146**	1870	1439	1170	739	537	422	347	295	257	227	203	184	169	155	*5915*
17-#11	.0229	**2240**	1932	1485	1207	824	602	474	391	333	289	256	230	208	190	175	*6704*
19-#11	.0256	**2334**	1994	1532	1244	907	665	525	434	369	322	285	256	232	212	195	*7493*
21-#11	.0283	**2427**	2055	1578	1280	986	726	575	476	406	353	313	281	255	233	215	*8282*
23-#11	.0310	**2521**	2117	1624	1317	1062	786	623	517	441	385	341	307	278	255	235	*9070*
25-#11	.0337	**2614**	2179	1670	1354	1135	843	671	557	476	416	369	332	301	276	254	*9859*
6-#14	.0117	**1849**	1671	1291	728	442	317	247	203	172	149	131	117	106	97	89	*3378*
7-#14	.0136	**1917**	1716	1324	836	511	367	287	235	199	173	153	137	124	113	104	*3941*
8-#14	.0156	**1984**	1760	1357	940	578	417	326	268	227	197	174	156	141	129	119	*4504*
9-#14	.0175	**2052**	1805	1390	1039	643	466	365	300	255	221	195	175	158	145	133	*5067*
10-#14	.0195	**2119**	1849	1423	1135	707	513	403	332	282	245	216	194	176	161	148	*5630*
11-#14	.0214	**2187**	1894	1456	1183	769	560	440	363	308	268	237	213	193	176	162	*6194*
13-#14	.0253	**2322**	1983	1522	1235	889	651	514	424	361	315	279	250	227	207	191	*7320*
15-#14	.0292	**2457**	2072	1588	1288	1002	739	585	484	413	360	319	287	260	238	219	*8446*
17-#14	.0331	**2592**	2160	1654	1340	1108	822	654	542	463	405	359	323	293	268	247	*9572*
19-#14	.0370	**2727**	2249	1720	1393	1170	902	720	599	513	448	398	358	325	298	275	*10698*
21-#14	.0409	**2862**	2338	1786	1445	1213	979	784	654	561	491	436	393	357	327	302	*11824*
6-#18	.0208	**2164**	1874	1439	1168	735	534	420	346	294	255	226	202	183	168	154	*5881*
7-#18	.0242	**2284**	1952	1497	1214	841	614	484	399	340	296	262	235	213	195	179	*6861*
8-#18	.0277	**2404**	2030	1555	1259	941	692	547	452	385	336	297	267	242	221	204	*7841*
9-#18	.0311	**2524**	2108	1612	1305	1037	766	608	504	430	375	332	299	271	248	229	*8822*
10-#18	.0346	**2644**	2186	1670	1351	1127	838	667	554	473	413	367	330	299	274	253	*9802*
11-#18	.0381	**2764**	2264	1727	1396	1171	907	724	602	516	451	401	360	327	300	277	*10782*
12-#18	.0415	**2884**	2342	1785	1442	1209	973	779	650	557	488	434	390	355	325	300	*11762*
13-#18	.0450	**3004**	2420	1842	1487	1247	1036	833	696	598	524	466	420	382	351	324	*12743*
14-#18	.0484	**3124**	2497	1899	1532	1284	1097	884	741	638	559	498	449	409	375	347	*13723*
15-#18	.0519	**3244**	2575	1957	1578	1322	1137	934	784	676	594	530	478	435	400	370	*14703*

Check availability of #14 and #18 bars.

All above columns require spirals of rod or cold drawn wire (f_y = 60,000 psi):—
¾ φ @ 2¾″

Outside diameter of spiral should be 3 in. less than side of column.
† Below zigzag horizontal line of each group, concrete governs; above, tension governs.
‡ M_o = capacity in pure bending, (N = 0); for extrapolation, see page 11-5.

SPIRALLY REINFORCED SQUARE COLUMNS—
Safe Load in Kips for Various Eccentricities in Inches
f'_c = 5000 psi (A431 Bars, f_y = 75,000 psi) f_s = 30,000 psi basis

COLUMN SIZE—35″ x 35″

f'_c = 5000 psi
f_y = 75,000 psi

Bars	p	M/N † = e (in.) 0	3	6	9	12	15	18	21	24	27	30	33	36	39	42	M_o ‡ (kip-in.)
8-#11	.0102	**1905**	1751	1361	733	438	312	242	198	167	145	128	114	103	94	87	*3267*
9-#11	.0115	**1952**	1783	1385	815	489	349	272	222	188	163	144	128	116	106	98	*3675*
10-#11	.0127	**1999**	1814	1408	895	540	386	301	246	208	181	159	143	129	118	108	*4084*
12-#11	.0153	**2092**	1877	1455	1050	639	459	358	294	249	216	190	170	154	141	130	*4901*
14-#11	.0178	**2186**	1940	1503	1196	735	530	414	340	289	251	221	198	179	164	151	*5717*
16-#11	.0204	**2280**	2003	1550	1264	827	599	470	386	328	285	252	226	204	187	172	*6534*
18-#11	.0229	**2373**	2066	1597	1302	916	667	524	431	367	319	282	253	229	209	193	*7351*
20-#11	.0255	**2467**	2129	1644	1339	1002	732	577	476	405	352	312	280	254	232	214	*8168*
22-#11	.0280	**2560**	2191	1691	1377	1085	796	629	519	443	385	341	306	278	254	234	*8985*
24-#11	.0306	**2654**	2254	1738	1415	1164	858	679	562	480	418	371	333	302	276	255	*9802*
26-#11	.0331	**2748**	2317	1785	1452	1224	918	729	604	516	450	399	359	326	298	275	*10619*
6-#14	.0110	**1936**	1771	1375	780	467	333	259	212	179	155	137	122	111	101	93	*3500*
7-#14	.0129	**2003**	1816	1409	895	540	386	301	246	208	181	159	142	129	118	108	*4083*
8-#14	.0147	**2071**	1861	1442	1006	611	438	342	280	237	206	182	162	147	134	124	*4666*
9-#14	.0165	**2138**	1906	1476	1113	680	490	382	314	266	231	204	182	165	151	139	*5250*
10-#14	.0184	**2206**	1951	1510	1216	748	540	422	347	294	255	226	202	183	167	154	*5833*
11-#14	.0202	**2273**	1996	1544	1258	814	589	462	380	322	280	247	222	201	183	169	*6416*
13-#14	.0239	**2408**	2086	1611	1312	941	685	539	444	378	328	291	260	236	216	199	*7583*
15-#14	.0276	**2543**	2177	1679	1366	1061	778	614	507	432	376	333	299	271	248	228	*8750*
17-#14	.0312	**2678**	2267	1746	1420	1174	866	686	568	485	423	375	336	305	279	257	*9916*
19-#14	.0349	**2813**	2356	1813	1473	1241	951	756	628	536	468	415	373	339	310	286	*11083*
21-#14	.0386	**2948**	2446	1880	1527	1286	1032	824	685	587	513	456	410	372	341	315	*12250*
6-#18	.0196	**2251**	1977	1527	1244	778	562	440	362	307	267	236	211	191	175	161	*6097*
7-#18	.0229	**2371**	2056	1586	1290	890	647	508	418	355	309	273	245	222	203	187	*7113*
8-#18	.0261	**2491**	2135	1644	1337	997	729	574	474	403	351	310	278	252	231	213	*8129*
9-#18	.0294	**2611**	2214	1703	1384	1099	808	638	528	450	392	347	311	283	258	238	*9146*
10-#18	.0327	**2731**	2293	1762	1431	1196	884	701	580	495	432	383	344	312	286	264	*10162*
11-#18	.0359	**2851**	2372	1821	1477	1243	957	761	632	540	472	419	376	342	313	289	*11178*
12-#18	.0392	**2971**	2451	1880	1524	1282	1027	820	682	584	510	453	408	371	339	313	*12194*
13-#18	.0424	**3091**	2530	1938	1571	1320	1094	876	731	627	548	488	439	399	366	338	*13211*
14-#18	.0457	**3211**	2609	1997	1617	1359	1159	931	778	668	586	521	469	427	392	362	*14227*
15-#18	.0490	**3331**	2688	2055	1664	1398	1205	984	824	709	622	554	500	455	417	386	*15243*

Check availability of #14 and #18 bars.

All above columns require spirals of rod or cold drawn wire (f_y = 60,000 psi):—
¾ φ @ 2½″

Outside diameter of spiral should be 3 in. less than side of column.

† Below zigzag horizontal line of each group, concrete governs; above, tension governs.

‡ M_o = capacity in pure bending, (N = 0); for extrapolation, see page 11-5.

ECCENTRICALLY LOADED CONCRETE COLUMNS
SECTION III—SPIRALLY REINFORCED ROUND COLUMNS

This section covers eccentric loads on spirally reinforced round concrete columns and parallels exactly the first section, so the explanation on pages 11-3 to 11-9 and 11-82 and -83 should be read before going on with the following description.

The necessary size and pitch of spiral reinforcement for each size of column is shown at the bottom of each page. Weights and percentages of spirals can also be taken from the tables on pages 11-176 to -179, inclusive. The vertical bars are spaced uniformly around a ring just inside of and in contact with the spiral.

While the scope of these tables is sufficient for most purposes, some illustrative examples are shown for those who wish to design beyond their range or merely to see how they were prepared.

Example I—For the table on page 11-144, verify the value $N = 205$ kips with an eccentricity of 2 in. for a 16 in. round spirally reinforced column of 3750 psi concrete reinforced with 6-#8 bars, using $f_s = 24{,}000$ psi, $f_c = 938$ psi, $n = 8.2$, $m = 18.8$.

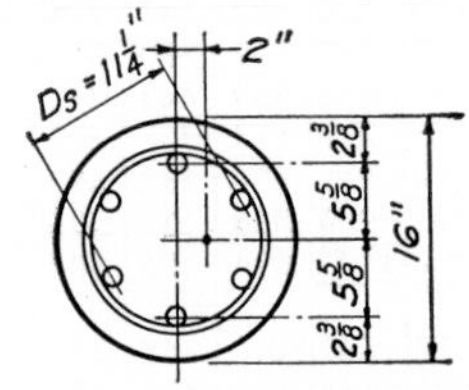

6-#8 Bars =
4.74 sq in. ⊃= 73.0 sq in.

Solution—Since the point of application is within R/4 of the center of the 16 in. round section the load apparently acts within the kern of the transformed section, producing compression over the entire area. To check whether tension or compression governs, e_b is determined from ACI 1407(a):—

$e_b = 0.43\,p_g m D_s + 0.14t = 0.43 \times 0.0236 \times 18.8 \times 11.25 + 0.14 \times 16 = 4.39$ in. > 2 in. so compression controls. Solve using the transformed section,* and $2n$.

Section	*Area of Transformed Section*	*Capacity (Axial Loading)*	*Moment of Inertia*
Concrete	$\frac{\pi}{4}(16)^2 = 201.0$	201 @ 938 = 188,500	$201 \times \frac{8^2}{4} = 3216$ in.^{4}
Bars	$(16.4\text{-}1) \times 6 \times 0.79 = 73.0$	6×0.79 @ 24,000 = 113,700	$73.0 \times \frac{(5.62)^2\,*}{2} = 1152$
	274.0 sq in.	302,200 lb	4368 in.^{4}

To check $\frac{f_a}{F_a} + \frac{f_b}{F_b} \lesssim 1$, $F_a = 0.34(1 + p_g m)f'_c$ $\qquad F_b = 1688$ psi

$$= 0.34(1 + 0.0236 \times 18.8)3750 = 1840 \text{ psi.}$$

$$\frac{N}{A_g F_a} + \frac{Nec}{IF_b} \lesssim 1;\ \frac{N}{201 \times 1840} + \frac{N \times 2 \times 8}{4368 + 1688} \lesssim 1;\ \frac{N}{370{,}000} + \frac{N}{460{,}000} \lesssim 1$$

$$2.24N = 460{,}000;\ N = \mathbf{205^k}, \text{ as in table.}$$

* The transformed steel area is assumed to be a ring with a mean radius r_m of 5.62 in.

$$I = \frac{\pi}{64}(D_1^4 - D_2^4) = \frac{Ar_m^2}{2}$$

ECCENTRICALLY LOADED SPIRALLY REINFORCED ROUND CONCRETE COLUMNS

Example II—Show that using the data from the previous example but increasing the eccentricity to 6 in. reduces the value of N to 85 kips.

Solution—Since the 6 in. eccentricity is greater than $e_b = 4.39$ in., tension governs. The most direct solution is to plot the load-moment interaction diagram (page 11-5) and use a linear interpolation between M_b and M_o, N_b and 0.

To locate point b, the dividing point between control by tension and compression:—

e_b, as in Ex. I, $= 4.39$ in.

$$\frac{N_b}{201 \times 1840} + \frac{N_b \times 4.39 \times 8}{4368 \times 1688} = 1 \qquad 2.77N_b = 370{,}000;\ N_b = 133{,}700 \text{ lb}$$

$M_b = N_b e_b = 133{,}700 \times 4.39 = 586{,}000$ lb-in.

To locate M_o, the capacity in pure bending, ($N = 0$):—

$M_o = 0.12\, A_{st} f_y D_s = 0.12 \times 4.74 \times 60{,}000 \times 11\frac{1}{4} = 384{,}000$ lb-in.

By reference to a plotted diagram, as in the accompanying figure, or by using the interpolation on page 11-5, one can compute:—

$$N_c = \frac{M_o}{e_c + \dfrac{M_o - M_b}{N_b}} = \frac{384{,}000}{6 + \dfrac{384{,}000 - 586{,}000}{133{,}700}}$$

$= 85^k +$ as in table.

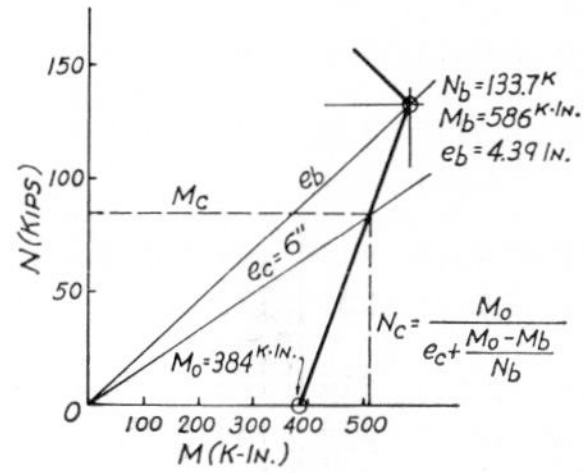

$$I = \frac{\pi D^4}{64} = A\frac{D^2}{16} = A \cdot \frac{4R^2}{16} = \frac{AR^2}{4}$$

SPIRALLY REINFORCED ROUND COLUMNS—
Safe Load in Kips for Various Eccentricities in inches
$f'_c = 3750$ psi (A61 or A432 Bars, $f_y = 60,000$ psi) $f_s = 24,000$ psi basis

COLUMN SIZE—12″ DIAMETER

$f'_c = 3750$ psi
$f_y = 60,000$ psi

Bars	p	M/N † = e (in.) 0	1	2	3	4	5	6	7	8	9	10	11	12	13	14	M_o ‡ (kip-in.)
6-#5	.0164	**150**	122	90	62	38	28	21	18	15	13	11	10	9	8	8	*102*
7-#5	.0192	**158**	126	93	69	44	32	25	20	17	15	13	12	11	10	9	*119*
8-#5	.0219	**165**	130	96	76	49	36	28	23	20	17	15	13	12	11	10	*136*
9-#5	.0247	**172**	134	99	78	54	39	31	26	22	19	17	15	14	12	11	*153*
6-#6	.0233	**169**	132	97	76	51	37	29	24	20	18	16	14	13	12	11	*142*
7-#6	.0272	**179**	138	101	80	57	42	34	28	24	21	18	16	15	13	12	*166*
8-#6	.0311	**190**	144	105	83	63	47	38	31	27	23	21	19	17	15	14	*190*
6-#7	.0318	**192**	145	105	83	63	47	38	31	27	23	21	19	17	15	14	*191*
7-#7	.0371	**206**	153	111	87	71	53	43	36	31	27	24	22	20	18	16	*223*
6-#8	.0419	**219**	159	115	90	74	58	47	39	34	29	26	24	21	20	18	*247*
7-#8	.0489	**238**	170	123	96	79	64	52	44	38	34	30	27	25	23	21	288
6-#9	.0531	**250**	175	126	98	81	67	55	46	40	35	32	29	26	24	22	307
7-#9	.0619	**274**	188	135	105	86	73	61	52	45	40	36	33	30	27	25	358
6-#10	.0674	**288**	195	139	108	88	75	63	54	47	42	38	34	31	29	27	382

Check availability of #14S and #18S bars.

All above columns require spirals of A432 rod or cold drawn wire ($f_y = 60,000$ psi):—
⅜ ϕ @ 1¾″

Outside diameter of spiral should be 3 in. less than outside diameter of column.
† Below zigzag horizontal line of each group, concrete governs; above, tension governs.
‡ M_o = capacity in pure bending, ($N = 0$); for extrapolation, see page 11-5.

SPIRALLY REINFORCED ROUND COLUMNS—
Safe Load in Kips for Various Eccentricities in Inches
$f'_c = 3750$ psi (A61 or A432 Bars, $f_y = 60{,}000$ psi) $f_s = 24{,}000$ psi basis

COLUMN SIZE—14″ DIAMETER

$f'_c = 3750$ psi
$f_y = 60{,}000$ psi

Bars	p	M/N † = e (in.) 0	1	2	3	4	5	6	7	8	9	10	11	12	13	14	M_o ‡ (kip-in.)
6-#5	.0121	**188**	166	126	96	55	38	29	24	20	17	15	13	12	11	10	*128*
7-#5	.0141	**196**	170	130	105	63	44	34	27	23	20	17	16	14	13	12	*150*
8-#5	.0161	**203**	175	133	108	70	49	38	31	26	23	20	18	16	15	13	*171*
9-#5	.0181	**211**	180	137	110	77	55	42	35	29	25	22	20	18	16	15	*193*
10-#5	.0201	**218**	185	140	113	84	60	47	38	32	28	25	22	20	18	17	*214*
11-#5	.0222	**226**	190	144	116	90	65	51	42	35	31	27	24	22	20	18	*236*
12-#5	.0242	**233**	194	148	119	96	70	55	45	38	33	29	26	24	22	20	*257*
6-#6	.0171	**207**	177	135	109	73	52	40	33	27	24	21	19	17	15	14	*180*
7-#6	.0200	**218**	184	140	113	82	59	46	37	32	27	24	22	19	18	16	*210*
8-#6	.0229	**228**	191	145	117	91	66	52	42	36	31	27	25	22	20	19	*240*
9-#6	.0257	**239**	198	150	120	99	72	57	47	40	35	31	27	25	23	21	*270*
10-#6	.0286	**249**	205	155	124	104	79	62	51	44	38	34	30	27	25	23	*300*
11-#6	.0314	**260**	211	160	128	107	85	67	56	48	41	37	33	30	27	25	*331*
6-#7	.0234	**230**	192	145	117	92	66	52	43	36	31	28	25	22	20	19	*243*
7-#7	.0273	**245**	201	152	122	102	75	59	49	42	36	32	29	26	24	22	*283*
8-#7	.0312	**259**	210	159	127	106	83	66	55	47	41	36	32	29	27	25	*324*
9-#7	.0351	**273**	219	165	133	111	91	73	60	52	45	40	36	33	30	28	*364*
10-#7	.0390	**288**	228	172	138	115	98	79	66	56	49	44	40	36	33	30	*405*
6-#8	.0308	**258**	209	157	126	105	82	65	53	46	40	35	32	29	26	24	*315*
7-#8	.0359	**277**	221	166	133	111	91	73	61	52	45	40	36	33	30	28	*368*
8-#8	.0411	**295**	233	175	140	117	100	81	68	58	51	45	41	37	34	31	*420*
9-#8	.0462	**314**	244	183	147	122	105	88	74	64	56	50	45	41	38	35	*473*
10-#8	.0513	**333**	256	192	153	128	109	95	80	69	61	55	49	45	41	38	*526*
6-#9	.0390	**288**	227	170	136	114	96	77	64	55	48	43	39	35	32	30	*394*
7-#9	.0455	**312**	242	181	145	121	103	86	72	62	55	49	44	40	37	34	*459*
8-#9	.0520	**336**	257	192	153	127	109	94	80	69	61	55	49	45	41	38	*525*
8-#9	.0585	**360**	272	203	162	134	115	100	87	75	67	60	54	50	46	42	*591*
10-#9	.0650	**384**	287	214	170	141	121	106	93	81	72	65	59	54	50	46	*656*
6-#10	.0495	**327**	250	187	149	124	106	90	76	66	58	52	47	43	39	36	*492*
7-#10	.0578	**357**	269	200	159	132	113	99	85	74	65	59	53	48	45	41	*574*
8-#10	.0660	**388**	288	214	170	141	121	105	93	81	72	65	59	54	50	46	*656*
6-#11	.0608	**368**	275	204	162	134	115	100	87	75	67	60	54	50	46	43	*595*
7-#11	.0709	**406**	297	220	175	145	124	108	96	84	75	67	61	56	52	48	*695*

Check availability of #14S and #18S bars.

Spirals. To provide required amount of spiral reinforcement and minimum clearance between turns (without complying with minimun spacing, $\left(\frac{D}{6}\right)$, all above columns can have spirals of A432 rod or cold drawn wire ($f_y = 60{,}000$ psi) as follows:

$\frac{3}{8}\ \phi$ @ $1\frac{3}{4}$″

Outside diameter of spiral should be 3 in. less than outside diameter of column.
† Below zigzag horizontal line of each group, concrete governs; above, tension governs.
‡ M_o = capacity in pure bending, ($N = 0$); for extrapolation, see page 11-5.

SPIRALLY REINFORCED ROUND COLUMNS—

Safe Load in Kips for Various Eccentricities in Inches

f'_c = 3750 psi (A61 or A432 Bars, f_y = 60,000 psi) f_s = 24,000 psi basis

COLUMN SIZE—16″ DIAMETER

f'_c = 3750 psi
f_y = 60,000 psi

Bars	p	M/N † = e (in.) 0	1	2	3	4	5	6	7	8	9	10	11	12	13	14	M_o ‡ (kip-in.)
7-#5	.0108	**240**	222	173	142	87	59	44	35	29	25	22	20	18	16	15	*181*
8-#5	.0123	**248**	227	177	146	97	66	50	40	33	29	25	22	20	18	17	*207*
9-#5	.0139	**255**	232	181	149	107	73	55	45	37	32	28	25	22	20	19	*233*
10-#5	.0154	**262**	238	185	152	116	80	61	49	41	35	31	28	25	23	21	*259*
11-#5	.0170	**270**	243	189	155	125	87	66	54	45	39	34	30	27	25	23	*285*
12-#5	.0185	**277**	248	193	158	133	93	72	58	49	42	37	33	30	27	25	*311*
14-#5	.0216	**292**	258	201	165	140	105	82	66	56	48	43	38	34	31	29	*363*
6-#6	.0131	**251**	230	179	147	101	69	52	42	35	30	26	23	21	19	17	*218*
7-#6	.0153	**262**	237	185	151	115	79	60	48	41	35	31	27	24	22	20	*255*
8-#6	.0175	**272**	244	190	156	127	88	68	55	46	40	35	31	28	25	23	*291*
9-#6	.0197	**283**	252	196	160	136	97	75	61	51	44	39	35	31	28	26	*327*
10-#6	.0219	**294**	259	202	165	140	106	82	67	56	49	43	38	34	31	29	*364*
12-#6	.0263	**315**	273	213	174	147	121	95	78	66	57	50	45	41	37	34	*437*
6-#7	.0179	**274**	245	191	156	128	89	68	55	46	40	35	31	28	26	23	*294*
7-#7	.0209	**289**	255	199	162	137	101	78	63	53	46	40	36	33	30	27	*343*
8-#7	.0239	**303**	265	206	169	143	112	87	71	60	52	46	41	37	34	31	*393*
9-#7	.0269	**318**	275	214	175	148	122	96	78	67	58	51	46	41	38	35	*442*
10-#7	.0298	**332**	285	221	181	153	132	104	86	73	63	56	50	45	41	38	*491*
12-#7	.0358	**361**	305	236	193	163	141	119	99	85	74	66	59	53	49	45	*589*
6-#8	.0236	**302**	264	205	167	142	110	85	70	59	51	45	40	36	33	30	*383*
7-#8	.0275	**321**	277	215	175	148	123	97	79	67	58	51	46	42	38	35	*447*
8-#8	.0314	**340**	290	225	183	155	134	107	88	75	66	58	52	47	43	40	*511*
9-#8	.0354	**359**	303	234	191	161	140	117	97	83	72	64	58	52	48	44	*575*
10-#8	.0393	**378**	316	244	199	168	145	126	105	90	79	70	63	57	53	49	*639*
12-#8	.0471	**416**	341	264	215	181	157	138	120	104	91	82	74	67	62	57	*767*
6-#9	.0298	**332**	284	220	179	151	130	102	84	71	62	55	49	44	41	37	*480*
7-#9	.0348	**356**	300	232	189	160	138	115	95	81	71	63	56	51	47	43	*560*
8-#9	.0398	**380**	316	245	199	168	145	126	105	90	79	70	63	57	53	49	*640*
9-#9	.0448	**404**	333	257	209	176	152	134	115	99	87	77	70	64	58	54	*720*
10-#9	.0497	**428**	349	269	219	185	160	140	124	107	94	84	76	69	64	59	*800*
12-#9	.0597	**476**	382	294	239	201	174	153	136	122	108	97	88	81	74	69	*960*
6-#10	.0379	**371**	309	239	194	164	142	121	100	86	75	67	60	54	50	46	*602*
7-#10	.0442	**401**	330	254	207	174	151	133	112	97	85	76	68	62	57	53	*702*
8-#10	.0505	**432**	350	270	219	185	159	140	124	107	94	84	76	70	64	59	*803*
9-#10	.0568	**462**	371	285	232	195	168	148	132	116	103	92	84	77	70	65	*903*
10-#10	.0632	**493**	391	301	244	205	177	156	139	125	111	100	91	83	77	71	*1004*
6-#11	.0466	**413**	336	259	210	177	153	134	115	100	88	78	70	64	59	54	*730*
7-#11	.0543	**450**	361	278	225	189	164	144	128	111	98	88	80	73	67	62	*852*
8-#11	.0621	**488**	387	296	240	202	174	153	137	122	108	97	89	81	75	69	*974*
9-#11	.0698	**525**	412	315	255	214	185	163	145	131	118	106	97	89	82	76	*1095*
6-#14S	.0671	**512**	400	305	246	207	178	156	139	126	112	101	92	84	78	72	*1026*
7-#14S	.0783	**566**	435	331	267	224	193	169	151	136	124	112	102	94	87	81	*1197*

Check availability of #14S and #18S bars.

All above columns require spirals of A432 rod or cold drawn wire (f_y = 60,000 psi):—
3/8 ϕ @ 2″

Outside diameter of spiral should be 3 in. less than outside diameter of column.
† Below zigzag horizontal line of each group, concrete governs; above, tension governs.
‡ M_o = capacity in pure bending, (N = 0); for extrapolation, see page 11-5.

SPIRALLY REINFORCED ROUND COLUMNS—
Safe Load in Kips for Various Eccentricities in Inches
$f'_c = 3750$ psi (A61 or A432 Bars, $f_y = 60{,}000$ psi) $f_s = 24{,}000$ psi basis

COLUMN SIZE—18″ DIAMETER

$f'_c = 3750$ psi
$f_y = 60{,}000$ psi

Bars	p	M/N † = e (in.) 0	1	2	3	4	5	6	7	8	9	10	12	14	16	18	M_o ‡ (kip-in.)
6-#6	.0104	**301**	289	230	191	140	90	66	53	44	37	32	26	21	18	16	*256*
7-#6	.0121	**312**	297	236	196	158	103	76	61	50	43	37	30	25	21	18	*299*
8-#6	.0138	**323**	304	242	202	172	115	86	69	57	49	43	34	28	24	21	*342*
9-#6	.0156	**333**	312	249	207	177	127	95	76	63	54	47	38	32	27	24	*384*
10-#6	.0173	**344**	320	255	212	181	138	104	84	70	60	52	42	35	30	26	*427*
12-#6	.0207	**365**	335	267	222	190	159	121	98	82	71	62	50	41	36	31	*513*
14-#6	.0242	**386**	351	279	232	198	173	137	111	94	81	71	57	48	41	36	*598*
16-#6	.0277	**407**	366	291	242	207	180	152	124	105	91	80	65	54	47	41	*684*
6-#7	.0141	**324**	305	243	202	173	116	87	69	58	49	43	34	28	24	21	*346*
7-#7	.0165	**339**	316	252	209	179	132	99	80	66	57	50	40	33	28	25	*404*
8-#7	.0189	**353**	326	260	216	184	147	111	89	75	64	56	45	38	32	28	*462*
9-#7	.0212	**368**	337	268	223	190	160	122	99	83	71	63	50	42	36	32	*520*
10-#7	.0236	**382**	348	276	229	196	171	133	108	91	78	69	55	46	40	35	*577*
12-#7	.0283	**411**	369	293	243	208	181	153	125	106	92	81	65	55	47	41	*693*
14-#7	.0330	**440**	390	309	257	219	191	170	141	120	104	92	75	63	54	48	*808*
6-#8	.0186	**352**	325	258	215	183	144	109	88	73	63	55	44	37	32	28	*452*
7-#8	.0217	**371**	339	269	223	191	162	124	100	84	72	63	51	43	37	32	*527*
8-#8	.0248	**390**	353	280	232	198	173	137	112	94	81	72	58	48	41	36	*602*
9-#8	.0279	**409**	366	291	241	206	180	150	123	104	90	79	64	54	46	41	*678*
10-#8	.0310	**428**	380	302	250	214	186	163	134	113	98	87	70	59	51	45	*753*
12-#8	.0373	**466**	408	323	268	229	199	177	153	131	114	101	83	70	60	53	*904*
14-#8	.0435	**504**	435	345	286	244	213	188	169	147	129	115	94	80	69	61	*1055*
6-#9	.0236	**382**	347	275	228	195	170	131	106	89	77	68	54	46	39	34	*566*
7-#9	.0275	**406**	364	289	239	204	178	147	120	102	88	78	63	53	45	40	*661*
8-#9	.0314	**430**	381	302	250	214	186	163	134	113	99	87	71	59	51	45	*755*
9-#9	.0354	**454**	399	316	261	223	195	172	146	125	109	96	78	66	57	50	*850*
10-#9	.0393	**478**	416	329	273	233	203	180	158	135	118	105	86	72	63	55	*944*
12-#9	.0472	**526**	451	357	295	251	219	194	174	155	136	121	100	85	74	65	*1133*
14-#9	.0550	**574**	485	384	317	270	236	209	187	170	152	136	113	96	84	74	*1322*
6-#10	.0299	**421**	374	296	245	209	182	156	128	108	94	83	67	56	48	43	*712*
8-#10	.0399	**482**	418	330	273	233	203	180	158	136	118	105	86	73	63	55	*949*
10-#10	.0499	**543**	462	365	301	257	223	198	178	159	140	125	103	88	76	68	*1186*
12-#10	.0599	**604**	505	399	329	280	244	216	194	176	160	144	119	102	89	79	*1424*
6-#11	.0368	**463**	403	319	263	224	195	173	148	126	110	97	79	67	58	51	*865*
7-#11	.0429	**500**	430	339	280	239	208	184	165	142	124	110	90	77	66	59	*1009*
8-#11	.0490	**538**	457	360	297	253	220	195	175	156	137	123	101	86	75	66	*1153*
9-#11	.0552	**575**	483	381	314	267	233	206	185	168	149	134	111	95	82	73	*1297*
10-#11	.0613	**612**	510	402	331	282	245	217	195	176	161	145	120	103	90	80	*1442*
11-#11	.0674	**650**	537	422	348	296	258	228	204	185	169	155	129	111	97	87	*1586*
6-#14S	.0531	**562**	471	371	305	259	225	199	179	161	142	127	105	90	78	69	*1220*
7-#14S	.0619	**616**	510	400	329	280	243	215	192	174	159	143	119	102	89	79	*1423*
8-#14S	.0707	**670**	548	429	353	300	260	230	206	187	171	156	131	113	99	88	*1627*
9-#14S	.0796	**724**	586	459	377	320	278	245	220	199	182	167	142	123	108	97	*1830*

Check availability of #14S and #18S bars.

All above columns require spirals of A432 rod or cold drawn wire ($f_y = 60{,}000$ psi):—
3/8 ϕ @ 2¼″

Outside diameter of spiral should be 3 in. less than outside diameter of column.
† Below zigzag horizontal line of each group, concrete governs; above, tension governs.
‡ M_o = capacity in pure bending, ($N = 0$); for extrapolation, see page 11-5.

SPIRALLY REINFORCED ROUND COLUMNS—
Safe Load in Kips for Various Eccentricities in Inches
$f'_c = 3750$ psi (A61 or A432 Bars, $f_y = 60,000$ psi) $f_s = 24,000$ psi basis

COLUMN SIZE—20″ DIAMETER

$f'_c = 3750$ psi
$f_y = 60,000$ psi

Bars	p	M/N † = e (in.) 0	1	2	3	4	5	6	7	8	9	10	12	14	16	18	M_o (kip-in.) ‡
6-#7	.0115	**380**	373	302	254	219	150	109	85	70	59	52	41	34	29	25	398
7-#7	.0134	**395**	384	311	262	226	170	124	98	81	69	60	47	39	33	29	464
8-#7	.0153	**409**	395	320	269	232	189	139	110	91	78	68	54	45	38	33	531
9-#7	.0172	**424**	406	329	276	238	207	153	122	101	86	75	60	50	43	37	597
10-#7	.0191	**438**	417	338	284	245	215	167	133	111	95	83	66	55	47	41	664
12-#7	.0229	**467**	439	356	299	258	226	192	155	129	111	97	78	65	56	49	797
14-#7	.0267	**496**	461	373	314	270	238	212	175	147	127	111	90	75	64	57	929
16-#7	.0306	**524**	483	391	329	283	249	222	193	163	142	125	101	85	73	64	1062
6-#8	.0151	**408**	393	319	268	231	186	137	108	89	76	66	53	44	37	32	520
7-#8	.0176	**427**	408	330	278	239	209	155	123	102	88	76	61	51	43	38	607
8-#8	.0201	**446**	422	342	287	248	218	173	138	115	99	86	69	57	49	43	693
9-#8	.0226	**465**	437	354	297	256	225	189	152	127	109	96	77	64	55	48	780
10-#8	.0251	**484**	451	365	307	264	232	205	165	139	119	105	84	70	60	53	867
12-#8	.0302	**522**	480	388	326	281	247	220	190	161	139	123	99	83	71	63	1040
14-#8	.0352	**559**	509	412	346	298	262	233	210	181	157	139	113	95	82	72	1214
16-#8	.0402	**597**	537	435	365	314	276	246	222	200	174	155	126	107	92	81	1387
6-#9	.0191	**438**	416	337	283	244	214	165	131	109	93	82	65	54	46	40	653
7-#9	.0223	**462**	434	351	295	254	223	186	149	125	107	94	75	63	54	47	762
8-#9	.0255	**486**	452	366	307	265	232	205	166	139	120	105	85	71	61	53	871
9-#9	.0286	**510**	470	380	319	275	242	215	182	153	132	116	94	79	68	59	979
10-#9	.0318	**534**	489	395	332	286	251	224	196	166	144	127	103	86	74	65	1088
12-#9	.0382	**582**	525	424	356	307	269	240	216	191	166	147	120	101	88	77	1306
14-#9	.0446	**630**	561	453	380	328	288	256	231	210	187	166	136	116	100	88	1524
16-#9	.0509	**678**	597	483	405	348	306	273	246	224	205	184	152	129	112	99	1742
6-#10	.0243	**477**	445	360	302	260	228	196	158	133	114	100	80	67	57	50	821
7-#10	.0283	**507**	468	378	317	273	240	214	178	150	130	114	92	77	66	58	958
8-#10	.0323	**538**	491	396	332	286	251	224	197	167	145	128	103	87	75	66	1095
10-#10	.0404	**599**	537	433	363	313	274	244	220	197	172	153	125	105	91	80	1369
12-#10	.0485	**660**	582	470	394	339	297	265	239	217	197	176	145	123	107	94	1643
14-#10	.0566	**721**	628	507	424	365	320	285	257	234	215	197	163	139	121	108	1917
6-#11	.0298	**519**	476	384	322	277	243	217	184	155	134	118	95	80	69	60	1000
7-#11	.0348	**556**	504	406	340	293	257	229	206	175	152	134	109	92	79	70	1166
8-#11	.0397	**594**	532	429	359	309	271	241	218	193	169	150	122	103	89	78	1333
9-#11	.0447	**631**	560	451	378	325	285	254	229	208	184	164	134	114	99	87	1500
10-#11	.0497	**668**	588	474	396	341	299	266	240	218	199	177	146	124	108	95	1666
11-#11	.0546	**706**	616	496	415	357	313	279	251	229	210	190	157	134	117	104	1833
13-#11	.0646	**781**	672	541	452	389	341	304	274	249	228	211	178	153	134	119	2166
6-#14S	.0430	**618**	548	441	368	317	277	247	222	201	176	156	128	108	94	83	1414
7-#14S	.0501	**672**	588	472	395	339	297	264	238	217	197	176	145	123	107	94	1650
8-#14S	.0573	**726**	628	504	421	362	317	282	254	231	212	193	160	137	119	106	1886
9-#14S	.0645	**780**	668	536	448	384	337	299	270	245	225	208	175	150	131	117	2122
10-#14S	.0716	**834**	708	568	474	407	356	317	285	259	238	220	188	162	143	127	2358
6-#18S	.0764	**870**	716	565	467	398	346	307	275	250	228	210	180	155	136	122	2285

Check availability of #14S and #18S bars.

All above columns require spirals of A432 rod or cold drawn wire ($f_y = 60,000$ psi):—
#14S and smaller—⅜ φ @ 2¼″
#18S only —⅜ φ @ 1¾″

Outside diameter of spiral should be 3 in. less than outside diameter of column.
† Below zigzag horizontal line of each group, concrete governs; above, tension governs.
‡ M_o = capacity in pure bending, ($N = 0$); for extrapolation, see page 11-5.

SPIRALLY REINFORCED ROUND COLUMNS—
Safe Load in Kips for Various Eccentricities in Inches
f'_c = 3750 psi (A61 or A432 Bars, f_y = 60,000 psi) f_s = 24,000 psi basis

COLUMN SIZE—22″ DIAMETER

f'_c = 3750 psi
f_y = 60,000 psi

Bars	p	M/N † = e (in.) 0	1	2	3	4	5	6	8	10	12	14	16	18	20	22	M_o ‡ (kip-in.)
7-#7	.0110	**457**	457	378	321	279	218	154	97	70	55	46	39	34	30	27	525
8-#7	.0126	**471**	470	387	329	286	242	172	109	80	63	52	44	38	34	30	600
9-#7	.0142	**485**	482	397	337	293	259	190	121	89	70	58	49	43	38	34	675
10-#7	.0158	**500**	493	406	345	300	265	207	133	98	77	64	55	48	42	38	750
12-#7	.0189	**529**	516	425	361	314	277	238	155	115	92	76	65	57	50	45	900
14-#7	.0221	**557**	539	443	377	327	290	260	177	132	105	88	75	65	58	52	1050
16-#7	.0253	**586**	561	462	393	341	302	271	197	148	119	99	85	74	66	59	1200
6-#8	.0125	**470**	469	386	328	285	238	169	107	78	62	51	43	38	33	30	588
7-#8	.0145	**489**	484	398	338	294	260	192	123	90	71	59	50	44	39	35	686
8-#8	.0166	**508**	499	410	349	303	268	214	138	102	81	67	57	50	44	39	784
9-#8	.0187	**527**	514	423	359	312	276	234	153	113	90	75	64	56	49	44	883
10-#8	.0208	**545**	529	435	369	321	284	254	167	124	99	82	70	61	54	49	981
12-#8	.0249	**583**	558	459	390	339	300	269	194	145	116	97	83	73	65	58	1177
14-#8	.0291	**621**	588	484	411	357	316	283	218	166	133	111	96	84	75	67	1373
16-#8	.0333	**659**	618	508	432	375	332	297	242	184	149	125	108	95	84	76	1569
6-#9	.0158	**500**	492	405	344	299	264	204	131	97	76	63	54	47	41	37	739
8-#9	.0210	**548**	530	436	370	321	284	254	168	125	99	83	71	62	55	49	986
10-#9	.0263	**596**	568	467	396	344	304	273	201	151	121	101	87	76	68	61	1232
12-#9	.0316	**644**	605	498	422	367	324	291	231	176	142	119	102	90	80	72	1479
14-#9	.0368	**692**	643	528	449	390	344	309	255	199	161	136	117	103	92	83	1725
16-#9	.0421	**740**	680	559	475	412	365	327	270	220	180	152	132	116	104	94	1972
6-#10	.0200	**539**	522	429	364	316	280	244	160	119	94	78	67	58	52	47	931
8-#10	.0267	**600**	570	468	397	345	305	273	202	152	122	102	87	76	68	61	1242
10-#10	.0334	**661**	618	507	430	374	330	296	239	183	148	124	107	94	84	75	1552
12-#10	.0401	**722**	665	546	463	402	356	318	263	211	172	145	125	110	98	89	1863
14-#10	.0468	**783**	713	585	496	431	381	341	282	236	194	164	143	126	113	102	2173
16-#10	.0535	**844**	760	624	529	460	406	364	301	257	215	183	159	141	127	115	2484
6-#11	.0246	**581**	554	455	386	335	296	265	188	141	113	94	80	70	62	56	1134
7-#11	.0287	**618**	583	479	406	353	311	279	212	160	129	108	93	81	72	65	1324
8-#11	.0328	**655**	613	503	426	370	327	293	234	179	144	121	104	92	82	74	1513
9-#11	.0369	**693**	642	527	446	387	342	306	253	196	159	134	116	102	91	82	1702
10-#11	.0410	**730**	671	550	467	405	358	320	265	213	173	146	127	112	100	90	1891
11-#11	.0451	**768**	700	574	487	422	373	334	276	228	187	158	137	121	108	98	2080
13-#11	.0533	**843**	758	622	527	457	404	362	299	255	213	181	158	140	125	114	2458
15-#11	.0616	**917**	816	669	567	492	435	389	322	274	236	202	177	157	141	129	2837
6-#14S	.0355	**680**	630	516	437	379	334	299	245	187	152	128	110	97	86	78	1609
7-#14S	.0414	**734**	671	550	465	403	356	319	263	211	172	145	126	111	99	89	1877
8-#14S	.0474	**788**	713	584	494	428	378	338	279	233	191	162	141	124	111	101	2145
9-#14S	.0533	**842**	755	618	523	453	400	358	295	251	209	178	155	137	123	112	2414
10-#14S	.0592	**896**	796	652	551	478	421	377	311	265	226	193	169	150	135	122	2682
12-#14S	.0710	**1004**	880	719	608	527	465	416	343	292	255	221	194	173	156	142	3218
6-#18S	.0631	**932**	808	653	548	472	414	369	303	257	219	187	164	146	131	119	2631
7-#18S	.0737	**1028**	880	710	595	512	449	400	329	279	242	209	184	164	148	135	3070

Check availability of #14S and #18S bars.

All above columns require spirals of A432 rod or cold drawn wire (f_y = 60,000 psi):—
#14S and smaller—3/8 φ @ 2¼″
#18S only —3/8 φ @ 1¾″

Outside diameter of spiral should be 3 in. less than outside diameter of column.
† Below zigzag horizontal line of each group, concrete governs; above, tension governs.
‡ M_o = capacity in pure bending, (N = 0); for extrapolation, see page 11-5.

SPIRALLY REINFORCED ROUND COLUMNS—
Safe Load in Kips for Various Eccentricities in Inches
$f'_c = 3750$ psi (A61 or A432 Bars, $f_y = 60,000$ psi) $f_s = 24,000$ psi basis

COLUMN SIZE—24″ DIAMETER

$f'_c = 3750$ psi
$f_y = 60,000$ psi

Bars	p	M/N † = e (in.) 0	1	2	3	4	5	6	8	10	12	14	16	18	20	22	M_o ‡ (kip.-in)
8-#7	.0106	**539**	539	461	396	346	308	212	129	93	73	60	50	44	39	34	*669*
9-#7	.0119	**553**	553	471	404	354	314	233	144	104	81	67	56	49	43	39	*753*
10-#7	.0133	**568**	568	481	412	361	321	254	158	114	90	74	62	54	48	43	*837*
12-#7	.0159	**596**	596	501	429	376	334	292	184	135	106	87	74	65	57	51	*1004*
14-#7	.0186	**625**	623	520	446	391	347	313	210	154	122	101	86	75	66	59	*1171*
16-#7	.0212	**654**	647	540	463	405	361	325	234	173	137	114	97	85	75	67	*1339*
6-#8	.0105	**537**	537	460	394	345	306	208	127	91	71	58	49	43	38	34	*656*
8-#8	.0140	**575**	575	486	416	364	324	263	164	119	93	77	65	57	50	45	*875*
10-#8	.0175	**613**	613	511	438	384	341	307	198	145	115	95	81	70	62	56	*1094*
12-#8	.0210	**651**	644	537	461	403	358	323	230	170	135	112	95	83	74	66	*1313*
14-#8	.0244	**689**	675	563	483	423	376	338	260	194	155	128	110	96	85	77	*1532*
16-#8	.0279	**727**	705	588	505	442	393	354	288	216	173	145	124	108	96	87	*1751*
6-#9	.0133	**568**	568	480	411	360	320	251	156	113	88	73	62	54	47	42	*826*
8-#9	.0177	**616**	615	512	439	384	342	307	199	146	115	95	81	70	62	56	*1101*
10-#9	.0221	**664**	653	545	467	409	363	327	239	177	141	117	100	87	77	69	*1376*
12-#9	.0265	**712**	692	577	495	433	385	347	275	206	165	137	118	103	91	82	*1652*
14-#9	.0309	**760**	731	609	523	457	407	366	305	234	188	157	135	118	105	95	*1927*
16-#9	.0354	**808**	769	642	550	482	428	386	321	259	210	176	152	133	119	107	*2202*
6-#10	.0168	**606**	606	506	433	379	337	300	190	139	110	90	77	67	59	53	*1041*
8-#10	.0225	**667**	656	547	468	410	364	328	240	178	142	118	100	88	78	70	*1388*
10-#10	.0281	**728**	705	587	503	440	391	352	285	215	172	143	123	108	96	86	*1735*
12-#10	.0337	**789**	754	628	538	471	419	377	314	248	200	168	144	127	113	102	*2082*
14-#10	.0393	**850**	803	669	574	502	446	402	335	279	227	191	165	145	129	117	*2429*
16-#10	.0449	**911**	852	710	609	533	473	426	355	304	252	213	184	163	146	132	*2776*
6-#11	.0207	**648**	640	533	456	399	355	319	224	165	131	108	92	81	71	64	*1269*
7-#11	.0241	**686**	670	558	478	418	371	334	253	188	150	125	106	93	82	74	*1481*
8-#11	.0276	**723**	700	583	499	437	388	349	280	210	168	140	120	105	93	84	*1692*
9-#11	.0310	**761**	730	608	521	455	405	364	303	231	186	155	133	117	104	94	*1904*
10-#11	.0345	**798**	760	633	542	474	421	379	316	251	203	170	146	128	114	103	*2116*
12-#11	.0414	**873**	820	683	585	512	455	409	341	288	234	198	171	151	134	122	*2539*
14-#11	.0483	**948**	880	733	628	549	488	439	366	313	264	224	194	172	154	139	*2962*
16-#11	.0552	**1023**	940	783	670	586	521	469	391	335	291	248	216	192	172	156	*3385*
6-#14S	.0298	**748**	718	597	511	446	396	357	293	221	177	148	127	111	99	89	*1803*
7-#14S	.0348	**802**	761	633	541	473	420	378	314	249	201	169	145	128	114	103	*2104*
8-#14S	.0398	**856**	804	668	572	500	444	399	332	276	224	189	163	143	128	116	*2404*
9-#14S	.0448	**910**	847	704	602	526	467	420	350	299	246	208	180	159	142	128	*2705*
10-#14S	.0497	**964**	890	740	633	553	491	441	367	315	266	226	196	173	155	141	*3006*
11-#14S	.0547	**1018**	933	775	663	579	515	463	385	330	285	243	212	188	168	153	*3306*
13-#14S	.0647	**1126**	1019	846	724	633	562	505	420	360	315	275	241	215	193	176	*3908*
6-#18S	.0531	**1000**	905	745	633	550	487	436	361	308	260	221	193	170	153	139	*2977*
7-#18S	.0619	**1096**	979	805	684	594	525	471	390	332	290	248	217	193	173	158	*3473*
8-#18S	.0707	**1192**	1053	865	734	638	564	505	418	357	311	273	240	214	193	176	*3969*
9-#18S	.0796	**1288**	1127	925	785	682	602	540	446	381	332	294	261	233	211	193	*4465*

Check availability of #14S and #18S bars.

All above columns require spirals of A432 rod or cold drawn wire ($f_y = 60,000$ psi):—
#14S and smaller—3/8 φ @ 2¼″
#18S only —3/8 φ @ 1¾″

Outside diameter of spiral should be 3 in. less than outside diameter of column.
† Below zigzag horizontal line of each group, concrete governs; above, tension governs.
‡ M_o = capacity in pure bending, ($N = 0$); for extrapolation, see page 11-5.

SPIRALLY REINFORCED ROUND COLUMNS—
Safe Load in Kips for Various Eccentricities in Inches
f'_c = 3750 psi (A61 or A432 Bars, f_y = 60,000 psi) f_s = 24,000 psi basis

COLUMN SIZE—26″ DIAMETER																f'_c = 3750 psi, f_y = 60,000 psi	
Bars	p	M/N † = e (in.)															M_o ‡ (kip-in.)
		0	2	4	6	8	10	12	14	16	18	20	22	24	26	28	
7-#8	.0104	**630**	555	422	290	172	122	94	77	65	56	50	44	40	36	33	846
8-#8	.0119	**649**	568	432	322	193	138	107	87	74	64	56	50	46	42	38	966
9-#8	.0134	**668**	581	443	353	214	153	119	98	83	72	63	57	51	47	43	1087
10-#8	.0149	**687**	595	453	366	233	168	131	108	91	79	70	63	57	52	48	1208
12-#8	.0179	**725**	621	473	382	271	197	155	127	108	94	83	75	67	62	57	1450
14-#8	.0208	**763**	648	494	399	307	225	177	147	125	109	96	86	78	71	66	1692
16-#8	.0238	**801**	675	514	416	340	251	199	165	141	123	109	98	89	81	75	1933
6-#9	.0113	**641**	562	428	308	183	131	101	83	70	60	53	48	43	39	36	912
8-#9	.0151	**689**	596	454	366	235	169	132	108	92	80	70	63	57	52	48	1216
10-#9	.0188	**737**	630	479	387	282	205	161	133	113	98	87	78	71	65	59	1520
12-#9	.0226	**785**	663	505	408	325	239	189	157	134	116	103	93	84	77	71	1824
14-#9	.0264	**833**	697	531	429	360	271	216	179	153	134	119	107	97	89	82	2129
16-#9	.0301	**881**	730	557	450	377	301	241	201	173	151	134	121	110	101	93	2433
18-#9	.0339	**929**	764	583	471	395	330	266	222	191	168	149	134	122	112	104	2737
6-#10	.0144	**680**	589	448	361	224	161	126	103	87	76	67	60	54	49	45	1151
8-#10	.0191	**741**	631	481	388	284	207	163	134	114	99	88	79	71	65	60	1534
10-#10	.0239	**802**	674	513	414	337	249	198	164	140	122	108	97	88	81	74	1918
12-#10	.0287	**863**	716	546	441	369	289	231	192	164	144	128	115	104	96	88	2302
14-#10	.0335	**924**	759	578	467	392	325	261	219	188	165	147	132	120	110	102	2685
16-#10	.0383	**985**	801	611	493	414	356	291	244	211	185	165	149	136	125	115	3069
18-#10	.0431	**1046**	844	643	520	436	376	318	269	232	205	183	165	151	139	128	3453
20-#10	.0478	**1107**	886	676	546	458	395	344	292	253	223	200	181	165	152	141	3836
6-#11	.0176	**722**	617	470	379	264	192	150	124	105	91	81	72	65	60	55	1404
7-#11	.0206	**759**	643	489	395	299	219	172	142	121	105	93	84	76	69	64	1638
8-#11	0235	**797**	669	509	411	331	244	194	160	137	119	106	95	86	79	73	1872
9-#11	.0264	**834**	695	529	427	358	269	214	178	152	133	118	106	96	88	81	2106
10-#11	.0294	**872**	721	549	443	371	292	234	195	167	146	130	117	106	97	90	2340
12-#11	.0353	**947**	773	589	475	399	336	271	227	195	171	153	137	125	115	106	2808
14-#11	.0411	**1021**	825	628	507	426	366	305	257	222	196	175	158	144	132	122	3277
16-#11	.0470	**1096**	877	668	540	453	390	338	286	248	219	196	177	162	149	138	3745
18-#11	.0529	**1171**	929	708	572	480	413	363	313	272	241	216	196	179	165	153	4213
6-#14S	.0254	**821**	684	520	419	347	257	204	170	145	126	112	101	91	84	77	1998
7-#14S	.0297	**875**	721	548	442	370	291	233	194	166	145	129	116	105	97	89	2331
8-#14S	.0339	**929**	759	577	465	390	322	259	217	186	163	145	131	119	109	101	2664
9-#14S	.0381	**983**	796	605	488	409	351	284	239	206	181	161	146	133	122	113	2997
10-#14S	.0424	**1037**	833	633	511	428	368	308	260	225	198	177	160	146	134	124	3330
11-#14S	.0466	**1091**	870	661	533	447	385	331	280	243	214	192	174	158	146	135	3663
13-#14S	.0551	**1199**	944	718	579	485	418	366	318	278	246	221	200	183	169	157	4329
15-#14S	.0636	**1307**	1018	775	625	524	451	395	352	310	275	248	225	207	191	177	4995
6-#18S	.0452	**1073**	841	633	508	424	363	305	257	223	196	175	159	145	133	123	3322
7-#18S	.0527	**1169**	904	680	545	455	390	340	289	252	223	200	181	165	152	141	3876
8-#18S	.0603	**1265**	968	727	583	486	417	365	319	279	247	222	202	185	171	158	4430
9-#18S	.0678	**1361**	1031	775	620	517	444	388	345	304	271	244	222	204	188	175	4984
10-#18S	.0753	**1457**	1094	822	658	548	470	412	366	327	293	265	241	222	205	191	5537

Check availability of #14S and #18S bars.

All above columns require spirals of A432 rod or cold drawn wire (f_y = 60,000 psi):—
#14S and smaller—3/8 φ @ 2¼″
#18S only —3/8 φ @ 1¾″

Outside diameter of spiral should be 3 in. less than outside diameter of column.
† Below zigzag horizontal line of each group, concrete governs; above, tension governs.
‡ M_o = capacity in pure bending, (N = 0); for extrapolation, see page 11-5.

SPIRALLY REINFORCED ROUND COLUMNS—
Safe Load in Kips for Various Eccentricities in Inches
f'_c = 3750 psi (A61 or A432 Bars, f_y = 60,000 psi) f_s = 24,000 psi basis

COLUMN SIZE—28″ DIAMETER

f'_c = 3750 psi
f_y = 60,000 psi

Bars	p	M/N † = e (in.) 0	2	4	6	8	10	12	14	16	18	20	22	24	26	28	M_o ‡ (kip-in.)
8-#8	.0103	**728**	658	507	395	226	158	121	99	83	72	63	56	51	46	42	*1057*
9-#8	.0115	**747**	672	518	421	250	176	135	110	93	80	71	63	57	52	48	*1190*
10-#8	.0128	**766**	685	529	430	273	193	149	122	103	89	78	70	63	57	53	*1322*
12-#8	.0154	**804**	713	550	448	317	226	176	144	122	105	93	83	75	69	63	*1586*
14-#8	.0180	**842**	740	572	465	359	258	202	166	140	122	107	96	87	79	73	*1851*
16-#8	.0205	**880**	768	593	483	398	289	227	187	158	138	122	109	99	90	83	*2115*
7-#9	.0114	**745**	669	516	419	245	172	133	108	91	79	69	62	56	51	47	*1165*
8-#9	.0130	**769**	687	529	431	275	194	150	122	103	89	79	70	63	58	53	*1331*
10-#9	.0162	**817**	721	556	453	330	236	184	150	127	110	97	87	79	72	66	*1664*
12-#9	.0195	**865**	756	584	475	380	275	216	177	150	131	115	103	94	85	79	*1997*
14-#9	.0227	**913**	791	611	497	420	312	246	203	173	150	133	119	108	99	91	*2330*
16-#9	.0260	**961**	825	638	520	438	347	275	228	195	170	150	135	122	112	103	*2663*
18-#9	.0292	**1009**	860	665	542	457	380	303	252	216	188	167	150	137	125	115	*2996*
6-#10	.0124	**760**	679	524	426	262	185	143	116	98	85	75	67	60	55	50	*1260*
8-#10	.0165	**821**	723	558	454	332	238	185	152	128	111	98	88	79	72	67	*1681*
10-#10	.0206	**882**	767	592	482	395	287	225	185	157	137	121	108	98	90	83	*2101*
12-#10	.0248	**943**	811	626	510	430	332	263	217	185	161	143	128	116	106	98	*2521*
14-#10	.0289	**1003**	855	660	538	454	375	299	248	212	185	164	148	134	123	113	*2941*
16-#10	.0330	**1064**	899	695	566	478	413	332	277	238	208	185	167	152	139	128	*3362*
18-#10	.0371	**1125**	943	729	594	501	434	364	305	263	231	205	185	169	155	143	*3782*
6-#11	.0152	**801**	709	546	444	309	220	171	140	118	102	90	81	73	67	61	*1539*
7-#11	.0177	**839**	736	567	461	350	252	196	161	136	118	104	93	85	77	71	*1795*
8-#11	.0203	**876**	763	588	479	388	281	221	181	154	134	118	106	96	88	81	*2052*
9-#11	.0228	**914**	789	609	496	418	310	244	201	171	149	132	118	107	98	90	*2308*
10-#11	.0253	**951**	816	630	513	432	337	267	221	188	164	145	130	118	108	100	*2565*
12-#11	.0304	**1026**	870	672	547	461	388	310	258	221	193	171	154	140	128	118	*3078*
14-#11	.0355	**1101**	923	713	581	490	424	350	293	251	220	196	177	161	148	136	*3591*
16-#11	.0405	**1176**	977	755	615	519	449	387	326	281	247	220	199	181	166	154	*4104*
18-#11	.0456	**1251**	1031	797	650	548	474	418	357	309	272	244	220	201	185	171	*4617*
20-#11	.0507	**1326**	1084	839	684	577	499	440	387	336	297	266	241	220	203	188	*5130*
6-#14S	.0219	**901**	778	600	488	407	297	233	192	163	142	126	113	102	93	86	*2192*
7-#14S	.0256	**955**	817	629	512	431	336	266	220	187	163	145	130	118	108	99	*2557*
8-#14S	.0292	**1009**	855	659	536	452	372	297	246	211	184	163	147	133	122	113	*2923*
9-#14S	.0329	**1063**	894	689	561	473	407	326	272	233	204	181	163	148	136	126	*3288*
10-#14S	.0365	**1117**	932	719	585	493	426	354	296	255	223	199	179	163	150	138	*3654*
12-#14S	.0438	**1225**	1009	778	634	534	462	406	342	296	261	233	210	192	176	163	*4385*
14-#14S	.0512	**1333**	1086	838	682	575	497	438	385	334	296	265	240	219	202	187	*5115*
16-#14S	.0585	**1441**	1162	898	731	617	533	469	419	370	329	295	268	245	226	210	*5846*
6-#18S	.0390	**1153**	943	721	584	491	423	352	295	254	223	199	179	163	150	138	*3668*
7-#18S	.0455	**1249**	1009	771	624	524	452	394	332	288	253	227	205	187	172	159	*4279*
8-#18S	.0520	**1345**	1074	821	665	558	481	423	367	319	282	253	229	209	193	179	*4891*
9-#18S	.0585	**1441**	1140	871	705	592	510	448	400	349	309	278	252	231	213	198	*5502*
10-#18S	.0650	**1537**	1206	922	746	626	539	474	423	377	335	302	275	252	233	216	*6113*
11-#18S	.0715	**1633**	1272	972	786	660	569	500	445	402	360	325	296	272	252	234	*6725*

Check availability of #14S and #18S bars.

All above columns require spirals of A432 rod or cold drawn wire (f_y = 60,000 psi):—
#14S and smaller—3/8 φ @ 2¼″
#18S only —3/8 φ @ 1¾″

Outside diameter of spiral should be 3 in. less than outside diameter of column.
† Below zigzag horizontal line of each group, concrete governs; above, tension governs.
‡ M_o = capacity in pure bending, (N = 0); for extrapolation, see page 11-5.

SPIRALLY REINFORCED ROUND COLUMNS—
Safe Load in Kips for Various Eccentricities in Inches
f'_c = 3750 psi (A61 or A432 Bars, f_y = 60,000 psi) f_s = 24,000 psi basis

COLUMN SIZE—30″ DIAMETER

f'_c = 3750 psi
f_y = 60,000 psi

Bars	p	M/N † = e (in.) 0	2	4	6	8	10	12	14	16	18	20	22	24	26	28	M_o ‡ (kip-in.)
8-#9	.0113	**854**	784	612	501	320	222	169	137	115	99	87	78	70	64	59	1447
9-#9	.0127	**878**	802	626	513	353	246	189	153	129	111	98	87	79	72	66	1627
10-#9	.0141	**902**	820	640	525	384	269	207	169	142	123	108	96	87	79	73	1808
12-#9	.0170	**950**	856	668	548	443	315	244	199	168	145	128	114	103	94	87	2170
14-#9	.0198	**998**	891	697	572	485	357	278	228	193	167	148	132	120	109	100	2532
16-#9	.0226	**1046**	927	725	595	505	397	312	256	218	189	167	150	136	124	114	2894
18-#9	.0255	**1094**	962	753	619	525	435	343	283	241	210	186	167	151	138	127	3255
20-#9	.0283	**1142**	998	781	642	545	472	374	310	264	230	204	183	166	152	140	3617
22-#9	.0311	**1190**	1034	810	665	565	491	403	335	287	250	222	200	182	166	153	3979
24-#9	.0340	**1238**	1069	838	689	585	508	431	360	308	270	240	216	196	180	166	4341
6-#10	.0108	**845**	777	606	496	306	211	161	130	109	94	83	74	66	60	55	1370
8-#10	.0144	**906**	822	642	526	387	272	209	170	143	124	109	97	88	80	73	1827
10-#10	.0180	**967**	867	677	555	461	328	255	208	176	152	134	120	109	99	91	2284
12-#10	.0216	**1028**	912	713	585	496	380	298	244	207	180	159	142	129	118	108	2741
14-#10	.0252	**1089**	957	749	615	521	429	338	279	237	207	183	164	149	136	125	3197
16-#10	.0287	**1150**	1002	784	644	546	475	377	312	267	232	206	185	168	154	142	3654
18-#10	.0323	**1211**	1048	820	674	572	497	413	344	295	258	229	206	187	171	158	4111
20-#10	.0359	**1272**	1093	856	703	597	518	448	374	322	282	251	226	205	188	174	4568
6-#11	.0132	**887**	808	630	516	361	252	193	157	132	114	100	89	81	73	67	1674
7-#11	.0154	**924**	835	651	534	408	288	222	181	152	132	116	104	93	85	78	1953
8-#11	.0177	**962**	863	673	552	453	322	250	204	172	149	131	117	106	97	89	2232
9-#11	.0199	**999**	890	695	570	483	354	276	226	192	166	147	131	119	108	100	2511
10-#11	.0221	**1037**	918	717	588	499	386	302	248	210	183	161	145	131	120	110	2790
12-#11	.0265	**1111**	973	761	624	529	444	351	290	247	215	191	171	155	142	131	3348
14-#11	.0309	**1186**	1028	804	660	560	486	397	330	282	246	219	196	178	163	151	3906
16-#11	.0353	**1261**	1083	848	696	591	513	440	367	315	276	246	221	201	184	170	4464
18-#11	.0397	**1336**	1138	891	732	622	540	477	403	347	305	272	245	223	205	189	5022
20-#11	.0441	**1411**	1194	935	769	652	567	501	437	378	333	297	268	245	225	208	5580
22-#11	.0486	**1486**	1249	979	805	683	593	525	470	407	359	322	291	266	244	226	6138
6-#14S	.0191	**986**	879	686	562	476	340	264	216	183	158	140	125	113	103	95	2386
7-#14S	.0223	**1040**	919	717	588	498	385	301	248	210	182	161	144	131	119	110	2784
8-#14S	.0255	**1094**	958	748	613	520	427	336	278	236	206	182	163	148	135	125	3182
9-#14S	.0286	**1148**	998	779	639	542	467	370	306	262	228	202	182	165	151	139	3580
10-#14S	.0318	**1202**	1037	810	665	563	489	402	334	286	250	222	200	181	166	153	3978
12-#14S	.0382	**1310**	1116	872	716	607	527	462	387	333	292	260	234	213	196	181	4773
14-#14S	.0446	**1418**	1195	935	767	651	565	499	436	377	332	296	268	244	224	208	5569
16-#14S	.0509	**1526**	1274	997	819	695	603	533	477	418	369	331	299	274	252	233	6365
18-#14S	.0573	**1634**	1353	1059	870	738	641	567	508	457	405	364	330	302	278	258	7160
6-#18S	.0340	**1238**	1050	815	666	562	487	402	335	287	251	223	200	182	167	154	4013
7-#18S	.0396	**1334**	1118	867	709	599	518	451	378	325	286	254	229	209	192	177	4682
8-#18S	.0453	**1430**	1186	920	752	635	550	485	418	362	318	285	257	234	215	199	5351
9-#18S	.0509	**1526**	1254	973	795	671	581	513	456	396	350	313	284	259	239	221	6020
10-#18S	.0566	**1622**	1322	1026	838	708	613	540	483	428	379	341	309	283	261	242	6689
11-#18S	.0622	**1718**	1390	1078	881	744	644	568	508	459	408	367	334	306	282	262	7358
12-#18S	.0679	**1814**	1458	1131	924	780	676	596	533	482	435	392	357	328	303	282	8027

Check availability of #14S and #18S bars.

All above columns require spirals of A432 rod or cold drawn wire (f_y = 60,000 psi):—
#14S and smaller—3/8 ϕ @ 2¼″
#18S only —3/8 ϕ @ 1¾″

Outside diameter of spiral should be 3 in. less than outside diameter of column.
† Below zigzag horizontal line of each group, concrete governs; above, tension governs.
‡ M_o = capacity in pure bending, (N = 0); for extrapolation, see page 11-5.

SPIRALLY REINFORCED ROUND COLUMNS—
Safe Load in Kips for Various Eccentricities in Inches
f'_c = 3750 psi (A61 or A432 Bars, f_y = 60,000 psi) f_s = 24,000 psi basis

COLUMN SIZE—32″ DIAMETER | f'_c = 3750 psi, f_y = 60,000 psi

Bars	p	M/N † = e (in.) 0	3	6	9	12	15	18	21	24	27	30	33	36	39	42	M_o ‡ (kip-in.)
9-#9	.0112	**969**	800	591	332	212	155	123	101	86	75	66	60	54	49	45	*1757*
10-#9	.0124	**993**	817	603	363	233	171	135	112	95	83	74	66	60	55	50	*1952*
12-#9	.0149	**1041**	849	628	422	274	202	161	133	114	99	88	79	72	65	60	*2343*
14-#9	.0174	**1089**	882	652	477	313	233	185	154	131	115	102	91	83	76	70	*2733*
16-#9	.0199	**1137**	914	677	529	350	262	209	174	149	130	116	104	94	87	80	*3124*
18-#9	.0224	**1185**	947	701	557	386	290	232	194	166	145	129	116	106	97	89	*3515*
20-#9	.0249	**1233**	979	726	576	421	318	255	213	183	160	143	129	117	107	99	*3905*
7-#10	.0111	**967**	798	589	327	208	153	121	100	85	74	65	59	53	48	45	*1726*
8-#10	.0126	**997**	819	604	367	235	173	137	113	96	84	74	67	60	55	51	*1973*
10-#10	.0158	**1058**	860	635	440	286	212	168	140	119	104	92	83	75	69	63	*2467*
12-#10	.0189	**1119**	901	666	507	335	250	199	166	142	124	110	99	90	82	76	*2960*
14-#10	.0221	**1180**	942	697	553	381	286	229	191	163	143	127	114	104	95	88	*3453*
16-#10	.0253	**1241**	983	728	578	424	321	258	215	185	162	144	130	118	108	100	*3947*
18-#10	.0284	**1302**	1024	759	603	466	354	286	239	206	181	161	145	132	121	112	*4440*
20-#10	.0316	**1363**	1065	790	628	505	386	313	263	226	199	177	160	146	134	124	*4934*
6-#11	.0116	**978**	805	594	341	217	160	126	104	89	77	68	61	55	51	47	*1808*
7-#11	.0136	**1016**	830	613	387	250	184	146	120	103	90	79	71	65	59	54	*2110*
8-#11	.0155	**1053**	855	632	432	281	208	165	137	117	102	90	81	74	67	62	*2411*
9-#11	.0175	**1090**	881	651	474	311	231	184	153	130	114	101	91	82	75	70	*2713*
10-#11	.0194	**1128**	906	669	514	340	254	202	168	144	126	112	100	91	84	77	*3014*
12-#11	.0233	**1203**	956	707	561	395	297	238	199	171	149	133	120	109	100	92	*3617*
14-#11	.0272	**1278**	1006	745	592	447	339	273	229	196	172	153	138	126	115	107	*4220*
16-#11	.0310	**1353**	1057	783	622	496	379	307	257	222	195	174	157	143	131	121	*4823*
18-#11	.0349	**1427**	1107	821	652	541	417	339	285	246	217	193	175	159	146	135	*5426*
20-#11	.0388	**1502**	1157	859	682	566	454	370	312	270	238	213	192	175	161	149	*6029*
23-#11	.0446	**1615**	1232	915	728	604	505	415	351	305	269	241	218	199	183	170	*6933*
6-#14S	.0168	**1077**	870	642	456	298	221	176	146	124	109	96	87	79	72	66	*2581*
7-#14S	.0196	**1131**	906	669	513	339	253	202	168	144	126	112	100	91	83	77	*3011*
8-#14S	.0224	**1185**	942	696	552	379	285	228	190	163	143	127	114	104	95	88	*3441*
9-#14S	.0252	**1239**	978	723	573	417	315	253	211	182	159	141	127	116	106	98	*3872*
10-#14S	.0280	**1293**	1014	750	595	454	344	278	232	200	175	156	141	128	117	108	*4302*
11-#14S	.0308	**1347**	1050	777	617	488	373	301	253	218	191	170	154	140	129	119	*4732*
13-#14S	.0364	**1455**	1122	831	660	547	427	347	292	253	222	199	179	164	150	139	*5592*
15-#14S	.0420	**1563**	1194	885	703	583	477	390	330	286	253	226	204	187	172	159	*6453*
17-#14S	.0476	**1671**	1266	939	746	619	525	432	367	319	282	252	229	209	192	178	*7313*
19-#14S	.0532	**1779**	1338	993	789	655	559	471	401	350	310	278	252	231	213	197	*8174*
6-#18S	.0298	**1329**	1024	753	595	456	347	280	234	202	177	158	142	129	119	110	*4359*
7-#18S	.0348	**1425**	1086	798	631	512	393	319	268	232	204	182	164	149	137	127	*5086*
8-#18S	.0398	**1521**	1147	843	667	551	437	356	301	260	229	205	185	169	155	144	*5812*
9-#18S	.0448	**1617**	1209	889	703	581	478	392	332	288	254	228	206	188	173	160	*6539*
10-#18S	.0497	**1713**	1271	934	739	611	516	425	362	315	278	250	226	207	190	176	*7265*
11-#18S	.0547	**1809**	1332	980	775	640	546	458	390	340	302	271	246	225	207	192	*7992*
12-#18S	.0597	**1905**	1394	1025	811	670	571	488	418	365	324	292	265	243	224	208	*8719*
13-#18S	.0647	**2001**	1456	1070	846	700	597	518	445	389	347	312	284	260	240	223	*9445*
14-#18S	.0696	**2097**	1517	1116	882	730	622	542	470	413	368	332	302	277	256	238	*10172*

Check availability of #14S and #18S bars.

All above columns require spirals of A432 rod or cold drawn wire (f_y = 60,000 psi):—
#14S and smaller—3/8 φ @ 2¼″
#18S only —3/8 φ @ 1¾″

Outside diameter of spiral should be 3 in. less than outside diameter of column.
† Below zigzag horizontal line of each group, concrete governs; above, tension governs.
‡ M_o = capacity in pure bending, (N = 0); for extrapolation, see page 11-5.

SPIRALLY REINFORCED ROUND COLUMNS—
Safe Load in Kips for Various Eccentricities in Inches
$f'_c = 3750$ psi (A61 or A432 Bars, $f_y = 60{,}000$ psi) $f_s = 24{,}000$ psi basis

COLUMN SIZE—34″ DIAMETER

$f'_c = 3750$ psi
$f_y = 60{,}000$ psi

Bars	p	M/N † = e (in.) 0	3	6	9	12	15	18	21	24	27	30	33	36	39	42	M_o ‡ (kip-in.)
10-#9	.0110	**1091**	922	688	415	260	189	149	123	104	91	80	72	65	59	55	*2096*
12-#9	.0132	**1139**	955	713	483	306	224	177	146	124	108	96	86	78	71	65	*2516*
14-#9	.0154	**1187**	988	739	545	350	258	204	168	144	125	111	99	90	82	76	*2935*
16-#9	.0176	**1235**	1022	764	604	392	290	230	191	163	142	126	113	103	94	87	*3354*
18-#9	.0198	**1283**	1055	790	631	432	322	256	213	182	159	141	127	115	105	97	*3774*
8-#10	.0112	**1095**	924	689	419	263	191	150	124	105	91	81	72	66	60	55	*2119*
10-#10	.0140	**1155**	966	721	503	320	235	185	153	130	113	100	90	82	75	69	*2649*
12-#10	.0168	**1216**	1008	753	580	375	277	219	181	155	135	120	107	97	89	82	*3179*
14-#10	.0196	**1277**	1050	786	628	426	317	252	209	179	156	138	124	113	103	95	*3709*
16-#10	.0224	**1338**	1093	818	654	475	355	284	236	202	177	157	141	128	118	108	*4239*
18-#10	.0252	**1399**	1135	850	680	522	393	315	263	225	197	175	158	143	132	121	*4769*
20-#10	.0280	**1460**	1177	882	706	567	429	345	288	248	217	193	174	158	145	134	*5299*
6-#11	.0103	**1075**	910	678	390	243	176	139	114	97	84	74	67	60	55	51	*1943*
7-#11	.0120	**1113**	936	698	443	279	204	160	132	112	98	86	77	70	64	59	*2267*
8-#11	.0137	**1150**	962	718	494	314	230	181	150	128	111	98	88	80	73	67	*2591*
9-#11	.0155	**1188**	987	737	542	348	256	202	167	143	124	110	99	90	82	75	*2915*
10-#11	.0172	**1225**	1013	757	588	380	281	223	185	157	137	122	109	99	91	84	*3239*
12-#11	.0206	**1300**	1065	796	636	443	330	263	218	187	163	145	130	118	108	100	*3887*
14-#11	.0241	**1375**	1117	836	668	501	376	301	251	215	188	167	150	137	125	116	*4535*
16-#11	.0275	**1450**	1168	875	700	557	421	338	283	243	213	189	171	155	142	131	*5182*
18-#11	.0309	**1525**	1220	915	732	609	463	374	314	270	237	211	190	173	159	147	*5830*
20-#11	.0344	**1599**	1272	954	763	636	504	409	343	296	260	232	210	191	175	162	*6478*
22-#11	.0378	**1674**	1323	993	795	663	543	442	373	322	283	253	229	208	192	177	*7126*
25-#11	.0430	**1787**	1401	1052	843	703	599	490	415	359	317	284	257	234	215	199	*8098*
6-#14S	.0149	**1175**	977	729	521	333	245	193	160	136	119	105	94	85	78	72	*2775*
7-#14S	.0173	**1229**	1014	757	588	380	281	223	184	157	137	122	109	99	91	84	*3238*
8-#14S	.0198	**1283**	1051	785	626	425	316	251	209	178	156	138	124	113	103	95	*3700*
9-#14S	.0223	**1337**	1088	813	649	468	350	279	232	199	174	154	139	126	116	107	*4163*
10-#14S	.0248	**1391**	1125	841	672	509	382	306	255	219	192	170	153	139	128	118	*4626*
11-#14S	.0273	**1445**	1162	869	694	548	414	333	278	239	209	186	168	152	140	129	*5088*
13-#14S	.0322	**1553**	1236	926	740	616	475	384	322	277	243	217	196	178	164	151	*6014*
15-#14S	.0372	**1661**	1310	982	785	654	531	432	364	314	277	247	223	203	187	173	*6939*
17-#14S	.0421	**1769**	1384	1038	830	692	585	478	404	350	309	276	250	228	210	194	*7864*
19-#14S	.0471	**1877**	1458	1094	876	730	626	522	443	385	340	304	276	252	232	215	*8789*
21-#14S	.0520	**1985**	1532	1150	921	768	658	564	480	418	370	332	301	275	254	235	*9715*
6-#18S	.0264	**1427**	1136	845	673	514	387	310	259	222	194	173	156	141	130	120	*4705*
7-#18S	.0308	**1523**	1200	893	711	577	439	354	296	255	224	199	179	163	150	138	*5489*
8-#18S	.0352	**1619**	1264	941	749	622	488	395	332	287	252	225	203	185	170	157	*6273*
9-#18S	.0397	**1715**	1327	988	787	654	534	435	367	317	280	250	226	206	189	175	*7057*
10-#18S	.0441	**1811**	1391	1036	825	686	578	473	401	347	306	274	248	226	208	193	*7841*
11-#18S	.0485	**1907**	1455	1083	863	717	613	510	433	376	332	298	270	247	227	210	*8626*
12-#18S	.0529	**2003**	1518	1131	901	749	641	545	464	404	358	321	291	266	245	228	*9410*
13-#18S	.0573	**2099**	1582	1179	939	781	668	578	494	431	382	344	312	286	263	244	*10194*
14-#18S	.0617	**2195**	1646	1226	977	812	695	607	523	457	406	366	332	305	281	261	*10978*
15-#18S	.0661	**2291**	1709	1274	1015	844	722	631	551	483	430	387	352	323	298	277	*11762*

Check availability of #14S and #18S bars.

All above columns require spirals of A432 rod or cold drawn wire ($f_y = 60{,}000$ psi):—
#14S and smaller—3/8 φ @ 2¼″
#18S only —3/8 φ @ 1¾″

Outside diameter of spiral should be 3 in. less than outside diameter of column.
† Below zigzag horizontal line of each group, concrete governs; above, tension governs.
‡ M_o = capacity in pure bending, ($N = 0$); for extrapolation, see page 11-5.

SPIRALLY REINFORCED ROUND COLUMNS—
Safe Load in Kips for Various Eccentricities in inches
f'_c = 3750 psi (A61 or A432 Bars, f_y = 60,000 psi) f_s = 24,000 psi basis

COLUMN SIZE—36″ DIAMETER

f'_c = 3750 psi
f_y = 60,000 psi

Bars	p	M/N † = e (in.) 0	3	6	9	12	15	18	21	24	27	30	33	36	39	42	M_o ‡ (kip-in.)
11-#9	.0108	**1218**	1051	792	513	316	228	178	146	124	108	95	85	77	70	65	*2464*
12-#9	.0118	**1242**	1068	805	551	341	247	193	159	135	117	103	93	84	77	70	*2688*
14-#9	.0138	**1290**	1102	832	622	390	284	223	184	156	136	120	108	97	89	82	*3137*
16-#9	.0157	**1338**	1136	858	689	437	320	252	208	177	154	136	122	111	101	93	*3585*
18-#9	.0177	**1386**	1171	885	711	482	355	280	232	198	172	153	137	124	114	105	*4033*
20-#9	.0196	**1434**	1205	911	733	526	389	308	255	218	190	168	151	137	126	116	*4481*
10-#10	.0125	**1259**	1079	814	574	357	259	203	167	142	123	109	97	88	81	74	*2832*
12-#10	.0150	**1320**	1123	847	662	418	305	240	198	168	146	130	116	105	96	89	*3399*
14-#10	.0175	**1380**	1166	881	707	475	349	276	228	195	169	150	135	122	112	103	*3965*
16-#10	.0200	**1441**	1209	914	735	530	392	311	258	220	192	170	153	139	127	117	*4532*
18-#10	.0225	**1502**	1252	947	762	583	434	345	287	245	214	190	171	155	142	131	*5099*
20-#10	.0250	**1563**	1295	981	789	633	474	378	315	270	236	210	189	171	157	145	*5665*
7-#11	.0107	**1216**	1048	789	506	311	224	175	144	122	106	94	84	76	69	64	*2424*
8-#11	.0123	**1253**	1075	810	564	350	254	199	163	139	120	106	95	86	79	73	*2771*
9-#11	.0138	**1291**	1101	830	619	388	282	222	183	155	135	119	107	97	88	81	*3117*
10-#11	.0153	**1328**	1128	851	671	424	310	244	201	171	149	132	118	107	98	90	*3463*
12-#11	.0184	**1403**	1181	892	716	494	364	288	238	203	177	157	141	128	117	108	*4156*
14-#11	.0215	**1478**	1234	933	750	560	415	330	274	234	204	181	163	148	136	125	*4849*
16-#11	.0245	**1553**	1287	974	783	622	465	371	309	265	231	205	185	168	154	142	*5542*
18-#11	.0276	**1628**	1340	1014	816	680	512	411	343	294	258	229	206	188	172	159	*6235*
20-#11	.0307	**1703**	1392	1055	850	711	558	449	376	323	283	252	227	207	190	175	*6927*
23-#11	.0352	**1815**	1472	1117	899	753	622	504	424	365	321	286	258	235	216	200	*7967*
27-#11	.0414	**1965**	1578	1198	966	809	696	574	484	419	369	330	298	272	250	232	*9352*
6-#14S	.0133	**1278**	1091	822	596	372	270	212	174	148	129	114	102	92	84	78	*2970*
7-#14S	.0155	**1332**	1129	851	671	424	310	244	201	171	149	132	118	107	98	90	*3465*
8-#14S	.0177	**1386**	1167	880	707	474	349	276	228	194	169	150	134	122	112	103	*3960*
9-#14S	.0199	**1440**	1205	909	730	522	386	306	254	217	189	167	150	136	125	115	*4455*
10-#14S	.0221	**1494**	1242	939	754	568	423	336	279	239	208	185	166	151	138	127	*4950*
12-#14S	.0265	**1602**	1318	997	802	655	492	394	328	282	246	219	197	179	164	152	*5940*
14-#14S	.0309	**1710**	1394	1055	849	710	557	449	376	323	283	252	227	207	190	175	*6930*
16-#14S	.0354	**1818**	1470	1114	896	750	619	501	421	363	319	284	257	234	215	199	*7920*
18-#14S	.0398	**1926**	1546	1172	944	790	677	551	465	402	354	316	286	260	239	221	*8910*
20-#14S	.0442	**2034**	1622	1230	991	830	714	599	507	439	387	347	314	286	263	244	*9900*
22-#14S	.0486	**2142**	1697	1289	1039	870	748	645	547	475	420	377	341	312	287	266	*10890*
6-#18S	.0236	**1530**	1256	944	756	575	429	341	284	243	212	188	169	154	141	130	*5050*
7-#18S	.0275	**1626**	1321	994	796	648	487	390	325	279	244	217	195	178	163	150	*5892*
8-#18S	.0314	**1722**	1386	1043	836	698	542	436	365	314	275	245	221	201	184	170	*6734*
9-#18S	.0354	**1818**	1452	1093	876	731	594	481	404	348	306	273	246	224	206	190	*7576*
10-#18S	.0393	**1914**	1517	1143	916	765	643	523	441	381	335	299	270	247	227	210	*8417*
11-#18S	.0432	**2010**	1583	1192	956	798	685	564	477	413	364	325	294	269	247	229	*9259*
12-#18S	.0472	**2106**	1648	1242	996	832	714	603	511	444	392	351	318	290	267	247	*10101*
13-#18S	.0511	**2202**	1714	1292	1036	865	743	640	545	474	419	376	341	312	287	266	*10943*
14-#18S	.0550	**2298**	1779	1341	1076	899	772	676	577	503	446	400	363	332	306	284	*11785*
15-#18S	.0589	**2394**	1845	1391	1116	932	800	701	608	531	472	424	385	353	325	302	*12626*
16-#18S	.0629	**2490**	1910	1441	1156	966	829	726	638	559	497	447	407	373	344	320	*13468*

Check availability of #14S and #18S bars.

All above columns require spirals of A432 rod or cold drawn wire (f_y = 60,000 psi):—
#14S and smaller—⅜ φ @ 2¼″
#18S only —⅜ φ @ 1¾″

Outside diameter of spiral should be 3 in. less than outside diameter of column.
† Below zigzag horizontal line of each group, concrete governs; above, tension governs.
‡ M_o = capacity in pure bending, (N = 0); for extrapolation, see page 11-5.

SPIRALLY REINFORCED ROUND COLUMNS—
Safe Load in Kips for Various Eccentricities in inches
$f'_c = 5000$ psi (A61 or A432 Bars, $f_y = 60,000$ psi) $f_s = 24,000$ psi basis

COLUMN SIZE—16″ DIAMETER — $f'_c = 5000$ psi, $f_y = 60,000$ psi

Bars	p	M/N † = e (in.) 0	1	2	3	4	5	6	7	8	9	10	11	12	13	14	M_o ‡ (kip-in.)
7-#5	.0108	303	285	223	181	89	59	44	35	29	25	22	19	17	16	14	177
8-#5	.0123	310	290	227	187	101	67	50	40	33	28	25	22	20	18	16	203
9-#5	.0139	318	295	231	190	111	75	56	45	37	32	28	25	22	20	18	228
10-#5	.0154	325	301	236	194	122	82	62	50	41	35	31	27	25	22	21	253
11-#5	.0170	333	306	240	197	132	89	68	54	45	39	34	30	27	25	23	279
12-#5	.0185	340	311	244	200	142	97	73	59	49	42	37	33	30	27	25	304
14-#5	.0216	355	322	252	207	161	110	84	68	57	49	43	38	34	31	29	355
6-#6	.0131	314	293	229	188	105	70	53	42	35	30	26	23	21	19	17	213
7-#6	.0153	325	300	235	193	120	81	61	49	41	35	30	27	24	22	20	249
8-#6	.0175	335	308	241	198	134	91	69	55	46	40	35	31	28	25	23	285
9-#6	.0197	346	315	247	202	148	101	77	62	52	44	39	35	31	28	26	320
10-#6	.0219	356	323	252	207	161	111	84	68	57	49	43	38	34	31	29	356
12-#6	.0263	378	338	264	217	184	129	99	80	67	58	51	45	41	37	34	427
6-#7	.0179	337	309	241	198	136	92	70	56	47	40	35	31	28	25	23	288
7-#7	.0209	352	319	249	205	154	105	80	64	54	46	41	36	33	30	27	336
8-#7	.0239	366	329	257	211	171	118	90	73	61	53	46	41	37	34	31	384
9-#7	.0269	380	339	265	217	184	130	100	81	68	59	52	46	41	38	35	432
10-#7	.0298	395	349	273	224	190	142	109	89	75	65	57	51	46	42	38	480
12-#7	.0358	424	370	288	237	200	164	128	104	88	76	67	60	54	50	46	576
6-#8	.0236	365	327	256	210	168	116	88	71	60	51	45	40	36	33	30	375
7-#8	.0275	384	341	266	218	185	132	101	82	69	59	52	47	42	38	35	437
8-#8	.0314	403	354	276	226	192	147	113	92	78	67	59	53	48	43	40	500
9-#8	.0354	421	367	286	235	199	161	125	102	86	75	66	59	53	49	45	563
10-#8	.0393	440	381	297	243	206	175	136	112	95	82	73	65	59	54	49	625
12-#8	.0471	478	407	317	260	220	190	158	130	111	96	85	77	69	63	58	750
6-#9	.0298	395	348	271	222	188	139	107	87	73	63	56	50	45	41	38	469
7-#9	.0348	419	365	284	233	197	158	122	100	84	73	64	57	52	47	43	547
8-#9	.0398	443	382	297	243	206	175	136	112	95	82	73	65	59	54	49	626
9-#9	.0448	467	398	310	253	214	186	150	123	105	91	81	72	65	60	55	704
10-#9	.0497	491	415	323	264	223	193	163	135	115	100	88	79	72	66	61	782
12-#9	·0597	539	448	348	285	241	208	184	155	133	117	104	93	85	78	72	939
6-#10	.0379	434	374	291	238	201	166	130	106	90	78	69	61	55	51	46	588
7-#10	.0442	464	395	307	251	212	184	147	121	103	89	79	71	64	58	54	686
8-#10	.0505	495	416	323	264	223	193	163	135	115	100	89	80	72	66	61	784
9-#10	.0568	525	438	339	277	234	203	178	148	126	111	98	88	80	73	68	883
10-#10	·0632	556	459	355	290	245	212	187	160	138	121	107	97	88	81	74	981
6-#11	.0466	475	402	312	255	215	186	151	124	106	92	81	73	66	60	56	713
7-#11	.0543	513	428	331	270	228	198	170	141	120	105	93	84	76	70	64	832
8-#11	.0621	550	453	351	286	241	209	184	156	134	117	104	94	85	78	72	951
9-#11	0698	588	479	370	302	255	220	194	171	147	129	115	104	95	87	80	1070
6-#14S	.0671	575	467	360	293	246	213	187	162	139	122	109	98	89	82	76	1001
7-#14S	.0783	629	504	387	315	265	229	201	180	156	138	123	111	102	93	86	1168

Check availability of #14S and #18S bars.

All above columns require spirals of A432 rod or cold drawn wire ($f_y = 60,000$ psi):—
½ ϕ @ 2″

Outside diameter of spiral should be 3 in. less than outside diameter of column.
† Below zigzag horizontal line of each group, concrete governs; above, tension governs.
‡ M_o = capacity in pure bending, ($N = 0$); for extrapolation, see page 11-5.

SPIRALLY REINFORCED ROUND COLUMNS—
Safe Load in Kips for Various Eccentricities in Inches
$f'_c = 5000$ psi (A61 or A432 Bars, $f_y = 60{,}000$ psi) $f_s = 24{,}000$ psi basis

COLUMN SIZE—18″ DIAMETER

$f'_c = 5000$ psi
$f_y = 60{,}000$ psi

Bars	p	M/N † = e (in.)															M_o ‡ (kip-in.)
		0	1	2	3	4	5	6	7	8	9	10	12	14	16	18	
6-#6	.0104	**381**	371	296	247	146	92	67	53	43	37	32	25	21	18	16	*251*
7-#6	.0121	**392**	379	303	252	166	106	78	61	50	43	37	30	24	21	18	*293*
8-#6	.0138	**402**	387	309	257	185	119	88	69	57	49	43	34	28	24	21	*335*
9-#6	.0156	**413**	395	315	263	204	132	98	77	64	55	48	38	31	27	23	*377*
10-#6	.0173	**423**	403	322	268	222	145	107	85	71	60	53	42	35	30	26	*419*
12-#6	.0207	**444**	419	335	279	239	169	126	101	84	72	63	50	42	36	31	*503*
14-#6	.0242	**465**	434	347	289	248	192	144	116	96	83	72	58	48	41	36	*587*
16-#6	.0277	**487**	450	360	300	257	213	162	130	109	94	82	66	55	47	41	*671*
6-#7	.0141	**404**	388	310	258	187	120	89	70	58	49	43	34	28	24	21	*340*
7-#7	.0165	**418**	399	318	265	212	138	102	81	67	57	50	40	33	28	25	*396*
8-#7	.0189	**433**	409	327	272	233	155	115	92	76	65	57	45	38	32	28	*453*
9-#7	.0212	**447**	420	336	279	239	171	128	102	85	73	63	51	42	36	31	*510*
10-#7	.0236	**462**	431	344	287	245	186	140	112	93	80	70	56	47	40	35	*567*
12-#7	.0283	**490**	453	361	301	258	215	163	132	110	95	83	67	55	48	42	*680*
14-#7	.0330	**519**	474	379	315	270	236	185	150	126	109	95	77	64	55	48	*793*
6-#8	.0186	**431**	408	326	271	231	152	113	90	74	64	56	44	37	31	27	*443*
7-#8	.0217	**450**	422	337	280	240	173	129	103	86	74	64	51	43	36	32	*517*
8-#8	.0248	**469**	436	348	290	248	192	145	116	97	83	73	58	49	42	36	*591*
9-#8	.0279	**488**	450	359	299	256	211	160	129	108	93	81	65	54	47	41	*665*
10-#8	.0310	**507**	464	371	308	264	229	175	141	118	102	89	72	60	52	45	*739*
12-#8	.0373	**545**	493	393	327	280	245	203	165	139	120	106	85	71	61	54	*887*
14-#8	.0435	**583**	521	416	346	296	259	228	187	158	137	121	98	82	71	62	*1035*
6-#9	.0236	**462**	430	343	285	244	183	137	110	92	79	69	55	46	39	34	*556*
7-#9	.0275	**486**	448	357	297	254	207	157	126	105	91	79	64	53	45	40	*648*
8-#9	.0314	**510**	465	371	309	264	230	175	142	119	102	90	72	60	52	45	*741*
9-#9	.0354	**534**	483	385	320	274	239	193	156	132	113	100	80	67	58	51	*834*
10-#9	.0393	**558**	501	399	332	284	248	209	171	144	124	110	88	74	64	56	*926*
12-#9	.0472	**606**	537	428	355	304	266	236	198	168	146	129	104	88	76	66	*1112*
14-#9	.0550	**654**	572	456	379	324	283	251	223	190	166	147	120	101	87	77	*1297*
6-#10	.0299	**500**	458	365	303	259	219	167	134	113	97	85	68	57	49	43	*698*
8-#10	.0399	**561**	503	400	332	284	248	210	171	144	125	110	89	74	64	56	*931*
10-#10	.0499	**622**	548	436	362	309	270	240	205	174	151	134	109	91	79	69	*1164*
12-#10	.0599	**683**	593	471	391	334	292	259	233	201	176	156	127	108	93	82	*1396*
6-#11	.0368	**542**	488	388	322	275	240	195	158	133	115	101	82	68	59	51	*848*
7-#11	.0429	**580**	515	410	340	290	254	220	180	152	132	116	94	79	68	60	*989*
8-#11	.0490	**617**	543	431	358	306	267	237	200	170	147	130	106	89	77	67	*1131*
9-#11	.0552	**655**	570	453	376	321	280	248	219	187	163	144	117	99	85	75	*1272*
10-#11	.0613	**692**	597	474	393	336	293	260	234	203	177	157	129	109	94	83	*1414*
11-#11	.0674	**729**	625	496	411	351	306	272	244	218	191	170	139	118	102	90	*1555*
6-#14S	.0531	**642**	558	442	366	312	272	241	208	177	154	136	111	93	81	71	*1196*
7-#14S	.0619	**696**	597	473	391	334	291	258	231	200	175	155	127	107	93	82	*1395*
8-#14S	.0707	**750**	636	503	416	355	309	274	246	221	194	173	142	120	104	92	*1594*
9-#14S	.0796	**804**	675	534	441	376	328	290	261	236	212	190	156	133	116	102	*1794*

Check availability of #14S and #18S bars.

All above columns require spirals of A432 rod or cold drawn wire ($f_y = 60{,}000$ psi):—
½ φ @ 2½″

Outside diameter of spiral should be 3 in. less than outside diameter of column.
† Below zigzag horizontal line of each group, concrete governs; above, tension governs.
‡ M_o = capacity in pure bending, ($N = 0$); for extrapolation, see page 11-5.

SPIRALLY REINFORCED ROUND COLUMNS—
Safe Load in Kips for Various Eccentricities in Inches
$f'_c = 5000$ psi (A61 or A432 Bars, $f_y = 60{,}000$ psi) $f_s = 24{,}000$ psi basis

COLUMN SIZE—20″ DIAMETER

$f'_c = 5000$ psi
$f_y = 60{,}000$ psi

Bars	p	M/N † = e (in.) 0	1	2	3	4	5	6	7	8	9	10	12	14	16	18	M_o ‡ (kip-in.)
6-#7	.0115	**479**	478	388	327	263	158	113	88	72	61	53	41	34	29	25	*398*
7-#7	.0134	**493**	489	398	335	290	181	130	101	83	70	61	48	40	34	29	*464*
8-#7	.0153	**507**	500	407	343	296	202	146	115	94	80	69	55	45	39	34	*531*
9-#7	.0172	**522**	512	416	351	303	223	162	127	105	89	77	61	51	43	38	*597*
10-#7	.0191	**536**	523	426	359	310	243	178	140	116	98	85	68	56	48	42	*664*
12-#7	.0229	**565**	545	444	375	324	281	208	165	136	116	101	81	67	57	50	*797*
14-#7	.0267	**594**	568	463	391	338	297	236	188	156	134	117	93	77	66	58	*929*
16-#7	.0306	**623**	591	482	406	352	310	263	210	175	150	132	105	88	75	66	*1062*
6-#8	.0151	**506**	499	406	342	295	199	144	112	92	78	68	54	44	38	33	*520*
7-#8	.0176	**525**	514	418	352	304	226	165	129	106	90	79	62	51	44	38	*607*
8-#8	.0201	**544**	528	430	362	313	252	185	146	120	102	89	71	59	50	44	*693*
9-#8	.0226	**563**	543	442	373	322	277	204	162	134	114	99	79	66	56	49	*780*
10-#8	.0251	**582**	558	454	383	331	292	223	177	147	125	109	87	72	62	54	*867*
12-#8	.0302	**620**	588	479	404	349	307	258	207	172	148	129	103	86	74	64	*1040*
14-#8	.0352	**658**	617	503	425	367	323	289	235	197	169	148	119	99	85	75	*1214*
16-#8	.0402	**696**	647	528	445	385	339	303	261	220	190	167	134	112	97	85	*1387*
6-#9	.0191	**536**	522	424	358	309	240	175	138	114	97	84	67	55	47	41	*653*
7-#9	.0223	**560**	541	440	371	320	271	200	158	131	112	97	77	64	55	48	*762*
8-#9	.0255	**584**	559	455	384	331	292	223	178	147	126	110	88	73	62	54	*871*
9-#9	.0286	**608**	578	470	397	343	302	246	196	163	140	122	98	81	70	61	*979*
10-#9	.0318	**632**	597	486	410	354	312	267	214	179	154	134	108	90	77	67	*1088*
12-#9	.0382	**680**	634	516	436	377	332	296	249	209	180	158	127	106	91	80	*1306*
14-#9	.0446	**728**	672	547	462	399	351	314	281	237	205	181	146	122	105	92	*1524*
16-#9	.0509	**776**	709	578	488	422	371	332	300	264	229	202	164	138	119	105	*1742*
6-#10	.0243	**575**	552	448	378	326	287	213	169	140	119	104	83	69	59	51	*821*
7-#10	.0283	**606**	575	468	394	340	300	241	193	160	137	120	96	80	68	60	*958*
8-#10	.0323	**636**	599	487	410	355	312	268	215	180	154	135	108	90	77	68	*1095*
10-#10	.0404	**697**	646	526	443	383	337	301	258	217	187	165	133	111	95	84	*1369*
12-#10	.0485	**758**	694	564	476	411	362	323	292	252	218	192	156	131	113	99	*1643*
14-#10	.0566	**819**	741	603	509	440	387	346	312	284	247	219	178	150	130	114	*1917*
6-#11	.0298	**617**	583	474	399	345	303	250	200	166	142	125	100	83	71	62	*1000*
7-#11	.0348	**654**	612	498	419	362	318	282	227	190	163	143	115	96	82	72	*1166*
8-#11	.0397	**692**	641	521	439	379	334	298	252	212	183	161	129	108	93	81	*1333*
9-#11	.0447	**729**	670	545	459	396	349	311	277	234	202	178	144	120	104	91	*1500*
10-#11	.0497	**767**	699	568	479	414	364	325	293	254	220	195	158	132	114	100	*1666*
11-#11	.0546	**804**	728	592	499	431	379	339	306	274	238	211	171	144	124	109	*1833*
13-#11	.0646	**879**	786	639	538	465	409	366	330	301	272	241	197	167	144	127	*2166*
6-#14S	.0430	**716**	658	534	449	387	340	304	264	222	192	169	136	114	98	86	*1414*
7-#14S	.0501	**770**	699	567	477	412	362	323	291	252	218	193	156	131	113	99	*1650*
8-#14S	.0573	**824**	741	601	505	436	383	342	309	279	243	215	175	147	127	112	*1886*
9-#14S	.0645	**878**	782	634	533	460	405	361	326	297	266	237	193	163	141	125	*2122*
10-#14S	.0716	**932**	823	668	562	484	426	380	343	313	287	257	211	179	155	137	*2358*
6-#18S	.0764	**968**	832	665	554	475	415	369	332	302	276	246	202	172	149	132	*2285*

Check availability of #14S and #18S bars.

All above columns require spirals of A432 rod or cold drawn wire ($f_y = 60{,}000$ psi):—
#14S and smaller—⅜ φ @ 1¾″
#18S only —½ φ @ 2½″

Outside diameter of spiral should be 3 in. less than outside diameter of column.
† Below zigzag horizontal line of each group, concrete governs; above, tension governs.
‡ M_o = capacity in pure bending, ($N = 0$); for extrapolation, see page 11-5.

SPIRALLY REINFORCED ROUND COLUMNS—
Safe Load in Kips for Various Eccentricities in Inches
$f'_c = 5000$ psi (A61 or A432 Bars, $f_y = 60{,}000$ psi) $f_s = 24{,}000$ psi basis

COLUMN SIZE—22″ DIAMETER | $f'_c = 5000$ psi, $f_y = 60{,}000$ psi

Bars	p	M/N † = e (in.) 0	1	2	3	4	5	6	8	10	12	14	16	18	20	22	M_o ‡ (kip-in.)
7-#7	.0110	**575**	575	485	413	360	232	161	99	72	56	46	39	34	30	27	525
8-#7	.0126	**590**	590	495	422	367	260	181	113	82	64	53	45	39	34	31	600
9-#7	.0142	**604**	604	505	430	374	286	201	126	91	72	59	50	43	38	34	675
10-#7	.0158	**619**	619	515	439	382	311	220	138	101	79	65	55	48	43	38	750
12-#7	.0189	**647**	647	535	455	397	351	257	163	120	94	78	66	58	51	46	900
14-#7	.0221	**676**	670	554	472	412	365	291	187	138	109	90	77	67	59	53	1050
16-#7	.0253	**705**	693	574	489	427	378	324	210	156	123	102	87	76	67	60	1200
6-#8	.0125	**588**	588	494	420	366	255	178	111	80	63	52	44	38	34	30	588
7-#8	.0145	**607**	607	507	431	376	290	204	128	93	73	60	51	44	39	35	686
8-#8	.0166	**626**	626	520	442	385	323	228	144	105	83	68	58	50	45	40	784
9-#8	.0187	**645**	645	532	454	395	350	252	160	117	93	76	65	56	50	45	883
10-#8	.0208	**664**	660	545	465	405	358	275	176	129	102	84	72	63	55	50	981
12-#8	.0249	**702**	691	571	487	424	376	319	207	153	121	100	86	75	66	59	1177
14-#8	.0291	**740**	721	597	509	444	393	353	236	175	140	116	99	86	77	69	1373
16-#8	.0333	**778**	752	622	531	463	410	369	264	197	158	131	112	98	87	78	1569
6-#9	.0158	**619**	619	514	437	381	308	217	136	99	78	64	55	48	42	38	739
8-#9	.0210	**667**	661	546	465	405	359	276	177	130	103	85	72	63	56	50	986
10-#9	.0263	**715**	700	579	493	430	380	331	215	159	126	105	89	78	69	62	1232
12-#9	.0316	**763**	739	611	521	454	402	361	251	187	149	124	106	93	82	74	1479
14-#9	.0368	**811**	777	643	549	478	424	381	285	214	171	143	122	107	95	86	1725
16-#9	.0421	**859**	816	676	577	503	446	400	318	240	193	161	138	121	108	97	1972
6-#10	.0200	**658**	653	539	459	400	354	264	168	123	97	80	68	59	53	47	931
8-#10	.0267	**719**	702	580	494	430	381	333	216	160	127	105	90	78	70	62	1242
10-#10	.0334	**779**	751	621	529	461	408	367	261	195	156	130	111	97	86	77	1552
12-#10	.0401	**840**	800	662	564	492	436	391	303	229	183	153	131	115	102	92	1863
14-#10	.0468	**901**	849	703	599	523	463	416	343	260	210	176	151	133	118	106	2173
16-#10	.0535	**962**	898	744	634	553	490	440	366	291	235	198	170	150	134	121	2484
6-#11	.0246	**699**	686	566	482	420	372	309	200	148	117	97	83	72	64	57	1134
7-#11	.0287	**737**	716	591	504	438	388	348	228	170	135	112	96	83	74	66	1324
8-#11	.0328	**774**	746	616	525	457	405	363	256	191	152	127	108	95	84	76	1513
9-#11	.0369	**812**	776	641	546	476	421	378	282	211	169	141	121	106	94	84	1702
10-#11	.0410	**849**	806	666	568	495	438	393	307	231	186	155	133	117	104	93	1891
11-#11	.0451	**887**	836	691	589	513	455	408	331	251	202	169	145	127	113	102	2080
13-#11	.0533	**961**	896	741	632	551	488	438	364	288	233	196	169	148	132	119	2458
15-#11	.0616	**1036**	956	791	675	588	521	468	389	323	263	222	192	169	151	136	2837
6-#14S	.0355	**799**	764	630	536	466	413	370	269	201	161	134	115	100	89	80	1609
7-#14S	.0414	**853**	807	666	566	493	436	391	304	230	184	154	132	116	103	93	1877
8-#14S	.0474	**907**	850	701	597	519	460	413	338	257	207	173	149	131	117	105	2145
9-#14S	.0533	**961**	892	737	627	546	483	434	360	283	229	192	166	146	130	117	2414
10-#14S	.0592	**1015**	935	772	658	573	507	455	377	308	250	211	182	160	143	129	2682
12-#14S	.0710	**1123**	1021	843	718	626	554	497	412	352	291	246	213	188	168	152	3218
6-#18S	.0631	**1051**	948	774	654	567	499	447	369	299	244	205	178	156	140	126	2631
7-#18S	.0737	**1147**	1021	834	704	610	537	480	396	336	276	233	203	179	160	145	3070

Check availability of #14S and #18S bars.

All above columns require spirals of A432 rod or cold drawn wire ($f_y = 60{,}000$ psi):—
#14S and smaller—3/8 ϕ @ 1¾″
#18S only —½ ϕ @ 2½″

Outside diameter of spiral should be 3 in. less than outside diameter of column.
† Below zigzag horizontal line of each group, concrete governs; above, tension governs.
‡ M_o = capacity in pure bending, ($N = 0$); for extrapolation, see page 11-5.

SPIRALLY REINFORCED ROUND COLUMNS—
Safe Load in Kips for Various Eccentricities in inches
f'_c = 5000 psi (A61 or A432 Bars, f_y = 60,000 psi) f_s = 24,000 psi basis

COLUMN SIZE—24″ DIAMETER

f'_c = 5000 psi
f_y = 60,000 psi

Bars	p	M/N † = e (in.) 0	1	2	3	4	5	6	8	10	12	14	16	18	20	22	M_o ‡ (kip-in.)
8-#7	.0106	**680**	680	593	509	446	334	222	133	95	74	60	51	44	39	35	*669*
9-#7	.0119	**695**	695	603	518	454	367	247	149	106	83	68	57	50	44	39	*753*
10-#7	.0133	**709**	709	614	527	462	399	270	164	117	92	75	63	55	48	43	*837*
12-#7	.0159	**738**	738	634	545	478	426	315	193	139	109	89	76	66	58	52	*1004*
14-#7	.0186	**767**	767	655	563	494	440	357	222	161	126	103	88	76	67	60	*1171*
16-#7	.0212	**795**	795	675	581	510	454	397	249	181	142	117	100	87	77	69	*1339*
6-#8	.0105	**679**	679	592	508	445	328	219	131	93	73	59	50	43	38	34	*656*
8-#8	.0140	**717**	717	619	531	466	413	281	171	123	96	78	66	57	51	45	*875*
10-#8	.0175	**755**	755	645	555	486	433	338	209	151	118	97	82	71	63	56	*1094*
12-#8	.0210	**793**	793	672	578	507	452	391	245	178	140	115	98	85	75	67	*1313*
14-#8	.0244	**830**	830	699	602	528	470	424	280	205	161	133	113	99	87	78	*1532*
16-#8	.0279	**868**	866	726	625	549	489	441	313	230	182	151	128	112	99	89	*1751*
6-#9	.0133	**709**	709	613	526	461	395	267	162	116	90	74	63	54	48	43	*826*
8-#9	.0177	**757**	757	646	556	487	434	340	210	152	119	97	83	72	63	57	*1101*
10-#9	.0221	**805**	805	680	585	513	457	406	255	186	146	120	102	89	79	71	*1376*
12-#9	.0265	**853**	852	714	614	539	480	433	298	219	173	143	122	106	94	84	*1652*
14-#9	.0309	**901**	892	748	644	565	504	454	339	250	199	165	140	122	109	97	*1927*
16-#9	.0354	**949**	932	782	673	591	527	475	378	281	224	186	159	139	123	111	*2202*
6-#10	.0168	**748**	748	639	549	481	428	324	199	144	113	92	78	68	60	54	*1041*
8-#10	.0225	**809**	809	682	586	514	458	408	257	187	147	121	103	90	79	71	*1388*
10-#10	.0281	**870**	865	725	624	547	487	439	310	228	181	149	127	111	98	88	*1735*
12-#10	.0337	**931**	916	768	661	580	517	466	361	268	213	176	151	132	117	105	*2082*
14-#10	.0393	**992**	966	810	698	613	546	493	408	305	244	203	174	152	135	121	*2429*
16-#10	.0449	**1053**	1016	853	735	646	576	519	434	341	274	228	196	172	153	137	*2776*
6-#11	.0207	**790**	790	668	574	503	448	380	238	173	136	112	95	82	73	65	*1269*
7-#11	.0241	**827**	827	694	596	523	466	420	271	198	156	129	110	95	84	76	*1481*
8-#11	.0276	**865**	860	720	619	543	484	436	304	223	177	146	124	108	96	86	*1692*
9-#11	.0310	**902**	891	746	642	563	501	452	335	248	196	163	139	121	107	96	*1904*
10-#11	.0345	**939**	922	772	664	583	519	468	365	271	216	179	153	134	118	106	*2116*
12-#11	.0414	**1014**	983	824	710	623	555	501	419	316	253	211	181	158	140	126	*2539*
14-#11	.0483	**1089**	1045	877	755	663	591	533	446	359	289	242	208	182	162	146	*2962*
16-#11	.0552	**1164**	1106	929	800	703	627	566	473	400	323	271	234	205	183	165	*3385*
6-#14S	.0298	**889**	879	735	631	553	493	444	320	236	187	155	132	115	102	91	*1803*
7-#14S	.0348	**943**	923	772	664	582	518	467	363	270	214	178	152	133	118	106	*2104*
8-#14S	.0398	**997**	967	809	696	610	543	490	403	302	241	201	172	150	133	120	*2404*
9-#14S	.0448	**1051**	1011	847	728	639	569	513	428	333	267	223	191	167	149	134	*2705*
10-#14S	.0497	**1105**	1055	884	760	667	594	536	448	363	292	244	210	184	164	148	*3006*
11-#14S	.0547	**1159**	1099	921	793	696	620	559	467	391	316	265	229	201	179	161	*3306*
13-#14S	.0647	**1267**	1187	996	857	752	671	605	505	434	363	306	264	233	208	188	*3908*
6-#18S	.0531	**1141**	1071	889	761	664	590	530	441	356	287	241	207	182	162	146	*2977*
7-#18S	.0619	**1237**	1147	952	814	711	631	567	472	401	326	274	237	208	186	168	*3473*
8-#18S	.0707	**1333**	1223	1015	868	758	673	605	503	431	362	306	265	234	209	189	*3969*
9-#18S	.0796	**1429**	1299	1078	922	805	715	642	534	457	396	336	292	258	231	210	*4465*

Check availability of #14S and #18S bars.

All above columns require spirals of A432 rod or cold drawn wire (f_y = 60,000 psi):—
#14S and smaller—3⁄8 φ @ 1¾″
#18S only —½ φ @ 2½″

Outside diameter of spiral should be 3 in. less than outside diameter of column.
† Below zigzag horizontal line of each group, concrete governs; above, tension governs.
‡ M_o = capacity in pure bending, (N = 0); for extrapolation, see page 11-5.

SPIRALLY REINFORCED ROUND COLUMNS—
Safe Load in Kips for Various Eccentricities in Inches
$f'_c = 5000$ psi (A61 or A432 Bars, $f_y = 60{,}000$ psi) $f_s = 24{,}000$ psi basis

COLUMN SIZE—26″ DIAMETER

$f'_c = 5000$ psi
$f_y = 60{,}000$ psi

Bars	p	M/N † = e (in.) 0	2	4	6	8	10	12	14	16	18	20	22	24	26	28	M_o ‡ (kip-in.)
7-#8	.0104	**796**	713	544	307	178	125	96	78	66	57	50	45	40	37	34	*846*
8-#8	.0119	**815**	727	555	344	201	142	109	89	75	65	57	51	46	42	38	*966*
9-#8	.0134	**834**	741	566	379	223	158	122	100	84	73	64	57	52	47	43	*1087*
10-#8	.0149	**853**	755	577	414	245	174	135	110	93	81	71	63	57	52	48	*1208*
12-#8	.0179	**891**	783	599	478	288	206	160	131	111	96	85	76	68	62	57	*1450*
14-#8	.0208	**929**	811	621	503	329	237	185	151	128	111	98	88	80	73	67	*1692*
16-#8	.0238	**967**	838	643	521	368	266	209	171	145	126	112	100	91	83	76	*1933*
6-#9	.0113	**807**	721	550	327	190	134	103	84	71	61	54	48	43	40	36	*912*
8-#9	.0151	**855**	756	578	416	247	175	136	111	94	81	71	64	58	53	48	*1216*
10-#9	.0188	**903**	791	605	490	300	215	167	137	116	100	89	79	72	65	60	*1520*
12-#9	.0226	**951**	826	633	513	350	253	198	162	138	120	106	95	86	78	72	*1824*
14-#9	.0264	**999**	861	660	535	398	290	228	187	159	138	122	110	99	91	84	*2129*
16-#9	.0301	**1047**	896	688	558	444	325	256	212	180	157	139	124	113	103	95	*2433*
18-#9	.0339	**1095**	931	715	581	488	359	285	235	201	175	155	139	126	115	106	*2737*
6-#10	.0144	**846**	749	572	397	235	166	129	105	89	77	68	60	55	50	46	*1151*
8-#10	.0191	**907**	793	606	491	302	217	169	138	117	101	89	80	72	66	61	*1534*
10-#10	.0239	**968**	838	641	519	365	264	207	170	144	125	111	99	90	82	75	*1918*
12-#10	.0287	**1029**	882	676	548	425	310	244	201	171	149	132	118	107	98	90	*2302*
14-#10	.0335	**1090**	926	711	577	480	354	280	231	197	172	152	137	124	113	104	*2685*
16-#10	.0383	**1151**	970	745	605	509	395	314	261	223	194	172	155	141	129	119	*3069*
18-#10	.0431	**1212**	1015	780	634	533	436	348	289	248	216	192	173	157	144	133	*3453*
20-#10	.0478	**1273**	1059	815	662	558	474	380	317	272	238	212	191	173	159	147	*3836*
6-#11	.0176	**888**	778	595	466	280	200	155	127	107	93	82	73	66	61	56	*1404*
7-#11	.0206	**925**	806	616	498	320	230	179	147	124	108	95	85	77	70	65	*1638*
8-#11	.0235	**963**	833	637	516	358	259	202	166	141	122	108	97	88	80	74	*1872*
9-#11	.0264	**1000**	860	658	533	395	287	225	185	158	137	121	108	98	90	83	*2106*
10-#11	.0294	**1038**	887	679	551	430	314	248	204	174	151	134	120	109	99	92	*2340*
12-#11	.0353	**1112**	941	722	585	492	367	291	241	205	179	159	142	129	118	109	*2808*
14-#11	.0411	**1187**	995	764	620	522	417	332	276	236	206	183	165	149	137	126	*3277*
16-#11	.0470	**1262**	1049	806	655	551	465	372	310	266	233	207	186	169	155	143	*3745*
18-#11	.0529	**1337**	1103	849	690	581	501	410	343	295	259	230	208	189	173	160	*4213*
6-#14S	.0254	**987**	848	648	525	378	274	215	177	150	130	115	103	93	85	79	*1998*
7-#14S	.0297	**1041**	887	679	549	428	313	246	203	173	151	133	119	108	99	91	*2331*
8-#14S	.0339	**1095**	926	709	574	476	351	277	229	196	170	151	136	123	112	104	*2664*
9-#14S	.0381	**1149**	964	739	599	503	387	307	255	218	190	168	151	137	126	116	*2997*
10-#14S	.0424	**1203**	1003	769	623	524	422	336	280	239	209	186	167	152	139	128	*3330*
11-#14S	.0466	**1257**	1042	799	648	545	455	365	304	261	228	203	182	166	152	140	*3663*
13-#14S	.0551	**1365**	1119	859	697	587	507	419	351	302	265	236	213	193	177	164	*4329*
15-#14S	.0636	**1473**	1197	920	747	629	543	470	396	341	300	268	242	220	202	187	*4995*
6-#18S	.0452	**1239**	1012	769	620	519	418	334	278	238	208	185	166	151	138	128	*3322*
7-#18S	.0527	**1335**	1078	819	661	554	471	379	317	272	239	212	191	174	160	147	*3876*
8-#18S	.0603	**1431**	1144	869	701	588	506	422	354	305	268	239	216	196	180	167	*4430*
9-#18S	.0678	**1527**	1210	920	742	622	535	463	390	337	297	265	240	218	201	186	*4984*
10-#18S	.0753	**1623**	1276	970	783	656	564	495	424	368	325	290	263	240	221	204	*5537*

Check availability of #14S and #18S bars.

All above columns require spirals of A432 rod or cold drawn wire ($f_y = 60{,}000$ psi):—
#14S and smaller—3/8 φ @ 1¾″
#18S only —½ φ @ 2½″

Outside diameter of spiral should be 3 in. less than outside diameter of column.
† Below zigzag horizontal line of each group, concrete governs; above, tension governs.
‡ M_o = capacity in pure bending, ($N = 0$); for extrapolation, see page 11-5.

SPIRALLY REINFORCED ROUND COLUMNS—

Safe Load in Kips for Various Eccentricities in Inches

f'_c = 5000 psi (A61 or A432 Bars, f_y = 60,000 psi) f_s = 24,000 psi basis

COLUMN SIZE—28″ DIAMETER | **f'_c = 5000 psi, f_y = 60,000 psi**

Bars	p	M/N † = e (in.) 0	2	4	6	8	10	12	14	16	18	20	22	24	26	28	M_o ‡ (kip-in.)
8-#8	.0103	**921**	846	653	423	235	162	124	100	84	72	64	57	51	47	43	*1057*
9-#8	.0115	**940**	860	665	466	261	181	139	112	94	81	71	64	57	52	48	*1190*
10-#8	.0128	**959**	874	676	507	287	200	153	124	104	90	79	71	64	58	53	*1322*
12-#8	.0154	**997**	903	699	571	336	236	182	148	124	107	94	84	76	69	64	*1586*
14-#8	.0180	**1035**	932	722	590	384	271	210	171	144	124	110	98	88	81	74	*1851*
16-#8	.0205	**1073**	960	745	609	430	305	237	193	163	141	125	111	101	92	84	*2115*
7-#9	.0114	**937**	857	663	458	256	178	136	110	92	80	70	62	56	51	47	*1165*
8-#9	.0130	**961**	876	677	510	288	201	154	125	105	91	80	71	64	58	54	*1331*
10-#9	.0162	**1009**	912	706	576	351	246	190	154	130	112	99	88	80	73	67	*1664*
12-#9	.0195	**1057**	948	735	600	410	290	225	183	155	134	118	105	95	87	80	*1997*
14-#9	.0227	**1105**	984	764	624	466	332	258	211	179	155	137	122	110	101	93	*2330*
16-#9	.0260	**1153**	1020	793	648	519	373	291	239	202	176	155	139	126	115	106	*2663*
18-#9	.0292	**1201**	1056	821	672	569	413	323	266	226	196	173	155	141	128	118	*2996*
6-#10	.0124	**952**	868	671	488	275	191	146	119	100	86	76	67	61	55	51	*1260*
8-#10	.0165	**1013**	914	707	577	354	249	192	156	131	113	100	89	81	73	67	*1681*
10-#10	.0206	**1074**	960	744	607	427	303	235	192	162	140	124	111	100	91	84	*2101*
12-#10	.0248	**1135**	1005	780	638	496	356	277	227	192	167	147	132	119	109	100	*2521*
14-#10	.0289	**1196**	1051	817	668	562	406	318	261	222	193	170	152	138	126	116	*2941*
16-#10	.0330	**1257**	1096	853	698	591	454	357	295	251	218	193	173	157	143	132	*3362*
18-#10	.0371	**1318**	1142	889	728	617	501	396	327	279	243	215	193	175	160	148	*3782*
6-#11	.0152	**994**	899	695	567	327	229	177	143	121	104	92	82	74	67	62	*1539*
7-#11	.0177	**1031**	927	717	585	374	264	204	166	140	121	106	95	86	78	72	*1795*
8-#11	.0203	**1069**	955	740	604	419	297	230	188	159	137	121	108	98	89	82	*2052*
9-#11	.0228	**1106**	983	762	622	462	330	256	209	177	153	135	121	109	100	92	*2308*
10-#11	.0253	**1144**	1011	784	641	503	361	282	231	195	169	150	134	121	111	102	*2565*
12-#11	.0304	**1218**	1066	829	677	573	422	331	272	231	201	178	159	144	132	121	*3078*
14-#11	.0355	**1293**	1122	873	714	604	480	378	312	266	231	205	184	167	152	140	*3591*
16-#11	.0405	**1368**	1178	917	751	636	535	424	351	300	261	232	208	189	173	159	*4104*
18-#11	.0456	**1443**	1234	962	788	667	579	468	389	333	291	258	232	211	193	178	*4617*
20-#11	.0507	**1518**	1290	1006	825	699	606	511	426	365	319	284	256	232	213	197	*5130*
6-#14S	.0219	**1093**	971	752	613	442	315	244	200	169	146	129	115	104	95	87	*2192*
7-#14S	.0256	**1147**	1011	784	640	502	360	281	230	195	169	149	133	121	110	101	*2557*
8-#14S	.0292	**1201**	1051	815	666	558	403	316	260	220	191	169	151	137	125	115	*2923*
9-#14S	.0329	**1255**	1091	847	692	585	445	350	289	245	213	189	169	153	140	129	*3288*
10-#14S	.0365	**1309**	1131	879	718	607	486	384	317	270	235	208	187	169	155	143	*3654*
12-#14S	.0438	**1417**	1211	942	771	652	563	448	372	318	277	246	221	201	184	170	*4385*
14-#14S	.0512	**1525**	1291	1005	823	697	604	508	424	363	318	283	255	231	212	196	*5115*
16-#14S	.0585	**1633**	1370	1069	876	742	643	566	474	408	358	319	287	261	240	222	*5846*
6-#18S	.0390	**1345**	1142	881	717	605	484	383	317	270	235	208	187	170	155	143	*3668*
7-#18S	.0455	**1441**	1210	934	761	641	547	435	362	309	270	240	215	196	179	165	*4279*
8-#18S	.0520	**1537**	1279	987	804	678	586	485	405	347	304	270	243	221	203	187	*4891*
9-#18S	.0585	**1633**	1347	1041	848	715	618	533	446	384	337	300	270	246	226	209	*5502*
10-#18S	.0650	**1729**	1416	1094	891	752	650	573	486	419	369	329	297	271	248	230	*6113*
11-#18S	.0715	**1825**	1484	1147	935	789	682	601	525	454	400	357	323	294	271	250	*6725*

Check availability of #14S and #18S bars.

All above columns require spirals of A432 rod or cold drawn wire (f_y = 60,000 psi):—
#14S and smaller—3/8 ϕ @ 1¾″
#18S only —½ ϕ @ 2½″

Outside diameter of spiral should be 3 in. less than outside diameter of column.
† Below zigzag horizontal line of each group, concrete governs; above, tension governs.
‡ M_o = capacity in pure bending, (N = 0); for extrapolation, see page 11-5.

SPIRALLY REINFORCED ROUND COLUMNS—
Safe Load in Kips for Various Eccentricities in Inches
f'_c = 5000 psi (A61 or A432 Bars, f_y = 60,000 psi) f_s = 24,000 psi basis

COLUMN SIZE—30″ DIAMETER | **f'_c = 5000 psi, f_y = 60,000 psi**

Bars	p	M/N † = e (in.) 0	2	4	6	8	10	12	14	16	18	20	22	24	26	28	M_o ‡ (kip-in.)
8-#9	.0113	**1075**	1005	786	628	336	229	174	140	117	101	88	79	71	64	59	1447
9-#9	.0127	**1099**	1023	801	658	373	255	194	157	131	113	99	88	79	72	66	1627
10-#9	.0141	**1123**	1042	816	670	408	281	214	173	145	125	110	98	88	80	74	1808
12-#9	.0170	**1171**	1079	846	696	477	331	253	205	172	149	131	117	105	96	88	2170
14-#9	.0198	**1219**	1116	876	721	542	379	292	237	199	172	151	135	122	111	102	2532
16-#9	.0226	**1267**	1153	906	746	604	426	329	268	226	195	172	154	139	126	116	2894
18-#9	.0255	**1315**	1190	936	771	656	471	365	298	252	218	192	172	155	142	130	3255
20-#9	.0283	**1363**	1227	966	796	678	514	400	328	277	240	212	190	172	157	144	3617
22-#9	.0311	**1411**	1264	996	822	699	557	435	357	302	262	232	207	188	171	158	3979
24-#9	.0340	**1459**	1301	1026	847	721	598	469	385	327	284	251	225	204	186	171	4341
6-#10	.0108	**1066**	997	779	602	320	218	165	133	111	96	84	74	67	61	56	1370
8-#10	.0144	**1127**	1044	817	671	412	284	216	175	146	126	111	99	89	81	74	1827
10-#10	.0180	**1188**	1091	855	703	497	346	265	215	181	156	137	122	110	101	92	2284
12-#10	.0216	**1249**	1138	893	735	578	406	313	255	215	185	163	146	132	120	110	2741
14-#10	.0252	**1310**	1185	931	767	652	464	359	293	248	214	189	169	153	139	128	3197
16-#10	.0287	**1371**	1232	969	799	679	519	404	331	280	242	214	191	173	158	145	3654
18-#10	.0323	**1432**	1278	1007	831	707	572	447	367	311	270	239	214	194	177	163	4111
20-#10	.0359	**1493**	1325	1045	862	734	623	489	403	342	297	263	236	214	195	180	4568
6-#11	.0132	**1108**	1029	805	661	382	262	199	161	135	116	102	91	82	74	63	1674
7-#11	.0154	**1145**	1057	828	680	436	301	230	186	156	134	118	105	95	86	79	1953
8-#11	.0177	**1183**	1086	851	700	488	339	260	211	177	153	134	120	108	98	90	2232
9-#11	.0199	**1220**	1115	874	719	538	376	289	235	198	171	150	134	121	110	101	2511
10-#11	.0221	**1257**	1144	897	738	586	412	318	259	218	189	166	148	134	122	112	2790
12-#11	.0265	**1332**	1201	944	777	661	482	374	305	258	224	197	176	159	145	134	3348
14-#11	.0309	**1407**	1258	990	816	694	548	428	351	297	258	228	204	184	168	155	3906
16-#11	.0353	**1482**	1315	1036	855	727	611	479	394	335	291	257	231	209	191	176	4464
18-#11	.0397	**1557**	1373	1083	894	761	662	529	437	372	324	287	257	233	213	197	5022
20-#11	.0441	**1632**	1430	1129	932	794	692	578	478	408	356	316	283	257	235	217	5580
22-#11	.0486	**1707**	1487	1175	971	828	721	625	519	444	387	344	309	281	257	237	6138
6-#14S	.0191	**1207**	1103	864	710	516	360	276	224	189	163	143	128	115	105	96	2386
7-#14S	.0223	**1261**	1144	897	738	584	411	317	258	218	188	166	148	134	122	112	2784
8-#14S	.0255	**1315**	1185	930	765	650	461	357	292	246	213	188	168	152	139	127	3182
9-#14S	.0286	**1369**	1226	963	793	674	509	396	324	274	238	210	188	170	155	143	3580
10-#14S	.0318	**1423**	1267	996	821	698	555	434	356	302	262	231	207	188	171	158	3978
12-#14S	.0382	**1531**	1349	1062	876	745	643	507	418	355	309	274	245	222	203	187	4773
14-#14S	.0446	**1639**	1431	1128	931	793	690	576	477	407	355	315	283	257	235	217	5569
16-#14S	.0509	**1747**	1513	1194	986	840	731	642	534	457	400	355	319	290	266	245	6365
18-#14S	.0573	**1855**	1595	1260	1042	887	773	685	589	506	443	394	355	323	296	273	7160
6-#18S	.0340	**1459**	1280	1001	821	696	557	436	358	303	263	233	209	189	172	159	4013
7-#18S	.0396	**1555**	1351	1057	868	736	629	496	409	348	303	268	240	218	199	184	4682
8-#18S	.0453	**1651**	1422	1113	914	775	673	553	458	391	341	302	272	247	226	208	5351
9-#18S	.0509	**1747**	1493	1168	960	815	707	608	506	433	378	336	302	274	251	232	6020
10-#18S	.0566	**1843**	1563	1224	1006	854	742	656	551	473	414	369	332	302	277	256	6689
11-#18S	.0622	**1939**	1634	1280	1052	893	776	686	595	512	450	401	361	329	302	279	7358
12-#18S	.0679	**2035**	1705	1336	1099	933	811	717	638	550	484	432	390	355	326	302	8027

Check availability of #14S and #18S bars.

All above columns require spirals of A432 rod or cold drawn wire (f_y = 60,000 psi):—
#14S and smaller—3/8 φ @ 1¾″
#18S only —½ φ @ 2½″

Outside diameter of spiral should be 3 in. less than outside diameter of column.

† Below zigzag horizontal line of each group, concrete governs; above, tension governs.

‡ M_o = capacity in pure bending, (N = 0); for extrapolation, see page 11-5.

SPIRALLY REINFORCED ROUND COLUMNS—
Safe Load in Kips for Various Eccentricities in Inches
f'_c = 5000 psi (A61 or A432 Bars, f_y = 60,000 psi) f_s = 24,000 psi basis

COLUMN SIZE—32″ DIAMETER

f'_c = 5000 psi
f_y = 60,000 psi

Bars	p	M/N † = e (in.) 0	3	6	9	12	15	18	21	24	27	30	33	36	39	42	M_o ‡ (kip-in.)
9-#9	.0112	**1221**	1027	760	347	218	158	125	103	87	76	67	60	54	50	46	1757
10-#9	.0124	**1245**	1044	773	381	240	175	138	114	97	84	74	67	60	55	51	1952
12-#9	.0149	**1293**	1078	799	448	284	208	164	136	115	100	89	80	72	66	61	2343
14-#9	.0174	**1341**	1112	826	511	327	240	190	157	134	117	103	93	84	77	71	2733
16-#9	.0199	**1389**	1146	852	572	369	272	216	178	152	133	118	106	96	88	81	3124
18-#9	.0224	**1437**	1180	878	630	410	303	241	200	170	149	132	118	107	98	91	3515
20-#9	.0249	**1485**	1215	905	687	449	334	265	220	188	164	146	131	119	109	100	3905
7-#10	.0111	**1218**	1024	758	342	214	156	122	101	86	74	66	59	53	49	45	1726
8-#10	.0126	**1249**	1046	774	385	243	177	139	115	98	85	75	67	61	56	51	1973
10-#10	.0158	**1310**	1089	808	468	298	218	172	142	121	106	93	84	76	69	64	2467
12-#10	.0189	**1371**	1132	841	546	351	259	205	170	145	126	112	100	91	83	77	2960
14-#10	.0221	**1432**	1175	874	621	403	298	237	196	168	146	130	116	106	97	89	3453
16-#10	.0253	**1492**	1219	907	692	453	337	268	223	190	166	147	132	120	110	102	3947
18-#10	.0284	**1553**	1262	941	750	502	375	299	248	213	186	165	148	135	123	114	4440
20-#10	.0316	**1614**	1305	974	777	549	412	329	274	235	205	182	164	149	137	126	4934
6-#11	.0116	**1229**	1031	763	356	224	163	128	105	90	78	69	62	56	51	47	1808
7-#11	.0136	**1267**	1058	783	408	258	189	149	122	104	91	80	72	65	60	55	2110
8-#11	.0155	**1304**	1084	804	459	292	214	169	139	119	103	91	82	74	68	63	2411
9-#11	.0175	**1342**	1111	824	507	325	239	189	156	133	116	103	92	83	76	70	2713
10-#11	.0194	**1379**	1137	844	555	357	263	208	172	147	128	114	102	92	85	78	3014
12-#11	.0233	**1454**	1190	885	645	420	311	247	205	175	153	135	122	110	101	93	3617
14-#11	.0272	**1529**	1243	926	730	480	358	285	237	203	177	157	141	128	117	108	4220
16-#11	.0310	**1604**	1296	966	770	539	403	322	268	230	201	178	161	146	134	123	4823
18-#11	.0349	**1679**	1348	1007	803	595	447	359	299	257	225	200	180	163	150	138	5426
20-#11	.0388	**1754**	1401	1047	836	649	491	394	329	283	248	221	199	181	166	153	6029
23-#11	.0446	**1366**	1480	1108	885	728	553	446	374	322	282	251	227	206	189	175	6933
6-#14S	.0168	**1329**	1100	815	486	310	228	180	149	127	110	98	88	79	73	67	2581
7-#14S	.0196	**1383**	1138	844	554	357	263	208	172	147	128	113	102	92	84	78	3011
8-#14S	.0224	**1437**	1175	873	619	402	297	236	196	167	146	129	116	105	96	89	3441
9-#14S	.0252	**1491**	1213	902	681	445	331	263	218	187	163	145	130	118	108	100	3872
10-#14S	.0280	**1545**	1251	931	740	488	364	290	241	206	180	160	144	131	120	110	4302
11-#14S	.0308	**1599**	1289	960	765	529	396	316	263	226	197	175	158	143	131	121	4732
13-#14S	.0364	**1707**	1364	1018	811	609	459	368	307	264	231	205	185	168	154	142	5592
15-#14S	.0420	**1815**	1440	1075	858	686	520	418	350	301	264	235	212	193	177	163	6453
17-#14S	.0476	**1923**	1515	1133	905	753	578	467	392	338	296	264	238	217	199	184	7313
19-#14S	.0532	**2031**	1590	1191	952	793	635	515	433	373	328	293	264	241	221	205	8174
6-#18S	.0298	**1581**	1261	933	741	492	367	293	244	209	182	162	146	132	121	112	4359
7-#18S	.0348	**1677**	1325	982	780	560	421	337	281	241	211	187	169	153	141	130	5086
8-#18S	.0398	**1773**	1390	1031	819	625	473	380	317	273	239	213	191	174	160	147	5812
9-#18S	.0448	**1869**	1455	1079	858	688	523	421	353	304	266	237	214	195	179	165	6539
10-#18S	.0497	**1965**	1519	1128	897	744	571	462	388	334	294	262	236	215	197	182	7265
11-#18S	.0547	**2061**	1584	1177	936	777	618	502	422	364	320	286	258	235	216	200	7992
12-#18S	.0597	**2157**	1649	1225	975	810	664	540	455	394	346	309	280	255	234	217	8719
13-#18S	.0647	**2253**	1713	1274	1014	842	708	578	488	422	372	333	301	275	252	234	9445
14-#18S	.0696	**2349**	1778	1323	1053	875	748	614	520	451	398	356	322	294	270	250	10172

Check availability of #14S and #18S bars.

All above columns require spirals of A432 rod or cold drawn wire (f_y = 60,000 psi):—
#14S and smaller—⅜ φ @ 1¾″
#18S only —½ φ @ 2¾″

Outside diameter of spiral should be 3 in. less than outside diameter of column.

† Below zigzag horizontal line of each group, concrete governs; above, tension governs.

‡ M_o = capacity in pure bending, (N = 0); for extrapolation, see page 11-5.

SPIRALLY REINFORCED ROUND COLUMNS—

Safe Load in Kips for Various Eccentricities in Inches

f'_c = 5000 psi (A61 or A432 Bars, f_y = 60,000 psi) f_s = 24,000 psi basis

COLUMN SIZE—34″ DIAMETER — **f'_c = 5000 psi, f_y = 60,000 psi**

Bars	p	M/N † = e (in.) 0	3	6	9	12	15	18	21	24	27	30	33	36	39	42	M_o ‡ (kip-in.)
10-#9	.0110	1374	1182	884	436	268	194	151	124	105	91	81	72	65	60	55	2096
12-#9	.0132	1422	1217	912	511	317	230	180	148	126	109	97	87	78	72	66	2516
14-#9	.0154	1470	1252	939	584	365	266	209	172	146	127	112	101	91	83	77	2935
16-#9	.0176	1518	1287	967	653	412	301	237	195	166	145	128	115	104	95	87	3354
18-#9	.0198	1566	1322	994	720	457	335	265	218	186	162	143	129	117	107	98	3774
8-#10	.0112	1378	1184	886	440	271	196	153	126	107	92	82	73	66	60	56	2119
10-#10	.0140	1439	1229	920	535	333	241	189	156	132	115	102	91	82	75	69	2649
12-#10	.0168	1500	1273	955	624	393	286	225	186	158	137	121	109	99	90	83	3179
14-#10	.0196	1561	1317	990	709	450	330	260	215	183	159	141	126	115	105	97	3709
16-#10	.0224	1622	1362	1024	790	507	373	295	244	208	181	160	144	131	119	110	4239
18-#10	.0252	1683	1406	1059	849	561	414	329	272	232	203	180	161	146	134	123	4769
20-#10	.0280	1744	1450	1093	877	614	455	362	300	256	224	199	178	162	148	137	5299
6-#11	.0103	1359	1170	874	408	250	180	141	115	98	85	75	67	61	55	51	1943
7-#11	.0120	1396	1197	895	467	288	208	163	134	114	99	87	78	71	65	59	2267
8-#11	.0137	1434	1224	916	525	326	236	185	153	129	112	99	89	81	74	68	2591
9-#11	.0155	1471	1251	938	580	363	264	207	171	145	126	112	100	91	83	76	2915
10-#11	.0172	1509	1278	959	634	399	291	229	189	161	140	124	111	100	92	85	3239
12-#11	.0206	1584	1333	1001	737	469	344	272	225	191	167	147	132	120	110	101	3887
14-#11	.0241	1659	1387	1043	833	537	396	314	260	221	193	171	154	139	127	117	4535
16-#11	.0275	1733	1441	1086	871	602	446	354	294	251	219	194	175	158	145	134	5182
18-#11	.0309	1808	1495	1128	905	665	495	395	328	280	245	217	195	177	163	150	5830
20-#11	.0344	1883	1549	1170	940	726	543	434	361	309	270	240	216	196	180	166	6478
22-#11	.0378	1958	1603	1212	974	785	590	472	394	338	296	263	237	215	197	182	7126
25-#11	.0430	2070	1684	1275	1026	858	658	529	442	380	333	296	267	243	223	206	8098
6-#14S	.0149	1458	1240	928	556	347	252	198	163	138	120	106	95	86	79	73	2775
7-#14S	.0173	1512	1279	958	634	399	291	229	189	161	140	124	111	100	92	84	3238
8-#14S	.0198	1566	1318	989	707	449	329	260	214	182	159	141	126	114	105	96	3700
9-#14S	.0223	1620	1357	1019	778	498	366	290	240	204	178	158	141	128	117	108	4163
10-#14S	.0248	1674	1395	1049	840	546	403	319	264	226	197	174	157	142	130	120	4626
11-#14S	.0273	1728	1434	1079	865	592	439	348	289	247	215	191	172	156	143	131	5088
13-#14S	.0322	1836	1512	1139	914	682	509	406	337	288	252	224	201	183	167	154	6014
15-#14S	.0372	1944	1589	1200	963	767	576	461	384	329	288	256	231	210	192	177	6939
17-#14S	.0421	2052	1666	1260	1013	846	641	515	430	370	324	288	259	236	216	200	7864
19-#14S	.0471	2160	1744	1320	1062	888	704	568	475	409	359	319	288	262	241	222	8789
21-#14S	.0520	2268	1821	1380	1111	929	766	619	520	448	393	351	316	288	264	244	9715
6-#18S	.0264	1710	1407	1053	841	553	408	324	268	229	200	177	159	144	132	122	4705
7-#18S	.0308	1806	1474	1104	883	629	468	373	309	264	231	205	184	167	153	141	5489
8-#18S	.0352	1902	1540	1155	924	703	526	420	350	299	262	233	209	190	174	161	6273
9-#18S	.0397	1998	1607	1206	965	773	582	466	389	334	292	260	234	213	195	180	7057
10-#18S	.0441	2094	1674	1257	1006	839	636	511	428	367	322	287	258	235	215	199	7841
11-#18S	.0485	2190	1740	1308	1048	874	689	555	465	400	351	313	282	257	236	218	8626
12-#18S	.0529	2286	1807	1359	1089	908	740	598	502	433	380	339	306	279	256	236	9410
13-#18S	.0573	2382	1873	1410	1130	943	789	640	539	465	409	365	329	300	276	255	10194
14-#18S	.0617	2478	1940	1461	1171	978	838	682	574	496	437	390	353	321	295	273	10978
15-#18S	.0661	2574	2007	1512	1213	1012	869	722	609	527	465	415	375	343	315	291	11762

Check availability of #14S and #18S bars.

All above columns require spirals of A432 rod or cold drawn wire (f_y = 60,000 psi):—
#14S and smaller—3/8 φ @ 1¾″
#18S only —½ φ @ 2¾″

Outside diameter of spiral should be 3 in. less than outside diameter of column.
† Below zigzag horizontal line of each group, concrete governs; above, tension governs.
‡ M_o = capacity in pure bending, (N = 0); for extrapolation, see page 11-5.

SPIRALLY REINFORCED ROUND COLUMNS—
Safe Load in Kips for Various Eccentricities in Inches
f'_c = 5000 psi (A61 or A432 Bars, f_y = 60,000 psi) f_s = 24,000 psi basis

COLUMN SIZE—36″ DIAMETER — f'_c = 5000 psi, f_y = 60,000 psi

Bars	p	M/N † = e (in.)															M_o ‡ (kip-in.)
		0	3	6	9	12	15	18	21	24	27	30	33	36	39	42	
11-#9	.0108	**1536**	1348	1019	541	326	233	181	148	126	109	96	86	78	71	65	*2464*
12-#9	.0118	**1560**	1366	1033	584	353	253	197	161	137	118	105	94	85	77	71	*2688*
14-#9	.0138	**1608**	1402	1061	666	406	292	228	187	159	138	122	109	98	90	83	*3137*
16-#9	.0157	**1656**	1438	1090	744	458	331	259	213	180	157	138	124	112	102	94	*3585*
18-#9	.0177	**1704**	1474	1118	820	509	369	289	238	202	176	155	139	126	115	106	*4033*
20-#9	.0196	**1752**	1510	1146	893	558	406	319	263	223	194	172	154	139	127	117	*4481*
10-#10	.0125	**1577**	1378	1042	610	370	266	207	170	144	125	110	98	89	81	75	*2832*
12-#10	.0150	**1638**	1424	1078	712	437	315	246	202	171	149	131	118	106	97	90	*3399*
14-#10	.0175	**1699**	1469	1114	809	501	363	285	234	199	173	153	137	124	113	104	*3965*
16-#10	.0200	**1760**	1514	1149	900	564	410	323	266	226	196	174	156	141	129	119	*4532*
18-#10	.0225	**1820**	1559	1185	956	624	456	360	297	252	220	194	174	158	145	133	*5099*
20-#10	.0250	**1881**	1605	1221	985	683	502	396	327	279	243	215	193	175	160	147	*5665*
7-#11	.0107	**1534**	1346	1016	533	321	230	179	146	124	107	94	84	76	70	64	*2424*
8-#11	.0123	**1571**	1373	1038	599	363	260	203	166	141	122	108	96	87	80	73	*2771*
9-#11	.0138	**1609**	1401	1060	662	404	291	227	186	158	137	121	108	98	89	82	*3117*
10-#11	.0153	**1646**	1429	1082	723	444	321	251	206	175	152	134	120	108	99	91	*3463*
12-#11	.0184	**1721**	1484	1126	840	523	379	298	245	208	181	160	143	130	118	109	*4156*
14-#11	.0215	**1796**	1540	1169	943	598	436	343	283	241	209	185	166	151	138	127	*4849*
16-#11	.0245	**1871**	1595	1213	979	671	492	388	321	273	238	211	189	171	157	144	*5542*
18-#11	.0276	**1946**	1651	1257	1015	741	546	432	358	305	266	236	211	192	176	162	*6235*
20-#11	.0307	**2021**	1706	1301	1051	809	599	475	394	336	294	260	234	212	194	179	*6927*
23-#11	.0352	**2133**	1789	1366	1105	907	676	538	448	383	335	297	267	243	222	205	*7967*
27-#11	.0414	**2283**	1899	1453	1177	989	775	620	517	443	388	345	311	282	259	239	*9352*
6-#14S	.0133	**1596**	1390	1050	635	387	278	217	178	150	131	115	103	93	85	78	*2970*
7-#14S	.0155	**1650**	1430	1082	723	444	321	251	206	175	152	134	120	109	99	91	*3465*
8-#14S	.0177	**1704**	1469	1113	807	501	363	284	234	198	172	152	137	124	113	104	*3960*
9-#14S	.0199	**1758**	1509	1144	887	555	404	317	261	222	193	171	153	139	127	117	*4455*
10-#14S	.0221	**1812**	1549	1176	947	608	444	350	288	245	214	189	169	154	140	129	*4950*
12-#14S	.0265	**1920**	1628	1238	999	711	523	413	342	291	254	225	202	183	168	154	*5940*
14-#14S	.0309	**2028**	1708	1300	1050	808	598	475	394	336	294	260	234	212	194	179	*6930*
16-#14S	.0354	**2136**	1787	1363	1101	901	672	535	445	381	333	295	265	241	221	204	*7920*
18-#14S	.0398	**2244**	1866	1425	1153	968	743	594	495	424	371	330	297	270	247	228	*8910*
20-#14S	.0442	**2352**	1945	1487	1204	1011	812	651	544	467	409	364	327	298	273	252	*9900*
22-#14S	.0486	**2460**	2024	1550	1255	1055	879	707	592	509	446	397	358	326	299	276	*10890*
6-#18S	.0236	**1848**	1562	1181	949	618	452	356	294	250	217	192	173	156	143	132	*5050*
7-#18S	.0275	**1944**	1631	1234	993	704	518	410	339	289	252	223	200	182	166	153	*5892*
8-#18S	.0314	**2040**	1699	1287	1036	786	582	462	383	327	285	253	227	206	189	174	*6734*
9-#18S	.0354	**2136**	1767	1340	1079	865	644	513	426	365	318	283	254	231	211	195	*7576*
10-#18S	.0393	**2232**	1836	1393	1123	940	704	563	469	401	351	312	281	255	234	216	*8417*
11-#18S	.0432	**2328**	1904	1446	1166	977	763	612	510	438	383	341	307	279	256	236	*9259*
12-#18S	.0472	**2424**	1973	1499	1209	1013	820	659	551	473	415	369	333	303	278	256	*10101*
13-#18S	.0511	**2520**	2041	1552	1253	1050	875	706	591	509	446	397	358	326	299	277	*10943*
14-#18S	.0550	**2616**	2109	1605	1296	1086	929	751	630	543	477	425	384	349	321	297	*11785*
15-#18S	.0589	**2712**	2178	1658	1339	1123	967	796	669	577	507	453	409	372	342	316	*12626*
16-#18S	.0629	**2808**	2246	1711	1382	1159	998	840	707	611	538	480	433	395	363	336	*13468*

Check availability of #14S and #18S bars.

All above columns require spirals of A432 rod or cold drawn wire (f_y = 60,000 psi):—
#14S and smaller—⅜ φ @ 1¾″
#18S only —½ φ @ 2¾″

Outside diameter of spiral should be 3 in. less than outside diameter of column.
† Below zigzag horizontal line of each group, concrete governs; above, tension governs.
‡ M_o = capacity in pure bending, (N = 0); for extrapolation, see page 11-5.

SPIRALLY REINFORCED ROUND COLUMNS—
Safe Load in Kips for Various Eccentricities in Inches
f'_c = 5000 psi (A431 Bars, f_y = 75,000 psi) f_s = 30,000 psi basis

COLUMN SIZE—16″ DIAMETER

f'_c = 5000 psi
f_y = 75,000 psi

Bars	p	M/N † = e (in.)															M_o ‡ (kip-in.)
		0	1	2	3	4	5	6	7	8	9	10	11	12	13	14	
6-#11	.0466	**532**	430	328	265	223	192	168	141	122	107	96	86	79	72	67	*892*
7-#11	.0543	**578**	460	350	283	237	204	179	157	136	120	108	98	89	82	76	*1040*
8-#11	.0621	**625**	490	372	300	251	216	190	169	149	132	119	108	99	91	85	*1189*
9-#11	.0698	**672**	520	394	317	266	228	200	178	160	143	129	118	108	100	93	*1338*
6-#14	.0671	**656**	506	382	307	257	221	193	172	153	136	123	112	102	95	88	*1252*
7-#14	.0783	**723**	548	413	331	277	237	208	185	167	150	136	124	115	106	99	*1461*

All above columns require spirals of rod or cold drawn wire (f_y = 60,000 psi):—
½ φ @ 2″

COLUMN SIZE—18″ DIAMETER

f'_c = 5000 psi
f_y = 75,000 psi

Bars	p	M/N † = e (in.)															M_o ‡ (kip-in.)
		0	1	2	3	4	5	6	7	8	9	10	12	14	16	18	
6-#11	.0368	**598**	518	407	335	285	247	219	182	155	135	120	98	82	71	63	*1060*
7-#11	.0429	**645**	550	432	355	301	262	231	202	174	152	135	111	94	81	72	*1237*
8-#11	.0490	**692**	583	456	375	318	276	244	219	191	168	150	124	105	91	81	*1414*
9-#11	.0552	**739**	615	481	395	335	290	257	230	206	183	164	136	116	101	89	*1590*
10-#11	.0613	**786**	647	505	414	351	305	269	241	218	196	176	147	126	110	98	*1767*
11-#11	.0674	**832**	680	530	434	368	319	282	252	228	208	188	157	135	119	106	*1944*
6-#14	.0531	**723**	601	469	384	325	282	249	223	197	174	156	129	110	96	85	*1495*
7-#14	.0619	**790**	647	503	412	349	302	266	238	216	193	174	145	124	109	96	*1744*
8-#14	.0707	**858**	693	538	440	372	322	284	254	230	210	190	159	137	121	107	*1993*
9-#14	.0796	**925**	739	573	468	395	342	302	270	244	222	204	173	150	132	118	*2242*

All above columns require spirals of rod or cold drawn wire (f_y = 60,000 psi):—
½ φ @ 2½″

Check availability of #14 and #18 bars.

Outside diameter of spiral should be 3 in. less than outside diameter of column.
† Below zigzag horizontal line of each group, concrete governs; above, tension governs.
‡ M_o = capacity in pure bending, (N = 0); for extrapolation, see page 11-5.

SPIRALLY REINFORCED ROUND COLUMNS—
Safe Load in Kips for Various Eccentricities in Inches
$f'_c = 5000$ psi (A431 Bars, $f_y = 75{,}000$ psi) $f_s = 30{,}000$ psi basis

COLUMN SIZE—20″ DIAMETER — $f'_c = 5000$ psi, $f_y = 75{,}000$ psi

Bars	p	M/N † = e (in.) 0	1	2	3	4	5	6	7	8	9	10	12	14	16	18	M_o ‡ (kip-in.)
6-#11	.0298	**673**	616	495	414	356	312	278	230	194	168	148	120	100	86	76	*1250*
7-#11	.0348	**720**	650	522	436	375	328	292	257	218	190	168	136	115	99	87	*1458*
8-#11	.0397	**767**	685	549	459	394	345	307	276	241	210	187	152	129	111	98	*1666*
9-#11	.0447	**813**	719	577	481	413	362	322	290	261	229	204	167	142	123	109	*1875*
10-#11	.0497	**860**	753	604	504	432	378	336	303	275	247	220	182	155	134	119	*2083*
11-#11	.0546	**907**	788	631	526	451	395	351	316	287	263	236	195	167	145	129	*2291*
13-#11	.0646	**1001**	856	685	571	489	428	380	342	311	285	263	220	189	166	148	*2708*
6-#14	.0430	**797**	705	564	470	403	353	313	282	250	219	195	159	135	117	103	*1768*
7-#14	.0501	**865**	754	602	502	430	376	334	301	273	244	218	180	153	133	118	*2063*
8-#14	.0573	**932**	803	641	533	457	399	355	319	290	266	239	199	170	148	132	*2358*
9-#14	.0645	**1000**	852	679	565	483	423	375	337	307	281	259	216	186	163	145	*2653*
10-#14	.0716	**1067**	901	718	596	510	446	396	356	323	296	273	232	201	177	158	*2947*
6-#18	.0764	**1112**	910	714	588	500	434	384	344	312	285	262	223	193	170	151	*2857*

All above columns require spirals of rod or cold drawn wire ($f_y = 60{,}000$ psi):—
#14 and smaller—3/8 ϕ @ 1¾″
#18 only —½ ϕ @ 2½″

COLUMN SIZE—22″ DIAMETER — $f'_c = 5000$ psi, $f_y = 75{,}000$ psi

Bars	p	M/N † = e (in.) 0	1	2	3	4	5	6	8	10	12	14	16	18	20	22	M_o ‡ (kip-in.)
6-#11	.0246	**755**	721	590	499	432	381	341	235	176	141	117	101	88	78	70	*1418*
7-#11	.0287	**802**	756	618	523	453	400	358	265	200	161	135	116	101	90	81	*1655*
8-#11	.0328	**849**	792	647	547	474	418	374	292	223	180	151	130	114	102	92	*1891*
9-#11	.0369	**896**	828	676	571	495	436	390	318	245	199	167	144	127	113	102	*2127*
10-#11	.0410	**943**	863	705	596	516	454	406	335	265	216	183	158	139	124	113	*2364*
11-#11	.0451	**989**	899	734	620	536	473	423	349	284	233	197	171	151	135	122	*2600*
13-#11	.0533	**1083**	970	791	668	578	509	455	375	318	264	225	196	174	156	142	*3073*
15-#11	.0616	**1177**	1042	849	716	620	546	488	402	342	292	250	219	195	176	160	*3546*
6-#14	.0355	**880**	813	663	560	484	427	382	305	234	190	159	137	121	108	97	*2011*
7-#14	.0414	**947**	864	704	594	514	453	405	333	263	214	181	157	138	124	112	*2346*
8-#14	.0474	**1015**	915	745	629	543	479	427	352	289	238	202	175	155	139	126	*2682*
9-#14	.0533	**1082**	966	786	663	573	504	450	371	313	259	221	193	171	153	139	*3017*
10-#14	.0592	**1150**	1017	827	697	602	530	473	390	331	280	239	209	186	167	152	*3352*
12-#14	.0710	**1285**	1119	909	766	661	582	519	428	363	316	273	240	214	194	177	*4023*
6-#18	.0631	**1195**	1032	830	693	596	522	465	381	323	271	233	204	181	163	148	*3289*
7-#18	.0737	**1315**	1119	898	750	643	563	501	410	347	300	259	228	204	184	168	*3837*

Check availability of #14 and #18 bars.

All above columns require spirals of rod or cold drawn wire ($f_y = 60{,}000$ psi):—
#14 and smaller—3/8 ϕ @ 1¾″
#18 only —½ ϕ @ 2½″

Outside diameter of spiral should be 3 in. less than outside diameter of column.
† Below zigzag horizontal line of each group, concrete governs; above, tension governs.
‡ M_o = capacity in pure bending, ($N = 0$); for extrapolation, see page 11-5.

SPIRALLY REINFORCED ROUND COLUMNS—
Safe Load in Kips for Various Eccentricities in Inches
f'_c = 5000 psi (A431 Bars, f_y = 75,000 psi) f_s = 30,000 psi basis

COLUMN SIZE—24″ DIAMETER

f'_c = 5000 psi
f_y = 75,000 psi

Bars	p	M/N † = e (in.) 0	1	2	3	4	5	6	7	8	9	10	11	12	13	14	M_o ‡ (kip-in.)
6-#11	.0207	**846**	835	693	592	517	459	412	280	207	164	136	116	101	89	80	*1587*
7-#11	.0241	**893**	871	723	618	539	479	430	316	236	188	156	133	116	103	93	*1851*
8-#11	.0276	**939**	908	753	644	562	498	448	350	263	210	175	150	131	117	105	*2116*
9-#11	.0310	**986**	945	784	669	584	518	466	381	288	232	194	167	146	130	117	*2380*
10-#11	.0345	**1033**	982	814	695	606	538	483	402	313	253	212	183	160	143	129	*2645*
12-#11	.0414	**1127**	1055	874	747	651	577	519	431	357	291	246	213	188	168	152	*3174*
14-#11	.0483	**1220**	1129	935	798	696	617	554	460	394	327	278	241	213	191	173	*3703*
16-#11	.0552	**1314**	1202	996	849	741	657	590	490	419	360	307	268	238	214	194	*4232*
6-#14	.0298	**970**	930	771	658	573	508	457	366	276	222	185	159	139	124	111	*2254*
7-#14	.0348	**1037**	983	814	694	605	537	482	400	311	251	211	182	159	142	128	*2630*
8-#14	.0398	**1105**	1036	857	731	637	565	507	421	343	279	235	203	179	160	144	*3006*
9-#14	.0448	**1172**	1088	900	767	669	593	532	442	373	305	258	224	198	177	160	*3382*
10-#14	.0497	**1240**	1141	943	804	701	621	557	462	395	330	280	244	216	193	175	*3757*
11-#14	.0547	**1307**	1194	987	841	732	649	582	483	413	353	301	263	233	209	190	*4133*
13-#14	.0647	**1442**	1299	1073	914	796	705	632	525	448	391	339	298	265	239	218	*4885*
6-#18	.0531	**1285**	1160	950	805	698	616	551	455	388	323	275	240	212	190	173	*3721*
7-#18	.0619	**1405**	1251	1023	865	750	662	592	489	416	359	308	269	240	216	196	*4341*
8-#18	.0707	**1525**	1341	1096	926	802	707	633	522	445	387	337	297	265	239	218	*4961*
9-#18	.0796	**1645**	1432	1169	987	854	753	673	555	473	411	363	321	288	261	239	*5582*

Check availability of #14 and #18 bars.

All above columns require spirals of rod or cold drawn wire (f_y = 60,000 psi):—
#14 and smaller—3/8 φ @ 1¾″
#18 only —½ φ @ 2½″

Outside diameter of spiral should be 3 in. less than outside diameter of column.
† Below zigzag horizontal line of each group, concrete governs; above, tension governs.
‡ M_o = capacity in pure bending, (N = 0); for extrapolation, see page 11-5.

SPIRALLY REINFORCED ROUND COLUMNS—
Safe Load in Kips for Various Eccentricities in Inches
f'_c = 5000 psi (A431 Bars, f_y = 75,000 psi) f_s = 30,000 psi basis

COLUMN SIZE—26″ DIAMETER

f'_c = 5000 psi
f_y = 75,000 psi

Bars	p	M/N † = e (in.)															M_o ‡ (kip-in.)
		0	2	4	6	8	10	12	14	16	18	20	22	24	26	28	
6-#11	.0176	**944**	805	610	491	331	240	188	155	132	114	101	90	82	75	69	*1755*
7-#11	.0206	**991**	836	634	510	374	274	216	178	152	132	117	105	95	87	80	*2048*
8-#11	.0235	**1038**	868	658	529	414	306	242	200	171	149	132	119	108	98	91	*2340*
9-#11	.0264	**1084**	900	681	548	451	336	267	222	190	166	147	132	120	110	101	*2633*
10-#11	.0294	**1131**	931	705	567	475	365	292	243	208	182	162	146	132	121	112	*2925*
12-#11	.0353	**1225**	994	753	606	506	418	337	283	243	214	190	172	156	143	133	*3511*
14-#11	.0411	**1318**	1057	800	644	538	463	379	320	276	243	218	197	179	165	152	*4096*
16-#11	.0470	**1412**	1120	848	682	570	490	418	354	308	272	243	220	201	185	172	*4681*
18-#11	.0529	**1506**	1183	895	720	602	517	454	387	337	299	268	243	223	205	190	*5266*
6-#14	.0254	**1068**	886	670	539	434	322	256	212	181	158	140	126	114	105	96	*2497*
7-#14	.0297	**1136**	931	704	566	473	363	290	242	207	181	161	145	132	121	112	*2913*
8-#14	.0339	**1203**	977	738	593	496	401	323	270	233	204	182	164	149	137	126	*3330*
9-#14	.0381	**1271**	1022	772	620	518	437	354	298	257	226	201	182	165	152	141	*3746*
10-#14	.0424	**1338**	1067	806	647	541	465	383	323	280	246	220	199	182	167	155	*4162*
11-#14	.0466	**1406**	1112	840	675	564	484	410	348	302	267	239	216	197	182	168	*4579*
13-#14	.0551	**1541**	1202	907	729	609	523	458	393	343	305	274	248	227	210	195	*5411*
15-#14	.0636	**1676**	1292	975	783	654	562	492	435	382	340	306	279	256	237	220	*6244*
6-#18	.0452	**1383**	1077	806	644	536	459	379	320	277	245	219	198	180	166	154	*4153*
7-#18	.0527	**1503**	1154	863	689	573	491	422	359	313	277	248	225	206	190	176	*4845*
8-#18	.0603	**1623**	1231	919	733	610	522	456	394	345	307	276	251	230	212	197	*5537*
9-#18	.0678	**1743**	1307	975	778	647	553	483	427	375	335	302	275	253	234	217	*6230*
10-#18	.0753	**1863**	1384	1031	822	683	585	511	453	403	361	327	298	275	254	237	*6922*

Check availability of #14 and #18 bars.

All above columns require spirals of rod or cold drawn wire (f_y = 60,000 psi):—
#14 and smaller—3/8 ϕ @ 1¾″
#18 only —½ ϕ @ 2½″

Outside diameter of spiral should be 3 in. less than outside diameter of column.
† Below zigzag horizontal line of each group, concrete governs; above, tension governs.
‡ M_o = capacity in pure bending, (N = 0); for extrapolation, see page 11-5.

SPIRALLY REINFORCED ROUND COLUMNS—
Safe Load in Kips for Various Eccentricities in Inches
f'_c = 5000 psi (A431 Bars, f_y = 75,000 psi) f_s = 30,000 psi basis

COLUMN SIZE—28″ DIAMETER

f'_c = 5000 psi
f_y = 75,000 psi

Bars	p	M/N † = e (in.) 0	2	4	6	8	10	12	14	16	18	20	22	24	26	28	M_o ‡ (kip-in.)
6-#11	.0152	**1050**	926	712	578	388	276	215	175	148	128	113	101	91	83	77	1924
7-#11	.0177	**1097**	959	737	598	439	315	246	202	171	148	131	117	106	97	89	2244
8-#11	.0203	**1144**	992	762	618	486	352	276	227	193	167	148	133	120	110	101	2565
9-#11	.0228	**1190**	1024	787	639	530	387	305	252	214	186	165	148	134	123	113	2886
10-#11	.0253	**1237**	1057	812	659	554	421	333	276	235	205	182	163	148	135	125	3206
12-#11	.0304	**1331**	1122	862	700	589	483	386	321	275	241	214	192	175	160	148	3848
14-#11	.0355	**1424**	1188	912	740	623	538	435	364	313	275	245	221	201	184	170	4489
16-#11	.0405	**1518**	1253	962	781	657	567	480	404	349	307	274	248	226	207	192	5130
18-#11	.0456	**1612**	1318	1012	822	691	597	522	442	383	338	303	274	250	230	213	5772
20-#11	.0507	**1705**	1383	1062	862	726	626	551	477	415	368	330	299	273	252	233	6413
6-#14	.0219	**1174**	1011	776	629	510	371	292	241	205	178	157	141	128	117	108	2740
7-#14	.0256	**1242**	1058	811	658	553	420	332	275	234	204	181	163	147	135	124	3197
8-#14	.0292	**1309**	1104	847	687	578	464	370	308	263	230	204	184	167	153	141	3654
9-#14	.0329	**1377**	1151	883	716	602	506	406	339	291	255	226	204	185	170	157	4111
10-#14	.0365	**1444**	1198	919	745	626	540	440	369	317	278	248	224	204	187	173	4567
12-#14	.0438	**1579**	1291	990	803	675	582	502	424	367	324	289	262	239	220	203	5481
14-#14	.0512	**1714**	1385	1061	860	723	624	549	475	414	366	328	298	272	251	233	6394
16-#14	.0585	**1849**	1478	1133	918	772	666	585	522	456	406	365	332	304	281	261	7308
6-#18	.0390	**1489**	1211	922	744	623	537	438	368	317	278	248	224	204	187	173	4585
7-#18	.0455	**1609**	1291	982	792	663	571	489	413	358	315	282	255	233	214	198	5349
8-#18	.0520	**1729**	1371	1042	840	703	605	531	455	396	350	314	285	261	240	222	6113
9-#18	.0585	**1849**	1451	1102	888	743	639	561	494	432	383	345	313	287	265	246	6878
10-#18	.0650	**1969**	1531	1162	936	783	674	591	526	465	414	374	340	312	289	268	7642
11-#18	.0715	**2089**	1611	1222	984	823	708	621	553	495	443	401	366	336	311	290	8406

Check availability of #14 and #18 bars.

All above columns require spirals of rod or cold drawn wire (f_y = 60,000 psi):—
#14 and smaller—3/8 φ @ 1¾″
#18 only —½ φ @ 2½″

Outside diameter of spiral should be 3 in. less than outside diameter of column.
† Below zigzag horizontal line of each group, concrete governs; above, tension governs.
‡ M_o = capacity in pure bending, (N = 0); for extrapolation, see page 11-5.

SPIRALLY REINFORCED ROUND COLUMNS—
Safe Load in Kips for Various Eccentricities in Inches
f'_c = 5000 psi (A431 Bars, f_y = 75,000 psi) f_s = 30,000 psi basis

COLUMN SIZE—30″ DIAMETER

f'_c = 5000 psi
f_y = 75,000 psi

Bars	p	M/N † = e (in.) 0	2	4	6	8	10	12	14	16	18	20	22	24	26	28	M_o ‡ (kip-in.)
6-#11	.0132	**1164**	1058	822	672	453	316	243	197	165	143	125	112	101	92	85	*2092*
7-#11	.0154	**1211**	1091	848	694	512	361	278	226	191	165	145	130	117	107	98	*2441*
8-#11	.0177	**1257**	1125	875	715	568	403	313	255	216	187	164	147	133	121	111	*2790*
9-#11	.0199	**1304**	1158	901	737	<u>619</u>	444	346	283	240	208	183	164	149	136	125	*3138*
10-#11	.0221	**1351**	1192	927	758	642	482	378	310	263	229	202	181	164	150	138	*3487*
12-#11	.0265	**1445**	1259	979	801	678	<u>554</u>	438	362	309	269	238	214	194	177	163	*4185*
14-#11	.0309	**1538**	1326	1032	844	714	619	494	411	352	307	273	245	223	204	188	*4882*
16-#11	.0353	**1632**	1394	1084	887	751	651	546	457	392	344	306	276	251	230	212	*5580*
18-#11	.0397	**1725**	1461	1137	930	787	682	<u>595</u>	500	431	379	338	305	278	255	236	*6277*
20-#11	.0441	**1819**	1528	1189	973	824	714	630	541	468	413	369	334	304	280	259	*6975*
22-#11	.0486	**1913**	1595	1242	1016	860	745	658	<u>579</u>	503	445	399	361	330	304	281	*7672*
6-#14	.0191	**1288**	1145	889	727	<u>596</u>	426	331	271	229	198	175	157	142	129	119	*2983*
7-#14	.0223	**1356**	1193	927	758	641	481	377	310	263	228	202	181	164	149	138	*3480*
8-#14	.0255	**1423**	1241	964	788	667	533	420	347	295	257	227	204	185	169	156	*3978*
9-#14	.0286	**1491**	1289	1002	819	693	<u>582</u>	462	382	327	285	253	227	206	188	174	*4475*
10-#14	.0318	**1558**	1337	1039	849	718	622	501	417	357	312	277	249	226	207	191	*4972*
12-#14	.0382	**1693**	1434	1114	911	770	667	<u>573</u>	480	414	363	324	292	266	244	225	*5967*
14-#14	.0446	**1828**	1530	1189	972	822	712	628	539	467	411	368	333	304	279	258	*6961*
16-#14	.0509	**1963**	1626	1264	1033	874	757	668	<u>593</u>	516	457	410	371	339	313	290	*7956*
18-#14	.0573	**2098**	1723	1338	1094	925	802	707	633	<u>562</u>	499	449	408	374	345	320	*8951*
6-#18	.0340	**1603**	1354	1045	851	717	620	501	418	358	313	278	250	228	209	192	*5017*
7-#18	.0396	**1723**	1436	1108	902	760	657	<u>561</u>	470	405	356	317	286	260	239	221	*5853*
8-#18	.0453	**1843**	1519	1171	953	803	694	611	519	449	396	354	320	292	268	248	*6689*
9-#18	.0509	**1963**	1602	1235	1004	846	731	644	<u>564</u>	491	434	389	352	322	297	275	*7526*
10-#18	.0566	**2083**	1685	1298	1055	889	768	676	604	529	470	422	383	351	324	300	*8362*
11-#18	.0622	**2203**	1768	1361	1107	932	805	709	633	<u>565</u>	503	453	413	379	350	325	*9198*
12-#18	.0679	**2323**	1851	1424	1158	975	842	741	662	598	<u>535</u>	483	441	405	375	349	*10034*

Check availability of #14 and #18 bars.

All above columns require spirals of rod or cold drawn wire (f_y = 60,000 psi):—
#14 and smaller—⅜ φ @ 1¾″
#18 only —½ φ @ 2½″

Outside diameter of spiral should be 3 in. less than outside diameter of column.
† Below zigzag horizontal line of each group, concrete governs; above, tension governs.
‡ M_o = capacity in pure bending, (N = 0); for extrapolation, see page 11-5.

SPIRALLY REINFORCED ROUND COLUMNS—
Safe Load in Kips for Various Eccentricities in Inches
f'_c = 5000 psi (A431 Bars, f_y = 75,000 psi) f_s = 30,000 psi basis

COLUMN SIZE—32″ DIAMETER

f'_c = 5000 psi
f_y = 75,000 psi

Bars	p	M/N † = e (in.) 0	3	6	9	12	15	18	21	24	27	30	33	36	39	42	M_o ‡ (kip-in.)
6-#11	.0116	**1286**	1055	776	428	273	200	158	130	111	97	86	77	70	64	59	*2261*
7-#11	.0136	**1332**	1085	798	486	313	230	182	151	129	112	99	89	81	74	68	*2637*
8-#11	.0155	**1379**	1116	821	542	352	260	207	171	146	127	113	101	92	84	78	*3014*
9-#11	.0175	**1426**	1146	843	594	389	289	230	191	163	143	127	114	103	94	87	*3391*
10-#11	.0194	**1473**	1177	866	644	425	318	253	211	180	158	140	126	114	105	96	*3768*
12-#11	.0233	**1566**	1237	911	721	494	372	298	249	213	187	166	150	136	125	115	*4522*
14-#11	.0272	**1660**	1298	956	757	558	423	341	285	245	215	192	173	157	144	133	*5275*
16-#11	.0310	**1754**	1359	1001	792	618	472	382	321	277	243	217	196	178	164	151	*6029*
18-#11	.0349	**1847**	1420	1046	828	673	519	422	355	307	270	241	218	199	182	169	*6783*
20-#11	.0388	**1941**	1481	1091	864	715	563	460	388	336	296	265	240	219	201	186	*7536*
23-#11	.0446	**2081**	1572	1159	918	759	625	513	436	379	335	300	272	248	228	212	*8667*
6-#14	.0168	**1410**	1134	833	571	373	277	220	182	156	136	121	108	98	90	83	*3226*
7-#14	.0196	**1477**	1177	865	643	425	317	253	210	180	157	140	126	114	105	96	*3764*
8-#14	.0224	**1545**	1221	898	709	474	356	285	238	204	178	158	143	130	119	110	*4302*
9-#14	.0252	**1612**	1264	930	735	521	394	316	264	227	199	177	159	145	133	123	*4840*
10-#14	.0280	**1680**	1308	962	761	566	430	346	290	250	219	195	176	160	147	136	*5377*
11-#14	.0308	**1747**	1351	994	786	608	465	376	316	272	239	213	192	175	161	148	*5915*
13-#14	.0364	**1882**	1438	1058	837	687	530	432	364	315	277	248	224	204	188	174	*6991*
15-#14	.0420	**2017**	1526	1123	888	734	591	485	410	356	314	281	255	232	214	198	*8066*
17-#14	.0476	**2152**	1613	1187	939	777	648	534	454	395	350	314	284	260	239	222	*9142*
19-#14	.0532	**2287**	1700	1251	990	819	698	581	496	433	384	345	313	287	264	245	*10217*
6-#18	.0298	**1725**	1320	965	761	569	433	350	293	252	221	197	178	162	149	137	*5449*
7-#18	.0348	**1845**	1395	1019	803	637	490	398	335	289	254	227	205	187	171	159	*6357*
8-#18	.0398	**1965**	1469	1073	846	697	543	443	375	324	286	256	231	211	194	179	*7265*
9-#18	.0448	**2085**	1544	1128	888	732	592	486	413	358	316	283	257	234	216	200	*8174*
10-#18	.0497	**2205**	1618	1182	930	767	639	527	449	391	346	310	281	257	237	220	*9082*
11-#18	.0547	**2325**	1693	1236	973	802	682	566	484	422	375	337	306	280	258	239	*9990*
12-#18	.0597	**2445**	1767	1290	1015	837	712	602	517	452	402	362	329	302	278	259	*10898*
13-#18	.0647	**2565**	1842	1344	1058	872	742	637	548	481	429	386	352	323	298	277	*11807*
14-#18	.0696	**2685**	1917	1398	1100	907	771	670	578	509	454	410	374	343	318	295	*12715*

Check availability of #14 and #18 bars.

All above columns require spirals of rod or cold drawn wire (f_y = 60,000 psi):—
#14 and smaller—3/8 φ @ 1¾″
#18 only —½ φ @ 2¾″

Outside diameter of spiral should be 3 in. less than outside diameter of column.
† Below zigzag horizontal line of each group, concrete governs; above, tension governs.
‡ M_o = capacity in pure bending, (N = 0); for extrapolation, see page 11-5.

SPIRALLY REINFORCED ROUND COLUMNS—
Safe Load in Kips for Various Eccentricities in Inches
f'_c = 5000 psi (A431 Bars, f_y = 75,000 psi) f_s = 30,000 psi basis

COLUMN SIZE—34″ DIAMETER

f'_c = 5000 psi
f_y = 75,000 psi

Bars	p	M/N † = e (in.) 0	3	6	9	12	15	18	21	24	27	30	33	36	39	42	M_o ‡ (kip-in.)
6-#11	.0103	**1415**	1194	888	490	305	221	174	143	121	105	93	83	76	69	64	*2429*
7-#11	.0120	**1462**	1225	911	557	350	255	201	165	141	122	108	97	88	80	74	*2834*
8-#11	.0137	**1509**	1257	935	620	394	288	227	188	160	139	123	110	100	91	84	*3239*
9-#11	.0155	**1556**	1288	958	680	436	320	253	210	179	156	138	124	112	103	95	*3644*
10-#11	.0172	**1602**	1319	982	737	477	352	279	231	197	172	152	137	124	114	105	*4049*
12-#11	.0206	**1696**	1382	1029	819	554	413	329	273	233	204	181	163	148	135	125	*4858*
14-#11	.0241	**1790**	1445	1076	857	626	470	376	314	269	235	209	188	171	157	145	*5668*
16-#11	.0275	**1883**	1507	1123	895	694	525	422	353	303	266	237	213	194	178	164	*6478*
18-#11	.0309	**1977**	1570	1170	932	757	577	466	391	337	296	263	238	216	199	183	*7288*
20-#11	.0344	**2070**	1632	1217	970	806	626	508	428	369	325	290	261	238	219	202	*8098*
22-#11	.0378	**2164**	1695	1264	1008	838	674	549	463	401	353	315	285	260	239	221	*8908*
25-#11	.0430	**2304**	1789	1334	1064	885	740	607	514	446	394	353	319	292	268	248	*10122*
6-#14	.0149	**1539**	1275	948	655	418	307	242	200	170	148	131	118	107	98	90	*3469*
7-#14	.0173	**1607**	1320	981	737	476	352	279	231	197	172	152	137	124	114	105	*4047*
8-#14	.0198	**1674**	1365	1015	808	532	395	314	261	223	195	173	155	141	129	119	*4626*
9-#14	.0223	**1742**	1410	1049	835	585	437	349	290	249	217	193	174	158	145	133	*5204*
10-#14	.0248	**1809**	1455	1082	862	635	478	383	319	274	240	213	192	174	160	147	*5782*
11-#14	.0273	**1877**	1500	1116	888	684	517	415	347	298	261	233	209	191	175	161	*6361*
13-#14	.0322	**2012**	1589	1183	942	773	591	478	401	346	304	271	244	222	204	189	*7517*
15-#14	.0372	**2147**	1679	1250	996	827	659	537	453	391	344	308	278	254	233	216	*8674*
17-#14	.0421	**2282**	1769	1317	1049	872	724	593	502	435	384	344	311	284	261	242	*9830*
19-#14	.0471	**2417**	1858	1384	1103	917	784	645	548	477	422	378	343	313	289	267	*10987*
21-#14	.0520	**2552**	1948	1452	1157	961	822	695	593	517	459	412	374	342	315	292	*12143*
6-#18	.0264	**1854**	1469	1087	863	642	483	387	323	277	243	216	195	177	162	150	*5881*
7-#18	.0308	**1974**	1546	1144	908	720	547	441	370	318	279	249	224	204	187	173	*6861*
8-#18	.0352	**2094**	1623	1201	953	790	607	493	414	358	314	281	253	231	212	196	*7841*
9-#18	.0397	**2214**	1700	1258	998	827	664	541	457	395	348	311	281	257	236	218	*8822*
10-#18	.0441	**2334**	1778	1315	1043	864	716	587	498	432	381	341	309	282	260	240	*9802*
11-#18	.0485	**2454**	1855	1372	1088	902	766	631	537	467	413	370	336	307	283	262	*10782*
12-#18	.0529	**2574**	1932	1428	1133	939	802	673	574	501	444	399	362	331	305	283	*11762*
13-#18	.0573	**2694**	2009	1485	1178	976	833	712	610	533	474	426	387	355	327	304	*12743*
14-#18	.0617	**2814**	2086	1542	1223	1013	865	750	644	565	502	453	412	378	349	324	*13723*
15-#18	.0661	**2934**	2163	1599	1268	1051	897	782	677	595	530	478	436	400	370	344	*14703*

Check availability of #14 and #18 bars.

All above columns require spirals of rod or cold drawn wire (f_y = 60,000 psi):—
#14 and smaller—3/8 φ @ 1¾″
#18 only —½ φ @ 2¾″

Outside diameter of spiral should be 3 in. less than outside diameter of column.
† Below zigzag horizontal line of each group, concrete governs; above, tension governs.
‡ M_o = capacity in pure bending, (N = 0); for extrapolation, see page 11-5.

SPIRALLY REINFORCED ROUND COLUMNS—
Safe Load in Kips for Various Eccentricities in Inches
f'_c = 5000 psi (A431 Bars, f_y = 75,000 psi) f_s = 30,000 psi basis

COLUMN SIZE—36″ DIAMETER

f'_c = 5000 psi
f_y = 75,000 psi

Bars	p	M/N † = e (in.) 0	3	6	9	12	15	18	21	24	27	30	33	36	39	42	M_o ‡ (kip-in.)
7-#11	.0107	**1599**	1375	1033	636	390	281	220	180	153	133	117	105	95	87	80	3030
8-#11	.0123	**1646**	1407	1057	709	439	318	249	205	174	151	133	119	108	99	91	3463
9-#11	.0138	**1693**	1439	1082	777	486	353	278	229	194	169	149	134	121	111	102	3896
10-#11	.0153	**1740**	1472	1106	842	532	388	306	252	215	187	165	148	134	123	113	4329
12-#11	.0184	**1833**	1536	1155	925	618	455	360	298	254	222	196	176	160	146	135	5195
14-#11	.0215	**1927**	1600	1204	965	699	519	413	343	293	256	227	204	185	169	156	6061
16-#11	.0245	**2021**	1664	1253	1004	775	580	464	386	331	289	257	231	210	192	177	6927
18-#11	.0276	**2114**	1728	1301	1044	847	638	512	428	367	322	286	258	234	215	198	7793
20-#11	.0307	**2208**	1793	1350	1083	904	694	559	468	403	353	315	284	258	237	219	8659
23-#11	.0352	**2348**	1889	1424	1142	954	772	626	527	454	400	357	322	293	269	249	9958
27-#11	.0414	**2535**	2017	1521	1221	1020	869	710	601	520	459	410	371	339	312	289	11690
6-#14	.0133	**1677**	1427	1071	748	466	338	265	218	186	161	143	128	116	106	97	3712
7-#14	.0155	**1744**	1473	1106	842	532	388	306	252	215	187	165	148	134	123	113	4331
8-#14	.0177	**1812**	1519	1141	914	594	437	345	285	243	212	188	168	153	140	129	4950
9-#14	.0199	**1879**	1565	1176	942	654	483	383	317	271	236	210	188	171	156	144	5569
10-#14	.0221	**1947**	1611	1211	970	710	528	420	349	298	261	231	208	189	173	159	6187
12-#14	.0265	**2082**	1703	1281	1026	816	614	492	410	352	308	274	246	224	205	189	7425
14-#14	.0309	**2217**	1795	1350	1082	903	693	559	468	403	353	315	284	258	237	219	8662
16-#14	.0354	**2352**	1887	1420	1139	950	768	623	524	452	397	355	320	292	268	248	9900
18-#14	.0398	**2487**	1979	1490	1195	997	837	683	577	499	440	393	355	324	298	276	11138
20-#14	.0442	**2622**	2071	1560	1251	1044	896	741	628	545	481	431	390	356	328	304	12375
22-#14	.0486	**2757**	2163	1630	1307	1091	937	795	676	588	521	467	423	387	357	331	13613
6-#18	.0236	**1992**	1627	1218	973	720	536	427	355	304	265	235	212	192	176	162	6313
7-#18	.0275	**2112**	1706	1277	1020	808	608	487	406	348	305	271	244	222	203	188	7365
8-#18	.0314	**2332**	1786	1336	1068	889	675	544	456	392	344	306	276	251	230	213	8417
9-#18	.0354	**2352**	1865	1396	1115	928	739	598	503	434	381	340	307	280	257	237	9470
10-#18	.0393	**2472**	1945	1455	1162	968	798	650	548	474	417	373	337	307	283	261	10522
11-#18	.0432	**2592**	2024	1514	1210	1007	854	699	592	513	453	405	366	335	308	285	11574
12-#18	.0472	**2712**	2103	1574	1257	1047	897	746	634	551	487	436	395	361	333	308	12626
13-#18	.0511	**2832**	2183	1633	1305	1086	930	791	674	587	520	467	423	387	357	331	13679
14-#18	.0550	**2952**	2262	1693	1352	1126	964	833	712	622	552	496	450	413	380	353	14731
15-#18	.0589	**3072**	2342	1752	1399	1165	998	873	749	656	583	525	477	437	404	375	15783
16-#18	.0629	**3192**	2421	1811	1447	1204	1032	902	785	688	613	553	503	462	426	396	16835

Check availability of #14 and #18 bars.

All above columns require spirals of rod or cold drawn wire (f_y = 60,000 psi):—
#14 and smaller—⅜ φ @ 2½″
#18 only —½ φ @ 2¾″

Outside diameter of spiral should be 3 in. less than outside diameter of column.
† Below zigzag horizontal line of each group, concrete governs; above, tension governs.
‡ M_o = capacity in pure bending, (N = 0); for extrapolation, see page 11-5.

DESIGN OF SPIRALS

Spirals are proportioned from ACI Equation (9-1):

$$p' = 0.45\left(\frac{A_g}{A_c} - 1\right)\frac{f'_c}{f_y}.$$

Spirals may be of hot rolled rod or cold drawn wire of a range of yield strengths. The spirals given in these tables are based upon f_y = 60,000 psi, requiring Grade 40 rod or wire of that minimum strength. If a different strength of material is used the cross-sectional area or pitch can be directly prorated.

Tables on page 2-19 give the maximum number of verticals that can be accommodated in spirals of various sizes. For a table giving the volumes of concrete in round columns, capitals and square columns see page 5-13.

The percentage of spirals in relation to core volume is given on pages 11-176 and 11-177. This saves calculation. The corresponding weight of spirals is given on pages 11-178 and 11-179.

The designer must keep in mind that beam bars often have to extend through the spaces between column verticals. It is generally considered permissible for the horizontal and vertical bars to have point contact in passing, after allowing for the projection of the deformations. Frequently a large-scale layout is helpful in establishing clearances and sometimes a full-size template is used in the field to get the correct orientation of column verticals before the beam bars are installed.

A few examples illustrate the application of the design formula.

Example I.* For the table on page 11-99 compute the pitch of ⅝″φ A432 spirals for a 30 in. square spirally reinforced column of 3750 psi concrete with vertical bars #14S or smaller.

Solution. $p' = 0.45\left[\frac{30 \times 30}{\pi(13.5)^2} - 1\right]\frac{3750}{60000} = 0.0161$

$$p' = \frac{\text{Volume of Steel in Vertical Foot}}{\text{Volume of Concrete}} = \frac{\pi D \frac{12}{\text{pitch}} A_s}{\frac{\pi D^2}{4}12} = \frac{4A_s}{D\ \text{pitch}}$$

$$\text{pitch} = \frac{4A_s}{p'D} \quad \frac{4 \times 0.31}{0.0161 \times 27} = 2.85'', \text{ hence } ⅝φ @ 2¾'' \text{ in table on page 11-99}$$

Example II.* Same as Example I, but with 5000 psi concrete. (Page 11-119).

Solution. Assume ⅝″φ rod will be suitable,

$$\text{pitch} = \frac{4 \times 0.31}{0.45\left[\frac{30 \times 30}{\pi(13.5)^2} - 1\right]\frac{5000}{60000} \times 27} = 2.14'', \text{ hence } ⅝''φ @ 2'' \text{ as on page 11-119.}$$

Example III.* Solve Example I if the column is 30 in. round instead of square.

Solution. Assuming ⅜″φ,

$$\text{pitch} = \frac{4 \times 0.11}{0.45\left[\frac{15^2}{13.5^2} - 1\right]\frac{3750}{60000} \times 27} = 2.47'', \text{ hence } ⅜''φ @ 2¼'' \text{ as on page 11-151.}$$

---

* These examples overestimate the volume of the spiral. Example I can be more precisely computed:—length of rod in one turn = $\sqrt{(\pi \times 26.375)^2 + (2.75)^2} = 82.7''$ as compared with $\pi 27 = 84.9''$ used in the example, but not in the tables.

SPIRALS AS PERCENTAGES OF CORE VOLUME (out to out of spirals)

See explanation on page 11-175

Core Dia (in.)	5/8 in. Dia Pitch (in.)							1/2 in. Dia Pitch (in.)						
	2	2¼	2½	2¾	3	3¼	3½	2	2¼	2½	2¾	3	3¼	3½
11														
12	5.17							3.33						
13	4.77							3.08						
14	4.44	3.94						2.86	2.54					
15	4.13	3.68	3.31					2.67	2.37	2.13				
16	3.88	3.45	3.10					2.50	2.22	2.00				
17	3.65	3.24	2.92	2.65				2.35	2.09	1.88	1.71			
18	3.45	3.06	2.76	2.51	2.30			2.22	1.97	1.78	1.62	1.48		
19	3.26	2.90	2.61	2.37	2.18			2.11	1.87	1.68	1.53	1.40		
20	3.10	2.76	2.48	2.25	2.07	1.91		2.00	1.78	1.60	1.45	1.33	1.23	
21	2.95	2.63	2.36	2.15	1.97	1.82	1.69	1.90	1.69	1.52	1.38	1.27	1.17	1.09
22	2.82	2.51	2.26	2.05	1.88	1.74	1.61	1.82	1.62	1.45	1.32	1.21	1.12	1.04
23	2.70	2.40	2.16	1.96	1.80	1.66	1.54	1.74	1.55	1.39	1.26	1.16	1.07	0.99
24	2.59	2.30	2.07	1.88	1.72	1.59	1.48	1.67	1.48	1.33	1.21	1.11	1.03	0.95
25	2.48	2.21	1.98	1.80	1.65	1.53	1.42	1.60	1.42	1.28	1.16	1.07	0.98	0.91
26	2.39	2.12	1.91	1.73	1.59	1.47	1.36	1.54	1.37	1.23	1.12	1.03	0.95	0.88
27	2.30	2.04	1.84	1.67	1.53	1.41	1.31	1.48	1.32	1.19	1.08	0.99	0.91	0.85
28	2.21	1.97	1.77	1.61	1.48	1.36	1.27	1.43	1.27	1.14	1.04	0.95	0.88	0.82
29	2.14	1.90	1.71	1.55	1.43	1.32	1.22	1.38	1.23	1.10	1.00	0.92	0.85	0.79
30	2.07	1.84	1.65	1.50	1.38	1.27	1.18	1.33	1.19	1.07	0.97	0.89	0.82	0.76
31	2.00	1.78	1.60	1.45	1.33	1.23	1.14	1.29	1.15	1.03	0.94	0.86	0.79	0.73
32	1.94	1.72	1.55	1.41	1.29	1.19	1.11	1.25	1.11	1.00	0.90	0.83	0.77	0.71
33	1.88	1.67	1.50	1.37	1.25	1.15	1.07	1.21	1.08	0.97	0.88	0.80	0.74	0.69
34	1.82	1.62	1.46	1.33	1.22	1.12	1.04	1.18	1.04	0.94	0.85	0.78	0.72	0.67
35	1.77	1.58	1.42	1.29	1.18	1.09	1.01	1.14	1.02	0.91	0.83	0.76	0.70	0.65
36	1.72	1.53	1.38	1.25	1.15	1.06	0.98	1.11	0.98	0.89	0.80	0.74	0.68	0.63
37	1.67	1.49	1.34	1.22	1.12	1.03	0.96	1.08	0.96	0.86	0.78	0.72	0.66	0.61
38	1.63	1.45	1.30	1.19	1.09	1.00	0.93	1.05	0.94	0.84	0.76	0.70	0.65	0.60
39	1.59	1.41	1.27	1.16	1.06	0.98	0.91	1.02	0.91	0.82	0.74	0.68	0.63	0.58
40	1.55	1.38	1.24	1.13	1.03	0.95	0.88	1.00	0.89	0.80	0.72	0.66	0.61	0.57
41	1.51	1.34	1.21	1.10	1.01	0.93	0.86	0.98	0.87	0.78	0.71	0.65	0.60	0.55
42	1.48	1.31	1.18	1.07	0.98	0.91	0.84	0.95	0.85	0.76	0.69	0.63	0.58	0.54
43	1.44	1.28	1.15	1.05	0.96	0.88	0.82	0.93	0.83	0.74	0.67	0.62	0.57	0.53
44	1.41	1.25	1.13	1.02	0.94	0.86	0.80	0.91	0.81	0.72	0.66	0.60	0.56	0.52
45	1.38	1.22	1.10	1.00	0.92	0.85	0.79	0.89	0.79	0.71	0.64	0.59	0.54	0.50
46	1.35	1.20	1.08	0.98	0.90	0.83	0.77	0.87	0.77	0.69	0.63	0.58	0.53	0.49
47	1.32	1.17	1.06	0.96	0.88	0.81	0.75	0.85	0.76	0.68	0.62	0.56	0.52	0.48
48	1.29	1.15	1.03	0.94	0.86	0.79	0.74	0.83	0.74	0.66	0.60	0.55	0.51	0.47

SPIRALS AS PERCENTAGES OF CORE VOLUME (out to out of spirals)

See explanation on page 11-175

⅜ in. Dia Pitch (in.)						
1¾	2	2¼	2½	2¾	3	3¼
2.29						
2.09	1.83					
1.93	1.69					
1.80	1.57	1.40				
1.68	1.47	1.30	1.17			
1.57	1.38	1.22	1.10			
1.48	1.29	1.15	1.03	0.94		
1.40	1.22	1.09	0.98	0.89	0.81	
1.32	1.16	1.03	0.93	0.84	0.77	
1.26	1.10	0.98	0.88	0.80	0.73	0.68
1.20	1.05	0.93	0.84	0.76	0.70	0.64
1.14	1.00	0.89	0.80	0.73	0.67	0.62
1.09	0.96	0.85	0.76	0.70	0.64	0.59
1.05	0.92	0.81	0.73	0.67	0.61	0.56
1.01	0.88	0.78	0.70	0.64	0.59	0.54
0.97	0.85	0.75	0.68	0.62	0.56	0.52
0.93	0.82	0.72	0.65	0.59	0.54	0.50
0.90	0.79	0.70	0.63	0.57	0.52	0.48
0.87	0.76	0.67	0.61	0.55	0.51	0.47
0.84	0.73	0.65	0.58	0.53	0.49	0.45
0.81	0.71	0.63	0.56	0.51	0.47	0.43
0.78	0.68	0.61	0.55	0.50	0.46	0.42
0.76	0.66	0.59	0.53	0.48	0.44	0.41
0.74	0.64	0.57	0.51	0.47	0.43	0.39
0.71	0.62	0.56	0.50	0.46	0.42	0.38
0.69	0.61	0.54	0.49	0.44	0.40	0.37
0.68	0.59	0.52	0.47	0.43	0.39	0.36
0.66	0.57	0.51	0.46	0.42	0.38	0.35
0.64	0.56	0.50	0.45	0.41	0.37	0.34
0.62	0.55	0.49	0.44	0.40	0.36	0.34
0.61	0.53	0.47	0.43	0.39	0.35	0.33
0.59	0.52	0.46	0.42	0.38	0.35	0.32
0.58	0.51	0.45	0.41	0.37	0.34	0.31
0.57	0.50	0.44	0.40	0.36	0.33	0.31
0.55	0.48	0.43	0.39	0.35	0.32	0.30
0.54	0.47	0.42	0.38	0.34	0.32	0.29
0.53	0.46	0.41	0.37	0.34	0.31	0.28
0.52	0.45	0.40	0.36	0.33	0.30	0.28

WEIGHTS OF SPIRALS PER VERTICAL FOOT *

See explanation on page 11-175

Core Dia (in.)	5/8 in. Dia Pitch (in.)							1/2 in. Dia Pitch (in.)						
	2	2¼	2½	2¾	3	3¼	3½	2	2¼	2½	2¾	3	3¼	3½
11														
12	19.7							12.6						
13	21.3							13.6						
14	22.9	20.4						14.7	13.0					
15	24.6	21.8	19.7					15.7	14.0	12.6				
16	26.2	23.3	21.0					16.8	14.9	13.4				
17	27.9	24.8	22.3	20.3				17.8	15.9	14.3	13.0			
18	29.5	26.2	23.6	21.4	19.7			18.9	16.8	15.1	13.7	12.6		
19	31.1	27.7	24.9	22.6	20.8			20.0	17.7	16.0	14.5	13.3		
20	32.8	29.1	26.2	23.8	21.8	20.2		21.0	18.6	16.8	15.3	14.0	12.9	
21	34.4	30.6	27.5	25.0	22.9	21.2	19.7	22.0	19.6	17.6	16.0	14.7	13.6	12.6
22	36.0	32.0	28.8	26.2	24.0	22.2	20.6	23.1	20.5	18.5	16.8	15.4	14.2	13.2
23	37.7	33.5	30.1	27.4	25.1	23.2	21.5	24.1	21.4	19.3	17.6	16.1	14.9	13.8
24	39.3	35.0	31.5	28.6	26.2	24.2	22.5	25.2	22.4	20.2	18.3	16.8	15.5	14.4
25	41.0	36.4	32.8	29.8	27.3	25.2	23.4	26.2	23.3	21.0	19.1	17.5	16.1	15.0
26	42.6	37.9	34.1	31.0	28.4	26.2	24.3	27.3	24.3	21.8	19.9	18.2	16.8	15.6
27	44.2	39.3	35.4	32.2	29.5	27.2	25.3	28.3	25.2	22.7	20.6	18.9	17.4	16.2
28	45.9	40.8	36.7	33.4	30.6	28.2	26.2	29.4	26.1	23.5	21.4	19.6	18.1	16.8
29	47.5	42.2	38.0	34.6	31.7	29.2	27.2	30.4	27.1	24.4	22.2	20.3	18.7	17.4
30	49.2	43.7	39.3	35.7	32.8	30.2	28.1	31.5	28.1	25.2	22.9	21.0	19.4	18.0
31	50.8	45.3	40.5	36.9	33.9	31.2	29.0	32.5	29.0	26.1	23.7	21.7	20.1	18.6
32	52.5	46.7	41.7	38.1	35.0	32.2	29.9	33.6	29.9	26.9	24.4	22.4	20.7	19.2
33	54.1	48.1	43.1	39.3	36.1	33.2	30.9	34.6	30.9	27.7	25.2	23.1	21.4	19.8
34	55.7	49.6	44.4	40.5	37.2	34.2	31.9	35.7	31.9	28.6	26.0	23.8	22.0	20.4
35	57.4	51.0	45.7	41.7	38.3	35.2	32.8	36.7	32.8	29.4	26.7	24.5	22.7	21.0
36	59.1	52.5	47.0	42.8	39.4	36.2	33.7	37.8	33.7	30.3	27.5	25.2	23.3	21.6
37	60.7	53.9	48.3	44.1	40.5	37.3	34.7	38.8	34.7	31.1	28.3	25.9	24.0	22.2
38	62.3	55.4	49.6	45.2	41.6	38.3	35.6	39.9	35.6	31.9	29.0	26.6	24.6	22.8
39	63.9	56.8	50.9	46.4	42.7	39.3	36.5	40.9	36.5	32.8	29.8	27.3	25.2	23.4
40	65.6	58.3	52.2	47.6	43.8	40.3	37.5	42.0	37.5	33.6	30.6	28.0	25.9	24.0
41	67.3	59.7	53.5	48.8	44.8	41.3	38.4	43.0	38.4	34.4	31.3	28.7	26.6	24.6
42	68.9	61.2	54.8	50.0	45.9	42.3	39.3	44.1	39.3	35.3	32.1	29.4	27.2	25.2
43	70.5	62.7	56.1	51.1	47.0	43.3	40.3	45.1	40.3	36.1	32.8	30.1	27.8	25.8
44	72.1	64.1	57.5	52.4	48.1	44.3	41.2	46.2	41.2	37.0	33.6	30.8	28.5	26.4
45	73.8	65.5	58.7	53.6	49.2	45.3	42.2	47.3	42.2	37.8	34.4	31.5	29.1	27.0
46	75.5	67.0	60.1	54.7	50.3	46.3	43.1	48.3	43.1	38.6	35.1	32.2	29.8	27.6
47	77.1	68.5	61.4	55.9	51.4	47.3	44.1	49.4	44.1	39.5	35.9	32.9	30.4	28.2
48	78.7	70.0	62.7	57.1	52.5	48.3	45.0	50.4	45.0	40.4	36.7	33.6	31.1	28.8

* The weights given include wire for regular loops only. Weight must be added for 1½ turns top and bottom equivalent to one-half the tabular weight for 2-in. pitch. Weight of spacers must also be added. A minimum section standard spacer is a 1″ × 1″ × ⅛″ angle weighing 0.80 lb per ft. Three spacers are required for spirals 24 in. or less in diameter, and four for spirals over 24 in. in diameter, or of ⅝″φ rods.

WEIGHTS OF SPIRALS PER VERTICAL FOOT *

See explanation on page 11-175

⅜ in. Dia Pitch (in.)							¼ in. Dia Nonstandard Spiral Pitch (in.)					
1¾	2	2¼	2½	2¾	3	3¼	1¾	2	2¼	2½	2¾	3
7.43							3.30					
8.10	7.09						3.60	3.15				
8.78	7.68						3.90	3.41				
9.45	8.27	7.35					4.20	3.67	3.26			
10.1	8.85	7.87	7.08				4.50	3.94	3.50	3.15		
10.8	9.44	8.39	7.55				4.80	4.20	3.73	3.36		
11.5	10.0	8.92	8.02	7.30			5.10	4.46	3.96	3.56	3.24	
12.1	10.6	9.44	8.50	7.73	7.08		5.40	4.72	4.20	3.78	3.43	3.15
12.8	11.2	9.97	8.97	8.15	7.48		5.70	4.98	4.43	3.98	3.62	3.32
13.5	11.8	10.5	9.44	8.59	7.87	7.28	6.00	5.25	4.66	4.20	3.82	3.50
14.2	12.4	11.0	9.92	9.02	8.26	7.64	6.30	5.51	4.90	4.41	4.01	3.67
14.8	13.0	11.5	10.4	9.45	8.66	8.00	6.60	5.77	5.13	4.62	4.20	3.85
15.5	13.6	12.1	10.9	9.88	9.05	8.36	6.90	6.03	5.36	4.83	4.39	4.02
16.2	14.2	12.6	11.3	10.3	9.45	8.72	7.20	6.30	5.60	5.04	4.58	4.20
16.9	14.8	13.1	11.8	10.7	9.84	9.09	7.50	6.56	5.83	5.25	4.77	4.37
17.5	15.4	13.6	12.3	11.2	10.2	9.45	7.80	6.82	6.06	5.46	4.96	4.55
18.2	15.9	14.2	12.7	11.6	10.6	9.81	8.10	7.08	6.30	5.67	5.15	4.72
18.9	16.5	14.7	13.2	12.0	11.0	10.2	8.40	7.34	6.53	5.88	5.34	
19.6	17.1	15.2	13.7	12.5	11.4	10.5	8.70	7.60	6.77	6.09	5.53	
20.2	17.7	15.7	14.2	12.9	11.8	10.9	8.99	7.87	7.00	6.30		
20.9	18.3	16.2	14.7	13.4	12.2	11.3	9.14	8.13	7.23	6.51		
21.6	18.9	16.8	15.2	13.8	12.6	11.7	9.57	8.39	7.46	6.72		
22.3	19.5	17.3	15.6	14.2	13.0	12.0	9.87	8.66	7.70			
22.9	20.1	17.8	16.1	14.6	13.4	12.4	10.2	8.92	7.93			
23.6	20.7	18.3	16.6	15.1	13.8	12.8	10.5	9.18	8.17			
24.3	21.3	18.9	17.1	15.5	14.2	13.1	10.8	9.44				
24.9	21.9	19.4	17.5	15.9	14.6	13.5	11.1	9.71				
25.6	22.4	19.9	18.0	16.4	15.0	13.8	11.4	9.97				
26.3	23.0	20.4	18.5	16.8	15.4	14.2	11.7	10.25				
27.0	23.6	21.0	19.0	17.2	15.8	14.6	12.0	10.50				
27.6	24.2	21.5	19.4	17.7	16.2	14.9	12.3					
28.3	24.8	22.0	19.9	18.1	16.6	15.3	12.6					
29.0	25.4	22.5	20.4	18.5	16.9	15.7	12.9					
29.6	26.0	23.0	20.8	18.9	17.3	16.0	13.2					
30.3	26.6	23.6	21.3	19.4	17.7	16.4	13.5					
31.0	27.2	24.1	21.8	19.8	18.1	16.8						
31.7	27.8	24.6	22.3	20.2	18.5	17.1						
32.4	28.3	25.1	22.7	20.7	18.9	17.5						

* The weights given include wire for regular loops only. Weight must be added for 1½ turns top and bottom equivalent to one-half the tabular weight for 2-in. pitch. Weight of spacers must also be added. A minimum section standard spacer is a 1″ x 1″ x ⅛″ angle weighing 0.80 lb per ft. Two spacers are required for spirals 20 in. or less in diameter, three for spirals 21 to 30 in., and four for spirals over 30 in. in diameter, or tor ½ in. or ⅜ in. rods.

SAFE LOAD TABLES

Footings, Pile Foundations

Section 12

FOUNDATIONS AND FOOTINGS

The function of a footing is to distribute the total down-load of a column, pier or wall (including the weight of the footing itself) over a sufficient area of soil to keep the bearing intensity within that allowable for the soil encountered (page 5-5). Also, the centroid of the down-load should coincide with that of the soil pressure prism to avoid eccentricities and overturning.

The first requirement is met by computing the total column load (with any live load reductions allowed, but including all walls, partitions, increased loads due to cantilevers, continuity, etc.), adding an allowance for the footing (still to be designed), and dividing by the allowable soil pressure.

A footing can usually be made square, centered on the column it carries, and of size such as those tabulated on pages 12-11 to 12-15. Rectangular footings can be substituted when space is restricted in one direction and not in the other. Round, octagonal and other shapes of bearing block can be used.

When the soil encountered is a soft stratum overlying a harder one some distance lower, end-bearing piles are often used to transfer the load through the soft to the harder bearing. Pile foundations are tabulated on pages 12-17 to 12-20. Another solution for going through a soft stratum to a harder layer is an open caisson, often circular, either large enough for a man to dig in, lined if necessary and belled out on the bottom to provide the bearing area required, or, with growing frequency, bored or drilled down to, and belled out in, a solid stratum with special boring rigs.

Some designers use pile foundations in a soft bearing stratum that is not underlain by a harder material, feeling that friction piles will transmit the load along their length and that their driving will consolidate the material into which they are driven. There is also a possibility of using a raft or mat foundation, spreading a solid slab of concrete over the whole area of the structure (and as far outside the actual building as loads require and property lines permit), designed along the lines of two-way flat slabs (Section 8), though, in these cases, the drop panels are most easily obtained by extra excavation so that they occur on the underside of the mat. Once again the two requirements govern that the total area of mat times the proposed bearing value should equal the total weight of structure and mat, and the centroid of the mat should coincide fairly well with that of the down-loads. Also, the mat should be structurally capable of transmitting the loads without excessive deflection or overstress.

Footings are further complicated (especially in congested districts) by property lines. Along street fronts, it is often possible to obtain permission for footings to project into the street and to use square footings as for interior columns. Along adjacent properties, this is practically never possible, and four common solutions of this problem are available:—(1) a mat foundation as just described; (2) setting the exterior columns back within the building lines and cantilevering the floors beyond them to the property lines, which is a simple and inexpensive solution when the columns can be concealed, as, for example, in the backgrounds of show windows; (3) using a "strap" or "cantilevered" footing, where the bearing block is made large enough to carry all of the fulcrum loads, and a strap or cantilevered beam is provided

For description of soil load test procedure, see page 12-16.

back to an opposite interior column to balance the exterior column load across the bearing block; * and (4) a combined footing where the bearing block is made large enough so that one or more exterior columns and one or more interior columns rest upon the same block, which then becomes a partial mat with the same requirements regarding capacity for down-loads, and coincidence of upward and down-loads.

Combined footings can differ so much in the ratio of loads on interior and exterior columns, the distance between column centers, and the like that it is practically impossible to tabulate a sufficient range of choices. Therefore, illustrative problems for both a strap footing and a combined one are presented.

A word of caution—no tables or methods of computation can replace judgment, especially in dealing with soil conditions, where a clay, for example, may look as hard and firm as could be desired during one season, and at another time may be very questionable as a foundation material.

1. DESIGN OF A STRAP FOOTING

Example—Given an exterior wall carrying 195 kips, whose exterior face is 20′-0″ from the center of an interior column, making the distance center to center 19′-6″. Using a soil pressure of not over 5000 psf, concrete strength of 3750 psi and steel at 24,000 psi, design a strap footing.

While some designers reduce the strength of concrete in footings, anticipating poor control, or placement directly against earth in neatly excavated pits, it seems better to use the quality of concrete contemplated throughout the structure and increase the outlines of the footing an inch or two all around for possible contamination.

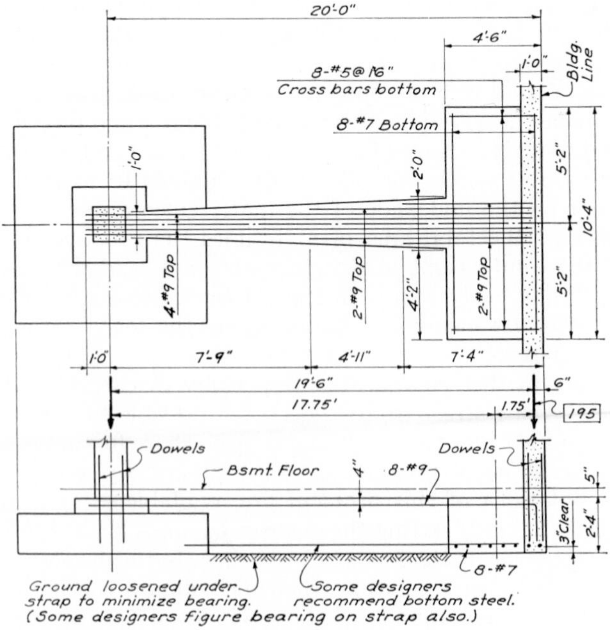

* A variation of this is to run a strap back into the building and, if there is no interior column readily available, provide sufficient dead weight of concrete to act as a balance for the eccentricity.

FOUNDATIONS AND FOOTINGS

Solution:—(See figure on page 12-4.)

Size of Bearing Block:— If the bearing block be assumed 4′-6″ wide, the distance from center of block to center of exterior column is 1.75 ft and to center of interior column is 17.75 ft, so, taking moments about the center of the bearing block, the uplift at the interior column (a downward load on the strap) is $\frac{1.75 \times 195{,}000}{17.75} = 19{,}200$ lb.

Column load	=	195,000 lb
Uplift reaction	=	19,200 lb
		214,200 lb
Weight of footing, assumed	=	18,000 lb
(Estimate as 8 to 9% of total load)		232,200 lb

Area required $= \frac{232{,}000}{5{,}000} = 46.4$ sf. Use 4′-6″ × 10′-4″ = 46.5 sf.

Net active bearing $= \frac{214{,}200}{4.5 \times 10.33} = 4610$ psf.

Assume projection beyond edge of strap as 4′-2″ and design as a cantilever, using a strip 1′-0″ wide:—

Shear at distance, d, from edge of strap (i.e. 4′-2″ − 2′-0″ = 2′-2″ from end of block) $= V = 4610 \times 2.17 = 9980$ lb

$$M = 4610 \times 4.17^2 \times \frac{12}{2} = 481{,}000 \text{ lb-in.}$$

Try 28 in. depth, $d = 24$ in.,

$$v = V/bd = \frac{9980}{12 \times 24} = 35 \text{ psi} < 67.4 \text{ psi}$$

Block might be sloped or stepped down towards outer end but may be more economical carried straight through.

$$R = M/bd^2 = \frac{481{,}000}{12 \times 24 \times 24} = 70 \text{ psi} < 271.$$

For bars in bearing block see page 12-6.

Size of Strap:—Neglecting weight of strap,

Zero shear (max. moment) is $\frac{195{,}000}{10.33 \times 4610} = 4.10$ ft. from bldg line.

$$M = 195{,}000 \left(\frac{4.10}{2} - 0.50\right) 12 = 3{,}625{,}000 \text{ lb-in.}$$

$V = 19{,}200$ lb

Try 28 in. depth, $d = 24$ in.,

$$b_m = M/Rd^2 = \frac{3{,}625{,}000}{271 \times 24 \times 24} = 23.2 \text{ in. at 4.10 ft from bldg line.}$$

$$b_v = V/vd = \frac{19{,}200}{67.4 \times 24} = 11.9 \text{ in. Use 12 in.}$$

Make strap 28 in. deep by 12 in. wide at cap of interior footing, and 24 in. wide at edge of exterior footing.

Steel in Strap:—$A_s = M/f_sjd = \frac{3{,}625{,}000}{24{,}000 \times 0.875 \times 24} = 7.2$ sq in.

8-#9 = 8.00 sq in.

Number of top bars left for bond at interior column:—

$$u = \frac{3.4\sqrt{3750}}{1.128} = 185 \text{ psi (page 3-13)}$$

$$N = \frac{V}{jdou} = \frac{19{,}200}{7/8 \times 24 \times 3.5 \times 185} = 1.4$$

(To keep bars at half stress ACI 918 (c)1, extend 4 bars and cut four short as below)

2—2/8 × 19.5 + 2′-0 = 6′-10″
2—4/8 × 19.5 + 2′-0 = 11′-9″
4—Full length

Steel in Bearing Block:—
$$A_s = \frac{M}{f_s jd} = \frac{481{,}000 \times 4.5}{21{,}000 \times 24} = 4.31 \text{ sq in.}$$

8-#7 = 4.80 sq in.

$$u = \frac{V}{\Sigma o jd} = \frac{4610 \times 4.17 \times 4.5}{21.99 \times 7/8 \times 24} = 188 < 336 \text{ psi}$$

At distance d, beyond face of strap (i.e., at 5′-2″ − 1′-0″ − 2′-0″ = 2′-2″ from end of bearing block):—

$$v_x = \frac{4610 \times 2.17}{12 \times 24} = 35 < 67.4 \text{ psi, so no stirrups are required.}$$

Cross bars are proportioned arbitrarily as 8-#5 @ 16 in.

Check Weight:—10.33 × 4.5 × 2.33 @ 150 = 16,300 lb (not including strap) < 18,000 lb, assumed.

2. DESIGN OF A COMBINED FOOTING

Example—Given an exterior wall carrying 195 kips as in the preceding problem, whose exterior face is 20′-0″ from the center of an interior column carrying 310 kips and 1.6 ft square, making the distance center to center 19′-6″. Using a soil pressure of not over 5000 psf, concrete strength of 3750 psi and steel at 24,000 psi, design a combined footing.

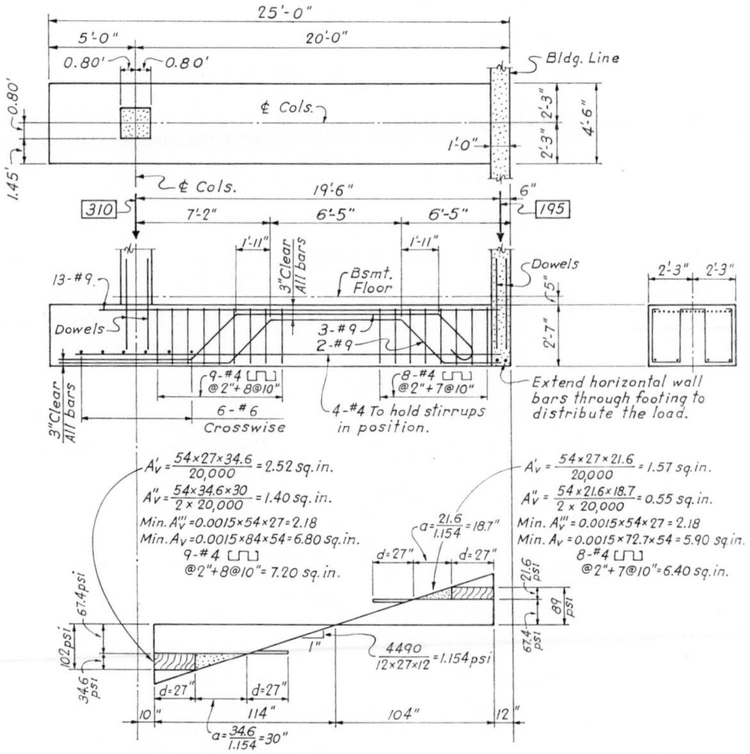

Solution—With columns 19.5 ft on centers and loads of 195 and 310 kips, the centroid of down-loads is $\left(0.5 + \frac{310}{505}\,19.5\right) = 12.47$ ft from the exterior face of the exterior column, so a rectangular footing must be 24.94 ft, say 25′-0″ long to center on the same line.

FOUNDATIONS AND FOOTINGS

The width is computed to furnish the required area:—

Load on exterior column	= 195,000 lb	505,000 lb
Load on interior column	= 310,000 lb	
Weight of footing, assumed (Estimate 9 to 10% of total load)	= 48,000 lb	
	553,000 lb	

$$b = \frac{553,000}{5000 \times 25.0} = 4.43 \text{ ft, say } 4'\text{-}6''.$$

$$\text{Net soil pressure} = \frac{505,000}{4.5 \times 25.0} = 4490 \text{ psf.}$$

From exterior face to zero shear is computed:— $x = \frac{195,000}{4.5 \times 4490} = 9.65$ ft (116 in.)

$$\text{Maximum bending moment, } M = 195,000 \times \left(\frac{9.65}{2} - 0.50\right) \times 12 = 10,120,000 \text{ lb-in.}$$

$$d = \sqrt{\frac{M}{Rb}} = \sqrt{\frac{10,120,000}{271 \times 54}} = 26.5, \text{ use 27 in.; } t = 2'\text{-}7''.$$

"Beam" shear is computed at distance d = 2.25 ft from the face of the interior column, (5.00 + 0.80 + 2.25 = 8.05 ft from inner end of footing):—
$V = 310,000 - 8.05 \times 4.5 \times 4490 = 148,000$ lb

$v = V/bd = \frac{148,000}{54 \times 27} = 102$ psi, so stirrups are required.

"Peripheral" shear around interior column:—$V = 310,000 - (1.60 + 2.25)^2\, 4490 =$ 243,500 lb. $v = \frac{V}{4(c+d)d} = \frac{243,500}{4(46.2)\,27} = 48.8 \text{ psi} < 2\sqrt{f'_c}$.

"Beam" shear at distance d from inside face of exterior wall $= 195,000 - 4.50 \times 3.25 \times 4490 = 129,500$ lb

$v = V/bd = \frac{129,500}{54 \times 27} = 89 > 67.4$ psi (stirrups)

"Peripheral" shear along exterior wall:—because of continuous wall, shear is more in the nature of "beam" shear.

Computation of stirrups is shown in the figure on page 12-6. (See also pages 4-23 ff.)

Top steel:—$A_s = M/f_sjd = \frac{10,120,000}{21,000 \times 27} = 17.8$ sq in.; 18-#9 = 18.0 sq in.

Number of straight top bars:—$N = \frac{V}{uojd} = \frac{310,000 - 5.80 \times 4.5 \times 4490}{185 \times 3.54 \times 7/8 \times 27} = 12.5$ straight.

Use 13 straight, bend 5.

Bottom bars in cantilever:—$M = \frac{4.50 \times 4490 \times 4.20^2 \times 12}{2} = 2,140,000$ lb-in.

$A_s = \frac{M}{f_sjd} = \frac{2,140,000}{21,000 \times 27} = 3.78$ sq in. 5-#9 = 5.00 sq in. (5 bent)

Since the point of inflection is only about 1.3 ft to the right of the interior column $(310 \times 1.3 = 403;\ 4.5 \times 4490 \times 6.3 \times 3.15 = 401)$, bottom bars in addition to truss bars and stirrup ties are not needed.

Bending bars:—(moment curve assumed parabolic and symmetrical about vertex at zero shear point)

Outside of zero shear:—

Bend 2 at $X_1 = 9.65\sqrt{2/18} = 3.20$ ft (6′-5″ from bldg line)

Bend 3 at $X_2 = 9.65\sqrt{5/18} = 5.10$ ft (1′-11″ outside of above)

Inside of zero shear:—

Bend 2 at $X_3 = 10.35 - 3.20 = 7.15$ ft (7′-2″ from ℄ col.)

Bend 3 at $X_4 = 10.35 - 5.10 = 5.25$ ft (1′-11″ outside of above)

Cross bending at interior column:—[design as a cantilever for $\frac{310,000}{2}$ lb with arm = (1′-1½″ − 5″) = 8½″; M = 1,320,000 lb-in.]

$A_s = \frac{M}{f_sjd} = \frac{1,320,000}{21,000 \times 27} = 2.33$ sq in. Use 6-#6 crosswise = 2.64 sq in.

Check assumed weight:—$4.50 \times 25.0 \times 2.58 \times 150 = 44,400$ lb

SAFE CARRYING CAPACITY OF SQUARE INDIVIDUAL COLUMN FOOTINGS

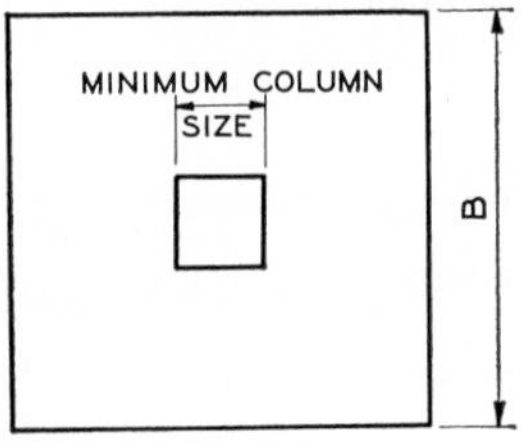

f_s = 24,000 psi*
f'_c = 3000 psi
f_c = 1350 psi
$v_c = 2\sqrt{f'_c} = 109.6$ psi
$u = \dfrac{4.8\sqrt{f'_c}}{D}$ psi (See page 3-13)

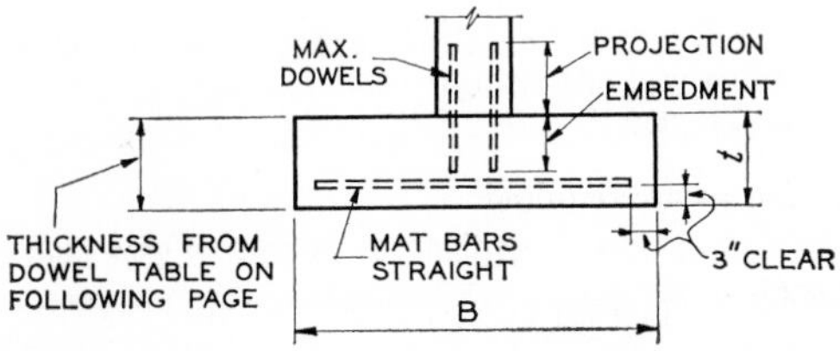

* Based only upon deformed bars grade (f_y = 60,000 psi)

These tables give the safe total superimposed load (with dead weight of the footing deducted) that can be carried by reinforced concrete square individual column footings for soil capacities of 1,000, 2,000, 3,000, 4,000, 5,000, 6,000, 8,000, 10,000, 12,000 and 14,000 psf. The 1963 ACI "Building Code Requirements for Reinforced Concrete" has been followed.

Shear and bond stresses are based upon reinforcing bars with deformations meeting the requirements of ASTM. With this type of bar, hooking of the mat reinforcement is unnecessary and straight bars are used. Plain round bars or bars with deformations not meeting ASTM Specifications cannot be used with these tables.

Designs are based upon a uniform depth, since the extra expense of sloped or stepped footings more than offsets the cost of added concrete to obtain the simple prism.

One grade of concrete is tabulated (f'_c= 3000 psi).

Development of Dowels in Footings

The following table gives the minimum depth of footing required to develop a deformed dowel by bond [ACI 2306(d)] for two cases:—

Case I Grade 60 (f_y = 60,000 psi)
Case II Grade 75 (f_y = 75,000 psi)

SAFE CARRYING CAPACITY OF SQUARE INDIVIDUAL COLUMN FOOTINGS

$$\text{Thickness of footing} = l + 3''; \; l = \frac{f_s D}{4u};$$

$$u = 6.5\sqrt{3000} = 356 \text{ psi.}$$

Case I: $t = 3 + 16.85D$ Case II: $t = 3 + 21.1D$

Minimum Footing Depth, t, required to develop Dowels. $f'_c = 3000$ psi									
Cases	Bar Sizes								
	#5	#6	#7	#8	#9	#10	#11	#14	#18
I	14	16	18	20	22	24	27	32	41
II	16	19	21	24	27	30	33	39	51

When dowel size exceeds the maximum tabulated for a given footing thickness:
Use a greater number of smaller diameter dowels to provide required steel area and development length within the thickness selected.

Not all possible designs are presented here. For those who wish to design beyond the scope of these tables, or merely see how they were prepared, the following example is presented:—

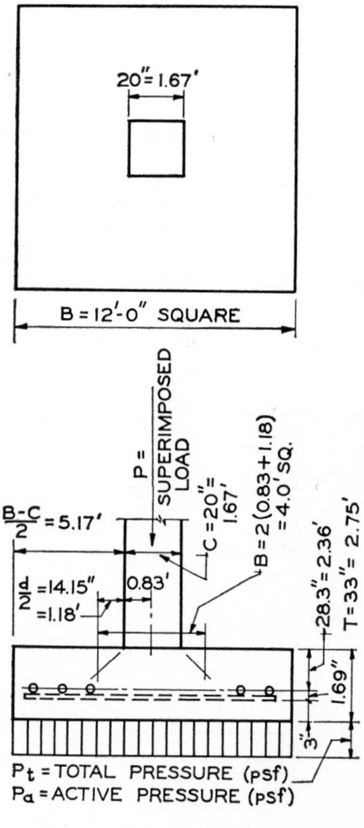

Example:—For the table on page 12-13 check the capacity of a 12 ft square footing on 5000 psf soil, $f'_c = 3000$ psi, $f_s = 24{,}000$ psi, $n = 9$.

Tables are worked in reverse of an actual design; i.e., by determining the net capacity of a selected footing.

Solution— $P = 660.6$ kips (from table on page 12-13)

$$\textit{Footing Wt} = \frac{12 \times 12 \times 2.75 \ @ \ 145}{1000} = \frac{57.4 \text{ kips}}{720.0 \text{ kips}} = 0.09\,P \text{ (for estimating weight)}$$

SAFE CARRYING CAPACITY OF SQUARE INDIVIDUAL COLUMN FOOTINGS

$$\text{Total Soil Pressure, } p_t = \frac{720.0 \times 1000}{12 \times 12} = 5{,}000 \text{ psf}$$

$$\text{Net Soil Pressure, } p_a = \frac{660.6 \times 1000}{12 \times 12} = 4575 \text{ psf}$$

Minimum column size:—Since bending moment is computed at the face of the column and increases as the column size decreases, an approximate minimum column size must be established.

$$P = 0.85A_g(0.25f'_c + f_s p_g) = 0.85A_g(750 + 0.05 \times 24{,}000) = 1657A_g$$

$$C = \sqrt{\frac{660.6}{1.657}} = 20 \text{ in.}$$

Shear on a Section 4.0 ft Square: *—

$$v = \frac{V}{bd} = \frac{(12 \times 12 - 4.0 \times 4.0)4575}{4 \times 48.3 \times 28.3} = 107 \text{ psi vs } 109 \text{ psi allowed}$$

Check beam shear at distance, d, from face of support:—

$L_{cantilever} = 2.81$ ft.

$V = 12 \times 2.81 \times 4575 = 154{,}200$ lb

$$v_c = \frac{V}{bd} = \frac{154{,}200}{144 \times 28.3} = 38 \text{ psi}$$

Moment on a Section at the Face of the Column:—

$$M = 4.575 \times 12 \times 5.17 \times \frac{5.17}{2} = 734 \ k\text{-ft.}$$

$$R = \frac{M}{bd^2} = \frac{734 \times 12 \times 1000}{144 \times 28.3 \times 28.3} = 77 < 204 \text{ so } \begin{cases} f_c < 1{,}350 \text{ psi (table on p. 3-12)} \\ j = 0.88 \end{cases}$$

$$A_s = \frac{M}{f_s jd} = \frac{734 \times 12}{24{,}000 \times 0.88 \times 28.3} = 14.73 \text{ sq in.}$$

15-#9 Bars = 15.00 sq in.

Bond on Bars at the Face of the Column:—

$$u = \frac{4.8\sqrt{f'_c}}{D} = \frac{4.8\sqrt{3000}}{1.128} = 234 \text{ psi}$$

Anchorage length at 0.8u

$$\text{Req'd } L = \frac{24{,}000 \times 1.128}{4 \times 0.8 \times 234} = 36 \text{ in.}$$

Furnished: 61 in.

Anchorage bond is less than $0.8u$ so that flexural bond need not be investigated.

Dowel anchorage:—Available embedment = 30″ in footing depth of 33″. Table on page 12-9 indicates that the maximum size for dowels is #11.

---

* It is possible to determine the depth required for shear in a fairly simple manner.

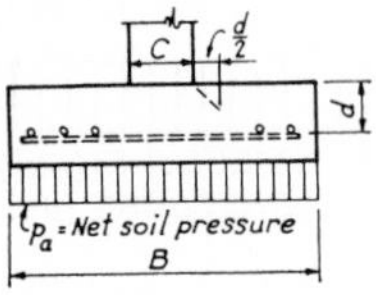

$$d = \frac{[B^2 - (C + d)^2]p_a}{4 \times 144v_c(C + d)}$$

$$\text{Let } A = \frac{p_a}{4 \times 144v_c} \text{ and } k = \frac{C}{B}, \text{ then:}$$

$$\frac{d}{B} = \frac{\sqrt{4A^2 + 4A + k^2} - k(1 + 2A)}{2(1 + A)}$$

For description of soil load test procedure, see page 12-16.

SAFE CARRYING CAPACITY
SQUARE INDIVIDUAL COLUMN FOOTINGS

f'_c = 3,000 psi
f_s = 24,000 psi

For explanation of these tables, see page 12-8

SOIL PRESSURE—1000 psf

Size B	Thick-ness t (in.)	Min. Col. Size (in.)	Mat Bars Each Way: Quant. of Bars	Mat Bars Each Way: Bar Size	Mat Bars Each Way: Spacing c/c (in.)	Weight of Bars per Footing (lb)	Volume of Concrete (cu yd)	Capacity (kips)
3′-0″	10	10	4	4	10	13.3	0.3	**7.9**
3′-6″	10	10	4	4	12	16.0	0.4	**10.7**
4′-0″	10	10	5	4	10½	23.3	0.5	**14.0**
4′-6″	10	10	5	4	12	26.7	0.6	**17.8**
5′-0″	10	10	6	4	10½	36.0	0.8	**21.9**
5′-6″	10	10	6	4	12	40.0	0.9	**26.5**
6′-0″	10	10	7	5	11	80.3	1.1	**31.6**
6′-6″	10	10	7	5	12	87.6	1.3	**37.1**
7′-0″	10	11	8	6	11	156.2	1.5	**43.0**
7′-6″	11	10	10	5	9	146.0	1.9	**48.7**
8′-0″	12	10	9	6	11	202.7	2.4	**54.7**
8′-6″	12	10	9	6	12	216.2	2.7	**61.7**
9′-0″	13	10	10	6	11	255.3	3.3	**68.2**
9′-6″	13	11	11	6	10½	297.3	3.6	**76.0**
10′-0″	14	10	12	6	10	342.4	4.3	**83.0**
10′-6″	15	10	12	6	10½	360.4	5.1	**90.2**
11′-0″	15	10	12	7	11	515.0	5.6	**99.0**
11′-6″	16	10	20	5	6½	458.9	6.5	**106.6**
12′-0″	17	10	13	7	11½	611.1	7.6	**114.4**
12′-6″	17	10	13	7	12	637.7	8.2	**124.1**
13′-0″	18	10	14	7	11½	715.3	9.4	**132.2**
13′-6″	18	10	15	7	11	797.1	10.1	**142.6**
14′-0″	19	10	15	7	11½	827.8	11.5	**151.0**
14′-6″	19	10	17	7	10½	972.9	12.3	**161.9**
15′-0″	20	10	17	7	10½	1007.6	13.9	**170.6**
15′-6″	20	11	19	7	10	1165.0	14.8	**182.1**
16′-0″	21	10	20	7	9½	1267.2	16.6	**191.0**

SOIL PRESSURE—2000 psf

Size B	Thick-ness t (in.)	Min. Col. Size (in.)	Mat Bars Each Way: Quant. of Bars	Mat Bars Each Way: Bar Size	Mat Bars Each Way: Spacing c/c (in.)	Weight of Bars per Footing (lb)	Volume of Concrete (cu yd)	Capacity (kips)
3′-0″	10	10	4	4	10	13.3	0.3	**16.9**
3′-6″	10	10	4	4	12	16.0	0.4	**23.0**
4′-0″	10	10	5	4	10½	23.3	0.5	**30.0**
4′-6″	10	10	7	4	8	37.4	0.6	**38.0**
5′-0″	10	11	6	6	10½	81.1	0.8	**46.9**
5′-6″	11	10	8	5	8½	83.4	1.0	**56.4**
6′-0″	12	11	7	6	11	115.6	1.3	**66.7**
6′-6″	13	10	7	6	12	126.1	1.7	**77.8**
7′-0″	14	10	8	6	11	156.2	2.1	**89.7**
7′-6″	15	10	9	6	10½	189.2	2.6	**102.3**
8′-0″	16	10	9	7	11	275.9	3.2	**115.6**
8′-6″	17	10	9	7	12	294.3	3.8	**129.6**
9′-0″	18	10	10	7	11	347.4	4.5	**144.3**
9′-6″	19	10	11	7	10½	404.7	5.3	**159.7**
10′-0″	20	10	11	7	11	427.1	6.2	**175.8**
10′-6″	20	12	13	7	10	531.4	6.8	**193.8**
11′-0″	22	10	13	7	10½	553.0	8.2	**209.8**
11′-6″	22	11	12	8	12	704.8	9.0	**229.3**
12′-0″	23	11	13	8	11½	798.3	10.2	**247.9**
12′-6″	24	11	14	8	11	897.1	11.6	**267.1**
13′-0″	25	11	14	8	11½	934.4	13.0	**286.9**
13′-6″	26	10	16	8	10	1110.7	14.6	**307.2**
14′-0″	26	12	17	8	10	1225.5	15.7	**330.4**
14′-6″	27	12	18	8	9½	1345.6	17.5	**351.9**
15′-0″	27	15	15	9	12	1479.0	18.8	**376.5**
15′-6″	28	14	16	9	12	1632.0	20.8	**399.2**
16′-0″	28	17	17	9	11½	1791.7	22.1	**425.3**

SAFE CARRYING CAPACITY
SQUARE INDIVIDUAL COLUMN FOOTINGS

For explanation of these tables, see page 12-8

$f'_c = 3{,}000$ psi
$f_s = 24{,}000$ psi

SOIL PRESSURE—3000 psf

Size B	Thick-ness t (in.)	Min. Col. Size (in.)	Mat Bars Each Way			Weight of Bars per Footing (lb)	Volume of Concrete (cu yd)	Capacity (kips)
			Quant. of Bars	Bar Size	Spacing c/c (in.)			
3′-0″	10	10	4	4	10	13.3	0.3	**25.9**
3′-6″	10	10	5	4	9	20.0	0.4	**35.2**
4′-0″	10	10	7	4	7	32.7	0.5	**46.0**
4′-6″	11	10	6	5	9½	50.0	0.7	**58.0**
5′-0″	12	11	6	6	10½	81.1	0.9	**71.3**
5′-6″	13	12	6	6	12	90.1	1.2	**85.9**
6′-0″	14	13	7	7	11	157.3	1.6	**101.9**
6′-6″	15	13	7	7	12	171.6	2.0	**119.0**
7′-0″	17	11	8	7	11	212.5	2.6	**136.9**
7′-6″	18	11	8	7	12	228.9	3.1	**156.5**
8′-0″	19	11	9	7	11	275.9	3.8	**177.3**
8′-6″	20	12	10	7	10½	327.0	4.5	**199.2**
9′-0″	21	13	10	8	11	453.8	5.3	**222.4**
9′-6″	22	13	10	8	12	480.5	6.1	**246.7**
10′-0″	24	11	11	8	11	558.0	7.4	**271.0**
10′-6″	25	11	12	8	10½	640.7	8.5	**297.4**
11′-0″	26	11	13	8	10½	728.9	9.7	**324.9**
11′-6″	26	14	14	8	10	822.3	10.6	**355.2**
12′-0″	27	15	13	9	11½	1016.5	12.0	**385.0**
12′-6″	29	13	13	9	12	1060.8	14.0	**413.9**
13′-0″	30	13	14	9	11½	1190.0	15.6	**445.7**
13′-6″	30	16	15	9	11	1326.0	16.9	**480.6**
14′-0″	31	16	16	9	10½	1468.8	18.8	**514.5**
14′-6″	32	16	17	9	10½	1618.3	20.8	**549.4**
15′-0″	33	17	15	10	12	1871.8	22.9	**585.2**
15′-6″	33	20	16	10	12	2065.4	24.5	**624.9**
16′-0″	34	20	17	10	11½	2267.6	26.9	**662.8**

SOIL PRESSURE—4000 psf

Size B	Thick-ness t (in.)	Min. Col. Size (in.)	Quant. of Bars	Bar Size	Spacing c/c (in.)	Weight of Bars per Footing (lb)	Volume of Concrete (cu yd)	Capacity (kips)
3′-0″	10	10	4	4	10	13.3	0.3	**34.9**
3′-6″	10	10	4	5	12	25.0	0.4	**47.5**
4′-0″	11	10	8	4	6	37.4	0.5	**61.8**
4′-6″	12	12	5	6	12	60.0	0.8	**78.0**
5′-0″	14	10	6	6	10½	81.1	1.1	**95.7**
5′-6″	15	11	7	6	10	105.1	1.4	**115.5**
6′-0″	16	13	7	7	11	157.3	1.8	**137.0**
6′-6″	18	11	7	7	12	171.6	2.3	**159.8**
7′-0″	19	12	8	7	11	212.5	2.9	**184.7**
7′-6″	20	13	9	7	10½	257.5	3.5	**211.4**
8′-0″	22	11	9	8	11	360.4	4.3	**238.9**
8′-6″	23	12	9	8	12	384.4	5.1	**268.9**
9′-0″	24	13	10	8	11	453.8	6.0	**300.5**
9′-6″	26	11	11	8	10½	528.6	7.2	**332.6**
10′-0″	26	15	11	9	11	710.5	8.0	**368.5**
10′-6″	28	13	11	9	12	748.0	9.5	**403.6**
11′-0″	29	14	12	9	11	856.7	10.8	**441.5**
11′-6″	30	15	13	9	11	972.3	12.2	**481.0**
12′-0″	31	16	14	9	10½	1094.8	13.8	**522.0**
12′-6″	32	16	15	9	10	1224.0	15.4	**564.5**
13′-0″	33	18	14	10	11½	1506.0	17.2	**608.6**
13′-6″	34	18	14	10	12	1566.2	19.1	**654.1**
14′-0″	35	19	15	10	11½	1742.7	21.2	**701.1**
14′-6″	36	20	16	10	11	1927.7	23.4	**749.5**
15′-0″	36	23	17	10	10½	2121.3	25.0	**802.1**
15′-6″	38	21	18	10	10½	2323.6	28.2	**850.6**
16′-0″	39	22	16	11	12	2635.2	30.8	**903.3**

SAFE CARRYING CAPACITY
SQUARE INDIVIDUAL COLUMN FOOTINGS

For explanation of these tables, see page 12-8

f'_c = 3,000 psi
f_s = 24,000 psi

SOIL PRESSURE—12,000 psf

Size B	Thickness t (in.)	Min. Col. Size (in.)	Mat Bars Each Way: Quant. of Bars	Mat Bars Each Way: Bar Size	Mat Bars Each Way: Spacing c/c (in.)	Weight of Bars per Footing (lb)	Volume of Concrete (cu yd)	Capacity (kips)
3′-0″	13	10	7	4	5	23.3	0.4	**106.5**
3′-6″	15	11	6	5	7	37.5	0.6	**144.7**
4′-0″	17	12	8	5	6	58.4	0.8	**188.7**
4′-6″	19	13	7	6	8	84.1	1.2	**238.3**
5′-0″	22	11	9	6	6½	121.6	1.7	**293.3**
5′-6″	24	12	11	6	6	165.2	2.2	**354.2**
6′-0″	25	15	9	7	8	202.3	2.8	**421.1**
6′-6″	28	14	11	7	7	269.8	3.7	**492.7**
7′-0″	29	16	13	7	6½	345.4	4.4	**570.8**
7′-6″	31	17	15	7	6	429.2	5.4	**653.9**
8′-0″	33	18	13	8	7½	520.6	6.5	**742.4**
8′-6″	35	18	15	8	6½	640.7	7.8	**836.4**
9′-0″	36	21	16	8	6½	726.2	9.0	**936.7**
9′-6″	38	22	18	8	6	865.0	10.6	**1041.5**
10′-0″	40	23	15	9	8	969.0	12.3	**1151.6**
10′-6″	42	23	17	9	7½	1156.0	14.3	**1267.0**
11′-0″	43	26	19	9	7	1356.5	16.1	**1389.1**
11′-6″	45	26	20	9	6½	1496.0	18.4	**1515.0**
12′-0″	47	27	22	9	6½	1720.3	20.9	**1646.2**
12′-6″	49	27	24	9	6	1958.3	23.6	**1782.4**
13′-0″	50	30	21	10	7½	2259.0	26.1	**1925.8**
13′-6″	52	31	22	10	7	2461.3	29.3	**2072.4**
14′-0″	53	33	24	10	7	2788.3	32.1	**2226.4**
14′-6″	55	34	25	10	7	3012.1	35.7	**2383.2**
15′-0″	57	34	27	10	6½	3369.2	39.6	**2545.0**
15′-6″	59	35	29	10	6	3743.6	43.7	**2711.7**
16′-0″	60	38	25	11	7½	4117.5	47.4	**2886.4**

SOIL PRESSURE—14,000 psf

Size B	Thickness t (in.)	Min. Col. Size (in.)	Mat Bars Each Way: Quant. of Bars	Mat Bars Each Way: Bar Size	Mat Bars Each Way: Spacing c/c (in.)	Weight of Bars per Footing (lb)	Volume of Concrete (cu yd)	Capacity (kips)
3′-0″	13	12	7	4	5	23.3	0.4	**124.5**
3′-6″	16	11	10	4	4	40.0	0.6	**169.1**
4′-0″	18	12	8	5	6	58.4	0.9	**220.5**
4′-6″	21	11	8	6	6½	96.1	1.3	**278.3**
5′-0″	23	12	10	6	6	135.1	1.8	**343.0**
5′-6″	25	13	12	6	5	180.2	2.3	**414.3**
6′-0″	27	14	10	7	7	224.8	3.0	**492.2**
6′-6″	28	17	12	7	6½	294.3	3.7	**577.2**
7′-0″	30	18	14	7	6	372.0	4.5	**668.2**
7′-6″	32	19	16	7	5½	457.8	5.6	**765.7**
8′-0″	34	20	14	8	6½	560.6	6.7	**869.7**
8′-6″	36	21	15	8	6½	640.7	8.0	**980.0**
9′-0″	38	22	17	8	6	771.6	9.5	**1096.8**
9′-6″	40	23	19	8	6	913.1	11.1	**1219.8**
10′-0″	42	24	21	8	5½	1065.3	13.0	**1349.2**
10′-6″	44	25	18	9	7	1224.0	15.0	**1484.8**
11′-0″	45	28	20	9	6½	1428.0	16.8	**1628.2**
11′-6″	48	27	22	9	6	1645.5	19.6	**1774.7**
12′-0″	49	30	24	9	6	1876.7	21.8	**1930.7**
12′-6″	51	30	26	9	5½	2121.6	24.6	**2091.2**
13′-0″	53	31	28	9	5½	2380.0	27.6	**2257.7**
13′-6″	54	35	23	10	7	2573.1	30.4	**2432.5**
14′-0″	56	35	25	10	6½	2904.5	33.9	**2611.3**
14′-6″	58	36	27	10	6	3253.0	37.6	**2796.1**
15′-0″	60	37	29	10	6	3618.8	41.7	**2986.8**
15′-6″	61	40	30	10	6	3872.6	45.2	**3186.4**
16′-0″	64	39	33	10	5½	4401.9	50.6	**3386.0**

SOIL LOAD TEST

Information on subsoil conditions is best obtained by:—

(1) Observation of nearby structures, and a determination of their bearing intensity and amount of settlement.

(2) Digging an open pit to a depth below the desired bearing level and judging the soil strata on the basis of familiarity with local soils.

(3) Exploratory borings, driving a casing by means of a drop weight (frequently 140 pounds dropping 30 in.), recording the number of blows to drive the casing a known distance, and comparing with data from other borings, to approximate the safe bearing capacity; also the obtaining of undisturbed samples from within the casing and, for clay, testing triaxial shear and free column compression as an added method of estimating safe bearing value.

(4) Applying physical load test to a square (sometimes circular) bearing block directly on the stratum where footings will rest, applied in the following manner:-

Method A (proving soil capacity):—

Assume a design load.
Build platform like sketch.
Load platform with assumed design load.
Leave until periodic measurements show no further settlement for a period of 24 hours.
Add four increments (each equal to 25 per cent of the design load) at 4-hour intervals.

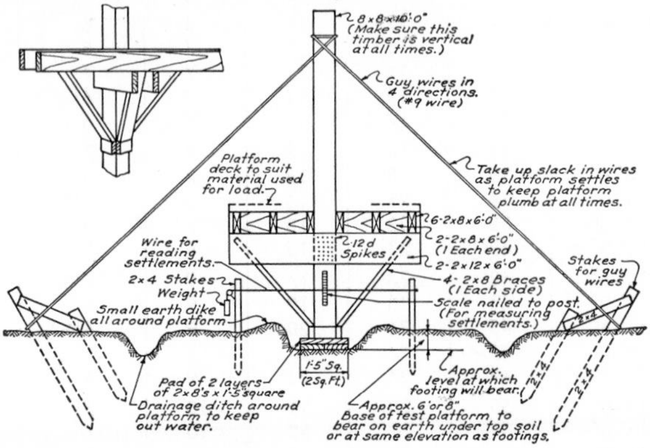

Leave total (double design) load until no measurable settlement occurs during a period of 24 hours.
Readings are to be taken to 1/32 in. every hour for the first 6 hours and every 12 hours thereafter.
When design load causes settlement of less than 3/8 in. and twice the design load of less than 1 in., the design load shall be allowed (but medium clay shall not exceed 4 tons psf, or soft clay 1 ton psf).

Method B (investigating soil capacity):—

When design load is not assumed in advance, place load in increments of, say, 2000 pounds or appropriate to the total load.
Add no further increment until readings at half-hour intervals show no further settlement at end of one hour.
Add second increment and check every half hour until there is no further settlement for a period of one hour.
Continue increments and measurements until total applied load is at least double the desired design load or until excessive settlement begins to occur.
If possible, leave load 48 hours, taking readings every 8 hours.
Remove the load, measure the recovery, plot a load-time-settlement curve to determine safe bearing value.

The accompanying graph shows such a curve, with slight time settlements at loads above 7000 psf, and a decided time settlement at 12,000 psf, and only a moderate recovery. In this case, 7000 psf was selected as a fairly high safe bearing value from such a curve.

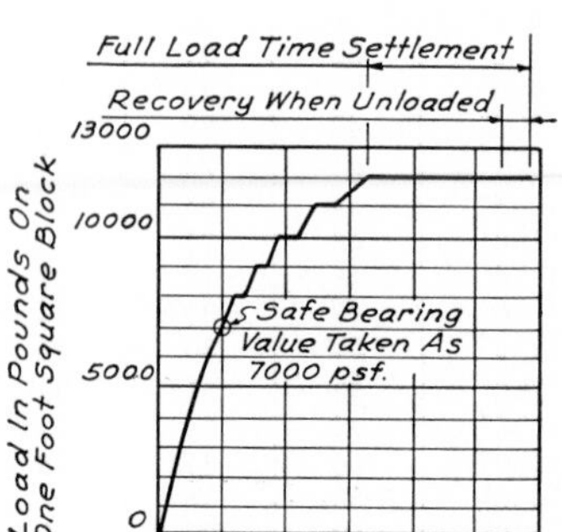

CONCRETE PILE FOOTINGS

30-Ton Piles 3′-0″ c. to c.*

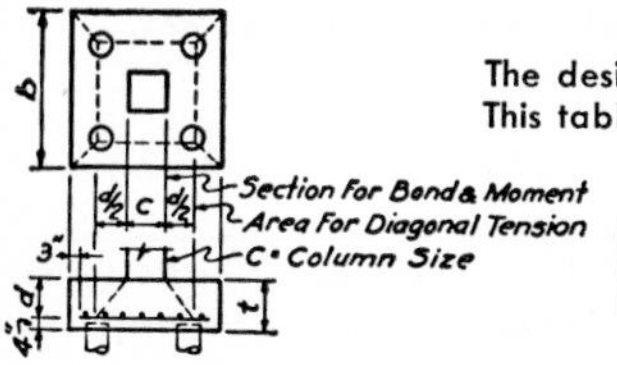

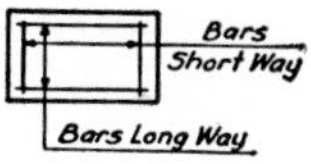

The design of pile caps involves many factors and is far from standardized. This table reproduced from Volume 1 is representative and has worked well.

No. Piles	PLAN	Column Load (kips)	d and t (in.)	Reinforcement Short way	Reinforcement Long way
2	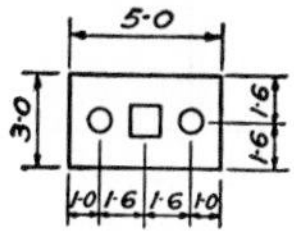 Min. column 12x12	115	18/22	4-#5	8-#5
			22/26	4-#5	7-#5
			24/28	3-#5	6-#5
3	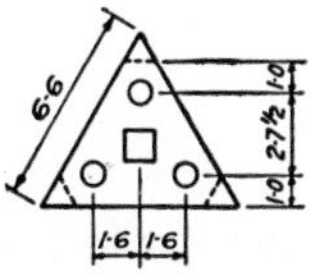 Min. column 12x12	174	18/22	3 ways ea. of: 10-#5	
			21/25	8-#5	
			24/28	7-#5	
4	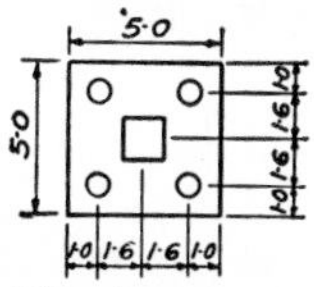 Min. column 16x16	231	17/21	17-#5	17-#5
			20/24	15-#5	15-#5
			24/28	12-#5	12-#5
5	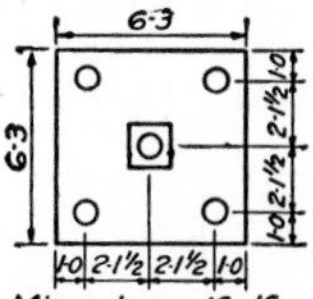 Min. column 16x16	286	23/27	17-#5	17-#5
			26/30	15-#5	15-#5
			30/34	13-#5	13-#5
6	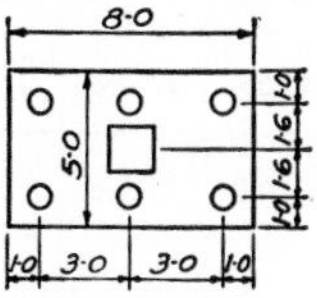 Min. column 18x18	343	26/30	17-#5	16-#6
			30/34	15-#5	14-#6
			34/38	13-#5	13-#6

No. Piles	PLAN	Column Load (kips)	d and t (in.)	Reinforcement Short way	Reinforcement Long way
7	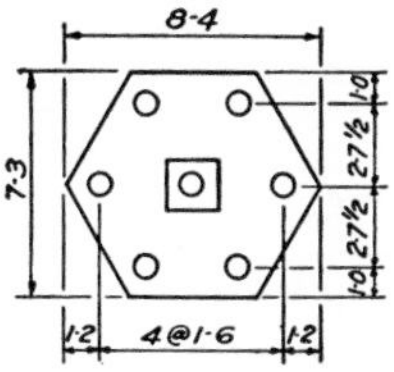 Min. column 20x20	396	28/32	12-#6	13-#6
			32/36	11-#6	11-#6
			34/38	10-#6	10-#6
8	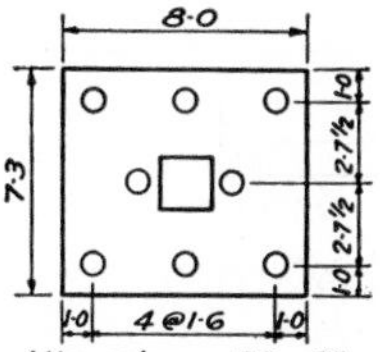 Min. column 20 x 20	452	30/34	17-#6	16-#6
			34/38	15-#6	14-#6
			36/40	14-#6	13-#6
9	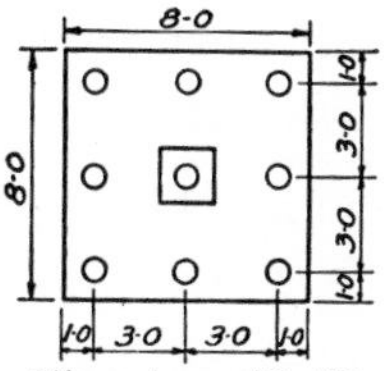 Min. column 22 x 22	506	34/38	17-#6	17-#6
			38/42	16-#6	16-#6
			42/46	14-#6	14-#6
10	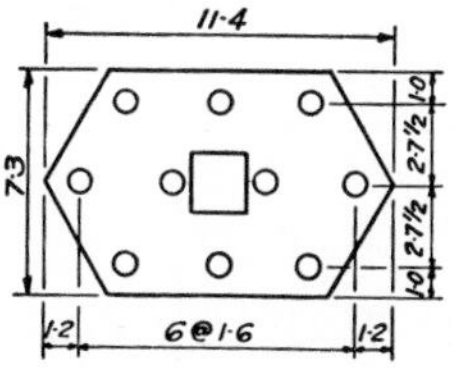 Min. column 24x24	562	37/41	18-#5	15-#7
			40/44	16-#5	14-#7
			44/48	15-#5	13-#7

* Piles are here assumed as carrying 30 tons each, with no reduction for the effect of neighboring piles in the cluster.

CONCRETE PILE FOOTINGS
30-Ton Piles 3′-0″ c. to c.*

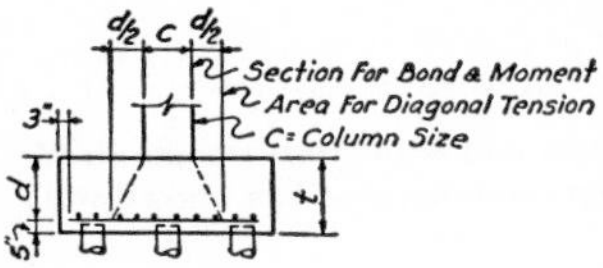

The design of pile caps involves many factors and is far from standardized. This table reproduced from Volume 1 is representative and has worked well.

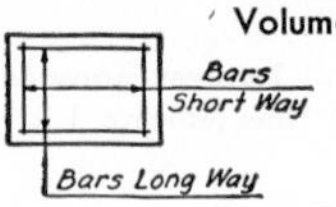

No. Piles	PLAN	Column Load (Kips)	d and t (in.)	Reinforcement Short way	Reinforcement Long way
12	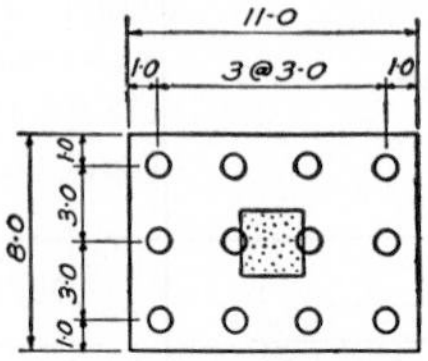 Min. Column 27 x 27	676	35/40	10-#8	19-#7
		668	42/47	8-#8	16-#7
		662	48/53	10-#7	14-#7
14	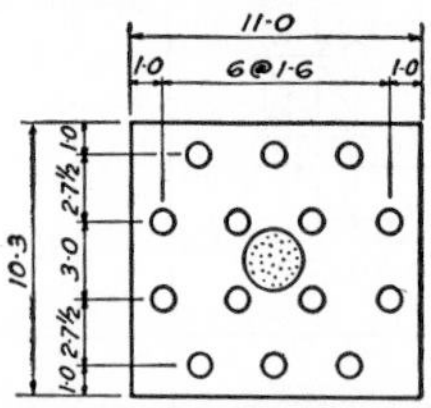 Min. Column 24″ φ	781	37/42	20-#7	20-#7
		772	43/48	17-#7	18-#7
		765	48/53	10-#9	16-#7
16	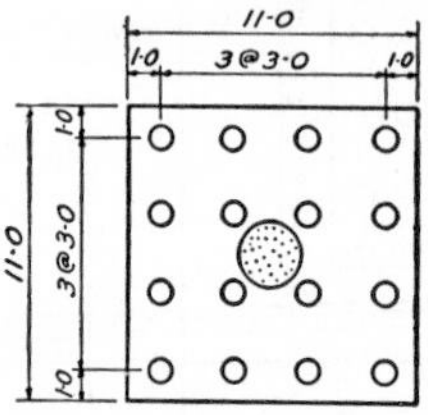 Min. Column 26″ φ	890	41/46	18-#8	18-#8
		883	46/51	21-#7	21-#7
		874	52/57	11-#9	11-#9
18	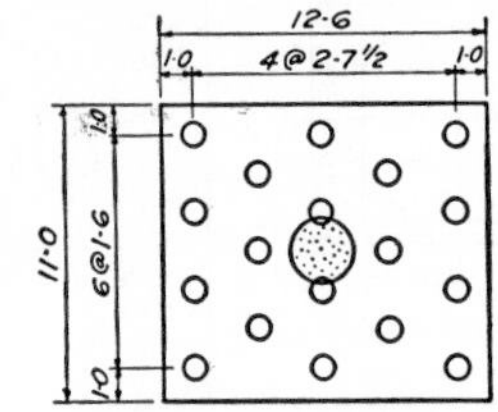 Min. Column 26″ φ	992	46/51	16-#8	22-#8
		982	52/57	14-#8	15-#9
		972	58/63	17-#7	17-#8
20	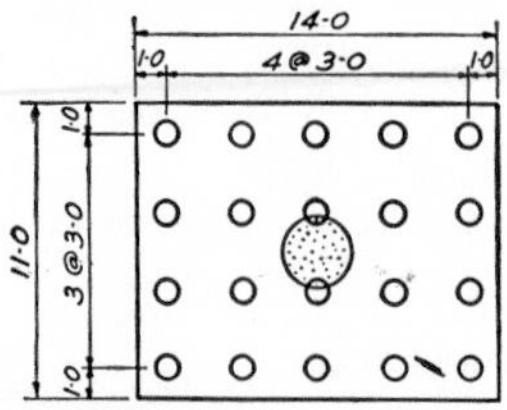 Min. Column 28″ φ	1100	47/52	19-#8	27-#8
		1086	54/59	17-#8	23-#8
		1075	60/65	15-#8	17-#9

* Piles are here assumed as carrying 30 tons each, with no reduction for the effect of neighboring piles in the cluster.

WOOD PILE FOOTINGS

15-Ton Piles 2′-6″ c. to c.*

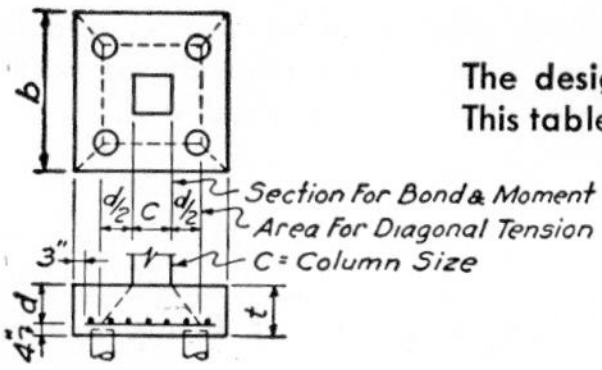

The design of pile caps involves many factors and is far from standardized. This table reproduced from Volume 1 is representative and has worked well.

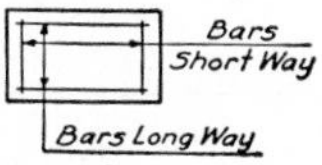

No. Piles	PLAN	Column Load (kips)	d and t (in.)	Reinforcement Short way	Reinforcement Long way
2	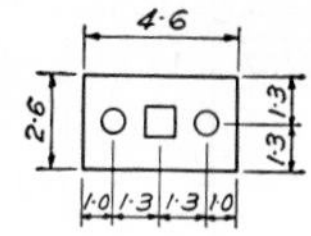 Min. column 12x12	58	9/13	4-#5	8-#5
			12/16	3-#5	6-#5
			15/19	3-#5	5-#5
3	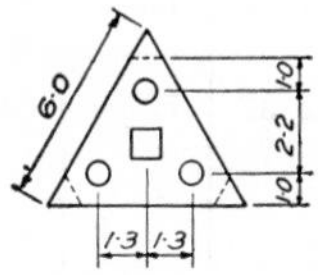 Min. column 12x12		12/16	3 ways ea. of: 7-#5	
		86	15/19	6-#5	
			18/22	5-#5	
4	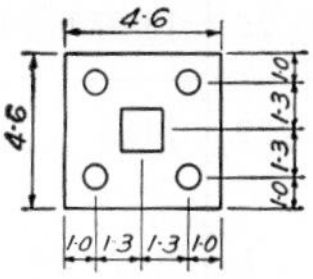 Min. column 12x12	115	13/17	12-#5	12-#5
			15/19	10-#5	10-#5
			18/22	8-#5	8-#5
5	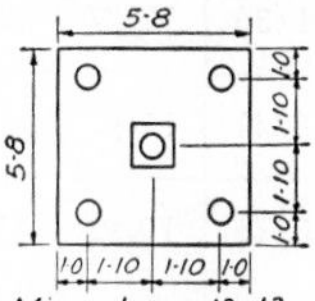 Min. column 13x13	141	15/19	12-#5	12-#5
			18/22	10-#5	10-#5
			20/24	9-#5	9-#5
6	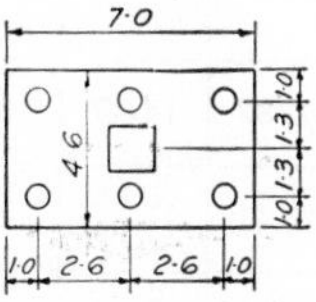 Min. column 14x14	171	18/22	12-#5	10-#6
			20/24	11-#5	9-#6
			23/27	10-#5	8-#6
7	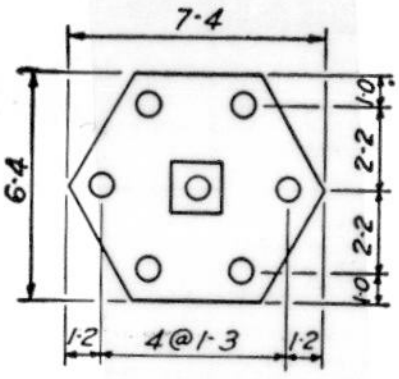 Min. column 15 x 15	199	19/23	11-#5	12-#5
			21/25	10-#5	11-#5
			24/28	9-#5	9-#5
8	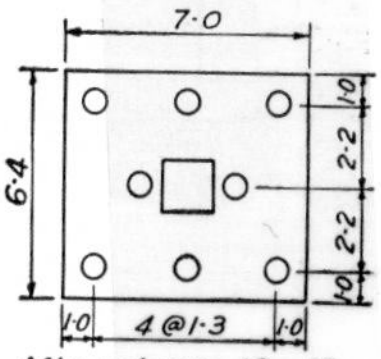 Min. column 16 x 16	226	18/22	12-#6	12-#6
			21/25	10-#6	10-#6
			24/28	9-#6	9-#6
9	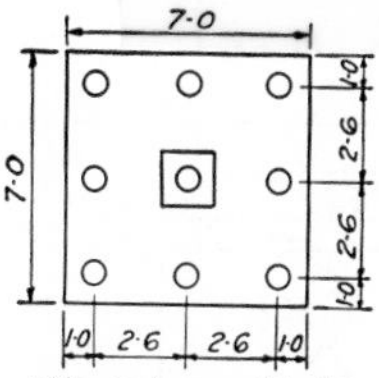 Min. column 17 x 17	253	21/25	14-#6	14-#6
			23/27	13-#6	13-#6
			26/30	10-#6	10-#6
10	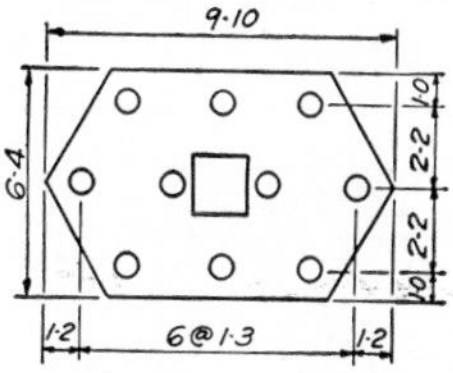 Min. column 18 x 18	281	23/27	14-#5	12-#7
			26/30	12-#5	11-#7
			30/34	11-#5	9-#7

* Piles are here assumed as carrying 15 tons each, with no reduction for the effect of neighboring piles in the cluster.

WOOD PILE FOOTINGS
15-Ton Piles 2′-6″ c. to c.*

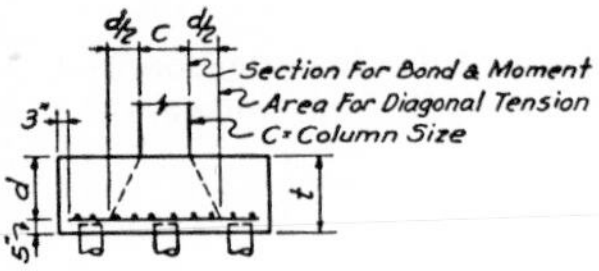

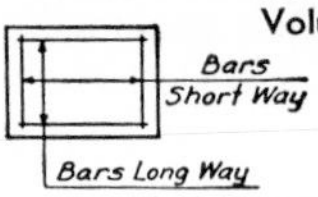

The design of pile caps involves many factors and is far from standardized. This table reproduced from Volume 1 is representative and has worked well.

No. Piles	PLAN		Column Load (Kips)	d and t (in.)	Reinforcement Short way	Reinforcement Long way
12	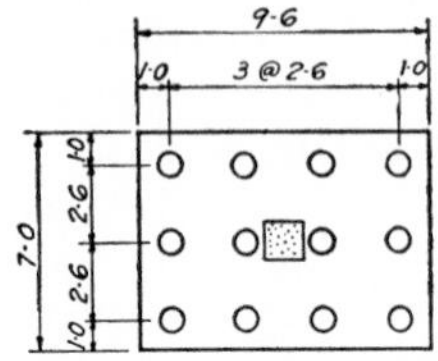	Min. Column 19 x 19	332	25/30	11-#6	12-#7
				28/33	10-#6	11-#7
				32/37	12-#5	13-#6
14	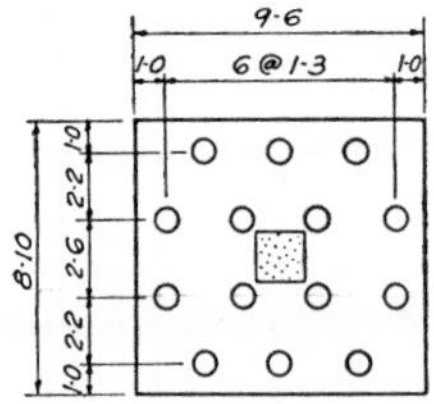	Min. Column 20 x 20	385	25/30	13-#7	12-#7
				28/33	11-#7	11-#7
				32/37	12-#6	13-#6
16	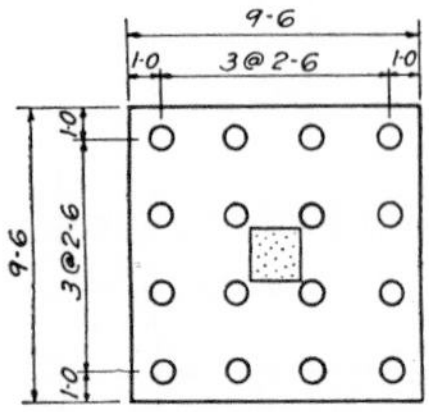	Min. Column 22 x 22	440	27/32	14-#7	14-#7
				30/35	13-#7	13-#7
				34/39	11-#7	11-#7
18	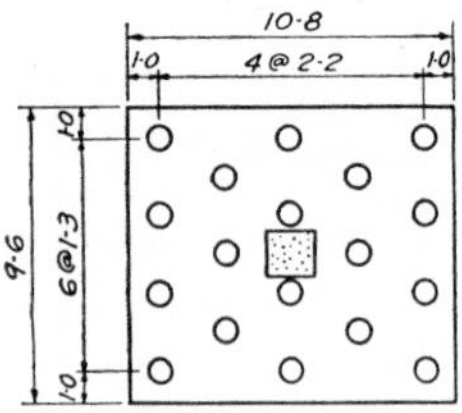	Min. Column 22 x 22	488	31/36	12-#7	17-#7
				36/41	11-#7	11-#8
				40/45	10-#7	13-#7
20	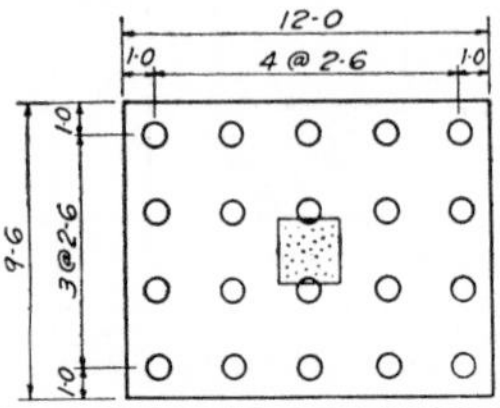	Min. Column 24 x 24	541	32/37	14-#7	13-#9
				36/41	17-#6	14-#8
				40/45	15-#6	17-#7

* Piles are here assumed as carrying 15 tons each, with no reduction for the effect of neighboring piles in the cluster.

SAFE LOAD TABLES

Retaining Walls

Section 13

CANTILEVERED RETAINING WALLS

The tables in this section give completely the dimensions and the reinforcement details for cantilevered retaining walls varying from 3 to 20 ft in height above the footing top, for four loading conditions:—(1) with horizontal backfill, (2) with backfill sloping upward at the angle of repose of the earth, (3) with horizontal backfill carrying a surcharge of 300 psf (highway loading),* and (4) a surcharge of 1000 psf (railroad loading). The tabulation also gives base pressure on the earth at the heel and toe, the resisting moment, overturning moment and factor of safety against overturning. (A tabulated heel pressure of zero does not necessarily mean that the vertex of a triangular pressure diagram is exactly at the heel, it may well be back underneath the foundation.) The stress allowances are given with each table. In all cases, the backfill is assumed to be well drained sand or gravel with an angle of internal friction (taken as the angle of repose) $\phi = 33°40'$.

To aid in computations regarding these walls, tables are given on pages 3-18 and 3-19 which record for vertical walls varying from 1 to 35 ft high the intensities of horizontal pressure for each foot of depth, the total horizontal pressure and the moment of the pressure about the bottom of the wall for the four loading conditions above noted and also for hydraulic pressure. These values were computed by the Rankine formula for earth pressure.

Very commonly the backfill material actually used will differ from that assumed for purposes of computation, with resulting differences, often considerable, in the magnitudes of the quantities. The determination of pressures for these variant conditions, determination of allowable base pressures, consideration of the influence of foundation strata and similar matters of judgment all lie within the province of the engineer trained in soil mechanics. Though it is probably sufficiently safe to select retaining wall designs from tables for heights up to, perhaps, a dozen or fifteen feet, when soil conditions are simple and approximately those here assumed, higher walls and those with difficult soil conditions demand the services of an expert.

The importance of drainage behind a wall can not be overemphasized. Weep holes through the vertical stem at intervals of perhaps 15 to 20 feet, draining out on top of the earth at the lower level, and a French drain of gravel, crushed stone or the equivalent, a foot or so thick, most of the height of the backwall are desirable. It is also usually desirable to provide weakened plane contraction joints at intervals of about 25 feet and keyed expansion joints about every fourth contraction joint, say, 100 feet apart. The exact spacing will depend upon the climate, exposure and similar factors. Weakened plane joints are made either with suitable rubber strips placed vertically full height in each face of the wall and left there or with wood strips similarly placed but eventually removed and the resulting slot filled with mastic caulking. Alternate longitudinal bars, at least, should be cut exactly opposite such weakened plane joints.

---

* The AASHO recommends 2 feet of added depth of fill for walls carrying a normal highway surcharge. These tables are, therefore, slightly more conservative.

CANTILEVERED RETAINING WALLS

The walls tabulated here are designed to have a factor of safety against overturning varying from a little less than 2 to a little over 2½, with a toe pressure not exceeding 4000 psf (except in the case of walls over 15 ft high with sloping backfill when the earth pressure runs up to 5000 psf). The passive resistance of any earth at the toe of the wall has been neglected. Generally, and especially in moist clay soils, a lug or key projecting down below the main footing level and with the front face cast directly against undisturbed earth, is desirable to assist in preventing sliding.

While these tables cover quite a wide range, it may be necessary to compute values beyond the scope of the book, or someone may want to see how the tabulated values were worked out, so the following example is included:—

Example—For the table on page 13-8, prepare the design of a cantilevered retaining wall 10 feet high from top of footing to top of wall, the surface of the earth fill being level at the top of the wall with no surcharge.

The outlines of the concrete, batter, and the location of the stem on the footing are matters of experience and of trial, quite a few proportions having been investigated before arriving at the values given. However, the checking of the tabulated values is fairly simple, taking concrete at 150 pcf and backfill at 100 pcf, with $\phi = 33°40'$, stresses being as tabulated at the head of the table.

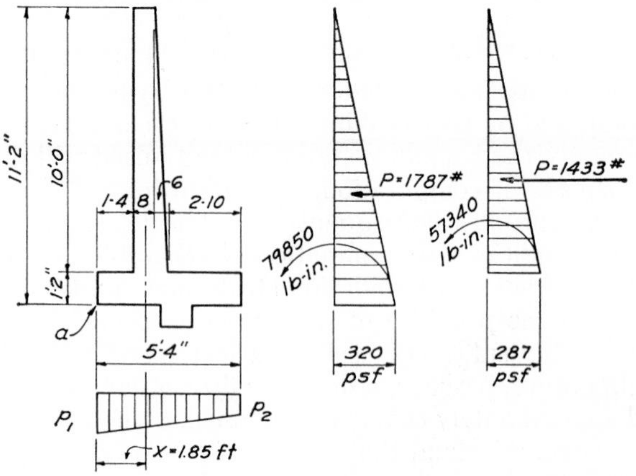

Stability—

Resisting Moment about point a—

			W	× x	= M
Footing:—	1.17 × 5.33 @ 150	=	935 lb	2.67 ft =	2,497 lb-ft
Stem:—	0.67 × 10.00 @ 150	=	1005 lb	1.67 ft =	1,678 lb-ft
	$0.50 \times \frac{10.00}{2}$ @ 150	=	375 lb	2.17 ft =	814 lb-ft
Earth:—	2.83 × 10.00 @ 100	=	2830 lb	3.92 ft =	11,094 lb-ft
	$0.50 \times \frac{10.00}{2}$ @ 100	=	250 lb	2.33 ft =	582 lb-ft
			5395 lb		16,665 lb-ft

Overturning Moment about point a (from the table on page 13-15):—

$0.5734\,wh^3 = 0.5734 \times 100 \times 11.17^3 = 79{,}850$ lb-in. $= -\ 6{,}654$ lb-ft

5395)10,011

Resultant base pressure acts at $x = 1.85$ ft from toe.

CANTILEVERED RETAINING WALLS

Factor against Overturning—$\frac{16,665}{6,654} = 2.50$ (as in table, page 13-9)

Pressure on Soil—Eccentricity of resultant pressure on base =

$\frac{5.33}{2} - 1.85 = 0.82 \text{ ft} < \frac{5.33}{6}$. So the force lies within the middle third of the base.

$$p_1 = \frac{P}{A} \pm \frac{Mc}{I} = \frac{P}{bh} + \frac{6Pe}{bh^2} = \frac{5395}{5.33} + \frac{6 \times 5395 \times 0.82}{1 \times (5.33)^2}$$

$$= 1012 + 932 = 1944 \text{ psf}$$

$$p_2 = 1012 - 932 = 80 \text{ psf}$$

} In table, p. 13-9

Stem

Shear at base of stem—From the table on page 13-18, the horizontal thrust for $h = 10$ is 1433 lb.

$$v = \frac{V}{bd} = \frac{1433}{12 \times 11\frac{1}{2}} = 11 \text{ psi} < 1.1\sqrt{3750} = 67.4 \text{ psi}$$

Moments at various levels—The bending moment increases rapidly (as the cube of the height) from top to bottom of stem. The effective depth of the reinforcing steel in the stem increases linearly from top to bottom. Economy results by selecting dowels

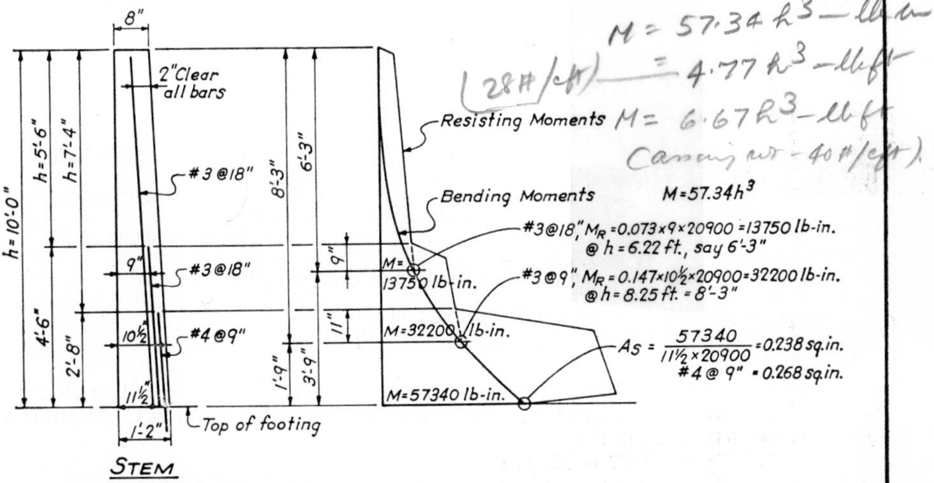

from the footing into the stem that are of proper size, spacing and length to take care of the peak of the curve for required A_s, while, at the top of these dowels, less reinforcement is necessary and only a portion of this need extend to the top of the wall. In these tables, the maximum spacing is arbitrarily limited to 18 in.

In the figure, curves of bending moments and resisting moments are superimposed. The dowel size and spacing are selected for the moment at the base of the stem. Vertical bars are selected for spacings that match the dowels, and are cut off on top to produce a simple pattern for the bar setters. The cut-off point of a bar is determined by locating a point below the top of the wall where the resisting moment of the uncut bars is equal to the bending moment and extending the cut bars 12 bar diameters or the effective depth of the stem above that point for anchorage. Bars must also lap 120% of 36 bar diameters or a distance to develop the stress at a bond value of $\left(\frac{0.75}{1.20} = 0.625\right)$ times $\left(\frac{4.8\sqrt{f'_c}}{D} \text{ or } 500 \text{ psi}\right)$.

Bond. Where verticals lap top of dowels. Length of lap must be $1.20 \times 36 \times \frac{1}{2} = 21.6$ in. < 2'-8", or $f_sD/4u$, where $u = \frac{5}{8} \times 500 = 313$ psi and $L = 24{,}000 \times 0.5/4 \times 313 = 9.6$ in. < 21.6 in.

Min. Embedment of dowels in footing. $L = f_sD/4u = 24{,}000 \times 0.5/4 \times 0.80 \times 500 = 7\frac{1}{2}$ in.

CANTILEVERED RETAINING WALLS

On dowels at bottom of stem (flexural bond). $u = \dfrac{V_s}{\Sigma_o j} = 11 \times 9/1.571 \times 0.875 = 72 < 500$ psi.

Toe

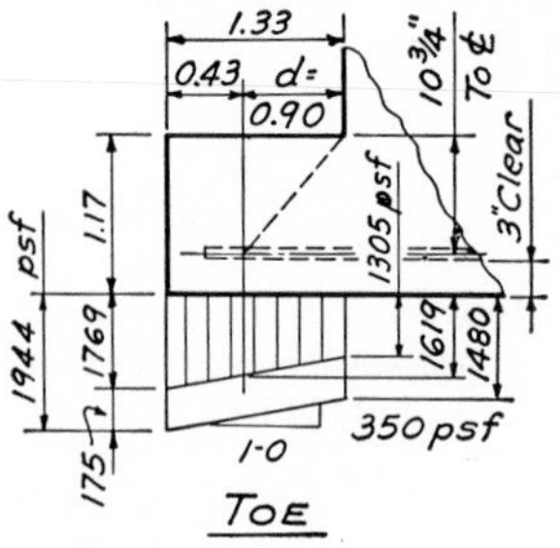

Loads—Concrete:—1.17 × 150 = 175 psf
At toe:—1944 − 175 = 1769 psf
Under face of stem:—1480 − 175 = 1305 psf

Shear—ACI 1201(c) (except for short cantilevers) permits computing shear on a plane at distance, *d*, from the face of the wall, where

$$V = 0.43\frac{1769 + 1619}{2} = 728 \text{ lb}$$

$$v = \frac{V}{bd} = \frac{728}{12 \times 10\frac{3}{4}} = 5.7 \text{ psi} < 67.4 \text{ psi}$$

More conservatively, shear can be computed on the face of the wall

$$V = 1.33\frac{1769 + 1305}{2} = 2044 \text{ lb}$$

$$v = \frac{V}{bd} = \frac{2044}{12 \times 10\frac{3}{4}} = 15.9 \text{ psi} < 67.4 \text{ psi}$$

For this wall, the shear is well on the conservative side.

Moment about Face of Stem:—1305 × 1.33 × 0.67 = 1163 lb-ft

$$464 \times \frac{1.33}{2} \times \frac{2 \times 1.33}{3} = +276 \text{ lb-ft}$$

1439 lb-ft = 17,300 lb-in.

$$A_s = \frac{M}{f_s jd} = \frac{17{,}300}{24{,}000 \times \frac{7}{8} \times 10\frac{3}{4}} = 0.078 \text{ sq in.}$$

#4 @ 27 = 0.089 sq in.

Bond—Bond is to be computed at the face of the wall, ACI 1301(a).

$$u = \frac{vs}{\Sigma_o j} = \frac{15.9 \times 27}{1.571 \times \frac{7}{8}} = 313 \text{ psi} < 500 \text{ psi}$$

Heel

Shear—While ACI 1201(c) (except for short cantilevers) permits computing shear on a plane at distance, *d*, from the back of the wall, it is more conservative to compute on a plane at the back of the wall

$$V = 3326 - 1627 = 1699 \text{ lb}$$

$$v = \frac{V}{bd} = \frac{1699}{12 \times 10\frac{3}{4}} = 13.2 \text{ psi} < 67.4 \text{ psi}$$

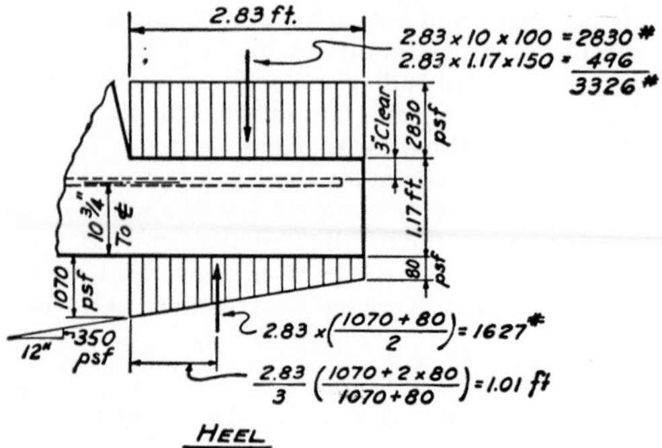

CANTILEVERED RETAINING WALLS

Moment about back of stem $= 3326 \times \frac{2.83}{2} = 4700$ lb-ft

$1627 \times 1.01 = -1643$ lb-ft

3057 lb-ft $= 36{,}700$ lb-in.

$$A_s = \frac{M}{f_s jd} = \frac{36{,}700}{24{,}000 \times 7/8 \times 10\tfrac{3}{4}} = 0.162 \text{ sq in.}$$

#5 @ 18 = 0.21 sq in. (from the table on page 13-8).

$$\textit{Bond—}u = \frac{vs}{\Sigma oj} = \frac{13.2 \times 18}{1.963 \times 7/8} = 139 < 470 \text{ psi}$$

Temperature reinforcement in stem:—

(ACI 807 does not apply; use ACI 2202)

Vertical bars at midheight (h = 5′-0″): Total $A_s = 0.0015 \times 12 \times 11 = 0.198$ sq in.

Rear face—#3 @ 9″ = 0.15
Front face—#3 @ 12″ = 0.11
0.26 sq in.

Horizontal bars at midheight (h = 5′-0″): Total $A_s = 0.0025 \times 12 \times 11 = 0.33$ sq in.

Rear face—#4 @ 12″ = 0.200
Front face—#4 @ 18″ = 0.133
0.333 sq in.

The designs in the other tables follow the same procedure. It is unnecessary to work out complete examples. A few observations will be helpful. For a sloping backfill, the resultant pressure is parallel to the slope. In computing overturning the resultant was applied against a vertical plane through the heel of the wall. The allocation of pressure to stem and heel is shown on the figure.

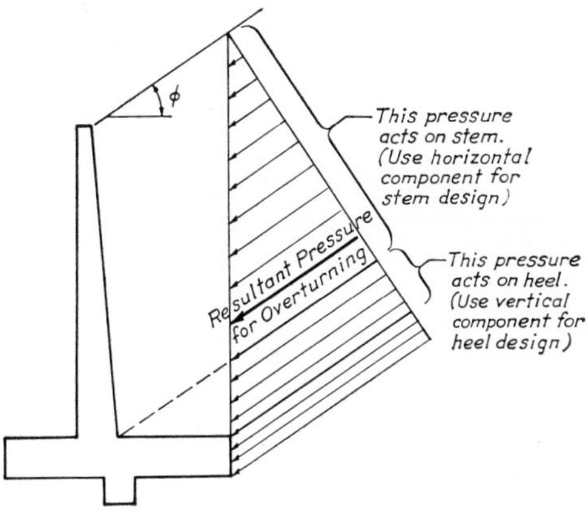
φ
This pressure acts on stem. (Use horizontal component for stem design)
This pressure acts on heel. (Use vertical component for heel design)
Resultant Pressure for Overturning

In the case of the highway and railroad surcharges, it was assumed that the increased intensity of thrust was effective the full height of the wall. If the line of travel is established somewhat back from the stem, it is possible to draw a sloping pressure line down from the nearest edge of the load to the back of the wall and omit the increased intensity above the intersection. (See the figure below.)

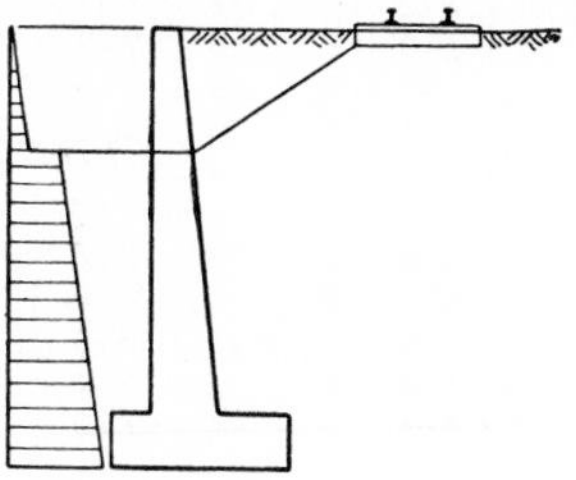

The case of an adjoining building exercising a thrust directly against the back of the wall is one requiring special study. Roughly, such a wall would work out about as much heavier than the case of a railroad surcharge as that case is heavier than a wall with an ordinary horizontal backfill.

In all of these tables, the top of the wall is arbitrarily taken as 8 in. thick. This is about the minimum through which proper concrete can be cast with all of the reinforcement in place. For the higher walls, some authorities recommend at least a 12 in. thickness. The user may increase the top thickness without changing the bottom thickness or reinforcing steel, if he cares to do so, the increased weight adding slightly to the resistance to overturning.

CANTILEVERED RETAINING WALLS—BACKFILL LEVEL—NO SURCHARGE

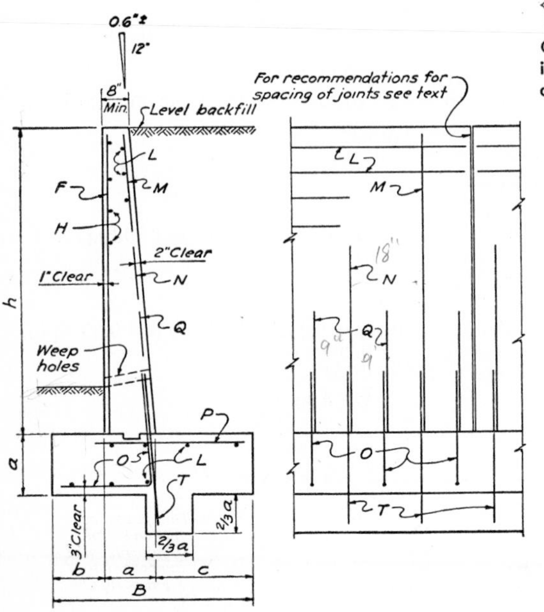

Vertical steel in back of wall may be:—

$\left\{\begin{matrix} O + T \text{ only} \\ O \text{ only} \\ M + N \text{ alt.} \end{matrix}\right.$ $\quad \left.\begin{matrix} M + Q + N + Q \\ \text{(as shown)} \end{matrix}\right\}$

Comparison of bar spacings in table will indicate combination, spacings being accumulative from a selected M or O bar.

Wt. of earth = 100 pcf

L of Internal Friction $= \phi = 33° 40'$

$f_s = 24{,}000$ psi

$f'_c = 3{,}750$ psi

$f_c = 1{,}688$ psi

$v = 1.1\sqrt{f'_c} = 67.4$ psi

$u = \dfrac{4.8\sqrt{f'_c}}{D}$ or $\dfrac{3.4\sqrt{f'_c}}{D}$ for top bars

(See table on p. 3-13)

O & T bars alternate, or occur O + T + T, except in walls without key, where only O bars are required.

REINFORCEMENT

Height of Wall = h (ft)	M			N			Q			P			O		
	Bar Size	Length (ft)	Spcg (in.)	Bar Size	Length (ft)	Spcg (in.)	Bar Size	Length (ft)	Spcg (in.)	Bar Size	Length (ft)	Spcg (in.)	Bar Size	Length (ft)	Spcg (in.)
3										#3	1′-3	18	#3	4′-3	18
4										#3	1′-8	18	#3	5′-5	18
5										#3	2′-2	18	#3	6′-5	18
6										#3	2′-6	18	#3	7′-10	18
7										#3	2′-8	12	#3	9′-2	12
8										#3	3′-0	10	#3	10′-5	10
9	#3	8′-10	12							#4	3′-6	12	#4	5′-3	24
10	#3	9′-10	18	#3	4′-6	18				#5	4′-0	18	#4	5′-8	18
11	#3	10′-10	18	#3	5′-6	18	#3	3′-8	18	#3	4′-0	6	#3	5′-7	12
12	#3	11′-10	18	#3	6′-6	18	#3	4′-8	18	#5	4′-8	12	#4	6′-9	18
13	#3	12′-10	18	#3	7′-6	18	#3	5′-7	9	#5	5′-0	9	#4	6′-8	9
14	#4	13′-10	16½	#4	6′-7	16½	#4	4′-2	16½	#4	5′-3	5½	#4	6′-4	11
15	#4	14′-10	15	#4	7′-3	15	#4	4′-7	15	#4	5′-6	5	#5	7′-0	10
16	#4	15′-10	18	#4	9′-0	18	#4	6′-7	9	#6	6′-4	9	#5	7′-10	9
17	#5	16′-10	18	#5	8′-7	18	#5	5′-9	18	#6	6′-8	6	#6	8′-2	12
18	#5	17′-10	18	#5	9′-5	18	#5	6′-7	9	#5	6′-6	4½	#5	7′-7	9
19	#6	18′-10	18	#6	9′-4	18	#6	6′-1	18	#6	7′-6	6	#7	8′-3	12
20	#6	19′-10	18	#6	10′-3	18	#6	7′-0	9	#7	8′-3	9	#6	8′-4	9

CANTILEVERED RETAINING WALLS—BACKFILL LEVEL—NO SURCHARGE

CONCRETE OUTLINES

Height of Wall = h (ft)	B (ft)	a (ft)	b (ft)	c (ft)	Base Pressure at Toe (psf)	Base Pressure at Heel (psf)	Resisting Moment (lb-ft)	Overturning Moment (lb-ft)	$\frac{M_R}{M_O}$	Concrete (cu ft per lin. ft of wall)
3	1′-9	0′-10½	0′-4	0′-6½	885	0	726	279	2.60	4.2
4	2′-2	0′-11	0′-5	0′-10	1,136	0	1,359	570	2.38	5.5
5	2′-8	0′-11	0′-5	1′-4	1,361	0	2,390	991	2.41	6.7
6	3′-3	1′-0	0′-8	1′-7	1,415	0	4,100	1,638	2.50	8.7
7	3′-10	1′-0	1′-0	1′-10	1,398	89	6,300	2,448	2.58	10.0
8	4′-3	1′-1	1′-1	2′-1	1,643	38	8,760	3,582	2.44	11.9
9	4′-9	1′-1	1′-1	2′-7	1,851	60	12,310	4,892	2.51	12.5
10	5′-4	1′-2	1′-4	2′-10	1,944	80	16,665	6,675	2.50	16.5
11	5′-10	1′-2	1′-6	3′-2	2,051	108	21,400	8,600	2.49	17.6
12	6′-6	1′-3	1′-8	3′-7	2,129	207	28,900	10,980	2.63	20.4
13	7′-0	1′-4	1′-8	4′-0	2,403	161	36,300	14,101	2.58	23.0
14	7′-8	1′-4	2′-1	4′-3	2,332	290	45,700	17,256	2.65	25.0
15	8′-1	1′-5	2′-1	4′-7	2,608	239	54,700	21,158	2.59	28.0
16	8′-6	1′-5	2′-2	4′-11	2,799	211	64,000	25,253	2.53	29.7
17	9′-0	1′-6	2′-3	5′-3	3,008	197	76,300	30,325	2.52	32.9
18	9′-6	1′-7	2′-4	5′-7	3,207	197	90,000	35,898	2.50	36.5
19	10′-2	1′-7	2′-6	6′-1	3,264	286	107,700	41,654	2.58	38.5
20	10′-5	1′-8	2′-6	6′-3	3,119	646	119,300	48,650	2.46	42.0

REINFORCEMENT

O a b		T			F			L			H			Weight of Bars (lb per lin. ft of wall)
a (ft)	b (ft)	Bar Size	Length (ft)	Spcg (in.)	Bar Size	Length (ft)	Spcg (in.)	Quant. of Bars	Bar Size	Spcg (in.)	Quant. of Bars	Bar Size	Spcg (in.)	
0′-10	3′-5				#3	2′-10	18	8	#3	10	3	#3	12	6.22
0′-11	4′-6				#3	3′-10	18	9	#3	10	4	#3	12	7.62
0′-11	5′-6				#3	4′-10	18	11	#3	10	6	#3	10	9.75
1′-3	6′-7				#3	5′-10	18	9	#4	14	4	#4	14	13.73
1′-7	7′-7				#3	6′-10	12	10	#4	16	5	#4	16	17.70
1′-9	8′-8				#3	7′-10	12	11	#4	16	6	#4	16	20.35
1′-9	3′-6	#4	4′-3	24	#3	8′-10	12	15	#4	12	6	#4	18	26.16
2′-1	3′-7	#4	4′-4	18	#3	9′-10	12	17	#4	12	7	#4	18	31.1
2′-3	3′-4	#4	4′-1	12	#4	10′-10	18	19	#4	12	7	#4	18	35.0
2′-6	4′-3	#4	5′-1	6, 12	#4	11′-10	18	20	#4	12	8	#4	18	42.1
2′-7	4′-1	#4	5′-0	9	#4	12′-10	18	21	#4	12	11	#4	14	52.4
3′-0	3′-4	#5	4′-3	11	#4	13′-10	18	23	#4	12	12	#4	14	58.5
3′-1	3′-11	#5	4′-10	10	#4	14′-10	18	25	#4	12	13	#4	14	70.1
3′-2	4′-8	#5	5′-7	9	#4	15′-10	18	27	#4	12	16	#4	12	84.1
3′-4	4′-10	#6	5′-10	12	#4	16′-10	18	28	#4	12	17	#4	12	100.0
3′-6	4′-1	#6	5′-3	9	#4	17′-10	18	29	#4	12	18	#4	12	106.5
3′-8	4′-7	#7	5′-8	12	#4	18′-10	18	30	#4	12	19	#4	12	126.3
3′-9	4′-7	#7	5′-8	9	#4	19′-10	18	31	#4	12	20	#4	12	141.6

CANTILEVERED RETAINING WALLS—SURFACE OF EARTH SLOPING ($\phi = 33°40'$)

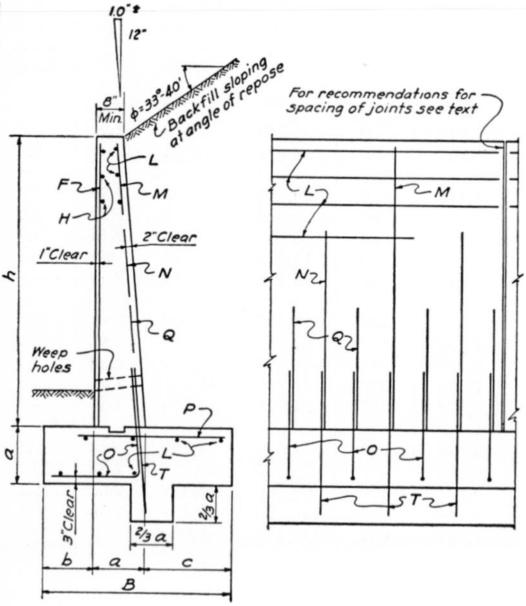

Vertical steel in back of wall may be:—

O + *T* only	*M* + *N* + 1Q
O only	*M* + Q + *N* + Q
M + *N* alt.	(as shown)

Comparison of bar spacings in table will indicate combination, spacings being accumulative from a selected *M* or O bar.

Wt of earth = 100 pcf
L of Internal Friction = ϕ = 33° 40′
f_s = 24,000 psi
f'_c = 3,750 psi
f_c = 1,688 psi
$v = 1.1\sqrt{f'_c} = 67.4$ psi
$u = \dfrac{4.8\sqrt{f'_c}}{D}$ or $\dfrac{3.4\sqrt{f'_c}}{D}$ for top bars
(See page 3-13)

O & *T* bars alternate, or occur O + O + *T* except in walls without key, where only O bars are required.

REINFORCEMENT

Height of Wall = *h* (ft)	M			N			Q			P			O		
	Bar Size	Length (ft)	Spcg (in.)	Bar Size	Length (ft)	Spcg (in.)	Bar Size	Length (ft)	Spcg (in.)	Bar Size	Length (ft)	Spcg (in.)	Bar Size	Length (ft)	Spcg (in.)
3										#3	1′-10	18	#3	4′-10	18
4										#3	2′-3	18	#3	6′-2	18
5										#3	2′-7	16	#3	7′-7	16
6										#4	2′-11	18	#3	8′-10	18
7										#3	3′-4	9	#4	6′-5	18
8	#4	7′-10	15							#5	3′-10	15	#4	6′-5	15
9	#4	8′-10	12							#5	4′-3	12	#4	7′-1	12
10	#3	9′-10	10	#4	4′-10	10				#5	4′-8	10	#4	6′-7	10
11	#4	10′-10	16	#5	5′-8	16				#5	5′-0	8	#6	8′-0	16
12	#4	11′-10	13	#5	6′-2	13				#7	6′-3	13	#6	8′-6	13
13	#4	12′-10	16½	#5	7′-10	16½	#5	5′-0	16½	#7	6′-8	11	#6	8′-11	11
14	#5	13′-10	18	#5	7′-8	18	#6	5′-6	18	#8	7′-6	12	#7	9′-5	12
15	#5	14′-10	15	#6	8′-2	15	#6	4′-10	15	#8	8′-0	10	#7	9′-9	10
16	#6	15′-10	18	#6	8′-8	18	#7	6′-0	18	#9	9′-2	12	#8	10′-2	12
17	#6	16′-10	15	#6	9′-0	15	#7	6′-2	15	#9	9′-6	10	#8	10′-8	10
18	#7	17′-10	16½	#7	8′-4	16½	#8	5′-10	16½	#10	10′-8	11	#8	11′-7	5½, 11
19	#7	18′-10	15	#7	10′-0	15	#8	6′-6	15	#10	11′-6	10	#8	12′-0	5, 10
20	#7	19′-10	16½	#8	11′-4	16½	#8	7′-4	16½	#11	12′-8	11	#9	13′-1	5½, 11

CANTILEVERED RETAINING WALLS—SURFACE OF EARTH SLOPING ($\phi = 33°40'$)

CONCRETE OUTLINES

Height of Wall = h (ft)	B (ft)	a (ft)	b (ft)	c (ft)	Base Pressure at Toe (psf)	Base Pressure at Heel (psf)	Resisting Moment (lb-ft)	Overturning Moment (lb-ft)	$\frac{M_R}{M_O}$	Concrete (cf per lf of wall)
3	2′-6	0′-11	0′-7	1′-0	1,072	25	2,397	1,130	2.12	5.05
4	3′-2	1′-0	0′-9	1′-5	1,421	49	5,072	2,527	2.01	6.93
5	3′-10	1′-1	1′-0	1′-9	1,699	62	9,092	4,660	1.95	9.04
6	4′-6	1′-2	1′-3	2′-1	1,990	62	14,900	7,750	1.92	11.39
7	5′-3	1′-3	1′-6	2′-6	2,238	105	23,400	12,100	1.93	13.97
8	5′-11	1′-4	1′-9	2′-10	2,512	118	33,600	17,600	1.91	16.7
9	6′-8	1′-5	2′-0	3′-3	2,753	176	47,900	25,000	1.92	19.8
10	7′-5	1′-6	2′-3	3′-8	3,018	210	65,800	34,300	1.92	23.0
11	8′-1	1′-7	2′-6	4′-0	3,298	210	85,300	44,900	1.90	26.3
12	8′-10	1′-8	2′-9	4′-5	3,536	266	111,000	57,900	1.91	30.0
13	9′-6	1′-9	3′-0	4′-9	3,805	286	139,000	72,800	1.90	33.7
14	10′-3	1′-10	3′-3	5′-2	4,058	329	173,000	90,900	1.91	37.8
15	11′-0	1′-11	3′-6	5′-7	4,310	375	214,000	112,000	1.91	42.1
16	11′-10	2′-0	3′-10	6′-0	4,477	470	262,000	135,000	1.94	46.7
17	12′-7	2′-1	4′-1	6′-5	4,719	524	314,000	162,000	2.04	51.5
18	13′-4	2′-2	4′-4	6′-10	4,959	582	373,000	193,000	1.94	56.6
19	14′-2	2′-3	4′-8	7′-3	5,104	696	443,000	226,000	1.96	61.9
20	15′-0	2′-4	5′-0	7′-8	5,300	774	521,000	264,000	1.97	67.4

REINFORCEMENT

O a b		T			F			L			H			Weight of Bars (lb per lin. ft of wall)
a (ft)	b (ft)	Bar Size	Length (ft)	Spcg (in.)	Bar Size	Length (ft)	Spcg (in.)	Quant. of Bars	Bar Size	Spcg (in.)	Quant. of Bars	Bar Size	Spcg (in.)	
1′-4	3′-6				#3	2′-10	18	8	#3	10	3	#3	12	6.52
1′-7	4′-7				#3	3′-10	18	10	#3	10	4	#3	12	8.38
1′-11	5′-8				#3	4′-10	18	8	#4	15	4	#4	15	12.09
2′-1	6′-9	#3	3′-10	18	#3	5′-10	16	9	#4	14	5	#4	14	15.45
2′-5	4′-0	#3	7′-11	18	#3	6′-10	16	11	#4	14	6	#4	14	19.79
2′-9	3′-8	#3	4′-6	15	#3	7′-10	14	13	#4	14	7	#4	14	28.11
3′-1	4′-0	#4	5′-0	12	#3	8′-10	12	16	#4	12	9	#4	12	38.45
3′-5	3′-2	#4	4′-2	10	#3	9′-10	12	17	#4	12	10	#4	12	44.50
3′-9	4′-3	#5	5′-3	16	#4	10′-10	18	19	#4	12	11	#4	12	55.7
4′-1	4′-5	#5	5′-5	13	#4	11′-10	18	22	#4	12	12	#4	12	70.3
4′-5	4′-6	#5	5′-8	11	#4	12′-10	18	21	#4	14	11	#5	14	84.7
4′-9	4′-8	#6	5′-10	12	#4	13′-10	18	23	#4	14	12	#5	14	102.5
5′-1	4′-8	#6	6′-0	10	#4	14′-10	18	24	#4	14	13	#5	14	124.5
5′-4	4′-10	#7	6′-2	12	#4	15′-10	16	29	#4	12	16	#5	12	154.4
5′-8	5′-0	#7	6′-4	10	#4	16′-10	16	31	#4	12	17	#5	12	176.8
6′-2	5′-5	#8	6′-10	16½	#4	17′-10	15	34	#4	12	18	#5	12	200.1
6′-9	5′-3	#8	6′-9	15	#4	18′-10	14	36	#4	12	19	#5	12	240.7
6′-10	6′-3	#9	7′-9	16½	#4	19′-10	14	37	#4	12	20	#5	12	279.8

CANTILEVERED RETAINING WALLS—HIGHWAY SURCHARGE

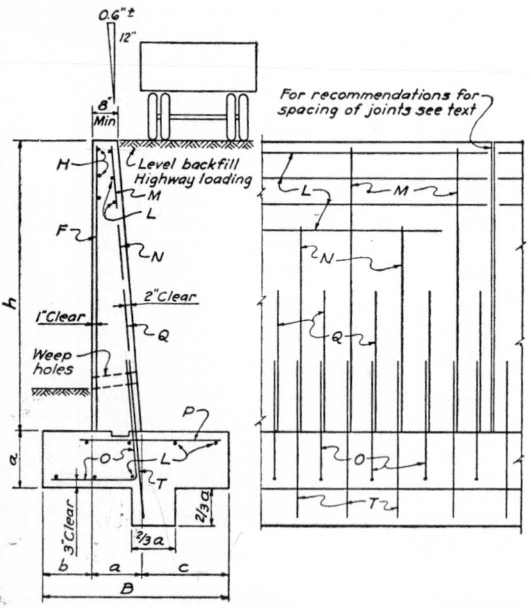

Vertical steel in back of wall may be:

O + *T* only	*M* + *N* + 1Q
O only	*M* + Q + *N* + Q
M + *N* alt.	(as shown)

Comparison of bar spacing in table will indicate combination, spacings being accumulative from a selected *M* or O bar.

Wt of earth = 100 pcf

Ί of Internal Friction = ϕ = 33° 40′

f_s = 24,000 psi

f'_c = 3,750 psi

f_c = 1,688 psi

$v = 1.1\sqrt{f'_c} = 67.4$ psi

$u = \dfrac{4.8\sqrt{f'_c}}{D}$ or $\dfrac{3.4\sqrt{f'_c}}{D}$ for top bars

(See page 3-13)

O & *T* bars alternate except in walls without key, where only O bars are required.

REINFORCEMENT

Height of Wall = *h* (ft)	M			N			Q			P			O		
	Bar Size	Length (ft)	Spcg (in.)	Bar Size	Length (ft)	Spcg (in.)	Bar Size	Length (ft)	Spcg (in.)	Bar Size	Length (ft)	Spcg (in.)	Bar Size	Length (ft)	Spcg (in.)
3										#3	2′-1	18	#3	5′-0	18
4										#3	2′-4	18	#3	6′-2	18
5										#4	2′-9	18	#3	7′-6	18
6										#4	3′-2	16	#3	8′-8	16
7										#5	3′-5	16	#4	6′-6	16
8	#4	7′-10	14							#5	3′-8	14	#4	5′-11	14
9	#5	8′-10	16							#4	4′-0	8	#5	6′-4	16
10	#4	9′-10	14	#4	4′-8	14				#6	4′-9	14	#5	6′-7	14
11	#4	10′-10	16	#5	5′-8	16				#7	5′-7	16	#6	7′-2	16
12	#4	11′-10	14	#5	6′-10	14				#7	5′-10	14	#6	7′-10	14
13	#4	12′-10	18	#5	8′-4	18	#5	5′-4	18	#7	6′-2	12	#6	7′-11	12
14	#4	13′-10	15	#5	8′-10	15	#5	5′-4	15	#7	6′-5	10	#6	8′-0	10
15	#5	14′-10	18	#6	9′-2	18	#6	5′-4	18	#8	7′-3	12	#7	8′-5	12
16	#5	15′-10	15	#6	9′-5	15	#6	5′-7	15	#8	7′-6	10	#7	8-7	10
17	#6	16′-10	18	#6	10′-2	18	#7	6′-8	18	#9	8′-9	12	#8	9′-5	12
18	#6	17′-10	16½	#6	10′-8	16½	#7	7′-0	16½	#9	9′-0	11	#8	9′-11	11
19	#7	18′-10	18	#7	10′-6	18	#7	6′-10	18	#10	9′-10	12	#9	10′-6	12
20	#7	19′-10	16½	#7	11′-2	16½	#7	7′-2	16½	#10	10′-0	11	#9	11′-2	11

CANTILEVERED RETAINING WALLS—HIGHWAY SURCHARGE

CONCRETE OUTLINES

Height of Wall = h (ft)	B (ft)	a (ft)	b (ft)	c (ft)	Base Pressure		Resisting Moment (lb-ft)	Over-turning Moment (lb-ft)	$\frac{M_R}{M_O}$	Concrete (cf per lf of wall)
					at Toe (psf)	at Heel (psf)				
3	3′-0	0′-10	1′-1	1′-1	752	0	1,899	900	2.11	5.04
4	3′-5½	0′-10½	1′-3	1′-4	878	0	3,418	1,581	2.16	6.42
5	4′-1	0′-11	1′-5	1′-9	1,092	0	5,186	2,501	2.07	8.07
6	4′-8	0′-11½	1′-7	2′-1½	1,230	0	7,833	3,698	2.12	9.75
7	5′-2	1′-0	1′-9	2′-5	1,384	0	10,967	5,194	2.11	11.41
8	5′-9	1′-1	2′-0	2′-8	1,524	0	15,162	7,133	2.12	13.7
9	6′-3	1′-1½	2′-2	2′-11½	1,683	0	19,820	9,372	2.11	15.7
10	6′-9½	1′-2	2′-4	3′-3½	1,824	0	25,641	12,017	2.13	17.8
11	7′-3½	1′-2½	2′-6	3′-7	1,974	0	32,183	15,121	2.13	19.8
12	7′-9	1′-3	2′-8	3′-10	2,143	0	39,207	18,681	2.10	21.9
13	8′-4	1′-4	2′-10	4′-2	2,281	0	48,979	22,890	2.14	24.9
14	8′-9½	1′-4½	3′-0	4′-5	2,452	0	58,266	27,538	2.11	27.3
15	9′-4	1′-5	3′-2	4′-9	2,591	0	69,950	32,765	2.13	29.8
16	9′-9½	1′-5½	3′-4	5′-0	2,751	0	81,599	38,550	2.12	32.2
17	10′-4	1′-6	3′-6	5′-4	2,880	0	96,094	45,000	2.14	34.9
18	10′-10	1′-7	3′-8	5′-7	3,052	0	111,690	52,371	2.13	37.6
19	11′-3	1′-7½	3′-10	5′-9½	3,232	0	126,583	60,228	2.10	41.4
20	11′-9	1′-8	4′-1	6′-0	3,303	9	145,196	68,800	2.11	44.1

REINFORCEMENT

O a_|b		T			F			L			H			Weight of Bars (lb per lin. ft of wall)
a (ft)	b (ft)	Bar Size	Length (ft)	Spcg (in.)	Bar Size	Length (ft)	Spcg (in.)	Quant. of Bars	Bar Size	Spcg (in.)	Quant. of Bars	Bar Size	Spcg (in.)	
1′-7	3′-5				#3	2′-10	18	8	#3	10	3	#3	12	6.63
1′-9	4′-5				#3	3′-10	18	9	#3	10	4	#3	12	7.98
2′-0	5′-6	#3	3′-1	18	#3	4′-10	18	11	#3	10	6	#3	10	11.53
2′-2	6′-6	#3	4′-0	16	#3	5′-10	18	9	#4	14	5	#4	14	15.91
2′-5	4′-1	#3	8′-6	16	#3	6′-10	12	10	#4	16	5	#4	16	20.96
2′-7	3′-4	#3	4′-0	14	#3	7′-10	12	11	#4	16	6	#4	16	26.70
3′-0	3′-4	#4	4′-0	16	#3	8′-10	12	15	#4	12	6	#4	18	34.28
3′-2	3′-5	#4	4′-2	14	#3	9′-10	12	17	#4	12	7	#4	18	42.28
3′-4	3′-10	#5	4′-8	16	#4	10′-10	18	19	#4	12	7	#4	18	52.5
3′-7	4′-3	#5	5′-2	14	#4	11′-10	18	20	#4	12	8	#4	18	61.7
3′-10	4′-1	#5	5′-0	12	#4	12′-10	18	22	#4	12	11	#4	14	72.8
4′-0	4′-0	#5	4′-10	10	#4	13′-10	18	24	#4	12	12	#4	14	85.6
4′-3	4′-2	#6	5′-2	12	#4	14′-10	18	26	#4	12	13	#4	14	101.8
4′-5	4′-2	#6	5′-2	10	#4	15′-10	18	27	#4	12	16	#4	12	116.1
4′-8	4′-9	#7	5′-9	12	#4	16′-10	18	29	#4	12	17	#4	12	140.9
4′-11	5′-0	#7	6′-0	11	#4	17′-10	18	30	#4	12	18	#4	12	157.4
5′-2	5′-4	#8	6′-4	12	#4	18′-10	18	33	#4	12	19	#4	12	184.6
5′-5	5′-9	#8	6′-10	11	#4	19′-10	18	35	#4	12	20	#4	12	208.4

CANTILEVERED RETAINING WALLS—RAILWAY SURCHARGE

Vertical steel in back of wall may be:

O + T only	M + N + 1Q
O only	M + Q + N + Q
M + N alt	(as shown)

Comparison of bar spacings in table will indicate combination, spacings being accumulative from a selected M or O bar.

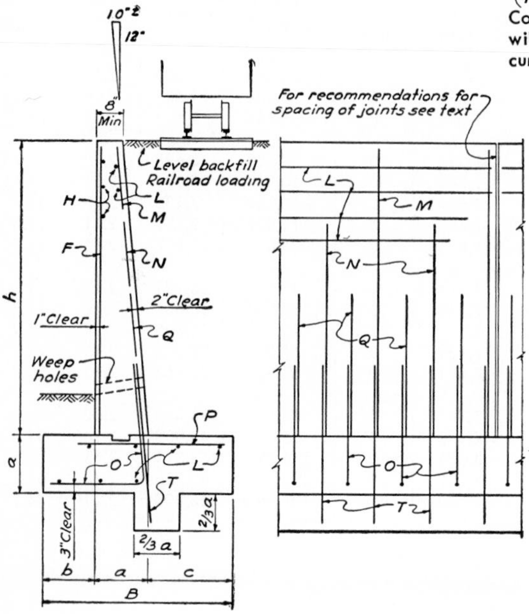

Wt. of earth = 100 pcf

L of Internal Friction = ϕ = 33° 40′

f_s = 24,000 psi

f'_c = 3,750 psi

f_c = 1,688 psi

$v = 1.1\sqrt{f'_c} = 67.4$ psi

$u = \dfrac{4.8\sqrt{f'_c}}{D}$ or $\dfrac{3.4\sqrt{f'_c}}{D}$ for top bars

(See page 3-13)

O & T bars alternate except in walls without key, where only O bars are required.

REINFORCEMENT

Height of Wall = h (ft)	M			N			Q			P			O		
	Bar Size	Length (ft)	Spcg (in.)	Bar Size	Length (ft)	Spcg (in.)	Bar Size	Length (ft)	Spcg (in.)	Bar Size	Length (ft)	Spcg (in.)	Bar Size	Length (ft)	Spcg (in.)
3										#5	3′-4	12	#3	5′-10	12
4										#6	4′-0	16	#3	7′-7	16
5										#5	3′-10	9	#4	8′-11	18
6										#6	4′-8	9	#5	10′-5	18
7	#5	6′-10	12							#7	5′-4	12	#4	7′-0	12
8	#4	7′-10	12	#4	4′-4	12				#7	5′-8	12	#5	7′-10	12
9	#4	8′-10	14	#4	5′-8	14				#8	6′-6	14	#6	9′-8	14
10	#5	9′-10	18	#5	6′-4	18				#7	6′-2	9	#7	10′-6	18
11	#5	10′-10	18	#6	7′-2	18				#7	6′-4	9	#8	11′-0	18
12	#6	11′-10	16	#6	6′-10	16				#7	6′-8	8	#8	11′-0	16
13	#5	12′-10	18	#5	10′-2	18	#6	7′-10	18	#7	7′-0	6	#7	12′-8	12
14	#6	13′-10	16½	#6	8′-10	16½	#6	5′-10	16½	#7	7′-4	5½	#7	11′-10	11
15	#6	14′-10	18	#6	10′-4	18	#7	7′-4	18	#7	7′-8	6	#8	12′-7	12
16	#6	15′-10	16½	#6	11′-0	16½	#7	8′-0	16½	#7	8′-0	5½	#8	13′-1	11
17	#6	16′-10	15	#6	11′-8	15	#7	8′-6	15	#7	8′-4	5	#8	14′-0	10
18	#6	17′-10	15	#7	13′-6	15	#7	8′-6	15	#9	10′-0	5, 10	#8	14′-7	10
19	#7	18′-10	18	#7	13′-2	18	#8	9′-8	18	#9	10′-4	6	#9	15′-10	12
20	#7	19′-10	15	#7	13′-4	15	#8	9′-4	15	#8	9′-0	5	#9	15′-3	10

CANTILEVERED RETAINING WALLS—RAILWAY SURCHARGE

CONCRETE OUTLINES

Height of Wall = *h* (ft)	*B* (ft)	*a* (ft)	*b* (ft)	*c* (ft)	Base Pressure at Toe (psf)	Base Pressure at Heel (psf)	Resisting Moment (lb-ft)	Overturning Moment (lb-ft)	$\frac{M_R}{M_O}$	Concrete (cf per lf of wall)
3	5′-1	0′-11	1′-10	2′-4	735	0	5,413	2,492	2.17	7.41
4	5′-11	1′-0	2′-4	2′-7	852	0	8,979	4,180	2.15	9.68
5	6′-7	1′-1	2′-8	2′-10	1,018	0	13,226	6,367	2.08	11.98
6	7′-4	1′-2	2′-11	3′-3	1,171	0	19,263	9,140	2.11	14.71
7	8′-0	1′-3	3′-3	3′-6	1,313	0	25,957	12,432	2.09	17.41
8	8′-8	1′-4	3′-7	3′-9	1,451	0	33,980	16,371	2.08	20.3
9	9′-4	1′-5	3′-11	4′-0	1,577	0	43,714	20,984	2.08	23.5
10	10′-0	1′-6	4′-3	4′-3	1,699	9	54,795	26,235	2.09	26.8
11	10′-6	1′-7	4′-5	4′-6	1,890	0	66,050	32,222	2.05	30.1
12	11′-2	1′-8	4′-8	4′-10	2,021	0	81,107	39,006	2.08	33.8
13	11′-9	1′-9	4′-10	5′-2	2,188	0	96,976	46,519	2.08	37.7
14	12′-4	1′-10	5′-0	5′-6	2,343	12	114,726	54,888	2.09	41.6
15	12′-11	1′-11	5′-3	5′-9	2,493	13	134,313	64,193	2.09	45.8
16	13′-6	2′-0	5′-4	6′-2	2,670	24	156,851	74,309	2.11	50.1
17	14′-1	2′-1	5′-6	6′-6	2,833	29	180,983	85,429	2.12	54.7
18	14′-9	2′-2	5′-8	6′-11	2,974	76	210,560	97,549	2.16	59.7
19	15′-3	2′-3	5′-10	7′-2	3,146	58	237,054	110,598	2.14	64.3
20	15′-10	2′-4	6′-0	7′-6	3,296	76	268,602	124,688	2.15	69.3

REINFORCEMENT

O *a* (ft)	*b* (ft)	*T* Bar Size	*T* Length (ft)	*T* Spcg (in.)	*F* Bar Size	*F* Length (ft)	*F* Spcg (in.)	*L* Quant. of Bars	*L* Bar Size	*L* Spcg (in.)	*H* Quant. of Bars	*H* Bar Size	*H* Spcg (in.)	Weight of Bars (lb per lin. ft of Wall)
2′-4	3′-6				#3	2′-10	18	6	#4	18	2	#4	18	11.74
2′-11	4′-5	#3	3′-4	16	#3	3′-10	18	7	#4	18	3	#4	18	15.25
3′-4	5′-7	#4	3′-9	18	#3	4′-10	18	10	#4	12	3	#4	18	20.04
3′-8	6′-9	#4	4′-0	18	#3	5′-10	16	12	#4	12	4	#4	18	30.69
4′-1	2′-11	#4	3′-9	12	#3	6′-10	16	15	#4	12	7	#4	12	41.75
4′-6	3′-4	#5	4′-2	12	#3	7′-10	14	17	#4	12	8	#4	12	51.49
4′-11	4′-9	#5	5′-8	14	#3	8′-10	12	19	#4	12	9	#4	12	62.61
5′-4	5′-2	#7	6′-2	18	#3	9′-10	12	21	#4	12	10	#4	12	75.09
5′-7	5′-5	#7	6′-4	18	#4	10′-10	18	23	#4	12	11	#4	12	86.0
5′-11	5′-1	#7	6′-1	16	#4	11′-10	18	24	#4	12	12	#4	12	108.3
6′-2	6′-6	#7	7′-7	12	#4	12′-10	18	26	#4	12	13	#4	12	124.4
6′-5	5′-5	#7	6′-7	11	#4	13′-10	18	25	#4	14	12	#5	14	137.3
6′-9	5′-10	#7	7′-0	12	#4	14′-10	18	26	#4	14	13	#5	14	147.7
6′-11	6′-2	#7	7′-5	11	#4	15′-10	16	31	#4	14	16	#5	12	172.3
7′-2	6′-10	#7	8′-2	10	#4	16′-10	16	33	#4	12	17	#5	12	202.5
7′-5	7′-2	#8	8′-7	10	#4	17′-10	15	35	#4	12	18	#5	12	237.2
7′-10	8′-0	#9	9′-6	12	#4	18′-10	14	36	#4	12	19	#5	12	269.0
7′-11	7′-4	#8	8′-11	10	#4	19′-10	14	36	#4	12	20	#5	12	277.9

SPECIAL ELL-SHAPED WALLS

Other types of retaining wall are frequently used, the most common being an ell shape, used where the face of the stem is exactly on a property line and the base can not project beyond this point. Two cases of ell-shaped walls are common:—(1) where the heel projects back under the earth which is at the high level with no projecting toe, (2) where the toe projects under the earth which is at the low level with no projecting heel. In the first case, a fair approximation can be made by shifting the position of the stem to the front of the toe for any of the four cases illustrated on pages 13-8 to 13-15. In the latter case, the base of the wall would have to be increased by 33⅓ to 50 per cent to obtain stability. The number of conditions of special walls is so great that it is impracticable to tabulate them all, but the above modifications to the tables, coupled with the earth pressure tables on pages 13-18 and 13-19 and the outline of a wall design illustrated in the example on page 13-4 ff, should enable the user to satisfy his needs.

BASEMENT WALLS SPANNED VERTICALLY

Another common case of walls resisting earth pressure occurs in basement walls spanned vertically from basement floor slab to first floor slab. The table on page 13-17 suggests suitable reinforcement for walls of 8-, 10-, 12- and 15-inch thickness on story heights from 7 to 18 feet, all based upon a surcharge of 300 psf to represent ordinary working loads on top of the backfill. Should neighboring buildings, adjoining railroad tracks, or other conditions impose a heavier surcharge, the wall reinforcement and thickness should be increased accordingly.

A table is also given for the maximum vertical heights of unreinforced basement walls of the same thicknesses to keep the tension developed by bending within 100 psi both for 300 psf surcharge and for no surcharge at all.

In all cases of vertically spanned walls, a word of caution on the design drawings is advisable to see that the contractor installs both the basement floor slab and the first floor slab and has them able to receive thrust before backfilling against the basement wall. Of course, both slabs should bear against the wall to afford horizontal support.

RETAINING WALLS

BASEMENT WALLS SPANNED VERTICALLY

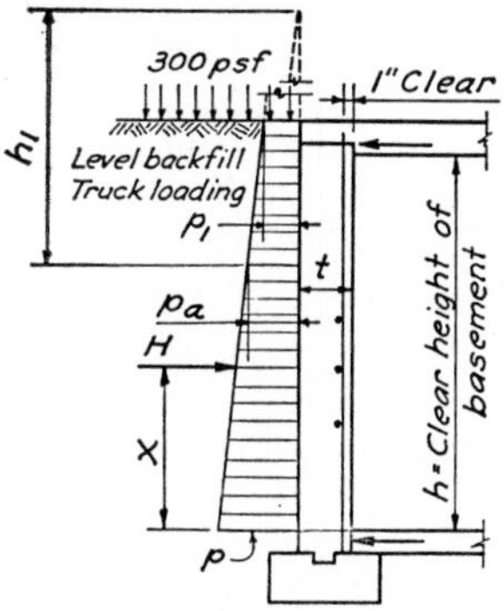

Angle of Repose $\phi = 33°40$

$$p_a = wh_1 \frac{1 - \sin\phi}{1 + \sin\phi} \qquad H = \frac{p + p_1}{2} h$$

$$w = 100 \qquad x = \frac{h}{3}\left(\frac{p + 2p_1}{p + p_1}\right)$$

STRESSES:—

$f_s = 24{,}000$ psi

$f'_c = 3{,}750$ psi

$f_c = 1{,}688$ psi

$v_c = 1.1\sqrt{3750} = 67.4$ psi

Wall Thickness (t)	8''		10''		12''		15''	
Clear Height of Basement (h)	Reinforcement on Interior Side of Wall							
	Vert.	Horiz.	Vert.	Horiz.	Vert.	Horiz.	Vert.	Horiz.
7'-0	#4 @ 16½''	#4 @ 10''	#4 @ 13''	#5 @ 12''	#4 @ 11''	#5 @ 10''	#5 @ 13½''	#6 @ 11½''
8'-0	#4 @ 16½''	#4 @ 10''	#4 @ 13''	#5 @ 12''	#4 @ 11''	#5 @ 10''	#5 @ 13½''	#6 @ 11½''
9'-0	#4 @ 13''	#4 @ 10''	#4 @ 13''	#5 @ 12''	#4 @ 11''	#5 @ 10''	#5 @ 13½''	#6 @ 11½''
10'-0	#4 @ 9½''	#4 @ 10''	#4 @ 12½''	#5 @ 12''	#4 @ 11''	#5 @ 10''	#5 @ 13½''	#6 @ 11½''
11'-0	#5 @ 11½''	#4 @ 10''	#4 @ 10''	#5 @ 12''	#4 @ 11''	#5 @ 10''	#5 @ 13½''	#6 @ 11½''
12'-0	#6 @ 12½''	#4 @ 10''	#5 @ 12''	#5 @ 12''	#4 @ 9½''	#5 @ 10''	#5 @ 13½''	#6 @ 11½''
13'-0	#7 @ 13½''	#4 @ 10''	#6 @ 13½''	#5 @ 12''	#5 @ 12''	#5 @ 10''	#5 @ 13½''	#6 @ 11½''
14'-0	#7 @ 11''	#4 @ 10''	#6 @ 11''	#5 @ 12''	#6 @ 14''	#5 @ 10''	#5 @ 12½''	#6 @ 11½''
15'-0	#8 @ 12''	#4 @ 10''	#7 @ 12½''	#5 @ 12''	#6 @ 11½''	#5 @ 10''	#5 @ 10½''	#6 @ 11½''
16'-0			#8 @ 13½''	#5 @ 12''	#7 @ 13''	#5 @ 10''	#6 @ 12½''	#6 @ 11½''
17'-0			#8 @ 11''	#5 @ 12''	#8 @ 14''	#5 @ 10''	#7 @ 14''	#6 @ 11½''
18'-0					#8 @ 12''	#5 @ 10''	#7 @ 12''	#6 @ 11½''

Often a pair of bars is added at top and at bottom of a wall to provide longitudinal beam action from footing to footing, pile cap to pile cap, or to bridge across soft and firm subsoil conditions.

MAXIMUM HEIGHTS IN FEET OF UNREINFORCED BASEMENT WALLS (KEEPING TENSION $\leqq$ 100 PSI).

Wall Thickness (t)	Surcharge = 300 psf (Diagram above)	No surcharge
8''	6.9	8.2
10''	8.0	9.7
12''	9.4	11.0
15''	11.1	12.7

RETAINING WALLS
EARTH AND WATER PRESSURES

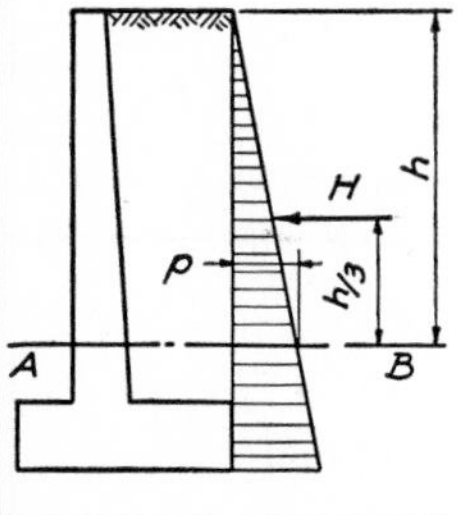

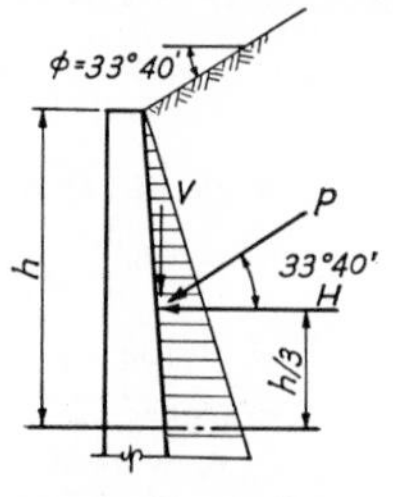

Use *p*, *H* and *M* for design of stem only (see page 13-17).

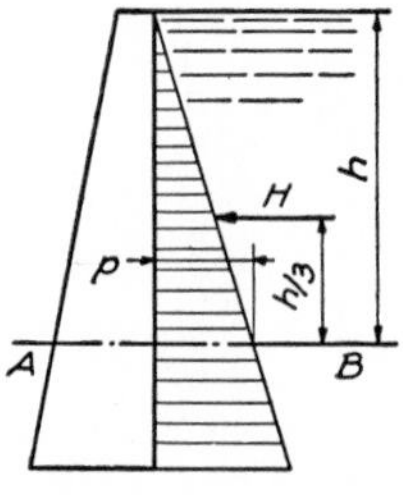

h—height that governs pressure.
p—Intensity of horizontal pressure (psf) at any depth (*h*).
H—Total horizontal pressure (lb) above A-B.
M—Moment (lb-in.) of *H* about an axis lying in Section A-B.
φ—Angle of repose = 33°40′ (1 on 1½). Rankine Theory.

Depth "*h*" (AB below surface)	Earth Horizontal (w = 100 pcf)			Earth Sloping Upward at $\phi = 33°\,40'$ (w = 100 pcf)			Water (w = 62.5 pcf)		
	$p = 0.2867\,wh$	$H = \frac{ph}{2} = 0.1434\,wh^2$	$M = \frac{Hh}{3}12 = 0.5734\,wh^3$	$p = 0.6927\,wh$	$H = \frac{ph}{2} = 0.3463\,wh^2$	$M = \frac{Hh}{3}12 = 1.3853\,wh^3$	$p = wh$	$H = \frac{wh^2}{2}$	$M = 2wh^3$ ($\frac{wh^3}{6} \times 12$)
ft	psf	lb	lb-in.	psf	lb	lb-in.	psf	lb	lb-in.
1	29	14	57	69	35	138	63	31	125
2	57	57	459	139	139	1,108	125	125	1,000
3	86	129	1,548	208	312	3,740	188	281	3,375
4	115	229	3,670	277	554	8,866	250	500	8,000
5	143	358	7,167	346	866	17,310	313	781	15,620
6	172	516	12,380	416	1,247	29,920	375	1,125	27,000
7	201	702	19,660	485	1,697	47,510	438	1,531	42,870
8	229	917	29,350	554	2,216	70,920	500	2,000	64,000
9	258	1,161	41,800	623	2,805	100,900	563	2,531	91,120
10	287	1,433	57,340	693	3,463	138,500	625	3,125	125,000
11	315	1,735	76,320	762	4,190	184,300	688	3,781	166,300
12	344	2,064	99,080	831	4,987	239,300	750	4,500	216,000
13	373	2,423	125,900	901	5,852	304,300	813	5,281	274,600
14	401	2,810	157,300	970	6,787	380,100	875	6,125	343,000
15	430	3,225	193,500	1039	7,792	467,500	938	7,031	421,800
16	459	3,670	234,800	1108	8,865	567,400	1000	8,000	512,000
17	487	4,143	281,700	1178	10,000	680,500	1063	9,031	614,100
18	516	4,645	334,400	1247	11,220	807,900	1125	10,120	729,000
19	545	5,175	393,200	1316	12,500	950,100	1188	11,280	857,300
20	573	5,734	458,700	1385	13,850	1,108,000	1250	12,500	1,000,000
21	602	6,322	531,000	1455	15,270	1,282,000	1313	13,780	1,157,000
22	631	6,938	610,500	1524	16,760	1,475,000	1375	15,120	1,331,000
23	659	7,583	697,600	1593	18,310	1,685,000	1438	16,530	1,520,000
24	688	8,257	792,600	1662	19,940	1,915,000	1500	18,000	1,728,000
25	717	8,959	895,900	1732	21,640	2,164,000	1563	19,530	1,953,000
26	745	9,690	1,007,000	1801	23,410	2,434,000	1625	21,120	2,197,000
27	774	10,450	1,128,000	1870	25,245	2,726,000	1688	22,780	2,460,000
28	803	11,230	1,258,000	1940	27,150	3,041,000	1750	24,500	2,744,000
29	831	12,050	1,398,000	2009	29,120	3,378,000	1813	26'280	3,048,000
30	860	12,900	1,548,000	2078	31,160	3,740,000	1875	28,120	3,375,000
	889	13,770	1,708,000	2147	33,270	4,126,000	1938	30,030	3,723,000
32	917	14,670	1,878,000	2217	35,460	4,539,000	2000	32,000	4,096,000
33	946	15,610	2,060,000	2286	37,710	4,978,000	2063	34,030	4,492,000
34	975	16,570	2,253,000	2355	40,030	5,444,000	2125	36,120	4,913,000
35	1003	17,560	2,458,000	2424	42,420	5,939,000	2188	38,280	5,359,000

RETAINING WALLS
EARTH PRESSURE WITH SURCHARGE

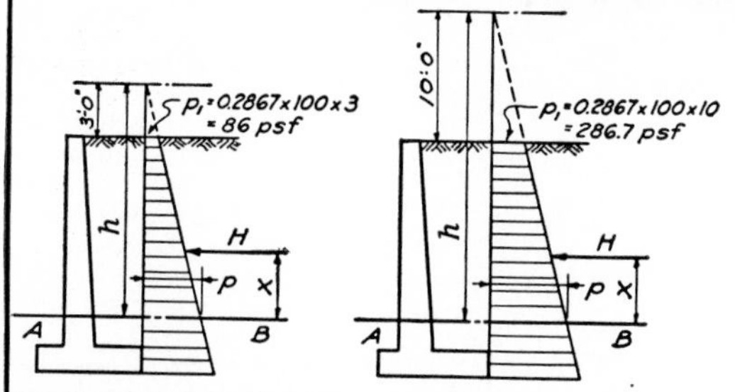

h—height that governs pressure.
p—Intensity of horizontal pressure (psf) at any depth (h − 3) or (h − 10).
H—Total horizontal pressure (lb) above A-B.
M—Moment (lb-in.) of H about an axis lying in Section A-B.
ϕ—Angle of repose = 33°40′ (1 on 1½).
w—Weight of earth = 100 pcf.
Rankine Theory.

Depth of AB below surface	Horizontal Surcharge—3′-0″ High = 300 psf				Horizontal Surcharge—10′-0″ High = 1000 psf			
	Intensity of Horizontal Pressure at A-B	Total Horizontal Pressure above A-B	Arm of Total Horiz. Pressure	Moment of H about Sect. A-B	Intensity of Horizontal Pressure at A-B	Total Horizontal Pressure above A-B	Arm of Total Horiz. Pressure	Moment of H about Sect. A-B
	p	$H = \frac{(h-3)}{2}(p+p_1)$	$x = \frac{(h-3)(p+2p_1)}{3(p+p_1)}$	$M = 12\,Hx$	p	$H = \frac{(h-10)}{2}(p+p_1)$	$x = \frac{(h-10)(p+2p_1)}{3(p+p_1)}$	$M = 12\,Hx$
ft	psf	lb	ft	lb-in.	psf	lb	ft	lb-in.
1	115	100	0.476	574	315	301	0.492	1,777
2	143	229	0.917	2,520	343	630	0.970	7,333
3	172	387	1.333	6,190	372	989	1.435	17,031
4	201	574	1.732	11,930	401	1,376	1.889	31,191
5	229	787	2.121	20,031	429	1,791	2.334	50,162
6	258	1,032	2.500	30,960	458	2,236	2.769	74,298
7	287	1,305	2.871	44,960	487	2,710	3.197	103,966
8	315	1,604	3.238	62,325	515	3,209	3.619	139,360
9	344	1,935	3.600	83,592	544	3,741	4.034	181,100
10	373	2,295	3.957	109,000	573	4,302	4.444	229,400
11	401	2,678	4.314	138,700	601	4,886	4.850	284,400
12	430	3,096	4.666	173,400	630	5,504	5.250	346,800
13	459	3,542	5.017	213,300	659	6,151	5.646	416,800
14	487	4,011	5.367	258,300	687	6,820	6.040	494,400
15	516	4,515	5.714	309,600	716	7,525	6.429	580,600
16	545	5,048	6.060	367,100	745	8,259	6.814	675,400
17	573	5,601	6.406	430,600	773	9,013	7.199	778,700
18	602	6,192	6.750	501,600	802	9,804	7.579	891,700
19	631	6,811	7.092	579,700	831	10,620	7.957	1,015,000
20	659	7,450	7.436	664,800	859	11,460	8.340	1,148,000
21	688	8,127	7.777	758,500	888	12,340	8.700	1,290,000
22	717	8,833	8.118	860,500	917	13,240	9.070	1,441,000
23	745	9,556	8.460	970,200	945	14,170	9.450	1,608,000
24	774	10,320	8.800	1,090,000	974	15,130	9.810	1,781,000
25	803	11,110	9.139	1,219,000	1003	16,130	10.180	1,972,000
26	831	11,920	9.479	1,356,000	1031	17,130	10.550	2,170,000
27	860	12,770	9.818	1,505,000	1060	18,180	10.910	2,380,000
28	889	13,650	10.150	1,663,000	1089	19,260	11.270	2,605,000
29	917	14,540	10.490	1,830,000	1117	20,360	11.640	2,845,000
30	946	15,480	10.830	2,012,000	1146	21,500	12.000	3,097,000
31	975	16,440	11.170	2,204,000	1175	22,660	12.350	3,358,000
32	1003	17,420	11.500	2,404,000	1203	23,840	12.710	3,636,000
33	1032	18,440	11.840	2,620,000	1232	25,070	13.070	3,932,000
34	1061	19,500	12.180	2,850,000	1261	26,320	13.430	4,243,000
35	1089	20,560	12.520	3,089,000	1289	27,580	13.780	4,561,000

SAFE LOAD TABLES

Miscellaneous Items

Section 14

Grain Storage Bins
Blast Resistant Structures
Lintels
Pits
Pipe Columns
Slabs on the Ground

WALLS FOR CIRCULAR GRAIN STORAGE BINS—INTERNAL PRESSURE

Because of the possibility of excessive cracking and consequent leakage with increasing elongation of hoop rods, these tables are reproduced from Volume I ($f'_c = 3000$, $f_s = 20{,}000$ psi). The designer may make whatever adjustment he wishes.

Horiz. radial pressure by Janssen's formula

$$L = \frac{wR}{\mu'}\left[1 - e^{-\left(\frac{k\mu'H}{R}\right)}\right]$$

where L = radial pressure (psf)
w = 50 (pcf) for soybeans, wheat, corn, etc.
$R = \frac{\text{area}}{\text{periphery}}$ (ft)
k = 0.60 for soybeans, wheat, corn, etc.
μ' = 0.42 for soybeans, wheat, corn, etc.
H = head of grain.

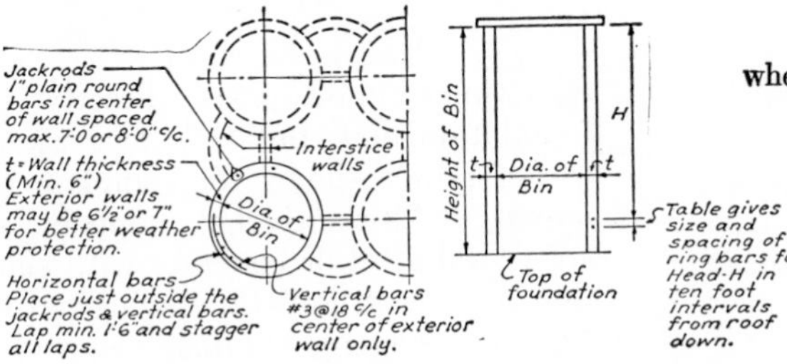

Jackrods 1" plain round bars in center of wall spaced max. 7'-0 or 8'-0" c/c.
t = Wall thickness (Min. 6")
Exterior walls may be 6½" or 7" for better weather protection.
Horizontal bars Place just outside the jackrods & vertical bars. Lap min. 1'-6 and stagger all laps.
Interstice walls
Dia. of Bin
Vertical bars #3@18 c/c in center of exterior wall only.
Height of Bin
H
t
Dia. of Bin
Top of foundation
Table gives size and spacing of ring bars for Head-H in ten foot intervals from roof down.

Reinforcement is based upon grain (max. weight 50 pcf, min. angle of repose 28°). For heavier material (such as portland cement), increase steel to suit.

Design is for single bin, internally loaded. For cluster, check arch action of bin wall when interstice bin is loaded.

Wall thickness is determined by allowable bearing (540 psi at bottom of wall) while carrying its own weight plus roof, and 80% of total weight of grain in bin. (Min. thickness 6".)

Height of single freestanding circular bin is limited by overturning under 30 psf wind against empty bin and includes all values above zig-zag line in table below. When bins are clustered, height may be increased greatly.

For convenience in placing, specify horizontal bars to lie in same horizontal plane through the entire structure, to supply tiers of bars at uniform vertical spaces for entire height, varying bar sizes to suit.

WALL REINFORCEMENT (All walls 6" min.)

Head H	Inside diameter of bin					
	13'-0	15'-0	18'-0	20'-0	22'-0	24'-0
10	#3 @ 8	#3 @ 8	#3 @ 8	#3 @ 8	#3 @ 8	#3 @ 8
20	#3 @ 8	#3 @ 8	#3 @ 8	#4 @ 12	#4 @ 10	#4 @ 9
30	#3 @ 8	#3 @ 8	#4 @ 12	#4 @ 12	#4 @ 9	#4 @ 8
40	#3 @ 8	#3 @ 8	#4 @ 12	#4 @ 9	#4 @ 8	#4 @ 7
50	#3 @ 8	#3 @ 8	#4 @ 10	#4 @ 9	#4 @ 7	#5 @ 9
60	#3 @ 8	#3 @ 8	#4 @ 10	#4 @ 8	#5 @ 11	#5 @ 9
70	#3 @ 8	#3 @ 8	#4 @ 10	#4 @ 8	#5 @ 10	#5 @ 9
80	#3 @ 8	#3 @ 8	#4 @ 10	#4 @ 8	#5 @ 10	#5 @ 9
90	#3 @ 8	#3 @ 8	#4 @ 10	#4 @ 8	#5 @ 10	#5 @ 9
100	#3 @ 8	#3 @ 8	#4 @ 10	#4 @ 8	#5 @ 10	#5 @ 9
110	#3 @ 8	#3 @ 8	#4 @ 10	#4 @ 8	#5 @ 10	#5 @ 9
120	#3 @ 8	#3 @ 8	#4 @ 10	#4 @ 8	#5 @ 10	#5 @ 9

CIRCULAR GRAIN STORAGE BINS—HOPPER BOTTOMS

Because of the possibility of excessive cracking and consequent leakage with increasing elongation of hoop rods, these tables are reproduced from Volume I ($f'_c = 3000$, $f_s = 20{,}000$ psi). The designer may make whatever adjustment he wishes.

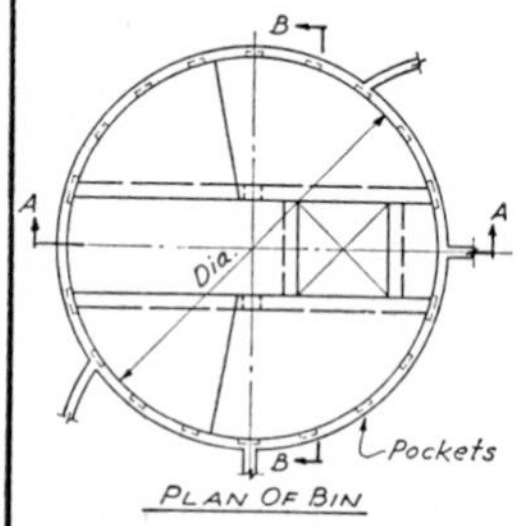

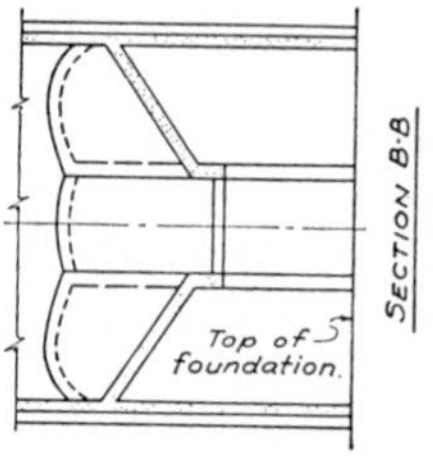

Sometimes grain rests directly on foundation mat, but this necessitates use of power shovel for complete removal. Alternatively, hoppers of structural steel or concrete with sides sloped at least 8-on-12, feeding onto a conveyor system, eliminate shoveling by providing gravity feed.

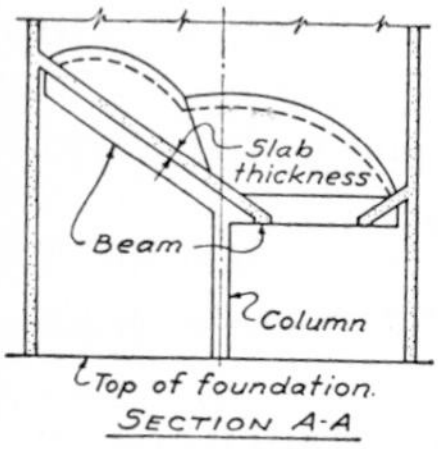

Concrete hoppers are economically constructed as shown in figure, dihedral angles filled in to provide for a slope of at least 8-on-12. Hoppers are supported by pockets in side walls and columns on foundation mat with slabs, beams, and columns designed for the vertical pressures given in the table. Vertical pressure on bin bottoms for conditions given on page 14-3:—

$$V = \frac{wR}{k\mu'}\left[1 - e^{-\left(\frac{k\mu' H}{R}\right)}\right]$$

VERTICAL PRESSURE ON BIN BOTTOM (psf)

Head H	Diameter of Bins					
	13′-0	15′-0	18′-0	20′-0	22′-0	24′-0
20	507	552	603	627	654	678
30	581	646	728	773	815	852
40	616	695	798	860	916	968
50	630	720	840	913	982	1043
60	638	728	862	942	1020	1095
70	642	738	875	962	1048	1128
80	645	742	883	974	1064	1148
90	645	745	886	983	1072	1164
100	645	745	893	992	1090	1172
110	645	745	893	992	1090	1190
120	645	745	893	992	1090	1190

DESIGN OF STRUCTURES TO RESIST NUCLEAR WEAPONS EFFECTS

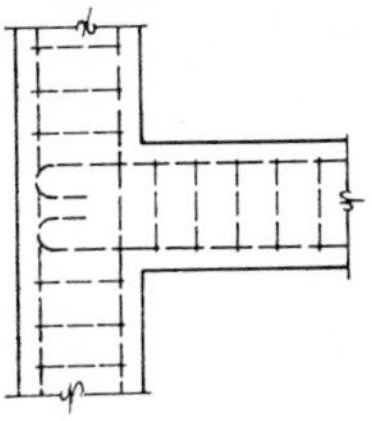

Structural design to resist the effects of moment reversals to resist unbalanced loads, wind, earthquake, or blast is pretty well covered in ASCE Manual No. 42, "Design of Structures to Resist Nuclear Weapon Effects," from which the following is quoted:—

"6.6 STRUCTURAL DETAILS"

"**Concrete Construction.** Reinforced concrete is an excellent material for blast resistant construction. However, strict attention must be paid to details in order to assure continuity, ductility, and resistance to loads in either direction. Thus, continuity of reinforcement by adequate lapping, and even welding, is required. Shear reinforcement, which is more necessary in blast resistant than in ordinary construction, should be normal to the axis of the member because inclined stirrups or main bars designed to carry shear become planes of weakness if the direction of loading or bending is reversed. Doubly-reinforced members with the reinforcing adequately tied have much more ductility than singly-reinforced members and accordingly offer great advantage for blast resistant construction.

"Joints are particularly important. They should be detailed and fabricated in such a way as to insure ductile behavior of the completed element. Further, the ultimate strength of the least strong connecting element should be developed in the joint, if at all practical. In no case shall the reinforcing index q exceed 0.45 in order to avoid brittle behavior: $q = (p - p')\frac{f_y}{f'_c}$. Further, the amount of reinforcing on one face of a beam or slab should not, in general, exceed 2% of the cross-sectional area of the element, unless special precautions are taken to tie adequately the compression steel. Steel bars with carbon content greater than 0.3% should not be welded unless adequate tests are made to demonstrate that such welding will not be brittle."

PRECAST REINFORCED CONCRETE LINTELS IN CONCRETE BLOCK WALLS

These lintel tables are taken bodily from Volume I, based on $f'_c = 3000$, $f_s = 20{,}000$, W.S.D. ACI 318-56. They have worked well. More precise design is not necessary.

Lintels are tabulated per 4 in. thickness of wall; for 8 in. thickness, double the width and reinforcement, and for a 12 in. wall, triple it. Lintels given have a capacity to carry only an equilateral triangle of 32 psf masonry with a base of (L + 8 in.) on a clear span of L; no provisions are made for beams, purlins, or other concentrated loads.

LINTELS IN BLOCK WALLS (per 4 in. thickness)

Clear Span L	Total Length L + 1'-4"	Min. f'_c (psi)	Height of Lintel (in.)	Reinforcement Bottom	Reinforcement Top	Weight of Lintel (lb)
4'-0	5'-4		7⅝	1-#3	1-#2	170
5'-0	6'-4	2000	7⅝	1-#3	1-#2	203
6'-0	7'-4		7⅝	1-#3	1-#2	235
7'-0	8'-4		7⅝	1-#4	1-#2	266
8'-0	9'-4	2500	7⅝	1-#4	1-#2	299
9'-0	10'-4		7⅝	1-#6	1-#2	331
10'-0	11'-4		11⅝	1-#5	1-#2	544
11'-0	12'-4	2000	11⅝	1-#5	1-#2	592
12'-0	13'-4		11⅝	1-#6	1-#2	640
13'-0	14'-4	2500	11⅝	1-#8	1-#3	688

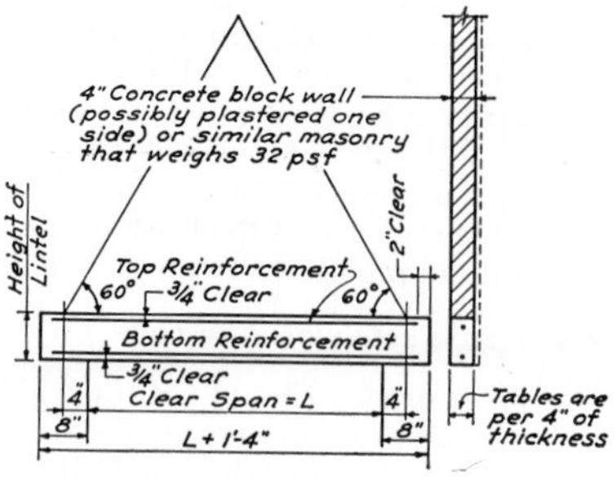

For wall to arch over opening and put only a triangular load on the lintel, there must be:—(1) an unbroken, solid wall above the vertex of the triangle equal to about one-third the height of the triangle, and (2) no included concentrations of load.

Bottom bars only may be used if the lintel is plainly marked, properly handled, and always kept right side up. If plainly marked, but likely to be stressed by drooping in handling, use top bars for transportation purposes. If lintel is not marked and can be installed upside down, use same size bars in top as are scheduled for bottom.

Check texture of exposed surfaces of lintel to harmonize with exposed blocks. Either light weight or standard concrete may be used.

For uniformly loaded lintels see page 14-7.

ALLOWABLE CONCENTRIC LOADS ON CONCRETE-FILLED STEEL PIPE COLUMNS

These tables are computed from ACI Equation (14-4).

STANDARD PIPE

Unbraced Length (ft)	Nominal Diameter—Weight Per Foot											
	12		10			8		6	5	4	3½	3
	49.56	43.77	40.48	34.24	31.20	28.55	24.70	18.97	14.62	10.79	9.11	7.58
6	350	323	272	243	229	185	167	117	87	60	49	39
8	347	320	269	240	226	182	165	114	83	56	45	34
10	344	317	265	237	223	178	161	109	79	51	40	29
12	340	313	261	233	219	173	156	104	73	45	33	
14	335	309	255	228	215	168	151	98	66	38		
16	329	303	249	222	209	161	145	91	59			
18	322	297	242	216	203	153	138	83	50			
20	315	290	234	209	196	145	131	74				
22	307	283	226	201	189	136	122	64				

EXTRA STRONG PIPE

Unbraced Length (ft)	Nominal Diameter—Weight Per Foot							
	12	10	8	6	5	4	3½	3
	65.42	54.74	43.39	28.57	20.78	14.98	12.51	10.25
6	424	339	254	161	114	79	63	50
8	421	335	250	156	110	73	58	44
10	417	330	244	150	104	67	51	36
12	412	325	238	143	96	59	43	
14	406	318	230	135	87	49		
16	399	310	221	125	77			
18	391	302	211	114	66			
20	383	292	199	101				
22	373	281	187					
24	363	270	173					

s are computed only for $h/K_s \leqq 120$. Properties of steel from which pipe is made are assumed to
se of ASTMA36.

CARRYING CAPACITY OF REINFORCED CONCRETE LINTELS

The table on page 14-6 gives lintel designs to carry an equilateral triangle of wall. These tables give the safe superimposed uniformly distributed load per lineal foot on 8 x 8 and 8 x 12 in. lintels on spans of 4′-0″ to 12′-0″, again based upon ACI 318-56, 3000/20,000.

8 x 8 in. Nominal Lintels (7⅝ x 7⅝)

Clear Opening L	Reinforcement					Length of Lintel	Weight of Lintel (lb)
	2-#3	#3 + #4	2-#4	#4 + #5	2-#5		
4′-0	697	1010	1320	1545	1870	5′-4″	340
5′-0	452	662	870	1130	1386	6′-4″	405
6′-0	309	460	612	800	980	7′-4″	469
7′-0	218	330	446	586	730	8′-4″	533
8′-0	157	247	336	446	556	9′-4″	597
9′-0	93	186	258	346	436	10′-4″	661
10′-0	78	136	192	264	338	11′-4″	725
11′-0	58	108	157	219	280	12′-4″	790
12′-0	40	82	124	176	228	13′-4″	854

To left of heavy line, f'_c = 2500 or 3000 psi but to right of heavy line $f'_c \gtrless$ 3000 psi.

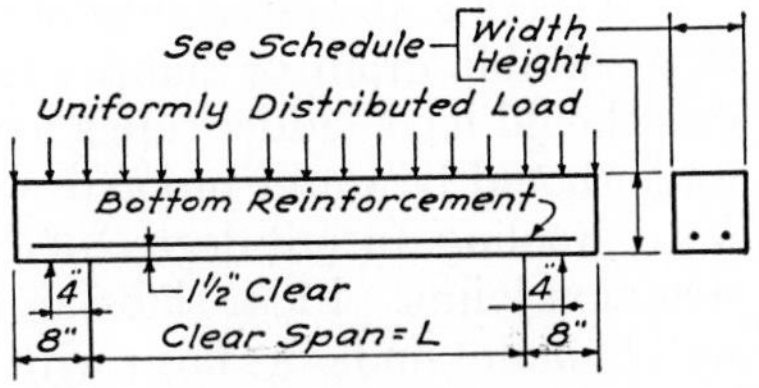

Concentrated loads can be approximated by the equivalent uniform loads on page 4-4, which are fairly accurate for flexure but should be investigated for shear.

The reinforcement *must* be placed in the bottom of the lintel, and can be the only reinforcement if lintel is plainly marked, carefully handled, and always kept right side up; otherwise see notes on page 14-6.

8 wide x 12 in. high Nominal Lintels (7⅝ x 11⅝)

Clear Opening L	Reinforcement						Length of Lintel	Weight of Lintel (lb)
	2-#4	#4 + #5	2-#5	#5 + #6	2-#6	#6 + #7		
4′-0″	2140	3020	3020	3020	3020	3020	5′-4″	513
5′-0″	1420	1830	2400	2400	2400	2400	6′-4″	609
6′-0″	995	1295	1445	1980	1980	1980	7′-4″	704
7′-0″	725	950	1065	1450	1690	1690	8′-4″	800
8′-0″	545	725	815	1115	1325	1460	9′-4″	896
9′-0″	420	565	635	880	1045	1255	10′-4″	992
10′-0″	315	430	490	680	815	980	11′-4″	1088
11′-0″	260	390	405	575	690	830	12′-4″	1184
12′-0″	205	290	330	470	570	690	13′-4″	1280

Below and to left of heavy line, f'_c = 2500 or 3000 psi, but above and to right of heavy line, $f'_c \gtrless$ 3000 psi. Either light weight or standard concrete may be used.

The above tables give uniformly distributed safe superimposed load per lineal foot; no allowance for beams, purlins, or other concentrations.

WALLS FOR PITS

Pits are frequent in industrial and commercial structures. There are so many ways of designing the walls and of appraising the lateral pressure of the earth, that the walls tabulated below, reproduced from Volume I, and designed for a surcharge of 300 psf, $f_s = 20{,}000$ psi, $f'_c = 3{,}000$ psi, $n = 10$, ($p = 28.6$ psf) are sufficiently precise except when a thorough analysis is required.

If there is any possibility of seepage or spillage, pit floors should be sloped to a suitable drain or sump (with grease or oil trap if conditions require). Pits should have ladder rungs for easy access. Under wet soil conditions, pit walls should be water proofed with exterior membrane, ironiting, or integral waterproofing, to suit degree of exposure, with a continuous waterstop in construction joints. Floor slabs around pits often rest in a recess around top of wall to maintain floors flush with top of pit. Provide inserts for any pipe railings, curb angles, floor beams, or gratings.

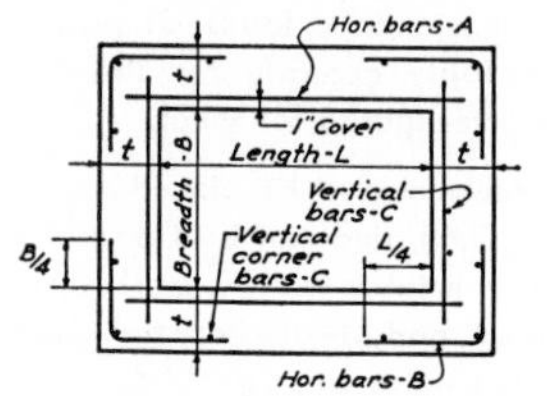

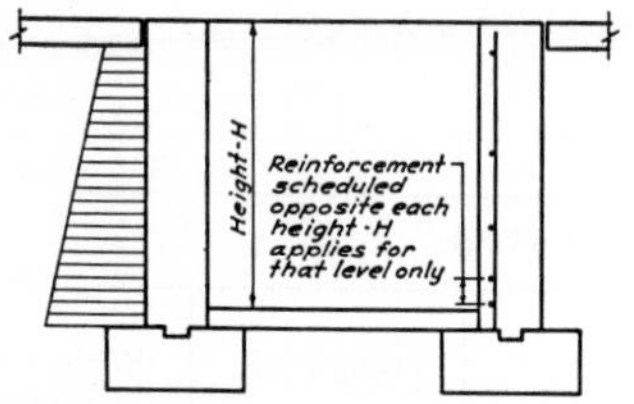

Case I—Rectangular, relatively deep, open-top pits of moderate length and width. For rectangular, moderately deep pits, especially when the bottom slab is not structurally integral, it is often economical to span the side walls as slabs from end wall to end wall, and the end walls from side wall to side wall, reinforcing around the corners to develop negative moments.

When $B \geq \frac{3}{4} L$, use distance L and same inside bars for all four walls; when $B < \frac{3L}{4}$, design as quadrangular frame.

Bars B are to be spaced same as Bars A and one size larger, viz., #5 for #4, and #6 for #5.

Height H	Bars A for Length L											Wall Thickness and Bars C
	10′-0	11′-0	12′-0	13′-0	14′-0	15′-0	16′-0	17′-0	18′-0	19′-0	20′-0	
7′-0	#4@12	#4@12	#4@12	#4@12	#4@12	#4@12	#4@12	#4@11	#4@10	#4@9	#4@8	t = 8″ C = #4@12
8′-0	#4@12	#4@12	#4@12	#4@11	#4@10	#4@9	#4@9	#4@8	#4@8	#5@12	#5@11	
9′-0	#4@12	#4@12	#4@11	#4@10	#4@9	#4@8	#5@12	#5@11	#5@10	#5@9	#5@9	
10′-0	#4@11	#4@10	#4@9	#4@8	#4@8	#5@11	#5@10	#5@9	#5@8	#5@8	#5@11	t = 10″ C = #4@10
11′-0	#4@10	#4@9	#4@8	#5@11	#5@10	#5@9	#5@8	#5@8	#5@10	#5@9	#5@9	
12′-0	#4@9	#4@8	#5@11	#5@10	#5@9	#5@8	#5@8	#5@10	#5@9	#5@8	#5@8	
13′-0	#4@8	#5@11	#5@10	#5@9	#5@8	#5@9	#5@10	#5@9	#5@8	#5@10	#5@9	t = 12″ C = #5@12
14′-0	#5@11	#5@10	#5@10	#5@8	#5@10	#5@9	#5@8	#5@8	#5@9	#5@9	#5@8	
15′-0	#5@10	#5@9	#5@8	#5@10	#5@9	#5@8	#5@8	#5@10	#5@8	#5@8	#6@10	

WALLS FOR PITS

Case II—Long, relatively shallow, open-top pits. For pits over, say, 20 ft on a side or with broken sides so that end walls can not lean against side walls, the simplest wall design is one vertically cantilevered from the floor slab. Wall thicknesses and reinforcement for various heights are scheduled.

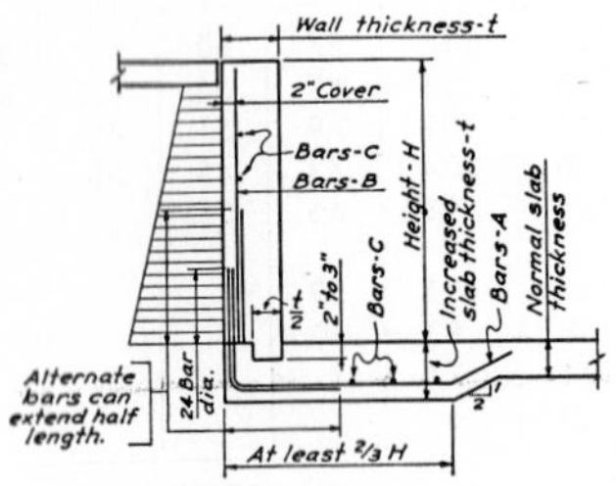

H	t	BARS		
		A	B	C
0 to 4′-0	8″	#4 @ 12	#4 @ 12	#4 @ 12
5′-0	8″	#5 @ 12	#4 @ 12	#4 @ 12
6′-0	8″	#5 @ 10	#4 @ 12	#4 @ 12
7′-0	8″	#6 @ 10	#4 @ 12	#4 @ 12
8′-0	10″	#6 @ 10	#5 @ 12	#5 @ 12
9′-0	10″	#7 @ 11	#5 @ 12	#5 @ 12
10′-0	10″	#7 @ 9	#5 @ 12	#5 @ 12

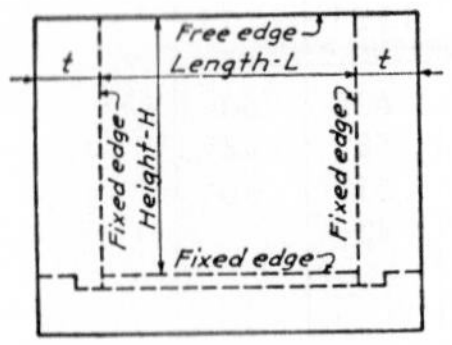

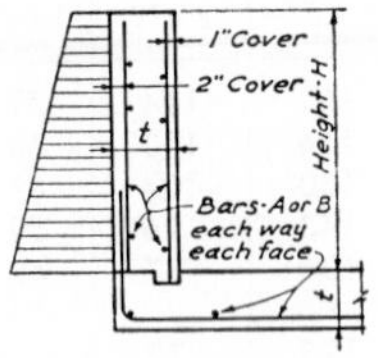

Case III—Cases I and II may combined into a wall fixed on th sides, free at the top, underg trapezoidal earth pressure, whic course, is somewhat more econ utilization of the reinforcemen

Height H	Bars A or B, Each Way, Each Face, in Length L										
	10′-0	11′-0	12′-0	13′-0	14′-0	15′-0	16′-0	17′-0	18′-0	19′-0	20′
7′-0	#4@12	#4@12	#4@12	#4@12	#4@12	#4@12	#5@12	#5@12	#5@12	#5@12	#
8′-0	#4@12	#4@12	#4@12	#5@12	#5@12	#5@12	#5@12	#5@12	#5@12	#5@12	
9′-0	#4@12	#4@12	#5@12	#5@12	#5@12	#5@12	#5@12	#5@12	#5@12	#5@1	
10′-0	#4@12	#5@12	#5@12	#5@12	#5@12	#5@12	#5@12	#5@12	#5@12	#5@	
11′-0	#5@12	#5@12	#5@12	#5@12	#5@12	#5@12	#5@12	#5@12	#5@12	#5	
12′-0	#5@12	#5@12	#5@12	#5@12	#5@12	#5@12	#5@12	#5@12	#5@12		
13′-0	#5@12	#5@12	#5@12	#5@12	#5@12	#5@12	#5@12	#5@12	#5@1		
14′-0	#5@12	#5@12	#5@12	#5@12	#5@12	#5@12	#5@12	#5@12	#5@		
15′-0	#5@12	#5@12	#5@12	#5@12	#5@12	#5@12	#5@12	#5@12	#5		

Case IV—Walls for pits with top slabs may be tre See page 13-17.

Value be tho

CARRYING CAPACITY OF REINFORCED CONCRETE LINTELS

The table on page 14-6 gives lintel designs to carry an equilateral triangle of wall. These tables give the safe superimposed uniformly distributed load per lineal foot on 8 x 8 and 8 x 12 in. lintels on spans of 4′-0″ to 12′-0″, again based upon ACI 318-56, 3000/20,000.

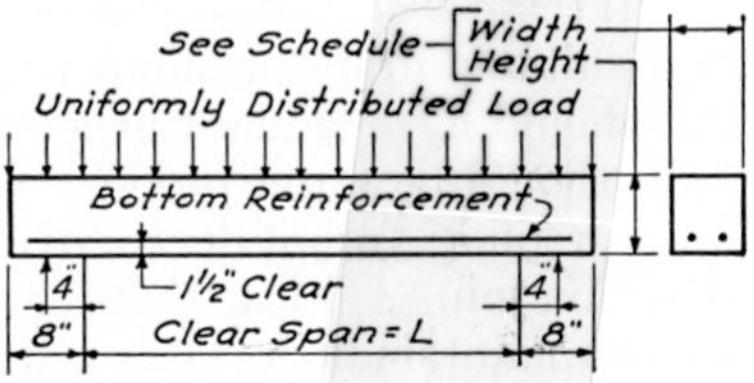

Concentrated loads can be approximated by the equivalent uniform loads on page 4-4, which are fairly accurate for flexure but should be investigated for shear.

The reinforcement *must* be placed in the bottom of the lintel, and can be the only reinforcement if lintel is plainly marked, carefully handled, and always kept right side up; otherwise see notes on page 14-6.

8 x 8 in. Nominal Lintels (7⅝ x 7⅝)

Clear Opening L	Reinforcement					Length of Lintel	Weight of Lintel (lb)
	2-#3	#3 + #4	2-#4	#4 + #5	2-#5		
4′-0	697	1010	1320	1545	1870	5′-4″	340
5′-0	452	662	870	1130	1386	6′-4″	405
6′-0	309	460	612	800	980	7′-4″	469
7′-0	218	330	446	586	730	8′-4″	533
8′-0	157	247	336	446	556	9′-4″	597
9′-0	93	186	258	346	436	10′-4″	661
10′-0	78	136	192	264	338	11′-4″	725
11′-0	58	108	157	219	280	12′-4″	790
12′-0	40	82	124	176	228	13′-4″	854

To left of heavy line, $f'_c = 2500$ or 3000 psi but to right of heavy line $f'_c \geqq 3000$ psi.

8 wide x 12 in. high Nominal Lintels (7⅝ x 11⅝)

Clear Opening L	Reinforcement						Length of Lintel	Weight of Lintel (lb)
	2-#4	#4 + #5	2-#5	#5 + #6	2-#6	#6 + #7		
4′-0″	2140	3020	3020	3020	3020	3020	5′-4″	513
5′-0″	1420	1830	2400	2400	2400	2400	6′-4″	609
6′-0″	995	1295	1445	1980	1980	1980	7′-4″	704
7′-0″	725	950	1065	1450	1690	1690	8′-4″	800
8′-0″	545	725	815	1115	1325	1460	9′-4″	896
9′-0″	420	565	635	880	1045	1255	10′-4″	992
10′-0″	315	430	490	680	815	980	11′-4″	1088
11′-0″	260	390	405	575	690	830	12′-4″	1184
12′-0″	205	290	330	470	570	690	13′-4″	1280

Below and to left of heavy line, $f'_c = 2500$ or 3000 psi, but above and to right of heavy line, $f'_c \geqq 3000$ psi. Either light weight or standard concrete may be used.

The above tables give uniformly distributed safe superimposed load per lineal foot; no allowance for beams, purlins, or other concentrations.

WALLS FOR PITS

Pits are frequent in industrial and commercial structures. There are so many ways of designing the walls and of appraising the lateral pressure of the earth, that the walls tabulated below, reproduced from Volume I, and designed for a surcharge of 300 psf, $f_s = 20{,}000$ psi, $f'_c = 3{,}000$ psi, $n = 10$, ($p = 28.6$ psf) are sufficiently precise except when a thorough analysis is required.

If there is any possibility of seepage or spillage, pit floors should be sloped to a suitable drain or sump (with grease or oil trap if conditions require). Pits should have ladder rungs for easy access. Under wet soil conditions, pit walls should be water proofed with exterior membrane, ironiting, or integral waterproofing, to suit degree of exposure, with a continuous waterstop in construction joints. Floor slabs around pits often rest in a recess around top of wall to maintain floors flush with top of pit. Provide inserts for any pipe railings, curb angles, floor beams, or gratings.

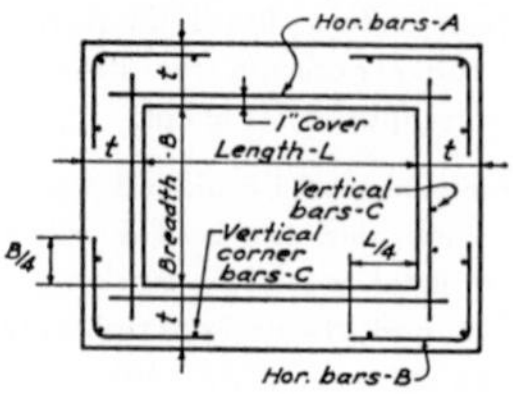

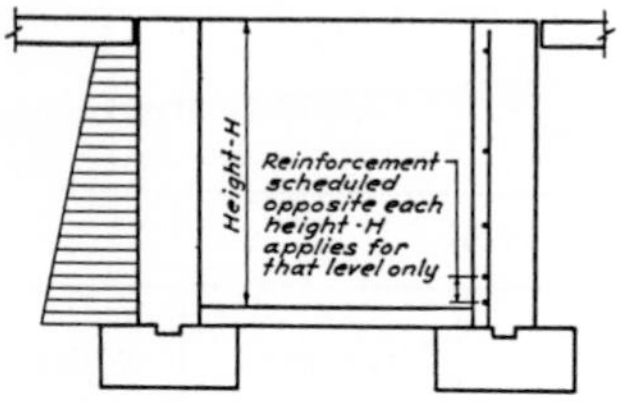

Case I—Rectangular, relatively deep, open-top pits of moderate length and width. For rectangular, moderately deep pits, especially when the bottom slab is not structurally integral, it is often economical to span the side walls as slabs from end wall to end wall, and the end walls from side wall to side wall, reinforcing around the corners to develop negative moments.

When $B \geq \frac{3}{4} L$, use distance L and same inside bars for all four walls; when $B < \frac{3L}{4}$, design as quadrangular frame.

Bars B are to be spaced same as Bars A and one size larger, viz., #5 for #4, and #6 for #5.

Height H	Bars A for Length L											Wall Thickness and Bars C
	10'-0	11'-0	12'-0	13'-0	14'-0	15'-0	16'-0	17'-0	18'-0	19'-0	20'-0	
7'-0	#4@12	#4@12	#4@12	#4@12	#4@12	#4@12	#4@12	#4@11	#4@10	#4@9	#4@8	t = 8" C = #4@12
8'-0	#4@12	#4@12	#4@12	#4@11	#4@10	#4@9	#4@9	#4@8	#4@8	#5@12	#5@11	
9'-0	#4@12	#4@12	#4@11	#4@10	#4@9	#4@8	#5@12	#5@11	#5@10	#5@9	#5@9	
10'-0	#4@11	#4@10	#4@9	#4@8	#4@8	#5@11	#5@10	#5@9	#5@8	#5@8	#5@11	t = 10" C = #4@10
11'-0	#4@10	#4@9	#4@8	#5@11	#5@10	#5@9	#5@8	#5@8	#5@10	#5@9	#5@9	
12'-0	#4@9	#4@8	#5@11	#5@10	#5@9	#5@8	#5@8	#5@10	#5@9	#5@8	#5@8	
13'-0	#4@8	#5@11	#5@10	#5@9	#5@8	#5@9	#5@10	#5@9	#5@8	#5@10	#5@9	t = 12" C = #5@12
14'-0	#5@11	#5@10	#5@10	#5@8	#5@10	#5@9	#5@8	#5@8	#5@9	#5@9	#5@8	
15'-0	#5@10	#5@9	#5@8	#5@10	#5@9	#5@8	#5@8	#5@10	#5@8	#5@8	#6@10	

WALLS FOR PITS

Case II—Long, relatively shallow, open-top pits. For pits over, say, 20 ft on a side or with broken sides so that end walls can not lean against side walls, the simplest wall design is one vertically cantilevered from the floor slab. Wall thicknesses and reinforcement for various heights are scheduled.

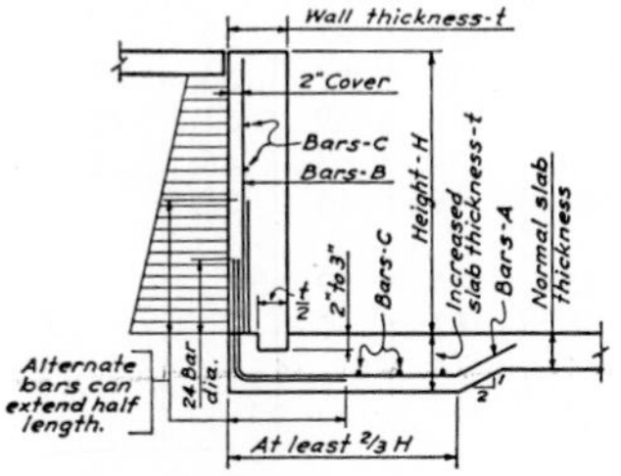

H	t	BARS		
		A	B	C
0 to 4′-0	8″	#4 @ 12	#4 @ 12	#4 @ 12
5′-0	8″	#5 @ 12	#4 @ 12	#4 @ 12
6′-0	8″	#5 @ 10	#4 @ 12	#4 @ 12
7′-0	8″	#6 @ 10	#4 @ 12	#4 @ 12
8′-0	10″	#6 @ 10	#5 @ 12	#5 @ 12
9′-0	10″	#7 @ 11	#5 @ 12	#5 @ 12
10′-0	10″	#7 @ 9	#5 @ 12	#5 @ 12

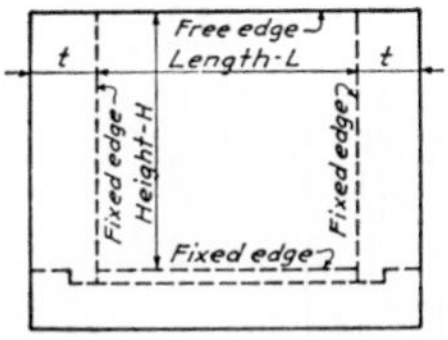

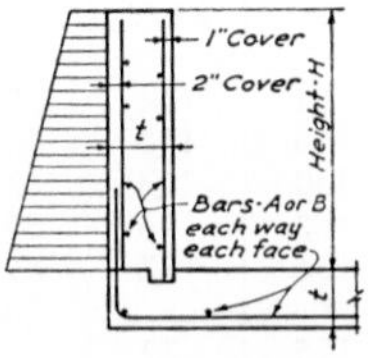

Case III—Cases I and II may be combined into a wall fixed on three sides, free at the top, undergoing trapezoidal earth pressure, which, of course, is somewhat more economical utilization of the reinforcement.

Height H	Bars A or B, Each Way, Each Face, in Length L											Wall Thickness t
	10′-0	11′-0	12′-0	13′-0	14′-0	15′-0	16′-0	17′-0	18′-0	19′-0	20′-0	
7′-0	#4@12	#4@12	#4@12	#4@12	#4@12	#4@12	#5@12	#5@12	#5@12	#5@12	#5@12	8″
8′-0	#4@12	#4@12	#4@12	#5@12	#5@12	#5@12	#5@12	#5@12	#5@12	#5@12	#5@12	10″
9′-0	#4@12	#4@12	#5@12	#5@12	#5@12	#5@12	#5@12	#5@12	#5@12	#5@12	#5@12	
10′-0	#4@12	#5@12	#5@12	#5@12	#5@12	#5@12	#5@12	#5@12	#5@12	#5@12	#5@12	12″
11′-0	#5@12	#5@12	#5@12	#5@12	#5@12	#5@12	#5@12	#5@12	#5@12	#5@12	#5@12	
12′-0	#5@12	#5@12	#5@12	#5@12	#5@12	#5@12	#5@12	#5@12	#5@12	#5@12	#5@12	15″
13′-0	#5@12	#5@12	#5@12	#5@12	#5@12	#5@12	#5@12	#5@12	#5@12	#5@12	#5@12	
14′-0	#5@12	#5@12	#5@12	#5@12	#5@12	#5@12	#5@12	#5@12	#5@12	#5@12		
15′-0	#5@12	#5@12	#5@12	#5@12	#5@12	#5@12	#5@12	#5@12	#5@12			

Case IV—Walls for pits with top slabs may be treated as basement walls. See page 13-17.

ALLOWABLE CONCENTRIC LOADS ON CONCRETE-FILLED STEEL PIPE COLUMNS

These tables are computed from ACI Equation (14-4).

STANDARD PIPE

Unbraced Length (ft)	Nominal Diameter—Weight Per Foot											
	12		10			8		6	5	4	3½	3
	49.56	43.77	40.48	34.24	31.20	28.55	24.70	18.97	14.62	10.79	9.11	7.58
6	350	323	272	243	229	185	167	117	87	60	49	39
8	347	320	269	240	226	182	165	114	83	56	45	34
10	344	317	265	237	223	178	161	109	79	51	40	29
12	340	313	261	233	219	173	156	104	73	45	33	
14	335	309	255	228	215	168	151	98	66	38		
16	329	303	249	222	209	161	145	91	59			
18	322	297	242	216	203	153	138	83	50			
20	315	290	234	209	196	145	131	74				
22	307	283	226	201	189	136	122	64				

EXTRA STRONG PIPE

Unbraced Length (ft)	Nominal Diameter—Weight Per Foot							
	12	10	8	6	5	4	3½	3
	65.42	54.74	43.39	28.57	20.78	14.98	12.51	10.25
6	424	339	254	161	114	79	63	50
8	421	335	250	156	110	73	58	44
10	417	330	244	150	104	67	51	36
12	412	325	238	143	96	59	43	
14	406	318	230	135	87	49		
16	399	310	221	125	77			
18	391	302	211	114	66			
20	383	292	199	101				
22	373	281	187					
24	363	270	173					

Values are computed only for $h/K_s \lesssim 120$. Properties of steel from which pipe is made are assumed to be those of ASTM A36.

SLABS ON GROUND *

For any slab on the ground, adequate preparation of subgrade for drainage and compaction is of prime importance. Dowelled expansion joints and weakened plane contraction joints should be carefully located, including expansion joints at all walls.

The design of slabs on the ground to distribute concentrated or uniform loads involves the elastic properties of the subsoil and the slab itself. An analysis can be made but is quite involved. Slabs for the very lightest occupancy should be not less than 4″ thick, and slabs for other occupancies may be empirically selected, the following being about minimum and sometimes less than what is required by ACI 807 for supported slabs:—

Occupancy **	Min. Slab Thickness	Reinforcement ‡
Sub-slabs under other slabs	2″	None
Domestic or light commercial (loaded less than 100 psf)	4″	One layer 6 x 6 10/10 welded wire fabric, minimum for ideal conditions; 6 x 6 8/8 for average conditions.
Commercial—institutional—barns (loaded 100-200 psf)	5″	One layer 6 x 6 8/8 welded wire fabric or one layer 6 x 6 6/6.
Industrial (loaded not over 400-500 psf) and pavements for industrial plants, gas stations, and garages	6″	One layer 6 x 6 6/6 welded wire fabric or one layer 6 x 6 4/4.
Industrial (loaded 600–800 psf) and heavy pavements for industrial plants, gas stations, and garages	6″	Two layers 6 x 6 6/6 welded wire fabric or two layers 6 x 6 4/4
Industrial (loaded 1500 psf) †	7″	Two mats of bars (one top, one bottom), each of #4 bars @ 12″ c/c, each way
Industrial (loaded 2500 psf) †	8″	Two mats of bars (one top, one bottom), each of #5 bars @ 12″ c/c, each way
Industrial (loaded 3000–3500 psf) †	9″	Two mats of bars (one top, one bottom), each of #5 bars @ 8″ to 12″ c/c, each way

* For further details, see "Concrete Floors on Ground," and "Concrete Airport Pavement," Portland Cement Association, 33 West Grand Avenue, Chicago, Illinois, 1952, and "Design of Concrete Floors on Ground for Warehouse Loadings," Aug. 1957 Journal, American Concrete Institute, P. O. Box 4754, Redford Sta., Detroit 19, Mich.

** For loads in excess of, say, 500 psf, use at least 3000 psi quality controlled concrete, and investigate subsoil conditions with extra care. Fill material and compaction should be equivalent to ordinary highway practice. If laboratory control of compaction is available, the load capacities can be increased in the ratio of the actual compaction coefficient, k, to 100.

† For loads in excess of, say, 1500 psf the subsoil conditions should be investigated with extra care.

‡ Place first layer of reinforcement 2 in. below top of slab; second layer, 2 in. up from bottom of slab.

Mathematical Tables

Section 15

TRIGONOMETRIC FORMULAS

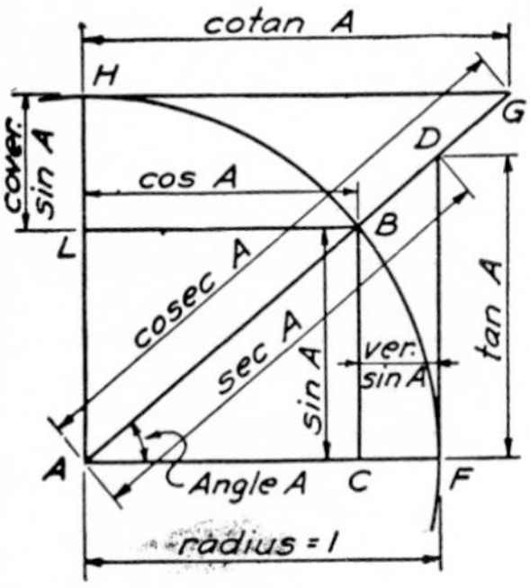

$$\text{Radius, } 1 = \sin^2 A + \cos^2 A = \sin A \operatorname{cosec} A = \cos A \sec A = \tan A \cot A$$

$$\text{Sine } A = \frac{\cos A}{\cot A} = \frac{1}{\operatorname{cosec} A} = \cos A \tan A = \sqrt{1 - \cos^2 A} = BC$$

$$\text{Cosine } A = \frac{\sin A}{\tan A} = \frac{1}{\sec A} = \sin A \cot A = \sqrt{1 - \sin^2 A} = AC$$

$$\text{Tangent } A = \frac{\sin A}{\cos A} = \frac{1}{\cot A} = \sin A \sec A = FD$$

$$\text{Cotangent } A = \frac{\cos A}{\sin A} = \frac{1}{\tan A} = \cos A \operatorname{cosec} A = GH$$

$$\text{Secant } A = \frac{\tan A}{\sin A} = \frac{1}{\cos A} = AD$$

$$\text{Cosecant } A = \frac{\cot A}{\cos A} = \frac{1}{\sin A} = AG$$

$$\sin (A \pm B) = \sin A \cos B \pm \cos A \sin B$$

$$\tan (A \pm B) = \frac{\tan A \pm \tan B}{1 \mp \tan A \tan B}$$

$$\cos (A \pm B) = \cos A \cos B \mp \sin A \sin B$$

$$\cot (A \pm B) = \frac{\cot A \cot B \mp 1}{\cot B \pm \cot A}$$

$$\sin A + \sin B = 2 \sin \tfrac{1}{2} (A + B) \cos \tfrac{1}{2} (A - B)$$

$$\tan A + \tan B = \frac{\sin (A + B)}{\cos A \cos B}$$

$$\sin A - \sin B = 2 \cos \tfrac{1}{2} (A + B) \sin \tfrac{1}{2} (A - B)$$

$$\tan A - \tan B = \frac{\sin (A - B)}{\cos A \cos B}$$

$$\cos A + \cos B = 2 \cos \tfrac{1}{2} (A + B) \cos \tfrac{1}{2} (A - B)$$

$$\cot A + \cot B = \frac{\sin (B + A)}{\sin A \sin B}$$

$$\cos B - \cos A = 2 \sin \tfrac{1}{2} (A + B) \sin \tfrac{1}{2} (A - B)$$

$$\cot A - \cot B = \frac{\sin (B - A)}{\sin A \sin B}$$

$$\sin 2A = 2 \sin A \cos A$$

$$\tan 2A = \frac{2 \tan A}{1 - \tan^2 A}$$

$$\cos 2A = \cos^2 A - \sin^2 A$$

$$\cot 2A = \frac{\cot^2 A - 1}{2 \cot A}$$

$$\sin \tfrac{1}{2}A = \sqrt{\frac{1 - \cos A}{2}} \qquad \cos \tfrac{1}{2}A = \sqrt{\frac{1 + \cos A}{2}}$$

$$\tan \tfrac{1}{2}A = \frac{\sin A}{1 + \cos A} \qquad \cot \tfrac{1}{2}A = \frac{\sin A}{1 - \cos A}$$

$$\sin^2 A = \frac{1 - \cos 2A}{2} \qquad \cos^2 A = \frac{1 + \cos 2A}{2}$$

$$\tan^2 A = \frac{1 - \cos 2A}{1 + \cos 2A} \qquad \cot^2 A = \frac{1 + \cos 2A}{1 - \cos 2A}$$

$$\sin^2 A - \sin^2 B = \sin (A + B) \sin (A - B)$$

$$\cos^2 A - \sin^2 B = \cos (A + B) \cos (A - B)$$

$$\frac{\sin A \pm \sin B}{\cos A + \cos B} = \tan \tfrac{1}{2}(A \pm B)$$

$$\frac{\sin A \pm \sin B}{\cos B - \cos A} = \cot \tfrac{1}{2}(A \mp B)$$

Quadrant	I	II	III	IV	Angle		
Angles	0° to 90°	90° to 180°	180° to 270°	270° to 360°	30°	45°	60°
Functions	Values vary from				Equivalent values		
sin	+0 to +1	+1 to +0	−0 to −1	−1 to −0	$\frac{1}{2}$	$\frac{1}{2}\sqrt{2}$	$\frac{1}{2}\sqrt{3}$
cos	+1 to +0	−0 to −1	−1 to −0	+0 to +1	$\frac{1}{2}\sqrt{3}$	$\frac{1}{2}\sqrt{2}$	$\frac{1}{2}$
tan	+0 to +∞	−∞ to −0	+0 to +∞	−∞ to −0	$\frac{1}{3}\sqrt{3}$	1	$\sqrt{3}$
cot	+∞ to +0	−0 to −∞	+∞ to +0	−0 to −∞	$\sqrt{3}$	1	$\frac{1}{3}\sqrt{3}$

Angle $a < 90°$				
Angle	sin	cos	tan	cot
$\phi°$	$\phi°$	$\phi°$	$\phi°$	$\phi°$
$0° \pm a$	$\pm \sin a$	$+\cos a$	$\pm \tan a$	$\pm \cot a$
$90° \pm a$	$+\cos a$	$\mp \sin a$	$\mp \cot a$	$\mp \tan a$
$180° \pm a$	$\mp \sin a$	$-\cos a$	$\pm \tan a$	$\pm \cot a$
$270° \pm a$	$-\cos a$	$\pm \sin a$	$\mp \cot a$	$\mp \tan a$

TRIGONOMETRIC SOLUTION OF TRIANGLES

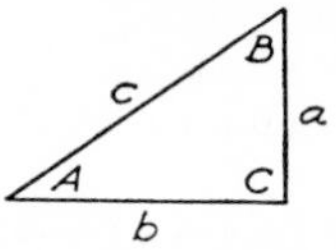

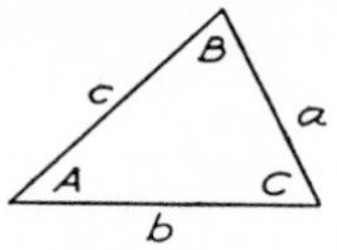

$$s = \frac{a+b+c}{2}$$

Given	Sought	Formulas
Right-Angled Triangles		
a, c	A, B, b	$\sin A = \frac{a}{c}$, $\cos B = \frac{a}{c}$, $b = \sqrt{c^2 - a^2}$
	Area	$\text{Area} = \frac{a}{2}\sqrt{c^2 - a^2}$
a, b	A, B, c	$\tan A = \frac{a}{b}$, $\tan B = \frac{b}{a}$, $c = \sqrt{a^2 + b^2}$
	Area	$\text{Area} = \frac{ab}{2}$
A, a	B, b, c	$B = 90° - A$, $b = a \cot A$, $c = \frac{a}{\sin A}$
	Area	$\text{Area} = \frac{a^2 \cot A}{2}$
A, b	B, a, c	$B = 90° - A$, $a = b \tan A$, $c = \frac{b}{\cos A}$
	Area	$\text{Area} = \frac{b^2 \tan A}{2}$
A, c	B, a, b	$B = 90° - A$, $a = c \sin A$, $b = c \cos A$
	Area	$\text{Area} = \frac{c^2 \sin A \cos A}{2} = \frac{c^2 \sin 2A}{4}$
Oblique-Angled Triangles		
a, b, c	A	$\sin \frac{1}{2} A = \sqrt{\frac{(s-b)(s-c)}{bc}}$, $\cos \frac{1}{2} A = \sqrt{\frac{s(s-a)}{bc}}$, $\tan \frac{1}{2} A = \sqrt{\frac{(s-b)(s-c)}{s(s-a)}}$
	B	$\sin \frac{1}{2} B = \sqrt{\frac{(s-a)(s-c)}{ac}}$, $\cos \frac{1}{2} B = \sqrt{\frac{s(s-b)}{ac}}$, $\tan \frac{1}{2} B = \sqrt{\frac{(s-a)(s-c)}{s(s-b)}}$
	C	$\sin \frac{1}{2} C = \sqrt{\frac{(s-a)(s-b)}{ab}}$, $\cos \frac{1}{2} C = \sqrt{\frac{s(s-c)}{ab}}$, $\tan \frac{1}{2} C = \sqrt{\frac{(s-a)(s-b)}{s(s-c)}}$
	Area	$\text{Area} = \sqrt{s(s-a)(s-b)(s-c)}$
a, A, B	b, c	$b = \frac{a \sin B}{\sin A}$, $c = \frac{a \sin C}{\sin A} = \frac{a \sin (A+B)}{\sin A}$
	Area	$\text{Area} = \frac{1}{2} ab \sin C = \frac{a^2 \sin B \sin C}{2 \sin A}$
a, b, A	B	$\sin B = \frac{b \sin A}{a}$
	c	$c = \frac{a \sin C}{\sin A} = \frac{b \sin C}{\sin B} = \sqrt{a^2 + b^2 - 2ab \cos C}$
	Area	$\text{Area} = \frac{1}{2} ab \sin C$
a, b, C	A	$\tan A = \frac{a \sin C}{b - a \cos C}$, $\tan \frac{1}{2}(A - B) = \frac{a-b}{a+b} \cot \frac{1}{2} C$
	c	$c = \sqrt{a^2 + b^2 - 2ab \cos C} = \frac{a \sin C}{\sin A}$
	Area	$\text{Area} = \frac{1}{2} ab \sin C$

$a^2 = b^2 + c^2 - 2bc \cos A$, $b^2 = a^2 + c^2 - 2ac \cos B$, $c^2 = a^2 + b^2 - 2ab \cos C$

NATURAL TRIGONOMETRIC FUNCTIONS

Degrees	SINES							Cosines
	0′	10′	20′	30′	40′	50′	60′	
0	0.00000	0.00291	0.00582	0.00873	0.01164	0.01454	0.01745	89
1	0.01745	0.02036	0.02327	0.02618	0.02908	0.03199	0.03490	88
2	0.03490	0.03781	0.04071	0.04362	0.04653	0.04943	0.05234	87
3	0.05234	0.05524	0.05814	0.06105	0.06395	0.06685	0.06976	86
4	0.06976	0.07266	0.07556	0.07846	0.08136	0.08426	0.08716	85
5	0.08716	0.09005	0.09295	0.09585	0.09874	0.10164	0.10453	84
6	0.10453	0.10742	0.11031	0.11320	0.11609	0.11898	0.12187	83
7	0.12187	0.12476	0.12764	0.13053	0.13341	0.13629	0.13917	82
8	0.13917	0.14205	0.14493	0.14781	0.15069	0.15356	0.15643	81
9	0.15643	0.15931	0.16218	0.16505	0.16792	0.17078	0.17365	80
10	0.17365	0.17651	0.17937	0.18224	0.18509	0.18795	0.19081	79
11	0.19081	0.19366	0.19652	0.19937	0.20222	0.20507	0.20791	78
12	0.20791	0.21076	0.21360	0.21644	0.21928	0.22212	0.22495	77
13	0.22495	0.22778	0.23062	0.23345	0.23627	0.23910	0.24192	76
14	0.24192	0.24474	0.24756	0.25038	0.25320	0.25601	0.25882	75
15	0.25882	0.26163	0.26443	0.26724	0.27004	0.27284	0.27564	74
16	0.27564	0.27843	0.28123	0.28402	0.28680	0.28959	0.29237	73
17	0.29237	0.29515	0.29793	0.30071	0.30348	0.30625	0.30902	72
18	0.30902	0.31178	0.31454	0.31730	0.32006	0.32282	0.32557	71
19	0.32557	0.32832	0.33106	0.33381	0.33655	0.33929	0.34202	70
20	0.34202	0.34475	0.34748	0.35021	0.35293	0.35565	0.35837	69
21	0.35837	0.36108	0.36379	0.36650	0.36921	0.37191	0.37461	68
22	0.37461	0.37730	0.37999	0.38268	0.38537	0.38805	0.39073	67
23	0.39073	0.39341	0.39608	0.39875	0.40142	0.40408	0.40674	66
24	0.40674	0.40939	0.41204	0.41469	0.41734	0.41998	0.42262	65
25	0.42262	0.42525	0.42788	0.43051	0.43313	0.43575	0.43837	64
26	0.43837	0.44098	0.44359	0.44620	0.44880	0.45140	0.45399	63
27	0.45399	0.45658	0.45917	0.46175	0.46433	0.46690	0.46947	62
28	0.46947	0.47204	0.47460	0.47716	0.47971	0.48226	0.48481	61
29	0.48481	0.48735	0.48989	0.49242	0.49495	0.49748	0.50000	60
30	0.50000	0.50252	0.50503	0.50754	0.51004	0.51254	0.51504	59
31	0.51504	0.51753	0.52002	0.52250	0.52498	0.52745	0.52992	58
32	0.52992	0.53238	0.53484	0.53730	0.53975	0.54220	0.54464	57
33	0.54464	0.54708	0.54951	0.55194	0.55436	0.55678	0.55919	56
34	0.55919	0.56160	0.56401	0.56641	0.56880	0.57119	0.57358	55
35	0.57358	0.57596	0.57833	0.58070	0.58307	0.58543	0.58779	54
36	0.58779	0.59014	0.59248	0.59482	0.59716	0.59949	0.60182	53
37	0.60182	0.60414	0.60645	0.60876	0.61107	0.61337	0.61566	52
38	0.61566	0.61795	0.62024	0.62251	0.62479	0.62706	0.62932	51
39	0.62932	0.63158	0.63383	0.63608	0.63832	0.64056	0.64279	50
40	0.64279	0.64501	0.64723	0.64945	0.65166	0.65386	0.65606	49
41	0.65606	0.65825	0.66044	0.66262	0.66480	0.66697	0.66913	48
42	0.66913	0.67129	0.67344	0.67559	0.67773	0.67987	0.68200	47
43	0.68200	0.68412	0.68624	0.68835	0.69046	0.69256	0.69466	46
44	0.69466	0.69675	0.69883	0.70091	0.70298	0.70505	0.70711	45
Sines	60′	50′	40′	30′	20′	10′	0′	Degrees
	COSINES							

NATURAL TRIGONOMETRIC FUNCTIONS

Degrees	COSINES 0′	10′	20′	30′	40′	50′	60′	Sines
0	1.00000	1.00000	0.99998	0.99996	0.99993	0.99989	0.99985	89
1	0.99985	0.99979	0.99973	0.99966	0.99958	0.99949	0.99939	88
2	0.99939	0.99929	0.99917	0.99905	0.99892	0.99878	0.99863	87
3	0.99863	0.99847	0.99831	0.99813	0.99795	0.99776	0.99756	86
4	0.99756	0.99736	0.99714	0.99692	0.99668	0.99644	0.99619	85
5	0.99619	0.99594	0.99567	0.99540	0.99511	0.99482	0.99452	84
6	0.99452	0.99421	0.99390	0.99357	0.99324	0.99290	0.99255	83
7	0.99255	0.99219	0.99182	0.99144	0.99106	0.99067	0.99027	82
8	0.99027	0.98986	0.98944	0.98902	0.98858	0.98814	0.98769	81
9	0.98769	0.98723	0.98676	0.98629	0.98580	0.98531	0.98481	80
10	0.98481	0.98430	0.98378	0.98325	0.98272	0.98218	0.98163	79
11	0.98163	0.98107	0.98050	0.97992	0.97934	0.97875	0.97815	78
12	0.97815	0.97754	0.97692	0.97630	0.97566	0.97502	0.97437	77
13	0.97437	0.97371	0.97304	0.97237	0.97169	0.97100	0.97030	76
14	0.97030	0.96959	0.96887	0.96815	0.96742	0.96667	0.96593	75
15	0.96593	0.96517	0.96440	0.96363	0.96285	0.96206	0.96126	74
16	0.96126	0.96046	0.95964	0.95882	0.95799	0.95715	0.95630	73
17	0.95630	0.95545	0.95459	0.95372	0.95284	0.95195	0.95106	72
18	0.95106	0.95015	0.94924	0.94832	0.94740	0.94646	0.94552	71
19	0.94552	0.94457	0.94361	0.94264	0.94167	0.94068	0.93969	70
20	0.93969	0.93869	0.93769	0.93667	0.93565	0.93462	0.93358	69
21	0.93358	0.93253	0.93148	0.93042	0.92935	0.92827	0.92718	68
22	0.92718	0.92609	0.92499	0.92388	0.92276	0.92164	0.92050	67
23	0.92050	0.91936	0.91822	0.91706	0.91590	0.91472	0.91355	66
24	0.91355	0.91236	0.91116	0.90996	0.90875	0.90753	0.90631	65
25	0.90631	0.90507	0.90383	0.90259	0.90133	0.90007	0.89879	64
26	0.89879	0.89752	0.89623	0.89493	0.89363	0.89232	0.89101	63
27	0.89101	0.88968	0.88835	0.88701	0.88566	0.88431	0.88295	62
28	0.88295	0.88158	0.88020	0.87882	0.87743	0.87603	0.87462	61
29	0.87462	0.87321	0.87178	0.87036	0.86892	0.86748	0.86603	60
30	0.86603	0.86457	0.86310	0.86163	0.86015	0.85866	0.85717	59
31	0.85717	0.85567	0.85416	0.85264	0.85112	0.84959	0.84805	58
32	0.84805	0.84650	0.84495	0.84339	0.84182	0.84025	0.83867	57
33	0.83867	0.83708	0.83549	0.83389	0.83228	0.83066	0.82904	56
34	0.82904	0.82741	0.82577	0.82413	0.82248	0.82082	0.81915	55
35	0.81915	0.81748	0.81580	0.81412	0.81242	0.81072	0.80902	54
36	0.80902	0.80730	0.80558	0.80386	0.80212	0.80038	0.79864	53
37	0.79864	0.79688	0.79512	0.79335	0.79158	0.78980	0.78801	52
38	0.78801	0.78622	0.78442	0.78261	0.78079	0.77897	0.77715	51
39	0.77715	0.77531	0.77347	0.77162	0.76977	0.76791	0.76604	50
40	0.76604	0.76417	0.76229	0.76041	0.75851	0.75661	0.75471	49
41	0.75471	0.75280	0.75088	0.74896	0.74703	0.74509	0.74314	48
42	0.74314	0.74120	0.73924	0.73728	0.73531	0.73333	0.73135	47
43	0.73135	0.72937	0.72737	0.72537	0.72337	0.72136	0.71934	46
44	0.71934	0.71732	0.71529	0.71325	0.71121	0.70916	0.70711	45
Cosines	60′	50′	40′	30′	20′	10′	0′ SINES	Degrees

NATURAL TRIGONOMETRIC FUNCTIONS

Degrees	TANGENTS 0′	10′	20′	30′	40′	50′	60′	Cotangents
0	0.00000	0.00291	0.00582	0.00873	0.01164	0.01455	0.01746	89
1	0.01746	0.02036	0.02328	0.02619	0.02910	0.03201	0.03492	88
2	0.03492	0.03783	0.04075	0.04366	0.04658	0.04949	0.05241	87
3	0.05241	0.05533	0.05824	0.06116	0.06408	0.06700	0.06993	86
4	0.06993	0.07285	0.07578	0.07870	0.08163	0.08456	0.08749	85
5	0.08749	0.09042	0.09335	0.09629	0.09923	0 10216	0.10510	84
6	0.10510	0.10805	0.11099	0.11394	0.11688	0.11983	0.12278	83
7	0.12278	0.12574	0.12869	0.13165	0.13461	0.13758	0.14054	82
8	0.14054	0.14351	0.14648	0.14945	0.15243	0.15540	0.15838	81
9	0.15838	0.16137	0.16435	0.16734	0.17033	0.17333	0.17633	80
10	0.17633	0.17933	0.18233	0.18534	0.18835	0.19136	0.19438	79
11	0.19438	0.19740	0.20042	0.20345	0.20648	0.20952	0.21256	78
12	0.21256	0.21560	0.21864	0.22169	0.22475	0.22781	0.23087	77
13	0.23087	0.23393	0.23700	0.24008	0.24316	0.24624	0.24933	76
14	0.24933	0.25242	0.25552	0.25862	0.26172	0.26483	0.26795	75
15	0.26795	0.27107	0.27419	0.27732	0.28046	0.28360	0.28675	74
16	0.28675	0.28990	0.29305	0.29621	0.29938	0.30255	0.30573	73
17	0.30573	0.30891	0.31210	0.31530	0.31850	0.32171	0.32492	72
18	0.32492	0.32814	0.33136	0.33460	0.33783	0.34108	0.34433	71
19	0.34433	0.34758	0.35085	0.35412	0.35740	0.36068	0.36397	70
20	0.36397	0.36727	0.37057	0.37388	0.37720	0.38053	0.38386	69
21	0.38386	0.38721	0.39055	0.39391	0.39727	0.40065	0.40403	68
22	0.40403	0.40741	0.41081	0.41421	0.41763	0.42105	0.42447	67
23	0.42447	0.42791	0.43136	0.43481	0.43828	0.44175	0.44523	66
24	0.44523	0.44872	0.45222	0.45573	0.45924	0.46277	0.46631	65
25	0.46631	0.46985	0.47341	0.47698	0.48055	0.48414	0.48773	64
26	0.48773	0.49134	0.49495	0.49858	0.50222	0.50587	0.50953	63
27	0.50953	0.51320	0.51688	0.52057	0.52427	0.52798	0.53171	62
28	0.53171	0.53545	0.53920	0.54296	0.54674	0.55051	0.55431	61
29	0.55431	0.55812	0.56194	0.56577	0.56962	0.57348	0.57735	60
30	0.57735	0.58124	0.58513	0.58905	0.59297	0.59691	0.60086	59
31	0.60086	0.60483	0.60881	0.61280	0.61681	0.62083	0.62487	58
32	0.62487	0.62892	0.63299	0.63707	0.64117	0.64528	0.64941	57
33	0.64941	0.65355	0.65771	0.66189	0.66608	0.67028	0.67451	56
34	0.67451	0.67875	0.68301	0.68728	0.69157	0.69588	0.70021	55
35	0.70021	0.70455	0.70891	0.71329	0.71769	0.72211	0.72654	54
36	0.72654	0.73100	0.73547	0.73996	0.74447	0.74900	0.75355	53
37	0.75355	0.75812	0.76272	0.76733	0.77196	0.77661	0.78129	52
38	0.78129	0.78598	0.79070	0.79544	0.80020	0.80498	0.80978	51
39	0.80978	0.81461	0.81946	0.82434	0.82923	0.83415	0.83910	50
40	0.83910	0.84407	0.84906	0.85408	0.85912	0.86419	0.86929	49
41	0.86929	0.87441	0.87955	0.88473	0.88992	0.89515	0.90040	48
42	0.90040	0.90569	0.91099	0.91633	0.92170	0.92709	0.93252	47
43	0.93252	0.93797	0.94345	0.94896	0.95451	0.96008	0.96569	46
44	0.96569	0.97133	0.97700	0.98270	0.98843	0.99420	1.00000	45
Tangents	COTANGENTS 60′	50′	40′	30′	20′	10′	0′	Degrees

NATURAL TRIGONOMETRIC FUNCTIONS

Degrees	COTANGENTS							Tangents
	0′	10′	20′	30′	40′	50′	60′	
0	∞	343.77371	171.88540	114.58865	85.93979	68.75009	57.28996	89
1	57.28996	49.10388	42.96408	38.18846	34.36777	31.24158	28.63625	88
2	28.63625	26.43160	24.54176	22.90377	21.47040	20.20555	19.08114	87
3	19.08114	18.07498	17.16934	16.34986	15.60478	14.92442	14.30067	86
4	14.30067	13.72674	13.19688	12.70621	12.25051	11.82617	11.43005	85
5	11.43005	11.05943	10.71191	10.38540	10.07803	9.78817	9.51436	84
6	9.51436	9.25530	9.00983	8.77689	8.55555	8.34496	8.14435	83
7	8.14435	7.95302	7.77035	7.59575	7.42871	7.26873	7.11537	82
8	7.11537	6.96823	6.82694	6.69116	6.56055	6.43484	6.31375	81
9	6.31375	6.19703	6.08444	5.97576	5.87080	5.76937	5.67128	80
10	5.67128	5.57638	5.48451	5.39552	5.30928	5.22566	5.14455	79
11	5.14455	5.06584	4.98940	4.91516	4.84300	4.77286	4.70463	78
12	4.70463	4.63825	4.57363	4.51071	4.44942	4.38969	4.33148	77
13	4.33148	4.27471	4.21933	4.16530	4.11256	4.06107	4.01078	76
14	4.01078	3.96165	3.91364	3.86671	3.82083	3.77595	3.73205	75
15	3.73205	3.68909	3.64705	3.60588	3.56557	3.52609	3.48741	74
16	3.48741	3.44951	3.41236	3.37594	3.34023	3.30521	3.27085	73
17	3.27085	3.23714	3.20406	3.17159	3.13972	3.10842	3.07768	72
18	3.07768	3.04749	3.01783	2.98869	2.96004	2.93189	2.90421	71
19	2.90421	2.87700	2.85023	2.82391	2.79802	2.77254	2.74748	70
20	2.74748	2.72281	2.69853	2.67462	2.65109	2.62791	2.60509	69
21	2.60509	2.58261	2.56046	2.53865	2.51715	2.49597	2.47509	68
22	2.47509	2.45451	2.43422	2.41421	2.39449	2.37504	2.35585	67
23	2.35585	2.33693	2.31826	2.29984	2.28167	2.26374	2.24604	66
24	2.24604	2.22857	2.21132	2.19430	2.17749	2.16090	2.14451	65
25	2.14451	2.12832	2.11233	2.09654	2.08094	2.06553	2.05030	64
26	2.05030	2.03526	2.02039	2.00569	1.99116	1.97680	1.96261	63
27	1.96261	1.94858	1.93470	1.92098	1.90741	1.89400	1.88073	62
28	1.88073	1.86760	1.85462	1.84177	1.82907	1.81649	1.80405	61
29	1.80405	1.79174	1.77955	1.76749	1.75556	1.74375	1.73205	60
30	1.73205	1.72047	1.70901	1.69766	1.68643	1.67530	1.66428	59
31	1.66428	1.65337	1.64256	1.63185	1.62125	1.61074	1.60033	58
32	1.60033	1.59002	1.57981	1.56969	1.55966	1.54972	1.53987	57
33	1.53987	1.53010	1.52043	1.51084	1.50133	1.49190	1.48256	56
34	1.48256	1.47330	1.46411	1.45501	1.44598	1.43703	1.42815	55
35	1.42815	1.41934	1.41061	1.40195	1.39336	1.38484	1.37638	54
36	1.37638	1.36800	1.35968	1.35142	1.34323	1.33511	1.32704	53
37	1.32704	1.31904	1.31110	1.30323	1.29541	1.28764	1.27994	52
38	1.27994	1.27230	1.26471	1.25717	1.24969	1.24227	1.23490	51
39	1.23490	1.22758	1.22031	1.21310	1.20593	1.19882	1.19175	50
40	1.19175	1.18474	1.17777	1.17085	1.16398	1.15715	1.15037	49
41	1.15037	1.14363	1.13694	1.13029	1.12369	1.11713	1.11061	48
42	1.11061	1.10414	1.09770	1.09131	1.08496	1.07864	1.07237	47
43	1.07237	1.06613	1.05994	1.05378	1.04766	1.04158	1.03553	46
44	1.03553	1.02952	1.02355	1.01761	1.01170	1.00583	1.00000	45
Cotangents	60′	50′	40′	30′	20′	10′	0′	Degrees
	TANGENTS							

NATURAL TRIGONOMETRIC FUNCTIONS

Degrees	SECANTS							Cosecants
	0′	10′	20′	30′	40′	50′	60′	
0	1.00000	1.00000	1.00002	1.00004	1.00007	1.00011	1.00015	89
1	1.00015	1.00021	1.00027	1.00034	1.00042	1.00051	1.00061	88
2	1.00061	1.00072	1.00083	1.00095	1.00108	1.00122	1.00137	87
3	1.00137	1.00153	1.00169	1.00187	1.00205	1.00224	1.00244	86
4	1.00244	1.00265	1.00287	1.00309	1.00333	1.00357	1.00382	85
5	1.00382	1.00408	1.00435	1.00463	1.00491	1.00521	1.00551	84
6	1.00551	1.00582	1.00614	1.00647	1.00681	1.00715	1.00751	83
7	1.00751	1.00787	1.00825	1.00863	1.00902	1.00942	1.00983	82
8	1.00983	1.01024	1.01067	1.01111	1.01155	1.01200	1.01247	81
9	1.01247	1.01294	1.01342	1.01391	1.01440	1.01491	1.01543	80
10	1.01543	1.01595	1.01649	1.01703	1.01758	1.01815	1.01872	79
11	1.01872	1.01930	1.01989	1.02049	1.02110	1.02171	1.02234	78
12	1.02234	1.02298	1.02362	1.02428	1.02494	1.02562	1.02630	77
13	1.02630	1.02700	1.02770	1.02842	1.02914	1.02987	1.03061	76
14	1.03061	1.03137	1.03213	1.03290	1.03368	1.03447	1.03528	75
15	1.03528	1.03609	1.03691	1.03774	1.03858	1.03944	1.04030	74
16	1.04030	1.04117	1.04206	1.04295	1.04385	1.04477	1.04569	73
17	1.04569	1.04663	1.04757	1.04853	1.04950	1.05047	1.05146	72
18	1.05146	1.05246	1.05347	1.05449	1.05552	1.05657	1.05762	71
19	1.05762	1.05869	1.05976	1.06085	1.06195	1.06306	1.06418	70
20	1.06418	1.06531	1.06645	1.06761	1.06878	1.06995	1.07115	69
21	1.07115	1.07235	1.07356	1.07479	1.07602	1.07727	1.07853	68
22	1.07853	1.07981	1.08109	1.08239	1.08370	1.08503	1.08636	67
23	1.08636	1.08771	1.08907	1.09044	1.09183	1.09323	1.09464	66
24	1.09464	1.09606	1.09750	1.09895	1.10041	1.10189	1.10338	65
25	1.10338	1.10488	1.10640	1.10793	1.10947	1.11103	1.11260	64
26	1.11260	1.11419	1.11579	1.11740	1.11903	1.12067	1.12233	63
27	1.12233	1.12400	1.12568	1.12738	1.12910	1.13083	1.13257	62
28	1.13257	1.13433	1.13610	1.13789	1.13970	1.14152	1.14335	61
29	1.14335	1.14521	1.14707	1.14896	1.15085	1.15277	1.15470	60
30	1.15470	1.15665	1.15861	1.16059	1.16259	1.16460	1.16663	59
31	1.16663	1.16868	1.17075	1.17283	1.17493	1.17704	1.17918	58
32	1.17918	1.18133	1.18350	1.18569	1.18790	1.19012	1.19236	57
33	1.19236	1.19463	1.19691	1.19920	1.20152	1.20386	1.20622	56
34	1.20622	1.20859	1.21099	1.21341	1.21584	1.21830	1.22077	55
35	1.22077	1.22327	1.22579	1.22833	1.23089	1.23347	1.23607	54
36	1.23607	1.23869	1.24134	1.24400	1.24669	1.24940	1.25214	53
37	1.25214	1.25489	1.25767	1.26047	1.26330	1.26615	1.26902	52
38	1.26902	1.27191	1.27483	1.27778	1.28075	1.28374	1.28676	51
39	1.28676	1.28980	1.29287	1.29597	1.29909	1.30223	1.30541	50
40	1.30541	1.30861	1.31183	1.31509	1.31837	1.32168	1.32501	49
41	1.32501	1.32838	1.33177	1.33519	1.33864	1.34212	1.34563	48
42	1.34563	1.34917	1.35274	1.35634	1.35997	1.36363	1.36733	47
43	1.36733	1.37105	1.37481	1.37860	1.38242	1.38628	1.39016	46
44	1.39016	1.39409	1.39804	1.40203	1.40606	1.41012	1.41421	45
Secants	60′	50′	40′	30′	20′	10′	0′	Degrees
	COSECANTS							

NATURAL TRIGONOMETRIC FUNCTIONS

Degrees	COSECANTS 0′	10′	20′	30′	40′	50′	60′	Secants
0	∞	343.77516	171.88831	114.59301	85.94561	68.75736	57.29869	89
1	57.29869	49.11406	42.97571	38.20155	34.38232	31.25758	28.65371	88
2	28.65371	26.45051	24.56212	22.92559	21.49368	20.23028	19.10732	87
3	19.10732	18.10262	17.19843	16.38041	15.63679	14.95788	14.33559	86
4	14.33559	13.76312	13.23472	12.74550	12.29125	11.86837	11.47371	85
5	11.47371	11.10455	10.75849	10.43343	10.12752	9.83912	9.56677	84
6	9.56677	9.30917	9.06515	8.83367	8.61379	8.40466	8.20551	83
7	8.20551	8.01565	7.83443	7.66130	7.49571	7.33719	7.18530	82
8	7.18530	7.03962	6.89979	6.76547	6.63633	6.51208	6.39245	81
9	6.39245	6.27719	6.16607	6.05886	5.95536	5.85539	5.75877	80
10	5.75877	5.66533	5.57493	5.48740	5.40263	5.32049	5.24084	79
11	5.24084	5.16359	5.08863	5.01585	4.94517	4.87649	4.80973	78
12	4.80973	4.74482	4.68167	4.62023	4.56041	4.50216	4.44541	77
13	4.44541	4.39012	4.33622	4.28366	4.23239	4.18238	4.13357	76
14	4.13357	4.08591	4.03938	3.99393	3.94952	3.90613	3.86370	75
15	3.86370	3.82223	3.78166	3.74198	3.70315	3.66515	3.62796	74
16	3.62796	3.59154	3.55587	3.52094	3.48671	3.45317	3.42030	73
17	3.42030	3.38808	3.35649	3.32551	3.29512	3.26531	3.23607	72
18	3.23607	3.20737	3.17920	3.15155	3.12440	3.09774	3.07155	71
19	3.07155	3.04584	3.02057	2.99574	2.97135	2.94737	2.92380	70
20	2.92380	2.90063	2.87785	2.85545	2.83342	2.81175	2.79043	69
21	2.79043	2.76945	2.74881	2.72850	2.70851	2.68884	2.66947	68
22	2.66947	2.65040	2.63162	2.61313	2.59491	2.57698	2.55930	67
23	2.55930	2.54190	2.52474	2.50784	2.49119	2.47477	2.45859	66
24	2.45859	2.44264	2.42692	2.41142	2.39614	2.38107	2.36620	65
25	2.36620	2.35154	2.33708	2.32282	2.30875	2.29487	2.28117	64
26	2.28117	2.26766	2.25432	2.24116	2.22817	2.21535	2.20269	63
27	2.20269	2.19019	2.17786	2.16568	2.15366	2.14178	2.13005	62
28	2.13005	2.11847	2.10704	2.09574	2.08458	2.07356	2.06267	61
29	2.06267	2.05191	2.04128	2.03077	2.02039	2.01014	2.00000	60
30	2.00000	1.98998	1.98008	1.97029	1.96062	1.95106	1.94160	59
31	1.94160	1.93226	1.92302	1.91388	1.90485	1.89591	1.88709	58
32	1.88708	1.87834	1.86970	1.86116	1.85271	1.84435	1.83608	57
33	1.83608	1.82790	1.81981	1.81180	1.80388	1.79604	1.78829	56
34	1.78829	1.78062	1.77303	1.76552	1.75808	1.75073	1.74345	55
35	1.74345	1.73624	1.72911	1.72205	1.71506	1.70815	1.70130	54
36	1.70130	1.69452	1.68782	1.68117	1.67460	1.66809	1.66164	53
37	1.66164	1.65526	1.64894	1.64268	1.63648	1.63035	1.62427	52
38	1.62427	1.61825	1.61229	1.60639	1.60054	1.59475	1.58902	51
39	1.58902	1.58333	1.57771	1.57213	1.56661	1.56114	1.55572	50
40	1.55572	1.55036	1.54504	1.53977	1.53455	1.52938	1.52425	49
41	1.52425	1.51918	1.51415	1.50916	1.50422	1.49933	1.49448	48
42	1.49448	1.48967	1.48491	1.48019	1.47551	1.47087	1.46628	47
43	1.46628	1.46173	1.45721	1.45274	1.44831	1.44391	1.43956	46
44	1.43956	1.43524	1.43096	1.42672	1.42251	1.41835	1.41421	45
Cosecants	60′	50′	40′	30′	20′	10′	0′	Degrees
	SECANTS							

FUNCTIONS OF NUMBERS, 1 to 50

No.	Square	Cube	Square Root	Cube Root	Logarithm	1000 x Reciprocal	No. = Diameter	
							Circum	Area
1	1	1	1.0000	1.0000	0.00000	1000.000	3.142	0.7854
2	4	8	1.4142	1.2599	0.30103	500.000	6.283	3.1416
3	9	27	1.7321	1.4422	0.47712	333.333	9.425	7.0686
4	16	64	2.0000	1.5874	0.60206	250.000	12.566	12.5664
5	25	125	2.2361	1.7100	0.69897	200.000	15.708	19.6350
6	36	216	2.4495	1.8171	0.77815	166.667	18.850	28.2743
7	49	343	2.6458	1.9129	0.84510	142.857	21.991	38.4845
8	64	512	2.8284	2.0000	0.90309	125.000	25.133	50.2655
9	81	729	3.0000	2.0801	0.95424	111.111	28.274	63.6173
10	100	1000	3.1623	2.1544	1.00000	100.000	31.416	78.5398
11	121	1331	3.3166	2.2240	1.04139	90.9091	34.558	95.0332
12	144	1728	3.4641	2.2894	1.07918	83.3333	37.699	113.097
13	169	2197	3.6056	2.3513	1.11394	76.9231	40.841	132.732
14	196	2744	3.7417	2.4101	1.14613	71.4286	43.982	153.938
15	225	3375	3.8730	2.4662	1.17609	66.6667	47.124	176.715
16	256	4096	4.0000	2.5198	1.20412	62.5000	50.265	201.062
17	289	4913	4.1231	2.5713	1.23045	58.8235	53.407	226.980
18	324	5832	4.2426	2.6207	1.25527	55.5556	56.549	254.469
19	361	6859	4.3589	2.6684	1.27875	52.6316	59.690	283.529
20	400	8000	4.4721	2.7144	1.30103	50.0000	62.832	314.159
21	441	9261	4.5826	2.7589	1.32222	47.6190	65.973	346.361
22	484	10648	4.6904	2.8020	1.34242	45.4545	69.115	380.133
23	529	12167	4.7958	2.8439	1.36173	43.4783	72.257	415.476
24	576	13824	4.8990	2.8845	1.38021	41.6667	75.398	452.389
25	625	15625	5.0000	2.9240	1.39794	40.0000	78.540	490.874
26	676	17576	5.0990	2.9625	1.41497	38.4615	81.681	530.929
27	729	19683	5.1962	3.0000	1.43136	37.0370	84.823	572.555
28	784	21952	5.2915	3.0366	1.44716	35.7143	87.965	615.752
29	841	24389	5.3852	3.0723	1.46240	34.4828	91.106	660.520
30	900	27000	5.4772	3.1072	1.47712	33.3333	94.248	706.858
31	961	29791	5.5678	3.1414	1.49136	32.2581	97.389	754.768
32	1024	32768	5.6569	3.1748	1.50515	31.2500	100.53	804.248
33	1089	35937	5.7446	3.2075	1.51851	30.3030	103.67	855.299
34	1156	39304	5.8310	3.2396	1.53148	29.4118	106.81	907.920
35	1225	42875	5.9161	3.2711	1.54407	28.5714	109.96	962.113
36	1296	46656	6.0000	3.3019	1.55630	27.7778	113.10	1017.88
37	1369	50653	6.0828	3.3322	1.56820	27.0270	116.24	1075.21
38	1444	54872	6.1644	3.3620	1.57978	26.3158	119.38	1134.11
39	1521	59319	6.2450	3.3912	1.59106	25.6410	122.52	1194.59
40	1600	64000	6.3246	3.4200	1.60206	25.0000	125.66	1256.64
41	1681	68921	6.4031	3.4482	1.61278	24.3902	128.81	1320.25
42	1764	74088	6.4807	3.4760	1.62325	23.8095	131.95	1385.44
43	1849	79507	6.5574	3.5034	1.63347	23.2558	135.09	1452.20
44	1936	85184	6.6332	3.5303	1.64345	22.7273	138.23	1520.53
45	2025	91125	6.7082	3.5569	1.65321	22.2222	141.37	1590.43
46	2116	97336	6.7823	3.5830	1.66276	21.7391	144.51	1661.90
47	2209	103823	6.8557	3.6088	1.67210	21.2766	147.65	1734.94
48	2304	110592	6.9282	3.6342	1.68124	20.8333	150.80	1809.56
49	2401	117649	7.0000	3.6593	1.69020	20.4082	153.94	1885.74
50	2500	125000	7.0711	3.6840	1.69897	20.0000	157.08	1963.50

FUNCTIONS OF NUMBERS, 51 to 100

No.	Square	Cube	Square Root	Cube Root	Logarithm	1000 x Reciprocal	No. = Diameter	
							Circum	Area
51	2601	132651	7.1414	3.7084	1.70757	19.6078	160.22	2042.82
52	2704	140608	7.2111	3.7325	1.71600	19.2308	163.36	2123.72
53	2809	148877	7.2801	3.7563	1.72428	18.8679	166.50	2206.18
54	2916	157464	7.3485	3.7798	1.73239	18.5185	169.65	2290.22
55	3025	166375	7.4162	3.8030	1.74036	18.1818	172.79	2375.83
56	3136	175616	7.4833	3.8259	1.74819	17.8571	175.93	2463.01
57	3249	185193	7.5498	3.8485	1.75587	17.5439	179.07	2551.76
58	3364	195112	7.6158	3.8709	1.76343	17.2414	182.21	2642.08
59	3481	205379	7.6811	3.8930	1.77085	16.9492	185.35	2733.97
60	3600	216000	7.7460	3.9149	1.77815	16.6667	188.50	2827.43
61	3721	226981	7.8102	3.9365	1.78533	16.3934	191.64	2922.47
62	3844	238328	7.8740	3.9579	1.79239	16.1290	194.78	3019.07
63	3969	250047	7.9373	3.9791	1.79934	15.8730	197.92	3117.25
64	4096	262144	8.0000	4.0000	1.80618	15.6250	201.06	3216.99
65	4225	274625	8.0623	4.0207	1.81291	15.3846	204.20	3318.31
66	4356	287496	8.1240	4.0412	1.81954	15.1515	207.35	3421.19
67	4489	300763	8.1854	4.0615	1.82607	14.9254	210.49	3525.65
68	4624	314432	8.2462	4.0817	1.83251	14.7059	213.63	3631.68
69	4761	328509	8.3066	4.1016	1.83885	14.4928	216.77	3739.28
70	4900	343000	8.3666	4.1213	1.84510	14.2857	219.91	3848.45
71	5041	357911	8.4261	4.1408	1.85126	14.0845	223.05	3959.19
72	5184	373248	8.4853	4.1602	1.85733	13.8889	226.19	4071.50
73	5329	389017	8.5440	4.1793	1.86332	13.6986	229.34	4185.39
74	5476	405224	8.6023	4.1983	1.86923	13.5135	232.48	4300.84
75	5625	421875	8.6603	4.2172	1.87506	13.3333	235.62	4417.86
76	5776	438976	8.7178	4.2358	1.88081	13.1579	238.76	4536.46
77	5929	456533	8.7750	4.2543	1.88649	12.9870	241.90	4656.63
78	6084	474552	8.8318	4.2727	1.89209	12.8205	245.04	4778.36
79	6241	493039	8.8882	4.2908	1.89763	12.6582	248.19	4901.67
80	6400	512000	8.9443	4.3089	1.90309	12.5000	251.33	5026.55
81	6561	531441	9.0000	4.3267	1.90849	12.3457	254.47	5153.00
82	6724	551368	9.0554	4.3445	1.91381	12.1951	257.61	5281.02
83	6889	571787	9.1104	4.3621	1.91908	12.0482	260.75	5410.61
84	7056	592704	9.1652	4.3795	1.92428	11.9048	263.89	5541.77
85	7225	614125	9.2195	4.3968	1.92942	11.7647	267.04	5674.50
86	7396	636056	9.2736	4.4140	1.93450	11.6279	270.18	5808.80
87	7569	658503	9.3274	4.4310	1.93952	11.4943	273.32	5944.68
88	7744	681472	9.3808	4.4480	1.94448	11.3636	276.46	6082.12
89	7921	704969	9.4340	4.4647	1.94939	11.2360	279.60	6221.14
90	8100	729000	9.4868	4.4814	1.95424	11.1111	282.74	6361.73
91	8281	753571	9.5394	4.4979	1.95904	10.9890	285.88	6503.88
92	8464	778688	9.5917	4.5144	1.96379	10.8696	289.03	6647.61
93	8649	804357	9.6437	4.5307	1.96848	10.7527	292.17	6792.91
94	8836	830584	9.6954	4.5468	1.97313	10.6383	295.31	6939.78
95	9025	857375	9.7468	4.5629	1.97772	10.5263	298.45	7088.22
96	9216	884736	9.7980	4.5789	1.98227	10.4167	301.59	7238.23
97	9409	912673	9.8489	4.5947	1.98677	10.3093	304.73	7389.81
98	9604	941192	9.8995	4.6104	1.99123	10.2041	307.88	7542.96
99	9801	970299	9.9499	4.6261	1.99564	10.1010	311.02	7697.69
100	10000	1000000	10.0000	4.6416	2.00000	10.0000	314.16	7853.98

PROPERTIES OF THE CIRCLE

Circumference of Circle of Diameter 1 = π = 3.14159265
Circumference of Circle = $2 \pi r$
Diameter of Circle = Circumference x 0.31831
Diameter of Circle of equal periphery as square = side x 1.27324
Side of Square of equal periphery as circle = diameter x 0.78540
Diameter of Circle circumscribed about square = side x 1.41421
Side of Square inscribed in Circle = diameter x 0.70711

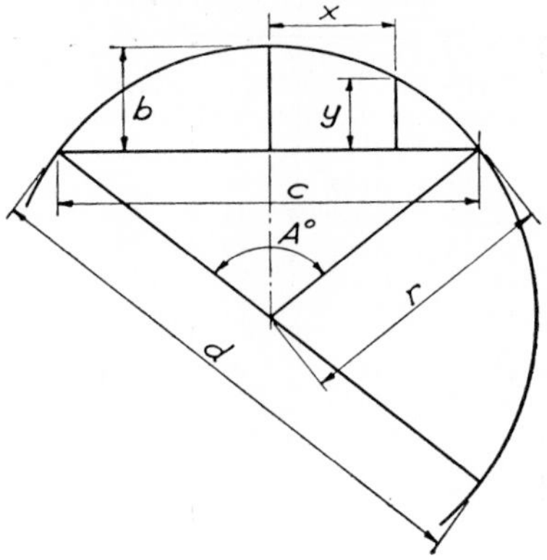

Arc, $a = \frac{\pi r A^\circ}{180} = 0.017453\, rA^\circ$

Angle, $A = \frac{180^\circ a}{\pi r} = 57.29578\,\frac{a}{r}$

Radius, $r = \frac{4b^2 + c^2}{8b}$ Diameter, $d = \frac{4b^2 + c^2}{4b}$

Chord, $c = 2\sqrt{2br - b^2} = 2r \sin\frac{A^\circ}{2}$

Rise, $b = r - \frac{1}{2}\sqrt{4r^2 - c^2} = \frac{c}{2}\tan\frac{A^\circ}{4} = 2r\sin^2\frac{A}{4}$

Rise, $b = r + y - \sqrt{r^2 - x^2}$, $y = b - r + \sqrt{r^2 - x^2}$, $x = \sqrt{r^2 - (r + y - b^2)}$

$\pi = 3.14159265$, log = 0.4971499

$\frac{1}{\pi} = 0.3183099$, log = 9.5028501-10

$\pi^2 = 9.8696044$, log = 0.9942997

$\frac{1}{\pi^2} = 0.1013212$, log = 9.0057003-10

$\sqrt{\pi} = 1.7724539$, log = 0.2485749

$\sqrt{\frac{1}{\pi}} = 0.5641896$, log = 9.7514251-10

$\frac{\pi}{180} = 0.0174533$, log = 8.2418774-10

$\frac{180}{\pi} = 57.2957795$, log = 1.7581226

AREAS OF CIRCULAR SEGMENTS

For Ratios of Rise and Chord

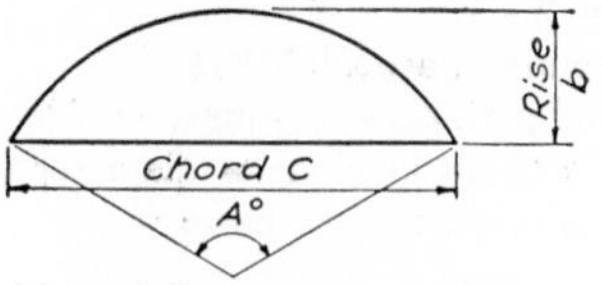

Area = b x C x coefficient

A°	Coeffi-cient	b/C	A°	Coeffi-cient	b/C	A°	Coeffi-cient	b/C	A°	Coeffi-cient	b/C
1	.6667	.0022	46	.6722	.1017	91	.6895	.2097	136	.7239	.3373
2	.6667	.0044	47	.6724	.1040	92	.6901	.2122	137	.7249	.3404
3	.6667	.0066	48	.6727	.1063	93	.6906	.2148	138	.7260	.3436
4	.6667	.0087	49	.6729	.1086	94	.6912	.2174	139	.7270	.3469
5	.6667	.0109	50	.6732	.1109	95	.6918	.2200	140	.7281	.3501
6	.6667	.0131	51	.6734	.1131	96	.6924	.2226	141	.7292	.3534
7	.6668	.0153	52	.6737	.1154	97	.6930	.2252	142	.7303	.3567
8	.6668	.0175	53	.6740	.1177	98	.6936	.2279	143	.7314	.3600
9	.6669	.0197	54	.6743	.1200	99	.6942	.2305	144	.7325	.3633
10	.6670	.0218	55	.6746	.1224	100	.6948	.2332	145	.7336	.3666
11	.6670	.0240	56	.6749	.1247	101	.6954	.2358	146	.7348	.3700
12	.6671	.0262	57	.6752	.1270	102	.6961	.2385	147	.7360	.3734
13	.6672	.0284	58	.6755	.1293	103	.6967	.2412	148	.7372	.3768
14	.6672	.0306	59	.6758	.1316	104	.6974	.2439	149	.7384	.3802
15	.6673	.0328	60	.6761	.1340	105	.6980	.2466	150	.7396	.3837
16	.6674	.0350	61	.6764	.1363	106	.6987	.2493	151	.7408	.3871
17	.6674	.0372	62	.6768	.1387	107	.6994	.2520	152	.7421	.3906
18	.6675	.0394	63	.6771	.1410	108	.7001	.2548	153	.7434	.3942
19	.6676	.0416	64	.6775	.1434	109	.7008	.2575	154	.7447	.3977
20	.6677	.0437	65	.6779	.1457	110	.7015	.2603	155	.7460	.4013
21	.6678	.0459	66	.6782	.1481	111	.7022	.2631	156	.7473	.4049
22	.6679	.0481	67	.6786	.1505	112	.7030	.2659	157	.7486	.4085
23	.6680	.0504	68	.6790	.1529	113	.7037	.2687	158	.7500	.4122
24	.6681	.0526	69	.6794	.1553	114	.7045	.2715	159	.7514	.4159
25	.6682	.0548	70	.6797	.1577	115	.7052	.2743	160	.7528	.4196
26	.6684	.0570	71	.6801	.1601	116	.7060	.2772	161	.7542	.4233
27	.6685	.0592	72	.6805	.1625	117	.7068	.2800	162	.7557	.4270
28	.6687	.0614	73	.6809	.1649	118	.7076	.2829	163	.7571	.4308
29	.6688	.0636	74	.6814	.1673	119	.7084	.2858	164	.7586	.4346
30	.6690	.0658	75	.6818	.1697	120	.7092	.2887	165	.7601	.4385
31	.6691	.0681	76	.6822	.1722	121	.7100	.2916	166	.7616	.4424
32	.6693	.0703	77	.6826	.1746	122	.7109	.2945	167	.7632	.4463
33	.6694	.0725	78	.6831	.1771	123	.7117	.2975	168	.7648	.4502
34	.6696	.0747	79	.6835	.1795	124	.7126	.3004	169	.7664	.4542
35	.6698	.0770	80	.6840	.1820	125	.7134	.3034	170	.7680	.4582
36	.6700	.0792	81	.6844	.1845	126	.7143	.3064	171	.7696	.4622
37	.6702	.0814	82	.6849	.1869	127	.7152	.3094	172	.7712	.4663
38	.6704	.0837	83	.6854	.1894	128	.7161	.3124	173	.7729	.4704
39	.6706	.0859	84	.6859	.1919	129	.7170	.3155	174	.7746	.4745
40	.6708	.0882	85	.6864	.1944	130	.7180	.3185	175	.7763	.4787
41	.6710	.0904	86	.6869	.1970	131	.7189	.3216	176	.7781	.4828
42	.6712	.0927	87	.6874	.1995	132	.7199	.3247	177	.7799	.4871
43	.6714	.0949	88	.6879	.2020	133	.7209	.3278	178	.7817	.4914
44	.6717	.0972	89	.6884	.2046	134	.7219	.3309	179	.7835	.4957
45	.6719	.0995	90	.6890	.2071	135	.7229	.3341	180	.7854	.5000

WEIGHTS AND MEASURES
UNITED STATES SYSTEM

Linear Measure

Inches		Feet		Yards		Rods		Furlongs		Miles
1.0	=	0.08333	=	0.02778	=	0.0050505	=	0.00012626	=	0.00001578
12.0	=	1.0	=	0.33333	=	0.0606061	=	0.000151515	=	0.00018939
36.0	=	3.0	=	1.0	=	0.1818182	=	0.00454545	=	0.00056818
198.0	=	16.5	=	5.5	=	1.0	=	0.025	=	0.003125
7920.0	=	660.0	=	220.0	=	40.0	=	1.0	=	0.125
63360.0	=	5280.0	=	1760.0	=	320.0	=	8.0	=	1.0

Square and Land Measure

Sq inches		Square feet		Square yards		Sq rods		Acres		Sq miles
1.0	=	0.006944	=	0.000772						
144.0	=	1.0	=	0.111111						
1296.0	=	9.0	=	1.0	=	0.03306	=	0.000207		
39204.0	=	272.25	=	30.25	=	1.0	=	0.00625	=	0.0000098
		43560.0	=	4840.0	=	160.0	=	1.0	=	0.0015625
				3097600.0	=	102400.0	=	640.0	=	1.0

Liquid Measure

Gills		Pints		Quarts		U. S. Gallons		Cubic feet
1.0	=	0.25	=	0.125	=	0.03125	=	0.00418
4.0	=	1.0	=	0.5	=	0.125	=	0.01671
8.0	=	2.0	=	1.0	=	0.250	=	0.03342
32.0	=	8.0	=	4.0	=	1.0	=	0.1337
						7.48052	=	1.0

Dry Measure

Pints		Quarts		Pecks		Cubic feet		Bushels
1.0	=	0.5	=	0.0625	=	0.01945	=	0.01563
2.0	=	1.0	=	0.125	=	0.03891	=	0.03125
16.0	=	8.0	=	1.0	=	0.31112	=	0.25
51.42627	=	25.71314	=	3.21414	=	1.0	=	0.80354
64.0	=	32.0	=	4.0	=	1.2445	=	1.0

Avoirdupois Weights

Grains		Drams		Ounces		Pounds		Tons
1.0	=	0.03657	=	0.002286	=	0.000143	=	0.0000000714
27.34375	=	1.0	=	0.0625	=	0.003906	=	0.00000195
437.5	=	16.0	=	1.0	=	0.0625	=	0.00003125
7000.0	=	256.0	=	16.0	=	1.0	=	0.0005
14000000.0	=	512000.0	=	32000.0	=	2000.0	=	1.0

CONVERSION FACTORS*

Multiplying	By	Gives
acres	0.404687	hectares
"	4.04687×10^{-3}	square kilometers
ares	1076.39	square feet
board feet	144 sq in. × 1 in.	cubic inches
" "	0.0833	cubic feet
centimeters	3.28083×10^{-2}	feet
"	0.3937	inches
cubic centimeters	3.53145×10^{-5}	cubic feet
" "	6.102×10^{-2}	cubic inches
cubic feet	2.8317×10^{4}	cubic centimeters
" "	2.8317×10^{-2}	cubic meters
" "	6.22905	gallons, British Imperial
" "	28.3170	liters
" "	2.38095×10^{-2}	tons, British Shipping
" "	0.025	tons, U. S. Shipping
cubic inches	16.38716	cubic centimeters
cubic meters	35.3145	cubic feet
" "	1.30794	cubic yards
cubic yards	0.764559	cubic meters
degrees, angular	0.0174533	radians
degrees, Fahrenheit (less 32° F)	0.5556	degrees, Centigrade
" Centigrade	1.8	degrees, Fahrenheit (less 32° F)
foot pounds	0.13826	kilogram meters
feet	30.4801	centimeters
"	0.304801	meters
"	304.801	millimeters
"	1.64468×10^{-4}	miles, nautical
gallons, British Imperial	0.160538	cubic feet
" " "	1.20091	gallons, U. S.
" " "	4.54596	liters
gallons, U. S.	0.832702	gallons, British Imperial
" "	0.13368	cubic feet
" "	231.	cubic inches
" "	3.78543	liters
grams, metric	2.20462×10^{-3}	pounds, avoirdupois
hectares	2.47104	acres
"	1.076387×10^{5}	square feet
"	3.86101×10^{-3}	square miles
inches	2.54001	centimeters
"	2.54001×10^{-2}	meters
"	25.4001	millimeters
kilograms	2.20462	pounds
"	9.84206×10^{-4}	long tons
"	1.10231×10^{-3}	short tons
kilogram meters	7.233	foot pounds
kilograms per meter	0.671972	pounds per foot
kilograms per square centimeter	14.2234	pounds per square inch
kilograms per square meter	0.204817	pounds per square foot
" " " "	9.14362×10^{-5}	long tons per square foot
kilograms per square millimeter	1422.34	pounds per square inch
" " " "	0.634973	long tons per square inch
kilograms per cubic meter	6.24283×10^{-2}	pounds per cubic foot
kilometers	0.62137	miles, statute
"	0.53959	miles, nautical

* These factors are for conversion from common metric units to American units, or from American to common metric. Systeme International (SI) bases all measurements upon six fundamentals and establishes the unit of force as the newton = 0.102 kgf and of pressure as the bar = 1.02 kgf/cm².

CONVERSION FACTORS*

Multiplying	By	Gives
liters	0.219975	gallons, British Imperial
“	0.26417	gallons, U. S.
“	3.53145×10^{-2}	cubic feet
meters	3.28083	feet
“	39.37	inches
“	1.09361	yards
miles, statute	1.60935	kilometers
“ “	0.8684	miles, nautical (knots)
miles, nautical (knots)	6080.204	feet
“ “ “	1.85325	kilometers
“ “ “	1.1516	miles, statute
millimeters	3.28083×10^{-3}	feet
“	3.937×10^{-2}	inches
pounds, avoirdupois	453.592	grams, metric
“ “	0.453592	kilograms
“ “	4.464×10^{-4}	tons, long
“ “	4.53592×10^{-4}	tons, metric
pounds per foot	1.48816	kilograms per meter
pounds per square foot	4.88241	kilograms per square meter
pounds per square inch	7.031×10^{-2}	kilograms per square centimeter
“ “ “ “	7.031×10^{-4}	kilograms per square millimeter
pounds per cubic foot	16.0184	kilograms per cubic meter
radians	57.29578	degrees, angular
square centimeters	0.1550	square inches
square feet	9.29034×10^{-4}	ares
“ “	9.29034×10^{-6}	hectares
“ “	0.0929034	square meters
square inches	6.45163	square centimeters
“ “	645.163	square millimeters
square kilometers	247.104	acres
“ “	0.3861	square miles
square meters	10.7639	square feet
“ “	1.19599	square yards
square miles	259.0	hectares
“ “	2.590	square kilometers
square millimeters	1.550×10^{-3}	square inches
square yards	0.83613	square meters
tons, long	1016.05	kilograms
“ “	2240.	pounds
“ “	1.01605	tons, metric
“ “	1.120	tons, short
tons, long, per square foot	1.09366×10^{-4}	kilograms per square meter
tons, long, per square inch	1.57494	kilograms per square millimeter
tons, metric	2204.62	pounds
“ “	0.98421	tons, long
“ “	1.10231	tons, short
tons, short	907.185	kilograms
“ “	0.892857	tons, long
“ “	0.907185	tons, metric
tons, British Shipping	42.00	cubic feet
“ “ “	0.952381	tons, U. S. Shipping
tons, U. S. Shipping	40.00	cubic feet
“ “ “	1.050	tons, British Shipping
yards	0.914402	meters

* These factors are for conversion from common metric units to American units, or from American to common metric. Systeme International (SI) bases all measurements upon six fundamentals and establishes the unit of force as the newton = 0.102 kgf and of pressure as the bar = 1.02 kgf/cm².

DECIMAL EQUIVALENTS OF AN INCH AND OF A FOOT

Fractions of Inch or Foot		Inch Equivalents to Foot Fractions	Fractions of Inch or Foot		Inch Equivalents to Foot Fractions	Fractions of Inch or Foot		Inch Equivalents to Foot Fractions	Fractions of Inch or Foot		Inch Equivalents to Foot Fraction
	.0052	1/16		.2552	3-1/16		.5052	6-1/16		.7552	9-1/16
	.0104	1/8		.2604	3-1/8		.5104	6-1/8		.7604	9-1/8
1/64	.015625	3/16	17/64	.265625	3-3/16	33/64	.515625	6-3/16	49/64	.765625	9-3/16
	.0208	1/4		.2708	3-1/4		.5208	6-1/4		.7708	9-1/4
	.0260	5/16		.2760	3-5/16		.5260	6-5/16		.7760	9-5/16
1/32	.03125	3/8	9/32	.28125	3-3/8	17/32	.53125	6-3/8	25/32	.78125	9-3/8
	.0365	7/16		.2865	3-7/16		.5365	6-7/16		.7865	9-7/16
	.0417	1/2		.2917	3-1/2		.5417	6-1/2		.7917	9-1/2
3/64	.046875	9/16	19/64	.296875	3-9/16	35/64	.546875	6-9/16	51/64	.796875	9-9/16
	.0521	5/8		.3021	3-5/8		.5521	6-5/8		.8021	9-5/8
	.0573	11/16		.3073	3-11/16		.5573	6-11/16		.8073	9-11/16
1/16	.0625	3/4	5/16	.3125	3-3/4	9/16	.5625	6-3/4	13/16	.8125	9-3/4
	.0677	13/16		.3177	3-13/16		.5677	6-13/16		.8177	9-13/16
	.0729	7/8		.3229	3-7/8		.5729	6-7/8		.8229	9-7/8
5/64	.078125	15/16	21/64	.328125	3-15/16	37/64	.578125	6-15/16	53/64	.828125	9-15/16
	.0833	1		.3333	4		.5833	7		.8333	10
	.0885	1-1/16		.3385	4-1/16		.5885	7-1/16		.8385	10-1/16
3/32	.09375	1-1/8	11/32	.34375	4-1/8	19/32	.59375	7-1/8	27/32	.84375	10-1/8
	.0990	1-3/16		.3490	4-3/16		.5990	7-3/16		.8490	10-3/16
	.1042	1-1/4		.3542	4-1/4		.6042	7-1/4		.8542	10-1/4
7/64	.109375	1-5/16	23/64	.359375	4-5/16	39/64	.609375	7-5/16	55/64	.859375	10-5/16
	.1146	1-3/8		.3646	4-3/8		.6146	7-3/8		.8646	10-3/8
	.1198	1-7/16		.3698	4-7/16		.6198	7-7/16		.8698	10-7/16
1/8	.1250	1-1/2	3/8	.3750	4-1/2	5/8	.6250	7-1/2	7/8	.8750	10-1/2
	.1302	1-9/16		.3802	4-9/16		.6302	7-9/16		.8802	10-9/16
	.1354	1-5/8		.3854	4-5/8		.6354	7-5/8		.8854	10-5/8
9/64	.140625	1-11/16	25/64	.390625	4-11/16	41/64	.640625	7-11/16	57/64	.890625	10-11/16
	.1458	1-3/4		.3958	4-3/4		.6458	7-3/4		.8958	10-3/4
	.1510	1-13/16		.4010	4-13/16		.6510	7-13/16		.9010	10-13/16
5/32	.15625	1-7/8	13/32	.40625	4-7/8	21/32	.65625	7-7/8	29/32	.90625	10-7/8
	.1615	1-15/16		.4115	4-15/16		.6615	7-15/16		.9115	10-15/16
	.1667	2		.4167	5		.6667	8		.9167	11
11/64	.171875	2-1/16	27/64	.421875	5-1/16	43/64	.671875	8-1/16	59/64	.921875	11-1/16
	.1771	2-1/8		.4271	5-1/8		.6771	8-1/8		.9271	11-1/8
	.1823	2-3/16		.4323	5-3/16		.6823	8-3/16		.9323	11-3/16
3/16	.1875	2-1/4	7/16	.4375	5-1/4	11/16	.6875	8-1/4	15/16	.9375	11-1/4
	.1927	2-5/16		.4427	5-5/16		.6927	8-5/16		.9427	11-5/16
	.1979	2-3/8		.4479	5-3/8		.6979	8-3/8		.9479	11-3/8
13/64	.203125	2-7/16	29/64	.453125	5-7/16	45/64	.703125	8-7/16	61/64	.953125	11-7/16
	.2083	2-1/2		.4583	5-1/2		.7083	8-1/2		.9583	11-1/2
	.2135	2-9/16		.4635	5-9/16		.7135	8-9/16		.9635	11-9/16
7/32	.21875	2-5/8	15/32	.46875	5-5/8	23/32	.71875	8-5/8	31/32	.96875	11-5/8
	.2240	2-11/16		.4740	5-11/16		.7240	8-11/16		.9740	11-11/16
	.2292	2-3/4		.4792	5-3/4		.7292	8-3/4		.9792	11-3/4
15/64	.234375	2-13/16	31/64	.484375	5-13/16	47/64	.734375	8-13/16	63/64	.984375	11-13/16
	.2396	2-7/8		.4896	5-7/8		.7396	8-7/8		.9896	11-7/8
	.2448	2-15/16		.4948	5-15/16		.7448	8-15/16		.9948	11-15/16
1/4	.2500	3	1/2	.5000	6	3/4	.7500	9	1	1.0000	12

Specifications
Section 16

Reinforcing Bar Specifications. Since all of the tables in this book (except some column tables) are based upon steel with a yield point of 60,000 psi; that is, Grade 60 bars, it is important that the designer be thoroughly familiar with the ASTM Specifications for these materials and particularly with the required rolled-on grade markings for deformed bars with f_y = 60,000 and 75,000 psi.

Such specifications are obtainable from the American Society for Testing and Materials or are reproduced in the CRSI Manual of Standard Practice for Reinforced Concrete Construction.*

ASTM Specifications establish the projection and spacing of deformations. "Building Code Requirements for Reinforced Concrete (ACI 318-63)," permits increased bond and diagonal tension values for bars meeting these specifications. These higher shear and bond values are used throughout the book. Consequently, only bars meeting the ASTM requirements for strength and deformations should be used with the tabulated values.

Specifications for Concrete Work. With the use of higher strength and better quality concrete, the designer must specify precisely what he requires and verify that this is what he obtains. Complete specifications for concrete work can be found in "Suggested Specifications for Structural Concrete for Buildings (ACI 301)" of the American Concrete Institute.†

---

* Available from Concrete Reinforcing Steel Institute, 228 North Lasalle Street, Chicago 1, Illinois.

† American Concrete Institute, P.O. Box 4754, Redford Station, Detroit 19, Michigan.

INDEX